PEARSON   ALWAYS LEARNING

David Krogh

Biology
A Guide to the Natural World

Third Custom Edition for Southern Maine Community College

Taken from:
Biology: A Guide to the Natural World, Fifth Edition
by David Krogh

Cover Art: Courtesy of PhotoDisc/Getty Images.

Taken from:

Biology: A Guide to the Natural World, Fifth Edition
by David Krogh
Copyright © 2011, 2009, 2005 by Pearson Education, Inc.
Published by Benjamin Cummings
San Francisco, California 94111

This special edition published in cooperation with Pearson Learning Solutions.

Pearson Learning Solutions, 501 Boylston Street, Suite 900, Boston, MA 02116
A Pearson Education Company
www.pearsoned.com

Printed in the United States of America

4 5 6 7 8 9 10 0BRV 16 15 14 13 12 11

000200010270767170

RH

ISBN 10: 1-256-14060-0
ISBN 13: 978-1-256-14060-3

About the Author

Author

DAVID KROGH has been writing about science for 27 years in newspapers, magazines, books, and for educational institutions. He is the author of *Smoking: The Artificial Passion,* an account of the pharmacological and cultural motivations behind the use of tobacco, which was nominated for the *Los Angeles Times* Book Prize in Science and Technology. In 1994, he began work on what would become *Biology: A Guide to the Natural World,* and in 1999 he completed its first edition. Since then, he has produced four more editions of *A Guide to the Natural World* along with a second textbook, *A Brief Guide to Biology.* He holds bachelor's degrees in journalism and history from the University of Missouri.

Art Development Editor

Kim Quillin received her B.A. in biology at Oberlin College and her Ph.D. in integrative biology from the University of California, Berkeley, and is now a lecturer in the Department of Biological Sciences at Salisbury University. Students and instructors alike have praised the illustration programs she has produced for three textbooks: David Krogh's *Biology: A Guide to the Natural World,* Colleen Belk and Virginia Borden's *Biology: Science for Life,* and Scott Freeman's *Biological Science.*

Preface

From the Author

Book titles may be the first thing any reader sees in a book, but they're often the last thing an author ponders. Not so with *Biology: A Guide to the Natural World.* The title arrived fairly early on, courtesy of the muse, and then stuck because it so aptly expresses what I think is special about this book.

Flip through these pages, and you'll see all the elements that students and teachers look for in any modern introductory textbook—rich, full-color art, an extensive study apparatus, and a full complement of digital learning tools. When you leaf slowly through the book and start to read a little of it, however, I think that something a little more subtle starts coming through. This second quality has to do with a sense of connection with students. The sensibility that I hope is apparent in *A Guide to the Natural World* is that there's a wonderful living world to be explored; that we who produced this book would like nothing better than to show this world to students; and that we want to take them on an instructive walk through this world, rather than a difficult march.

All the members of the teams who have produced the five editions of *A Guide to the Natural World* have worked with this idea in mind. We felt that we were taking students on a journey through the living world and that, rather like tour guides, we needed to be mindful of where students were at any given point. Would they remember this term from earlier in the chapter? Had we created enough of a bridge between one subject and the next? The idea was never to leave students with the feeling that they were wandering alone through terrain that lacked signposts. Rather, we aimed to give them the sense that they had a companion—this book—that would guide them through the subject of biology. *A Guide to the Natural World,* then, really is intended as a kind of guide, with its audience being students who are taking biology but not majoring in it.

Biology is complex, however, and if students are to understand it at anything beyond the most superficial level, details are necessary. It won't do to make what one faculty member called "magical leaps" over the difficult parts of complex subjects. Our goal was to make the difficult comprehensible, not to make it disappear altogether. Thus, the reader will find in this book fairly detailed accounts of such subjects as cellular respiration, photosynthesis, immune system function, and plant reproduction. It was in covering such topics that our concern for student comprehension was put to its greatest test. We like the way we handled these subjects and other key topics, however, and we hope readers will feel the same way.

What's New in the Fifth Edition?

The numerous changes made to the *Guide* for its fifth edition have added up to one global change in the book that longtime users may be able to perceive just by picking it up: It's shorter than it used to be. We had 791 numbered pages in the fourth edition, but this time around we have 725. The usual course for textbooks is to get larger as they get older, but we ended up going the other way in this edition after concluding that, in certain areas, we were providing more coverage than faculty thought was desirable. (You can see which areas have been trimmed by reading to the end of this section.) No book can perfectly meet the needs of all faculty with respect to content, but we've done our best to produce a book that has only as much content in it as most faculty say they need. Apart from this change, the fifth edition revision also includes:

- **A greatly revised lineup of essays.** Eighteen new essays have been written for this edition, most of them taking an applied slant. For example, on page 150, you'll find the essay "Using Photosynthesis to Fight Global Warming," which reviews some of the ways photosynthesis stands to be utilized as a tool societies can employ in their efforts to lessen climate change. Chapter 15's "Biotechnology Gets Personal" provides students with some idea of what they could expect to learn by having their own genomes scanned for signs of predispositions toward sickness or health (page 274). Then the essay "An Evolving Ability to Drink Milk" should apply in a personal way to every student in a classroom, as it shows how the forces of mutation and natural selection have worked with human culture to place all human adults alive today into one of two camps: those who can digest milk and those who can't (page 294).

- **An expanded set of review questions.** Faculty have made clear how important review questions are to student comprehension of biology, and we've responded by producing an edition that has more questions in it than any of its predecessors. The in-chapter "So Far" questions that made their debut in the fourth edition have been retained, while the end-of-chapter Multiple-Choice questions that existed up through the third edition have been brought back. The more detailed Brief Review and Applying Your Knowledge questions also appear at the end of each chapter and we're continuing to supply a host of review questions on the web.

- **Stand-alone chapters on plants, fungi, the nervous system, and the endocrine system.** In the *Guide's* fourth edition, plants and fungi were covered in a single chapter, and the same thing was true of the nervous and endocrine systems. In the fifth edition, each of these subjects gets its own chapter. One effect of this change is that the book's endocrine coverage has been significantly expanded, as you can see by turning to page 532.

- **A completely revised chapter on the immune system.** The *Guide's* coverage of the immune system has been revamped from start to finish and as such is right up-to-date. As you can see by turning to page 550, the chapter includes not only information on how the immune system works but information on two promising forms of immune therapy. This coverage is then complemented by two new essays that stand to be relevant to student lives: "Why is There No Vaccine for AIDS?" on page 566 and "Unfounded Fears about Vaccination" on page 568.

- **New coverage of applied topics.** Numerous applied topics are being covered for the first time in this edition, often in the essays mentioned earlier. Subjects taken up include the intertwining of science and big business in the development of new cancer drugs (page 12); the nature of the new targeted therapies for cancer (page 168); the pluses and minuses of making genetic information public (page 206); a research breakthrough in the fight against herpes (page 386); endorphin release as a possible motivation for the use of tanning beds (page 495); and the controversy about how much vitamin D Americans ought to be getting (page 602). We also have a greatly expanded table on methods of contraception, which you can see on page 642. Last but not least, the fourth edition of the *Guide* had a section on avian flu, but for reasons that may be obvious, the fifth edition has a section on swine flu (page 384).

- **New coverage of basic science topics.** The *Guide's* Chapter 14, on transcription, translation, and genetic regulation, is completely predictable in one way: Its section on transcription and translation never changes much while its section on genetic regulation never stops changing (page 253). Writing about genetic regulation in an age of RNA interference and alternatively spliced genes is like posting dispatches from the Lewis and Clark expedition: You're not sure where you're going to end up, but reports about the journey are fascinating. Genetic regulation is, however, only one of the basic science topics that's been greatly revised in the fifth edition. Chapter 15, on biotechnology, now has a long section on a topic whose name only came into wide circulation in the last couple of years: cell reprogramming. Material on both embryonic stem cells and induced pluripotent stem cells is included in this section, which starts on page 270. Chapter 19's coverage of the history of life on Earth has a greatly revised section on origin-of-life theories (page 342), and as you might expect the *Guide's* coverage of global warming and environmental issues in general has changed considerably since the fourth edition came out (page 704). In human evolution studies, a rough draft of the Neanderthal genome was completed in the last year, and the *Guide's* Chapter 20 includes coverage of that, along with an essay that explores the question of whether the discovery of cooking speeded up the evolution of human intelligence (page 371).

- **A different way of approaching animals.** For several editions, the *Guide* has covered the animal kingdom through the traditional means of taking students on a long walk through its major phyla. With this edition, we've taken a different tack, in accordance with advice we got from faculty. All the phyla are still covered, but in much less detail than before. What's been added is a look *across* the phyla at four subjects: reproduction, egg fertilization and protection, organs and circulation, and skeletons and molting. The end result is not only a different chapter, but a shorter one—something that was consistent with our goal of providing only as much coverage as faculty think is desirable.

- **A different way of approaching plants.** In the fourth edition of the *Guide*, plants were covered in three chapters: one in the book's evolution and diversity unit and two in the plant unit of the book, which was completely devoted to angiosperm anatomy and physiology. With this edition, some of the angiosperm A&P material has been moved to the plant diversity chapter, while the number of chapters in the plant unit has been reduced from two to one. Here again, we were following the advice of faculty, who told us we have been giving them more angiosperm A&P material than they needed. And here again the result was a reduction in the number of *Guide* pages.

- **The elimination of animal behavior.** The *Guide* has closed out nearly every one of its editions with an animal behavior chapter that was part of a larger ecology unit. Reviewing faculty liked this chapter and I certainly liked it, but it seemed to be used scarcely at all in non-majors classes and thus didn't fit in with our goal of producing a book that has only as much material in it as faculty recommend. So with the fifth edition of the *Guide*, we've eliminated animal behavior altogether.

Electronic Media and the Fifth Edition: MasteringBiology®

With the fifth edition of the *Guide*, departments or individual instructors will have the option of utilizing a set of electronic tools that stand to greatly enhance biology instruction in two ways: For students, they will provide new ways to learn about biology, while for faculty they will provide powerful new methods of monitoring student performance and preparedness.

These tools go under the umbrella title of MasteringBiology®— a term whose "Mastering" part may be familiar to you if you have colleagues who use Pearson textbooks to teach in physics or chemistry. In just the past year, Pearson's Mastering system has been broadened to include less-quantitative disciplines, such as biology, and the early results have been impressive. There is so much to MasteringBiology® that it defies brief explanation, but let me try to summarize some of its high points by walking through a couple of typical class exercises.

Suppose that you or your department have made the decision both to adopt the *Guide* and to designate any course using the book as a "Mastering" course. Now suppose you've reached a point in an academic term in which you are teaching one of biology's difficult subjects, such as photosynthesis. Students who have registered for their Mastering course go to its website and learn—either through a full-term syllabus you've posted on it or through a more recently posted note to them—that the subject of this Wednesday's lecture will be photosynthesis. Further, they learn that the sections of the book to read before this lecture are 8.1 through 8.5, and that they need to go to the Mastering website and complete a 10-question multiple-choice quiz on this material at least one hour before coming to class. Now, just before class, you look at the results of the quiz—automatically graded because all the questions on it were multiple-choice—and you find out what you need to emphasize in lecture and what you can cut back on. You find out not only which questions students got right or wrong, but how *long* it took them to answer each question, how many *tries* it took them to answer each question—assuming you decided to give them more than one try per question—and how their performance stacked up against a national database of other students who have taken the same quiz. These data are aggregated for the entire class, but finding out about individual students in it is as simple as clicking on their individual records.

Now, when this same kind of procedure is replicated across many class assignments, you end up with an electronic matrix for the class, with the students on the Y axis and the term's assignments on the X axis. From this, what you ultimately can see is the big picture of performance across an entire academic term. Issue a command to color-code assignment performances that fell below a certain threshold and you can instantly see where either the class as a whole, or individual students in it, were having trouble. Midway through an academic term, a student who comes to office hours with only a vague idea of where he or she is having trouble can now be shown where the trouble has existed—this kind of material rather than that, this kind of testing rather than that.

In addition, all these teaching and course management tools are customizable. Quizzes, for example, come with default settings, but the number of questions, their order, the weighting of points for them, whether to give extra credit for some of them—all these things and more can be decided upon by the instructor. They can also be edited by instructors to match their personal style or exam questions.

For the student, MasteringBiology® provides a wealth of learning tools. For starters, all students enrolled in a MB class will have their own eText version of the *Guide,* available on the web. In it, students can post notes to themselves about certain sections of the book, electronically highlight pieces of text, and instantly bring up any of the world-class BioFlix animations—18 of them in this edition—which they can start and stop as they read along, thus integrating visual learning with linear text comprehension. In a similar vein, an instructor can compose notes that can automatically be posted to the eText of every student in the class. More help for students is available in the "Study Area" of the MasteringBiology site in the form of practice quizzes and flash cards.

There's much more to MasteringBiology® than an account such as this one can provide, but the best way to see all that it offers is to go to www.masteringbiology.com, register, and start investigating it. I think you'll agree that it integrates teaching and learning in biology in ways that haven't existed before.

The *Guide to the Natural World* Team

Textbooks are such enormous collective efforts that it's difficult for an author to thank all the people who've helped out, for the simple reason that the author hasn't *met* a good number of the people who've helped out. The best I can do, therefore, is name a few of the people whose assistance has been valuable to me personally as I've worked on the fifth edition of *A Guide to the Natural World.*

Developmental Editor Debbie Hardin gave the *Guide* the most thorough review it's had since it first came out. Every word, drawing, and photo in the book went under Debbie's microscope and the *Guide* is much better for having been analyzed in this way. The terrific artist and biologist Kim Quillin continued to produce nearly all the new and revised art for the book, working as usual with her winning combination of good cheer and devotion to clear scientific illustration. Among the people at Benjamin Cummings I'm indebted to are Production Supervisor Camille Herrera, who made sure all the pieces of the book moved forward together on time, and Design Manager Marilyn Perry, who gave the *Guide* its stylish fifth-edition look. Sylvia Rebert and her colleagues at Progressive Publishing Alternatives took thousands of pieces of *Guide* art and text and made a book out of them, doing so in a manner that allowed all parties to remain calm—no small feat, as anxiety about getting to the finish line on time is a built-in feature of producing a textbook. Overall direction for the *Guide*'s fifth edition came from a leader who provided a steady hand on the tiller, Star MacKenzie, whose devotion to producing a better book never wavered. Finally, I'm indebted to Project Editor Leata Holloway, who over a period of two years ably moved the *Guide* forward in a thousand different ways.

Apart from these publishing team members, more than 350 faculty have now carefully critiqued every word and image you see in the *Guide.* The names of reviewing faculty can be found beginning on page ix.

Finally, the test of any textbook is its effect in the classroom. As a consequence, for any textbook author, there is no such thing as too much feedback from those who stand at the front of the class. So, if you teach using the *Guide,* or if you've merely looked at it in some detail, here's an invitation: Write me and tell me what you think. Whether your reactions are positive or negative doesn't matter; the book stands to be improved by both kinds of responses. The more faculty I hear from, the better the book's sixth edition stands to be. My e-mail address is: rdkrogh@pacbell.net.

DAVID KROGH
Kensington, California

Student Supplements

Study Guide

0-321-68303-X / 978-0-321-68303-8

This tool is an effective and interactive study guide that helps students concentrate their study efforts. The Study Guide contains quizzes, word roots, key term reviews, and helpful summaries.

Study Card

0-321-68280-7 / 978-0-321-68280-2

This laminated quick-reference Study Card is developed specifically for *Biology: A Guide to the Natural World* and can be value-packaged with the book at no additional charge. The Study Card provides a brief, chapter-by-chapter review, including key figures, to help students review the most important topics in biology.

MasteringBiology Study Area

This comprehensive study resource has been revised to include new BioFlix™ animations on the toughest topics in biology and customized study plans for individual students. Also included are Web Links and references, Vocabulary Study Tools, Cumulative Tests, Web Animations with accompanying quizzes, Discovery Channel video clips, Tutoring Services, Lab Bench, Graph It! Activities, and MP3 lectures.

URL: http://www.masteringbiology.com/

Scientific American *Current Issues in Biology*

Volume 1: 0-8053-7507-4 / 978-0-8053-7507-7

Volume 2: 0-8053-7108-7 / 978-0-8053-7108-6

Volume 3: 0-8053-2146-2 / 978-0-8053-2146-3

Volume 4: 0-8053-3566-8 / 978-0-8053-3566-8

Volume 5: 0-321-54187-1 / 978-0-321-54187-1

Give your students the best of both worlds—accessible, dynamic, relevant articles from *Scientific American* magazine that present key issues in biology, paired with the authority, reliability, and clarity of Benjamin Cummings' non-majors biology texts. Articles include questions to help students check their comprehension and make connections to science and society. This resource is available at no additional charge when packaged with a new text.

Instructor Supplements

Instructor Resource DVD

0-321-68276-9 / 978-0-321-68276-5

The Instructor Resource CD-ROM includes PowerPoint® lectures that integrate figures and new BioFlix™ animations, BLAST animations, Discovery Channel® videos, all figures, art, and photos in JPEG format, label-edit PowerPoints, and over 200 Instructor Animations that accurately depict complex topics and dynamic

processes described in the book. New, innovative Classroom Response System questions are offered for each chapter as a way to directly engage students in lectures.

Instructor Guide

0-321-68277-7 / 978-0-321-68277-2

This comprehensive guide provides chapter-by-chapter instructor and student objectives, chapter outlines, key terms, interactive activities with handouts, and answers to the Applying Your Knowledge critical thinking questions from the textbook. A separate section offers chapter-by-chapter media guides to aid teaching and learning introductory biology. The Instructor Guide is available in print and as a Microsoft® Word document

Transparency Acetates

0-321-72376-7 / 978-0-321-72376-5

Selected full-color acetates include illustrations and tables from the text.

Test Bank

0-321-72377-5 / 978-0-321-72377-2

All of the exam questions in the Test Bank have been peer reviewed, thus providing questions that set the standard for quality and accuracy. Test questions are ranked according to Bloom's taxonomy, and improved TestGen® software makes assembling tests easier. The Test Bank is also available in Course Management Systems and in Word® format on the Instructor Resource CD-ROM.

Course Management

CourseCompass™

This nationally hosted, dynamic, interactive online course management system is powered by Blackboard. This easy-to-use and customizable program enables professors to tailor content to meet individual course needs! Every CourseCompass™ course includes preloaded content, such as testing and assessment question pools. CourseCompass is also available with an E-Book.

URL: http://www.aw-bc.com/coursecompass

Blackboard

This open-access course management system contains preloaded content such as testing and assessment question pools. More content is also available in a premium version.

URL: http://www.aw-bc.com/blackboard

Reviewers

Fifth Edition Reviewers

Stephanie Aamodt, *Louisiana State University, Shreveport*

Stephen Ballard, *Hillyer College*

Cheryl Boice, *Lake City Community College*

Peggy Brickman, *University of Georgia*

Lisa G. Bryant, *Arkansas State University, Beebe*

Sara G. Carlson, *University of Akron*

Sanjoy Chakraborty, *New York City College of Technology, CUNY*

Gregory A. Dahlem, *Northern Kentucky University*

Kathleen DeCicco-Skinner, *American University*

Jean DeSaix, *University of North Carolina, Chapel Hill*

M. Omar Faison, *Virginia State Community College*

Elizabeth A. Fitch, *Motlow State Community College*

Tammy R. Gamza, *Arkansas State University, Beebe*

Anthony J. Gaudin, *Ivy Technical Community College*

George W. Gilchrist, *College of William and Mary*

Beverly Glover, *Western Oklahoma State University*

Jeanette Gore, *St. Petersburg College*

Kelly A. Hogan, *University of North Carolina, Chapel Hill*

Sue Hum-Musser, *Western Illinois University*

Diana E. Hurlbut, *Irvine Valley Community College*

Robert Iwan, *Inver Hills Community College*

Malcolm Ian Jenness, *New Mexico Institute of Mining and Technology*

Kyoungtae Kim, *Missouri State University*

Eliot Krause, *Seton Hall University*

Rukmani Kuppuswami, *Laredo Community College*

Dale Lambert, *Tarrant County Community College*

David Lambert, *Louisiana School for Math, Science, and the Arts*

Johnathan Lochamy, *Georgia Perimeter College*

Madeleine Love, *New River Community College*

Roger F. Martin, *Brigham Young University*

Bram Middeldorp, *Minneapolis Community and Technical College*

Martin M. Matute, *University of Arkansas*

Alice J. Monroe, *St. Petersburg College*

James Murphy, *Monroe Community College*

Kathryn Nette, *Cuyamaca College*

Rachel S. Potti, *Mountain View Community College*

Gregory Podgorski, *Utah State University*

Angela R. Porta, *Kean University*

Wendy M. Rappazzo, *Harford Community College*

Adam Rechs, *California State University, Sacramento*

Beverly Schieltz, *Wright State University*

Bo Sisnicki, *Piedmont Virginia Community College*

Colleen Smith Sisnicki, *Ashford University*

Marc A. Smith, *Sinclair Community College*

Meredith Somerville-Norris, *University of North Carolina, Charlotte*

Anthony Stancampiano, *Oklahoma City Community College*

Brian Sturtevant, *Oakland University*

Brent Todd, *Lake Land Community College*

Edward L. Vezey, *Oklahoma State University, Oklahoma City*

Robert L. Wallace, *Ripon College*

Jane M. Wattrus, *College of St. Scholastica*

Robert R. Wise, *University of Wisconsin, Oshkosh*

Past Edition Reviewers

Kim Anthony Aaronson, *Truman College*

Dawn Adams, *Baylor University*

Julie Adams, *Ohio Northern University*

John Alcock, *Arizona State University*

David L. Alles, *Western Washington University*

Sylvester Allred, *Northern Arizona University*

Gary Anderson, *University of California, Davis*

Marjay A. Anderson, *Howard University*

Michael F. Antolin, *Colorado State University*

Kerri Armstrong, *Community College of Philadelphia*

Mary Ashley, *University of Illinois, Chicago*

Bert Atsma, *Union County College*

Jessica Baack, *Montgomery College*

Kemuel Badger, *Ball State University*

James W. Bailey, *University of Tennessee*

Peter Bednekoff, *Eastern Michigan University*

Michael C. Bell, *Richland College*

William J. Bell, *University of Kansas*

Carla Bundrick Benejam, *California State University, Monterey Bay*

David Berrigan, *University of Washington*

Lois A. Bichler, *Stephens College*

Ian M. Bird, *University of Wisconsin, Madison*

A.W. Blackler, *Cornell University*

Andrew Blaustein, *Oregon State University*

Nancy Boury, *Iowa State University*

Robert S. Boyd, *Auburn University*

Bonnie L. Brenner, *Wilbur Wright College (City College of Chicago)*

Mimi Bres, *Prince George's Community College*

Leon Browder, *University of Calgary*

Arthur L. Buikema, *Virginia Polytechnic Institute and State University (Allegheny College)*

Steven K. Burian, *Southern Connecticut State University*

Janis K. Bush, *University of Texas, San Antonio*

Linda Butler, *University of Texas, Austin*

W. Barkley Butler, *Indiana University of Pennsylvania*

David Byres, *Florida Central Community College, South Campus*

James Cahill, *University of Alberta*

Chantae Calhoun, *Lawson State Community College*

Don Canfield, *University of Southern Denmark*

John Capeheart, *University of Houston-Downtown*

Kelly Sue Cartwright, *College of Lake County*

Marnie Chapman, *University of Alaska, Southeast Sitka*

Van D. Christman, *Ricks College*

Deborah C. Clark, *Middle Tennessee State University*

William S. Cohen, *University of Kentucky*

Karen A. Conzelman, *Glendale Community College*
Tricia Cooley, *Laredo Community College*
Richard Copping, *Lane College*
Lee Couch, *University of New Mexico*
Patricia Cox, *University of Tennessee, Knoxville*
John Crane, *Washington State University*
Robert Curry, *Villanova University*
Garry Davies, *University of Alaska, Anchorage*
Paula Dedmon, *Gaston College*
Miriam del Campo, *Miami-Dade Community College*
Brent DeMars, *Lakeland Community College*
Llewellyn Densmore, *Texas Technical University*
Jean Dickey, *Clemson University*
Christopher Dobson, *Front Range Community College*
Deborah Dodson, *Vincennes University*
Carolyn Doege, *Cy-Fair College*
Cathy Donald-Whitney, *Collin County Community College*
Matthew M. Douglas, *Grand Rapids Community College (University of Kansas)*
Lee C. Drickamer, *Southern Illinois University*
JodyLee Duek, *Pima College*
Albia Dugger, *Miami-Dade College*
Charles Duggins, Jr., *University of South Carolina*
Susan A. Dunford, *University of Cincinnati*
Douglas Eder, *Southern Illinois University*
Ron Edwards, *University of Florida*
Douglas J. Eernisse, *California State University, Fullerton*
Jamin Eisenbach, *Eastern Michigan University*
George Ellmore, *Tufts University*
Patrick E. Elvander, *University of California, Santa Cruz*
Michael Emsley, *George Mason University*
Elyce Ervin, *University of Toledo*
David W. Essar, *Winona State University*
Richard H. Falk, *University of California, Davis*
Michael Farabee, *Estrella Mountain Community College*
Rita Farrar, *Louisiana State University*
John Philip Fawley, *Westminster College*
Eugene J. Fenster, *Longview Community College*
Rebecca Ferrell, *Metropolitan State College at Denver*
Leanne H. Field, *University of Texas, Austin*
Teresa Fischer, *Indian River Community College*
Christine M. Foreman, *University of Toledo*
Carl S. Frankel, *Pennsylvania State University*
Ralph Fregosi, *University of Arizona*
Lawrence Friedman, *University of Missouri, St. Louis*

Carol Friesen, *Ball State University*
John L. Frola, *University of Akron*
Larry Fulton, *American River College*
Gail E. Gasparich, *Towson University*
Matt Geisler, *University of California, Riverside*
Mita Ghosh, *FCCJ*
Tejendra S. Gill, *University of Houston*
Claudette Giscombe, *University of Southern Indiana*
Carolyn Glaubensklee, *University of Southern Colorado*
Jack M. Goldberg, *University of California, Davis*
Elliott Goldstein, *Arizona State University*
Judith Goodenough, *University of Massachusetts, Amherst*
David M. Gordon, *Pittsburg State University*
Glenn A. Gorelick, *Citrus College*
Becky Graham, *The University of West Alabama*
Melvin H. Green, *University of California, San Diego*
G.A. Griffith, *South Suburban College*
Sherri Gross, *Ithaca College*
Edward Hale, *Ball State University*
Gail Hall, *Trinity College*
Linnea S. Hall, *California State University, Sacramento*
Madeline Hall, *Cleveland State University*
Kelly Hamilton, *Shoreline Community College*
James Hampton, *Salt Lake Community College*
Christopher Harendza, *Montgomery County Community College*
Steven C. Harris, *Clarion University*
Barbara Harvey, *Kirkwood Community College*
Steve Heard, *University of Iowa*
Walter Hewitson, *Bridgewater State College*
Jane Aloi Horlings, *Saddleback College*
Eva Horne, *Kansas State University*
Michael Hudecki, *State University of New York, Buffalo*
Michael Hudspeth, *Northern Illinois University*
Terry L. Hufford, *The George Washington University*
Carol A. Hurney, *James Madison University*
Catherine J. Hurlbut, *Florida Community College*
Andrea Huvard, *California Lutheran University*
Martin Ikkanda, *Los Angeles Pierce College*
Rose M. Isgrigg, *Ohio University*
Rebecca Jann, *Queens University of Charlotte*
Thomas W. Jurik, *Iowa State University*
Arnold J. Karpoff, *University of Louisville*
Karry Kazial, *SUNY Fredonia*
Anne Keddy-Hector, *Austin Community College*
Kathleen Keeler, *University of Nebraska*

Nancy Keene, *Pellissippi State Technical Community College*
Kevin M. Kelley, *California State University, Long Beach*
Jeanette J. Kiem, *Guilford Technical Community College*
Tom Knoedler, *Ohio State University, Lima Campus*
Don E. Krane, *Wright State University*
Jocelyn Krebs, *University of Alaska, Anchorage*
Kate Lajtha, *Oregon State University*
Kirkwood Land, *University of the Pacific*
Erika Ann Lawson, *Columbia College*
Mike Lawson, *Missouri Southern State College*
Brenda Leicht, *University of Iowa*
Harvey Liftin, *Broward Community College*
Lynne Lisenby, *Florida Community College at Jacksonville*
Ann S. Lumsden, *Florida State University*
Paul Lurquin, *Washington State University*
James Manser, *Harvey Mudd College*
Michael M. Martin, *University of Michigan, Ann Arbor*
Paul Mason, *Butte Community College*
Michel Masson, *Santa Barbara City College*
Andrea Mastro, *Pennsylvania State University*
Mary Victoria McDonald, *University of Central Arkansas*
Mary Colleen McNamara, *Albuquerque T-VI A Community College*
Hugh A. Miller, III, *East Tennessee University*
Leslie R. Miller, *Iowa State University*
Lee H. Mitchell, *Mount Hood Community College*
Robert Mitchell, *Community College of Philadelphia*
Jeremy Montague, *Barry University*
Scott M. Moody, *Ohio University*
Janice Moore, *Colorado State University*
Joseph Moore, *California State University*
Jorge A. Moreno, *University of Colorado*
Michael D. Morgan, *University of Wisconsin, Green Bay*
David Mork, *Saint Cloud State University*
Deborah A. Morris, *Portland State University*
Allison Morrison-Shetlar, *Georgia Southern University*
Richard Mortensen, *Albion College*
Christopher B. Mowry, *Berry College*
Michelle Murphy, *University of Notre Dame*
Courtney Murren, *University of Tennessee, Knoxville*
Richard L. Myers, *Missouri State University*
Royden Nakamura, *California Polytechnic State University*
Leann Naughton, *University of Wyoming*

Judy M. Nesmith, *University of Michigan, Dearborn*
Harry Nickla, *Creighton University*
James A. Nienow, *Valdosta State University*
Jane Noble-Harvey, *University of Delaware*
Paul Nolan, *Ithaca College*
Ray Ochs, *St. John's University*
Hunter O'Reilly, *University of Wisconsin, Milwaukee*
Marcy P. Osgood, *University of Michigan*
Andrea Ostrofsky, *University of Maine*
Onesimus Otieno, *Oakwood College*
Charles Owens, *King College*
Maya Patel, *Ithaca College*
Eckle L. Peabody, *Tulsa Community College*
Kathleen Pelkki, *Saginaw Valley State University*
Patricia A. Peroni, *Davidson College*
Rhoda E. Perozzi, *Virginia Commonwealth University*
Carolyn Peters, *Spoon River College*
John S. Peters, *College of Charleston*
Kim M. Peterson, *University of Alaska, Anchorage*
Raleigh K. Pettegrew, *Denison University*
Gary W. Pettibone, *State University of New York, College at Buffalo*
Holly C. Pinkart, *Central Washington University*
Barbara Pleasants, *Iowa State University*
John M. Pleasants, *Iowa State University*
Lynn Polasek, *Los Angeles Valley College*
F. Harvey Pough, *Arizona State University, West*
Don Pribor, *University of Toledo*
Michelle Priest, *University of Southern California*
Louis Primavera, *Hawaii Pacific University*
Paul Ramp, *Pellissippi State and Technical Community College*
Ameed Raoof, *University of Michigan Medical School*
Marceau Ratard, *Delgado Community College*
Regina Rector, *William Rainey Harper College*
Robert J. Reinsvold, *University of Northern Colorado*
Rick Relyea, *University of Pittsburgh*
Michael H. Renfroe, *James Madison University*
Dennis Richardson, *Quinnipiac University*
Todd Rimkus, *Marymount University*
Sonia J. Ringstrom, *Loyola University*
David A. Rintoul, *Kansas State University*
Darryl Ritter, *Okaloosa-Walton Community College*

Carolyn Roberson, *Roane State Community College*
Laurel Roberts, *University of Pittsburgh*
Jay Robinson, *San Antonio College*
Rodney A. Rogers, *Drake University*
William H. Rohrer, *Union County College*
Leslie Ann Roldan, *Massachusetts Institute of Technology*
Amanda Rosenzweig, *Delgado Community College*
Heidi Rottschafer, *University of Notre Dame*
John Rueter, *Portland State University*
Ron Ruppert, *Cuesta College*
Brian Sailer, *Sam Houston State University*
Nancy Sanders, *Northeast Missouri Sate University*
Gary Sarinsky, *City University of New York, Kingsborough Community College*
Julie Schroer, *Bismarck State College*
Steven Scott, *Merritt College*
Edna Seaman, *University of Massachusetts, Boston*
Ralph W. Seelke, *University of Wisconsin, Superior*
Prem P. Sehgal, *East Carolina University*
C. Thomas Settlemire, *Bowdoin College*
Robert Shetlar, *Georgia Southern University*
Cara Shillington, *Eastern Michigan University*
Mark A. Shotwell, *University of Slippery Rock*
Linda Simpson, *University of North Carolina, Charlotte*
Peter Slater, *University of St. Andrews, UK*
Ellen Smith, *Arizona State University, West*
Linda Smith-Staton, *Pellissippi State Technical Community College*
Philip J. Snider, *University of Houston*
Nancy G. Solomon, *Miami University*
Salvatore A. Sparace, *Clemson University*
Frederick W. Spiegel, *University of Arkansas*
Bryan Spohn, *Florida Community College at Jacksonville–Kent Campus*
Kathleen M. Steinert, *Bellevue Community College*
Allan R. Stevens, *Snow College*
Donald P. Streubel, *Idaho State University*
Gerald Summers, *University of Missouri, Columbia*
Christine Tachibana, *University of Washington*
Steven Tanner, *University of Missouri*
Todd Templeton, *Metropolitan Community College*
Rebekah J. Thomas, *Saint Leo University*
Joanne Tornow, *University of Southern Mississippi*

Todd T. Tracy, *Colorado State University*
Robin W. Tyser, *University of Wisconsin, LaCrosse*
Rani Vajravelu, *University of Central Florida*
Joseph W. Vanable, Jr., *Purdue University*
William A. Velhagen, Jr., *Longwood College*
Tanya Vickers, *University of Utah*
Janet Vigna, *Grand Valley State University*
Allan Hayes Vogel, *Chemeketa Community College*
Dennis Vrba, *North Iowa Area Community College*
Stephen Wagener, *Western Connecticut State University*
Jyoti R. Wagle, *Houston Community College*
John H. Wahlert, *Baruch College, The City University of New York*
Carol Wake, *South Dakota State University*
Timothy S. Wakefield, *John Brown University*
Charles Walcott, *Cornell University*
Gene Walton, *Tallahassee Community College*
Yunqiu Wang, *University of Miami*
Sarah Ward, *Colorado State University*
Jennifer M. Warner, *University of North Carolina, Charlotte*
Cheryl Watson, *Central Connecticut State University*
Richard Weinstein, *University of Tennessee, Knoxville*
Richard Barry Welch, *San Antonio College*
Jamie Welling, *South Suburban College*
Elizabeth Forston Wells, *George Washington University*
Mary Pat Wenderoth, *University of Washington*
Susan Whittemore, *Keene State University*
Allison Wiedemeier, *University of Missouri-Columbia*
Sandra Winicur, *Indiana University, South Bend*
William Wischusen, *Louisiana State University*
James Wise, *Hampton University*
Deborah Wisti-Peterson, *University of Washington*
Rachel Witcher, *University of Central Florida*
Mark A. Woelfe, *Vanderbilt University*
Lorne Wolfe, *Georgia Southern University*
Wade B. Worthen, *Furman University*
Robert Yost, *Indiana University Purdue University Indianapolis*
Calvin Young, *Fullerton College*
Martha C. Zúñiga, *University of California, Santa Cruz*
Victoria Zusman, *Miami-Dade Community College*

Navigate the World of Biology

Give your biology students an indispensable tour guide

Author David Krogh *guides* your students through the world of biology with his accessible and easy-to-understand writing style. The book is a helpful companion that *guides* non-majors students on their voyage through biology by placing unfamiliar topics in context with everyday life.

Krogh's engaging writing style walks students step by step through complex biological processes.

An accessible writing style means your students will actually enjoy reading this book!

" To understand what this latter role means in practice, let's think about what happens when you eat something—say, a candy bar. The result of doing this is that you'll get a surge of simple sugar coursing through your veins; this is blood-sugar that needs to move into your cells to satisfy their energy needs. "

— Excerpt from page 157

" In a corporation, there may be several individuals making up an office, several offices making up a department, several departments making up a division, and so forth. In life, there is one set of organized "building blocks" making up another, as you can see. "

— Excerpt from page 10

The text captures students' interest with analogies from everyday life, history, art, and literature.

" Why this change in form? This condensing before cell division has the same effect as you taking all your scattered belongings and packing them into boxes just before moving from one apartment to another. Remember that DNA is packing up to leave as well, in this case for life in a successor cell. Were it not to tighten into its duplicated chromosomal form, its elongated fibers would get tangled up in the move. "

— Excerpt from page 163

Engaging visuals lead students to better understanding

A strong illustration program *guides* students through structures and processes with clear three-dimensional detail; key information from the text is reinforced in the illustrations.

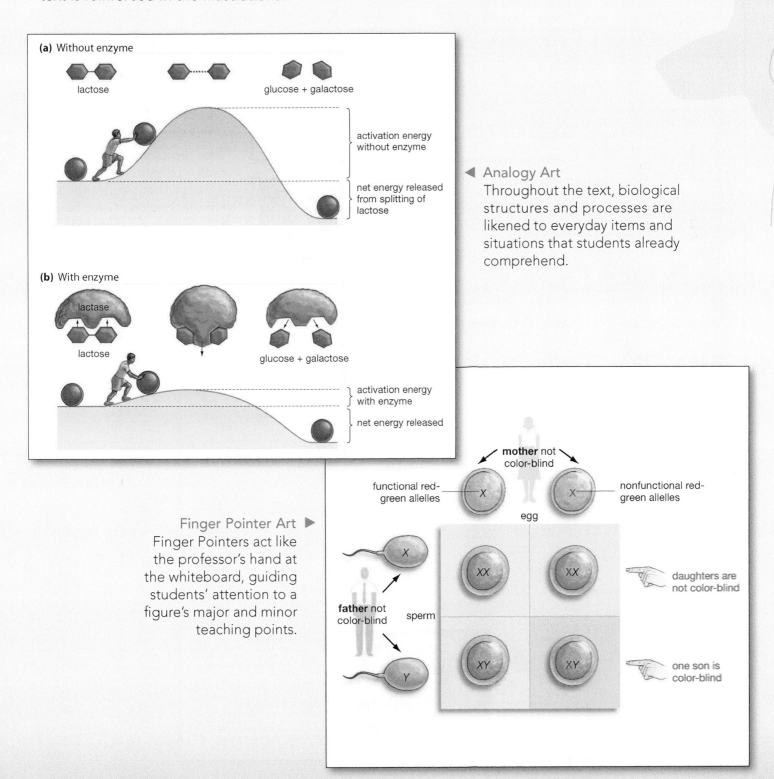

(a) Without enzyme

lactose

glucose + galactose

activation energy without enzyme

net energy released from splitting of lactose

(b) With enzyme

lactase

lactose

glucose + galactose

activation energy with enzyme

net energy released

◄ Analogy Art
Throughout the text, biological structures and processes are likened to everyday items and situations that students already comprehend.

Finger Pointer Art ▶
Finger Pointers act like the professor's hand at the whiteboard, guiding students' attention to a figure's major and minor teaching points.

mother not color-blind

functional red-green allelles

nonfunctional red-green allelles

X

X

egg

XX

XX

daughters are not color-blind

X

Y

father not color-blind

sperm

XY

XY

one son is color-blind

A Guide Like No Other

Scenic outlooks help students interpret biology in a meaningful way

Essays provide helpful insights that resonate with today's students.

ESSAY

PGD: Screening for a Healthy Child

"Is the baby OK?" In a life full of questions, it's possible that none carries more weight than this one. In most cases, the answer will be reassuring, but in some it will be devastating. Small wonder, then, that scientists constantly are trying to perfect ways to know in advance whether a new... healthy. You have seen the... of debilitating human co... netic causes. Further, you... every kind of cell in a per... tains a complete copy of... genome, or set of genes... check on someone's gene... that is necessary is to hav... collection of that person'... exist, of course, in embry... newborn babies and adu... hard to see what the pro... for prenatal genetic testi... onic cells and examine th... chromosomes.

This kind of testing h... in ever-more-refined for... 1960s. From that time u... ever, most prospective pa... bad news from a genetic... choices: abort the fetus... with an incurable condit... world. Now, an ever-grov... of reproductive clinics ar... third choice. Parents wh... undertake so-called in vi... fertilization of the moth... laboratory—can have ea... early-stage embryos that... process tested for geneti... initial group of embryos... to be genetically healthy...

be inserted back into the mother. The hope is that at least one of them will implant in the mother's uterus and result in a child.

Right now, some clinics allow parents to use PGD to...

such as Huntington, but there is a difference. In amniocentesis, cells are obtained from an embryo that has been developing in a mother's uterus for a minimum of 14 weeks. By the time the results of amniocentesis are in, more than four months of a nine-month pregnancy may have elapsed. Most prospective parents would make a distinction between aborting a

---

ESSAY

When Energy Harvesting Ends at Glycolysis, Wine Can Be the Result

For yeasts, alcohol is simply a by-product of the fermentation they carry out.

For some bacteria—and even sometimes for people—energy harvesting ends with the set of steps called glycolysis rather than pr... the Krebs cycle and ox... electron transport cha... happens, organisms n... their energy transfer r... that doesn't depend o... they produced in glyco... added electrons and b... so it can be reused in... tion to this dilemma i... dumping, the product... to be some of the mos... in the world.

Fermentation in

Yeasts provide a good... in which this works b... busy single-celled fur... glycolysis alone, or th... aerobic respiration. S... are working away on... glycolysis, but doing... environment. Recall t... strate" product of gly... cules of a substance c... In yeasts, the pyruvi... with is converted to a... acetaldehyde, and it t... from NADH, meanin... problem is now solve... NADH's electrons, th... now is converted to s... familiar: ethanol, bet... drinking alcohol.

Human beings put... ments in which this w...

because this is how we make wine and beer. Imagine yeast cells inside a dark, airless wine cask, working

---

ESSAY

When the Cell Cycle Runs Amok: Cancer

The cell cycle reviewed in this chapter is, in one sense, a common natural process: Cells grow; they duplicate their chromosomes; these chromosomes separate; one cell divides into two. This goes on like clockwork, millions of times a second in each one of us. Then one day we learn that an aunt, a grandfather, or a friend is experiencing an *unrestrained* division of cells. Things aren't explained to us in this way, of course. We are simply told that someone we know has cancer.

At root, all cancers are failures of the cell cycle. Put another way, all cancers represent a failure of cells to limit their multiplication in the cell cycle. What is liver cancer, for example? It is a damaging multiplication of liver cells. First one, then two, then four, then eight liver cells move repeatedly through the cell cycle, and as their numbers increase, they destroy the liver's working tissues. Given that cancer manifests in this way, it's not surprising that a large portion of modern cancer research is *cell-cycle* research. The logic here is simple: To the extent that uncontrolled cell division can be stopped, cancer can be stopped.

In recent years, cell-cycle research has brought about a remarkable change in the kinds of treatments that are being developed for cancer. For decades, the basic idea behind cancer treatment was to kill as many cancer cells as possible, either by removing these cells from the body altogether (in surgery) or by destroying them with radiation or drugs. In contrast, nearly all the cancer drugs being developed today are intended not to kill cancerous cells. Instead, they are intended to disrupt the process by which these cells multiply. The idea is that, just as a light can be switched off by disrupting an electrical circuit, so cell division can be switched off by disrupting a *molecular* circuit—the chain of chemical reactions that keeps a cancerous cell moving constantly through cell division. The new breed of cancer treatments that are built on this idea are called targeted therapies.

To get a feel for what this approach means in practice, consider the first targeted therapy ever developed: a drug called Gleevec, which is aimed at combating a form of cancer, called chronic myeloid leukemia (CML), that results in an uncontrolled proliferation of certain types of white blood cells. In the 1990s, the researcher most responsible for Gleevec's use in CML treatment, Oregon Health and Sciences University Professor

Brian Druker, began to focus on the process by which CML cells come to their out-of-control state. Druker knew that CML begins in a single white blood cell when two of its chromosomes undergo an unusual form of segment-swapping with one another. When a segment from chromosome A fuses with a segment of chromosome B in this process, the result is that information from both chromosomes combines to create a mutant gene—a gene that does not exist in any normal white blood cell. Of course, this mutant gene (dubbed *BCR-ABL*) then results in a protein that is capable of carrying out some task in the white blood cell. Unfortunately, what the BCR-ABL protein does is flip a molecular switch; through it, the white blood cell starts multiplying more rapidly, even as it and its daughter cells start undergoing further destabilizing changes that ultimately result in full-blown leukemia.

Druker's key insight into stopping CML was to look very carefully at the BCR-ABL protein, which you can see represented in **Figure 1**. He realized that BCR-ABL is powered into activity following its binding with the energy-transfer molecule ATP. So, he wondered, what would happen if the ATP binding site on the BCR-ABL protein became unavailable—what would happen if this binding site became *occupied* by another molecule? The substance he eventually hit upon that takes on this occupying role

Figure 9.11
Cytokinesis in Animals

Cytokinesis in animal cells begins with an indentation of the cell surface, a cleavage furrow, shown here in a dividing frog egg.

through the tightening of a cellular waistband that is composed of two sets of protein filaments working together. These filaments—the same type that allow your muscles to contract—form a *contractile ring* that narrows along the cellular equator (**Figure 9.11**). An indentation of the cell's surface (called a cleavage furrow) results from the ring's contraction; consequently, the fibers in the mitotic spindle are pushed closer and closer together, eventually forming one thick pole that is destined to break.

The dividing cell now assumes an hourglass shape; as the contractile ring continues to pinch in, one cell becomes two by means of something you looked at in Chapter 4: membrane fusion. The membranes on each

---

NEW! Essays

Many new Essays focus on social concerns and personal applications, helping your students apply what they are learning in class to their own experiences.

New topics include:
- Using Photosynthesis to Fight Global Warming
- Biotechnology Gets Personal
- An Evolving Ability to Drink Milk

Navigate the World of Biology

Give your biology students an indispensable tour guide

Author David Krogh *guides* your students through the world of biology with his accessible and easy-to-understand writing style. The book is a helpful companion that *guides* non-majors students on their voyage through biology by placing unfamiliar topics in context with everyday life.

Krogh's engaging writing style walks students step by step through complex biological processes.

An accessible writing style means your students will actually enjoy reading this book!

> To understand what this latter role means in practice, let's think about what happens when you eat something—say, a candy bar. The result of doing this is that you'll get a surge of simple sugar coursing through your veins; this is blood-sugar that needs to move into your cells to satisfy their energy needs.

— Excerpt from page 157

> In a corporation, there may be several individuals making up an office, several offices making up a department, several departments making up a division, and so forth. In life, there is one set of organized "building blocks" making up another, as you can see.

— Excerpt from page 10

The text captures students' interest with analogies from everyday life, history, art, and literature.

> Why this change in form? This condensing before cell division has the same effect as you taking all your scattered belongings and packing them into boxes just before moving from one apartment to another. Remember that DNA is packing up to leave as well, in this case for life in a successor cell. Were it not to tighten into its duplicated chromosomal form, its elongated fibers would get tangled up in the move.

— Excerpt from page 163

All of the Tools You Need for a Memorable Experience

The Mastering platform is the most effective and widely used online tutorial, homework, and assessment system for the sciences.

- Over one million active student users
- Data-supported efficacy
- A proven history with over 8 years of student use
- Active users in all 50 states and in 30 countries
- 99.8% server reliability

Make Learning Part of the Grade®

Mastering**BIOLOGY**®

www.masteringbiology.com

Study tools prepare students for their adventure

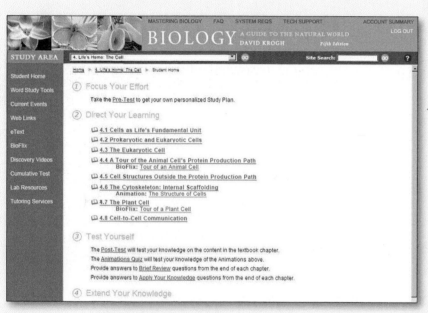

◄ MasteringBiology® Study Area
The Study Area offers customized study plans for students presented in an easy-to-use chapter guide interface. Features found in the Study Area include Chapter Pre-tests, Vocabulary Review, an Audio Glossary, Animations, and Chapter Post-tests.

Pearson eText ▶
Give students access to the text whenever and wherever they can access the Internet. The eText pages look exactly like the printed text, and include powerful interactive and customization functions.

Easy-to-use resources get you on your way

MasteringBiology provides you with a variety of multimedia resources, coaching activities, and pre-built assignments, making it easier for you to engage your students and help them succeed in your class.

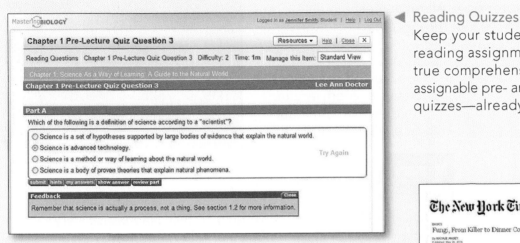

◀ Reading Quizzes
Keep your students on track with your reading assignments and test their true comprehension with these easily assignable pre- and post-lecture reading quizzes—already prepared for you.

Current Events ▶
Easily assignable *New York Times* articles and Discovery Channel videos engage non-majors students in course concepts and allow you to easily assess their scientific literacy.

BioFlix® Coaching Activities
Easily assign a key selection of coaching activities and tutorials on the toughest topics in biology. Built around the BioFlix 3D movie-quality animations, these tutorials coach students to better understanding.

GraphIt!
Easily assignable activities help students better understand how to work with and interpret graphs and real data.

Ensuring a Successful Journey for You

Instructor Resource DVD (IR-DVD)
978-0-321-68276-5 • 0-321-68276-9

Everything you need for lectures is in one place. Enhanced menus make locating and assessing the digital resources for each chapter easy. All resources found on the IR-DVD are also available through the Instructor Resources Area of MasteringBiology.®

BioFlix® animations ▶
Invigorate classroom lectures with effective, 3-minute, movie quality, 3D graphics.

◀ These brief 3–5 minute Discovery Channel video clips cover topics from fighting cancer to antibiotic resistance and introduced species.

▲
Over 200 extra animations are scientifically clear, accurate, and available in PowerPoint.

◀ Customizable PowerPoint® Lectures serve as lecture outlines and are included for each textbook chapter.

▼

Expanded Test Bank questions are available as downloadable Microsoft® Word files and in TestGen.®

All of the art, stepped-art, tables, and photos from the book are available with customizable labels and are also available in PowerPoint.

▼

www.pearsonhighered.com/virtualbiologylabs

◄ NEW! MasteringBiology: Virtual Labs is an online environment that promotes critical thinking skills using virtual experiments and explorations that may be difficult to perform in a wet lab environment due to time, cost, or safety concerns. The MasteringBiology: Virtual Labs upgrade option provides unique learning experiences in the areas of Microscopy, Molecular Biology, Genetics, Ecology, and Systematics.

Additional Student Supplements

Study Guide
978-0-321-68303-8 • 0-321-68303-X

This tool is an effective and interactive study guide presenting information in short modules, which allows students to decide where to concentrate their study efforts. The Study Guide features a consistent format and uniform organization so students can quickly assimilate the layout and use the guide effectively.

Study Card
978-0-321-68280-2 • 0-321-68280-7

This laminated quick reference Study Card has been developed specifically for *Biology: A Guide to the Natural World.* The Study Card provides a brief, chapter-by-chapter review, including key figures, to help students review the most important topics in biology.

Scientific American Current Issues in Biology
www.pearsonhighered.com/currentissues

Articles include questions to help students check their comprehension and make connections to science and society.

Contents

CHAPTER 4

Life's Home:
The Cell

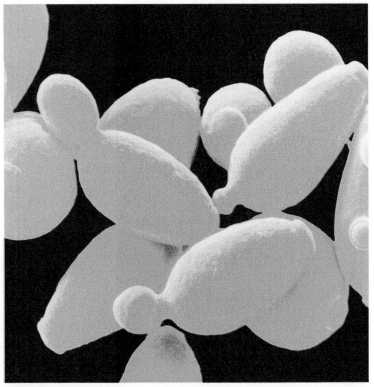

CHAPTER 5

Life's Border:
The Plasma Membrane

Unit 2

Energy and Its Transformations

Unit 3
How Life Goes On: Genetics

CHAPTER 14

How Proteins Are Made:
Genetic Transcription, Translation, and Regulation   244

CHAPTER 13

Passing on Life's Information:
DNA Structure and Replication   232

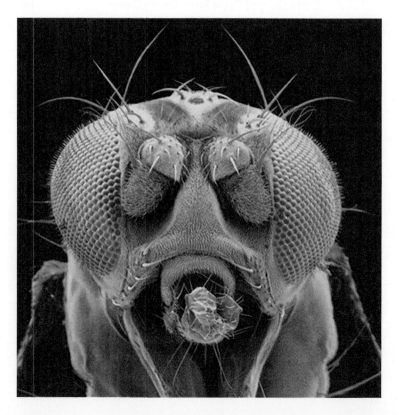

CHAPTER 15

The Future Isn't What It Used to Be: Biotechnology

Unit 4

Life's Organizing Principle: Evolution and the Diversity of Life

CHAPTER 16

An Introduction to Evolution:
Charles Darwin, Evolutionary Thought, and the Evidence for Evolution

CHAPTER **17**

The Means of Evolution:
Microevolution   300

CHAPTER **18**

The Outcomes of Evolution:
Macroevolution   318

CHAPTER **21**

Viruses, Bacteria, Archaea, and
Protists: The Diversity of Life 1   378

CHAPTER 22

Fungi:
The Diversity of Life 2

CHAPTER 23

Animals:
The Diversity of Life 3

CHAPTER 24

Plants:
The Diversity of Life 4

Unit 5

A Bounty That Feeds Us All: Plants

CHAPTER 25

The Angiosperms:

Form and Function in Flowering Plants

Unit 6

What Makes the Organism Tick? Human Anatomy and Physiology

CHAPTER 26

Body Support and Movement:

The Integumentary, Skeletal, and Muscular Systems

CHAPTER 36

An Interactive Living World 3:

Ecosystems and Biomes

Science as a Way of Learning:

A Guide to the Natural World

Science has great impact on our lives now and stands to have greater impact on them in the future. Science is both a body of knowledge and a means of acquiring knowledge. Biology, a branch of science, is the study of life.

Measurement plays a part in almost every scientific investigation. Here, an ecologist in Borneo measures a rafflesia plant (*Rafflesia keithii*), whose flower is believed to be the largest in the world.

I n September 2008, the editors of *Nature* magazine noted an anniversary that had just occurred: Exactly 10 years earlier, the first employee of Google walked into the suburban garage that was serving as Google's headquarters at the time. In the intervening years, of course, Google became the largest distributor of information on the planet—something that

prompted the *Nature* editors to pose a question to a group of cutting-edge science and technology analysts: What technology, currently at the stage Google was at in 1998, will have changed our world in the *next* 10 years as much as Google did in the past 10?

Of the six sets of predictions that *Nature* received, the most mind-bending came from Ian Pearson, an Englishman who makes his living consulting about the future. Pearson foresees a mash-up of our computer worlds and our everyday physical worlds that will come to us via a digital tool called the video visor, which may end up looking something like a set of wrap-around ski goggles spiked by a small wireless antenna. Each visor would be outfitted with a global positioning system and a high-speed Internet connection, thus giving its wearer a constant stream of information about his or her surroundings.

"So as you're walking down a busy city street," Pearson says, "you will be able to see reviews of shops and restaurants, adverts for services, other people who have similar interests to you, or whatever." All this will be customizable according to your interests. On a given day, you might be interested only in Chinese restaurants or perhaps in people you pass who play bridge (and who likewise are seeking out bridge players themselves). But the fun wouldn't stop there. As Pearson has written elsewhere, "Building appearance will depend on the taste of the person looking at it. So will the appearance of other people. People, buildings, and objects will emit a digital aura that contains alternative digital appearances as well as lots of marketing information. . . . You may well broadcast a different image according to the viewer. So your portable will act as a digital filter, deciding what you want to see and how you want to see it, and a personal advertiser, marketing you to the rest of the world."

And if you're thinking that the real stumbling block to this is that nobody would want to walk around with a set of ski goggles on, well, think how ordinary it now seems to see a person on the street talking out loud into a cell phone headset when only a few years ago such behavior seemed a little bizarre.

1.1 How Does Science Impact the Everyday World?

The future that Pearson foresees may not come to pass, of course, but the thing that makes his vision so riveting is that we can imagine such leaps taking place in the near future because we've seen so many like them taking place in the recent past. The touch screen on an iPhone manages to seem like magic to us, even though it's fully *functional* magic, ready to enlarge a picture or get us to a website. A satellite image of our own house may cause us to shake our heads in disbelief that such a thing is possible, and yet there's our house, right in front of us on a computer screen.

We may categorize most of this change under the umbrella heading of *technology,* but when we look deeply enough into the roots of any technological innovation what we generally find is a contribution made by the endeavor we call science. The fundamental discovery that brought about modern electronics, including the computer, was research done on materials science that culminated with the invention of the transistor at Bell Labs in 1947. And most of the software that runs our electronic devices has its roots in university-based computer science research. What has happened in the years since World War II is that the fruits of this kind of research have been made ever more personal—moving from the laboratory, to businesses, and finally into our homes—even as the pace of technological innovation has been gaining speed over time.

To look at these events in connection with computer technology, average Americans heard about computers for 30 years following the invention of the transistor, but not until the mid-1980s were they *using* computers right on their desktops. Once this revolution in circuits got going, however, things came in a torrent. CD players were newfangled devices in the mid-1980s; now, people are downloading MP3 files into their portable global positioning systems. Then again, we need not go back to the 1980s to see how fast technological change is coming. On a typical day, do you send an e-mail to someone, talk on a cell phone, or visit a website? As late as the mid-1990s, the average person would not have done any of these things (**Figure 1.1**).

A similar story has taken place in connection with the raft of new products and processes that go under the heading of biotechnology. The fundamental breakthrough that brought about biotech was the description of the DNA molecule in 1953 by James Watson and Francis Crick. Some 25 years elapsed, however, between this discovery and the appearance of the first genetically engineered medicine (human

insulin). But now? Eighty percent of U.S.-grown corn is genetically modified, criminals are regularly convicted (and innocent people freed) through use of DNA "fingerprints," cloned goats can provide us with human medicines, and in the near future you may be able to get a copy of your own personal genome—the inventory of all your DNA information—for less than $1,000, whereas in 2006 the cost of getting this information stood at more than $1 million.

It may go without saying that these various innovations and discoveries entail value judgments on the part of society. Research involving embryonic stem cells seems to have great potential to cure or alleviate the suffering caused by such conditions as spinal cord injuries and Parkinson's disease. Yet this research is dependent on the removal of cells from embryos that would otherwise be discarded by fertility clinics—a procedure that kills the embryos. After looking at both sides of this issue, California voters decided in 2004 that, over the ensuing 10 years, they would spend $3 billion of state money on embryonic stem cell research. They did so, however, only after *national* political leaders came to a very different conclusion about this research. From 2001 to 2009, federal funding of it was severely restricted by order of President George Bush, who believed that the killing of human embryos amounted to a taking of human life. The Bush funding restrictions lasted only as long as the Bush presidency, however. The change in voter sentiment that brought Barack Obama to office in 2009 resulted in a directive from him that loosened federal limitations on stem cell research. Of course, stem cells are not the only science-driven issue that society is grappling with. Think of genetically modified foods, the dizzying possibility of a human clone, and suspects who are listed on arrest warrants not by their names but by their DNA profiles.

Note that all these issues have been brought to society by science. We might say that science has presented society with *options*, about which society then makes decisions. But things also work the other way around—society brings issues to science. Why? To get advice. Since scientists are in the business of investigating nature, they function, in effect, as society's eyes and ears on the natural world. Thus, if we want to know whether Earth really is warming, whether we're in danger from an errant comet, or what the likelihood is of swine flu spreading, then it's not politicians, economists, or business executives who are going to tell us; it is scientists. In line with this, scarcely a week goes by without scientists rendering judgments on vital issues that touch on nature's processes. Do polar bears need protection as an endangered species? Does the practice of thinning out forests reduce the risk of catastrophic forest fires? What are the risk factors for diabetes? In all these instances, governments and average citizens look to

Figure 1.1
Then and Now

(a) A technician enters data into the world's first programmable computer, run initially in 1948. Called "Baby," the computer was more than 6 feet tall and almost 16 feet wide but had a total memory of only 128 bytes.

(b) In contrast, this MSI touch-screen computer, displayed at the 2010 Las Vegas Consumer Electronics Show, was two feet across, less than three inches thick, and had a total memory of 640 billion bytes.

(a)

(b)

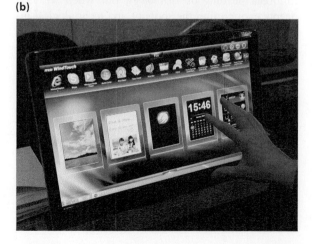

science to provide answers (after which it's up to governments and average citizens to act on the advice they get).

If we take a step back from all this, the message is that science and technology are now woven more tightly into the fabric of society than ever before. Accordingly, to fully participate in the workforce, to make informed choices at the ballot box, or simply to make routine decisions, the average person must now be more scientifically literate than ever before. To get a sense of how this plays out in everyday life, let's look at some biology-related news that came to Americans through one magazine (*Time*) during one short period (June through October 2008). In the process, you'll see how learning something about science can provide a foundation for understanding the kind of science-related news that comes our way every day.

How Safe Are Vaccines? *Time* asked in its June 2 cover story, which noted that a small but growing number of children in the United States are not being vaccinated against common childhood diseases because of their parents' belief that vaccination serves to cause illness, rather than prevent it (**Figure 1.2**).

Figure 1.2
Science in the News

The importance of science to everyday life is reflected in the large number of news stories that focus on science. Pictured are several magazines whose cover stories concerned science-related issues.

Time didn't have the space to fill in its readers on how vaccination works or what kinds of illnesses it's aimed at stopping, but readers of this book can learn about both topics by turning to the *Guide*'s Chapter 29, on the human immune system, which begins on page 550.

It's Not Just Genetics, said *Time* in its story of June 12 on the reasons for the national epidemic of childhood obesity. Factors other than genes, such as poverty and place of residence, also play a part in predisposing children to being obese. But how common is it for genes to work in concert with "environmental" factors such as these to produce a given physical condition? And what is it about being overweight that's so hazardous to human health? Readers interested in the first question can turn to Chapter 11's primer on inheritance, which begins on page 190, while readers interested in the second question should see "Why Fat Matters and Why Exercise May Matter More" in Chapter 26 on page 492.

Mopping Up the CO_2 Deluge, in *Time*'s July 3 issue, was about ways to combat global warming by getting rid of the excess carbon dioxide that human beings have put into the atmosphere over the last couple of hundred years. One of these proposed "geoengineering" techniques is to fertilize the world's oceans with iron, thus allowing algae to flourish on a scale large enough to soak up significant amounts of atmospheric CO_2. Both the algae and the carbon within them would then sink to the bottom of the ocean when the algae die—or so the proposal goes. But why do algae soak up CO_2? To find out, see Chapter 8, on photosynthesis, beginning on page 140. And what are the root causes of global warming? Chapter 36 provides some answers, beginning on page 704.

He Won His Battle with Cancer, in *Time*'s September 4 edition, was on the glacially slow progress the United States is making in its fight against cancer. "Overall, the death-rate from cancer dropped just 5 percent from 1950 to 2005," *Time* noted, while during the same period, "deaths from heart disease dropped 64 percent." Though there are many different kinds of cancer, all of them are the result of a breakdown in a basic biological process: cell division, which you can read about in Chapter 9, beginning on page 156. And what causes these breakdowns? Mutations to DNA, which you can read about in Chapter 13, beginning on page 232.

The Forgotten Plague, in *Time*'s October 2 edition, was about the resurgence of a disease that at one time seemed to be all but vanquished: tuberculosis, which has recently appeared in forms that are resistant to all the tuberculosis-fighting antibiotics we have. But what is an antibiotic, and why have many of these drugs begun losing their effectiveness against diseases such as tuberculosis? To find out, see "Bacteria and Human Disease" in Chapter 21, beginning on page 389.

1.2 What Is Science?

Having looked a little at the impact that science has, it might be helpful now to consider the question of what science *is*. The point here is to give you some sense of the underpinnings of science—to review something about the how and why of it before you begin looking at the nature of one of its disciplines, biology.

Science as a Body of Knowledge

Science is in one sense a process—a *way* of learning. In this respect, it is an activity carried out under certain rules, which we'll get to shortly. **Science** is also a body of knowledge about the natural world. It is a collection of unified insights about nature, the evidence for which is an array of facts. The unified insights of science are commonly referred to as *theories.*

It is unfortunate but true that the word *theory* means one thing in everyday speech and something almost completely different in scientific communication. In everyday speech, a theory can be little more than a hunch. It is an unproven idea that may or may not have any supportive evidence. In science, meanwhile, a **theory** is a general set of principles, supported by evidence, that explains some aspect of nature. There is, for example, a Big Bang theory of the universe. It is a general set of principles that explains how our universe began and then developed over time. Among its principles are that a cataclysmic explosion occurred about 13.7 billion years ago, and that after it, matter first developed in the form of gases, which then coalesced into the stars we can see all around us. There are numerous facts supporting these principles, such as the current size of the universe and its average temperature.

As you might imagine, with any theory this grand some *pieces* of it are in dispute; some facts don't fit the theory, and scientists disagree about how to interpret this piece of information or that. On the whole, though, these insights have withstood the questioning of critics and stand as a scientific theory.

The Importance of Theories

Far from being a hunch, a scientific theory actually is a much more valued entity than is a scientific fact because the theory has an *explanatory* power, while a fact generally is an isolated piece of information. That the universe is about 13.7 billion years old is a wonderfully interesting fact, but it explains little in comparison with the Big Bang theory. Facts are important; theories could not be supported or refuted without them. But science is first and foremost in the theory-building business, not the fact-finding business.

Science as a Process: Arriving at Scientific Insights

So how does a body of facts and theories come about? What is the process of scientific investigation, in other words? When science is viewed as a process, it could be defined as a means of coming to understand the natural world through observation and the testing of hypotheses. This process is referred to as the **scientific method** (**Figure 1.3**). The starting state for scientific inquiry is always *observation*: A piece of the natural world is observed to work in a certain way. Then follows the *question,* which broadly speaking is one of three types: a "what" question, a "why" question, or a "how" question. Biologists have asked, for example: What are genes made of? Why does the number of species decrease as we move from the equator to the poles? How does the brain make sense of visual images?

Following the formulation of the question, various hypotheses are proposed that might answer it. A **hypothesis** is a tentative, testable explanation for an observed phenomenon. In almost any scientific question, several hypotheses are proposed to account for the same observation. Which one is correct? Most fre-

Figure 1.3
Scientific Method

The scientific method enables us to answer questions by testing hypotheses.

quently in science, the answer is provided by a series of experiments, which are controlled tests of the question at hand. Scientists don't regard all hypotheses as equally worthy of undergoing experimental test. By the time scientists arrive at the experimental stage, they usually have an idea of which is the most promising hypothesis among the contenders and then proceed to put that hypothesis to the test. Let's see how this worked in an example from history.

The Scientific Method at Work: Pasteur and Spontaneous Generation

Does life regularly arise from anything *but* life, or can it be created "spontaneously," through the coming together of basic chemicals? The latter idea had wide acceptance from the time of the ancient Romans, and

as late as the nineteenth century it was championed by some of the leading scientists of the day. So, how could the issue be decided? The famous French chemist and medical researcher Louis Pasteur formulated a hypothesis to address this question (**Figure 1.4**). He believed that many purported examples of life arising spontaneously were simply instances of airborne microscopic organisms landing on a suitable substance and then multiplying in such profusion that they could be seen. Life came from life, in other words, not from spontaneous generation. But how could this be demonstrated? In 1860, Pasteur sterilized a meat broth in glass flasks by heating it, while at the same time heating the glass *necks* of the flasks, after which he bent the necks into a "swan" or S shape. The ends of the flasks remained open to the air, but

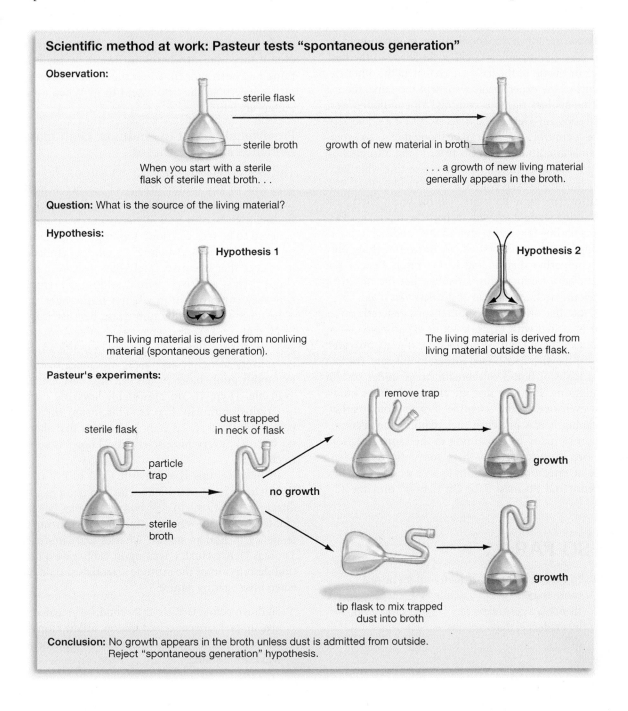

Scientific method at work: Pasteur tests "spontaneous generation"

Observation:

sterile flask

sterile broth   growth of new material in broth

When you start with a sterile flask of sterile meat broth. . .   . . . a growth of new living material generally appears in the broth.

Question: What is the source of the living material?

Hypothesis:

Hypothesis 1

The living material is derived from nonliving material (spontaneous generation).

Hypothesis 2

The living material is derived from living material outside the flask.

Pasteur's experiments:

remove trap

sterile flask

dust trapped in neck of flask

particle trap

no growth

growth

sterile broth

tip flask to mix trapped dust into broth

growth

Conclusion: No growth appears in the broth unless dust is admitted from outside. Reject "spontaneous generation" hypothesis.

**Figure 1.4
Pasteur's Experiments and the Scientific Method**
Nineteenth-century observation made clear that life would appear in a medium, such as broth, that had been sterilized, but what was the source of this life? One hypothesis was that it arose through *spontaneous generation,* meaning it formed from the simple chemicals in the broth. Conversely, Pasteur hypothesized that it originated from airborne microorganisms. He designed an experiment that offered evidence for this hypothesis. The device he used was an S-shaped flask, which enabled air to enter the flask freely while trapping all particles (including invisible microorganisms) in a bend in the neck.

inside the flasks there was not a sign of life. Why? The broth remained sterile because microbe-bearing dust particles got trapped in the bend of the flask's neck. When Pasteur broke the neck off before the bend, however, the flask soon had a riot of bacterial life growing within it. In another test, Pasteur tilted the flask so that the broth *touched* the bend in the neck, a change that likewise got the microbes growing.

Elements in Pasteur's Experiments

Now, note what was at work here. Pasteur had a preconceived notion of what the truth was, and he designed experiments to test his hypothesis. Critically, he performed the same set of steps several times in the experiments, keeping all elements the same each time—except for one. The nutrient broth was the same in each test; it was heated the same amount of time and in the same kind of flask. What *changed* each time was one critical **variable:** an adjustable condition in an experiment. In this case, the variable was either the shape of the flask neck or the tilt of the flask. Given that all the other elements of the experiments were kept the same, the experiments had rigorous controls: All conditions were held constant over several trials except for a single variable. A control *condition* can be thought of as an experimental condition that exists prior to the introduction of any variables tested. Pasteur was testing what happened with a broken-necked flask and a tilted flask. The control condition, therefore, was the broth-filled flask left sitting straight up with its particle trap intact. Pasteur's finding that no life grew in this condition is interesting but tells little by itself. We learn something only by comparing this finding to the result Pasteur got when he introduced his variables: that life *did* grow when the neck was broken or the flask was tilted.

Note that the idea of spontaneous generation was not banished with this one set of experiments—nor should it have been. Pasteur's experiments provided one of the *facts* mentioned earlier; in this case, the fact that flasks of liquid will remain sterile under certain conditions. The idea that life arises only from life is, however, one of the scientific *theories* noted earlier, meaning it is a principle that requires the accumulation of many facts pointing in the same direction. (If you want to see how these conventions of scientific investigation play out in today's world, see "How Science and Business Take On Cancer" on page 12.)

SO FAR ...

1. In everyday speech, a theory might be little more than a _____, while in science a theory is a general set of _____, supported by evidence, that explains some aspect of _____.

2. In science, a tentative, testable explanation for an observed phenomenon is referred to as a _____.

3. All properly executed scientific experiments must have rigorous controls, meaning that all aspects of the experiment must be held _____ except for the condition, known as a _____, which is being tested for.

When Is a Theory Proven?

At what point does a theory become proven? An irony of the orderly undertaking called science is that there's nothing orderly about this transition. No scientific supreme court exists to make a decision. Scientists aren't polled for their views on such questions, and even if they were, at what point would we say something had been proven: when more than 50 percent of the experts in the field assent to it? When no dissenters are left?

Provisional Assent to Findings: Legitimate Evidence and Hypotheses

This lack of finality in science actually fits, however, with one of the central tenets of science, which is that nothing is ever finally proven. Instead, every finding is given only *provisional* assent, meaning it is believed to be true for now, pending the addition of new evidence. This principle is so deeply embedded in science that scientists rarely have reason to think about it (just as drivers would seldom contemplate why they come to a stop when a traffic light turns red). Yet it is profoundly important because it is the thing that most starkly separates science from belief systems, such as those that operate in politics or religion. Every principle and "fact" in science is subject to modification based solely on the best evidence available. There are no immutable laws and no unquestioned authority figures. This means there is a paradox in science: Its only bedrock is that there is no bedrock; everything scientists "know" is subject to change.

In practice, this is a difficult ideal to live up to. Even when a body of evidence starts to point in a new direction, scientists—like anybody else—may be reluctant to give up old ways of thinking. Recognizing this tendency in human nature, Charles Darwin's friend Thomas Henry Huxley, writing in 1860, gave a beautiful description of the attitude scientists should have when investigating nature:

> Sit down before fact as a little child, be prepared to give up every preconceived notion, follow humbly wherever and whatever abysses nature leads, or you will learn nothing.

This principle of science's openness to revision is one of three important scientific principles having to do with the scientific process. Here are all three:

- Every assertion regarding the natural world is subject to challenge and revision based solely on evidence.
- Any scientific hypothesis or claim must be *falsifiable,* meaning open to negation through scientific inquiry. The assertion that "UFOs are visiting Earth" does not rise to the level of a scientific claim because there is no way to prove that this is *not* so.
- Scientific inquiry concerns itself only with natural explanations for natural phenomena. Put another way, *supernatural* explanations for the workings of nature lie outside the realm of science and thus cannot be examined through the scientific process.

At first blush, this third principle may seem a little strange. If science is about the testing of hypotheses through open inquiry, then when carrying out such inquiry, why can't scientists test all possible explanations—including supernatural explanations? For example, if we find (as we do) that the Hawaiian Islands have a wildly uneven representation of living things—there are 500 species of one kind of fly on the islands but not a single native species of reptile—then why can't scientists investigate a claim such as this: Hawaii has the mix of creatures it does because an intelligent designer arranged things in this way?

The primary answer to this question is that an intelligent designer would, by definition, have abilities that lie outside those in the natural world. Any entity that could arrange species on the Hawaiian Islands as it saw fit would be free to violate all the principles that underlie science: the laws of physics and chemistry, to say nothing of biology. And if this is the case, then scientists would have little more ability than, say, artists to investigate intelligent design in Hawaii because scientific principles need not apply to the question at hand.

SO FAR ...

1. Every finding in science is subject to _____ based on the accumulation of new _____.

2. Any scientific claim must be falsifiable, meaning open to _____ through means of scientific inquiry.

3. Science concerns itself only with _____ explanations for natural phenomena, as opposed to _____ explanations for these phenomena.

1.3 The Nature of Biology

Let's shift now from an overview of science to a more narrow focus on **biology,** which can be defined as the study of life. But what is life? It may surprise you to learn that there is no standard short answer to this question. Indeed, the only agreement among scholars seems to be that there is not, and perhaps cannot be, a short answer to this question. The main impediment to such a definition is that any quality common to all living things is likely to exist in some non-living things as well. Some living things may "move under their own power," but so does the wind. Living things may grow, but crystals and fire do the same thing. Therefore, biologists generally define life in terms of a group of characteristics possessed by living things. Looked at together, these characteristics are sufficient to separate the living world from the non-living. We can say that living things:

- Can assimilate (take in) and use energy
- Can respond to their environment
- Can maintain a relatively constant internal environment
- Possess an inherited information base, encoded in DNA, that allows them to function
- Can reproduce through use of the information encoded in DNA
- Are composed of one or more cells
- Evolved from other living things
- Are highly organized compared to inanimate objects

Every one of these qualities exists in all the varieties of Earth's living things. The simplest bacterium needs an energy source no less than any human being. Our energy source is the food that's familiar to us; the bacterium's might be the remains of vegetation in the soil. The bacterium responds to its environment, just as we do. You would take action if you smelled gas in your house; the bacterium would move away if it encountered something it regarded as noxious. Humans maintain a relatively stable internal environment by, for example, sweating when they are hot. When the bacterium's external environment becomes too hot, it has certain genes that will switch on to keep it functioning. Both humans and bacteria use the molecule DNA as a repository of the information necessary to allow them to live. Bacteria and human beings both reproduce—bacteria through simple cell division, human beings through the use of two kinds of reproductive cells (egg and sperm). A bacterium is a single-celled life form, while humans are a 10-trillion-celled life form. Bacteria and humans both evolved from complex living things and ultimately share a single common ancestor.

There are some exceptions to these "universals." For example, the overwhelming majority of honeybees

atom
(hydrogen)

molecule
(water)

organelle
(nucleus)

cell
(neuron)

tissue
(nervous tissue)

organ
(brain)

**Figure 1.5
Levels of
Organization in
Living Things**

and ants are sterile females; they can't reproduce, but no one would doubt that they're alive. In general, however, if something is living, it has all these qualities.

Life Is Highly Organized in a Hierarchical Manner

One item on the list of qualities requires a little more explanation. Living things are indeed highly organized compared to inanimate objects. But to put a finer point on this, living things are organized in a "hierarchical" manner, meaning one in which lower levels of organization are progressively integrated to make up higher levels. The main levels in this hierarchy could be compared to the organization of a business. In a corporation, there may be several individuals making up an office, several offices making up a department, several departments making up a division, and so forth. In life, there is one set of organized "building blocks" making up another, as you can see in **Figure 1.5**.

When we begin to think about life in terms of the integration of these many structural levels, we can see that it is not just "highly" organized. Nothing else comes *close* to it in organizational complexity. The sun is a large thing, but it is an uncomplicated thing compared to even the simplest organism. Consider that you have about 10 trillion cells in your body and that, with some exceptions, each type of cell has in it a complement of DNA that is made up of chemical building blocks. How many building blocks? Three billion of them. Now, you probably know that most cells divide regularly: one cell becoming two, the two becoming four, and so on. Each time this happens, each of the 3 billion DNA building blocks must be faithfully *copied* so that both cells resulting from cell division have their own complete copy of DNA. And this copying of the molecule—before anything is

actually done with it—is carried out in almost all the varieties of the 10 trillion cells we have. Complex indeed. Let's see what life's levels of organization are.

Levels of Organization in Living Things

The building blocks of matter, called *atoms*, lie at the base of life's organizational structure (see Chapter 2 for more about them). Atoms come together to form *molecules*, which are entities consisting of a defined number of atoms that exist in a defined spatial relationship to one another. A molecule of water is one atom of oxygen bonded to two atoms of hydrogen, with these atoms arranged in a precise way. Molecules in turn form *organelles*, meaning "tiny organs," in a cell. Each of your cells has, for example, a structure called a nucleus that contains the cell's primary complement of DNA. Such an organelle is not just a collection of molecules that exist close to one another. It is a highly organized structure, as you can tell just from looking at the rendering of it in the sea lion in Figure 1.5.

Atoms, molecules, and organelles are all component parts of life, but they are not themselves living things. At the next step up the organizational chain, however, we reach the entities that are living. These are *cells*, the fundamental units of life; the simplest, smallest entities that carry out all of life's basic processes. Indeed, if we ask where life exists *outside* cells, the answer most experts would give is: nowhere at all. Every product of life—the material that makes up our bones, the wood that helps make up a tree—comes from cells, and every process that enables life is initiated by cells.

Large organisms such as the sea lion in Figure 1.5 then go on to have *tissues*, meaning *collections* of cells that serve a common function. The sea lion has, for example, collections of the nerve cells called neurons,

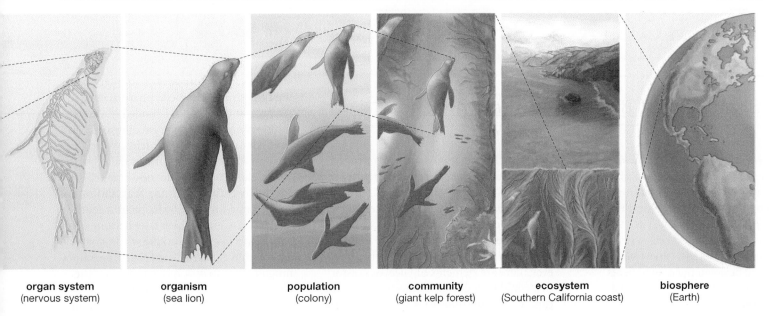

organ system
(nervous system)

organism
(sea lion)

population
(colony)

community
(giant kelp forest)

ecosystem
(Southern California coast)

biosphere
(Earth)

all of which serve the common function of transmitting electrical signals. Each collection of these cells is referred to as neural tissue. Several kinds of tissues can then come together to form a functioning unit known as an *organ*. The sea lion's brain, for example, is made up not only of neurons but of cells called *glia* that help support neurons. Several organs and related tissues then can be integrated into an *organ system*. The sea lion's brain, its spinal cord, and all the nerves that extend from these organs constitute the sea lion's nervous system. An assemblage of cells, tissues, organs, and organ systems can then form a multicelled *organism* such as the sea lion. (However, back down at the cell level, a one-celled bacterium is also an organism; it's just not one that has organs, tissues, and so forth.)

From this point out, life's levels of organization all involve many organisms living together. Members of a single type of living thing (a species), living together in a defined area, make up what is known as a *population*. When you look at *all* the kinds of living things in a given area, you are looking at a *community*. When you consider the members of a community and the non-living elements with which they interact (such as climate and water), the result is an *ecosystem*. Finally, all the communities of Earth—and the physical environment with which they interact—make up the *biosphere*.

Life's Spectacular Diversity

Life at the level of populations, communities, and ecosystems is tremendously complex for the simple reason that life at these levels is tremendously diverse. We can get an intuitive sense of this diversity by just thinking about the stunning *forms* that life comes in: whales, bats, trees, toadstools, algae. But life's diversity also exists in forms that are less visible to us. A single gram of fertile midwestern soil—an amount of soil about the size of a quarter of a teaspoon—is likely to contain 10,000 different *species* of bacteria, along with an assortment of roundworms, fungi, insects, and perhaps plant root fragments. When we look at the living world as a whole, we find that the lowest estimate for the total number of species in it is about 4 million, while higher-end estimates come in at 10 to 15 million, and the highest of them all is 100 million. We really have no idea which of these estimates best approximates the truth, however. In all the time that scientists have been looking at the living world, they simply have been unable to catalogue its vast diversity.

1.4 Special Qualities of Biology

Biology traces its origins to the ancient Greeks. In the work of such Greeks as Hippocrates and Galen, we can find the origins of modern medical science. In the work of Aristotle and others, we can find the origins of "natural history," which led to what we think of today as mainstream biology and the larger category of the **life sciences:** a set of disciplines that focus on varying aspects of the living world. Apart from biology, the life sciences include such areas of study as veterinary medicine and forestry.

Despite its ancient origins, biology is, in a sense, a much younger science than, say, physics, which is one of the physical sciences, meaning the natural sciences not concerned with life. Western Europe's revolution in the physical sciences probably can be dated from the sixteenth century, when Nicholas Copernicus published his work *On the Revolution of Heavenly Spheres*, which demonstrated that Earth moves around the sun. Meanwhile, biology did not come into its own as a science until the *nineteenth* century. Prior to the

THE PROCESS OF SCIENCE

How Science and Business Take On Cancer

At one time, getting a diagnosis for the form of cancer known as chronic myeloid leukemia, or CML, was tantamount to receiving a death sentence, because up through the late 1990s this disease of white blood cells was inevitably fatal. On average, three to five years elapsed between the date patients were diagnosed with CML and the date they died from it. Today, however, 85 to 90 percent of CML patients are alive five years after diagnosis, and it seems likely that the vast majority of these patients will be alive a great deal longer. The reason their future looks bright is that CML has been transformed. Whereas once it was a deadly disease, it now has taken on the qualities of a chronic, manageable disorder—a condition that can be controlled in the manner of, say, diabetes or asthma.

What has made the difference with CML is a single drug, called Gleevec, that was approved for medical use by the U.S. Food and Drug Administration in 2001. Gleevec is extremely expensive—it would not be unusual for a single patient's supply to cost $30,000 per year—and it is not a cure for CML, because patients must keep taking it for as long as they live. But for most of the 5,000 Americans diagnosed with CML each year, it has meant the difference between life and death.

For a single drug to have made this kind of difference in the treatment of a particular cancer is almost without precedent in cancer therapy. But Gleevec is remarkable in several other respects as well. To an unusual degree, it resulted from the vision and persistence of a single researcher, Brian Druker, who since 1993 has been at the Oregon Health and Science University in Portland, Oregon (**Figure 1**). Apart from this, Gleevec is now seen as the drug that pointed the way toward the future in cancer research, in that it was the first drug to target what might be called the circuitry of a particular cancer—the chemical pathway by which a given form of cancer gets started. (For more on this aspect of Gleevec, see "When the Cell Cycle Runs Amok" on page 168.) Despite all this, however, there are elements of Gleevec's history that could be found in connection with any cancer drug. In some ways, its development is a textbook example of how science and big business work together in tackling the daunting challenge of cancer.

Gleevec's story began in the 1980s, when Druker, then fresh out of medical school at the University of California, San Diego, was carrying out a type of research that underlies the development of any cancer treatment. This is so-called basic research, which is aimed at coming to a better understanding of either cancer in general or of a particular cancer—how does it get started, how does it change over time, what might its weak points be? Such research can be funded by private foundations, but in the United States today, the largest single funder of this research by far is the federal government—specifically a branch of the federal government known as the National Institutes of Health (NIH), which is made up of 27 separate institutes and centers. In 2008, NIH's National Cancer Institute provided researchers across the country with about $4.9 billion in cancer research funding. This large federal investment in cancer research, however, does not extend to developing the cancer *drugs* that end up being administered by physicians. In nearly every case, the research on such drugs is funded by pharmaceutical companies, which are almost invariably *large* companies because of the costs involved: Some experts put the current cost of bringing a single drug to market at an average of $1.2 billion.

Gleevec was a product of an intertwining of both this "applied," pharmaceutical research and basic, NIH-funded research. In the 1980s, Druker was carrying out basic research on a family of proteins, called the tyrosine kinases, that promote the process by which human cells divide—one cell becoming two, two becoming four, and so on. At the same time, the Swiss pharmaceutical giant Ciba-Geigy (which later became Novartis) was likewise working with tyrosine kinases and came to Druker's lab, beginning in 1986, to seek out expertise on the effectiveness of a set of drugs that were aimed at *inhibiting* the activity of tyrosine kinases. The idea was that drugs that could disrupt the activity of these kinases could be used to stop the uncontrolled division of cells that is a hallmark of all forms of cancer.

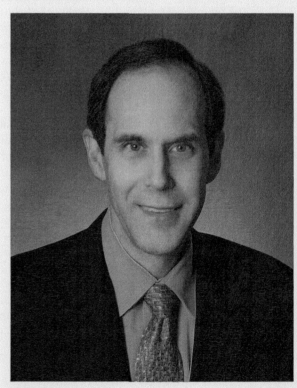

Figure 1
Cancer Research Pioneer
Cancer researcher and physician Brian Druker of the Oregon Health and Science University.

By 1990, Druker was focusing strictly on CML and had come to believe it might be arrested by means of disabling a mutant protein, called BCR-ABL, that becomes active in the white blood cells of all CML patients. The challenge was to find a compound that could carry out this disabling task. When, in 1993, Druker began to search for such a compound, he contacted Ciba-Geigy biochemist Nicholas Lydon, who sent him several tyrosine kinase inhibitors developed in his lab, one of which went on to show promise in laboratory

that serve as the make-or-break test for all human medicines: clinical trials.

No drug can be prescribed for use in the United States without having first been approved by the U.S. Food and Drug Administration. And to gain FDA approval, every drug must be put through a series of rigorous tests on human beings that demonstrate, first, that the drug is safe and, second, that it has a positive effect on the condition it is intended to combat. The gold standard for demonstrating both things to the FDA is the

of CML patients who had not responded to the standard therapy of the time, which was a form of the drug interferon. This trial, which went on for a little less than a year, was intended only to measure the safety of Gleevec, but a strange thing happened during this test: Gleevec demonstrated an astounding *effectiveness* among the patients. White blood cell counts returned to normal in 53 of 54 patients who received high doses of Gleevec—a 98 percent response rate in a type of trial that would have been counted as a success had it achieved a 10 percent response rate. With the Phase I results in, Novartis moved quickly into Phase II trials, and the results there were equally stellar. So effective was Gleevec in Phase II that it gained FDA approval as a prescription drug before its Phase III trials were ever completed. Three years elapsed from the time a volunteer first took a dose of Gleevec to the time it was approved for use in CML patients. By way of comparison, the FDA normally takes between five and eight years to approve a drug.

Gleevec is now seen as the drug that pointed the way toward the future in cancer research.

tests that Druker and Lydon reported on together. This was the compound that became Gleevec. The problem was that Ciba-Geigy's successor, Novartis, had little interest in proceeding with *human* tests of this substance—that is, with tests of it in CML patients. One of the problems with such testing was that no one had ever given a tyrosine kinase inhibitor to a human being before, and the assumption of many experts was that doing so could be dangerous. Apart from this, however, proceeding with the development of Gleevec seemed to make little sense to Novartis as a business proposition. The 5,000 Americans who are diagnosed with CML each year represent a small number of cancer patients compared to, say, the 46,000 Americans who are diagnosed with kidney cancer or the 215,000 who are diagnosed with lung cancer. Thus, even if Gleevec worked—which was far from certain following the lab tests of it—demand for it was bound to be small, while the costs of developing it were bound to be large. As a simple matter of economics, then, Novartis had little incentive to find out whether it would be effective as a cancer treatment. Eventually, however, Druker convinced the company to see it through the expensive set of evaluations

clinical trial, which is a set of tests that typically operate in three stages: a Phase I trial that seeks to demonstrate nothing more than the safety of the drug, as measured by its effect among a few dozen patients; a Phase II trial that expands the patient-base to several hundred volunteers and that is looking for both safety and effectiveness; and a Phase III trial that often enrolls thousands of patients at dozens of clinical settings that may be located around the world. These trials are models of the scientific method in that they must adhere to two watchwords: they must be *controlled* and they must be *randomized*. They are controlled in that the drug must demonstrate its effectiveness *compared to* another therapy—generally the therapy that is standard for the disease in question at the time. And they are randomized in that patients will randomly be assigned to get either the new drug or the standard therapy. The costs for all three phases of a clinical trial are borne entirely by the pharmaceutical firm developing the drug in question, and these costs are considerable; a given company could easily spend $400 million testing a drug that goes through Phase III trials.

Novartis began its Phase I trial of Gleevec in June 1998 with a small group

Today, Gleevec is used not just for CML, but for nine other forms of cancer as well; as a result, it is now administered to some 200,000 cancer patients worldwide. Druker receives no income from any sales of Gleevec, as he began his work with it only after it had been patented as a potential medicine. His achievements in connection with it have, however, been widely recognized by both cancer patients and cancer researchers. In 2009, he and Nicholas Lydon were named winners of the Lasker-DeBakey Clinical Medical Research Award—sometimes called the American Nobel Prize—for their work in developing Gleevec. The two shared the award with Charles Sawyers of Memorial Sloan-Kettering Cancer Center in New York, who was instrumental in developing compounds that are effective in treating CML patients whose cancers have become resistant to Gleevec.

1800s, biology was almost purely "descriptive," meaning that the naturalists whom we would today call biologists largely confined themselves to describing living things—what kinds there were, where they lived, what features they had, and so forth. Beginning in about the 1820s, however, biologists began to formulate biological theories as that term was defined earlier. They began to postulate that all life exists within cells, that life comes only from life, that life is passed on through small packets of information that we now call genes, and so on. To put this another way, biologists in the nineteenth century began describing the *rules* of the living world, whereas before they were largely describing *forms* in the living world.

This change moved biology closer to the same scientific footing as physics, but biology was then, and remains now, a very different kind of science from any of the physical sciences, with physics a clear case in point. One reason for this difference is that the component parts of physics are uniform and far fewer than is the case in biology. Physics deals with only 92 stable elements, such as hydrogen and gold, and to a first approximation, if you've seen one electron, you've seen them all.

Meanwhile, in biology, if you've seen one species, you've seen just that—one species. Each species is at least marginally different from another, and many are greatly dissimilar. Moreover, each species has all the organizational levels of elements in physics *and more*. (They not only have electrons and atoms, but organelles, cells, tissues, and so on.) Biology is concerned with the rules that govern all species, and

you've seen that there are some biological "universals." However, when cancer researchers are looking for the principles that underlie cell division, they are likely to be looking at only one of two main kinds of cells; when ecologists are looking at what causes dry grassland to turn into desert, their findings are likely to have little relevance to the rain forest. Put simply, the living world is tremendously diverse compared to the non-living world, and such diversity means that biology is concerned less with universal rules than is the case in the physical sciences.

Evolution: Biology's Chief Unifying Principle

Almost all biologists would agree that the most important thread that runs through biology is **evolution:** the gradual modification of populations of living things over time, with this modification sometimes resulting in the development of new species. Evolution is central to biology because every living thing has been shaped by it. (There are no known exceptions to this universal.) Given this, the explanatory power of evolution is immense. Why do peacocks have their finery, or frogs their coloration, or trees their height (**Figure 1.6**)? All these things stand as wonders of nature's diversity, but with knowledge of evolution they are wonders of diversity that *make sense*. For example, why do so many unrelated stinging insects look alike? Evolutionary principles suggest that they *evolved* to look alike because of the general protection this provides from predators. Think of yourself for a moment as a bee predator.

(a) A peacock displaying his plumage

(b) A red-eyed tree frog from Central America

(c) Pine trees in the South Pacific

Figure 1.6
Evolution Has Shaped the Living World

(a) Leafcutter bee

(b) Paper wasp

Figure 1.7
Similar Enough to Yield a Benefit
These are two of the many stinging insects that have the black-and-yellow striped coloration that warns away predators.

Having once gotten stung, would you annoy any roundish insect that had a black-and-yellow striped coloration? You probably learned your lesson about this in connection with one species, but many species of insects are now protected from you simply by virtue of the coloration they share (**Figure 1.7**). Thus, there were reproductive benefits to individual insects that, through genetic chance, happened to get a slightly more striped coloration: They left more offspring because they were bothered less by predators. Over time, entire populations moved in this direction. They evolved, in other words.

The means by which living things can evolve is a topic this book takes up beginning in Chapter 16. For now, just keep in mind that a consideration of evolution is never far from most biological observations. So strong is evolution's explanatory power that in uncovering something new about, say, a sequence of DNA or the life cycle of a given organism, one of the first things a biologist will ask is: What evolutionary advantage can this have provided?

On to Chemistry

How do you get a handle on something as diverse and complex as life? One way is to start small, with life's building blocks, and then see how these units come together to make up complete organisms. We'll be taking this approach over the next several chapters—starting small and working our way up, you might say. We'll actually be starting *very* small in this tour, with the building blocks called atoms. For us, the central question concerning these tiny entities will be: How do they come together to make up life's larger molecules? As you'll see, the short answer to this question is: They obey the laws of chemistry.

SO FAR ...

1. Arrange the following levels of organization in living things, going from least inclusive to most inclusive: cell, community, molecule, organ, ecosystem, organism.

2. The most important principle in biology, the theory of evolution, concerns the gradual _____ of populations of living things over time, sometimes resulting in the development of new _____.

3. Biology can be defined as the study of _____.

Go to the Study Area at www.masteringbiology.com for practice quizzes, myeBook, BioFlix™ 3-D animations, MP3 Tutor Sessions, videos, current events, and more.

Mastering
BIOLOGY™

CHAPTER 1 REVIEW

Summary

1.1 How Does Science Impact the Everyday World?

- Science is increasingly important to society, which often turns to scientists to answer questions about health, the environment, and other domains of life. (p. 3)

1.2 What Is Science?

- Science is a body of knowledge: a collection of unified insights about nature. Science is also a way of learning: a process of coming to understand the natural world through observation and experimentation. (p. 6)

- The unified insights of science are known as theories. A theory is a general set of principles, supported by evidence, that explains some aspect of nature. (p. 6)

- Science uses the scientific method, in which an observation leads to a question about the natural world. Then comes a hypothesis—a tentative, testable explanation that most often will be tested through a series of experiments. (p. 6)

- In science, every assertion is subject to challenge and revision; scientific claims must be falsifiable, meaning open to negation through scientific inquiry; and scientific inquiry is limited to investigating natural explanations for natural phenomena. (p. 9)

1.3 The Nature of Biology

- Biology is the study of life. Life is defined by a group of characteristics: Living things can assimilate energy, respond to their environment, maintain a relatively constant internal environment, and reproduce. In addition, they possess an inherited information base, encoded in DNA, that allows them to function; they are composed of one or more cells; they are evolved from other living things; and they are highly organized compared to inanimate objects. (p. 9)

- Life is organized in a hierarchical manner in increasing complexity: from atoms to molecules, organelles, cells, tissues, organs, organ systems, organisms, populations, communities, ecosystems, and the biosphere. (p. 10)

1.4 Special Qualities of Biology

- The living world is exceedingly diverse, and as such, biology focuses less on universal rules than is the case in the physical sciences. (p. 14)

- Biology's chief unifying principle is evolution, defined as the gradual modification of populations of living things over time, with this modification sometimes resulting in the development of new species. Evolution helps explain the forms and processes seen in living things. (p. 14)

Key Terms

biology 9

evolution 14

hypothesis 6

life sciences 11

science 6

scientific method 6

theory 6

variable 8

Understanding the Basics

Multiple-Choice Questions

(Answers are in the back of the book.)

1. Which of the following statements best describes the nature of a scientific hypothesis?
   a. A hypothesis is an idea that is widely accepted as a description of objective reality by a majority of scientists.
   b. A hypothesis must stand alone and not be based on prior knowledge.
   c. A hypothesis is a tentative explanation that can be tested, usually through experimentation.
   d. A hypothesis must deal with an aspect of the natural world never dealt with before.
   e. A hypothesis, when accepted, becomes a scientific law.

2. A theory, as defined in scientific discourse, is:
   a. an established fact about the natural world, such as the distance from Earth to the sun.
   b. a long-accepted belief about the natural world.
   c. a concept that is in doubt among most scientists.
   d. a set of principles, supported by evidence, that explains some aspect of nature.
   e. an initial assumption about how some aspect of nature works.

3. Pasteur's experiments on spontaneous generation made correct use of a variable in that Pasteur:
   a. varied the bacteria he employed with each experiment.
   b. used statistics to prove his hypothesis.
   c. observed the bacteria as they were growing in the flasks.
   d. held all conditions constant in each test except one.
   e. was willing to vary to the extent necessary from the standard hypotheses of his day.

4. Which of the following characteristics are true of all scientific claims? (Select all that apply.)
   a. They are capable of negation through further scientific inquiry.
   b. They can be negated by expert opinion.
   c. They are natural explanations for either natural or supernatural phenomena.

d. They stand or fall solely on the basis of evidence.

e. They are regarded as provisional, pending the addition of new evidence.

5. Evolution is a central, unifying theme in biology because:
   a. it is not a falsifiable hypothesis.
   b. humans have evolved from ancestors we share with present-day monkeys.
   c. the enormously diverse forms of life on Earth have all been shaped by it.
   d. it has occurred in the past, even though it no longer operates today.
   e. almost all biologists believe in it.

6. Biologists generally define life in terms of a group of characteristics possessed by living things. Which of the following is *not* a characteristic of living things?
   a. All living things possess an inherited information base, encoded in DNA, that allows them to function.
   b. All living things can respond to their environment.
   c. All living things can maintain a relatively constant internal environment.
   d. All living things evolved from other living things.
   e. All living things are composed of more than one cell.

Brief Review

(Answers are in the back of the book.)

1. What is science? In what ways is science different from a belief system such as religious faith?

2. What is a controlled experiment?

3. How did Louis Pasteur cast doubt on the idea of spontaneous generation?

4. Describe the defining features of life as we know it on Earth.

5. Living things are organized in a hierarchical manner. List all the levels of the biological hierarchy that you can.

Applying Your Knowledge

1. Would you agree that it is valuable for a nation to have a citizenry that is reasonably well versed in science? Give reasons for your answer. Would you say this need has become especially urgent in the last two decades? If so, why?

2. Although science cannot investigate the supposed workings of the supernatural, the scientific method can be used to investigate some *claims* that the supernatural has been at work. Can an astrologer know something about you just by knowing the place and time of your birth? A scientific test of this question, carried out in the 1980s, involved providing a group of 30 top-level astrologers with nothing but birth information for a group of people and then seeing whether the astrologers could predict anything about the personalities of these people (as measured by a standard personality "inventory"). The result was that the astrologers did no better than chance in trying to predict personality. Many of the standard tools of science were at work in this test of astrology—for example, controls (the test was the same for each astrologer) and statistical analysis (used to see whether the astrologers did better than chance). Using this test as a case in point, are all claims of supernatural effects open to scientific investigation? Can you think of other claims that could be investigated or any that could not?

3. If you were sent on an interplanetary mission to investigate the presence of life on Mars, what would you look for? Would you explore the land and the atmosphere? Imagine you discover an entity you suspect is a living being. Realizing that life elsewhere in the universe may not be organized by the same rules as on Earth, which of the features of life on Earth, if any, would you insist that the entity display before you would declare it living?

2

Fundamental Building Blocks:
Chemistry, Water, and pH

Life is carried on through chains of chemical reactions. The qualities of water have shaped life. The degree to which substances are acidic or basic has strong effects on living things.

Life began as a series of chemical reactions in water, and water remains indispensable to all living things today. Here, a red-eyed tree frog (*Agalychnis callidryas*) sits under a plant leaf during a rainstorm.

Cities are made of buildings and buildings are made of bricks; bricks are made of earth, and earth is made of ...? To answer this question, in this chapter we will look at what the material world is made of. Biology is our subject, but to fully understand it, you need to learn a little about what underlies biology. You need to learn a little about what *biology* is

made of, in a sense. To do this, you need to understand some of the basics in another field: chemistry.

How is chemistry relevant to biology? Well, the average person probably is aware that living things are made up of individual units called cells, but beyond this bit of knowledge, reality fades and a kind of fantasy takes over. In it, the cells that populate people, plants, or birds carry on their activities under the direction of their own low-level consciousness. A cell *decides* to move, it *decides* to divide, and so on. Not so. By the time our story is finished, many chapters from now, it will be clear that the cells that make up complex living things do what they do as the result of a chain of chemical reactions. Repulsion and bonding, latching on and re-forming, depositing and breaking down—what makes people, plants, and birds function at this cellular level is *chemistry*. Given this, the basic principles of chemistry are important to biology—important enough that we'll spend most of this chapter reviewing them. Once this is done, we'll touch on one of life's most important substances, water. Then we'll finish the chapter with a look at pH, a chemistry-related concept that has to do with how acidic or "basic" watery solutions are.

2.1 Chemistry's Building Block: The Atom

What is chemistry concerned with? Look around you. Do you see a table, light from a lamp, a patch of night or daytime sky? Everything that exists can be viewed as falling into one of two categories: matter or energy. You will learn something about energy in this chapter, but we are most concerned here with *matter and its transformations,* which is the subject of chemistry. Matter can be defined as anything that takes up space

and has **mass.** This latter term is a measure of the *quantity* of matter in any given object. How much space does an object occupy—how much volume, to put it another way—and how *dense* is the matter within that space? These are the things that define mass. For our purposes, we may think of mass as equivalent to weight, although physics makes a distinction between these two things.

As we behold matter all around us, it is natural to ask, What is its nature? A child sees a grain of sand, pounds it with a rock, sees the smaller bits that result, and wonders: What is this stuff like at the end of these divisions? Not surprisingly, adults also have wondered about this question—for centuries. About 2,400 years ago, the Greek philosopher Plato accepted the notion that all matter is made up of four primary substances: earth, air, fire, and water. A near-contemporary of his, Democritus, believed that these substances were in turn made up of smaller units that were both invisible and in*div*isible—they could not be broken down further. He called these units *atoms* (**Figure 2.1**, on the next page).

Well, let's give at least one cheer for Democritus because he had it partly right. Centuries of painstaking work between his time and ours has confirmed that matter is indeed composed of tiny pieces of matter, which we still call atoms, but these atoms are not indivisible, as Democritus thought. Rather, they are themselves composed of constituent parts. A superficial account of *all* the parts scientists have discovered to date would go on for pages and still be incomplete. Physicists are continually slamming together parts of atoms with ever-greater force in an effort to determine what else there may be at the heart of matter. This is what the machines called "atom smashers" do. (The physicists who run them could be compared to people who, in trying to find out what parts a watch has, throw it on the ground and record the way its

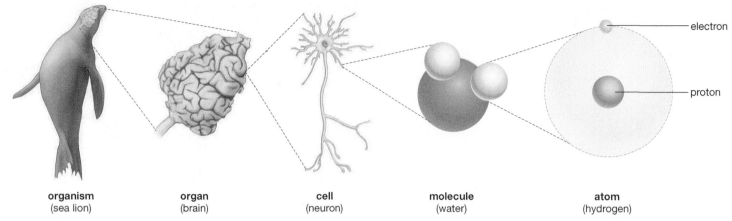

| organism (sea lion) | organ (brain) | cell (neuron) | molecule (water) | atom (hydrogen) |

Figure 2.1
The Building Blocks of Life

Viewing this sea lion at increasing levels of magnification, we eventually arrive at the building block of all matter, the atom. The atom selected here, from among a multitude that make up the sea lion, is a single hydrogen atom, composed of one proton and one electron.

various mechanisms fly out on impact.) This is interesting stuff, but it is purely the business of physics, with little relation to biology. We are not concerned here with what's at the very end of matter's divisions. We do care a good deal, however, about what's nearly at the end of them.

Protons, Neutrons, and Electrons

For our purposes, there are three important constituent parts of an atom: **protons, neutrons,** and **electrons.** These three parts exist in a spatial arrangement that is always the same, regardless of what atom we're dealing with. Protons and neutrons are packed tightly together in a core (the atom's **nucleus**), and electrons move around this core some distance away (**Figure 2.2**). The one variation on this theme is the substance hydrogen, the lightest of all the kinds of matter we will run into. Hydrogen has no neutrons but rather only one proton in its nucleus and one electron in motion around it.

These three "subatomic" particles have mind-bending sizes and proportions. As the chemist P. W.

Atkins has pointed out, an atom is so small that 100 million carbon atoms would lie end to end in a line of carbon about this long: _____ (3 centimeters). Things are just as disorienting when we consider the size of an atom as a whole relative to the nucleus. The whole atom, with electrons at its edge, is 100,000 times bigger than the nucleus. So, if you were to draw a model of an atom *to scale* and began by sketching a nucleus of, say, half an inch, you'd have to draw some of its electrons more than three-quarters of a mile away.

Although the nucleus accounts for little of the space an atom takes up, it accounts for almost all of the mass an atom has. So negligible are electrons in this regard, in fact, that all of the mass (or weight) of an atom is considered to reside with the protons and neutrons of the nucleus.

The components of atoms have another quality that interests us: electrical charge. Protons are positively charged, and electrons are negatively charged. Neutrons—as their name implies—have no charge; they are electrically neutral. Because all these particles do not exist separately but *combine* to form an atom, as a whole the atom may be electrically neutral as well. The negative charge of the electrons balances out the positive charge of the protons. Why? Because in this state the number of protons an atom has is exactly equal to the number of electrons it has (although we'll see a different, "ionic" state later in this chapter). In contrast, the number of neutrons an atom has can vary in relation to the other two particles.

With this picture of atoms in mind, we can begin to answer the question that has been handed down to us through history: What is matter? We certainly have a common sense answer to this question. Matter is any substance that exists in our everyday experience. For example, the iron that goes into cars is matter. But what is it that differentiates this iron from, say, gold? The answer is that an iron atom has 26 protons in its nucleus, while a gold atom has 79.

electron shell

nucleus

electron (negative charge)

proton (positive charge)

neutron (no charge)

Hydrogen (H)   Helium (He)

Figure 2.2
Representations of Atoms

One conceptualization of two separate atoms, hydrogen and helium. The model is not drawn to scale; if it were, the electrons would be perhaps a third of a mile away from the nuclei. The model also is simplified, giving the appearance that electrons exist in track-like orbits around an atom's nucleus. In fact, electrons spend time in volumes of space that have several different shapes.

Fundamental Forms of Matter: The Element

Gold is an **element**—a substance that is "pure" in that it cannot be reduced to any simpler set of component substances through chemical processes. And the thing that defines each element is the number of protons it has in its nucleus. A solid-gold bar, then, represents a huge collection of identical atoms, each of which has 79 protons in its nucleus (**Figure 2.3**). In making gold jewelry, an artist may combine gold with another metal such as silver or copper to form an alloy that is stronger than pure gold, but the gold atoms are still present, all retaining their 79-proton nuclei.

Given what you've just read about protons, neutrons, and electrons, you may wonder why gold—or any other element—cannot be reduced to any simpler set of component substances. Aren't protons and neutrons components of atoms? Yes, but they are not component *substances* because they cannot exist by themselves as matter. Rather, protons and neutrons must *combine* with each other to make up atoms.

Assigning Numbers to the Elements

In the same way that buildings can be defined by a location and thus have a street number assigned to them, elements, which are defined by protons in their nuclei, have an **atomic number** assigned to them. Scientists have constructed the atomic numbering system so that it goes from the smallest number of protons to the largest. So, hydrogen, which has only one proton in its nucleus, has the atomic number 1. The next element, helium, has two protons, so it is assigned the atomic number 2. Continuing on this scale all the way through the elements found in nature, we end with uranium, which has an atomic number of 92. (You can see all of these elements laid out for you in a periodic table at the back of the book, in Appendix 2, on page AP3.)

Given this view of the nature of matter, we are now in a position to answer the question posed at the beginning of the chapter: What is a handful of earth—or anything else—made of? The answer is: one or more elements. If you look at **Figure 2.4**, you can see the most important elements that go into making up both Earth's crust and human beings.

Figure 2.3
Pure Gold

Gold is an element because it cannot be reduced to any simpler set of substances through chemical means. Each gold bar is made up of a vast collection of identical atoms—those with 79 protons in their nuclei.

Earth's crust

other | 8%
oxygen (O) | 50%
silicon (Si) | 26%
aluminum (Al) | 8%
calcium (Ca) | 3%
iron (Fe) | 5%

Human body

7% | other
10% | hydrogen (H)
65% | oxygen (O)
18% | carbon (C)

Figure 2.4
Constituent Elements

The major chemical elements found in Earth's crust (including the oceans and the atmosphere) and in the human body.

Isotopes

All this seems like a nice, tidy way to identify elements—one element, one atomic number, based on number of protons—except that we're leaving out something. Recall that atoms also have neutrons in their nuclei; that these neutrons add weight to the atom; and that the number of neutrons can vary independently of the number of protons. What this means is that, in thinking about an element in terms of its weight, we have to take neutrons into account. Furthermore, because the number of neutrons in an element's nucleus may vary, we can have various *forms* of elements, called **isotopes.** Most people have heard of one example of an isotope, whether or not they recognize it as such. The element carbon has six protons, giving it an atomic number of 6. In its most common form, it also has six neutrons. However, a relatively small amount of carbon exists in a form that has *eight* neutrons. Well, the element is still carbon, and in this form the number of its protons and neutrons equals 14, so the *isotope* is carbon-14 (which is used in determining the age of objects ranging from pyramids to plants, as you can see in "Finding the Iceman's Age in an Isotope" on page 26).

Most elements have several isotopes. Hydrogen, for example, which usually has one proton and one electron, also exists in two other forms: deuterium, which has one proton, one electron, and one neutron; and tritium, which has one proton, one electron, and two neutrons (**Figure 2.5**).

The Importance of Electrons

In our account so far of the subatomic trio, we have had much to say about protons and neutrons but little to say about electrons. This was necessary because we needed to discuss the nature of matter, but in a sense, you can regard what has been set forth to this point as so much stage-setting because what's most important in biology is the way elements *combine* with other elements. And in this combining, it is the outermost electrons that play a critical role. Just as you come into contact with the world through what lies at your surface—your eyes, your ears, your hands—so atoms link with one another through what lies at their periphery.

2.2 Chemical Bonding: The Covalent Bond

The process of chemical combination and rearrangement is called **chemical bonding,** and for us it represents the heart of the story in chemistry. When the outermost electrons of two atoms come into contact, it becomes possible for these electrons to reshuffle themselves in a way that allows the atoms to become attached to one another. This can take place in two ways: One atom can *give up* one or more electrons to another, or one atom can *share* one or more electrons with another atom. Giving up electrons is called *ionic bonding;* sharing electrons is called *covalent bonding.* A third type of bonding, which we'll discuss shortly, is also important for our purposes; it's known as hydrogen bonding.

Energy Always Seeks Its Lowest State

Atoms that undertake bonding with one another do so because they are in a more stable state after the bonding than before it. A frequently used phrase is helpful in understanding this kind of stability: Energy always seeks its lowest state. Imagine a boulder perched precariously on a hill. A mere shove might send it rolling toward its lower energy state—at the

Figure 2.5
Same Element, Different Forms
Pictured are three isotopes of hydrogen. Like all isotopes, they differ in their number of neutrons.

Hydrogen	Deuterium	Tritium
1 proton	1 proton	1 proton
0 neutrons	1 neutron	2 neutrons

Unstable, very reactive atoms   **Stable, unreactive atoms**

hydrogen (H)   helium (He)

carbon (C)   neon (Ne)

sodium (Na)   argon (Ar)

Outermost electron
shells *unfilled*   Outermost electron
shells *filled*

Figure 2.6
Electron Configurations in Some Representative Elements

The concentric rings represent energy levels or "shells" of the elements, and the dots on the rings represent electrons. Hydrogen has but a single shell and a single electron within it, while carbon has two shells with a total of six electrons in them. Helium, neon, and argon have filled outer shells and are thus unreactive. Hydrogen, carbon, and sodium do not have filled outer shells and are thus reactive—they readily combine with other elements.

bottom of the hill. It would not then roll *up* the hill, either spontaneously or with a light shove, because it is now existing in a lower energy state than it did before—one that is clearly more stable than its former precarious perch. With electrons, the energy is not gravitational but electrical. Atoms bond with one another to the extent that doing so moves them to a lower, more stable energy state. The critical thing for our purposes is that atoms move to this more stable state by filling what is known as their *outer shells*.

Seeking a Full Outer Shell: Covalent Bonding

What are the outer shells? Electrons reside in certain well-defined "energy levels" outside the nuclei of atoms. The number of these energy levels varies depending on the element in question. Here, we only need to note the practical effect of these levels on bonding: *Two* electrons are required to fill the first energy level (or shell) of any given atom, but *eight* are

required to fill all the levels thereafter in most of the elements that make up the living world. If you look at the electron configurations in **Figure 2.6**, you can see that two elements pictured there—hydrogen and helium—have so few electrons in orbit around them that they have nothing *but* a first energy level, while the other elements pictured have two or three energy levels. This means that hydrogen and helium each require only two electrons in orbit around their nuclei to have filled outer shells, but that the other elements pictured require eight electrons to complete their outer electron shells.

Chemical Bonding in One Instance: Water

To see how chemical bonding works in connection with this concept of filled outer shells, take a look at the bonding that occurs with the constituent parts of one of the most simple (and important) substances on Earth, water. In so doing, you'll see one of the kinds of bonding we talked about—covalent bonding.

The familiar chemical symbol for water is H_2O. This means that two atoms of hydrogen (H_2) have combined with one atom of oxygen (O) to form water. (See "Getting to Know Chemistry's Symbols" on page 29 for an explanation of the notation used in chemistry.) Recall that hydrogen has only one electron running around in its single energy level. Also recall, however, that this first level is not completed until it has *two* electrons in it. Next, consider the oxygen atom, which has eight electrons. Looking at Figure 2.7, you can see what this means: Two electrons fill oxygen's first energy level, which leaves six for its second. But remember that the second shells of the atoms we're concerned with are not completed until they hold eight electrons. Therefore oxygen, like hydrogen, would welcome a partner. It needs two electrons to fill its outer shell—something that two *atoms* of hydrogen could provide. The outcome is a bonding of two hydrogen atoms with one atom of oxygen. And each of the hydrogen atoms is linked to the oxygen in a **covalent bond**—a chemical bond in which atoms share pairs of electrons. The oxygen atom and first hydrogen atom donate one electron each for the first pair, and these electrons can now be found orbiting the nuclei of both atoms. Then the oxygen and second hydrogen atom each donate one electron for the second pair. The result? Three atoms covalently bonded together, and all of them "satisfied" to be in that condition.

Note that when this pairing of electrons happens, no matter has been gained or lost. We started with two atoms of hydrogen and one atom of oxygen, and we finish that way. The difference is that these atoms are now bonded. This points up an important principle known as the **law of conservation of mass,** which states that matter is neither created nor destroyed in a chemical reaction.

What Is a Molecule?

When two or more atoms combine in this kind of covalent reaction, the result is a **molecule:** an entity consisting of a defined number of atoms covalently bonded together. Here, one atom of oxygen has covalently bonded with two atoms of hydrogen to

create *one water molecule.* (What we commonly think of as water, then, is an enormous, linked collection of these individual water molecules.) A molecule need not be made of two different elements, however. Two hydrogen atoms can covalently bond to form one hydrogen molecule. Conversely, a molecule can contain many different elements bonded together. Consider the sucrose molecule—better known as table sugar—which is $C_{12}H_{22}O_{11}$ (12 carbon atoms bonded to 22 hydrogen atoms and 11 oxygen atoms).

Reactive and Unreactive Elements

The elements considered so far all welcome bonding partners because all of them have incomplete outer shells. This is not true of all elements, however. There is, for example, the helium atom, which has two electrons. It therefore *comes equipped*, we might say, with a filled outer shell. As such, it is extremely stable—it is unreactive with other elements. At the opposite end of the spectrum are elements that are extremely reactive. Look again at the representation of the sodium atom in Figure 2.6. It has 11 electrons: two in the first shell and eight in the second, which leaves but one electron in the third shell—a very unstable state. Between the extremes of sodium and helium are elements with a range of outer (or *valence*) electrons. So there is a spectrum of stability in the chemical elements, based on the number of outer-shell electrons each element has—from one to eight, with one being the most reactive and eight being the least reactive.

Covalent Polar and Nonpolar Bonding

Not all covalent bonds are created alike. When two hydrogen atoms come together, the result is a hydrogen molecule (H_2). Now, in the hydrogen molecule, the electrons are shared *equally*. That is, the two electrons the hydrogen atoms share are equally attracted to each hydrogen atom. This is not the case, however, with the water molecule.

Figure 2.7
Covalent Bonding

(a) A covalent bond is formed when two atoms share one or more pairs of electrons. The starting state in this reaction is two hydrogen atoms and one oxygen atom. Note that none of these atoms has outer-shell stability—each hydrogen atom would need one more electron to achieve stability, while the oxygen atom would need two more.

(b) In bonding, all the atoms achieve this stability; in this case, two pairs of electrons are shared—one pair between one hydrogen atom and the oxygen atom and the other pair between the second hydrogen and the oxygen. The result is the creation of a water molecule.

hydrogen (H) atom

hydrogen (H) atom

oxygen (O) atom

(a) Two hydrogen atoms and one oxygen atom

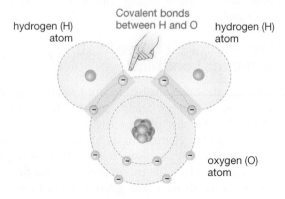

hydrogen (H) atom

Covalent bonds between H and O

hydrogen (H) atom

oxygen (O) atom

(b) One water molecule

Look at the representation of the water molecule in **Figure 2.8a**. As it turns out, the oxygen atom has greater power to attract electrons to itself than do the hydrogen atoms. The term for measuring this kind of pull is **electronegativity.** Because the oxygen atom has more electronegativity than do the hydrogen atoms, it tends to pull the shared electrons away from the hydrogen and toward itself. When this happens, the molecule takes on a **polarity,** or a difference in electrical charge at one end as opposed to the other. Because electrons are negatively charged and because they can be found closer to the oxygen nucleus, the oxygen end of the molecule becomes slightly negatively charged, while the hydrogen regions become slightly positively charged. We still have a covalent bond, but it is a specific type: a **polar covalent bond.** Conversely, with the hydrogen molecule—where electrons are shared equally—we have a **nonpolar covalent bond.**

To grasp the importance of this, consider the water molecule with its positive and negative regions. What's going to happen when it comes into contact with *other* polar molecules? The oppositely charged parts of the molecules will attract, and the similarly charged parts will repel. It's like having a bar magnet and trying to bring its positive end into contact with the positive end of another magnet; left on its own, the second magnet just flips around, so that positive is now linked to negative. In the same way, molecules flip around in relation to their polarity.

It is possible for atoms with different electronegativity to link and still have the resulting molecule be nonpolar. Water is polar because the atom with more electronegativity (the oxygen) lies to one *side* of the two hydrogen atoms. Meanwhile, in the methane molecule shown, four hydrogen atoms are arranged in a symmetrical way around a central, and more electronegative, carbon atom (**Figure 2.8b**). In this arrangement, the differing charges balance each other out, leaving methane with no positive or negative end—meaning it is nonpolar. (Keep this quality of methane in mind, as it will be important in

the consideration of why oil and water don't mix.) In summary, some molecules are polar while others are nonpolar, and this difference has significant consequences for chemical bonding.

> ## SO FAR . . .
>
> 1. Atoms tend to bond with one another to the extent that they do not have a _____ outer shell, which means having _____ outer-shell electrons for most elements in living things, but only _____ outer-shell electrons for the simple elements hydrogen and helium.
>
> 2. When two atoms share one or more pairs of electrons, they have become linked through a _____ bond.
>
> 3. In some of these bonds, one of the linked atoms may exert a greater pull on the shared electrons. When this happens, the result can be a _____ bond, a bond in which differing regions of the resulting molecule take on a difference in _____ in one region, as compared to another.

2.3 The Ionic Bond

So we've gone from nonpolar covalent bonding, in which electrons are shared equally, to polar covalent bonding, in which electrons are pulled to one side of the resulting molecule. What if we carried this just one step further and had instances when the electronegativity differences between two atoms were so extreme that electrons were pulled *off* one atom, only to latch on to the atom that was attracting them? This is what happens in our second type of

Figure 2.8
Polar and Nonpolar Covalent Bonding

(a) In the water molecule, the oxygen atom exerts greater attraction on the shared electrons than do the hydrogen atoms. Thus, the electrons are shifted toward the oxygen atom, giving the oxygen atom a partial negative charge (because electrons are negatively charged) and the hydrogen atoms a partial positive charge. ("Partial" here is indicated by the Greek symbol δ.)

(b) In the methane molecule, the carbon atom is more electronegative than the hydrogen atoms, but the methane molecule as a whole is nonpolar because its hydrogen atoms are arranged symmetrically around the central carbon atom, meaning the partial charges that exist balance each other out.

(a) Polar water molecule

(b) Nonpolar methane molecule

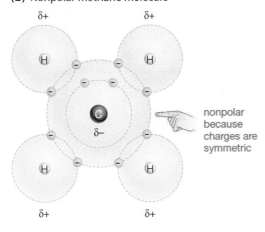

Finding the Iceman's Age in an Isotope

In September 1991, two German hikers walking in a mountain pass that spanned the border between Austria and Italy were startled to see a human body protruding from a section of ice at the bottom of some rock outcroppings (Figure 1). The couple's discovery was initially investigated by Austrian police, who at first wondered whether the body might be that of a music teacher who had disappeared from the Italian city of Verona in 1939. In the days that followed, investigators removed the corpse from the ice and then helicoptered it to a research institute at the University of Innsbruck in Austria. There, an expert on prehistoric cultures looked at both the body and some articles found with it and estimated that the frozen

corpse was not 50 years old, but more like 4,000 years old. The man in the ice—dubbed Oetzi for the Otzal section of the Alps in which he was found—had made a

Carbon-14 dating has taken us from the realm of guessing about dates in the distant past to the realm of knowing about them.

fatal journey over the mountains long before the countries of Austria or Italy ever existed. But exactly when had Oetzi lived? The 4,000-year figure was just a rough guess, based mostly on the articles found with the body. To get a more precise date, scientists employed a kind of atomic

clock—one that begins ticking in the remains of all living things from the moment of their death. As it turns out, this clock runs on a special variety of the element carbon.

All living things take in carbon each day in order to live, and the pathway by which they obtain this carbon is well understood. Plants take in carbon dioxide from the atmosphere and incorporate the carbon from it into their tissues; then animals eat plants, thus incorporating the carbon into *their* tissues. The vast majority of the carbon atoms that move through this system are carbon-12 atoms, but a very small proportion of them are carbon-14 atoms, which are constantly being produced in the atmosphere. Each carbon-14 atom is unstable, however; each is fated to emit an energetic particle from its nucleus and thus be transformed into an atom of ordinary nitrogen. This process goes under a name that may sound familiar: radioactive decay. Carbon-14 is a radioactive isotope of carbon.

Several features of carbon-14's decay are critical in allowing it to serve as an atomic clock. First, its decay takes a long time. Take any sample of carbon-14 atoms, and half of them will decay into nitrogen in 5,730 years; of the carbon atoms that remain in the sample, another half will decay into nitrogen in the *next* 5,730 years, and so on (Figure 2). In living things, this manifests as a steady ticking away of one carbon-14 atom after another within living tissue, each atom emitting its energetic particle, thereby becoming nitrogen. Critically, we know what this tick rate is: In every gram of carbon from a living thing, about 14 atoms of carbon-14 will decay each

Figure 1
A Startling Find
The remains of the "iceman" Oetzi as they looked when they were discovered in the mountainous border region of Austria and Italy in 1991.

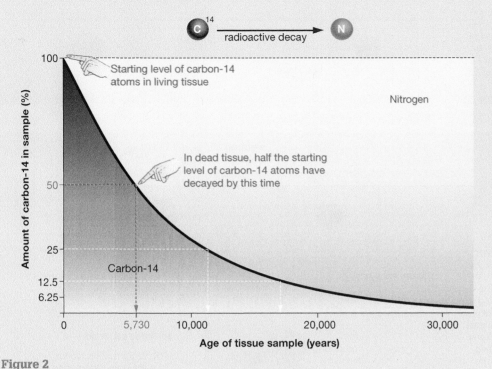

Figure 2
Using Carbon as a Clock
Carbon-14 decays into nitrogen at such a steady rate that scientists can use it to calculate the approximate age of almost any object 50,000 years or younger that was composed originally of living tissue.

minute. Just as important, we can *count* these ticks; the emission of an energetic particle from one carbon-14 atom as it is transforming into nitrogen will register as one tick on a radioactive counter.

With all this in mind, here's how carbon-14 dating worked in the case of Oetzi. On the day this hardy traveler died, we know he had eaten some grain and some deer meat, meaning the movement of carbon atoms through plants and animals and then through him was proceeding as usual. The critical thing, however, comes with Oetzi's death, for it's at this point that *carbon stopped flowing into him.* He quit taking in carbon from the outside world, including carbon-14. With this, no newly formed carbon-14 atoms entered him, but all of the carbon-14 atoms *already* present in his tissues were

decaying away at their usual rate. On the day he died, 14 ticks per minute would have taken place for every gram of carbon in his body. But go, say, 2,800 years out from his death and the number of ticks drops to 10.5 per minute. Why? Because by this time, 25 percent of the carbon-14 atoms in his body had become nitrogen and therefore were no longer emitting energetic particles. All that was necessary to determine the approximate date of his death, therefore, was to get a sample of carbon from his tissues and count the number of carbon-14 ticks being emitted from it. The lower the number of ticks, the longer ago he lived. Two labs performed a modern variation on this type of analysis, and they both came to the same conclusion: there is a 95.4 percent chance that Oetzi lived sometime between 5,111 and 5,381 years ago.

If you compare these relatively precise dates with the rough estimate that Oetzi lived about 4,000 years ago, you can see what carbon-14 dating has done for human knowledge: It has taken us from the realm of guessing about dates in the distant past to the realm of knowing about them. Critically, it's not just human or even just animal tissues that can be dated. Wood found in an ancient Egyptian pyramid once was a part of a living tree, so it can be dated; cloth that made up a medieval tapestry once was a part of a living plant, so it can be dated. Trees knocked down by an ancient glacier can give us an approximate date for the glacier's advance. Given this wide utility, it's not surprising that tens of thousands of samples of once-living tissue go through carbon-14 analysis each year at laboratories around the world. The primary limitation on the technique is that it doesn't work on items that are more than about 50,000 years old; at that point, the carbon-14 in any sample has run out.

For many years, carbon-14 dating was done through the counting method outlined above; scientists had to get gram-sized samples of tissue and then count up particle emissions over several days. More recently, this method has been replaced by a technique called accelerator mass spectrometry, which not only can directly count the number of carbon-14 atoms in a sample, but can do so on samples that are only thousandths of a gram in size. The basic principle behind carbon-14 dating has remained unchanged, however, from the time chemist Willard Libby first developed it at the University of Chicago in the 1940s. Then as now, the idea was to find out how many carbon-14 atoms remain in a sample of once-living tissue. In 1960, Libby received the ultimate in thanks for a job well done in science when he was awarded the Nobel Prize in chemistry for giving the world the gift of carbon-14 dating.

Figure 2.9
Ionic Bonding

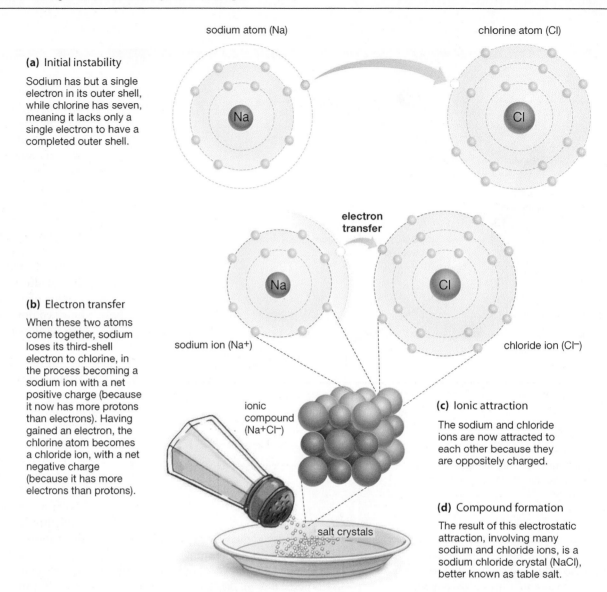

sodium atom (Na)

chlorine atom (Cl)

(a) Initial instability

Sodium has but a single electron in its outer shell, while chlorine has seven, meaning it lacks only a single electron to have a completed outer shell.

electron transfer

Na

Cl

(b) Electron transfer

When these two atoms come together, sodium loses its third-shell electron to chlorine, in the process becoming a sodium ion with a net positive charge (because it now has more protons than electrons). Having gained an electron, the chlorine atom becomes a chloride ion, with a net negative charge (because it has more electrons than protons).

sodium ion (Na+)

chloride ion (Cl−)

ionic compound (Na+Cl−)

(c) Ionic attraction

The sodium and chloride ions are now attracted to each other because they are oppositely charged.

(d) Compound formation

The result of this electrostatic attraction, involving many sodium and chloride ions, is a sodium chloride crystal (NaCl), better known as table salt.

salt crystals

bonding, ionic bonding. The classic illustration of this type of bonding involves the sodium we looked at earlier and the element chlorine. Recall that sodium has 11 electrons, meaning that there is a lone electron flying around in its outer, third electron shell. Chlorine, in contrast, has 17 electrons, meaning it has 7 electrons in the third shell. Remember that 8 usually is the magic number for outer-shell stability. Sodium could get to this number by *losing* one electron, while chlorine could get to it by *gaining* one electron. That's just how this encounter occurs: Sodium does in fact lose its one electron, chlorine gains it, and both parties become stable in the process (**Figure 2.9**).

What Is an Ion?

But this story has a postscript. Having lost an electron (with its negative charge), sodium (Na) then takes on an overall *positive* charge. Having gained an electron,

chlorine (Cl) takes on a negative charge. Each is then said to be an **ion**—a charged atom or, to put it another way, an atom whose number of electrons differs from its number of protons. We denote the ionized forms of these atoms like this: Na^+, Cl^-. Were an atom to gain or lose more electrons, a number would be put before the charge sign. For example, to show that the magnesium atom has lost two electrons, we would write Mg^{2+}.

Note that we now have two ions, Na^+ and Cl^-, with differing charges in proximity to one another. They are therefore attracted to one another through an *electrostatic attraction* and have therefore become bonded through **ionic bonding:** a chemical bonding in which two or more ions are linked by virtue of their opposite charge. This hardly ever happens with just two ions, of course. Many billions of them are bonded in this way, up, down, and sideways from each other, thus forming the kind of solid, crystal structure you can see in **Figure 2.9c**. What's produced through this

Getting to Know Chemistry's Symbols

One of the "languages of science" is the system of symbols that chemistry uses. Somewhat intimidating at first viewing, this system soon comes to serve its intended purpose of conveying a lot of information quickly.

Our starting place is that each chemical element has its own symbol, so that hydrogen is represented by H, carbon by C, and platinum by Pt. When we begin to combine these elements into molecules, it is necessary to specify how *many* atoms of each element are part of the molecule. If we have two atoms of oxygen together—which is the way oxygen is usually packaged in our atmosphere—we have the molecule O_2. Three molecules of O_2 is written as $3O_2$. This kind of notation is known as a **molecular formula.** It is helpful in stipulating the makeup of molecules, from the simple, such as oxygen, to the complex, such as chlorophyll, which is notated $C_{55}H_{72}MgN_4O_5$.

Anyone who sees a molecular formula learns a lot about which atoms are in a molecule but nothing about the way the atoms are *arranged* in relation to one another. (Look at chlorophyll's formula. Is there a line of 55 carbon atoms followed by 72 hydrogen atoms? From the molecular formula, how could you tell?) To convey this ordering information, chemists and biologists use **structural formulas**—two-dimensional representations of a given molecule. Methane (CH_4) is a very simple molecule composed, as the molecular formula shows, of one atom of carbon and four of hydrogen. In a structural formula, these constituent parts are conceptualized like this:

$$
\begin{array}{c}
\text{H} \\
| \\
\text{H} - \text{C} - \text{H} \\
| \\
\text{H}
\end{array}
$$

methane

Note that there is a single line between each hydrogen atom and the central carbon atom. This signifies that the bond between any of the hydrogen atoms and carbon is a single bond: Each line represents *one* pair of electrons being shared. Thus:

$$
\text{H} : \overset{\cdot\cdot}{\underset{\text{H}}{\text{C}}} : \text{H}
$$
electron pairs

There can also be double bonds and triple bonds. When carbon dioxide forms, there are two oxygen atoms. Each shares two pairs of electrons with a lone carbon atom. Here's how we would notate the double bond in a carbon dioxide (CO_2) molecule:

$$
\text{O} = \text{C} = \text{O}
$$
carbon dioxide

Although structural (or "skeletal") formulas can tell us a good deal about the ordering of atoms in a molecule, they tell us little about the *three-dimensional* arrangements of atoms. For this, we rely on two other kinds of representations, the **ball-and-stick model** and the **space-filling model.** An ammonia molecule (NH_3) is pictured next in both forms, with the molecular and structural formulas added to show the progression:

$$NH_3$$
molecular formula

$$
\text{H} - \overset{\cdot\cdot}{\text{N}} - \text{H} \\
| \\
\text{H}
$$
structural formula

ball-and-stick model   space-filling model

Note that the ball-and-stick model gives us a better idea of molecular angles of the atoms, but that the space-filling model gives us a better idea of the relative size of these atoms and how one actually hugs the other. (The dots above the "N" in the structural formula represent an unshared pair of electrons.)

Finally, it is useful to have a way to notate the "before" and "after" stages of a chemical reaction. This is done by employing a simple arrow, as when carbon reacts with hydrogen to form methane: $C + 4H \rightarrow CH_4$. The carbon and hydrogen atoms on the left are **reactants,** the arrow means "yields," and the methane molecule on the right is the **product** of the reaction. Here's a graphic representation of what is happening:

$$
\underbrace{\text{C} \quad + \quad 4\text{H}}_{\text{reactants}} \xrightarrow{\text{yield}} \underbrace{\text{CH}_4}_{\text{product}}
$$

An important thing to keep in mind about notation goes back to the law of conservation of mass: Matter is neither created nor destroyed in a chemical reaction. It follows that reactions such as the one above must be *balanced:* We must have the same number of atoms when the reaction is finished (on the right) as when it started (on the left). So we couldn't have $C_2 + 4H \rightarrow CH_4$. This is an unbalanced reaction. We started out with two atoms of carbon on the left but somehow ended up with one atom of carbon on the right. Nature doesn't play that way.

process is an **ionic compound:** a collection of the atoms of two or more elements that have become linked through ionic bonding.

Note that this compound is not a *molecule* as H_2O is. It does not have a defined number of atoms—as in H_2O's two atoms of hydrogen and one of oxygen—and the many atoms that do make it up are linked through ionic bonds, rather than covalent bonds. The particular ionic compound pictured in Figure 2.9 actually is familiar. Sodium and chlorine combine to create sodium chloride, which is better known as table salt. The notation for it should properly be written Na^+Cl^-, but it is usually denoted just as NaCl.

2.4 The Hydrogen Bond

We now turn to a final variant on bonding called *hydrogen bonding.* Recall that in any water molecule, the stronger electronegativity of the oxygen atom pulls the electrons shared with the hydrogen atoms toward the oxygen nucleus, giving the oxygen end of the molecule a partial negative charge and the hydrogen end of the molecule a partial positive charge. So what happens when you place several water molecules together? A positive hydrogen atom of one molecule is weakly attracted to the negative, *unshared* electrons of its oxygen neighbor. Thus is created the **hydrogen bond,** which links an already covalently bonded hydrogen atom with an electronegative atom (in this case, with oxygen; **Figure 2.10**). Hydrogen bonding is a linkage that, in the living world, nearly always pairs hydrogen with either oxygen or nitrogen. Hydrogen bonds, usually indicated by a dotted line in illustrations, are important in many of the molecules of life—in DNA, in proteins, and elsewhere. These bonds are, however, relatively weak compared to either covalent or ionic bonds. In collections of water molecules, the result is a set of bonds that are constantly breaking and then re-forming. Each water molecule can be bonded to four others, but no individual set of bonds lasts for long. Nevertheless, hydrogen bonding manages to strongly shape the qualities of water, as you'll soon see.

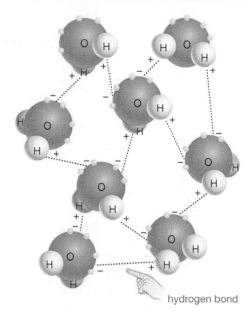

hydrogen bond

Figure 2.10
Hydrogen Bonding

The hydrogen bond, in this case between water molecules, is indicated by the dotted line. It exists because of the attraction between hydrogen atoms, with their partial positive charge, and the unshared electrons of the oxygen atom, with their partial negative charge.

2.5 Three-Dimensional Shape in Molecules

We now need to make more explicit what has been noted only by implication in our diagrams of water molecules: that molecules and ionic compounds have a three-dimensional shape. It is useful to depict them as two-dimensional chains, rings, and such, but in real life a molecule is as three-dimensional as a sculpture. A fair number of shapes are possible; atoms may be lined up in a row, in triangles, or in pyramid shapes. As an example, look at the water and methane molecules in **Figure 2.11**. You can see that in water there is a definite spatial configuration: its hydrogen atoms are splayed out from its oxygen atom at an angle of 104.5°. In methane, meanwhile, the hydrogen atoms have an angle of 109.5° between them.

Figure 2.11
Three-Dimensional
Representations of
Molecules

(a) In the case of water, there is an angle of 104.5° between hydrogen atoms.

(b) Methane is a molecule with an angle of 109.5° between hydrogen atoms.

(a) Water (H_2O)

104.5°

(b) Methane (CH_4)

109.5°

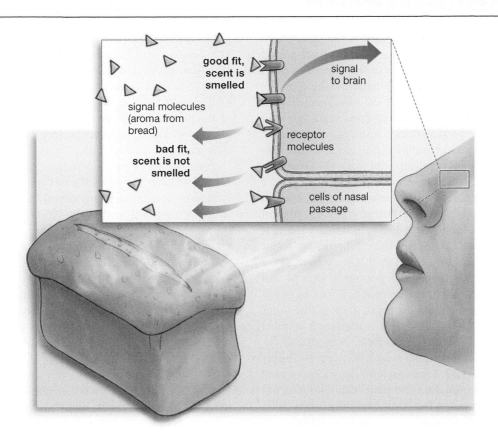

Figure 2.12
Figure 2.12
The Importance of Molecular Shape
Gas molecules wafting off bread (the triangles) bind with specific receptors on the surface of the cell, thus acting as signaling molecules that set a cellular process in motion. For this binding to take place, the gas and nasal receptor molecules must fit together.

Why does molecular shape matter? It is critical in enabling biological molecules to carry out their activities. This is because molecular shape determines the capacity of molecules to latch on to or "bind" with one another. When, for example, you smell the aroma of fresh-baked bread, gas molecules wafting off the bread bind with receptor molecules in your nasal passages, thus sending a message to the brain about the presence of bread. It is the precise shape of the gas molecules and nasal receptor molecules that allows them to bind with one another. Look at **Figure 2.12** to see how this works. If you look at **Figure 2.13**, then you can get an idea of how large some biological molecules are relative to the simple molecules considered so far.

SO FAR...

1. An ionic bond occurs when one atom _____ one or more _____ to another atom and the resulting ions become attached because of their differing _____.

2. A hydrogen bond links an already covalently bonded hydrogen atom with a more _____ atom. In biology, such bonds almost always occur between hydrogen and either _____ or _____.

3. Molecular shape is important in biology because it determines the ability that molecules have to _____ with one another.

Figure 2.13
Complex Binding
A computer model of some real-life molecular binding. In this case, a protein (the yellow atoms) binds to a length of DNA. This space-filling model provides some idea of the enormous number of atoms and the complicated shapes that make up some of the molecules employed by living things.

2.6 Water and Life

Having looked at some of the ways in which atoms form the world's substances, we now look in detail at just *one* substance, water. Why such emphasis on water? Because of its great importance to our central subject, which is life.

How are life and water related? Well, consider how the two things have been intertwined over time. Life got started in water and then existed almost nowhere *but* water for eons. More than 3 billion years passed between the time life began (in the ancient oceans) and the time living things first came onto land (in the form of ancient plants). Since the movement to land occurred no more than 450 million years ago, this means that life on land came about only in the last 11 percent of life's history. With this in mind, it's not surprising that when organisms did make the transition to land, they could only manage this feat by carrying a watery environment with them—inside themselves. The plant pioneers had this characteristic 450 million years ago, dinosaurs had it 100 million years ago, and human beings have it today. Human bodies are about 66 percent water by weight, so that if we have, say, a 128-pound person, about 85 pounds of that person will be water. And this proportion is low by some standards: Among most vertebrate animals, the water proportion is more like 70 or 80 percent, and for most plant tissues, the figure is 90 percent. Not surprisingly, then, almost all organisms must have a regular supply of water to survive. Some bacteria can go into a kind of suspended animation and remain alive for long periods without water, but no living thing can be fully *functional* without water. To reproduce, to move, to obtain nutrients—to carry out most of life's basic processes, in other words—all living things must have water. Given this, if we ask how important water is to life, the answer is that the two things are inseparable.

Water Is a Major Player in Many of Life's Processes

But what gives water this status? Recall the notion we touched on earlier of life being, at one level, a series of chemical reactions. It makes sense that these reactions would best take place in some liquid medium—since liquid allows for the easy distribution of materials— and that medium turns out to be water. However, water is not just a passive medium in which reactions take place. It *facilitates* many of these reactions thanks to its chemical structure. To understand this, it's important to know something about three terms that start with an *s*: solution, solute, and solvent.

Pour some salt into a container of water, stir the water, and what happens? The salt quickly disappears. It hasn't actually gone anywhere, of course; it has simply mixed with the water. Now, if it has mixed thoroughly, so that there are no lumps of salt here or there, you have created a **solution**—a mixture of two or more kinds of molecules, atoms, or ions that is *homogenous,* meaning uniform throughout. The salt is what's being dissolved, so it is the **solute.** The water is doing the dissolving, so it is the **solvent.** And with this, we get to the point about water: it's a terrific solvent, which is to say it has a great ability to dissolve other substances.

If you look at **Figure 2.14**, you can get a detailed view of water's solvent power in connection with the salt we just talked about. Remember that water is a polar molecule, which is to say a molecule that has differing electric charges at one end as opposed to the other. Attracted by the polar nature of the water molecule, the sodium and chloride ions that make up a salt crystal separate from the crystal—and from each other. Each ion is then surrounded by several water molecules. These units keep the sodium and chloride ions from getting back together. In other words, they keep the ions evenly dispersed throughout the water, which is what makes this a solution. Water works as a solvent here because the ionic compound sodium chloride carries an electrical charge. What *generally*

Figure 2.14
Water's Power as a Solvent

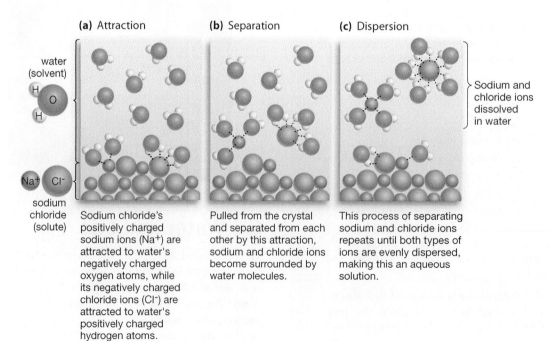

(a) Attraction   **(b)** Separation   **(c)** Dispersion

water (solvent)

H O H

Na+ Cl-
sodium chloride (solute)

Sodium and chloride ions dissolved in water

Sodium chloride's positively charged sodium ions (Na+) are attracted to water's negatively charged oxygen atoms, while its negatively charged chloride ions (Cl-) are attracted to water's positively charged hydrogen atoms.

Pulled from the crystal and separated from each other by this attraction, sodium and chloride ions become surrounded by water molecules.

This process of separating sodium and chloride ions repeats until both types of ions are evenly dispersed, making this an aqueous solution.

makes water work as a solvent, however, is its ability to form, with other molecules, the hydrogen bonds we talked about earlier.

Water's Unusual Properties

When we note water's ability to act as a solvent, we're actually not giving water its due. Water is not just *a* solvent: Over the range of substances, nothing can match it as a solvent. It can dissolve more compounds in greater amounts than can any other liquid.

But solvency power is merely the beginning of water's abilities. It is a multitalented performer. And it achieves this status because it is ... odd. Compared to other molecules, water is like some zany eccentric whose powers stem precisely from its eccentricity. Consider the fact that ice floats on water. This is so because the solid form of H_2O is less dense than the liquid form—a strange reversal of nature's normal pattern. Things work this way because of water's hydrogen bonding. You may remember that, in a collection of water molecules, the hydrogen bonds between individual molecules are constantly breaking and then re-forming. This allows the molecules to pack relatively closely together, as you can see in **Figure 2.15**. Start to move water toward freezing, however, and things change; now the water molecules are able to form the maximum number of hydrogen bonds with each other, and the effect of this is that each water molecule sits *farther apart* from its neighbor. The more space there is between molecules of any substance, the less dense that substance is. In this case, the result is that ice is less dense than liquid water.

This may seem like some minor, quirky quality, but it actually has the effect of making possible life as we know it. Ice on the surface of water insulates the water beneath it from the freezing surface temperatures and wind above, creating a warmer environment for organisms such as fish. If ice *sank,* on the other hand, then the entire body of water would freeze solid at colder latitudes, creating an environment in which few living things could survive for long.

Moderating Temperature: Specific Heat

Water serves as an insulator not only when it is frozen, but also when it is liquid or gas. This has to do with a quality called **specific heat:** the amount of energy required to raise the temperature of a substance by 1°Celsius. As it turns out, water has a high specific heat. Put a gram container of drinking alcohol (ethyl alcohol) side by side with one of water, heat them both, and it will take almost twice as much energy to raise the temperature of the water 1°C as it will the alcohol. Having absorbed this much heat, however, water then has the capacity to *release* it when the environment around it is colder than the water itself. The result? Water acts as a great heat buffer for Earth.

ice

In ice, the maximum number of hydrogen bonds form, causing the molecules to be spread far apart.

liquid water

In liquid water, hydrogen bonds constantly break and re-form, enabling a more dense spacing than in ice.

Figure 2.15
Life Made Possible under the Ice
Water is unusual in that its solid form (ice) is less dense than its liquid form. This means that ice floats, and this in turn means that life can flourish in cold-weather aquatic environments. Pictured is a harp seal swimming under the ice in Canada's Gulf of St. Lawrence.

The oceans absorb tremendous amounts of radiant energy from the sun only to release this heat when the temperature of the air above the ocean gets colder. Without this buffering, temperature on Earth would be less stable. People who have spent a day and a night in a desert can attest to this effect. The searing heat of the desert day radiates off the desert floor; but at night, with little water vapor in the air to capture this heat, the desert cools dramatically. In the same way, our *internal* temperature can remain much more stable because the water that makes up so much of us is able to first absorb and then release great amounts of heat. The sweat created in exercise has considerable cooling power because each drop of perspiration carries with it a great deal of heat.

Water derives these powers once again from its hydrogen bonds. Weak and shifting though individual hydrogen bonds may be, collectively they have great strength. Heat is the motion of molecules. To get molecules moving, though, chemical bonds must first be broken. Because water has a formidable set of hydrogen bonds, it takes a lot of energy to break the bonds and get its molecules moving.

Cohesion and Surface Tension

This tendency of water molecules to stay together is called *cohesion,* and it is very important in the plant world; thanks to this quality, evaporation can work with a process called osmosis to draw water from a plant's roots all the way to its leaves and out into the air as water vapor. Cohesion also imparts the quality of *surface tension* to water in places where water meets air. Water molecules below the surface are equally attracted in all directions to other water molecules. *At the surface, however, water molecules have no such attraction to the air above them—they are pulled down and to the side, but not up.* This causes the "beading" that water droplets do on surfaces. More important for our purposes, surface water molecules pack together more closely than do interior molecules, allowing all kinds of small animals to move across the surface of water, rather than sinking into it. Note the familiar water strider in **Figure 2.16**.

Having looked at the qualities of water, you may be tempted to think how *uncanny* it is that water has all these characteristics that are conducive to life. But remember that life went on solely in water for billions of years before living things ever came onto land. Thus, water has fundamentally conditioned life as we know it. Being surprised about water's life-enhancing qualities is like being surprised that a stage is a good place to put on a play.

Hydrophobic and Hydrophilic Molecules

With its great complexity, life requires molecules that *cannot* be dissolved by water. Such is the case with

(a) Walking on water

(b) Beading up

Figure 2.16
Walking on Water
(a) Water's high surface tension enables small animals, such as this water strider, to walk on it.
(b) This same surface tension also causes water to bead up on waxy or oily surfaces, such as this bird feather.

nonpolar covalent molecules, one example of which is the methane molecule, CH_4. Compounds such as methane are known as **hydrocarbons** because they are made up solely of hydrogen and carbon atoms. Petroleum products are more complex hydrocarbons than methane, but they also are nonpolar, and you can see a vivid demonstration of their lack of water solubility in oil spills. Oil doesn't dissolve in water because the

Figure 2.17
Oil and Water Do Not Mix
When there is an oil spill in the ocean, the oil stays concentrated even as it spreads because oil and water do not form chemical bonds with each other. Here, trawlers are using a boom to clean up after an oil spill in Great Britain.

oil carries almost no electrical charge that water can bond with; thus water has no way to separate one oil molecule from another (**Figure 2.17**).

The ability of molecules to form bonds with water has a couple of important names attached to it. Compounds that will interact with water—such as the sodium chloride considered earlier—are known as **hydrophilic** ("water loving"), while compounds that do not interact with water, such as oil, are known as **hydrophobic** ("water fearing"). Both terms are misleading in that no substance has any emotional relationship with water. *Hydrophobic* is particularly off the mark because water does not repel hydrophobic molecules; instead, the strong bonds that water molecules form with each other cause them to form circles around concentrations of hydrophobic molecules, as if they had lassoed them. (You can see this at home anytime you pour some cooking oil into a pan of water.)

The importance of hydrophobic molecules can be illustrated in part by the common milk carton. Why is the milk carton important? Because it can keep milk separate from everything else. We living organisms need some kind of "carton" that can separate the world outside of us from ourselves. Likewise, organisms have great use *within* themselves for compartments that can be sealed off to one degree or another. If water broke down every molecule of life it came in contact with, then it would break down all these divisions of living systems. Molecules do not have to be

completely hydrophilic or hydrophobic. Indeed, as you'll see, a number of important molecules have both hydrophilic and hydrophobic portions.

SO FAR . . .

1. Pour some salt into a container of water and stir until the salt is no longer visible. In this situation, the salt is the _____, the water is the _____, and the uniform mixture of the two substances is a _____.

2. Thanks to the _____ linking them, water molecules have great _____, meaning a tendency to stay together, and a high _____, with the result that it takes a relatively large amount of energy to raise their temperature.

3. Oil is an example of a substance that will not readily bond with water and thus is _____, while sodium chloride is an example of a substance that is _____ because it will readily bond with water.

2.7 Acids and Bases

When considering the question of the water-based or "aqueous" solutions so common in nature, an important concept is that of acids, bases, and the pH scale used to measure their levels.

We all have had experience with acids and bases, whether we've called them by these names or not. Acidic substances tend to be a little more familiar: lemon juice, vinegar, tomatoes. Substances that are strongly acidic have a well-deserved reputation for being dangerous: The word *acid* is often used to mean something that can sear human flesh. It might seem to follow that bases are benign, but ammonia is a strong base, as are many oven cleaners. The safe zone for living tissue in general lies with substances that are neither strongly acidic nor strongly basic. Science has developed a way of measuring the degree to which something is acidic or basic—the pH scale. So widespread is pH usage that it pops up from time to time in television advertising ("It's pH-balanced!").

Acids Yield Hydrogen Ions in Solution, Bases Accept Them

The *H* in pH stands for hydrogen, while the *p* can be thought of as standing for power. Thus, we get "hydrogen power," which describes what lies at the root of pH. An **acid** is any substance that *yields hydrogen ions* when put in aqueous solution. A **base** is any substance that *accepts* hydrogen ions in aqueous solution.

How might this yielding or accepting come about? Recall first that an ion is a charged atom, and that atoms become charged through the gain or loss of one or more electrons. Because electrons carry a negative charge, the loss of an electron leaves an atom with a net positive charge. Also recall that the hydrogen atom amounts to one central proton and one electron that circles around it. A hydrogen ion, then, is a lone proton that has lost its electron—a positively charged ion whose symbol is H^+.

Now, suppose you put an acid—hydrochloric acid (HCl)—into some water. What happens is that HCl *dissociates* or breaks apart into its ionic components, H^+ and Cl^-. The HCl has therefore yielded a hydrogen ion (H^+). Now, with a greater concentration of hydrogen ions in it, the water is more acidic than it was (**Figure 2.18**).

What about bases? There is a compound called sodium hydroxide (NaOH)—better known as lye—that, when poured into water, dissociates into Na^+ (sodium) and OH^- (hydroxide) ions. The place to look in this case is the OH^- ions. Negatively charged as they are, they would readily bond with positively charged H^+ ions. In other words, they would *accept* H^+ ions in solution, which is the definition of a base. This accepting of the H^+ ions makes the solution more basic—or to look at it another way, less acidic. Thus, acids and bases are something like the two ends of a teeter-totter: When one goes up, the other comes down. As you might have guessed, in the right proportions they can balance each other out perfectly. Look at Figure 2.18 to see how this would play out with the solutions you've looked at so far. Mixing them, the collection of H^+ and OH^- ions now comes

Figure 2.18
Hydrogen Ions and pH

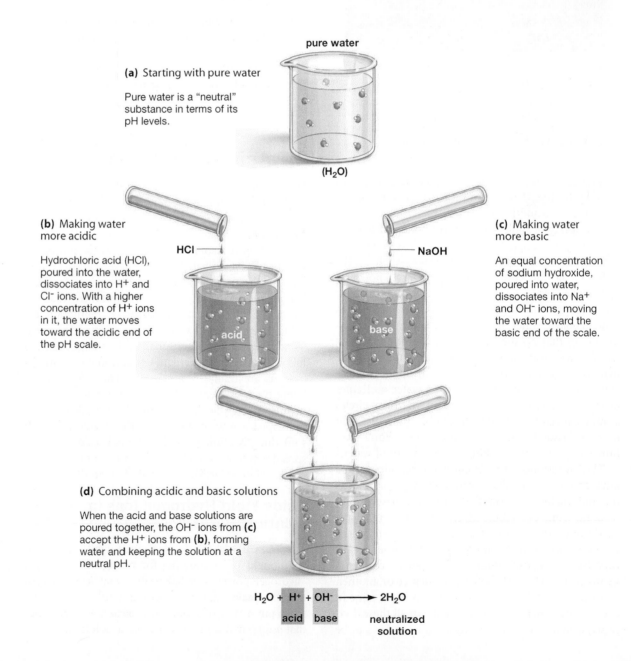

pure water

(a) Starting with pure water

Pure water is a "neutral" substance in terms of its pH levels.

(H_2O)

(b) Making water more acidic

Hydrochloric acid (HCl), poured into the water, dissociates into H^+ and Cl^- ions. With a higher concentration of H^+ ions in it, the water moves toward the acidic end of the pH scale.

HCl

acid

NaOH

base

(c) Making water more basic

An equal concentration of sodium hydroxide, poured into water, dissociates into Na^+ and OH^- ions, moving the water toward the basic end of the scale.

(d) Combining acidic and basic solutions

When the acid and base solutions are poured together, the OH^- ions from **(c)** accept the H^+ ions from **(b)**, forming water and keeping the solution at a neutral pH.

$$H_2O + H^+ + OH^- \longrightarrow 2H_2O$$

acid base   neutralized solution

together in water, and for each pair of ions that inter-acts, the result is:

$$H^+ + OH^- \rightarrow H_2O$$

Water, which is neutral on the pH scale. The acid and the base have perfectly balanced one another out. The OH^- ion, generally referred to as the **hydroxide ion,** is important because compounds that yield them in quantity are strongly basic and can be used to move solutions from the acidic toward the basic.

Ranking Substances on the pH Scale

Look at **Figure 2.19**, on the next page, for an idea of how acidic or basic some common substances are. Following from the notion of what pH amounts to, it's clear that battery acid, for example, is strongly acidic because when it dissociates in solution it yields a large number of hydrogen ions. As you move on to lemon juice and then tomatoes, how-ever, the acids are weaker, which is to say they are substances that yield fewer H^+ ions in solution. By the time you get to human blood, you've arrived at substances that *accept* hydrogen ions.

The net effect of all this yielding and accepting of hydrogen ions is the concentration of H^+ ions in so-lution. Through this concentration, the notion of pH can be *quantified*—can have numbers attached to it. What is employed here is the **pH scale,** a scale used in measuring the relative acidity of a sub-stance. Look at Figure 2.19 again, this time in con-nection with the numbers on the right of the scale. You can see that 0 on the scale is the most acidic, while 14 is the most basic. It's important to note that the pH scale is *logarithmic:* A substance with a pH of 9 is 10 times as basic as a substance with a pH of 8 and 100 times as basic as a substance with a pH of 7.

Some pH Terminology

Now here are some notes on pH terminology:

- As a solution becomes more basic, its pH *rises.* Thus, the higher the pH, the more basic the solu-tion; the lower the pH, the more acidic the solu-tion. Oven cleaner is said to have a high pH, while lemon juice has a low pH.
- Given that a hydrogen ion amounts to a single proton, it is also correct to say that an acid is something that yields *protons* in solution, while a base is something that accepts protons. This is how you will often hear hydrogen ions discussed in biology.
- A solution that is basic is also referred to as an **alkaline** solution.

Why Does pH Matter?

So, why do we care about pH? The brief answer is be-cause living things are sensitive to its levels in many ways. There is, for example, a class of proteins called enzymes that you'll be reading about in Chapter 3. Enzymes are chemical tools that must retain a specific shape to function. However, if you put an enzyme in a solution with a pH that is too acidic, the enzyme loses its shape. Why? The charged nature of the acidic solu-tion starts breaking down the enzyme's hydrogen bonds. (Remember, lots of positively charged protons are floating around in an acidic solution.) Likewise, cell membranes—which to some degree perform the milk carton function noted earlier—can start to break down if pH levels begin to go outside normal limits. Membranes and enzymes are so fundamental to life that when they are interfered with, death can result. It is not surprising, then, that many organisms have de-veloped so-called acid-base **buffering systems,** mean-ing physiological systems that function to keep pH within normal limits. What are these limits? The usual range for living things is about 6–8, with the pH of the human cell being about 7 and that of the blood in our arteries about 7.4. However, some parts of the body have special pH requirements. The interior of your stomach, for example, can have a pH as low as 1—an extremely acidic environment that not only helps break down food but that also kills most bacteria that ride in on the food. Even a stomach can become too acidic, however (perhaps because of what we've eaten), in which case people may turn to the *pharmaceutical* pH buffers commonly known as antacids. These sub-stances do just what their name implies: They raise pH levels in the stomach, thus helping to alleviate the symptoms of "heartburn."

Beyond its effects on individuals, pH can affect en-tire communities of living things. You may have heard of acid rain as a phenomenon that affects forests, streams, and lakes. Well, **acid rain** is just what it sounds like: rain whose pH level has been skewed to-ward the acidic side of the pH scale, with air pollution being the cause of this shift. As you can imagine, when rain itself has an altered pH, there can be widespread trouble for living things. Starting in the 1970s, this began to be the case in many environments world-wide, and this remains true today. (In the United States, the problem has been most severe in an area stretching from Michigan eastward through Pennsyl-vania and New York State.) Air pollution regulations have lessened the severity of acid rain in recent years, but it remains a long-term problem that requires con-stant monitoring.

On to Biological Molecules

In this chapter, you've learned a fair amount about some of nature's most fundamental building blocks:

Figure 2.19
Common Substances and the pH Scale

Chemists use units called moles per liter to measure the concentration of substances in solution. The pH scale, derived from this framework, measures the concentration of hydrogen ions per liter of solution. The most acidic substances on the scale have the greatest concentration of hydrogen ions, while the most basic (or alkaline) substances have the lowest concentration of hydrogen ions. The scale is logarithmic, so that wine, for example, is 10 times as acidic as tomatoes and 100 times as acidic as black coffee.

H+ concentration (moles/liter)

pH

acidic

10^0	0	battery acid
10^{-1}	1	hydrochloric acid
10^{-2}	2	lemon juice, gastric (stomach) juice
10^{-3}	3	cola, beer, wine, vinegar
10^{-4}	4	tomatoes
10^{-5}	5	black coffee
10^{-6}	6	urine
10^{-7}	7	water
		human blood
10^{-8}	8	seawater
10^{-9}	9	baking soda
10^{-10}	10	Great Salt Lake
10^{-11}	11	household ammonia
10^{-12}	12	
10^{-13}	13	household bleach
		oven cleaner
10^{-14}	14	lye

neutral 10^{-7}

basic

human blood is slightly basic

atoms, ions, the simple substance water, and a special ion (the H^+ ion) whose levels govern pH. Now it's time to see how these building blocks fit together to create some of the larger-scale component parts of life. These component parts usually are referred to as *biological molecules*. Everyone has heard of at least some biological molecules. Carbohydrates are one variety of them, for example, and it's easy to name foods that we think of as carbohydrates. But what *is* a carbohydrate? What is the fundamental nature of this component part of life? To sharpen the point, how does a carbohydrate differ from a protein? In Chapter 3, you'll find out as we explore the types of molecules that make up the living world.

SO FAR . . .

1. An acid is any substance that _____ hydrogen _____ when put into an aqueous solution, while a base is any substance that _____ them.

2. The neutral point on the pH scale is _____, while the most acidic point is _____, and the most basic or alkaline point is _____.

3. Living things tend to have internal pH environments that hover around _____.

C H A P T E R

2 REVIEW

Go to the Study Area at www.masteringbiology.com for practice quizzes, myeBook, BioFlix™ 3-D animations, MP3 Tutor Sessions, videos, current events, and more.

Mastering BIOLOGY™

Summary

2.1 Chemistry's Building Block: The Atom

- The fundamental unit of matter is the atom, whose most important constituent parts are protons, neutrons, and electrons. Protons and neutrons exist in the atom's nucleus; electrons move at some distance around the nucleus. Protons are positively charged; electrons are negatively charged; neutrons carry no charge. (p. 20)

- An element is any substance that cannot be reduced to a simpler set of constituent substances through chemical means. Each element is defined by the number of protons in its nucleus. (p. 21)

- The number of neutrons in an atom can vary independently of the number of protons. Thus, a single element can exist in various forms, called isotopes. (p. 22)

2.2 Chemical Bonding: The Covalent Bond

- Atoms can link to one another in the process of chemical bonding. One form

this bonding can take is covalent bonding, in which atoms share one or more electrons. (p. 22)

- Chemical bonding comes about as atoms "seek" their lowest energy state. An atom achieves this state when it has a filled outer electron shell. (p. 22)

- A molecule is an entity consisting of a defined number of atoms covalently bonded together. (p. 24)

- Atoms of different elements differ in their power to attract electrons. The term for measuring this power is electronegativity. Through electronegativity, a molecule can take on a polarity, meaning a difference in electrical charge at one end compared to the other. Covalent chemical bonds can be polar or nonpolar. (p. 25)

2.3 The Ionic Bond

- Two atoms will undergo a process of ionization when the electronegativity differences between them are great enough that one atom loses one or more electrons to the other. This process creates ions: atoms whose number of electrons differs from

their number of protons. The charge differences that result from ionization can produce an electrostatic attraction between ions. This attraction is an ionic bond, and the product of this bonding is an ionic compound: a collection of the atoms of two or more elements that have become linked through ionic bonding. (p. 25)

2.4 The Hydrogen Bond

- Hydrogen bonding links an already covalently bonded hydrogen atom with an electronegative atom. (p. 30)

2.5 Three-Dimensional Shape in Molecules

- Three-dimensional molecular shape determines the capacity molecules have to bind with one another. (p. 30)

2.6 Water and Life

- No living thing can be fully functional without a steady supply of water. Water's chemical properties allow it to facilitate many of the chemical reactions that take place in living things. (p. 31)

- Water has several other qualities that have affected life on Earth, among them cohesion and high specific heat. (p. 33)

- Some molecules do not interact with water and are called hydrophobic. Molecules or ions that do interact with water, by virtue of being charged or polar, are called hydrophilic. (p. 34)

2.7 Acids and Bases

- An acid is any substance that yields hydrogen ions when put in an aqueous (water) solution. A base is any substance that accepts hydrogen ions in solution. A base added to an acidic solution makes that solution less acidic, while an acid added to a basic solution makes that solution less basic. (p. 35)

- The concentration of hydrogen ions a solution has determines how basic or acidic that solution is, as measured on the pH scale (running from 0 to 14, with 0 most acidic, 14 most basic, and 7 neutral). (p. 37)

- The pH scale is logarithmic; a substance with a pH of 9 is 10 times as basic as a substance with a pH of 8. Living things function best in a near-neutral pH. (p. 37)

Key Terms

acid   35
acid rain   37
alkaline   37
atomic number   21
ball-and-stick model   29
base   35
buffering system   37
chemical bonding   22
covalent bond   24
electron   20
electronegativity   25
element   21
hydrocarbon   34
hydrogen bond   30
hydrophilic   35
hydrophobic   35
hydroxide ion   37
ion   28
ionic bonding   28

ionic compound   30
isotope   22
law of conservation of mass   24
mass   19
molecular formula   29
molecule   24
neutron   20
nonpolar covalent bond   25
nucleus   20
pH scale   37
polar covalent bond   25
polarity   25
product   29
proton   20
reactant   29
solute   32
solution   32
solvent   32
space-filling model   29
specific heat   33
structural formula   29

Understanding the Basics

Multiple-Choice Questions

(Answers are in the back of the book.)

1. Carbon is an element with an atomic number of 6. Based on this information, which of the following statements is true? (More than one may be true.)
   a. Carbon can be broken down into simpler component substances.
   b. Carbon cannot be broken down into simpler component substances.
   c. Each carbon atom will always have 6 neutrons.
   d. Each carbon atom will always have 6 protons.
   e. Number of protons + number of electrons = 6

2. Neon has an atomic number of 10 and thus has eight electrons in its second energy level. Thus neon (select all that apply):
   a. has a strong tendency to form covalent bonds.
   b. has a filled outer shell.
   c. has no tendency to form covalent bonds.

   d. is polar.
   e. all of these

3. Oxygen and hydrogen differ in their electronegativity. Thus:
   a. They can share electrons, but unequally.
   b. Sometimes oxygen takes electrons completely away from hydrogen.
   c. They can share electrons equally.
   d. Hydrogen is attracted to oxygen but does not bond with it.
   e. They have the same number of protons.

4. A molecule that does not have a net electrical charge at one end as opposed to the other is:
   a. an isotope.
   b. a polar molecule.
   c. a reactant.
   d. a nonpolar molecule.
   e. a solvent.

5. You add sugar to your coffee, and the sugar dissolves. Thus the coffee is the _____ and the sugar is the _____.
   a. solute; solvent
   b. solvent; solute
   c. polar covalent bond; nonpolar covalent bond
   d. nonpolar covalent bond; polar covalent bond
   e. ionic bond; hydrogen bond

6. Near an ocean or other large body of water, air temperatures do not vary as much with the seasons as they do in the middle of a continent. This tendency of water to resist changes in temperature is the result of water's:
   a. high density.
   b. low density.
   c. being a good solvent.
   d. low specific heat.
   e. high specific heat.

7. Janine has dry skin, so she uses body oil every morning. The oil seals in some of the water on her skin, so that it doesn't get as dry. This is possible because oils:
   a. are hydrophilic.
   b. are rare in nature.
   c. have a high specific heat.
   d. are more dense than water.
   e. are hydrophobic.

8. Some plants live in bogs in which the pH is about 2. Thus these plants are able to survive in a(n) _____ external environment.
   a. basic
   b. buffered
   c. acidic
   d. neutral
   e. alkaline

Brief Review

(Answers are in the back of the book.)

1. As with most elements, carbon comes in several forms, one of which is carbon-14. What are these forms called, and how does one differ from the other?

2. Compare the size of an atom with the size of its nucleus. Where are the electrons? In light of this, what makes up most of the volume of an atom?

3. Draw a line and label one end "complete + or − charge" and the other end "no charge" to indicate the charges on the molecules or ions after bonding has occurred. Along the line, indicate where polar covalent bonds, nonpolar covalent bonds, and ionic bonds should be placed.

4. Why are atoms unlikely to react when they have their outer shell filled with electrons?

5. Give two examples of the ways in which water acts as a heat buffer.

6. Why do living things need to keep such a tight control on their internal pH?

Applying Your Knowledge

1. In the Middle Ages, alchemists labored to turn common materials such as iron into precious metals such as gold. If you could journey back in time, how could you convince an alchemist that iron cannot be changed into gold?

2. Why does a balloon filled with helium float? Hydrogen can make balloons float, but it is not used for this purpose today because it is flammable. Based on chemical principles reviewed in the chapter, can you see why helium is not flammable? (*Hint:* Think what you are adding to a fire when you blow on it.)

3. How is water's importance to life reflected in the normal range of internal pH values that living things are likely to have?

Life's Components:
Biological Molecules

*Four kinds of carbon-based
molecules form the living world.*

Living things such as this giant redwood tree (*Sequoia sempervirens*) can
grow to enormous sizes thanks to the
strength of materials they themselves
produce.

We are stardust . . .

Billion-year-old carbon

from "Woodstock," by Joni Mitchell

Songwriters usually specialize in emotional truth, so it's no small feat that, in just a couple of lines, Joni Mitchell could sum up the literal truth of what we are made of. Admittedly, her billion-year-old figure is off—Earth actually is about 4.6 billion years old, and its carbon is older yet. Even so, she was right about the essentials. Are we stardust? To a large extent, yes. All the heavy elements in our bodies—calcium, iron, carbon—were first cooked up in the fiery interior of stars and then dispersed into space when these stars exploded. Over time, these elements became a part of planets such as the Earth.

But surely we're more than carbon, right? Well, by weight we are more oxygen than anything else, mostly because oxygen is a principal element in water, which makes up so much of our bodies. Even so, it's carbon that really is life's element. How so? Well, consider the way in which living things amount to *concentrations* of carbon when compared to the makeup of the nonliving world around them. As the environmental scientist Vaclav Smil has noted, Earth's crust is about 0.05 percent carbon, and Earth's atmosphere is about 0.01 percent carbon. Yet Earth's *organisms* are 18 percent carbon, even when water is taken into account, and nearly 50 percent carbon when water is factored out.

Given such figures, it's not surprising that, just as money must flow through an economy for it to operate, so carbon must flow through the living world for it to operate. First, plants and other photosynthesizers take in carbon from the atmosphere—over 100 billion tons of it per year, in the form of atmospheric CO_2. Then the plants, and all the organisms that eat them, use this carbon to make up their tissues and to power their activities. Finally, all these organisms die, and as their remains are broken down, some of the carbon in them is released into the atmosphere. But this is not a one-way trip; sooner or later, this same carbon is likely to move back into the living world, to be made part of a tree or a mushroom or a human being once again.

3.1 Carbon's Place in the Living World

So, why does carbon have this special place in life? The answer can be summed up in one word: linkage. Recall from Chapter 2 that carbon has four outer-shell,

or "valence" electrons but that most elements need *eight* outer-shell electrons for maximum stability. This means that carbon achieves maximum stability by linking up with four more electrons, which in turn means that carbon's bonding capacity is great. It can form very large and complex molecules, which is exactly what is needed in connection with the tremendous complexity of living things. Moreover, the bonds that carbon creates are covalent—it is *sharing* electrons with other atoms—which means its linkages are more stable than those formed by elements that bond ionically. Given the natural forces that can buffet life, such as ultraviolet radiation and heat, this stability is an important quality first in getting life going and then in keeping it going. So important is carbon that it forms one whole area of chemistry—**organic chemistry,** a branch of chemistry devoted to the study of molecules that have carbon as their central element (**Figure 3.1,** on the next page).

How does carbon link up with itself or other atoms? Last chapter, you had a look at a model of a very simple carbon-based molecule, methane. Here it is again:

$$\begin{array}{c} \text{H} \\ | \\ \text{H}-\text{C}-\text{H} \\ | \\ \text{H} \end{array}$$

Note that the only elements present are hydrogen and carbon, which makes this molecule a **hydrocarbon.** Now, observe a slightly more complex hydrocarbon, the familiar gas propane (C_3H_8).

$$\begin{array}{c} \text{H} \quad \text{H} \quad \text{H} \\ | \quad | \quad | \\ \text{H}-\text{C}-\text{C}-\text{C}-\text{H} \\ | \quad | \quad | \\ \text{H} \quad \text{H} \quad \text{H} \end{array}$$

You can see that, instead of being surrounded by four hydrogen atoms, the carbons here link with other carbons as well as with the hydrogens. This process of

Figure 3.1
Pure Carbon, Mostly Carbon

A diamond is pure carbon and the hardest natural material known. Surrounding the diamond is a lump of coal, which has a high carbon content because it is made up mostly of the remains of carbon-rich, ancient vegetation.

extension keeps going with still more complex hydrocarbons. For obvious reasons, the preceding configuration is known as a *straight-chain* carbon molecule. But carbon has more tricks up its sleeve than simple straight-line extensions. The next hydrocarbon up the line is butane, the fuel in cigarette lighters. It can be just another straight-chain extension, looking like this:

$$H-\underset{\underset{H}{|}}{\overset{\overset{H}{|}}{C}}-\underset{\underset{H}{|}}{\overset{\overset{H}{|}}{C}}-\underset{\underset{H}{|}}{\overset{\overset{H}{|}}{C}}-\underset{\underset{H}{|}}{\overset{\overset{H}{|}}{C}}-H$$

But it can also look like this:

$$H-\underset{\underset{H}{|}}{\overset{\overset{H}{|}}{C}}-\underset{\underset{\underset{\underset{H}{|}}{H-C-H}}{|}}{\overset{\overset{H}{|}}{C}}-\underset{\underset{H}{|}}{\overset{\overset{H}{|}}{C}}-H$$

These two forms of butane are known as *isomers*—molecules that have the same chemical formulas but differ in the spatial arrangement of their atoms.

Carbon can also form rings. Here is the structure of benzene (C_6H_6), which is found in petroleum products:

Note the three sets of double lines in the molecule. Recall that this means there are double *bonds* between these atoms; the atoms involved share *two* pairs of electrons.

It just so happens that all the carbon-based molecules introduced so far are hydrocarbons, but this is

the exception rather than the rule. Here are two representations of a molecule mentioned already—glucose, better known as blood sugar:

So here are some added oxygen atoms. Notice how the second model, below the first, with its heavy line down at the bottom, looks a little different than the benzene ring? Such a model is meant to give you a slightly more realistic picture of the actual arrangement of atoms when a carbon ring is present. Think of the ring as lying at an angle to the paper, with the heavy line closer to you than the line in the back; the H and OH groups then lie above and below the plane of the ring, as shown. You may also notice that when things get this complicated, space starts getting a little tight for writing in the letters that stand for the various atoms that are a part of the molecule. Because most rings are formed predominantly of carbon, it is common to dispense with the Cs when a structural formula is presented. Here is a third representation of the glucose model, written in this stripped-down form:

You can see that carbon is *assumed* to exist at each bond juncture in the ring; if some other element occupies one of these points, it is explicitly noted. Often the solitary Hs that are attached to carbons are left out as well.

Such models as these, as you'll recall from the last chapter, don't show the actual three-dimensional form of a molecule. To do so, ball-and-stick or space-filling models are required. Examples of these models are shown in **Figure 3.2**. With them, you can start to see how carbon is literally central to the molecules of the living world. Note how the carbon atoms form the core of the glucose molecule, with the hydrogen and oxygen atoms on the periphery.

3.2 Functional Groups

Having seen how carbon-based molecules start to become specialized through the addition of other kinds of atoms, it's worth noting that such atoms often are affixed in *groups*. Each of these units is a **functional group**: a group of atoms that confers a special property on a carbon-based molecule. Just as an attachment on a power tool might make the difference between a drill and a screwdriver, so a functional group can make the difference between one molecule and another. Look here at the formula for the hydrocarbon ethane, which is a flammable gas:

$$
\begin{array}{c}
\text{H} \quad \text{H} \\
| \quad\quad | \\
\text{H} - \text{C} - \text{C} - \text{H} \\
| \quad\quad | \\
\text{H} \quad \text{H}
\end{array}
$$

Now let's substitute a functional group, called the hydroxyl or –OH group, for the rightmost hydrogen atom in ethane and thus get:

$$
\begin{array}{c}
\text{H} \quad \text{H} \\
| \quad\quad | \\
\text{H} - \text{C} - \text{C} - \text{OH} \\
| \quad\quad | \\
\text{H} \quad \text{H}
\end{array}
$$

With this, we no longer have a gas; we have a liquid—the drinkable liquid ethyl alcohol. Anytime an –OH group is added to a hydrocarbon chain, some sort of alcohol is formed, be it the isopropyl alcohol used to disinfect cuts, the methanol used to power turbine engines, or some other variety. Thus, the –OH group has a generalized function in connection with hydrocarbons and is therefore referred to as a *functional group*. Now note another effect of this group. The ethane we started with was *nonpolar*—there was no difference in charge at one end of the ethane molecule as opposed to the other. But the addition of the group changed this; the oxygen atom it contains has such strong electronegativity that ethyl alcohol does have a polarity, meaning it can bond with other charged or polar molecules, including water. This exemplifies a general characteristic of functional groups, which is that they often impart an electrical charge, or at least a polarity, onto molecules, which makes a big difference in their bonding capacity. The –OH group serves this polarizing function not only when it is added to hydrocarbons, but also when it is part of other molecules as well. If you look at **Table 3.1**, you can see some of the functional groups that are most important in living

ball-and-stick model of glucose   space-filling model of glucose

Figure 3.2
Ball-and-Stick and Space-Filling Models of Glucose
The simple sugar glucose is the single most important energy source for our bodies. Because it has several –OH groups, it is highly hydrophilic and thus readily breaks down in water. Note how the carbon atoms (in black) form the core of the molecule, with oxygen (in red) and hydrogen (in white) at the periphery.

things. You'll be seeing all of these groups as the chapter progresses: the carboxyl group when we look at fats (or lipids), the amino group when we go over proteins, and the phosphate group when we review both lipids and DNA.

SO FAR ...

1. The element _____ is central to the molecules that make up the living world. This element comes to its special status because of the great power it has to form stable _____.

2. A functional group is a group of _____ that confers a special property on a _____ molecule.

Table 3.1

Functional Groups

Group	Structural Formula	Found in
Carboxyl (–COOH)	$-\text{C} \overset{\displaystyle O}{\underset{\displaystyle OH}{}}$	fatty acids, amino acids
Hydroxyl (–OH)	— OH	alcohols, carbohydrates
Amino (–NH$_2$)	$-\text{N}\overset{\displaystyle H}{\underset{\displaystyle H}{}}$	amino acids
Phosphate (–PO$_4$)	$-\text{O}-\overset{\displaystyle O}{\underset{\displaystyle O^-}{\overset{\|}{\|}}}\text{P}-\text{O}^-$	DNA, ATP

Table 3.2

Monomers, Polymers

If the monomer is . . .	The polymer is . . .
A monosaccharide (for example, glucose, fructose)	A polysaccharide (for example, starch, glycogen, cellulose)
An amino acid (for example arginine, leucine)	A polypeptide or protein (A- and B-chains of insulin are polypeptides and insulin is a protein)
A nucleotide (sugar, phosphate, base in combination)	A nucleic acid (for example, DNA, RNA)

3.3 Carbohydrates

With this overview of carbon structures under your belt, you're ready to begin looking at some of the classes of carbon-based molecules—the molecules of living things. You'll explore four groupings of these organic molecules: carbohydrates, lipids, proteins, and nucleic acids.

As you get into this section, it will be a great help to keep in mind that *complex* organic molecules often are made from *simpler* molecules. Many of the molecules you'll be reading about have a building-blocks quality to them. Take a simple sugar, or monosaccharide, such as glucose, put it together with another monosaccharide (fructose), and you have a larger *di*saccharide called sucrose (better known as table sugar). Put *many* monosac-

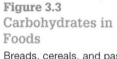

Figure 3.3
Carbohydrates in Foods

Breads, cereals, and pasta make up a significant proportion of our diets. These foods are all rich in carbohydrates, one of the four main types of biological molecules.

charide units together, and you have a polysaccharide, such as starch. The starch is an example of a **polymer**—a large molecule made up of many similar or identical subunits. Meanwhile, the glucose is an example of a **monomer**—a small molecule that can be combined with other similar or identical molecules to make a polymer. Look at **Table 3.2** for examples of both.

Carbohydrates: From Simple Sugars to Cellulose

Happily, for purposes of memory, the elements in the first molecules we'll look at, carbohydrates, are all hinted at in the name: **Carbohydrates** are organic molecules that always contain carbon, oxygen, and hydrogen and that in many instances contain nothing *but* carbon, oxygen, and hydrogen. Furthermore, they usually contain exactly twice as many hydrogen atoms as oxygen atoms. For example, the carbohydrate glucose ($C_6H_{12}O_6$) contains 12 atoms of hydrogen and 6 of oxygen. Most people think of carbohydrates purely in terms of foods such as breads and pasta (**Figure 3.3**), but as you'll see, carbohydrates have more roles than this in nature.

The building blocks of the carbohydrates are the **monosaccharides** mentioned earlier. These are the monomers of carbohydrates, collectively referred to as **simple sugars.** You've already seen several views of one of these monomers, glucose. Glucose has a use in and of itself: Much of the food we eat is broken down into it, at which point it becomes our most important energy source. Glucose can also bond with other monosaccharides, however, to form more complex carbohydrates. Let's take a look at how this happens. If you look at **Figure 3.4**, you can see an example of two glucose molecules bonding to create the disaccharide called maltose.

Several things are worth noting here. In maltose, as you can see, the link that joins the two glucose monomers is a single oxygen atom linked to carbons of each of the glucose units. To get this, two atoms of hydrogen and one atom of oxygen are split off (on the left side of the equation) from the original glucose molecules. What becomes of these three atoms? Look at the far right-hand side of the reaction and see the $+ H_2O$. The products of this reaction are a molecule of maltose and a molecule of water.

Now note the arrows in the middle of the reaction. You've been used to seeing a single, rightward-pointing arrow, but here the arrows go both ways. This means that this is a reversible reaction—it can proceed in either of the two directions. Maltose can be split apart to yield two *glucose* molecules. Finally, note the existence of the −OH functional group in both the glucose and maltose molecules.

Kinds of Simple Carbohydrates

You have thus far seen examples of one of the simplest carbohydrates, the monosaccharide glucose, and one

| glucose | + | glucose | = | maltose | + | water |

Figure 3.4
Carbohydrates Follow a Building-Blocks Model
In this example, two units of the monosaccharide (or simple sugar) glucose link to form the disaccharide maltose. In addition to maltose, the reaction yields water.

slightly more complex carbohydrate, a disaccharide called maltose. There are many kinds of mono- and disaccharides, however. Among the monosaccharides are, for example, fructose and deoxyribose. Among disaccharides, there are sucrose and lactose. At the risk of pointing out the obvious, note that all these sugars have –*ose* at the end of their name: If it's an –*ose,* it's a sugar (**Figure 3.5**).

Complex Carbohydrates

If you go another couple of bumps up in complexity from disaccharides, you get to the polymers of carbohydrates, the **polysaccharides.** The *poly-* in polysaccharide means "many," while *saccharide* means "sugars," and the term is apt. In the polysaccharide molecule cellulose, for example, there may be 10,000 glucose units linked with one another. The basic unit here is the six-carbon monosaccharide glucose $C_6H_{12}O_6$ from which chains of glucose units are built. The complexity of these molecules gives them their alternate name, *complex carbohydrates.* Four different types of complex carbohydrates interest us: starch, glycogen, cellulose, and chitin (**Table 3.3**, on the next page).

Starch is a complex carbohydrate found in plants; it exists in the form of such foods as potatoes, rice, carrots, and corn. In plants, these starches serve as the main form of carbohydrate *storage,* sometimes as seeds (rice and wheat grains) or sometimes as roots (carrots or beets) (Table 3.3).

Another complex carbohydrate, **glycogen,** serves as the primary form of carbohydrate storage in animals. Thus, glycogen does for animals what starch does for plants. For this reason, glycogen is sometimes called animal starch. The starches or sugars we eat are broken down eventually into glucose, at which point some of this glucose may be used immediately as an energy source. Some may not be needed right away, however, in which case it's moved into muscle and liver cells to be stored as the more complex carbohydrate glycogen (Table 3.3).

Cellulose is a structural, complex carbohydrate produced by plants and other organisms. Despite this in-

nocuous-sounding function, cellulose is important because it makes up so much of the natural world. It is easily the most abundant carbohydrate on Earth: Trees, cotton, leaves, and grasses are largely made of it. The dry-weight of a single white oak tree, for example, is about 4,200 pounds, of which 1,200 pounds might be cellulose. When you think of how many trees there are in the world—to say nothing of the uncountable acres of grass, cotton, and so forth—you begin to get an idea of how much cellulose there is on Earth. When this carbohydrate is enmeshed with a hardening substance called lignin, the result is a set of cell walls that can hold up giant redwood trees. Because cellulose is so dense and rigid, it is not surprising that human beings cannot digest it. This statement may make you wonder about grass-eating *cows,* but in fact cows have cellulose digested for them by special bacteria in their digestive tract. Cellulose is important to humans because it is our major source of insoluble fiber, which helps move foods through the digestive tract. Because cellulose exists in the cell walls of plants, we can get our fiber from such foods as whole grains.

Figure 3.5
Sugars Come in Many Forms

Sucrose or table sugar comes to us from sugarcane or sugar beets, and glucose is found in corn syrup. Fructose comes to us in sweet fruits and in high-fructose corn syrup, which often is used to sweeten soft drinks.

Our fourth complex carbohydrate, **chitin,** forms the external skeleton of the arthropods—all insects, spiders, and crustaceans, for example. In these animals, chitin plays a structural role similar to that of cellulose in plants: It gives shape and strength to the structure of the organism (Table 3.3).

SO FAR ...

1. Biological molecules often have a building-blocks quality to them, with smaller _____ linked together to form larger _____.

2. Carbohydrates are organic molecules that always contain _____, _____, and _____. The building blocks of carbohydrates are the simple sugars or _____, which link to form _____.

3. The four most important varieties of complex carbohydrates in the living world are _____, which serves as a carbohydrate storage molecule in plants; _____, which serves this same function in animals; _____, which makes up a large portion of plant stems and leaves; and _____, which forms the external skeleton of all arthropods.

Table 3.3

Four Examples of Complex Carbohydrates

	Starch	Glycogen	Cellulose	Chitin
Structure				
Function	Serves as a form of carbohydrate storage in many plants	Serves as a form of carbohydrate storage in animals	Provides structural support for plants and other organisms	Makes up a large portion of the outer "skin" or cuticle of arthropods
Example	Starch granules within cells of a raw potato slice	Glycogen granules (black dots) within a liver cell	Cellulose fibers within the cell wall of a marine algae cell	The chitinous cuticle of a tick

3.4 Lipids

We turn now to our second major group of biological molecules, the **lipids,** a class of molecules whose defining characteristic is that they do not readily dissolve in water. It turns out that lipids are made of the same elements as carbohydrates—carbon, hydrogen, and oxygen. But lipids have much more hydrogen, relative to oxygen, than do the carbohydrates. We're all familiar with some lipids; they exist as fats, oils, cholesterol, and as hormones such as testosterone and estrogen. Unlike the other biological molecules you'll be studying, however, a lipid is not a polymer composed of component-part monomers; no single structural unit is common to all lipids. Thus, the one characteristic shared by pure lipids is that they do not readily dissolve or "break down" in water. Remember a discussion last chapter about the need living things have for internal compartments that are sealed off from one another? Well, thanks to their insolubility, lipids are able to serve this function. In addition, lipids have considerable powers to store energy and to provide insulation (think of the abundant fat on a polar bear).

The Glyceride Lipids

The most common kind of lipid, the glyceride, can be thought of as a molecule in two parts. The first part is a "head" composed of the alcohol glycerol:

$$H-C-OH$$
$$H-C-OH$$
$$H-C-OH$$

The second part is one or more fatty acids; an example can be seen in **Figure 3.6**. This is stearic acid, one of the fatty acids in animal fat. As you can see, it amounts to a long chain of hydrogen and carbon atoms—its hydrocarbon portion—that terminates with a COOH or "carboxyl" functional group on the left. Now, bringing the carboxyl part of this fatty acid chain together with the –OH group of glycerol is what makes a glyceride. But you can see that the glycerol has *three* –OH groups on the right. Thus there is, you might say, docking space on glycerol for three fatty acids, and in the synthesis of many glycerides, this

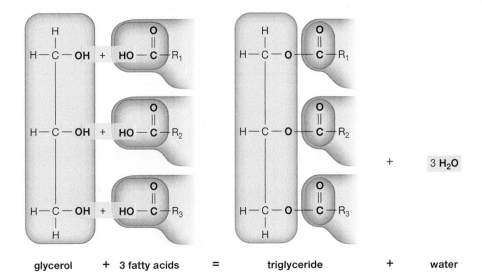

glycerol   +   3 fatty acids   =   triglyceride   +   water

linkage takes place: Three fatty acids link with glycerol to form a triglyceride, which is the most important dietary form of lipid. **Figure 3.7** shows how it works schematically.

The Rs on the right end of the COOH group stand for whatever the hydrocarbon chain is of that particular fatty acid. To get a better idea of the shape of a completed triglyceride, look at the space-filling model in **Figure 3.8**, on the next page. This particular triglyceride, called tristearin, has three stearic fatty acids that stem like tines on a fork from the glycerol. This is only one possibility among many and is exceptional, rather than usual, in that all three fatty acids are the same. Among the dozens of fatty acids that exist, several *different* kinds of fatty acids generally will hook up in glycerol's three –OH "slots" to form a triglyceride. Actual fat products, such as butter, are composed of different proportions of various fatty acids.

We've seen three fatty acids linking with glycerol to form *triglycerides*, but monoglycerides (one fatty acid joined to glycerol) and diglycerides (two fatty acids joined with glycerol) can be formed as well. Triglycerides are the most important of the glycerides, however, because they constitute about 90 percent of the lipid weight in foods.

With all this under your belt, you're ready for a couple of definitions. A **triglyceride** is a lipid molecule formed from three fatty acids bonded to glycerol. A **fatty acid** is a molecule found in many lipids that is composed of a hydrocarbon chain bonded to a carboxyl group.

Figure 3.7
Formation of a Triglyceride

Figure 3.6
Structural Formula for Stearic Acid

Figure 3.8
The Triglyceride Tristearin

This lipid molecule is composed of three stearic fatty acids, stemming rightward from the glycerol –OH "head." Tristearin is found in both beef fat and the cocoa butter that helps make up chocolate.

Saturated and Unsaturated Fatty Acids in Triglycerides

If you now look at **Figure 3.9**, you can see three different fatty acids: palmitic, oleic, and linoleic. There is an obvious difference among them in that the oleic and linoleic hydrocarbon chains are "bent" compared to the straight-line palmitic chain. On closer inspection, you can see that the palmitic acid has an unbroken line of single bonds linking its carbon atoms. Meanwhile, the oleic acid has one double bond between the carbons in its chain, and the linoleic acid has two. Furthermore, note that these double bonds exist precisely where the "kinks" appear in these molecules.

What these variations describe are the differences between three *kinds* of fatty acids. First, there is a **saturated fatty acid**—a fatty acid with no double bonds between the carbon atoms of its hydrocarbon chain. Then, there is a **monounsaturated fatty acid** (a fatty acid with one double bond between carbon atoms) and a **polyunsaturated fatty acid** (a fatty acid with two or more double bonds between carbon atoms). What a saturated fatty acid is saturated *with* is hydrogen atoms. A given monounsaturated fatty acid could theoretically have its lone carbon-carbon double bond replaced with a *single* bond between the carbons. This change would entail the addition of two more hydrogen atoms at the bond sites. Once this happened, this fatty acid would contain the maximum number of hydrogen atoms possible, meaning it would be a saturated fatty acid.

This may not sound like much of a difference, but it has several important consequences. First, at room temperature, as you move from saturated to unsaturated, you also move from fats in their solid form to fats in their liquid form, which we call **oils.** Why does saturation make this kind of difference? Remember that saturated fatty acids have a straight-chain form; as such, they can pack together tightly in a triglyceride,

like so many boards in a lumberyard. In contrast, unsaturated fatty acids stick out at varying angles to one another; thus, they have a disorder that generally makes them liquid at room temperature. In short, the "kinks" in unsaturated fatty acids have consequences.

The distinction between saturated and unsaturated fatty acids also has another important effect, this one related to human health. Think of it this way: To the degree that *fatty acids* are saturated, the *fats* they make up will be saturated. And consumption of saturated fats has long been linked with heart disease—saturated fats raise total blood cholesterol levels, and high cholesterol levels are a risk factor for heart disease. The picture on dietary fats in general is more complex, however; some are neutral with respect to health and others actually are beneficial. You can read more about this in "From Trans Fats to Omega-3s" on page 54.

Lipid and Carbohydrate Energy Storage and Use

Lipids and the carbohydrates we looked at have something in common in connection with energy use on the one hand and energy storage on the other. To be used for energy, the fats we eat must first be broken down into their glycerol and fatty acid components. To be stored away, however, these component parts must be combined, thus producing triglycerides. Carbohydrates, meanwhile, may come to us in their complex starch form, but to be used for energy expenditure, they must first be broken down into their simple carbohydrate building blocks, usually meaning glucose (**Figure 3.10**, on page 52). Should we not need glucose immediately for energy expenditure, glucose units will be combined into larger glycogen molecules, which are stored in muscle and liver cells. This process of alternately building up molecules for energy storage or breaking them down for energy expenditure is a major task of living things.

(a) Palmitic acid

saturated (no double bonds)

(b) Oleic acid

The "kinks" imparted by double carbon-bonds make unsaturated fatty acids more likely to be liquid oils, rather than solid fats, at room temperature

monounsaturated (one double bond)

(c) Linoleic acid

polyunsaturated (more than one double bond)

Figure 3.9
Saturated and Unsaturated Fatty Acids

The degree to which fatty acid hydrocarbon chains are "saturated" with hydrogen atoms has consequences for both the form these lipids take and for human health.

(a) The hydrocarbon "tail" in palmitic acid is formed by an unbroken line of carbons, each with a single bond to the next, making this a saturated fatty acid.

(b) In oleic acid, a double bond exists at one point between two carbon atoms, making this a monounsaturated fatty acid.

(c) The carbons in linoleic acid have double bonds in two locations, making this a polyunsaturated fatty acid.

Figure 3.10
Storage and Use of Carbohydrates and Lipids
Carbohydrates and lipids generally are stored in one form but used in another.

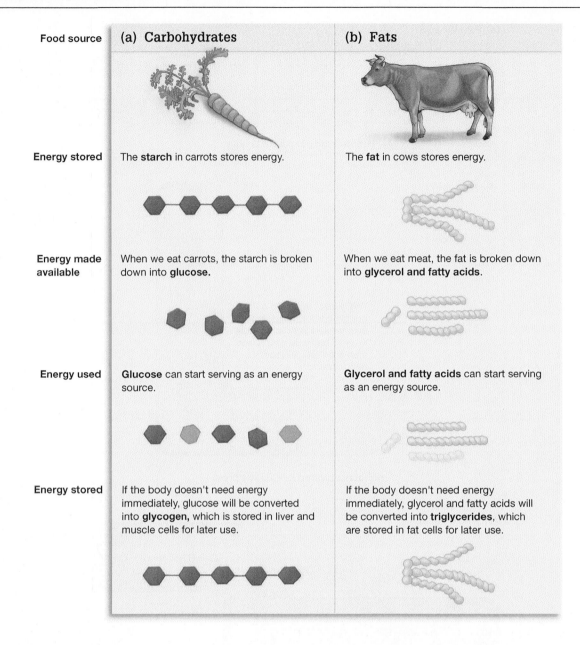

Food source	(a) Carbohydrates	(b) Fats
Energy stored	The **starch** in carrots stores energy.	The **fat** in cows stores energy.
Energy made available	When we eat carrots, the starch is broken down into **glucose.**	When we eat meat, the fat is broken down into **glycerol and fatty acids**.
Energy used	**Glucose** can start serving as an energy source.	**Glycerol and fatty acids** can start serving as an energy source.
Energy stored	If the body doesn't need energy immediately, glucose will be converted into **glycogen,** which is stored in liver and muscle cells for later use.	If the body doesn't need energy immediately, glycerol and fatty acids will be converted into **triglycerides,** which are stored in fat cells for later use.

The Steroid Lipids

Our second variety of lipid molecules, the **steroids,** can be defined as a class of lipids that have, as a central element in their structure, four carbon rings. What separates one steroid from another are the various side chains that can be attached to these rings (**Figure 3.11**). When you see how different steroids are structurally from the triglycerides, you can understand why the monomers-to-polymers framework doesn't apply to lipids.

Among the most well-known steroids are cholesterol and two of the steroid hormones, testosterone and estrogen. Like fats in general, cholesterol has a bad reputation, but also like fats in general, it serves good purposes, too. **Cholesterol** is a steroid molecule that forms part of the outer membrane of all animal cells and that acts as a precursor for many other steroids.

One of the steroids formed from it is the principal "male" hormone testosterone; another is the principal "female" hormone estrogen. (Both hormones actually are produced in both sexes, though in differing amounts.) The term *steroids* by itself undoubtedly rings a bell because the phrase "on steroids" has come to mean artificially bulked up or supercharged. In this common usage, steroids refers to manufactured drugs that are close chemical cousins of one variety of natural steroids, the muscle-building steroid hormones.

The Phospholipids

Our next class of lipids, phospholipids, has something of the same makeup as triglycerides in that a phospholipid has a glycerol head with fatty acids attached to it. But where triglycerides have three fatty acids stemming from the glycerol, phospholipids have only two (**Figure 3.12a**). Linking up with glycerol's third –OH group is a charged **phosphate group,** which is a phosphorus atom surrounded by four oxygen atoms. Thus, we can define a **phospholipid** as a charged lipid molecule composed of two fatty acids, glycerol, and a phosphate group.

The combination of a phosphate group and fatty acid tails is extremely important because it gives phospholipids a dual nature: Being hydrocarbons, the fatty acid tails are hydrophobic, but the phosphate head is hydro*philic*—it will readily bond with water—because it is charged. In Figure 3.12b, you can see the effect of this structure in solution. Imagine a phospholipid as a marker buoy in deep water. No matter how you push the hydrocarbon tail around, it's going to end up waving free *out* of the water, while the head is going to be submerged in it. You will learn more about these molecules later, when you study cells; for now, just note that the material on the periphery of cells—the outer membrane of a cell—is largely made of phospholipids. Living things need the kind of partitions described earlier, and these partitions are composed to a significant extent of phospholipids.

A Fourth Class of Lipids Is Wax

Ever wonder why water rolls off a duck's back? It's because the duck's feathers are coated by another variety of lipid: a wax. Likewise, beehives are made largely of wax (beeswax, of course), and an apple can

(a) Four-ring steroid structure

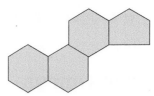

(b) Side chains make each steroid unique

testosterone

estrogen

cholesterol

Figure 3.11
Structure of Steroids

(a) The basic unit of steroids, four interlocked carbon rings.

(b) Types of steroids, each differentiated from the other by the side chains that extend from the four-ring skeleton.

Figure 3.12
A Dual-Natured Molecule

(a) Phospholipids are composed of two long fatty acid "tails" attached to a "head" containing a phosphate group (which carries a negative charge) and another variable group (which often carries a charge).

(b) Because the head is polarized, it can bond with water and thus will remain submerged in it; the tails have no such bonding capability.

(a) Phospholipid structure

variable group   phosphate group   glycerol

polar head   **nonpolar tails**

(b) Phospholipid orientation

"like attracts like"

oil (nonpolar)

water (polar)

nonpolar hydrophobic tails
(fatty acids) exposed to oil

polar hydrophilic heads
exposed to water

ESSAY

From Trans Fats to Omega-3s: Fats and Health

Saturated and unsaturated fats, trans fats, omega-3's. What a confusing situation. Average Americans might understandably throw up their hands, assume that all fats are unhealthy, and try to reduce their intake of every variety. But a closer look at the various kinds of fats reveals that, while some are indeed bad for the heart, others don't affect its health one way or another, and still others are actually good for it. Thus it's possible to rate various kinds of fats based on their health effects and it's easy to learn which fats are contained in various foods. Here is a hierarchy of dietary fats starting with the most healthful and going to the most harmful:

- Polyunsaturated fats containing omega-3 fatty acids

- Monounsaturated fats and polyunsaturated fats that do not contain omega-3s

- Saturated fats

- Trans fats

To understand this ranking, it's important to understand the effects these various fats have on two substances produced in the body: low-density lipoproteins, or LDLs, and high-density lipoproteins, or HDLs. The LDLs (or "bad cholesterol") can be thought of as capsules of protein that carry cholesterol from the liver and small intestines *to* various places in the body, including the arteries of the heart. Meanwhile, HDLs (or "good cholesterol") can be thought of as protein capsules that carry cholesterol to the liver *from* the heart and other tissues, thus clearing this cholesterol from the system. It is the lodging of LDL-cholesterol molecules in the heart's arteries that initiates the most prevalent form of heart disease. Therefore, any food that raises LDL cholesterol levels ought to be avoided, while any food that raises HDL cholesterol levels ought to be sought out. So where do the various forms of dietary fat rank on this and other measures of health? Here is the rundown on all of them, looking at them again from most healthy to least healthy.

Polyunsaturated Fats Containing Omega-3s

Standing at the top of the "good fats" list are fats that contain omega-3 fatty acids. Omega-3s are one variety of polyunsaturated fatty acid—fatty acids that have two or more carbon-carbon double bonds somewhere in their hydrocarbon chains. Now, the far end of the hydrocarbon chain (away from the glycerol head) is called the *omega end*. When a carbon double bond is located between the third and fourth carbons up from the omega end, the result is an omega-3 fatty acid. Polyunsaturated fats containing these fatty acids raise HDL levels, guard against blood clot formation, reduce fat levels generally in the bloodstream, and reduce the growth of the fatty deposits that clog heart arteries. Omega-3 fatty acids are found most abundantly in certain kinds of fatty fish, including salmon, albacore tuna, mackerel, lake trout, and sardines; and in lesser amounts in plant-based foods such as canola oil, walnuts and the soybean-based product tofu.

Monounsaturated Fats and Other Polyunsaturated Fats

Monounsaturated fats, which are mostly found in oils, leave both LDL and HDL levels unchanged. However, one particular source of monounsaturated fats may actually work to prevent heart disease. Several studies have shown that residents of Mediterranean countries have significantly lower levels of heart disease than people in other parts of the developed world. What these residents have in common, in terms of

---

Figure 3.13
A Waxy Outer Covering

Wax can form a tight seal, which is just what plants need to help them keep water in while keeping microbial invaders out. Pictured is a cross section of a Haworthia leaf, which like all leaves has a waxy outer covering called a cuticle, visible as the layer of material running across the top of the leaf. Cuticles on leaves are pock-marked with microscopic pores, called stomata, that can open to allow the plant to take in the carbon dioxide it needs to perform photosynthesis.

be polished because its outer surface has a wax coating that takes on a shine when the apple is rubbed. As these examples show, waxes often serve in nature to seal one thing off from another—the duck from water and the apple from the world around it. Waxes are extremely widespread in plants; almost all plant surfaces exposed to air will have a thin covering (called a cuticle) that is composed largely of wax (**Figure 3.13**). These coverings conserve water even as they protect the plant from outside invaders, such as fungi. Waxes are solid yet pliable at lower temperatures, but they will melt at higher temperatures. Like the triglycerides and the phospholipids we looked at, waxes are composed partly of fatty acid chains. However, whereas triglycerides have three fatty acids linked to a small alcohol (glycerol), a **wax** can be defined as a lipid composed of a single fatty acid linked to a long-chain alcohol.

diet, is consumption of large amounts of the monounsaturated fats in olive oil. In 2005, researchers uncovered a reason that olive oil may be beneficial: It contains a naturally occurring substance (called oleocanthal) that stands to work against heart disease by cutting down on the inflammation that helps it get going. Other sources of monounsaturated fats are peanut oil and avocados.

When we look at polyunsaturated fats other than those that contain omega-3s, we find that they leave LDL levels unchanged, although they do slightly lower the "good" HDL cholesterol levels. Even so, most experts regard them, at worst, as neutral to health. This type of polyunsaturated fat can be found in safflower and corn oil.

Saturated Fats

Nothing in your diet will raise LDL levels as much as saturated fats do. Most studies have found that each 1 percent increase in these fats leads to a 2 percent increase in LDL cholesterol levels. Given an effect such as this, the American Heart Association recommends limiting calories from saturated fats to less than 7 percent of total daily calories. The usual source for saturated fats is animal fat—primarily fatty meat and dairy products—but they can also be found in a few plant products, such as coconut oil and cocoa butter.

Trans Fats

Trans fats stand apart from all the other fats we've looked at in that they are produced not by nature but by an industrial process, called *hydrogenation,* in which hydrogen is bubbled into mono- or polyunsaturated oils. Food manufacturers do this for several reasons: It turns these oils into fats at room temperature, it often gives them a creamy texture that consumers like, and it increases the shelf life of the foods that result. The problem is that hydrogenation changes the chemical structure of fatty acids in ways that make them unhealthful. In most instances, this process has the effect of changing the *orientation* of the hydrogen atoms that already exist at carbon-carbon double bonds. Normally these pairs of hydrogens are on the same side, like this:

cis form (hydrogen atoms on same side of chain)

With so-called partial hydrogenation, they can end up on the opposite or *trans* sides, like this:

trans form (hydrogen atoms on opposite sides of chain)

Thus, we get the term *trans* fatty acids. The trans fats that result from this change are found in a dwindling, but still significant, number of packaged and fast foods: cookies, French fries, cakes, crackers, doughnuts, popcorn, and candy, to name a few. Trans fats earned their reputation as the least healthy fats by having a twin set of bad effects that not even saturated fats can manage: They raise LDL levels while lowering HDL levels. In addition, they appear to boost fat levels in general in the blood while impairing the ability of blood vessels to open or "dilate." As such, the American Heart Association recommends limiting trans fat intake to less than 1 percent of total daily calories.

How can you know how much trans fat you are consuming? For packaged foods, it's easy. Beginning in 2006, the federal Food and Drug Administration (FDA) required food producers to list trans fats separately on the Nutrition Facts labels seen on all packaged products. Check these labels to find out the amount of trans fats you're getting. Chances are, however, that you won't be getting much in the future. The FDA labeling requirement produced a surge of activity among packaged producers to rid their products of trans fats. Hence, what you'll often see on the Nutrition Facts labels these days is "Trans fat 0 g," meaning zero grams of trans fat.

SO FAR . . .

1. The defining characteristic of lipids is that they do not _____ in _____.

2. The fats in foods are composed mostly of triglycerides, which are formed from three _____ bonded to a _____. A saturated fatty acid is one that has no double bonds between the _____ of its _____ chain.

3. Steroids are a class of lipids whose central structure includes four _____. Examples include the reproductive hormones _____ and _____. Another class of lipids is important in making up the outer membrane of cells; these are the _____, composed of glycerol, two fatty acids, and a _____ group.

3.5 Proteins

Living things must accomplish a great number of tasks just to get through a day, and the diverse biological molecules you've been looking at allow this to happen. You've seen carbohydrates do some things, and you've seen lipids do some more, but in the range of tasks that molecules accomplish, proteins reign supreme. Witness the fact that almost every chemical reaction that takes place in living things is hastened—or, in practical terms, *enabled*—by a particular kind of protein called an enzyme. These molecules function in nature like some vast group of tools, each taking on a specific chemical task. Accordingly, an animal cell might contain up to 4,000 different types of enzymes.

We might marvel at proteins solely because of what enzymes can do, but the amazing thing is that

Figure 3.14
Made of Protein

A human hair, shown here emerging from a follicle in the skin, is composed mostly of the protein keratin. Each hair is composed of many groups of keratin strands that wrap around each other, giving hair its structure, which is flexible and much longer than it is wide.

enzymes are only one class of proteins. Proteins also form the scaffolding, or structure, of a good deal of tissue; they're active in transporting molecules from one site to another; they allow muscles to contract and cells to move; some hormones are made from them. If you factor out water, they account for about half the weight of the average cell. In short, it's hard to overestimate the importance of these molecules (**Figure 3.14**). **Table 3.4** lists some of the different kinds of proteins.

Proteins Are Made from Chains of Amino Acids

Proteins are prime examples of the building-block type of molecule described earlier. The monomers in this case are called amino acids. String a minimum number of them together in a chain—some say 10, some say 30—and you have a **polypeptide,** defined as a series of amino acids linked in linear fashion. When the polypeptide chain *folds up* in a specific three-dimensional manner, you have a **protein,** defined as a large, folded chain of amino acids. As a practical matter, proteins are likely to be made of hundreds of amino acids strung together and folded up. As you'll see, it's not unusual for two or more polypeptide chains to be part of a single protein.

Figure 3.15a gives the fundamental structural unit for amino acids, followed by a couple of examples. You can see carbon at the center of this unit, an amino functional group off to its left, and a carboxyl group to its right. What differentiates one amino acid from another is the group of atoms that occupies the R or "side-chain" position. In **Figure 3.15b**, you can see examples of the actual amino acids tyrosine and glutamine with their different occupants of the R position.

(a) What all amino acids have in common is an amino group and a carboxyl group attached to a central carbon.

(b) What makes the 20 amino acids unique are the side-chains attached to the central carbon.

Figure 3.15
Structure of Amino Acids

(a) Basic amino acid structure.

(b) Two examples of actual amino acids, tyrosine and glutamine.

Table 3.4		
Types of Proteins		
Type	**Role**	**Examples**
Enzymes	Quicken chemical reactions	Sucrase: Positions sucrose (table sugar) in such a way that it can be broken down into component parts of glucose and fructose.
Hormones	Chemical messengers	Growth hormone: Stimulates growth of bones
Transport	Move other molecules	Hemoglobin: Transports oxygen through blood
Contractile	Movement	Myosin and actin: Allow muscles to contract
Protective	Healing; defense against invader	Fibrinogen: Stops bleeding Antibodies: Combat microbial invaders
Structural	Mechanical support	Keratin: Hair, Collagen: Cartilage
Storage	Stores nutrients	Ovalbumin: Egg white, used as nutrient for embryos
Toxins	Defense, predation	Bacterial diphtheria toxin
Communication	Cell signaling	Glycoprotein: Receptors on cell surface

A Group of Only 20 Amino Acids Is the Basis for All Proteins in Living Things

Although only two examples are shown here, it is a group of 20 amino acids that is the basis for all proteins in living organisms. The thousands of proteins that exist can be made from a mere 20 amino acids because these amino acids can be strung together in different *orders*. Substitute an alanine here for a glutamine there, and you've got a different protein. In this, amino acids commonly are compared to letters of the alphabet. In English, substituting one letter can take us from *bat* to *hat*. In the natural world, 20 amino acids can be put together in different order to create a multitude of proteins, each with a different function. (A list of all 20 primary amino acids can be found in Chapter 14, on page 245.)

The stringing together of amino acids happens in a regular way: The carboxyl group of one amino acid joins to the amino group of another. Look at **Figure 3.16** to see how three amino acids come together.

Shape Is Critical to the Functioning of All Proteins

As a protein's amino acids are strung together in sequence, all the kinds of chemical forces discussed in Chapter 2 begin to work on them. With this, the chain begins to twist, turn, and fold into its unique three-dimensional shape. It turns out that, in the functioning of proteins, this shape, or protein conformation, is utterly crucial. Here's an example of why. If you look at the top illustration in **Figure 3.17**, on the left you can see a computerized model of a protein found on the surface of the influenza virus. If you look on the right, you will see a model of an immune system protein, called an antibody, that fights foreign invaders such as influenza viruses. Now, how does the antibody interact with a virus? It binds to it as shown in the lower illustration, and this process is made possible by the exact fit of antibody to invading virus. Look at the shape of the two molecules to see how closely they conform to one another. The binding of an antibody to an invader sounds important enough, but recall that proteins are the chemical enablers called enzymes, and they're transport molecules, and so forth. In all these functions, shape is critical. The architect Frank Lloyd Wright had a famous dictum about his designs: "Form and function are one." The same thing can be said of proteins.

There Are Four Levels of Protein Structure

So, what forms do proteins take? Well, the answer to this depends on what vantage point you adopt in looking at them, as there are four levels of structure

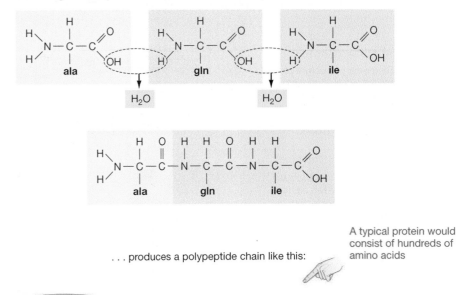

The linkage of several amino acids . . .

ala   gln   ile

H_2O H_2O

ala   gln   ile

. . . produces a polypeptide chain like this:

A typical protein would consist of hundreds of amino acids

| ala | leu | ser | glu | glu | his | ala | gln | ile | ser | tyr | ala | ser | glu | glu |

Figure 3.16
Beginnings of a Protein
Amino acids join together to form polypeptide chains, which fold up to become proteins. The linking of amino acids yields water as a by-product. In this figure, alanine (ala) first joins with glutamine (gln), which then is linked to isoleucine (ile).

(a)

(b)

Figure 3.17
Hand-in-Glove Fit
Molecular shape is a critical element in the functioning of most proteins.

(a) The computer-model on the left is of a molecule found on the surface of an influenza virus. On the right is a model of a portion of human protein, called an antibody, that attacks invaders such as viruses.

(b) The antibody helps disable the virus by binding with it, as shown. The antibody is able to carry out this binding because it has a shape that is complementary to that of the virus molecule.

Four Levels of Structure in Proteins

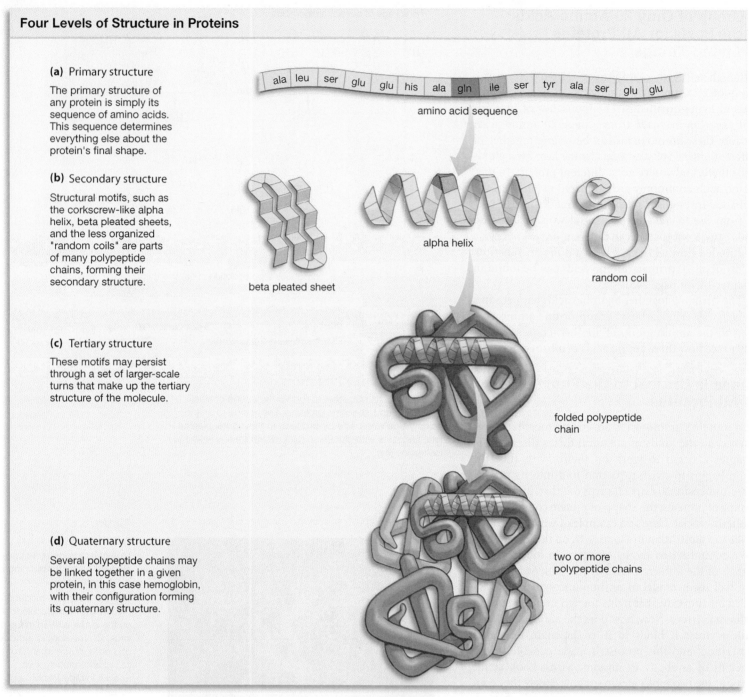

(a) Primary structure

The primary structure of any protein is simply its sequence of amino acids. This sequence determines everything else about the protein's final shape.

(b) Secondary structure

Structural motifs, such as the corkscrew-like alpha helix, beta pleated sheets, and the less organized "random coils" are parts of many polypeptide chains, forming their secondary structure.

(c) Tertiary structure

These motifs may persist through a set of larger-scale turns that make up the tertiary structure of the molecule.

(d) Quaternary structure

Several polypeptide chains may be linked together in a given protein, in this case hemoglobin, with their configuration forming its quaternary structure.

ala leu ser glu glu his ala gln ile ser tyr ala ser glu glu

amino acid sequence

beta pleated sheet

alpha helix

random coil

folded polypeptide chain

two or more polypeptide chains

Figure 3.18
Four Levels of Structure in Proteins

in proteins. You can see all four levels in **Figure 3.18.** The first of these, the **primary structure** of a protein, is simply its sequence of amino acids. Everything about the final shape of a protein is dictated by this sequence. Electrochemical attraction and repulsion forces act on this structure, and the result is the folded-up protein.

As it turns out, when these forces begin to operate on the amino acid sequence, a couple of common shapes begin to emerge in the **secondary structure** of proteins, defined as the structure that proteins assume after folding up. The *alpha helix,* a common secondary structure of proteins, has a shape much like a corkscrew. Another common secondary structure in proteins, the *beta pleated sheet,* takes a form like the folds of an accordion. Proteins can be made almost entirely of alpha helices. This is the case with hair, nails, horns, and the like. Likewise, proteins can be made entirely of beta pleated sheets. The most familiar example of this is silk, in which the beta sheets lie pancake-style on one another. Often, however, alpha helices and beta pleated sheets form what we might think of as design motifs within a larger protein structure; they periodically give way to the less-regular segments called random coils. The larger-scale three-dimensional shape that a protein takes is its **tertiary structure.** The way in which *two or more* polypeptide chains come together to form a protein results in that protein's **quaternary structure.**

Proteins Can Come Undone

As noted, proteins fold up into a precise conformation in order to function. However, proteins can *lose* their shape and thus their functionality. We noted this last chapter in connection with pH and enzymes. In the wrong pH environment, an enzyme can unfold, losing its tertiary structure and thus losing its ability to accelerate a chemical process. Alcohol works as a disinfectant on skin because it *denatures* or alters the shape of the proteins of bacteria.

Lipoproteins and Glycoproteins

Some molecules in living things are hybrids or combinations of the various types of molecules you've been looking at. **Lipoproteins,** as their name implies, are molecules that are a combination of lipids and proteins. Active in transporting fats throughout the body, lipoproteins are transport molecules that amount to a capsule of protein surrounding a globule of fat. Almost everyone has heard of two varieties of lipoproteins: high-density lipoproteins and low-density lipoproteins, also known as HDLs and LDLs, which are important components of our diet. What makes them high or low in density is the ratio of protein to lipid in them; lipid is less dense than protein, so a low-density lipoprotein has a relatively large amount of lipid compared to protein. The LDLs have acquired a reputation as dietary villains because they carry cholesterol *to* outlying tissues, including the coronary arteries of the heart, where this cholesterol may come to reside, thickening eventually into "plaques" that can block coronary arteries and bring about a heart attack. The HDLs, meanwhile, are regarded as the cavalry; they carry cholesterol *away* from outlying cells to the liver. A high proportion of HDLs in relation to cholesterol is predictive of keeping a healthy heart.

Glycoproteins are combinations of proteins and *carbohydrates.* Where do we find these molecules? One place is the surface of cells, which usually are peppered with a profusion of antenna-like structures, called *receptors,* that allow a cell to receive signals from outside itself. A typical receptor is likely to be composed of both protein and carbohydrate, with the protein forming the "stem" of the receptor and the carbohydrate forming side chains that extend from the stem and serve as the actual binding sites for signaling molecules that may pass by. Some hormones are glycoproteins, along with many other proteins released from cells.

3.6 Nucleic Acids

Nucleic acids are the last major class of biological molecule we'll look at. The building blocks for them, called nucleotides, can be important molecules in and of themselves, as you'll see in Chapter 6 when we look at an energy-transferring nucleotide called ATP (adenosine triphosphate). Here, however, we'll look primarily at just one nucleic acid, which has the distinction of being perhaps the most famous biological molecule of them all.

DNA: Information for the Construction of Proteins

You've learned that proteins perform a large number of biological functions and that one class of proteins, the enzymes, may be represented with up to 4,000 types in a single animal cell. If you had a factory that turned out 4,000 different kinds of tools, you would obviously need some direction on how each of these tools was to be manufactured: This part of the tool goes here first, and then that goes there, and so on. There is a molecule that in essence provides this kind of information for the construction of proteins. It is **DNA,** or **deoxyribonucleic acid:** the primary information-bearing molecule of life, composed of two linked chains of nucleotides. How many nucleotides? In human beings, about 3 billion of them are strung together to form the DNA that comes packaged in the units called chromosomes.

The information contained in the DNA molecule is much like the information contained in a cookbook, only what the DNA "recipes" call for are precisely ordered chains of amino acids—those that go into making up different proteins. "Start with an alanine, then add a cysteine, then a tyrosine . . . ," and so on for hundreds of steps, the DNA-encoded instructions will say, after which, through a series of steps, a protein becomes synthesized and then gets busy on some task. A player in this series of steps is another nucleic acid, **ribonucleic acid** or **RNA,** a molecule composed of nucleotides that is active in the synthesis of proteins. The functions of RNA include ferrying the DNA-encoded instructions to a kind of workbench in the cell, called a ribosome, where proteins are put together. A different sort of RNA actually helps make up this workbench as well, as you'll see next chapter.

Figure 3.19
Nucleotides Are the
Building Blocks
of DNA

(a) The basic unit of the DNA
molecule is the nucleotide, a
molecule in three parts: a
sugar (deoxyribose), a phosphate group, and a nitrogen-
containing base.

(b) A computer-generated
space-filling model of DNA.

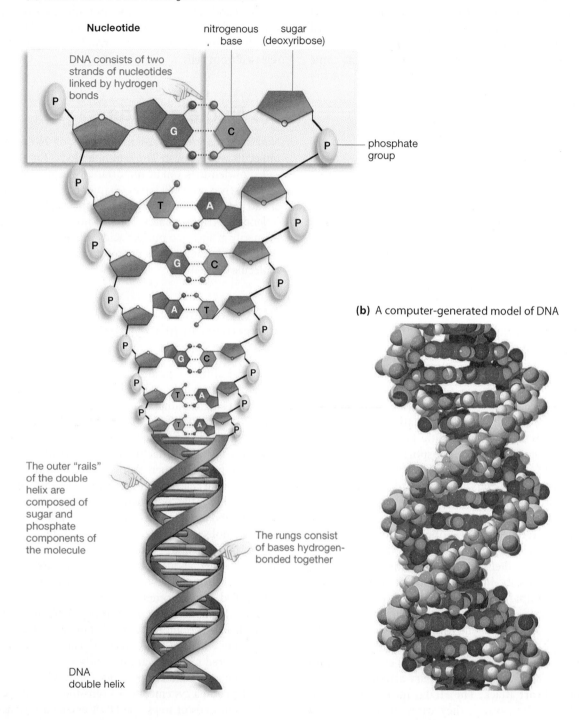

(a) Nucleotides are the building blocks of DNA.

DNA consists of two
strands of nucleotides
linked by hydrogen
bonds

Nucleotide

nitrogenous base sugar (deoxyribose)

phosphate group

(b) A computer-generated model of DNA

The outer "rails"
of the double
helix are
composed of
sugar and
phosphate
components of
the molecule

The rungs consist
of bases hydrogen-
bonded together

DNA
double helix

The Structural Unit of DNA Is the Nucleotide

Look at **Figure 3.19**, and you'll see the structure of the monomers that make up the nucleic acid polymer of DNA. These are **nucleotides,** each of which is a molecule in three parts: a phosphate group, a sugar (deoxyribose), and one of four nitrogen-containing bases: adenine (A), guanine (G), cytosine (C), or thymine (T). The sugar and phosphate components of the nucleotides link to one another to form the outer "rails" of the DNA molecule, while the bases point toward the molecule's interior. Two chains of nucleotides are linked, via hydrogen bonds, to form DNA's famous double helix.

On to Cells

Before getting to the story of this elegant DNA molecule, you need to learn a little bit about the territory in which it does its work. What you'll be looking at is a profusion of jostling, roiling, ceaselessly working

Table 3.5

Summary Table of Biological Molecules

Type of Molecule	Subgroups	Examples and Roles
Carbohydrates	Monosaccharides	Glucose: energy source
	Disaccharides	Sucrose: energy source
	Polysaccharides	Glycogen: storage form of glucose
		Starch: carbohydrate storage in plants; used by animals in nutrition
		Cellulose: plant cell walls, structure; fiber in animal digestion
		Chitin: external skeleton of arthropods
Lipids	Triglycerides: 3 fatty acids and glycerol	Fats, oils (butter, corn oil): food, energy, storage, insulation
	Fatty acids: components of triglycerides	Stearic acid: food, energy sources
	Steroids: four-ring structure	Cholesterol: fat digestion, hormone precursor, cell membrane component
	Phospholipids: polar head, nonpolar tails	Cell membrane structure
Proteins	Enzymes: chemically active	Sucrase: breaks down sugar
	Structural	Keratin: hair
	Lipoproteins: protein-lipid molecule	HDLs, LDLs: transport of lipids
	Glycoproteins: protein-sugar molecule	Cell surface receptors
Nucleic acids	Deoxyribonucleic acid (DNA)	DNA contains information for the production of proteins
	Ribonucleic acid (RNA)	One variety of RNA carries DNA's information to the sites of protein production, the ribosomes; another variety of RNA helps make up ribosomes.

chemical factories that make up all living things. These factories are called cells, the subject of Chapter 4. Look at **Table 3.5** and you'll find a summary of all the types of molecules reviewed in this chapter.

SO FAR . . .

1. Each protein is made from a chain of _____ that folds up into a specific shape that allows the protein to take on its working role. The primary structure of a protein is simply its sequence of _____, while its secondary structure is the shape the protein assumes after having _____.

2. HDL and LDL are acronyms for high-density and low-density _____. These molecules are combinations of _____ and _____.

3. DNA and RNA are nucleic acids, which are polymers composed of the monomers called _____, each of which is in turn composed of a _____, a _____, and one of four _____.

CHAPTER 3 REVIEW

Summary

3.1 Carbon's Place in the Living World

- Carbon is central to life because most biological molecules are built on a carbon framework. Carbon's outer shell has four of the eight outer-shell electrons necessary for maximum stability in most elements. Carbon atoms are thus able to form stable, covalent bonds with a wide variety of atoms, a capacity that allows carbon to serve as the central element in the large, complex molecules that make up living things. (p. 43)

3.2 Functional Groups

- Groups of atoms known as functional groups can confer special properties on carbon-based molecules, thus altering the molecule's function. (p. 45)

3.3 Carbohydrates

- Carbohydrates are formed from the building blocks or monomers of simple sugars. These monomers can be linked to form larger carbohydrate polymers (polysaccharides, or complex carbohydrates). Four polysaccharides are critical in the living world: starch, the nutrient storage form of carbohydrates in plants; glycogen, the nutrient storage form of carbohydrates in animals; cellulose, a rigid structural carbohydrate produced by plants and other organisms; and chitin, a tough carbohydrate that forms the external skeleton of arthropods. (p. 46)

3.4 Lipids

- The defining characteristic of all lipids is that they do not readily dissolve in water. No one structural element is common to all lipids. (p. 49)

- Among the most important lipids are: triglycerides, composed of a glyceride and three fatty acids; steroids, which have a core of four carbon rings; phospholipids, composed of two fatty acids, glycerol, and a charged phosphate group; and waxes, which are composed of a single fatty acid linked to a long-chain alcohol. (p. 49)

3.5 Proteins

- Proteins are a diverse group of biological molecules composed of the monomers called amino acids. Sequences of amino acids are strung together to produce polypeptide chains, which then fold up into working proteins. Important groups of proteins include enzymes, which hasten chemical reactions, and structural proteins. (p. 55)

- The primary structure of a protein is its amino acid sequence; this sequence determines a protein's secondary structure—the form a protein assumes after having folded up. The tertiary structure is the larger-scale three-dimensional shape that a protein assumes; the way two or more polypeptide chains come together to form a protein results in that protein's quaternary structure. The activities of proteins are determined by their final folded shapes. (p. 57)

- Lipoproteins are combinations of lipids and proteins. (p. 59)

- Glycoproteins are combinations of carbohydrates and proteins. (p. 59)

3.6 Nucleic Acids

- Nucleic acids are polymers composed of nucleotides. The nucleic acid DNA (deoxyribonucleic acid) is composed of nucleotides that contain a sugar (deoxyribose), a phosphate group, and one of four nitrogen-containing bases. DNA is a repository of genetic information. The sequence of its bases contains the information for the production of the huge array of proteins produced by living things. (p. 60)

Key Terms

carbohydrate 46
cellulose 47
chitin 48
cholesterol 52
deoxyribonucleic acid (DNA) 59
fatty acid 49
functional group 45
glycogen 47
glycoprotein 59
hydrocarbon 43
lipid 49
lipoprotein 59
monomer 46
monosaccharide 46
monounsaturated fatty acid 50
nucleotide 60
oil 50
organic chemistry 43
phosphate group 53
phospholipid 53
polymer 46
polypeptide 56
polysaccharide 47
polyunsaturated fatty acid 50
primary structure 58
protein 56
quaternary structure 59
ribonucleic acid (RNA) 59
saturated fatty acid 50
secondary structure 58
simple sugar 46
starch 47
steroid 52
tertiary structure 59
triglyceride 49
wax 54

Understanding the Basics

Multiple-Choice Questions

(Answers are in the back of the book.)

1. Carbon is able to serve as life's central element because it:
   a. is able to bond with hydrogen atoms to form hydrocarbon chains.
   b. will readily bond with water molecules.
   c. has four outer-shell electrons and thus can form stable bonds with many other elements.
   d. has six outer-shell electrons and thus can form stable bonds with many other elements.
   e. forms strong ionic bonds with many other elements.

2. Functional groups often confer the general property of _____ on _____ molecules.
   a. hydrophilia; water-based
   b. hydrophobia; water-based
   c. stability; carbon-based
   d. stability; unstable
   e. polarity; carbon-based

3. Glucose and the amino acid tyrosine are members of different classes of biological molecules, but they are alike in that both are _____ that go into making up _____.
   a. monomers; polymers
   b. monosaccharides; polysaccharides
   c. polysaccharides; monosaccharides
   d. polymers; monomers
   e. nucleotides; DNA

4. When you eat starch such as spaghetti, an enzyme in your mouth breaks it down to maltose. Eventually, the maltose enters your small intestine, where it is broken down to glucose, which you can absorb into your bloodstream. The starch is a(n) _____, the maltose is a _____, and the glucose is a(n) _____.
   a. protein; dipeptide; amino acid
   b. monosaccharide; disaccharide; polysaccharide
   c. triglyceride; fatty acid; glycerol
   d. amino acid; dipeptide; protein
   e. polysaccharide; disaccharide;, monosaccharide

5. Which of these is not a difference between saturated and unsaturated fats?
   a. Saturated fats are more likely to be solid at room temperature; unsaturated fats are more likely to be liquid.
   b. Saturated fats are a type of cholesterol or steroid, whereas unsaturated fats are a triglyceride.
   c. Saturated fats have fatty acids that pack closely together, owing to their straight-line construction. Unsaturated fats have fatty acids arranged at varying angles to one another, because of their double bonds.
   d. Saturated fats are composed of fatty acids that have no double bonds in their chemical structure. Unsaturated fats are composed of fatty acids that have one or more double bonds in their chemical structure.
   e. All of the above are differences between saturated and unsaturated fats.

6. The myoglobin protein, which carries oxygen in muscle cells, has only the first three levels of protein structure. In other words, it lacks a quaternary level. From this you can conclude that myoglobin:
   a. is made of nucleic acids.
   b. is made of only one polypeptide chain.
   c. lacks hydrogen bonds.
   d. is not helical or pleated.
   e. is a fiber.

7. You received your genetic information from your parents in the form of DNA. This DNA carried the instructions for making:
   a. carbohydrates such as glycogen.
   b. fatty acids.
   c. phospholipids for making the membranes of your cells.
   d. proteins.
   e. all of the above.

8. John is lactose intolerant. The -ose ending indicates that John cannot digest a certain:
   a. sugar.
   b. polysaccharide.
   c. protein.
   d. steroid.
   e. enzyme.

Brief Review

(Answers are in the back of the book.)

1. Why is it accurate to look at life as "carbon based," and what quality gives carbon this special role?

2. Both low-density lipoproteins (LDLs) and high-density lipoproteins (HDLs) are involved with carrying fats through the bloodstream. If your LDL count is unusually high, should you be concerned? What if your HDL count is high? Why are they different?

3. What are steroids, as that term is defined in biochemistry? What are steroids in the popular sense of the term?

4. List as many functions of proteins as possible. Why are proteins able to do so many different types of jobs?

5. Why is it accurate to think of DNA as an information-bearing molecule?

Applying Your Knowledge

1. Scientists who look for life outside Earth have a favorite candidate for an element that could take on the role that carbon does here on Earth. The element is silicon, which has 14 electrons, compared to carbon's 6. Based on the rules of chemical bonding you learned about last chapter, why should silicon's electron number make it a candidate for a central biological element?

2. One piece of advice that nutritionists give today is to favor complex carbohydrates, such as those found in whole-grain bread, over simple carbohydrates, such as those found in soft drinks. One reason for this is that simple sugars result in "spikes" in blood sugar levels, while complex carbohydrates usually do not. Why should the two kinds of carbohydrates differ in this regard?

3. Many species of beans produce a poisonous group of glycoproteins called lectins, which cause red blood cells to clump together (agglutinate) and cease to function. (Fortunately, cooking destroys most of them.) Using what you learned about the structure and function of glycoproteins, suggest how they might do this. What benefit do you think plants might get just by causing red blood cells to clump together?

4

Life's Home:
The Cell

All life exists within cells. These tiny entities can be compared to factories whose products maintain life.

Cells are the fundamental units of life. Pictured is an artificially colored human embryonic cell.

The United States Senate has 100 members in it, and all of them do occasionally gather to consider given issues. But if you want to know how the Senate actually gets something done, you must look elsewhere. The business of the nation is simply too complex for all Senate members to deal with all issues. Instead, issues are dealt with one at a time within the specialized working units of the Senate known as committees.

Something similar to this goes on in the natural world. If we look at birds, trees, or people and ask how any of these living things actually gets something done, the answer again is through working units—in this case the working units known as cells.

4.1 Cells as Life's Fundamental Unit

Muffins are in the oven, and you are in the living room. Gas molecules from the baking muffins waft into the living room, and some of them happen to make their way to your nose, there to travel a short distance to your upper nasal cavity and land on a set of ceaselessly waving hair-like projections called cilia. These actually are the extensions of some specialized nerve cells. If enough gas molecules bind with enough of the cilia, an impulse is passed along (through other nerve cells) to trigger not only the *sensation* of smell but also the *association* of this smell with muffins you have smelled in the past. How do we know muffins are in the oven? Through cells. How do we move our hands or read this page? Through cells. Life's working units are cells, and in our amazingly complex natural world, there is great specialization in them (**Figure 4.1**, on the next page). The nerve cells in human beings are specialists in transmitting nerve signals, red blood cells are specialists in transporting oxygen, and muscle cells are specialists in contracting.

Running like a thread through this diversity, however, is the unity of cellular life. Every form of life either is a single cell or is composed of cells. The one possible exception to this is viruses, but even they must use the machinery of cells to reproduce. There is unity, too, in the way cells come about: Every cell comes *from* a cell. Human beings are incapable of producing cells from scratch in the laboratory, and so far as we can tell, nature has fashioned cells from simple molecules only once—back when life on Earth got started. The fact that all cells come from cells means that each cell in your body is a link in a cellular chain that stretches back more than 3.5 billion years.

Life's Fundamental Unit

(a) Human red and white blood cells inside a blood vessel. The large, dark ovals that can be seen in the background are flat cells that form the interior lining of the blood vessel.

(b) Cells of the fungus brewer's yeast, which is used to make wine, beer, and bread.

(c) Cells of a spinach leaf, with the leaf seen in cross section. Two layers of outer or "epidermal" cells can be seen at top and bottom; most of the cells in between perform photosynthesis.

(a)

(b)

(c)

Figure 4.1
Cells Specialize

Several kinds of cells are active at the site of any injury to the human body. Blood circulation increases at such a site, with the result that more oxygen-bearing red blood cells pass through it. Meanwhile, the body's immune system will launch an attack against microbes that entered the injured site. The yellow cells visible at the center of the photo are immune system cells called leukocytes that will take part in this attack. The site of any injury also will be sealed off partly through the activity of a group of cell fragments called platelets, visible in the photo as the smaller pink objects.

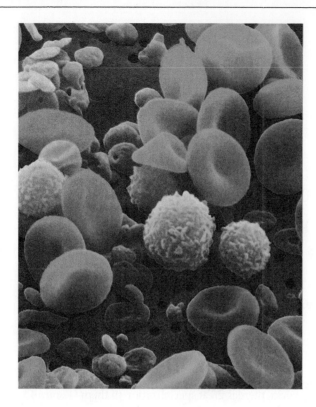

4.2 Prokaryotic and Eukaryotic Cells

So, what are these tiny working units we call cells? It follows, from the variety of cells that exist, that there is no such thing as a "typical" cell. There are, however, certain *categories* of cells that are important, and the two most important of these are prokaryotic and eukaryotic cells. Every cell that exists is one or the other, and this simple either-or quality extends to the organisms that fall into these camps. All prokaryotic cells either are bacteria or another microscopic form of life known as archaea. Setting bacteria and archaea aside, *all other cells* are eukaryotic. This means all the cells in plants, in animals, in fungi—all the cells in every living thing except in the bacteria and the archaea.

Prokaryotic and Eukaryotic Differences

The name *eukaryote* comes from the Greek *eu,* meaning "true," and *karyon,* meaning "nucleus," while *prokaryote* means "before nucleus." These terms describe the most critical distinction between the two cell types. **Eukaryotic cells** are cells whose primary complement of DNA is enclosed within a nucleus. **Prokaryotic cells** are cells whose DNA is not enclosed within a nucleus. To complete this circle, a **nucleus** is a membrane-lined compartment that encloses the primary complement of DNA in eukaryotic cells.

While having a nucleus is the most important difference between eukaryotic and prokaryotic cells, it is not the only difference. It may seem sensible to think of two single-celled creatures—one a prokaryotic bacterium, the other a eukaryotic amoeba—as very similar, but the distance between them as life-forms is immense. Human beings and chimpanzees are nearly identical in comparison. Eukaryotic cells tend to be much larger than their prokaryotic counterparts; indeed, thousands of bacteria could easily fit into an average eukaryotic cell (see "The Size of Cells" on page 68). Eukaryotes are often multicelled organisms, while prokaryotes are always single-celled (**Figure 4.2**). Beyond this, eukaryotic cells are *compartmentalized* to a far greater degree than is the case with prokaryotes. The nucleus in eukaryotic cells turns out to be only one variety of **organelle:** a highly organized structure, internal to a cell, that serves some specialized function. Eukaryotic cells contain several different kinds of these "tiny organs." There are organelles called mitochondria, for example, that transform energy from food, and organelles called lysosomes that recycle the raw materials of the cell. In prokaryotic cells, meanwhile, there is only a single type of organelle—a kind of workbench for producing proteins we'll look at later.

If we look at eukaryotes that are familiar to us, such as trees, mushrooms, and horses, it's easy to see that there is a fantastic diversity in the *forms* of eukaryotes compared to the strictly single-celled prokaryotes. It does not follow from this, however, that prokaryotes are uniform; on the contrary, they actually differ greatly from one another with respect to, say, the ways they obtain their nutrition and the environments in which they live. And they are extremely successful, if success is defined as inhabiting these environments in great numbers. As the biologists Lynn Margulis and Karlene Schwartz have observed, more bacteria are living in your mouth right now than the number of people who have ever existed. But for the range of biological structures and processes we want to look at, eukaryotic cells are more diverse and hence are the initial focus of our study. (For an account of the first person ever to behold the micro-world of cells, see "First Sightings: Anton van Leeuwenhoek" on page 88.)

4.3 The Eukaryotic Cell

What are the constituent parts of eukaryotic cells? Here are five larger structures that in turn are composed of component parts. The first two have been mentioned already (**Figure 4.3**):

- The cell's nucleus
- Other organelles (which lie outside the nucleus)

Figure 4.2
Prokaryotic and
Eukaryotic Cells
Compared

Prokaryotic cells	Eukaryotic cells
DNA spread through much of cell	within membrane-bound nucleus
Size much smaller	much larger
Organization always single-celled	often multicellular
Organelles only one type of organelle	many types of organelles

- The **cytosol,** a protein-rich, jelly-like fluid in which the cell's organelles are immersed
- The *cytoskeleton,* a kind of internal scaffolding consisting of three sorts of protein fibers; some of these can be likened to tent poles, others to monorails
- The **plasma membrane,** the outer lining of the cell

In any discussion of a cell, you are likely to hear the term **cytoplasm,** which simply means the *region* of the cell inside the plasma membrane but outside the nucleus. The cytoplasm is different from the cyto*sol*. If you removed all the structures of the cytoplasm—meaning the organelles and the cytoskeleton—what would be left is the cytosol, which is mostly water. This does not mean that the cytosol is simply a passive medium for the other structures, but it is not an organized structure in the way the organelles are. Almost all the organelles you'll be seeing are encased in their own membranes, just as the whole cell is encased in its plasma membrane. What are membranes? Until you get the formal definition next chapter, think of a membrane as the flexible, chemically active outer

Figure 4.3
Eukaryotic Cell

This cutaway view of a eukaryotic cell displays the elements that nearly all such cells possess.

Components of eukaryotic cells

nucleus   other organelles   cytosol   cytoskeleton   plasma membrane

ESSAY

The Size of Cells

For several chapters, you've been going over atoms, ions, molecules, and such—things small enough to be invisible to the unaided eye. For the most part, you've had to imagine what these entities look like, simply because most of them are so small that such images as we have of them don't tend to be very informative. If you flip through the pages of this chapter and those to come, however, you begin to see a fair number of actual photographs. They don't have the same quality as summer vacation snapshots, but they are recognizable as pictures, or more properly as **micrographs,** meaning pictures taken with the aid of a microscope. Micrographs enable us to see surprising things; for example, hundreds of bacteria on the tip of a pin (**Figure 1**). So, with the cells that are introduced in this chapter, there has obviously been a bump up in size into a world that is more easily visible with the help of various kinds of technology.

In taking stock of the micro-world, two units of measure are particularly valuable. The smaller of them is the **nanometer,** abbreviated as nm; the larger is the **micrometer,** abbreviated μm. (The unfamiliar-looking first letter is the Greek symbol for a small *m*. Scientists are not trying to be obscure in using it; another unit of the metric system, the millimeter, lays claim to the mm abbreviation.) What these abbreviations stand for is a billionth of a meter (nm) and a millionth of a meter (μm). A meter equals about 39.6 inches, or just over a yard, which gives you some starting sense of physical reality in understanding the rest of these sizes.

Now look at **Figure 2** to see what size various objects are. Atoms are at the bottom of the scale, at about a tenth of a nanometer. Something less than a 10-fold increase gets you to the size of the protein building blocks, called amino acids, that you looked at in Chapter 3. Another

10-fold-plus increase and you've reached the upper limit on proteins.

You have to go better than 10 times larger than this, however, before you arrive at the size of something that is actually *living* as opposed to something that is a component part of life. The living entities here are cells, specifically bacterial cells that measure 200–300 nm. This extreme on the small side of cells has a counterpart on the large side with the single cells we call chicken or ostrich eggs and with certain nerve cells that can stretch out to a meter in length. In general, however, we just cross into the micrometer range with the smaller bacterial cells: about 1–10 μm. The cell size for most plants and animals falls in a range that is a little less than 10 times larger than this, about 10–30 μm. At 10 μm perhaps a billion cells could fit into the tip of your finger. And how about in your whole body? A standard estimate of the actual number of human cells is 10 trillion.

So, Why So Small?

Having learned how small cells are, you might then well ask: *Why* are they so small? As noted, cells are small chemical factories,

(a) Bacteria on a pin, magnified x 85

(b) Magnified x 425

(c) Magnified x 2100

Figure 1
Hidden Life
Microscope enlargements of the tip of this pin show an abundance of life—in this case bacteria—thriving on an object that we normally think of as devoid of living organisms.

and just like any factory, they are constantly shipping things in and out. The primary size-limiting factor for cells is having enough surface area to export and import all that they need.

This constraint comes about because of a fundamental mathematical principle: As the surface area of an object increases, its *volume* increases even more. Say you have a cube 1 inch long on each of its sides. Its surface area is 6 square inches (Length × Width × Number of sides), while its volume is 1 cubic inch (Length × Width × Height). Now, say you increase the side dimension to 8 inches. The surface area goes from 6 to 384 square inches, but the *volume* goes from 1 to 512 cubic inches. At a 1-inch dimension, there were *six* square inches of surface area for every cubic inch of volume; now, there are only *three-quarters* of an inch of surface for every cubic inch of volume. Beyond a certain volume, then, a cell simply would not have enough surface area to import and export all the materials it needs. This effectively sets an upper limit on how big cells can be and helps explain why most of the cells in an elephant are no bigger than those in an ant, although the elephant does have more cells than the ant. **Figure 3** shows you some size comparisons in the micro-world.

100 m
10 m ------- blue whale
1 m ------- human
10 cm
------ chicken egg ------
1 cm
------- frog egg ------
1 mm

100 µm
------ plant and animal cells ------
10 µm ------ cell nucleus
------ most bacteria ------
1 µm ------ mitochondria

------ smallest bacteria
100 nm ------ large virus ------

10 nm ------ proteins ------
------ lipids ------
1 nm

0.1 nm ------ atoms ------

1 meter (m) = 1.09 yards
1 centimeter (cm) = 10^{-2} (1/100) meter (**1 cm = 0.4 inch**)
1 millimeter (mm) = 10^{-3} (1/1000) meter
1 micrometer (µm) = 10^{-6} (1/1,000,000) meter
1 nanometer (nm) = 10^{-9} (1/1,000,000,000) meter

Figure 2
Little and Big
The sizes of some selected objects in the natural world.

poliovirus

section of DNA molecule

ribosome

glucose (blood sugar) molecule

carbon atom

5 nm

Figure 3
Small Is a Relative Thing
The sizes and shapes of five natural-world entities, each magnified a million times.

lining of a cell or of one of its compartments. In the balance of this chapter, we'll explore all of the constituent parts listed above except for the plasma membrane, which is so special it gets its own chapter.

BioFlix

Tour of an Animal Cell

Figure 4.4
The Animal Cell

The Animal Cell

To get a sense of what eukaryotic cells are like, it's convenient to look at two types of them: animal cells and plant cells. These cell types have more similarities than they do differences, but they are different enough that it will be helpful to look at them separately. We'll start by examining animal cells and then look at how plant cells differ from them.

Insofar as we can characterize that elusive creature, the "typical" animal cell (**Figure 4.4**), it is roughly spherical, surrounded by, and linked to, cells of similar type, immersed in a watery fluid, and about 25 micrometers (μm) in diameter, meaning that about 30 of them could fit side by side within the period at the end of this sentence.

SO FAR ...

1. Every form of life either is a _____ or is composed of _____, each of which can arise only from another _____.

2. The two most fundamentally different kinds of cells are _____ cells, each of which has its primary complement of DNA enclosed inside a membrane-lined _____; and _____ cells, whose DNA is not enclosed within this structure.

3. In a eukaryotic cell, the cytoplasm is the region that lies inside the _____ but outside the _____. The jelly-like fluid filling much of this region is called the _____, while the individual highly organized structures within it are called _____.

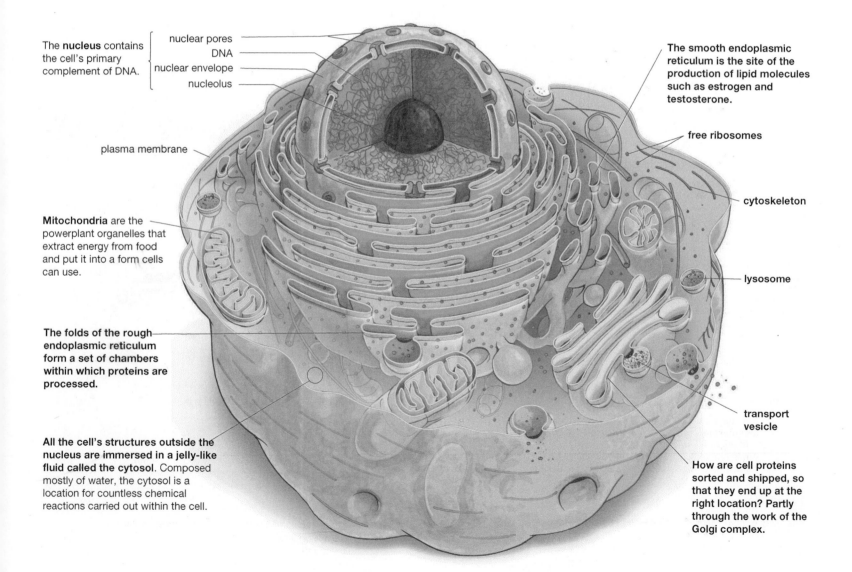

The **nucleus** contains the cell's primary complement of DNA.

nuclear pores
DNA
nuclear envelope
nucleolus

The smooth endoplasmic reticulum is the site of the production of lipid molecules such as estrogen and testosterone.

free ribosomes

plasma membrane

cytoskeleton

Mitochondria are the powerplant organelles that extract energy from food and put it into a form cells can use.

lysosome

The folds of the rough endoplasmic reticulum form a set of chambers within which proteins are processed.

transport vesicle

All the cell's structures outside the nucleus are immersed in a jelly-like fluid called the **cytosol**. Composed mostly of water, the cytosol is a location for countless chemical reactions carried out within the cell.

How are cell proteins sorted and shipped, so that they end up at the right location? Partly through the work of the Golgi complex.

4.4 A Tour of the Animal Cell's Protein Production Path

You are now going to take an extended tour of the animal cell, which can be thought of as a living factory. Much of the first part of your trip will be spent tracing the way this factory puts together a product—a protein—for export outside itself. Just as a new employee might tour an assembly line as a means of learning about factory equipment, so you are going to follow the path of protein production as a means of learning about cell equipment.

Figure 4.5 shows the path you'll be taking, from nucleus to the outer edge of the cell. Don't be bothered by the unfamiliar terms in Figure 4.5 because they'll all be explained in the text. The important thing is that, before we begin our tour, you have some sense of the path that protein production takes.

Beginning in the Control Center: The Nucleus

As noted in Chapter 3, proteins are critical working molecules in living things, and DNA contains the information for putting proteins together from a starting set of the building blocks called amino acids. Our entire complement of DNA is like a cookbook that contains individual protein recipes, which we call genes. A given gene's chemical sequence in effect says, "Connect this amino acid to this one, then add this one, then this one . . . ," the final result being the specifications for a completed protein. In the eukaryotic cell, as you've seen, DNA is largely confined within a nucleus bound by a membrane. If you look at **Figure 4.6** on the next page, you can see the nature of this membrane. It is the **nuclear envelope:** the double membrane that lines the nucleus in eukaryotic cells.

There comes a point in the life of most cells when they divide, one cell becoming two. Because (with a few exceptions) all cells must possess the set of instructions that are contained in DNA, it follows that when a cell divides, its original complement of DNA must *double,* so that both cells that result from the cell division can have their own DNA. The nucleus, then, is not just the site where DNA exists; it is the site where new DNA is put together, or "synthesized," for this doubling.

Messenger RNA

At the end of Chapter 3, you saw that, while DNA exists in a cell's nucleus, the proteins that DNA codes for are put together in a cell's cytoplasm. Thus, the information contained in a length of DNA has to be transported from the nucleus to the cytoplasm. How does this happen? DNA's instructions are copied onto

a second long-chain molecule, called RNA, and *it* ferries the DNA information out of the nucleus to the site of protein synthesis. RNA actually comes in several forms, but the form that DNA's instructions are copied onto is the well-named *messenger RNA* or mRNA for short. Given that mRNA goes to the cytoplasm, it must, of course, have some way of getting out of the nucleus; its exit points turn out to be thousands of channels that stud the surface of the nuclear envelope—the *nuclear pores* that you can see in Figure 4.6.

mRNA Moves Out of the Nucleus

Imagine shrinking in size so that the nucleus seems about as big as a house, with you standing outside it. What you would see in protein synthesis is lengths of

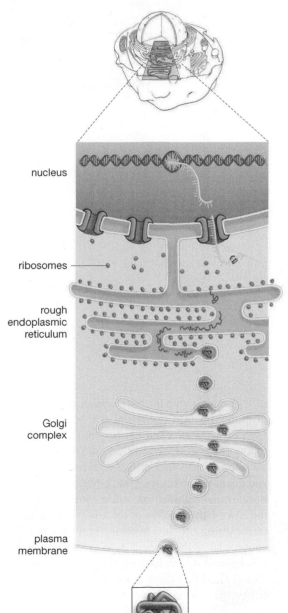

**Figure 4.5
Path of Protein
Production in Cells**

nucleus

ribosomes

rough
endoplasmic
reticulum

Golgi
complex

plasma
membrane

1. Instructions from DNA are copied onto mRNA.

2. mRNA moves to ribosome.

3. Ribosome moves to endoplasmic reticulum and "reads" mRNA instructions.

4. Amino acid chain growing from ribosome is dropped inside endoplasmic reticulum membrane. Chain folds into protein.

5. Protein moves to Golgi complex for additional processing and for sorting.

6. Protein moves to plasma membrane for export.

Figure 4.6
The Cell's Nucleus

The DNA of eukaryotic cells is sequestered inside a compartment, the nucleus, which is lined by a double membrane known as the nuclear envelope. Compounds pass into and out of the nucleus through a series of microscopic channels called nuclear pores. Protein production depends on the information encoded in DNA's sequence of chemical building blocks. This information is copied onto a length of messenger RNA (mRNA), which then exits from the nucleus through a nuclear pore. (Micrograph: × 4,400)

mRNA rapidly moving out through nuclear pores and dropping off into the cytoplasm. Several varieties of RNA actually come out like this, but for now, let's just follow the trail of the mRNA. You're about ready to leave the nucleus to continue your cell tour, but before you do, note two things. First, DNA contains information for making proteins, and the mRNA chains coming out of the nuclear pores amount to a means of transmitting this information. Thus, it's not hard to conceptualize the nucleus as a control center for the cell. Beyond this, in looking at Figure 4.6 you've probably noticed that there is a rather imposing structure *within* the nucleus, called the nucleolus. For now, just *hold that thought;* the mRNA chains have come out of the nuclear pores and are making a short trip to another part of the cell.

Ribosomes

Small structures called ribosomes are the destinations for our lengths of mRNA. For now, we can define the **ribosome** as an organelle that serves as the site of protein synthesis in the cell. If an mRNA chain amounts to a set of instructions for putting a protein together, a ribosome amounts to a machine that carries out these instructions. Each ribosome acts as a site through which an mRNA chain is run; as this happens, the ribosome "reads" the chemical sequence in the mRNA chain and starts putting together amino acids in the order specified by the mRNA sequence. The result is a chain of amino acids that grows from the ribosome—a chain that eventually will fold up into the molecule we call a protein (**Figure 4.7**). You may remember that the kind of protein we are tracking will eventually be exported out of the cell altogether. The synthesis of this kind of protein actually stops when only a very short sequence of the amino acid (or "polypeptide") chain has grown from the ribosome. Why? "Export" polypeptide chains need to be processed within other structures in the cell before they can become fully functional proteins. The first step in this process is for the ribosome, and its associated cargo, to migrate a short distance in the cell and then attach to another cell structure.

The Rough Endoplasmic Reticulum

If you look again at Figure 4.4, you can see that, though the nucleus cuts a roughly spherical figure out of the cell, there is in essence a folded-up continuation of the nuclear envelope on one side. This mass of membrane has a name that is a mouthful: the **rough endoplasmic reticulum**. This structure can be defined as a network of membranes that aids in the processing of proteins in eukaryotic cells. The rough endoplasmic reticulum is rough because it is studded with ribosomes; it is endoplasmic because it lies within (*endo*) the cyto*plasm*; and it is a reticulum because it is a net-

work, which is what *reticulum* means in Latin. Understandably, it is generally referred to as the rough ER or the RER.

Our ribosome, bound with its attached mRNA and polypeptide chains, will migrate to the rough ER and dock on its outside face, thus joining a multitude of other ribosomes that have done the same thing. As noted, the polypeptide chain that is output from the ribosome is in essence an unfinished protein that needs to go through more processing before it can be exported. The first step in this processing leads only to the other side of the ER wall in which the ribosome is embedded. As the ribosome goes on with its work, the polypeptide chain it is producing drops into chambers inside the rough ER.

If you look at Figure 4.7, you can see that the entire rough ER takes the shape of a set of flattened sacs. The membrane that the rough ER is composed of forms the periphery of these sacs. Inside are the internal spaces of the rough ER. As polypeptide chains enter the internal spaces, they first fold up into their protein shapes, as you saw in Chapter 3. Beyond this, most proteins exported from cells have sugar side chains added to them here. Quality control of the production line is in operation in the rough ER as well. Polypeptide chains that have

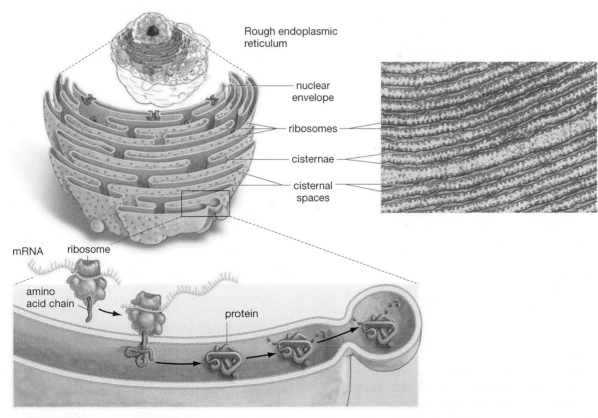

Figure 4.7
Proteins Taking Shape: Ribosomes and the Rough Endoplasmic Reticulum

The steps of the lower figure begin with a length of messenger RNA (mRNA) that has migrated from the nucleus of a cell.

Rough endoplasmic reticulum

nuclear envelope

ribosomes

cisternae

cisternal spaces

mRNA

ribosome

amino acid chain

protein

1. mRNA docks on ribosome. Amino acid chain production begins.

2. Ribosome docks on ER. As it is completed, amino acid chain moves into ER's internal space.

3. Amino acid chain folds up making a protein.

4. Sugar side chains added to protein.

5. Vesicle formed to house protein while in transport.

faulty sequences are detected in the rough ER internal space and ejected out of the protein production line altogether, after which they are broken down into their component parts, which will be recycled. Other proteins will pass the quality control tests, however, and will then move out of the rough ER for more processing.

Several Locations for Ribosomes

All of the mRNA that comes out of the nuclear pores goes to ribosomes, but only some of these ribosomes end up migrating to the rough ER. A multitude of ribosomes will remain "free ribosomes," which is to say ribosomes that remain free-standing, in the cytosol. What makes the difference? Remember how, in the ribosome we looked at, only a small stretch of the polypeptide chain it was producing emerged before the ribosome first halted its work and then migrated to the rough ER? That small stretch of the chain contained a chemical signal that said, in effect, "rough ER processing needed." The result was the ribosome's move to the rough ER. In general, these rough ER-linked ribosomes produce proteins that will reside in the cell's membranes or that will be exported out of the cell altogether (making them "secretory" proteins). Meanwhile, free ribosomes tend to produce proteins that will be used within the cell's cytoplasm or nucleus.

A Pause for the Nucleolus

Before you continue on the path of protein processing, think back a bit to the discussion about the nucleus, when you were asked to hold the thought about the large structure *inside* the nucleus called the nucleolus. This is the point where its story can be told because now you know what ribosomes are.

It turns out that ribosomes are mostly made of RNA. (They are made of a mixture of proteins and *ribo*nucleic acid.) So great is the cell's need for ribosomes that a special section of the nucleus is devoted to the synthesis of RNA. This is the nucleolus. The *type* of RNA that's part of the ribosomes is, fittingly enough, called ribosomal RNA or rRNA, and it's one of the multiple varieties of RNA mentioned before. With this in mind, we can define the **nucleolus** as the area within the nucleus of a cell devoted to the production of ribosomal RNA.

Ribosomes are brought only to an unfinished state within the nucleolus, after which they pass through the nuclear pores and into the cytoplasm; when put together in final form there, they begin receiving mRNA chains. They are the one variety of cellular organelle that is not lined by a membrane. (They are also the one variety of organelle that prokaryotic cells have.) The cell's traffic in ribosomes is considerable; with millions of them in existence, lots are going to be wearing out all the time. Perhaps a thousand need to be replaced every minute.

Elegant Transportation: Transport Vesicles

The proteins that have been processed within the rough ER need to move out of it and to their "downstream" destinations before being exported. But how do proteins move from one location to another within the cell? Recall that the rough ER and the nuclear membrane amount to one long, convoluted membrane. And, as just noted, all the organelles in the cell except ribosomes are "membrane-bound," meaning they have membranes at their periphery. Each of these membranes has its own chemical structure, but collectively they have an amazing ability to work together: A piece of one membrane can *bud off*, as the term goes, carrying inside it some of our proteins-in-process. Moving through the cytosol, this tiny sphere of membrane can then *fuse* with another membrane-bound organelle, releasing its protein cargo in the process. You can see how this works in **Figure 4.8**, which offers a closer view of

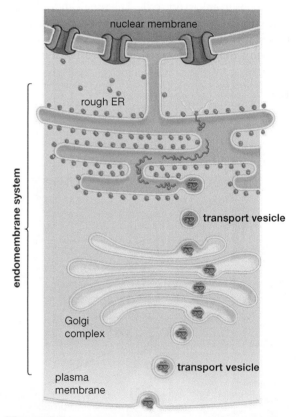

Figure 4.8
Cellular Transportation:
The Endomembrane System

Proteins and other cellular materials are transported through eukaryotic cells within membrane-lined spheres called transport vesicles. These vesicles can emerge, soap bubble-like, from one membrane-lined organelle, travel through the cell's cytosol, and then fuse with a second membrane-lined organelle, unloading their cargo in the process. The cell's interactive network of transport vesicles and membrane-lined organelles is referred to as its endomembrane system.

one part of the protein-production path. The membrane-lined spheres that move within this network, carrying proteins and other molecules, are called **transport vesicles.** The network itself is known as the **endomembrane system:** an interactive group of membrane-lined organelles and transport vesicles within eukaryotic cells.

This system gives cells a remarkable capability. One minute a piece of membrane may be an integral part of, say, the rough ER; the next, it is separating off as a spheroid vesicle and moving through the cytosol, carrying proteins within it. (These vesicles are not moving under their own power, however. As you'll see later, they are propelled along the "monorails" of the cell's internal skeleton.) Many different kinds of proteins are being processed at any one time in the rough ER sacs, but most of those under construction are initially bound for the same place—the Golgi complex.

Downstream from the Rough ER: The Golgi Complex

Once a transport vesicle, bearing proteins, has budded off from the rough ER, it then moves through the cytosol to fuse with the membrane of another organelle, one first noticed by Italian biologist Camillo Golgi at the beginning of the twentieth century. The **Golgi complex** is a network of membranes that processes and distributes proteins that come to it from the rough ER. Some side chains of sugar may be trimmed from proteins here, or phosphate groups may be added, but the Golgi complex does something else as well. Recall that some proteins in this production line are bound for export outside the cell, while others will end up being used within various membranes in the cell. It follows that proteins have to be *sorted and shipped* appropriately, and the Golgi does just this, acting as a kind of distribution center. Chemical "tags" that are part of the proteins often allow for this routing. Remember how, in the rough ER, carbohydrate side chains might be attached to a newly formed protein? Often, these side chains serve as the routing tags; other times, a section of the protein's amino acid sequence will serve this function.

The Golgi is similar to the ER in that it amounts to a series of connected membranous sacs with internal spaces (**Figure 4.9**). Proteins arrive at the Golgi housed in transport vesicles that fuse with the Golgi "face" nearest the rough ER, at which point the vesicles release their protein cargo into the Golgi internal spaces for processing. Once processed, proteins of the sort we are following eventually bud off from the outside face of the Golgi, now housed in their final transport vesicles.

From the Golgi to the Surface

For secretory proteins, the journey that began with the copying of DNA information onto mRNA is almost over. Once a vesicle buds off from the Golgi, all that remains is for it to make its way through the cytosol to the plasma membrane at the outer reaches of

**Figure 4.9
Processing and Routing: The Golgi Complex**

The vesicles in the micrograph at right are the pink and purple spheres.

Golgi complex

1. Transport vesicle from RER fuses with Golgi

2. Protein undergoes more processing in Golgi

Side chains are edited (sugars may be trimmed, phosphate groups added).

3. Proteins are sorted and shipped…

for export out of cell

to plasma membrane

to cytosol

cisternae

cisternal space

vesicle

the cell. There, the vesicle fuses with the plasma membrane, and the protein is ejected into the extracellular world. With it, one finished product of the cellular factory has rolled out the door.

SO FAR ...

1. The cell's nucleus holds the cell's primary complement of _____, which contains information for the production of _____.

2. Proteins of the sort followed in the text are put together within tiny organelles called _____ that lie outside the nucleus. During their production, these proteins fold up upon entering the _____, where they undergo editing, after which they move to the _____, where they undergo further editing and are sorted for distribution.

3. Proteins and other materials move through the cell within membrane-lined spheres called _____, which, together with membrane-lined organelles, make up the _____ system.

4.5 Cell Structures Outside the Protein Production Path

A functioning cell engages in more activities than the protein synthesis and shipment just reviewed for the simple reason that cells do a lot more than produce proteins.

The Smooth Endoplasmic Reticulum

If you look back to Figure 4.4, you can see that there actually are *two* kinds of endoplasmic reticuli. The part of the ER membrane, farther out from the nucleus, that has no ribosomes is called the smooth endoplasmic reticulum or smooth ER. It's "smooth" because it is not peppered with ribosomes, and this very quality means it is not a site of protein synthesis. Instead, the **smooth endoplasmic reticulum** is a network of membranes that is the site of the synthesis of various lipids and a site at which potentially harmful substances are detoxified within the cell. The tasks the smooth ER undertakes, however, will vary in accordance with cell type. The lipids we normally think of as "fats" are put together and stored in the smooth ER of liver and fat cells, while the "steroid" lipids reviewed last chapter—testosterone and estrogen—are put together in the smooth ER of the ovaries and testes. The detoxification of potentially harmful substances, such as alcohol, takes place largely in the smooth ER of liver cells.

Tiny Acid Vats: Lysosomes and Cellular Recycling

Any factory must be able to get rid of some old materials while recycling others. A factory also needs new materials, brought in from the outside, that probably will have to undergo some processing before use. A single organelle in the animal cell aids in doing all these things. It is the **lysosome,** an organelle found in animal cells that digests worn-out cellular materials and foreign materials that enter the cell. Several hundred of these membrane-bound organelles may exist in any given cell. You could think of them as sealed-off acid vats that take in large molecules, break them down, and then return the resulting smaller molecules to the cytosol. What they cannot return, they retain inside themselves or expel outside the cell. They carry out this work not only on molecules entering the cell from the outside (say, invading bacteria) but also on materials that exist inside the cell—on worn-out organelle parts, for example (**Figure 4.10**).

A given lysosome may be filled with as many as 40 different enzymes that can break larger molecules into their component parts—an enzymatic array that allows each lysosome to break down most of what comes its way. A lysosome generally gets hold of its macromolecule prey through the work of a larger network of membrane-lined vesicles. One of these vesicles engulfs, say, a worn-out organelle part and then fuses with a lysosome, which then goes to work breaking the organelle fragment down. The small molecules that result then pass freely out of the lysosome and into the cytosol for reuse elsewhere. Thus, there is recycling at the cellular level. Cells carry out this kind of self-renewal at an amazing rate. Christian de Duve, who with his colleagues discovered lysosomes in the 1950s, has noted the effect of this activity on human brain cells. In an elderly person, he noted,

such cells have been there for decades. Yet, most of their mitochondria, ribosomes, membranes, and other organelles are less than a month old. Over the years, the cells have destroyed and remade most of their constituent molecules from hundreds to thousands of times, some even more than 100,000 times.

Molecular house cleaning of this sort operates continually within all eukaryotic cells, but the *pace* of this activity changes in accordance with an organism's nutritional state. The organelles and proteins of a person who is starving will be dismantled at a much higher rate than is the case in a person who has had plenty to eat. Indeed, when nutrition is running low, perfectly *functional* cellular components seem to be taken apart in this process, after which the resulting molecules are used to meet the energy needs of the cell—the cellular equivalent of throwing furniture into a fireplace as a means of keeping warm. On the other side of this coin, we now have evidence indicating that an *underactive* molecular recycling system plays a part in producing Alzheimer's disease. In this case, faulty protein fragments are allowed to build up in brain cells, rather than being degraded through lysosomal activity. The result is a set of brain cells that end up dying because of the proteins that have accumulated in them.

Extracting Energy from Food: Mitochondria

Just as there is no such thing as a free lunch, there is no such thing as free lysosome activity, or ribosomal action, or protein export. There is a price to be paid for all these things, and it is called energy expenditure. The fuel for this energy is contained in the food that cells ingest. But the energy in this food has to be extracted and transferred to a molecule that can easily dispense it as needed—a molecule called ATP (adenosine triphosphate). And where does this energy extraction and transfer take place? Mostly in the tiny "power plant" organelles of the cell, called mitochondria. Just as a city's power plant takes in coal and turns out electricity, so mitochondria take in food and turn out ATP. Thus, **mitochondria** can be defined as organelles that are the primary sites of energy conversion in eukaryotic cells. While cells that don't use much energy might only have one or two mitochondria, an energy-ravenous liver cell might have a thousand. Most of the heat in our bodies is generated within mitochondria, and almost all the food we eat is ultimately consumed in them.

Figure 4.11, on the next page, gives you an idea of the structure of a mitochondrion. Note that there is a continuous outer membrane enclosing an inner membrane that has a series of folds in it. The effect of these infoldings is to give mitochondria a larger internal surface area for carrying out their energy transformation activities.

Few details about mitochondria are included here because much of Chapter 7 is devoted to them. Suffice it to say that to carry out their work, mitochondria need not only food but oxygen. (Ever

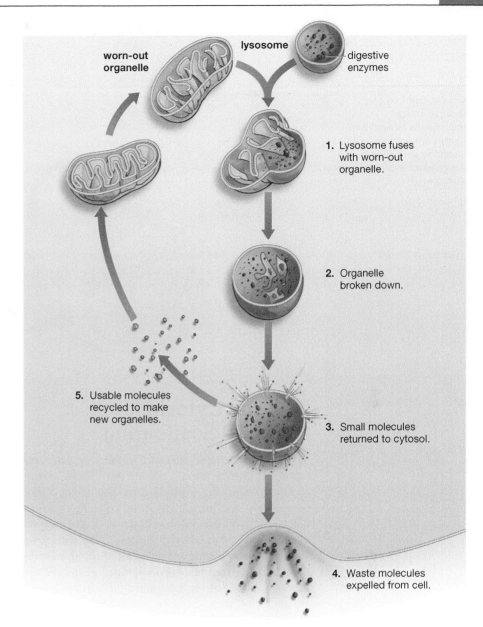

1. Lysosome fuses with worn-out organelle.

2. Organelle broken down.

3. Small molecules returned to cytosol.

4. Waste molecules expelled from cell.

5. Usable molecules recycled to make new organelles.

Figure 4.10
Cellular Recycling: Lysosomes

Lysosomes are membrane-bound organelles that contain potent enzymes capable of digesting large molecules, such as worn-out organelles. The useful parts of such organelles will be returned to the cytosol and used elsewhere—a form of cellular recycling.

wonder why you need to breathe?) The *products* of mitochondrial activity, meanwhile, are the ATP we talked about along with water and carbon dioxide. (Ever wonder where the carbon dioxide you exhale comes from?) Another thing to note about mitochondria is that they are the descendants of resident aliens. They started out as bacterial cells that invaded eukaryotic precursor cells more than 1.5 billion years ago only to end up becoming part of these larger cells (see "The Stranger Within," on page 80).

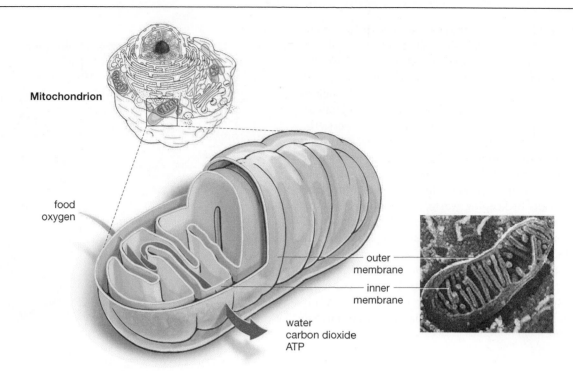

Figure 4.11
Energy Transformers:
Mitochondria
Just as a power plant
converts the energy con-
tained in coal into useful
electrical energy,
mitochondria convert the
energy contained in food into
a useful form of chemical
energy, which is stored in the
molecule ATP.

4.6 The Cytoskeleton: Internal Scaffolding

When you see a set of cells in action, the word that comes to mind is *hyperactive*. Cells are not passive entities. Jostling, narrowing, expanding, moving about, capturing objects and bringing them in, expelling other objects: This is life as a bubbling cauldron of activity. It was once thought that cells did all these things with pretty much the equipment you've looked at so far, meaning that the Golgi complex, the ribosomes, and so forth were thought to be floating in a featureless soup that was the cytosol. But improved work with microscopes showed that there is, in fact, a complex forest within the cytoplasm. It is the **cytoskeleton,** a network of protein filaments that functions in cell structure, cell movement, and the transport of materials within the cell. This network is found in its full form only in eukaryotic cells, but in the last few years scientists have confirmed that bacteria have several types of cytoskeletal fibers as well.

Some of the cytoskeleton's fibers are permanent and relatively static, but many are moving, and some are assembled or disassembled very rapidly. The cytoskeleton usually is divided into three component parts. Ordered by size, going from smallest to largest in diameter, these are microfilaments, intermediate filaments, and microtubules (**Figure 4.12**). Let's take a look at some of the characteristics of each.

Microfilaments

The most slender of the cytoskeletal fibers, **microfilaments** are made of the protein *actin* and serve as a support or "structural" filament in almost all eukaryotic cells. Microfilaments can also help cells move or capture prey, essentially by growing very rapidly at one end—in the direction of the movement or extension—while decomposing rapidly at the other end. You can see a vivid example of microfilament-aided cell extension in **Figure 4.13**.

Intermediate Filaments

Intermediate filaments are filaments of the cytoskeleton intermediate in diameter between microfilaments and microtubules. These in-between-sized proteins are the most permanent of the cytoskeletal elements, perhaps coming closest to our everyday notion of what a skeleton is like. They stabilize the positions of the nucleus and other organelles within the cell.

Microtubules

Microtubules are the largest of the cytoskeletal filaments, taking the form of tubes composed of the protein tubulin. Microtubules play a structural role in the cell; in fact, theirs seems to be the preeminent structural role in the sense of determining the shape of the cell. But they take on several other tasks in addition. They serve, for example, as the monorails of the cell's internal skeleton discussed earlier. Recall that protein-laden vesicles move from one organelle to another in the cell. These spheres are moving along the "rails" of microtubules, while sitting atop the "engine" of one of the so-called motor proteins (**Figure 4.14** on page 80). How does this work? One family of motor proteins serves to move vesicles toward a cell's periphery while a second family of proteins serves to move vesicles toward a cell's center. If you've ever "walked" a fork across a flat surface, you understand the kind of motor-protein movement that's pictured in Figure 4.14. One of the

(a) Microfilaments (in red)

(b) Intermediate filaments

(c) Microtubules

7 nm
Main function: changes
in cell shape

10 nm
Main function: maintenance
of cell shape

25 nm
Main functions: maintenance
of cell shape, movement of
organelles, cell mobility
(cilia and flagella)

Figure 4.12
Structure and
Movement: The
Cytoskeleton
Three types of fibers form the
inner scaffolding or cytoskeleton of the eukaryotic cell:
microfilaments, intermediate
filaments, and microtubules.

protein's "feet" detaches from the microtubule and
swings around in front of the other foot, after which
the process is reversed. Each of these steps is 8 nanome-
ters long, and each is powered by a release of energy
from an ATP molecule.

Cell Extensions Made of
Microtubules: Cilia and Flagella

Microtubules also form the underlying structure for
two kinds of cell extensions, cilia and flagella. **Cilia** are
microtubular extensions of cells that take the form of a
large number of active, hair-like growths stemming
from them. The function of cilia is simple: Move back
and forth very rapidly, perhaps 10 to 40 times per second. The effect of this movement can be either to propel a cell or to move material *around* a cell. Cilia are
extremely common among single-celled organisms
and in some of the cells of simple animals (sponges, jellyfish). You saw an example of cilia in humans earlier in
connection with our sense of smell. Our lungs also are
lined with cilia whose job it is to sweep the lungs clean
of whatever foreign matter has been inhaled. These
cilia, like most others, all beat at once in the same direction, acting like rowers in a crew.

Figure 4.13
Microfilaments in Action
Certain cells can move or capture prey by sending out
extensions of themselves called pseudopodia ("false feet").
It is the rapid construction of actin microfilaments—in the
direction of the extension—that makes this possible. Here,
a type of blood-borne guard cell called a macrophage is
about to use a pseudopodium it is constructing to capture
a green bacterium.

ESSAY

The Stranger Within: Endosymbiosis

If pressed to think about it, most people would probably agree that there's something slightly creepy about being made up of cells. Jostling and dividing as they are, working and dying within us without so much as asking permission, they give us the feeling that the unitary *self* that we so cherish actually amounts to an unruly collection of creatures within.

How sobering it is, then, to realize that we almost certainly are composite beings in more ways than one. Each of our *cells* has within it the vestiges of other living things: the descendants of bacteria that long ago invaded our ancestors' cells, only to take up residence there. In animal cells, the mito-chondria that serve as cellular "power-houses" are almost certainly the descendants of bacteria (**Figure 1**). Plant and algae cells have mitochondria, too, but then go on to have an additional set of bacterial descendants in them: the chloroplasts that carry out photosynthesis.

The idea that these structures are descended from free-standing bacteria is called the endosymbiotic theory—*endo* for "within" the cell and *symbiotic* for "symbiosis," meaning a situation in which two organisms not of the same species live in close association. What makes us think that endosymbiosis really happened? First, mitochondria and chloroplasts—which,

Figure 1
Once Invaders, Now Organelles
The mitochondria within this cell, colored yellow, are the descendants of bacteria that invaded a set of host eukaryotic cells billions of years ago. Over evolutionary time, these bacteria were transformed into energy-converting organelles that today are found in almost all eukaryotic cells.

Figure 4.14
Several Functions for Microtubules

(a) They are the "rails" on which vesicles move through the cell, carried along by "motor proteins."

(b) They exist outside the cell in the form of cilia, which are profuse collections of hair-like projections that beat rapidly, forming currents that can propel a cell or move material around it.

(c) They are also found outside cells in the form of flagella. The flagellum on this sperm cell is enabling it to seek entry into an egg.

(a) Transport monorails

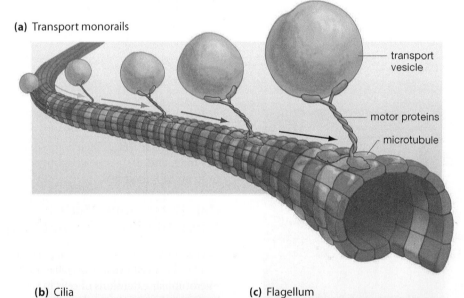

transport vesicle

motor proteins

microtubule

(b) Cilia

(c) Flagellum

remember, are *organelles* within eukaryotic cells—have many of the characteristics of free-standing *cells,* specifically free-standing bacterial cells. They have their own ribosomes and their own DNA, both of a bacterial type, and they reproduce through a bacteria-like division, partly under their own genetic control. Moreover, the sequencing of mitochondrial DNA indicates that all mitochondria are descended from a single species of bacteria whose closest modern relatives make a living by invading other cells. (As it happens, the single closest living relative of the ancient mitochondrial invaders is *Rickettsia prowazekii*, the cause of modern typhus.)

Mitochondria appear to have completed the transition to endosymbiotic living somewhere between 2.2 and 1.5 billion years ago—so far in the past that the receiving or "host" cells for their initial invasion were a kind of early version of today's eukaryotic cells. The reason this invasion turned into a long-lasting merger was straightforward: Both the bacterial and eukaryotic cells benefited from the new arrangement, though in different ways. At the time, oxygen was making up more and more of Earth's atmosphere, and the mitochondrial ancestors were able to use or "metabolize" oxygen in the extraction of energy from food, while the early eukaryotes they invaded were fairly intolerant of oxygen. Once the two kinds of organisms began living together, the host eukaryote provided food to the bacterium, and the bacterium allowed the host to thrive in an oxygenated world. Then, over time, through a process of internal gene transfer, the bacteria made a transition from organisms that were living inside a host to organelles that were simply part of the host.

This union of the two types of cells was an important event in the evolution of living things in that it scaled up the energy available to eukaryotes. This is so because oxygen-aided energy transfer is terrifically *efficient* compared to energy transfer that does not use oxygen. In our own bodies, the oxygen-aided or "aerobic" energy transfer that takes place in our mitochondria allows us to extract perhaps 15 times as much energy from each bite of an apple than would be the case with energy transfer that doesn't use oxygen. Large organisms require large amounts of energy, and the only way they can get such quantities is by metabolizing oxygen. Thus, the sheer size of the living world is to some degree a product of a microbial merger that began as a microbial invasion billions of years ago.

Cilia grow from eukaryotic cells in great profusion, but it is a different story with **flagella**—the relatively long, tail-like extensions of some cells that function in cell movement (Figure 4.14). It is sometimes the case that several flagella will sprout from a given cell, but often there is but a single flagellum. Only one kind of animal cell is flagellated, and it scarcely needs an introduction: A sperm is a single cell that whips its flagellum in a corkscrew motion to get to an unfertilized egg.

In Summary: Structures in the Animal Cell

In your tour of the cell so far, you've pictured a cell as a factory, one that synthesizes proteins in a "production line" that starts with DNA in the nucleus and then goes to the ribosomes (via mRNA), to the rough ER, to the Golgi complex, and finally to the protein's destination (the plasma membrane, export, and so on). You've also seen that cells have other structures, such as lysosomes for digestion and recycling, mitochondria for energy extraction, the smooth endoplasmic reticulum for lipid synthesis, and the cytoskeleton for structure and movement. If you look at **Figure 4.15**, you can see, in metaphorical form, a "map" of these component parts within the cell. **Table 4.1**, on the next page, lists cellular elements found in plant and animal cells as well as some elements found only in plant cells.

Figure 4.15
The Cell as a Factory
This comparison may help you to remember some roles of the different parts of the cell.

Table 4.1

Structures in Plant and Animal Cells

Name	Function and Location	Name	Function and Location
Nucleus	Site of most of the cell's DNA Location: Inside nuclear envelope	Mitochondria	Transform energy from food Location: Cytoplasm
Nucleolus	Synthesis of ribosomal RNA Location: Nucleus	Rough endoplasmic reticulum	Protein processing Location: Cytoplasm
Ribosomes	Sites of protein synthesis Location: Rough ER, Free-standing in cytoplasm	Smooth endoplasmic reticulum	Lipid synthesis, storage; detoxification of harmful substances Location: Cytoplasm
Cytoskeleton	Maintains cell shape, facilitates cell movement and movement of materials within cell Location: Cytoplasm	Vesicles	Transport of proteins and other cellular materials Location: Cytoplasm
Cytosol	Protein-rich fluid in which organelles and cytoskeleton are immersed Location: Cytoplasm	Central vacuole (in plant cells only)	Nutrient storage, cell pressure maintenance, pH balance Location: Cytoplasm
Golgi complex	Processing, sorting of proteins Location: Cytoplasm	Chloroplasts (in plant cells only)	Photosynthesis Location: Cytoplasm
Lysosomes (in animal cells only)	Digestion of imported materials and cell's own used materials Location: Cytoplasm	Cell walls (in plant cells only)	Limit water uptake; maintain cell membrane shape, protect from outside influences Location: Outside plasma membrane

SO FAR...

1. Lipids, including fats, are put together in the organelle called the _____, while worn-out cellular materials are broken down and recycled in the organelles called _____.

2. The organelles called mitochondria transform the _____ from food into a usable chemical form, contained in a molecule called _____.

3. The cell's internal scaffolding, made up of different types of protein fibers, is called the _____.

4.7 The Plant Cell

The animal cell you just looked at has lots in common with the cells that you'd see in any eukaryotic living thing. If you looked at the cells that make up plants or fungi, for example, you'd see that they have a nucleus, ribosomes, mitochondria, and so forth. But, as you can imagine, the cells of a fungus have to be *somewhat* different from those of an animal since fungi and animals are such different types of organisms. To give you an idea of some of the kinds of differences found in the cells of life's various kingdoms, we'll look briefly now at the plant cell, which differs from an animal cell in several basic ways.

A quick look at **Figure 4.16** will confirm for you the first part of this story—how structurally similar plant and animal cells are. As you see, a plant cell has a nucleus (with a nucleolus), the smooth and rough ERs, a cytoskeleton—most of the things you've just gone over in animal cells. Indeed, there is only one struc-

ture present in the animal cells you've looked at that plant cells don't have: the lysosome. What jumps out at you when you look at plant cells is not what they lack compared to animal cells, but what they *have* that animal cells do not. As you can see in **Figure 4.17** on the next page, these additions are:

- A thick cell wall
- Structures called chloroplasts
- A large structure called a central vacuole

The Central Vacuole

The central vacuole pictured in Figure 4.17 is so prominent that it appears to be a kind of organelle continent surrounded by a mere moat of cytosol. And, indeed, in a mature plant cell, one or two central vacuoles may comprise 90 percent of cell volume. Although animal cells can have vacuoles, the imposing central vacuole in plants is different. For a start, it is composed mostly of water, which demonstrates just how watery plant cells are. A typical animal cell may be 70 percent water, but for plant cells the water proportion is likely to be 90 to 98 percent.

The watery environment of the central vacuole contains hundreds of other substances. Many of these are nutrients; others are waste products. There are also hydrogen ions, pumped in to keep the cell's cytoplasm at a near-neutral pH. The sheer number of larger molecules or "solutes" in the central vacuole spurs the movement of *water* into it through an effect called osmosis (which we'll be looking at next chapter). As a result of this influx of water, the central vacuole expands, pushing up against the cell's cytosol and giving the plant cell as a whole a healthy internal pressure. Given this task and the others, we can define the **central vacuole** as a large, watery plant organelle whose functions include the maintenance of cell pressure, the storage of cell nutrients, and the retention and degradation of

BioFlix

Tour of a Plant Cell

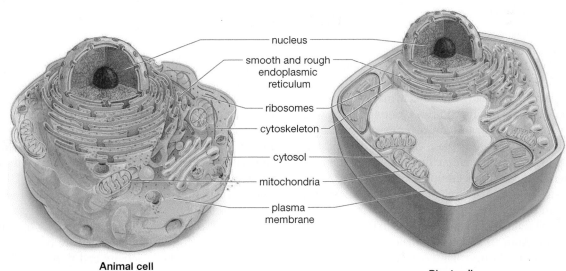

**Figure 4.16
Common Structures in Animal and Plant Cells**

nucleus

smooth and rough endoplasmic reticulum

ribosomes

cytoskeleton

cytosol

mitochondria

plasma membrane

Animal cell

Plant cell

Plant cells have a cell wall, chloroplasts, and a central vacuole, while animal cells do not.

cytoskeleton

nuclear envelope
nuclear pores
DNA
nucleolus

} nucleus

cell wall

chloroplast

central vacuole

rough endoplasmic reticulum
smooth endoplasmic reticulum
free ribosomes
Golgi complex
cytosol
plasma membrane
mitochondrion

Figure 4.17
The Plant Cell

cell waste products. Despite the vacuole's size, however, it is the other two structures—the cell wall and the chloroplasts—that interest us most as they tell us the most about differences among the cells of various types of living things. Let's have a look at these two structures.

The Cell Wall

Plant cells have an outer protective lining, called a **cell wall,** that makes their plasma membrane, just inside the cell wall, look rather thin and frail by comparison. This is because it *is* thin and frail by comparison; the plasma membrane of a plant cell may be 0.01 μm thick, while the combined units of a cell wall may be 700 times this width—7 μm or more. Cell walls are nearly always present in plant cells. And they exist in many organisms that are neither plant nor animal— bacteria, fungi, and a group of living things called protists—although the cell walls of these life-forms differ in chemical composition from those of plants. Thus, cell walls are the rule, rather than the exception, in nature. Animals are the one major group of living things whose cells never have cell walls.

What do cell walls do for plant cells? They provide them with structural strength, put a limit on their absorption of water (as you'll see in the next chapter), and generally protect plants from harmful outside influences. So, if they're so useful, why don't *animal* cells have them? Cell walls make for a rather rigid, inflexible organism—like plants, which are fixed in one place. Animals, meanwhile, need to be mobile, both to catch prey and to avoid *being* prey, which means they have to be flexible.

Cell walls in plants can come in several forms, but all such forms will be composed chiefly of a molecule you were introduced to last chapter: cellulose, a complex sugar or "polysaccharide" that is embedded within cell walls in the way reinforcing bars run through concrete. In some cell walls, cellulose is joined by a compound called lignin, which imparts considerable structural strength. You can see a vivid demonstration of this in the material we know as wood, which is largely made of cell walls (**Figure 4.18a**).

Cell walls can serve different functions over the life of an organism. Generally, they are the site of a good deal of metabolic activity and thus should not

(a)

(b)

secondary xylem (wood)   inner bark   outer bark

Figure 4.18
Great Strength from Small Things

(a) Trees can reach great heights because of the strength of their secondary xylem—better known as wood—which is largely made of cell walls. Pictured is an American basswood tree (*Tilia americana*).

(b) Cell walls play important roles in living cells, but they also are valuable as the strong, remaining components of dead cells. The outer bark of the basswood tree, seen in the blow-up at right, is composed mostly of dead cells whose cell walls are infused with a waxy substance that acts to protect the tree from invading insects and microorganisms.

be considered mere barriers. On the other hand, the outer portion of tree bark consists mostly of *dead* cell walls, which clearly are serving a barrier function (**Figure 4.18b**).

Chloroplasts

Everyone knows that a major difference between plants and animals is that, while animals must get their food from outside themselves, plants make their own food through the process of photosynthesis. Where does photosynthesis take place in plants? Inside the organelles known as chloroplasts. It's hard to overstate the importance of these tiny, oblong structures, given that they are the food factories for most of the living world. Lions may eat zebras, but zebras eat grass, and grass is essentially produced inside chloroplasts. Thanks to their ability to harness the sun's power, these membrane-laden organelles can start with nothing more than water, a few minerals, and atmospheric carbon dioxide and end up turning out a sugar that builds an entire plant. A by-product of this operation—a kind of refuse of photosynthesis—is the oxygen that sustains most of Earth's organisms (**Figure 4.19** on the next page). **Chloroplasts** can be defined as organelles that are the sites of photosynthesis in algae cells, as well as plant cells. No other organisms possess these specialized organelles, although

certain bacteria are able to perform photosynthesis without them. In plants, chloroplasts are especially abundant in the cells of leaves. A cell that lies toward a leaf's interior might contain hundreds of these organelles, each of which is capable of performing photosynthesis on its own.

Also note that, as with mitochondria, chloroplasts are the descendants of resident aliens. They originally were a form of free-standing bacteria that were capable of performing photosynthesis. Ancient eukaryotic cells then ingested these bacteria and, over time, the two organisms came to live as one, with the bacteria eventually being transformed into mere organelles within the larger eukaryotic cells. Thus, the green world of trees and plants and algae—this massive edifice that sustains nearly all animals—ultimately was powered into being through the activity of some of the smallest living things we know of.

4.8 Cell-to-Cell Communication

Most of what you've seen so far has made the cell seem like an isolated entity, but this is not the case. Single-celled organisms can exist as separate entities, along with certain plant or animal cells (red blood

water
carbon dioxide
minerals

outer membrane

inner membrane

sugar (food)
oxygen

cells, for example), but most plant and animal cells are linked together in organized collections referred to as *tissues*. Not surprisingly, these assemblages of cells—whether plant or animal—have the ability to communicate with one another.

Communication among Plant Cells

Having noted the thickness of something like the cell walls in plants, you might wonder how one plant cell could interact with another. Communication between plant cells takes place quite readily, however, through a series of tiny channels in the plant cell wall called **plasmodesmata** (singular, plasmodesma). The structure of these channels is such that the cytoplasm of one plant cell is continuous with that of another—so much so that the cytoplasm of an entire plant can be properly looked at as one continuous whole (**Figure 4.20a**). The structure of plasmodesmata is more complex than that of a simple opening, but the basic idea is of a channel-like linkage between two plant cells.

Communication among Animal Cells

There are no plasmodesmata in animal cells, but there are three other kinds of *cell junctions,* or linkages, one of which serves to facilitate cell communication. It is called

a gap junction, and it consists of clusters of protein structures that shoot through the plasma membrane of a cell from one side to the other, forming a kind of tube. When these tubes line up in adjacent cells, the result is a channel for passage of small molecules and electrical signals (**Figure 4.20b**). Thus, we can define a **gap junction** as a protein assemblage that forms a communication channel between adjacent animal cells. Note that animal gap junctions and plant plasmodesmata are very different kinds of channels. Plasmodesmata can be thought of as permanent channels between plant cells, whereas gap junctions open only as necessary.

On to the Periphery

Having looked at what is inside the cell, you've arrived at the cell's periphery, the plasma membrane, which is where you'll be staying for a while. It may at first seem strange to devote a whole chapter to an outer boundary. How much attention would you pay, after all, to a factory's wall as opposed to its contents? The answer is: A lot, if that wall could facilitate communication with the outer world, continually renew itself, and let some things in while keeping others out. Such is the case with the plasma membrane, a slender lining that manages to make one of the most fundamental distinctions on Earth: Inside, life goes on; outside it does not. We'll look at its story in the chapter that's coming up.

Plant tissues

plasmodesmata

plasma membrane

cell walls

cytoplasm

(a) Plasmodesmata

In plants, a series of tiny pores between plant cells, the plasmodesmata, allow for the movement of materials among cells. Thanks to the plasmodesmata channels, the cytoplasm of one cell is continuous with the cytoplasm of the next; the plant as a whole can be thought of as having a single complement of continuous cytoplasm.

Animal tissues

gap junction

plasma membranes

cytoplasm

(b) Gap junctions

In animals, protein assemblies come into alignment with one another, forming communication channels between cells. A cluster of many such assemblies—perhaps several hundred—is called a gap junction.

Figure 4.20
Cell Communication

SO FAR...

1. Plant cells have two organelles and one structure that animal cells do not have. The organelles are _____, which are the sites of photosynthesis, and a large _____, which performs multiple functions, including the storage of nutrients and the maintenance of internal cell pressure. The structure is the _____, which provides protection and limits the plant cell's uptake of water.

2. Animal cells have only a single organelle that plant cells do not have. This is the _____, which breaks down and recycles materials in the cell.

3. In plants, the channels that facilitate cell-to-cell communication are called _____, while in animals, the tube-like protein structures that facilitate such communication are called _____.

THE PROCESS OF SCIENCE

First Sightings: Anton van Leeuwenhoek

To the list of explorers that includes Columbus and Balboa we could add the name Anton van Leeuwenhoek. This unassuming Dutchman was the great early voyager into another world, the micro-world.

It was not until the seventeenth century that human beings realized that things as small as cells existed. Leeuwenhoek began to report in the 1670s on what he saw with the aid of a device invented at the end of the 1500s—the microscope (**Figure 1**). One of Leeuwenhoek's contemporaries, Englishman Robert Hooke, coined the term *cell* after viewing a slice of cork under a simple microscope, but Hooke's purpose was to reveal the detailed structure of familiar, small objects, such as the flea. Leeuwenhoek, by contrast, revealed the *existence* of creatures unimagined until his time. Moreover, he carried out this work in the most extraordinary fashion: Laboring alone in the small town of Delft with palm-sized magnifiers he himself had created, looking at anything that struck his fancy. (And many things struck his fancy; he once looked at exploding gunpowder under a microscope, nearly blinding himself in the process.) For 50 years, while working as shopkeeper and minor city official, this un-trained amateur of boundless curiosity ex-amined the micro-world and reported on it in letters he posted to the Royal Society in London.

Who could believe what he uncovered? How was it possible that there was a buzzing, blooming universe of "animal-cules" (little animals) whose existence had been completely unsuspected? Prior to his work, no one thought that any creature smaller than a worm could exist within the human body. Yet, examining scrapings from his own mouth, Leeuwen-hoek tells us:

> I saw, with as great a wonderment as ever before, an inconceivably great number of little animalcules, and in so unbelievably small a quantity of the foresaid stuff, that those who didn't see it with their own eyes could scarce credit it.

The animalcules that Leeuwenhoek be-held over his career were single-celled or-ganisms that today are known as bacteria and protists. It would be two hundred years before Leeuwenhoek's findings were fully integrated into a modern theory of cells. Yet the man from Delft had shown that only a small portion of the world's living things are visible things.

(a) What Leeuwenhoek could see

(b) Leeuwenhoek with two of his microscopes

Figure 1

(a) What Leeuwenhoek Could See
Biologist Brian Ford used an actual 300-year-old Leeuwenhoek microscope to capture this image of spiny spores from a truffle. (Micrograph: × 600)

(b) Leeuwenhoek's Microscopes Were Handheld and Paddle-Shaped
Leeuwenhoek revealing the micro-world to Queen Catherine of England, wife of King Charles II (1630–1685).

Go to the Study Area at www.masteringbiology.com for practice quizzes, myeBook, BioFlix™ 3-D animations, MP3 Tutor Sessions, videos, current events, and more.

Mastering
BIOLOGY

Summary

4.1 Cells as Life's Fundamental Unit

- With the possible exception of viruses, every living thing is a cell or is composed of cells and all cells come into existence only through the activity of other cells. (p. 65)

4.2 Prokaryotic and Eukaryotic Cells

- All cells are either prokaryotic (bacteria or archaea) or eukaryotic (all other cells). Eukaryotic cells store most of their DNA in their cell nucleus while prokaryotic cells do not have a nucleus. Eukaryotic cells tend to be much larger than prokaryotic cells and they have more organelles. Many eukaryotes are multicelled organisms while all prokaryotes are single-celled. (p. 66)

4.3 The Eukaryotic Cell

- The five principal components of the eukaryotic cell are the nucleus, other organelles, the cytosol, the cytoskeleton, and the plasma membrane. Organelles are highly organized structures within the cell that carry out specialized functions. The cytosol is the jelly-like fluid outside the nucleus in which most organelles are immersed. The cytoplasm is the region of the cell inside the plasma membrane but outside the nucleus. The cytoskeleton is a network of protein filaments that have diverse functions. The plasma membrane is the outer lining of the cell. (p. 66)

4.4 A Tour of the Animal Cell's Protein Production Path

- Information for constructing proteins is contained in the DNA located in the cell nucleus. This information is copied onto a length of messenger RNA (mRNA) that departs the nucleus through its nuclear pores and goes to ribosomes. Many ribosomes that receive mRNA chains then migrate to and embed in a membrane network called the rough endoplasmic reticulum (RER). The polypeptide chains produced by the ribosomal "reading" of the mRNA sequences are dropped from ribosomes into the internal spaces of the RER, where they undergo folding and editing. (p. 71)

- Materials move from one structure to another in the cell via the endomembrane system, in which a piece of membrane, with proteins inside, can bud off from one organelle as a transport vesicle that moves through the cell and then fuses with another membrane-lined structure. (p. 74)

- Once protein processing is finished in the RER, proteins undergoing processing move to the Golgi complex where they are processed further and marked for shipment to appropriate cellular locations. (p. 75)

BioFlix™

Tour of an Animal Cell

4.5 Cell Structures Outside the Protein Production Path

- The smooth ER is a network of membranes that functions to synthesize lipids and to detoxify harmful substances. Lysosomes are organelles that break down worn-out cellular structures or foreign materials that come into the cell and return their components to the cytoplasm for re-use. Mitochondria are organelles that extract energy from food and transfer this energy to an energy-dispensing molecule, ATP. (p. 76)

4.6 The Cytoskeleton: Internal Scaffolding

- The cytoskeleton provides the cell with structure, facilitates the movement of materials inside the cell, and facilitates cell movement. (p. 78)

- From smallest to largest in diameter, the three principal types of cytoskeleton elements are microfilaments, intermediate filaments, and microtubules. Microfilaments help the cell move and capture prey by forming rapidly in the direction of movement. Intermediate filaments provide support and structure to the cell. Microtubules provide structure to cells and facilitate the movement of materials inside the cell by serving as transport "rails." (p. 78)

- Cilia and flagella are extensions of cells composed of microtubules. Cilia extend from cells in great numbers, serving to either move the cell or to move material around the cell. In contrast, one—or at most a few—flagella extend from cells that have them and serve to facilitate cell movement. (p. 79)

4.7 The Plant Cell

- Plant cells have two organelles not found in animal cells—chloroplasts and central vacuoles—and have one structure not found in animal cells, the cell wall. Conversely, plant cells lack one organelle found in animal cells, the lysosome. The cell wall gives the plant structural strength and helps regulate the intake of water; the central vacuole stores nutrients, degrades waste products, and helps maintain internal cell pressure; and chloroplasts are the sites of photosynthesis. (p. 83)

BioFlix

Tour of a Plant Cell

4.8 Cell-to-Cell Communication

- Plant cells have plasmodesmata: channels that are always open and that hence make the cytoplasm of one plant cell continuous with that of another. Adjacent animal cells have gap junctions that are composed of protein assemblages that open only as necessary, allowing the movement of small molecules and electrical signals between cells. (p. 85)

Key Terms

cell wall   84

central vacuole   83

chloroplast   85

cilia   79

cytoplasm   67

cytoskeleton   78

cytosol   67

endomembrane system   75

eukaryotic cell   66

flagella   81

gap junction   86

Golgi complex   75

intermediate filament   78

lysosome   76

microfilament   78

micrograph   68

micrometer   68

microtubule   78

mitochondria   77

nanometer   68

nuclear envelope   71

nucleolus   74

nucleus   66

organelle   66

plasma membrane   67

plasmodesmata   86

prokaryotic cell   66

ribosome   72

rough endoplasmic reticulum   73

smooth endoplasmic reticulum   76

transport vesicle   75

Understanding the Basics

Multiple-Choice Questions

(Answers are in the back of the book.)

1. Jerome has strep throat, a bacterial infection. The cause of the infection is:
   a. the growth of a virus.
   b. the presence of archaea.
   c. eukaryotic cells dividing in his throat.
   d. organelles that take control of his organs—in this case, his throat.
   e. prokaryotic cells.

2. Where would you expect to find a cytoskeleton?
   a. primarily inside the nucleus
   b. as the internal structure of a mitochondrion
   c. between bacterial cells
   d. throughout the cytosol
   e. as an outer coat on an insect

3. Suppose you found a cell that had many mitochondria, a nucleus, and a cell wall made of cellulose. You would assume that you had found:
   a. a plant cell.
   b. an animal cell.
   c. a bacterial cell.
   d. one of these three types, but you will not know which type without further investigation.
   e. either a plant cell or an animal cell, but not a bacterial cell.

4. Cells in the pancreas manufacture large amounts of protein. Which of these would you expect to find a large amount of, or number of, in pancreatic cells?
   a. lysosomes
   b. rough endoplasmic reticulum
   c. smooth endoplasmic reticulum
   d. chloroplasts
   e. plasma membrane

5. Suppose that a cell could be seen to lack microtubule filaments. Which of these would be the most likely effect of this condition?
   a. an inability to get energy out of food
   b. an inability to manufacture proteins
   c. an inability to break down worn-out organelles
   d. an inability of the skeletal muscles to contract
   e. an inability to move proteins from one part of the cell to another

6. Heart muscle cells have a number of gap junctions connecting them to their adjoining cells. From this you can conclude that heart muscle cells:
   a. exchange nuclei very frequently.
   b. have plasmodesmata.
   c. move vacuoles from cell to cell.
   d. communicate frequently.
   e. lack the ability to divide.

7. Which is the correct ranking of these "small" things, from smallest to largest? (Use typical sizes.)
   a. animal cells<atoms<bacteria< proteins<amino acids
   b. atoms<amino acids<proteins< bacteria<animal cells
   c. atoms<proteins<amino acids< animal cells<bacteria
   d. bacteria<atoms<amino acids< proteins<animal cells
   e. bacteria<animal cells<atoms <amino acids<proteins

8. Cells need large amounts of ribosomal RNA to make proteins. The ribosomal RNA is made in a specialized structure known as _____, which is found in _____.
   a. a chloroplast; the cytosol
   b. a ribosome; the cytosol
   c. the endoplasmic reticulum; the nucleus
   d. the nuclear envelope; the nucleus
   e. the nucleolus; the nucleus

Brief Review

(Answers are in the back of the book.)

1. Why are cells necessarily so small? Why couldn't a brain cell, for example, be large enough to be seen with the naked eye?

2. What are some of the differences between eukaryotic cells and prokaryotic cells?

3. Insulin, a hormone that reduces blood-sugar levels in the body, is a protein that is exported from special cells in the pancreas. Describe the set of steps that leads from a length of insulin-coding DNA in the nucleus to the release of insulin in the bloodstream.

4. What are cilia and flagella? What are some of the roles they play in the human body?

5. Consider what plants would be like if they had no plasmodesmata. Explain why this would be a problem.

6. What is a gap junction, and what is its function?

Applying Your Knowledge

1. The text notes that animals could not function as they do if their cells were encased in the thick cell walls that surround plant cells. What about the reverse case? Why would plants be unable to function if their cells lacked cell walls?

2. The earliest organisms we have evidence of were all single-celled. Why do you think life had to "start small" like this?

3. Why do membranes figure so prominently in eukaryotic cells? What essential function do they serve?

Life's Border:
The Plasma Membrane

The outer lining of cells is in a sense the outer border of life. In its roles as protector, gatekeeper, and message carrier, this lining is indispensable to life.

Every cell has, at its periphery, a plasma membrane that serves as the interface between the cell and the world outside it.

Things have steadily been getting better for the estimated 30,000 Americans who suffer from the disease cystic fibrosis (CF). At one time, 80 percent of the victims of this illness didn't make it to their first birthday. But with each passing year, small advances in the treatment of CF have led to small increases in life expectancy. Even so, today's average CF patient lives only to age 37. How does CF bring about this shortening of lives? Although its effects are many, its lethal effects usually have to do with the lungs. More specifically, CF causes a dangerous layer of mucus to accumulate in the passageways of the lungs. The lungs of healthy people are lined by a layer of mucus, too. But in their case, the layer is thin and wet—it's pliable enough, we might say, that it can be regularly swept away by the hair-like cilia that function like tiny brooms in the lung passageways. Cystic fibrosis patients, conversely, have a mucus layer that is thicker and drier and that becomes a site for repeated bacterial infections. In time, these infections can result in the destruction of the lung passageways.

So, what accounts for the difference between the lungs of a healthy person and those of a person suffering from CF? Because of a faulty gene, the substance chloride cannot be transported in sufficient quantity from the inside of a CF patient's lung cells to the outside of them (where the mucus builds up). Healthy individuals have a protein that acts as a channel for chloride—a kind of tunnel that spans the cell's outer membrane. In contrast, the cells of CF patients have either defective chloride channels or none at all. The result is a lack of chloride outside their cells, which gets the mucus buildup going.

As noted last chapter, life goes on only inside cells. The fact that the cell's outer, or "plasma," membrane is out on life's edge may prompt the thought that it's *merely* at the edge, as if the real action is taking place deep within the cell. But consider, as in CF, the effect of having a *defective* plasma membrane. The focus in this chapter is to learn more about this important cell lining.

5.1 The Nature of the Plasma Membrane

So, what is the nature of the plasma membrane? First, it's worth noting that it's very much like the membranes described in Chapter 4. Much of what follows about the plasma membrane could also be said of the various membranes that are internal to the cell—those that line lysosomes or that make up the Golgi complex, for example. There are some important differences between the plasma and other membranes, however, because the plasma membrane is constantly interacting with the world outside the cell, whereas internal membranes are not.

When we start to consider the qualities of the plasma membrane, we find that, even in the microworld of cells, it is an extremely *thin* entity. If you stacked 10,000 of them on top of one another, their combined depth would be about that of a sheet of paper. Next, the plasma membrane has a fluid and somewhat fatty makeup. If we looked for a counterpart to it in our everyday world, a soap bubble might come close, meaning this membrane is very flexible. Yet it is stable enough to stay together despite being constantly re-formed, thanks to the endless movement of materials in and out of it. If you imagine half the surface of your skin remaking itself every 30 minutes or so, you begin to get the picture about how dynamic this membrane is. Let's look now at the most important component parts of it. All these components are illustrated in **Figure 5.1** on the next page. They are:

- **The phospholipid bilayer.** Just as bread is made mostly from flour, the plasma membrane is made

Figure 5.1
The Plasma
Membrane

The cell's outer lining or plasma membrane is composed of four main structural elements, as shown in the figure.

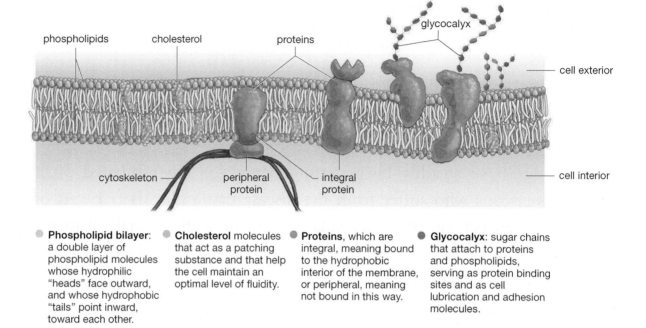

phospholipids   cholesterol   proteins   glycocalyx   cell exterior

cytoskeleton   peripheral protein   integral protein   cell interior

● **Phospholipid bilayer**: a double layer of phospholipid molecules whose hydrophilic "heads" face outward, and whose hydrophobic "tails" point inward, toward each other.

● **Cholesterol** molecules that act as a patching substance and that help the cell maintain an optimal level of fluidity.

● **Proteins**, which are integral, meaning bound to the hydrophobic interior of the membrane, or peripheral, meaning not bound in this way.

● **Glycocalyx**: sugar chains that attach to proteins and phospholipids, serving as protein binding sites and as cell lubrication and adhesion molecules.

mostly from two layers of phospholipid molecules, with "tails" that mingle together, but "heads" that point in opposite directions—to the interior of the cell in one direction and to the world outside the cell in the other.

- **Cholesterol.** Like mortar between bricks, cholesterol acts as a "patching" material for the membrane in animal cells; it also keeps the membrane at an optimal level of fluidity.

- **Proteins.** These molecules shoot through the membrane and lie on either side of it, serving as support structures, signaling antennas, identification markers, and cellular passageways.

- **Glycocalyx.** This is the collective term for a set of carbohydrate chains that form a layer on the outside of the membrane, functioning in cell lubrication, adhesion, and signaling.

Now let's look at each of these components in greater detail.

First Component: The Phospholipid Bilayer

You may recall the discussion in Chapter 3 of phospholipids—molecules that have two long fatty acid chains linked to a phosphate-bearing group (**Figure 5.2**). You may also recall that, because fatty acid chains are lipids, they are hydrophobic or "water fearing," meaning they will not bond with water. Conversely, phosphate groups are charged, hydro*philic* molecules, meaning they are "water loving" and will readily bond with water. When such phosphate and lipid components are put together, the resulting phospholipid is a molecule with a dual nature. Its phosphate "head" will seek water, but its fatty acid "tail" will avoid it. Drop a

group of phospholipids in water, and they will arrange themselves into the form you see in Figure 5.2: two *layers* of phospholipids sandwiched together, the tails of each layer pointing inward (thus avoiding water) and the heads pointing outward (thus bonding with the watery environment that lies both inside and outside the cell). With this in mind, the **phospholipid bilayer** can be defined as a chief component of the plasma membrane, composed of two layers of phospholipids, arranged with their fatty acid chains pointing toward each other.

This phospholipid structure has a couple of important consequences for the plasma membrane. First, it helps give the membrane its fluid nature—the bilayer's fatty acid tails have a chemical makeup that is more like that of oil than shortening. Second, because these are two hydrophobic layers of tails, the only substances that can pass through them with ease are other hydrophobic substances or a few very small molecules that aren't hydrophobic. This stems from a rule of thumb in chemistry: Like dissolves like. Fats dissolve in fats, charged molecules dissolve in charged molecules. Thus, various steroid hormones (which, remember, are lipids) gain fairly easy entry into the cell, as do fatty acids, because these substances will dissolve in the lipid bilayer. Conversely, hydrophilic substances—ions, amino acids, all kinds of polar molecules—will not dissolve in the membrane and thus cannot make it past the fatty acid chains without help. What kind of help? Stay tuned.

Second Component: Cholesterol

Molecules of the lipid material cholesterol nestle between phospholipid molecules throughout the plasma membrane in animal cells, performing two

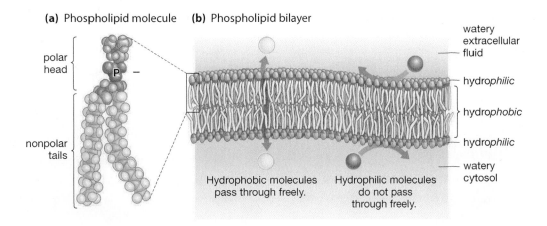

(a) Phospholipid molecule   **(b)** Phospholipid bilayer

polar head

nonpolar tails

P −

watery extracellular fluid

hydro*philic*

hydro*phobic*

hydro*philic*

watery cytosol

Hydrophobic molecules pass through freely.

Hydrophilic molecules do not pass through freely.

Figure 5.2
Dual-Natured Lining

(a) The essential building block of the cell's plasma membrane is the phospholipid molecule, which has two elements: a hydrophilic "head," containing a charged phosphate group that bonds with water; and hydrophobic "tails," composed of fatty acids that do not bond with water.

(b) Two layers of phospholipids sandwich together to form the plasma membrane.

functions. First, they act as a kind of patching substance on the bilayer, keeping some small molecules from getting through. Second, they help keep the membrane at an optimum level of fluidity. Without cholesterol, the plasma membrane would react to low temperatures the same way butter does: It would change from a flexible substance to a hardened one—a dysfunctional condition for a cell. The cholesterol molecules nestled between the phospholipid's fatty acid tails keep this from happening by keeping these chains from packing too closely together. When temperatures rise, however, the carbon rings of the cholesterol molecule interfere with the movement of the phospholipid's fatty acid tails, thus keeping the membrane from becoming too fluid.

Third Component: Proteins

Embedded within, or lying on, the phospholipid bilayer is a third major group of membrane components, *membrane proteins*, of which there are two principal types, integral and peripheral. **Integral proteins** are plasma membrane proteins that are bound to the membrane's hydrophobic interior. In some cases, these proteins span the entire membrane—popping out on either side of it—while in other cases, they extend only partway in. **Peripheral proteins** are plasma membrane proteins that lie on either side of the membrane but are not bound to its hydrophobic interior. They are usually attached to integral proteins at the surface of the membrane.

It is hard to overstate the importance of proteins to the plasma membrane. By itself, the lipid bilayer has a handful of capabilities. With the addition of proteins, it is turned into a structure with a huge array of capabilities. Here is a selected set of the roles that membrane proteins play.

Structural Support

Peripheral proteins that lie on the interior or "cytoplasmic" side of the membrane often are attached to elements of the cell's cytoskeleton. Thus anchored,

they help to stabilize various parts of the cell and play a part in giving animal cells their characteristic shape (**Figure 5.3** on the next page). (Why not plant cells? Because their shape is determined by the cell wall.)

Recognition

Much like military sentries, some cells need to know the answer to a critical question: Who goes there, friend or foe? These sentries are immune system cells, which circulate through the body in a never-ending search for cells that have been infected by viruses or other microbial invaders. The way immune cells can tell a friend (a normal cell) from a foe (an infected cell) is that almost all cells in the body constantly take part in a kind of molecular show-and-tell: They put on display, within proteins that extend from their plasma membranes, fragments of proteins they've recently been producing. Immune system cells have receptors that can *bind with* the resulting protein complexes. In most cases, the message that will be conveyed by this binding is, "Normal cell here; pass on by." But a cell that's been infected with a virus will be putting a set of *viral* protein fragments on display within one of its recognition proteins, thus conveying the message, "I've been infected; begin an immune system attack."

Communication

Cells communicate with one another in various ways. Signals can be sent from one cell to a neighboring cell, and communication over longer distances is possible through the chemical messengers known as hormones. These signals are likely to be channeled through a **receptor protein**—a plasma membrane protein that binds with a signaling molecule.

Receptor proteins—usually just called receptors—have binding sites on them with a shape that is so specific they generally will bind only to a single type of signaling molecule. To take one example of this, the hormone insulin is a signaling molecule. The message it conveys to cells is: "Glucose levels are rising in the bloodstream; construct some channels in your plasma membranes so that you can take some of this glucose

Figure 5.3
Roles of Membrane Proteins

Plasma membrane proteins serve four principal functions, as shown in the figure.

(a) Structural support   **(b)** Recognition   **(c)** Communication   **(d)** Transport

cell exterior

cell interior

Membrane proteins can provide structural support, often when attached to parts of the cell's scaffolding or "cytoskeleton."

Protein fragments held within recognition proteins can serve to identify the cell as "normal" or "infected" to immune system cells.

Receptor proteins, protruding out from the plasma membrane, can be the point of contact for signals sent to the cell via traveling molecules, such as hormones.

Proteins can serve as channels through which materials can pass in and out of the cell.

in." Now, how does insulin transmit this message? It binds with an insulin receptor protein whose binding site lies outside the cell, and this binding causes a chemical change on the portion of the protein that lies *inside* the cell. The result is a cascade of cellular reactions that puts in motion the construction of the channels. Note that, through this means, a signaling molecule need not come into the cell to have an effect; it merely needs to bind with a receptor protein that spans the plasma membrane.

Transport

You have seen that most materials cannot simply pass through the cell's plasma membrane. Yet, cells need many of these very materials. How do they get in? Different kinds of integral proteins take on a transport task—they act as channels through which materials pass both into cells and out of them. In some cases, these proteins form what might be called passive passageways—microtunnels that simply provide a hydrophilic opening through a hydrophobic environment. In other cases, however, these protein channels are actively involved in moving materials through the membrane. We'll review all the forms of protein-aided transport shortly. For now, just note the existence of **transport proteins:** proteins that facilitate the movement of molecules or ions from one side of the plasma membrane to the other.

Fourth Component: The Glycocalyx

If you look at Figure 5.1 and focus on the extracellular face of the plasma membrane, you can see, protruding from proteins and phospholipids alike,

a number of short, branched extensions. These are simple carbohydrate chains, meaning sugar chains. It turns out that these chains serve as the actual binding sites for many signaling molecules, including insulin. (Remember in Chapter 4 how many of the proteins that were constructed had sugar side chains added to them? Well, now you can see what some of these chains do.) Sugar chains also serve to lubricate cells and allow them to stick to other cells by acting as an adhesion layer. Collectively, all these chains form the **glycocalyx:** an outer layer of the plasma membrane composed of short carbohydrate chains that attach to membrane proteins and phospholipid molecules.

The Fluid-Mosaic Membrane Model

With this review of component parts under your belt, you're ready for a definition of the **plasma membrane.** It is a membrane, forming the outer boundary of many cells, composed of a phospholipid bilayer that is interspersed with proteins and cholesterol and coated on its exterior face with carbohydrate chains.

Taking a step back, the general message is that the plasma membrane is a loose, lipid structure peppered with proteins and coated with sugars. A better image, however, might be of a *sea* of lipids that is peppered with proteins, some of which are fixed in place but some of which have a great deal of freedom to move sideways or "laterally" across the membrane, something like icebergs on an ocean. When we overlay this quality of movement on the basic membrane structure just reviewed, the result is the contemporary view of the plasma membrane, the **fluid-mosaic model:** a conceptualization of the plasma membrane as a fluid, phospholipid bilayer that has within it a mosaic of both stationary and mobile proteins.

SO FAR . . .

1. The plasma membrane of an animal cell has four principal components. These are the _____, which is composed of two layers of molecules with fatty acid tails that point toward each other; the lipid molecule _____, which serves as a patching and fluidity control substance; many _____, which serve in such diverse roles as passageways and communication molecules; and the _____, which is a collective term for a set of carbohydrate chains attached to the outside of the membrane.

2. The phospholipid molecules of the plasma membrane are dual natured. The "heads" of these molecules are _____, meaning they will readily bond with _____. Meanwhile, the tails point inward, toward each other, because they are _____, meaning they will not bond with _____.

3. Plasma membrane proteins serve in the role of _____ by binding with signaling molecules that come from outside the cell and in the role of _____ by acting as channels for substances moving into and out of the cell.

5.2 Diffusion, Gradients, and Osmosis

It may be obvious that one of the main roles of the plasma membrane is to let in substances that are needed within the cell while keeping out substances that aren't needed or that actually are harmful. Having learned something about the membrane's makeup, you will now see how it carries out this task of passage and blockage.

It is necessary to begin this story, however, not with the cell but with the more general notion of how substances go from places where they are more concentrated to places where they are less concentrated. Anyone who has put some food dye in water has a sense of how this works: A few drops of, say, red dye will tumble into the liquid and start dispersing; eventually, the result is a solution that is uniformly more reddish than plain water (**Figure 5.4**). The question we'll look at is why this takes place.

Random Movement and Even Distribution

All molecules are constantly in motion, and this motion is random. Because liquid molecules are bonded together so weakly, they can *act* on this motion—they can slide past each other and thus go from one location to another. (Meanwhile, the molecules that make up solids are so tightly bonded together that their motion amounts simply to vibrating in place.) Because liquid molecules move randomly, they will naturally move from any initial *ordered* state—in our example,

(a) Dye is dropped in. **(b)** Diffusion begins. **(c)** Dye is evenly distributed.

water molecules

dye molecules

Figure 5.4
From Concentrated to Dispersed

Diffusion is the movement of molecules or ions from areas of their greater concentration to areas of their lesser concentration. In this sequence of photos and diagrams, a few drops of red dye, added to a beaker of water, are at first heavily concentrated in one area but then begin to diffuse, eventually becoming evenly distributed throughout the solution.

their concentrated state when first dropped in the container—to their most disordered state, meaning evenly distributed throughout a given volume.

What is at work here is **diffusion**: the movement of molecules or ions from a region of their higher concentration to a region of their lower concentration. This notion carries with it the concept of a gradient. A **concentration gradient** is defined as the difference between the highest and lowest concentration of a solute within a given medium. In our example, the solute is the dye, and the medium is water. As with bicycles coasting down a grade, the natural tendency for any solute is to move down its concentration gradient, from higher concentration to lower. Our dye did just that. Bikes and solutes can move *up* a grade or gradient, but there is a price to be paid, and that price is the expenditure of energy. (On its own, would red dye ever come back to its concentrated state in the container? No. Some work would have to be performed for this to happen, which means that some energy would have to be expended.)

Diffusion through Membranes

So far, you have looked at molecules diffusing in an undivided container. But the subject here is divisions—those provided by the plasma membrane. Let us consider, therefore, what happens to a solution in a container that is divided by a membrane. If that membrane is *permeable* to both water and the solute—that is, if both water and the solute can freely pass through it—and the solute lies only on one side of the membrane, then the predictable happens: The solute moves down its concentration gradient, diffusing right through the membrane, eventually becoming evenly distributed on both sides of it.

Now let's imagine a *semi*permeable membrane, one that water can freely move through but that solutes cannot. **Figure 5.5** shows you what happens if more solute—in this case, salt—is put on the right side of the membrane than the left. Water flows through the membrane both ways, but *more* water flows into the right chamber, which has a greater concentration of solutes in it. The result is that the solution on the right side rises to a higher level than the one on the left.

This seems strange on first viewing, as if gravity were taking a vacation on the right side of the container. But what has been demonstrated here is **osmosis**: the net movement of water across a semipermeable membrane from an area of lower solute concentration to an area of higher solute concentration. Why should this occur? In the case of a solute like salt, water molecules will surround and bond with the sodium and chloride ions that salt separates into in solution. Because these solutes are not free to pass through the membrane, the water molecules bound to them will likewise remain confined to the right side. This means that more "free" water will exist on the left side—water that is free to act on the natural tendency of liquid molecules to remain in motion. The result is a net movement of water into the right side (see Figure 5.5b). Looked at one way, this is just another example of diffusion—of a substance moving from an area of its higher concentration to an area of its lower concentration. Once the solute binds with the water molecules on the right side of the container, there is a greater concentration of free water molecules on the left than on the right. By moving to the right, the molecules are simply moving down their concentration gradient.

The Plasma Membrane as a Semipermeable Membrane

So, what does movement of water have to do with the cell's outer lining? The cell's phospholipid bilayer is itself a semipermeable membrane. It is somewhat permeable to water and lipid substances but not permeable to larger substances that carry a positive or negative charge. Thus, osmosis can take place across

(a) An aqueous solution divided by a semipermeable membrane has a solute —in this case, salt— poured into its right chamber.

(b) As a result, though water continues to flow in both directions through the membrane, there is a net movement of water toward the side with the greater concentration of solutes in it.

(c) Why does this occur? Water molecules that are bonded to the sodium (Na⁺) and chloride (Cl⁻) ions that make up salt are not free to pass through the membrane to the left chamber of the container.

salt
solute
solvent
semipermeable membrane
osmosis
pure water
water bound to salt ions

Figure 5.5
Osmosis in Action

the plasma membrane—indeed, it does all the time. It is the primary means by which plants *get* water, and it is a player in all sorts of routine metabolic processes in animals. In humans, for example, much of the fluid portion of blood is at one point driven out of the blood vessels called capillaries by the force of blood pressure. How does this fluid get back in? Osmosis. Proteins that remain in the capillaries after the fluid has moved out function like the salt in the container: They bring about an osmosis that pulls the fluid back into the blood vessels.

Or think about a more extreme example. Why are we always told that someone who is stranded at sea should never drink salt water? Because doing so would provide an enormous concentration of sodium chloride ions in the watery fluid that lies *outside* the cells. This is no different in principle than dumping more solutes into the right side of the container in Figure 5.5. The result would be water flowing out of cells, dehydration of the cells, and in extreme cases, death. (What actually kills people in this situation is a shrinkage of brain cells due to the dehydration.)

This is an example of an *osmotic imbalance,* which is a situation in which osmotic pressure is either drying out cells or flooding them. In the case of flooding,

plant cells have a great advantage over animal cells— their cell walls. Remember from Chapter 4 that one function of the cell wall is to regulate water uptake? Well, now we can see why this is so valuable. Animal cells, which do not have a cell wall, can expand until they burst when water comes in. Plant cells, conversely, will expand only until their membranes push up against the cell wall with some force, setting up a pressure level that keeps more water from coming in. Such tight quarters actually are an optimal condition for plants. A nice, crisp celery stick is one that has achieved this kind of *turgid* state, while a droopy celery stick that has lost this quality has cells that are *flaccid;* flowers or leaves in the latter condition are *wilted* (**Figure 5.6**).

Osmosis and Cell Environments

Is a given cell likely to lose water to its surroundings, gain water from them, or have a balanced flow back and forth with them? Any of these things is possible, depending on what the solute concentration is outside the cell as opposed to inside. Three terms are helpful in describing the various conditions that can exist. A fluid that has a higher concentration of solutes than another is said to be a **hypertonic**

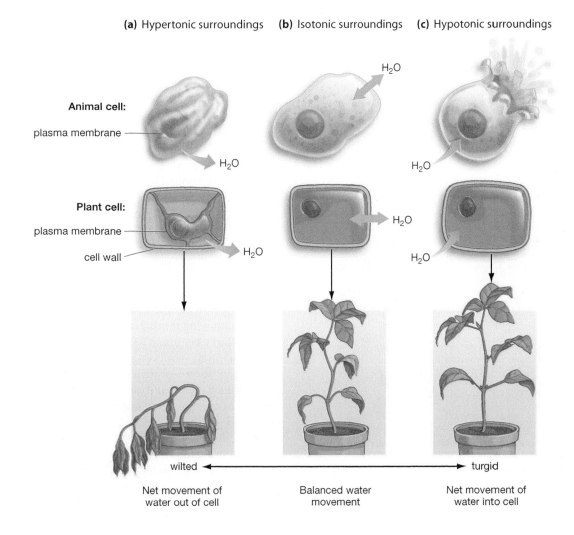

(a) Hypertonic surroundings   **(b)** Isotonic surroundings   **(c)** Hypotonic surroundings

Animal cell:

plasma membrane

H_2O

H_2O

H_2O

H_2O

Plant cell:

plasma membrane

cell wall

H_2O

H_2O

H_2O

wilted ◄──────────────────► turgid

Net movement of water out of cell

Balanced water movement

Net movement of water into cell

Figure 5.6
Osmosis in Cells

(a) When solutes (such as salt) exist in greater concentration outside the cell than inside, water moves out of the cell by osmosis, and the cell shrinks.

(b) When solute concentrations inside and outside the cell are balanced, water movement into and out of the cell is balanced as well.

(c) When solutes exist in greater concentration inside the cell than outside, water moves into the cell by osmosis.

solution. If a cell's surroundings are hypertonic to the cell's cytoplasm, water will flow out of the cell. Two solutions that have equal concentrations of solutes are said to be **isotonic.** If one of these solutions is the cell's cytoplasm and the other is the fluid surrounding the cell, water flow will be balanced between cell and surroundings. Finally, a fluid that has a lower concentration of solutes than another is a **hypotonic solution.** If a cell's surroundings are hypotonic to the cell's cytoplasm, water will flow into the cell. Figure 5.6 gives examples of what can happen to cells in all three types of environments.

SO FAR ...

1. Diffusion, the movement of molecules or ions from a region of their _____ to a region of their _____ takes place spontaneously in liquids, meaning it takes place without the input of any _____.

2. Osmosis is the net movement of water across a _____ membrane, from an area of lower _____ to an area of higher _____.

3. If a cell is surrounded by a fluid that is hypertonic to the cell's cytoplasm, water will flow _____ the cell. If a cell is surrounded by a fluid that is hypotonic to the cell's cytoplasm, water will flow _____ the cell.

Figure 5.7
Transport through the Plasma Membrane

5.3 Moving Smaller Substances In and Out

This excursion into the land of diffusion and osmosis has prepared us to start looking at the ways materials actually move into and out of the cell, across the plasma membrane. The big picture here is that some molecules are able to cross with no more assistance than is provided by diffusion. Other molecules require diffusion and the protein channels we talked about, and still others require channels and the expenditure of energy to get across. Different terms are applied to these different kinds of transport. **Active transport** is any movement of molecules or ions across a cell membrane that requires the expenditure of energy. **Passive transport** is any movement of molecules or ions across a cell membrane that does not require the expenditure of energy (**Figure 5.7**). Our review of transport begins with two varieties of passive transport.

Passive Transport

Simple Diffusion

Gases such as oxygen and carbon dioxide are such small molecules that they need only move down their concentration gradients to pass into or out of the cell. Having been delivered by blood capillaries to an area just outside the cell, oxygen exists there in greater concentration than it does inside the cell. Moving down its concentration gradient, it diffuses through the plasma membrane and emerges on the other side. This is an example of **simple diffusion,** which is diffusion through a cell membrane that does not require a special protein channel. Molecules that are larger than oxygen but that are fat soluble, such as the steroid hormones mentioned before, also move into the cell in this manner because of their ability to dissolve in the bilayer of the membrane. Carbon dioxide, which is formed *in* the cell as a result of the transfer of energy from food, has a net movement *out* of the cell through simple diffusion.

Facilitated Diffusion: Help from Proteins

Water can traverse the lipid bilayer through simple diffusion, moving through *despite* its hydrophilic nature primarily because it's such a small molecule. Yet, with water itself—and certainly with polar molecules larger than water—protein channels begin to be required for passage in and out of the cell. With this, the method of passage is no longer *simple* diffusion; it is **facilitated diffusion,** which is passage of materials through the plasma membrane that is aided by a transport protein.

With this, we get to the protein specificity referred to earlier. Each transport protein acts as a conduit for only one substance or at most a small family of related

Passive transport

simple diffusion

Materials move down their concentration gradient through the phospholipid bilayer.

facilitated diffusion

The passage of materials is aided both by a concentration gradient and by a transport protein.

Active transport

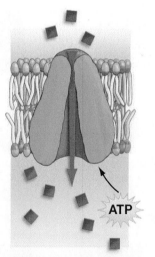

ATP

Molecules again move through a transport protein, but now energy must be expended to move them against their concentration gradient.

substances. Transport through these proteins begins with the kind of binding explained earlier. A circulating molecule of glucose, for example, latches onto the binding site of a glucose transport protein, as you can see in **Figure 5.8**. This binding causes the protein to change its shape, thus allowing the glucose molecule to pass through the membrane. In addition to glucose, other hydrophilic molecules, such as amino acids, move through the plasma membrane in this way. Note that this facilitated diffusion does not require the expenditure of energy because it has a concentration gradient working in its favor. Glucose exists in greater concentration outside most cells than inside them. It is moving down its concentration gradient, then, by passing into the cell through a protein channel. So facilitated diffusion has something in common with simple diffusion. *Both* processes are driven by concentration gradients, meaning that neither requires metabolic energy. Thus, both are specific examples of passive transport.

Although the glucose in our example moved only one way in facilitated diffusion (into the cell), in general transport proteins are a channel for movement either way through the membrane. All that is required is a concentration gradient and binding of the material with the transport protein.

Active Transport

If passive transport—either in simple or facilitated diffusion—were the only means of membrane passage available, cells would be totally dependent on concentration gradients. If, for example, molecules of a given amino acid come to exist in the same concentration on both sides of the plasma membrane, these amino acid travelers will continue to be transported, but they will be flowing out of the cell at the same rate they are flowing in. For cells, the problem is that some solutes are *needed* in greater concentration, say, outside the cell. So, how do cells deal with a situation like this? They use pumps: They expend energy and pump the needed materials out of themselves. This is active transport at work. The energy for this transport usually is supplied by a molecule we've had occasion to note before, ATP (adenosine triphosphate). One of the most important and best-studied of the ATP-driven transport mechanisms is called the sodium-potassium pump.

The Sodium-Potassium Pump

The sodium-potassium pump allows the cell to maintain high concentrations of potassium ions (K^+) inside the cell and sodium ions (Na^+) outside the cell. Imagine for a moment being able to take a snapshot of a cell at a moment in time that would allow us to see these two ion concentrations. With lots of Na^+ ions outside the cell, the result is predictable: These ions leak slowly into the cell through transport proteins as they follow not only their concentration gradient but an electrochemical gradient—these positively charged Na^+ ions are attracted to a net *negative* charge that tends to exist inside cells. But our fantasy snapshot of this scene would also reveal something else: An abundance of protruding proteins that are

BioFlix

Membrane Transport

1. The transport protein has a binding site for glucose that is open to the outside of the cell.
2. Glucose binds to the binding site.
3. This binding causes the protein to change shape, exposing glucose to the inside of the cell.
4. Glucose passes into the cell and the protein returns to its original shape.

Figure 5.8
Facilitated Diffusion
Owing to its size and hydrophilic nature, a molecule such as glucose cannot move into a cell through simple diffusion, even when it has a concentration gradient working in its favor. Its movement must be facilitated by a transport protein, such as the one pictured in the figure. This movement of glucose is passive transport, however, in that no expenditure of cellular energy is required to bring it about.

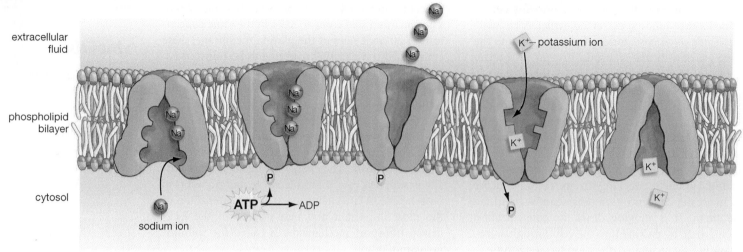

1. Three sodium ions (Na⁺) located within the cell's cytoplasm bind with a transport protein.

2. The energy molecule ATP gives up an energetic phosphate group to the transport protein.

3. This binding causes the protein to open its channel to the extracellular fluid; to lose its Na⁺ binding sites, thus releasing the ions into the fluid; and to create binding sites for potassium ions (K⁺).

4. Two K⁺ move into the protein's K⁺ binding sites, which brings about the release of the phosphate group.

5. This loss returns the protein to its original shape, releasing the K⁺ into the cytoplasm and readying the protein for binding with another set of Na⁺.

**Figure 5.9
The Sodium-
Potassium Pump**

busy pumping these Na⁺ ions the *other way,* acting like so many bilge pumps moving seawater that has leaked into a ship back out into the ocean. The result is maintenance of a high concentration of Na⁺ ions outside the cell (and K⁺ ions inside). If you look at **Figure 5.9**, you can see how this works.

As may be obvious, this is an energy-intensive operation. As such, you may wonder: Why would a cell spend so much energy to maintain this imbalance in sodium and potassium ions? Well, nerve cells undertake this task for the same reason you undertake the task of charging your cell phone batteries: to have ready access to a capability. In your case, the capability is talking on the phone. In the nerve cell's case, the capability is being able to rapidly take in a large number of Na⁺ ions as a means of transmitting a nerve signal—something you can read more about in Chapter 27.

5.4 Moving Larger Substances In and Out

Pumps and channels, diffusion and osmosis—these mechanisms move substances in and out of the cell, but as it turns out they only move relatively *small* substances. Remember an earlier discussion about the immune system cells that check to see if a given cell is friend or foe? Well, if an immune sentry finds a bacterial foe, it may have to ingest this *whole cell.* As you might guess, a cell cannot do this by employing little channels or pumps. You learned a bit in Chapter 4 about what does happen in these cases; now, you'll be looking at it in somewhat greater detail.

The methods in question here are *endocytosis,* which brings materials into the cell, and *exocytosis,* which sends them out. What these mechanisms have in common is their use of vesicles—the membrane-lined enclosures you learned about last chapter that alternately bud off from membranes or fuse with them.

Movement Out: Exocytosis

Exocytosis is defined as the movement of materials out of the cell through a fusion of a transport vesicle with the plasma membrane. As **Figure 5.10** shows, exocytosis involves a transport vesicle making its way to the plasma membrane and fusing with it, whereupon the vesicle's contents are released into the extracellular fluid. You observed in Chapter 4 that cells use exocytosis when they are exporting proteins. For single-celled creatures, waste products may also be released into the extracellular fluid through this process.

Movement In: Endocytosis

Endocytosis is the movement of relatively large materials into the cell by an infolding of the plasma membrane. It can take two major forms: pinocytosis, which brings in molecules that are larger than those we've looked at so far, and phagocytosis, which brings in much larger molecules yet, as you'll see.

Pinocytosis

There actually are several varieties of pinocytosis, but we'll only look at one representative form here, called clathrin-mediated endocytosis or CME. This means of bringing materials into cells was once known as

(a) Exocytosis

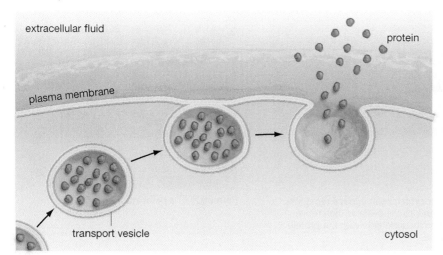

extracellular fluid

protein

plasma membrane

transport vesicle

cytosol

(b) Micrograph of exocytosis

Figure 5.10
Movement Out of the Cell

(a) In exocytosis, a transport vesicle—perhaps loaded with proteins or waste products—moves to the plasma membrane and fuses with it. This section of the membrane then opens, and the contents of the former vesicle are released to the extracellular fluid.

(b) Micrograph of material expelled from the cell through exocytosis.

receptor-mediated endocytosis, but it turns out that almost all forms of endocytosis employ receptors. The receptors active in CME first bind with molecules of the material that's brought into the cell. Then, while the receptors are holding onto their molecular cargo, they move laterally across the membrane and congregate in a depression referred to as a coated pit. What the pit is coated *with,* on its underside, is the chemically active protein clathrin (hence the term clathrin-mediated endocytosis). Eventually, the pit deepens (or "invaginates") and pinches off, creating the familiar vesicle moving into the cell. CME is very important in getting nutrients and other substances into cells. It is the way cholesterol gets into our cells, for example. Alas, it is also the way certain invaders get into our cells: Polio and flu viruses are among the molecules that can bind to human CME receptors, thus giving them access to our cells. Taking a step back, in CME, we can see an example of **pinocytosis:** the movement of relatively large materials into a cell by means of the creation of transport vesicles that are produced through an invagination of the plasma membrane (**Figure 5.11** on the next page).

Phagocytosis

Phagocytosis literally means "cell eating," and the term can be apt since this is the means by which many one-celled creatures take in food. It's also the means, mentioned earlier, by which human immune system cells ingest whole bacteria. Given functions like these, it will come as no surprise to learn that phagocytosis is bringing *large* materials into the cell. Indeed, the vesicles used in it might be 10 times the size of the vesicles used in pinocytosis.

Phagocytosis begins when the cell sends out extensions of its plasma membrane called *pseudopodia* ("false feet"). These surround the food and fuse their ends together. What was once outside is now inside, encased in a vesicle and moving toward the cell's interior. Once this happens, lysosomes in the cell move to the vesicle, fuse with it, and begin breaking down the material in it. **Phagocytosis** can be defined as the movement of large materials into a cell by means of wrapping extensions of the plasma membrane around the materials and fusing the extensions together. While phagocytosis is seen fairly often in one-celled organisms, there are only three types of cells in the human body that are capable of carrying it out, all of them immune system cells. While these cells sometimes serve in the role of warrior by ingesting whole invaders, they also have a less-exalted function, which is that of janitor. They clean up debris within the body—fragments of the body's own cells or larger molecules—by ingesting these materials, after which they are broken down into their component parts.

On to Energy

Your tour of the cell and its plasma membrane is now complete. What's coming up next is something called bioenergetics. In our story of biology so far, there have been continuing vague references to proteins that are called enzymes, to a molecule called ATP, and to energy expenditures. This has been rather like a description of an elephant that avoids the subject of its trunk. We will now dive into the subject of bioenergetics, however, which describes forces that are so basic that the entire living world is shaped by them.

(a) Pinocytosis

receptors

captured molecules

coated pit

vesicle

In this form of pinocytosis, called clathrin-mediated endocytosis, cell-surface receptors bind to individual molecules of the substance to be taken into the cell and then move laterally across the plasma membrane to a pit, coated on its underside with the protein clathrin, that will become a vesicle that moves into the cell.

Formation of a pinocytosis vesicle.

(b) Phagocytosis

bacterium (or food particles)

pseudopodium

vesicle

In phagocytosis, food particles—or perhaps whole organisms—are taken in by means of "false feet" or pseudopodia that surround the material. Pseudopodia then fuse together, forming a vesicle that moves into the cell's interior with its catch enclosed.

A human immune system cell called a macrophage (colored blue) uses phagocytosis to ingest an invading yeast cell.

Figure 5.11
Two Ways to Get Relatively Large Materials into the Cell

SO FAR ...

1. Smaller materials move into and out of the cell through one means that requires the expenditure of energy, _____, and one means that does not require the expenditure of energy, _____. In turn, there are two varieties of the latter means of transport: simple diffusion, meaning diffusion through a cell membrane that does not require a special _____; and facilitated diffusion, meaning diffusion that does require a _____.

2. Active transport allows for the net movement of molecules into or out of a cell even when there is a _____ working against this movement.

3. Exocytosis is the movement of materials out of the cell through the fusion of a _____ with the _____. The movement of relatively large materials into the cell takes two forms: _____, in which entire cells or other large materials may be ingested through use of plasma membrane extensions called pseudopodia; and _____, in which somewhat smaller materials are brought in through an infolding or "invagination" of the membrane to create a vesicle that then moves inside the cell.

Go to the Study Area at www.masteringbiology.com for practice quizzes, myeBook, BioFlix™ 3-D animations, MP3 Tutor Sessions, videos, current events, and more.

Summary

5.1 The Nature of the Plasma Membrane

- The plasma membrane is a thin, fluid entity that manages to be very flexible and yet is stable enough to stay together despite constant movement of materials in and out of it. The four principal components of the plasma membrane in animal cells are a phospholipid bilayer, molecules of cholesterol interspersed within the bilayer, proteins that are embedded in or that lie on the bilayer, and short carbohydrate chains on the cell surface, collectively called the glycocalyx, that function in cell adhesion and as binding sites. (p. 93)

- Phospholipids are composed of two fatty acid chains linked to a charged phosphate group. The fatty acid chains are hydrophobic; the phosphate group is hydrophilic. Phospholipids arrange themselves into bilayers, with the fatty acid "tails" of each layer pointing inward and the phosphate "heads" pointing outward. (p. 94)

- The cholesterol molecules that, in animal cells, are interspersed between phospholipid molecules in the plasma membrane act as patching that helps keep some small molecules from moving through the membrane and keeps the membrane at an optimal level of fluidity. (p. 94)

- Membrane proteins function in structural support; in cell identification, by serving as external recognition proteins that interact with immune system cells; in communication, by serving as external receptors for signaling molecules; and in transport, by providing channels for the movement of compounds into and out of the cell. (p. 95)

- The fluid-mosaic model views the plasma membrane as a fluid, phospholipid bilayer that has a mosaic of proteins either fixed within it or capable of moving laterally across it. (p. 96)

5.2 Diffusion, Gradients, and Osmosis

- Diffusion is the movement of molecules or ions from a region of their higher concentration to a region of their lower concentration. A concentration gradient defines the difference between the highest and lowest concentrations of a solute within a given medium. Through diffusion, compounds naturally move from higher to lower concentrations, meaning down their concentration gradients. Energy must be expended, however, to move compounds against their concentration gradients. (p. 97)

- A semipermeable membrane allows some compounds to pass through freely while blocking passage of others. Osmosis is the net movement of water across a semipermeable membrane from an area of lower solute concentration to an area of higher solute concentration. (p. 98)

- Osmosis is responsible for much of the movement of fluids into and out of cells. Osmotic imbalances can cause cells either to dry out from losing too much water or, in the case of animal cells, to break from taking too much water in. Plant cells generally do not have the latter problem because their cell walls limit their uptake of water. (p. 98)

- Cells will gain or lose water relative to their surroundings in accordance with what the solute concentration is inside the cell as opposed to outside it. A cell will lose water to a surrounding solution that is hypertonic to the cytoplasmic fluid; a cell will gain water when the surrounding solution is hypotonic. Water flow will be balanced between the cell and its surroundings when the surrounding fluid and the cytoplasmic fluid are isotonic to each other. (p. 99)

5.3 Moving Smaller Substances In and Out

- Some compounds are able to cross the plasma membrane strictly through diffusion; others require diffusion and special protein channels; still others require protein channels and the expenditure of cellular energy. Active transport is any movement of molecules or ions across a cell membrane that requires the expenditure of energy. Passive transport is any movement of molecules or ions across a cell membrane that does not require the expenditure of energy. (p. 100)

- Simple diffusion and facilitated diffusion are two forms of passive transport. For either form to bring about a net movement of materials into or out of a cell, a concentration gradient must exist. Facilitated diffusion requires both a concentration gradient and a protein channel. (p. 100)

- To maintain differing concentrations of substances on opposite sides of the plasma membrane, cells employ chemical pumps, through which they expend energy to move compounds across the plasma membrane against their concentration and electrochemical gradients. This is active transport. (p. 101)

BioFlix™

Membrane Transport

5.4 Moving Larger Substances In and Out

- Larger materials are brought into the cell through endocytosis and moved out through exocytosis. Both mechanisms employ vesicles. In exocytosis, a transport vesicle moves from the interior of the cell to the plasma membrane and fuses with it, at which point the contents of the vesicle are released to the environment outside the cell. (p. 102)

- There are two principal forms of endocytosis: pinocytosis, the movement of moderate-sized molecules into a cell by means of the creation of transport vesicles produced through an infolding of a portion of the plasma membrane; and phagocytosis, in which certain cells use pseudopodia to first surround and then engulf whole cells, fragments of them, or other large organic materials. As in pinocytosis, such materials are brought into the cell inside vesicles that bud off from the plasma membrane. (p. 102)

Key Terms

active transport   100

concentration gradient   98

diffusion   98

endocytosis   102

exocytosis   102

facilitated diffusion   100

fluid-mosaic model   96

glycocalyx   96

hypertonic solution   99

hypotonic solution   100

integral protein   95

isotonic solution   100

osmosis   98

passive transport   100

peripheral protein   95

phagocytosis   103

phospholipid bilayer   94

pinocytosis   103

plasma membrane   96

receptor protein   95

simple diffusion   100

transport protein   96

Understanding the Basics

Multiple-Choice Questions

(Answers are in the back of the book.)

1. Which of the following groupings describes the four principal components of the plasma membrane?
   a. Phospholipid bilayer, proteins, DNA, ribosomes
   b. Phospholipid bilayer, ribosomes, glycocalyx, proteins
   c. Phospholipid bilayer, proteins, cholesterol, glycocalyx
   d. Phospholipid bilayer, lipoproteins, glycocalyx, cholesterol
   e. Phospholipid bilayer, DNA, proteins, cholesterol

2. Because of the fatty acid chains that help make up the phospholipid bilayer, the only substances that can pass through the plasma membrane purely by means of diffusion are:
   a. small proteins.
   b. amino acids and lipids.
   c. small carbohydrates.
   d. lipids or very small polar molecules.
   e. lipids or polar molecules of any size.

3. True or false: You eat spaghetti for dinner and digest the starch in it to glucose. The glucose is now in high concentration in the cells of your small intestine, relative to its concentration in your bloodstream. Predictably, with the help of a transport protein, the glucose diffuses across the plasma membrane of your intestinal cells, into your bloodstream.
   a. True.
   b. False, because molecules cannot move across membranes by diffusion.
   c. False, because diffusion moves materials from low concentration to high concentration.
   d. False, because molecules are too large to move across membranes.
   e. False, because energy is required for diffusion.

4. In osmosis, water moves across a semi-permeable membrane:
   a. wherever energy pulls it.
   b. toward an area of lower solute concentration.
   c. toward an area of higher solute concentration.
   d. independently of solutes.
   e. any of the above could be true in different situations.

5. Tyrone gave Lakeisha a rose for the anniversary of their first date. Now the rose has wilted, because:
   a. the cells have taken too much water in and burst.
   b. the cell walls have broken down.
   c. the plasma membrane has lost the proteins that keep water in.
   d. the phospholipid bilayer has broken down.
   e. the plant's cells have insufficient water in them to push against their cell walls.

6. You get a cut on your finger and some bacteria enter. Your immune system cells kill off the invaders by ingesting them. This is an example of:
   a. pinocytosis.
   b. phagocytosis.
   c. receptor-mediated endocytosis.
   d. exocytosis.
   e. active transport.

7. According to the fluid-mosaic model of membrane structure, the membrane is made up of a:
   a. continuous base of proteins with phospholipids in it that have fairly free lateral movement.
   b. bilayer of phospholipids with proteins interspersed in it that have fairly free lateral movement.
   c. bilayer of protein with layers of phospholipids on the outside and inside.
   d. bilayer of phospholipid with layers of proteins on the outside and inside.
   e. bilayer of phospholipids sandwiched between two bilayers of proteins.

8. Endocytosis and exocytosis are similar in that both involve the use of:
   a. vesicles that carry materials into and out of the cell.
   b. the Golgi apparatus to package materials.
   c. diffusion to carry food and wastes across the plasma membrane.
   d. starch to supply large amounts of energy.
   e. the rough ER to manufacture proteins.

Brief Review

(Answers are in the back of the book.)

1. Imagine a receptor on the surface of one of your muscle cells that responds only to glucose. Plenty of insulin molecules are passing by this receptor, but it does not respond to them. Why not?

2. You often hear how dangerous it is for athletes to take steroids to "bulk up" and how many problems steroids cause in various parts of the body. Why do these drugs affect all parts of the body—not just the muscles?

3. Explain why the phospholipid "heads" of the plasma membrane are always pointed toward the cytosol and extracellular fluid, whereas the "tails" are always oriented toward the middle of the membrane.

4. Describe the form of endocytosis, called clathrin-mediated endocytosis, that is reviewed in the text.

5. As you saw in this chapter, all cellular membranes are similar in structure.

However, what differences are likely to exist between plasma membranes and the membranes that exist in the interior of the cell?

Applying Your Knowledge

1. All life-forms on Earth arguably exist either as single cells or as collections of cells. All such cells have a plasma membrane at their periphery (although many cells have cell walls outside their plasma membrane). Why do you think the plasma membrane exists in all living things? Why aren't there living things that don't have a membrane at their periphery?

2. Because materials move from high concentration to low concentration via simple diffusion, and because they move the same way via facilitated diffusion, why do cells make proteins to carry out facilitated diffusion? Isn't this just a waste of energy?

3. Place a number of marbles on one end of a cafeteria tray. Shake the tray gently a few times, keeping it level. What happens to the marbles? Start over and shake faster the next time. What happens now? Explain how this is like chemical diffusion.

6

Life's Mainspring:
An Introduction to Energy

Energy flows through life in a never-ending pattern of acquisition, storage, and use.

All living things must have a constant supply of energy. Here, a golden stonefly (*Hesperoperla pacifica*) expends considerable energy getting from one place to another near the banks of Oregon's Metolius River.

to the lump of coal causes the coal's carbon atoms to react with oxygen. Chemical bonds are broken through this process, and the energy stored in these bonds is released as heat. But heat is the random motion of molecules, and these molecules have no tendency to stay concentrated. Thus, it's clear that we have gone from the *ordered, concentrated* energy in the chemical bonds of coal to the *disordered, dispersed* energy of heat.

The Second Law of Thermodynamics: The Natural Tendency toward Disorder

And this gets us to the critical thing. Energy transformations will spontaneously run *only* from greater order to lesser order. Some of the heat produced in a steam engine is useful; it's driving a piston. Some of it is not, however—it's simply dissipated. But *all* of it amounts to a form of energy that is more dispersed than the chemical bonds in coal and that will quickly disperse further. Once this happens, there is no chance that it will spontaneously convert into anything *but* heat. We expect to see a lump of coal burn to ashes and to feel the hot air that results disperse, but we do not expect to see the ashes re-form into a lump of coal or to feel the hot air concentrate itself again.

In yielding energy, matter goes from a more-ordered state to a less-ordered state. The scientific principle that speaks to this is the **second law of thermodynamics:** Energy transfer always results in a greater amount of disorder in the universe. In connection with this law, there is a term you will hear—*entropy,* which is a measure of the amount of disorder in a system. The greater the entropy, the greater the disorder. **Figure 6.2** summarizes the principles of the first and second laws of thermodynamics. **Figure 6.3** shows you how much energy is lost to heat in several energy systems.

The Consequences of Thermodynamics

All of this may seem like just so much … *hot air,* but it turns out that few things so profoundly condition the universe we live in as these thermodynamic rules. Indeed, the relentless increase in entropy that the second law entails may dictate nothing less than the fate of the universe.

Allow yourself, for a second, to think of the universe as consisting solely of the sun, the Earth, and the space between them. The sun is a concentration of hydrogen that is undergoing a nuclear reaction, thus releasing light. Living things on Earth manage to capture buckets of the solar energy in this light through the activities of plants and the other photosynthesizers. But every time one of these buckets is poured into another—every time solar energy from the sun is transformed into energy stored in plants,

for example—there is some spillage into heat. And once heat is generated, there is no spontaneous way it can make its way back into the orderly form of sunlight or carbohydrates. With every firing of a car's cylinder or contraction of a muscle, then, some amount of energy is lost to heat.

Against this, life as we know it is made possible by ordered concentrations of energy. The sun can sustain life, but dispersed heat will not. One day, our sun will have wound down like the spring in a music box, bringing to an end the energy source for life on Earth.

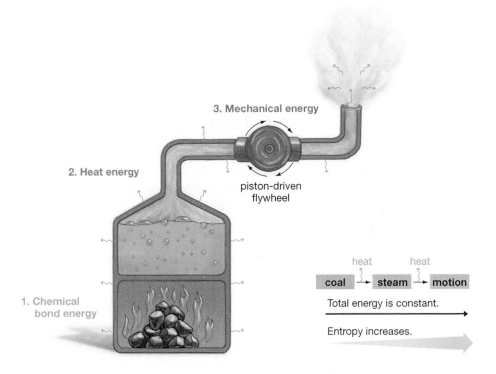

Figure 6.2
Energy Transformed

In a steam engine, energy locked up in the chemical bonds of coal is transformed into heat energy and mechanical energy. No energy is lost in this process, but energy is transformed from a more-ordered form (the chemical bonds of coal) to a less-ordered form (heat). Thus, the amount of disorder—or entropy—increases in the transaction.

Figure 6.3
Energy Efficiency

The efficiency of several energy systems, as measured by the proportion of energy they receive relative to what they then make available to perform work. In measuring the efficiency of the car engine, the question is: How much of the energy contained in the chemical bonds of gasoline is converted by the car into the kinetic energy of wheel movement? In each system, most of the energy not available for work is lost to heat.

One possible scenario for the universe as a whole is that all its stars eventually will darken, leaving a cold universe with little potential for life—indeed, with little activity of any sort. The laws of thermodynamics are powerful indeed.

SO FAR ...

1. Energy that is stored is _____ energy, while energy in motion is _____ energy.

2. The first law of thermodynamics says that energy is never _____ or _____ but is only _____. The second law of thermodynamics says that energy transfer always results in a greater amount of _____ in the universe.

3. Whenever energy is transferred—for example, from the chemical bonds in gasoline to the movement of a car's pistons—some of the original quantity of energy is lost to _____.

6.3 How Is Energy Used by Living Things?

A sprouting plant is constantly building itself up; it is making larger, more complex molecules (proteins, starches) from smaller, simpler ones (amino acids, simple sugars). This increasing organization stands in contrast to the spontaneous course of things—breakdown and disorder—and thus may seem to be a violation of the second law, but it is not. In the context of the universe as a whole, living things are contributors to its entropy. Any given biological activity, such as building a leaf, generates heat and thus increases the disorder in the universe as a whole. But living things can bring about *local* increases in order (in themselves) by using the energy that comes ultimately from the sun.

Up and Down the Great Energy Hill

The building up of complex molecules from simpler ones is an example of work, and in it, we begin to see how living things use energy. A starchy carbohydrate is a more complex thing than the simple sugars it is made of. It is a more *ordered* arrangement of atoms than is a group of individual simple sugars. As such, the second law tells us, it should *take* energy to make a starch from simple sugars, and this is indeed the case. Going in the opposite direction, the breakdown of a starchy carbohydrate into simple sugars is an action favored by the second law because it brings about *less* order. Such a process therefore should not take energy. Indeed, this process should *release* energy, and this too is the case.

Breakdown operations, such as starches breaking down into sugars, are examples of **exergonic reactions:** reactions in which the starting set of molecules (the reactants) contains more energy than the final set of molecules (the products). Meanwhile, buildup operations are examples of **endergonic reactions:** reactions in which the products contain more energy than the reactants. This is what happens when, for example, simple glucose molecules are brought together to form glycogen, which is a storage form of carbohydrates (**Figure 6.4**).

Figure 6.4
Energy Stored and Released

It takes energy to build up a more complex molecule (in this case, glycogen) from simpler molecules (in this case, glucose units). Such a buildup is thus an endergonic or uphill reaction. Conversely, energy is released in reactions in which more complex molecules are broken down into simpler ones. Such reactions are exergonic or downhill reactions.

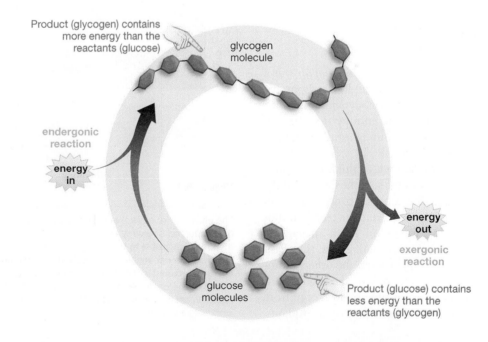

Product (glycogen) contains more energy than the reactants (glucose)

glycogen molecule

endergonic reaction

energy in

energy out

exergonic reaction

glucose molecules

Product (glucose) contains less energy than the reactants (glycogen)

Coupled Reactions

With this as background, we arrive at an important insight: Endergonic and exergonic reactions are linked in living things. Why should this be so? If you want to get something uphill—into a higher energy state—you have to power that process, which means *using* some energy. Just as it takes energy to get a bicycle uphill, so it takes energy to power the endergonic reaction that takes us from glucose molecules to glycogen. Now, where is this energy going to come from? It must come from an energy-releasing *exergonic* reaction. The result is a **coupled reaction**: a chemical reaction in which an exergonic reaction powers an endergonic reaction.

With this, we reach a critical point about how living things operate: through an endless series of coupled reactions. Want to move a muscle? Two kinds of long, slender muscle protein filaments must slide past each other for this to happen. For this to work, a huge number of tiny, pivoting extensions on one kind of muscle filament must first latch onto and then pull the other kind of filament (**Figure 6.5**). Now, how are these extensions going to "cock" themselves and get ready for a pull? This cocking is an endergonic reaction—it is a movement up the energy hill. Once our muscle extensions are cocked, they will be in a higher energy state, just as the bar on a mousetrap is in a higher energetic state after it's pulled back. Following what was just said, an endergonic reaction such as this must be powered by an exergonic reaction—energy must be released from somewhere for those muscle extensions to be moved into their cocked state. Now, where does the energy for this come from? To follow the whole trail, this energy came originally from the sun, after which it was captured by a photosynthesizing organism—a peach tree, for example. Then, say

we ate a peach from the tree; now, the energy that was locked up in the peach is locked up in us in the form of glucose molecules. So, does the energy to pull back the muscle extensions go directly from the glucose to the extensions? No. One more energy transfer must be made first. The energy in the glucose must be transferred into a molecule called ATP.

6.4 The Energy Dispenser: ATP

It is ATP that will release the energy that allows the muscle extensions to be cocked. Only with the energy dispensed by ATP can our muscles contract. You could think of ATP as a kind of "middleman"—it receives the energy from food and then doles it out for activities such as muscle contraction. Why do we need an intermediate molecule of this sort? Well, think of it this way. Power plants have considerable use for coal because, as we've seen, coal can yield energy. But it may go without saying that most people don't use coal's energy *directly* in their homes. Instead, power plants must convert the energy in coal into a form that people *can* use in their homes—electricity. In this same way, the energy contained in food must be converted into a form the human body can use, and this form is overwhelmingly the molecule known as ATP, which can accept relatively large amounts of energy from a food source and then proceed to pass on this energy to a wide range of the molecules found in the body. The upshot is that every time a muscle contracts or a nerve signal fires, ATP is doling out the energy for these operations. Every time a sperm cell whips its tail, ATP is supplying the energy. And what goes for energy use in human beings goes for energy use in all forms of life.

A muscle shortens when many segments such as these contract.

Myofibril (contracting unit within muscle cell)

Extensions at rest

ATP

Extensions "cocked"

Cocking the muscle extensions is an endergonic ("uphill") reaction. Where does this energy come from? ATP

Direction of muscle pull

Figure 6.5
Powering a Coupled Reaction

For any muscle to contract, one set of muscle filaments must pull on a second set, thus shortening the muscle segment that both are part of. To accomplish this, extensions of the active filaments must be put in a "cocked" position. Energetically, this is a movement up the energy hill and thus is an energy-using or endergonic reaction that must be powered by an energy-releasing or exergonic reaction. Together, the two reactions constitute a single reaction—a coupled reaction. This coupled reaction, like so many in living things, is powered by energy released from the molecule ATP.

The simplest bacterium is as dependent on ATP as we are. In sum, **ATP** can be defined as the most important energy transfer molecule in living things.

So, what's the structure of this molecule? To answer this question, let's start by thinking about where ATP's full name, **adenosine triphosphate,** comes from. ATP has a sugar (called ribose) and a nitrogen-containing base (called adenine) that together make up a compound called adenosine, as you can see in **Figure 6.6.** Phosphate groups are also linked to adenosine—three phosphate groups, which gives us adenosine *tri*phosphate. The place to look for energy storage in ATP is in the phosphate groups. Notice that they all are negatively charged. This is the key to understanding why ATP serves as such an effective energy transfer molecule. Remember that like charges repel each other, and in this case three phosphate groups are doing just that. Energy was required to put these phosphate groups together as they are, in this relatively unstable state. This linkage represents a move *up* the energy hill. With ATP, it is as though someone squeezed a jack-in-the-box back into the box and shut

the lid. It should be no surprise that when the lid is opened, a good deal of energy will be released.

If you look now at **Figure 6.7,** you can see the details of how ATP does its job in the muscle contraction we just touched on. The essence of the operation is that a muscle-filament extension is moved from a 45-degree angle to a "cocked" *90*-degree angle thanks to the energy input from ATP—a position from which the extension can now pull the muscle filament to the left. The result, when carried out by a huge number of extensions and filaments, is contraction of a muscle.

The ATP/ADP Cycle

There is another side to this ATP-driven reaction, however. Note that once ATP loses its outer phosphate group, it is not ATP anymore, but two molecules—one called ADP and another labeled P (for phosphate). ATP works by losing (or "donating") a phosphate group in this way, but once this happens, it becomes a molecule with only *two* phosphate groups: adenosine *di*phosphate or ADP. However, this is a temporary condition. Once an ADP molecule is finished with a reaction, it is free to have a third phosphate group added to it again. This is just what happens: ADP returns to being ATP, which is capable of providing energy for yet another reaction. This shuttling from ATP to ADP and back, illustrated in Figure 6.6, takes place constantly in cells.

Between Food and ATP

The essence of our story so far is that, in animals, energy that comes originally from the sun is first stored in the food we eat and is then transferred to ATP, which then dispenses the energy to power our daily activities. But if you think about it, there's a piece missing here. How does that third phosphate group get onto ADP, making it ATP? This is an uphill reaction. So, where's the energy-*yielding* reaction that allows it to take place? Put another way, by which reactions does energy get from food to ATP? It is almost time to answer this question—it will be answered in Chapter 7—but first you need to know something about a group of proteins that living things use to control energy.

Figure 6.6

Life's Most Important Energy Transfer Molecule

ATP stores energy in the form of chemical bonds between its phosphate groups. When the bond between the second and outermost phosphate group is broken, the outermost phosphate separates from ATP, and energy is released. This separation transforms ATP into adenosine diphosphate or ADP, which then goes on to pick up another phosphate group, becoming ATP again.

SO FAR ...

1. Coupled reactions combine an endergonic reaction, in which the _____ have more energy than the _____, and an exergonic reaction, in which the _____ have more energy than the _____.

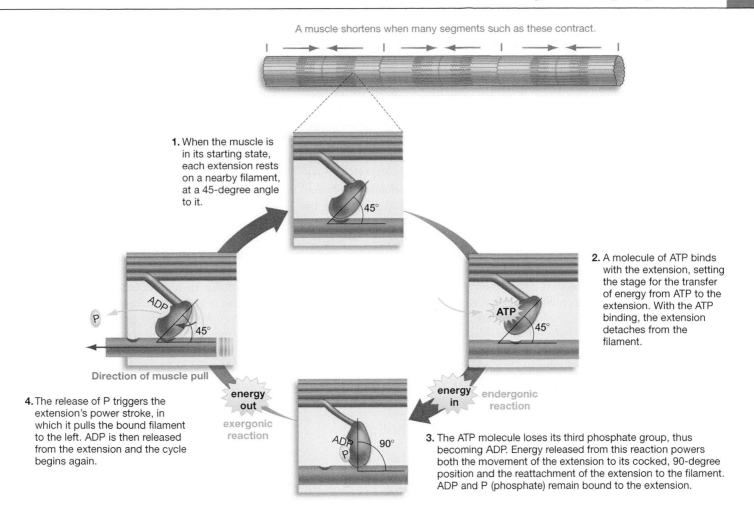

A muscle shortens when many segments such as these contract.

1. When the muscle is in its starting state, each extension rests on a nearby filament, at a 45-degree angle to it.

2. A molecule of ATP binds with the extension, setting the stage for the transfer of energy from ATP to the extension. With the ATP binding, the extension detaches from the filament.

ADP

P

45°

Direction of muscle pull

4. The release of P triggers the extension's power stroke, in which it pulls the bound filament to the left. ADP is then released from the extension and the cycle begins again.

energy out

exergonic reaction

ATP

45°

energy in   *endergonic reaction*

ADP P   90°

3. The ATP molecule loses its third phosphate group, thus becoming ADP. Energy released from this reaction powers both the movement of the extension to its cocked, 90-degree position and the reattachment of the extension to the filament. ADP and P (phosphate) remain bound to the extension.

Figure 6.7
Muscle Contraction, Powered by ATP

2. The energy for most coupled reactions in the body is supplied by the molecule _____, in particular by the splitting off of this molecule's third or outer _____.

3. After powering a reaction, ATP becomes the molecule _____, which, with the addition of another _____, becomes ATP once more.

6.5 Efficient Energy Use in Living Things: Enzymes

Lactose—better known as milk sugar—is composed of two simple sugars, glucose and galactose, that are linked together by a single atom of oxygen. It follows from what you've seen so far that lactose will split into its glucose and galactose parts without any energy requirement. Indeed, a little energy will be released in this process because chemical bonds have been broken and two smaller molecules have been produced. Such a splitting is therefore a downhill reaction.

If we actually took a small amount of lactose, however, and put it in some plain water, it would certainly be hours—it might be days—before any of the lactose molecules would break down into glucose and galactose. How can this be? Millions of people around the world drink milk, and it doesn't seem to pile up in them.

Accelerating Reactions

The secret is that when lactose is metabolized in living things, it isn't being split up in plain water. Something else is present that speeds up this process immensely, accelerating it perhaps a billionfold. That something is an **enzyme,** a type of protein that accelerates a chemical reaction. In the case of lactose, the particular enzyme is called lactase, but it is merely one of thousands of enzymes known to exist. Each of these compounds works on some chemical process, but not all are involved in splitting molecules. Some enzymes combine molecules; some rearrange them.

Given their numbers, it may be apparent that enzymes are involved in a lot of different activities, but this doesn't begin to give them the recognition they deserve. Enzymes facilitate nearly every chemical process that takes place in living things. No organism could survive without them. Technically, these compounds are only accelerating chemical reactions that would happen anyway, as with lactase splitting lactose. But in practical terms, they are *enabling* these reactions because no living thing could wait days or months for the milk sugar it ingests to be broken down, or for hormones to be put together, or for bleeding to stop.

To get an idea of the importance of enzymes, consider the millions of Americans who are known as lactose intolerant because, after childhood, their bodies reduced their production of lactase. When these people consume milk, the lactose in it *does* simply stay in their intestines. It is eventually digested not by them but by the bacteria that live in the human digestive tract (something that causes bloat and gas). Troublesome as this affliction may be, it is minor compared to other conditions caused by enzyme dysfunction. All newborn babies in the United States are screened for a list of inherited diseases, three of which are Tay-Sachs disease, phenylketonuria, and congenital adrenal hyperplasia. Each of these diseases is caused by an enzyme deficiency. In the case of Tay-Sachs disease, the lack of an enzyme leads to a buildup of fat deposits within nerve cells, and the result usually is death by age 4.

Specific Tasks and Metabolic Pathways

From the sheer number of enzymes that exist, you can probably get a sense of how specifically they are matched to given tasks. Although some enzymes can work on groups of similar substances, a specific enzyme usually facilitates a specific reaction: It works on one or perhaps two molecules and no others. Thus,

lactase breaks down lactose—and *only* lactose—and the products of its activity are always glucose and galactose. The substance that is worked on by an enzyme is known as its **substrate.** Thus, lactose is the substrate for lactase. The *-ase* ending you see in lactase is common to most enzymes. As you can see, the substrate (lactose) is identified in the enzyme's name (lactase).

Certain activities in living things, such as blood clotting, are much more complex than the breakdown of lactose. They are multistep processes, each step of which requires its own enzyme. Most large-scale activities in living things work this way: leaf growth, digestion, hormonal balance. The result is a **metabolic pathway:** a set of enzymatically controlled steps that results in the completion of a product or process in an organism. In such a sequence, each enzyme does a particular job and then leaves the succeeding task to the next enzyme, with the product of one reaction becoming the substrate for the next (**Figure 6.8**). This is the way that, for example, cholesterol gets produced: One cholesterol precursor leads to another through a series of enzymatically enabled reactions, with the final product being cholesterol itself. The sum of all the chemical reactions that a cell or larger organism carries out is known as its **metabolism.** To put things simply, enzymes are active in all facets of the metabolism of all living things.

6.6 Enzymes and the Activation Barrier

All this information about enzymes is well and good, you may be saying at this point, but what does it have to do with energy? The answer is that in carrying out their tasks, enzymes are in the business of lowering the amount of energy needed to get chemical reactions going. And this means that the reactions can get going faster.

An analogy may be helpful here. Consider the now-familiar rock perched at the top of a hill. Situated in this way, it has a good deal of potential energy. If it rolled down the hill, it would release this potential energy as kinetic energy. But here is the critical question: What would be required to get this rock going? It is perched at the top of the hill because it is *stable* at the top of the hill. To get it going would require *additional* energy in the form of, say, a push.

Now consider the lactose molecule. It is "perched" like the rock, in a sense, because it lies "uphill" from the glucose and galactose it can break into. But just as the rock is stable because of its position in the ground, so the lactose is stable because it has a strong set of chemical bonds holding its atoms in a fixed position. Now, some energy is going to be required to break those bonds, thus getting the reaction going. But is there anything that can *lower* the amount of energy

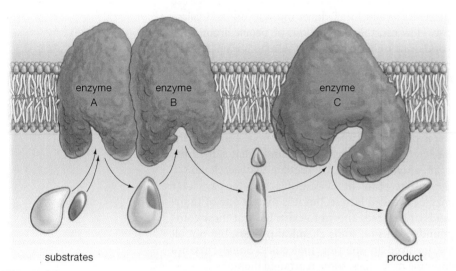

substrates   product

Figure 6.8
Metabolic Pathway: Sequence of Enzyme Action

Most processes in living organisms are carried out through a metabolic pathway—a sequential set of enzymatically controlled reactions in which the product of one reaction serves as the substrate for the next. Enzymes perform specific tasks on specific substrates. In this example, enzyme A combines two substrates, enzyme B removes part of its substrate, and enzyme C changes the shape of its substrate.

required to set this process in motion? The answer is yes—an enzyme. If you look at **Figure 6.9**, you can see this in schematic terms. Imagine that you had to push a boulder up the hill in (a) to get it to roll down the other side. Now imagine that you only had to push a boulder up the hill in (b) to get the same result. In which situation would you be able to get your desired result *faster*? What is at work here is lowering of **activation energy:** the energy required to initiate a chemical reaction.

How Do Enzymes Work?

How do enzymes carry out this task of lowering activation energy? As you'll see shortly, they bind to their substrates and in so doing make these substances more vulnerable to chemical alteration. The amazing thing is that they do this without being permanently altered themselves. Enzymes are **catalysts**—substances that retain their original chemical composition while bringing about a change in a substrate. At the end of its splitting of the lactose molecule, lactase has exactly the same chemical structure as it did prior to this operation. It is thus free to pick up another lactose molecule and split *it*. And all this takes place in a flash: The fastest-working enzymes can carry out 100,000 chemical transformations per second.

Enzymes generally take the form of globular or ball-like proteins with a shape that includes a kind of pocket into which the substrate fits. If you look at **Figure 6.10**, you can see a space-filling model of one enzyme, called hexokinase. You can also see, buried there in the middle, its substrate—glucose, which is better known as blood sugar. As with all proteins, enzymes are made up of amino acids, but only a few of the hundreds of amino acids in an enzyme are typically involved in actually binding with the substrate. Five or six would be common. These amino acids help form the substrate pocket, known as the **active site:** the portion of an enzyme that binds with a substrate, thus helping transform it.

In some cases, the participants at the active site include, along with amino acids, one or more accessory molecules. One variety of these molecules is the **coenzymes:** molecules other than amino acids that facilitate the work of enzymes by binding with them. If you've ever wondered what vitamins do, a big part of the answer is: function as coenzymes. All the B vitamins, for example, serve as coenzymes that sit in the active site of an enzyme and provide an added chemical attraction or repulsion that allows the enzyme to do its job.

An Enzyme in Action: Chymotrypsin

The details of how enzymes carry out their work are complex, and they vary according to enzyme. Let's consider in a general way, however, the activity of a much-studied enzyme called chymotrypsin.

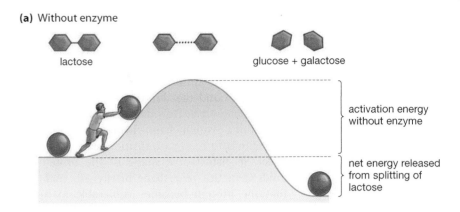

(a) Without enzyme

lactose   glucose + galactose

activation energy without enzyme

net energy released from splitting of lactose

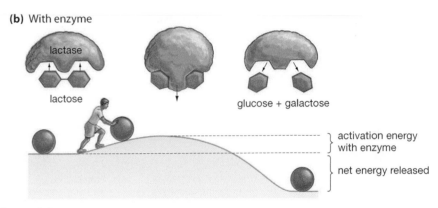

(b) With enzyme

lactase

lactose   glucose + galactose

activation energy with enzyme

net energy released

Figure 6.9
Enzymes Accelerate Chemical Reactions
Without an enzyme, the amount of energy necessary to split lactose is high. In the presence of the enzyme lactase, however, a low activation energy is sufficient to get the process started.

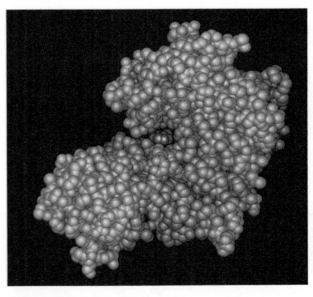

Glucose molecule (shown in red) binding to active site of hexokinase enzyme

Figure 6.10
Shape Is Important in Enzymes
Substrates generally fit into small grooves or pockets in enzymes. The location at which the enzyme binds the substrate is known as the enzyme's active site. Pictured is a computer-generated model of a glucose molecule (in red) binding to the active site of an enzyme called hexokinase (in blue).

Chymotrypsin is delivered from the human pancreas to the small intestine, where it works with water to break down proteins we have ingested. Its function is to snip protein chains in between their building block amino acids. It does this by breaking the single bond that binds one amino acid to the next (**Figure 6.11**). How does it work? After binding to part of a protein chain, chymotrypsin then interacts with it to create a transition-state molecule. In effect, it distorts the shape of the protein—and holds it in this new shape briefly—in such a way that the protein becomes vulnerable to bonding with ionized water molecules. This allows carbon and nitrogen atoms to latch on to new partners, and the protein chain is cut in two. Chymotrypsin then returns to its original form and proceeds to a new reaction.

Figure 6.11
How the Enzyme Chymotrypsin Works

In this example, the enzyme chymotrypsin is facilitating the breakdown of a protein by changing the protein's shape. In the absence of chymotrypsin, this process would take a billion times longer.

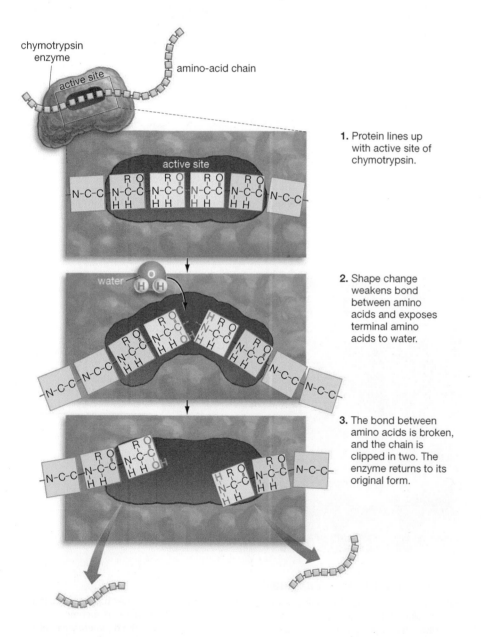

1. Protein lines up with active site of chymotrypsin.

2. Shape change weakens bond between amino acids and exposes terminal amino acids to water.

3. The bond between amino acids is broken, and the chain is clipped in two. The enzyme returns to its original form.

6.7 Regulating Enzymatic Activity

The activity of enzymes doesn't proceed in a monotonous, clock-like way, but instead is regulated through several different means. To put this another way, several factors influence the amount of "product" an enzyme turns out. One of these factors, logically, is the amount of substrate in the enzyme's vicinity. If there's no substrate to work on, no product can be turned out.

The work of enzymes can, however, be reduced in other ways. For example, some molecules that are not the normal substrate for an enzyme can nevertheless bind to the enzyme's active site. This happens all the time in natural ways in our bodies, but to sharpen the point, consider the well-known drug Lipitor, which millions of people take to lower their cholesterol levels. How does this drug work? Recall that there is a metabolic pathway by which cholesterol is produced—one cholesterol precursor after another is modified in a set of reactions, each one of which is facilitated by an enzyme. But one of these enzymes has an active site that *Lipitor* can fit into. When this happens, this enzyme is occupied—it can't bind with the cholesterol precursor that is its normal substrate. And this effect is dose dependent: The greater the number of enzyme molecules that are occupied by Lipitor, the fewer the number of enzyme molecules that can help produce cholesterol. Thus, the ultimate effect of Lipitor is to lower the amount of cholesterol produced in the body. What we see with Lipitor is an example of **competitive inhibition:** a reduction in the activity of an enzyme by means of a compound other than the enzyme's usual substrate binding with it in its active site.

Allosteric Regulation of Enzymes

Living things routinely regulate enzyme activity by another means. Earlier, you saw a model of an enzyme called hexokinase, which works on the substrate glucose. The product of this reaction is something called glucose-6-phosphate. Although this is an enzymatic product, it can bind to hexokinase at a site *other* than its active site and in so doing change the shape of hexokinase. This change renders hexokinase less able to bind with its substrate, glucose, meaning hexokinase's work is temporarily reduced. If you look at **Figure 6.12**, you can see how this process works schematically.

This is but one example of the process known as **allosteric regulation**—the regulation of an enzyme's activity by means of a molecule binding to a site on the enzyme other than its active site. Many variations on this theme are possible. In the case of hexokinase, its own product (glucose-6-phosphate) bound with it and cut down on its activity, but molecules other than the enzymatic product can bind with an enzyme at one of its additional binding sites. Furthermore, the effect of such binding need not be negative; allosteric binding can increase the activity of enzymes as well as reduce it.

The importance of such regulation is that enzymes are not simply fated to turn out product as long as there is substrate to work on. If a cell has too much of a product, allosteric control can cut down on it; if there is too little, its concentration can be increased.

On to Energy Harvesting

Our story of energy concluded in this chapter with a look at enzymes and energy. Next chapter, however, we'll pick up the story of energy with a more detailed look at a process touched on earlier—the transfer of energy from food to ATP. The question we will tackle is this: What are the steps by which our bodies extract energy from food and then channel this energy into pushing phosphate groups onto ADP, thus making it ATP? Put another way, how does our primary energy-dispensing molecule become energized?

SO FAR . . .

1. An enzyme is a type of _____ that _____ a chemical reaction.

2. The substance that an enzyme works on is known as its _____. A metabolic pathway is a linked series of enzymatically controlled reactions in which the _____ of one reaction becomes the _____ for the next.

3. Activation energy is the energy required to _____ a chemical reaction. Enzymes work by _____ activation energy.

(a) Substrate becomes product.

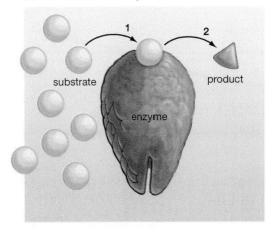

1. Substrate binds to enzyme.

2. Enzyme transforms substrate to product.

(b) Product feeds back on enzyme.

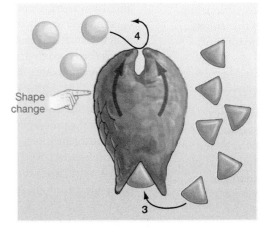

3. Product binds to a *different* site on the enzyme, causing the enzyme to change shape.

4. The new shape of the enzyme prevents it from binding to any more substrate.

Figure 6.12
Allosteric Regulation of Enzymes
The frequency of chemical reactions can be controlled by the binding of a molecule to an enzyme at a site other than its active site. In this instance, the enzyme's own product binds with the enzyme in this way, thereby reducing the enzyme's activity.

CHAPTER

6 REVIEW

Go to the Study Area at www.masteringbiology.com for practice quizzes, myeBook, BioFlix™ 3-D animations, MP3 Tutor Sessions, videos, current events, and more.

Mastering
BIOLOGY

Summary

6.1 Energy Is Central to Life

- All living things require energy. The sun is the ultimate source of energy for most living things. The sun's energy is captured on Earth by photosynthesizing organisms, which then pass this energy on to other organisms in the form of food. (p. 109)

6.2 The Nature of Energy

- Energy is the capacity to bring about movement against an opposing force. Energy can be conceptualized as either potential energy, meaning stored energy; or kinetic energy, meaning energy in motion. The study of energy is known as thermodynamics. (p. 109)

- The first law of thermodynamics states that energy is never created or destroyed, but is only transformed; the second law of thermodynamics states that energy transfer will always result in a greater amount of disorder in the universe. (p. 110)

- In every energy transaction, some energy will be lost to heat, the most disordered form of energy. Entropy is a measure of the amount of disorder in a system. (p. 111)

6.3 How Is Energy Used by Living Things?

- Living things can bring about local increases in order (in themselves) through their metabolic processes, but it takes energy to do this. (p. 112)

- Energy in living things is stored in endergonic reactions in which the products of the reaction contain more energy than the starting substances (or reactants). Energy is released in exergonic reactions, in which the reactants contain more energy than the products. Endergonic and exergonic reactions are linked in coupled reactions

in which an energy-yielding exergonic reaction powers an energy-requiring endergonic reaction. (p. 112)

6.4 The Energy Dispenser: ATP

- Adenosine triphosphate (ATP) is the most important energy transfer molecule in living things. Energy that is extracted from food is transferred to ATP, and the energy in it is then used to drive a vast array of metabolic processes. (p. 113)

- ATP drives chemical reactions by donating one of its three phosphate groups to them. In the process, it becomes the two-phosphate molecule adenosine diphosphate (ADP). To again become ATP, it must have a third phosphate group attached to it. (p. 114)

6.5 Efficient Energy Use in Living Things: Enzymes

- An enzyme is a type of protein that accelerates the rate at which a chemical reaction takes place in an organism. Nearly every chemical process that takes place in living things is facilitated by an enzyme. (p. 115)

- The substance that an enzyme helps transform through chemical reaction is called its substrate. Many activities in living things are controlled by metabolic pathways, in which a series of reactions is undertaken in sequence, each facilitated by its own enzyme. In such a series, the product of one reaction becomes the substrate for the next. The sum of all the chemical reactions that a cell or larger living thing carries out is its metabolism. (p. 116)

6.6 Enzymes and the Activation Barrier

- Enzymes work by lowering activation energy, meaning the energy required to initiate a chemical reaction. Enzymes are catalysts: They bring about a change in

their substrates without being chemically altered themselves. (p. 116)

- Enzymes generally take the form of globular proteins whose shape includes a pocket, called the active site, into which the enzyme's substrate fits. Only a few of the hundreds of amino acids that typically make up an enzyme will be involved in substrate binding. In some cases, substrate binding is facilitated by coenzymes. (p. 117)

6.7 Regulating Enzymatic Activity

- Enzyme activity can be controlled by competitive inhibition (a reduction in the activity of an enzyme by means of a compound other than the enzyme's usual substrate binding with the enzyme in its active site) or allosteric regulation (a molecule binding with the enzyme at a site other than its active site). Through such means, enzyme activity can be finely tuned in accordance with cellular needs. (p. 118)

Key Terms

activation energy   117
active site   117
adenosine triphosphate (ATP)   114
allosteric regulation   118
catalyst   117
coenzyme   117
competitive inhibition   118
coupled reaction   113
endergonic reaction   112
energy   109
enzyme   115
exergonic reaction   112
first law of thermodynamics   110
kinetic energy   110
metabolic pathway   116
metabolism   116

Understanding the Basics

Multiple-Choice Questions

(Answers are in the back of the book.)

1. According to the first law of thermodynamics, energy:
   a. is never lost or gained, but is only transformed.
   b. always requires an ultimate source such as the sun.
   c. can never be gained, but can be lost.
   d. can never really be harnessed.
   e. can never be transformed.

2. Each time there is a chemical reaction, some energy is exchanged. According to the second law of thermodynamics, with each exchange:
   a. some energy is lost, but other energy is created.
   b. some energy must come from the sun.
   c. some energy is transformed into heat.
   d. energy is gained for future use.
   e. some energy is permanently destroyed.

3. ATP stores energy in the form of:
   a. mechanical energy.
   b. heat.
   c. complex carbohydrates.
   d. chemical bonds.
   e. amino acids.

4. People who are lactose intolerant lack a compound called lactase in their digestive tract. You know that this compound, lactase, is probably a(n):
   a. hormone, because it causes a change in the person.
   b. coenzyme, because it helps the enzyme, lactose, do its job.
   c. vitamin, because it is essential to health.
   d. substrate, because it is involved with food.
   e. enzyme, because its name ends in -ase.

5. Glycolysis is a metabolic pathway that helps living things extract energy from food. From this we know that glycolysis:
   a. consists of a series of chemical reactions.
   b. uses a number of enzymes.
   c. involves the modification of a series of substrates.
   d. proceeds by means of each enzyme leaving a succeeding reaction to a different enzyme.
   e. all of the above

6. Each molecule of ATP stores a good deal of energy because:
   a. ATP is such a large protein.
   b. ATP captures energy directly from the sun.
   c. ATP's third phosphate group exists in a highly energetic state.
   d. a long metabolic pathway is required for the production of ATP.

7. Enzymes:
   a. accelerate specific chemical reactions.
   b. are not chemically altered by binding with a substrate.
   c. lower the activation energy of specific chemical reactions.
   d. all of the above
   e. a and c only

8. The active site of enzyme A is occupied by a molecule other than its substrate. Enzyme B has had its activity reduced by means of a molecule binding to it at a site other than its active site. What is taking place in connection with enzyme A and then enzyme B?
   a. a reaction acceleration, a coupled reaction
   b. a lowering of activation energy, ATP use
   c. allosteric regulation, competitive inhibition
   d. allosteric regulation, coenzyme participation
   e. competitive inhibition, allosteric regulation

Brief Review

(Answers are in the back of the book.)

1. A plant leaf is more ordered and complex than are carbon dioxide and water. In photosynthesis, plants take small, relatively disordered carbon dioxide, water, and mineral molecules and make complex, ordered sugars out of them. How is it possible for this to happen without violating the second law of thermodynamics?

2. The text notes that, in connection with muscle contraction, extensions of one kind of muscle filament are "cocked" in an uphill reaction, and that ATP plays a part in this. Explain how this is a coupled reaction.

3. Where does the energy come from that is stored and released by ATP? In what way is ATP an energy transfer molecule?

4. The average person thinks of enzymes only as substances in their digestive tract that break down food. How would you explain the role of enzymes to your little sister, who has heard about digestion in grade-school biology?

5. What is meant by allosteric regulation of an enzyme?

Applying Your Knowledge

1. In light of the laws of thermodynamics, explain why you get so much hotter when you run than when you are sitting still.

2. Which is easier to have: a messy, disordered room or a neat, ordered room? Is the second law of thermodynamics at work in this situation? What is the price of bringing order to a room?

3. Physicists say that it is impossible to create a perpetual motion machine—a machine whose own activity keeps it running perpetually. What energy principle precludes the possibility of a perpetual motion machine?

Vital Harvest:
Deriving Energy from Food

To remain alive, living things must put the energy they acquire into a form they can use—ATP.

How do living things extract energy from food? Through the process of cellular respiration. Here, a snowcap hummingbird (*Microchera albocoronata*) feeds from a flower in a Costa Rican rain forest.

In May of 1996, the world's attention was riveted on news coming out of Nepal, in Southeast Asia. Disaster had struck several groups of mountain climbers who had been attempting to scale the world's highest peak, Mt. Everest. A vicious storm had taken the members of two Everest expeditions by surprise as they were moving down from Everest's summit, toward the safety of lower altitudes. Within 36 hours, five climbers had lost their lives, and another was so badly frostbitten that one of his hands had to be amputated.

One of the expeditions was led by a highly respected guide from New Zealand, Rob Hall. Courageously remaining near the summit in an effort to bring down one of his clients (who had collapsed), Hall ended up spending a night in a howling storm on Everest without a tent. When the sun rose the next day, the factors working against him included cold and wind, which he might have encountered in lots of inhospitable places on Earth. Also bedeviling him, however, was something that human beings rarely encounter: a lack of oxygen. At his altitude—sitting in the snow at about 28,500 feet—the oxygen he took in with each breath was little more than a third of the amount he would have inhaled with each breath at sea level. Technology might have come to his aid, as he had two oxygen bottles with him, but his intake valve for them had become clogged with ice.

Down at Everest's lower altitudes, other climbers—some of them Hall's friends—had to endure the agony of talking to him by two-way radio while not being able to reach him physically. All of them knew that a lack of oxygen was draining not only his muscles but his mind. Here is Hall in one of his radio transmissions asking about another guide on the ill-fated expedition: "Harold was with me last night, but he doesn't seem to be with me now. Was Harold with me? Can you tell me that?" In the end, the mountain without mercy claimed Rob Hall. He never got up from the place where he spent his night on Everest.

The tragedy of the 1996 Everest expeditions drives home a point and raises a paradox: No one needs to be reminded that we need to breathe in order to live, and most people are aware that oxygen is the most important thing that comes in with breath. That said, of the next 100 people you meet, how many could tell you what oxygen is doing to sustain life? Put another way, why do we need to breathe?

The short answer is that breathing and oxygen are in the energy transfer business. They are part of a system that allows us to extract, from food, energy that is then used to put together the "energy-dispensing" molecule, ATP. As you'll recall from Chapter 6, the body uses ATP (adenosine triphosphate) to power activities that range from muscle contraction to thinking to cell repair. Living things need large amounts of ATP to live, and organisms such as ourselves use oxygen to produce most of our ATP. If we don't get enough oxygen to keep making ATP, our bodies and minds start failing.

Exhausted Near the Summit

Two members of the ill-fated expeditions that climbed Mount Everest in May 1996 approach the mountain's peak.

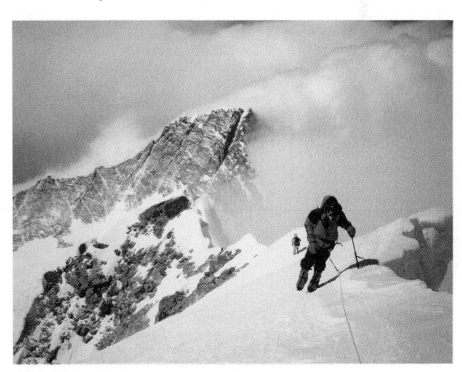

Oxygen is not required for all the "harvesting" we do of the energy contained in food. When you lift a box, the short burst of energy that is required comes largely from a different sort of energy harvesting, which you'll learn more about shortly. But even here, the essential *product* of energy harvesting is ATP. Keep that in mind, and you won't get lost in the byways of energy transfer. How does the body produce enough ATP to allow us to read a book or climb a mountain? In this chapter, you'll find out.

7.1 Energizing ATP

Given the importance of ATP to this story, let us begin with a brief review of how this molecule works. Recall from Chapter 6 that each ATP molecule has three phosphate groups and that ATP powers a given reaction by losing the outermost of these phosphate groups. In this process, ATP is transformed into a molecule with *two* phosphate groups, adenosine diphosphate, or ADP. To return to its more "energized" ATP state, it must have a third phosphate group attached again. This is, however, a trip *up* the energy hill because the product (ATP) contains more energy than the reactants (ADP + a phosphate group). Thus, getting that third phosphate group onto ADP requires energy. It is like preparing a spring-loaded mousetrap for action. It takes energy to pull a mousetrap bar back, and the same is true of putting a third phosphate group onto ATP (**Figure 7.1**). Where does the energy come from? For animals such as ourselves, it comes from food; energy that is extracted from food powers the phosphate group up the energy hill—and literally onto ADP.

In tracking the story of *how* energy goes from food to ATP, we will use as an example one particular food molecule, glucose, to see how energy is harvested from it. Although the details here are complex, the essential story is simple. Electrons derived from glucose, which is high in energy, will be running

downhill; they will be channeled off, a few at a time, and their downhill drop will power the *uphill* push needed to attach a phosphate group onto ADP. The glucose-derived electrons will be transferred to several intermediate molecules in their downhill journey, but the *final* molecule that will receive them at the bottom of the energy hill is oxygen. We need to breathe because we need oxygen to serve as this final electron acceptor.

As you are following this process, you may well wonder why so many steps are required to transfer energy from food to ATP. Why isn't there just one step in energy transfer—food to ATP? It turns out that the gradual transfer of energy, through many steps, allows the body to make the most of the energy it receives. Think of it this way. You could have water drop 1,000 feet straight off a cliff onto a waterwheel below. In this case, the wheel would simply be pulverized by the water crashing onto it. In the process, the potential energy that had been contained in the water at the top of the cliff would be transformed almost entirely into useless heat. Conversely, you could have a stream that ran briskly downhill for 1,000 vertical feet with waterwheels spaced periodically to channel the energy off a little at a time, thereby conserving the energy for work. The steps you are going to read about amount to this kind of controlled channeling off of energy— the energy that's contained in food.

Redox Reactions

The basis for electron transfers down the energy hill is straightforward: Some substances more strongly attract electrons than do others. A substance that loses one or more electrons to another is said to have undergone **oxidation.** We hear the related word *oxidized* all the time—when paint on an outdoor surface has become dulled, for example, or when metal rusts (**Figure 7.2**). Meanwhile, the substance that *gains* electrons in this reaction is said to have undergone **reduction.** (This seems about as logical as saying a

Figure 7.1
Storing and Releasing Energy
Adenosine triphosphate (ATP) is the most important energy-dispensing molecule in our bodies. The energy it contains is used to power everything from muscle contraction to thinking.

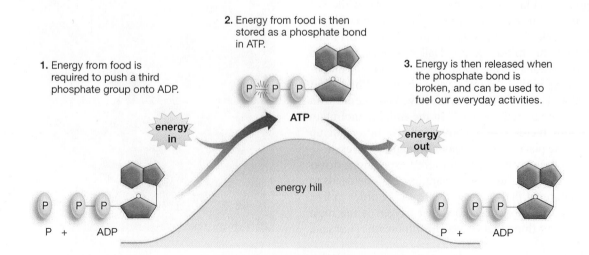

1. Energy from food is required to push a third phosphate group onto ADP.

2. Energy from food is then stored as a phosphate bond in ATP.

3. Energy is then released when the phosphate bond is broken, and can be used to fuel our everyday activities.

energy in

ATP

energy out

energy hill

P + ADP

P + ADP

Figure 7.2
An Effect of Oxidation
Rust has formed on a hook atop a corroded steel sheet.

country lost a war by winning. The way to think about it is that, because electrons carry a negative charge, any substance that gains electrons has had a reduction in its *positive charge*.)

In cells, oxidation and reduction never occur independently. If one substance is oxidized, another must be reduced. It's like a teeter-totter; if one side goes down, the other must come up. The combined operation is known as a reduction-oxidation reaction, or simply a **redox reaction:** the process by which electrons are transferred from one molecule to another. Critically, the substance oxidized in a redox reaction has its electrons traveling energetically downhill.

Many Molecules Can Oxidize Other Molecules

The term *oxidation* might give you the idea that oxygen must be involved in any redox reaction, but this is not the case. Any compound that serves to pull electrons from another is a so-called oxidizing agent. In living things, a large number of molecules are involved in energy transfer, and each has a certain tendency to gain or lose electrons relative to the others.

This is how electrons can be passed down the energy hill: The starting, energetic molecule of glucose is oxidized by another molecule, which in turn is oxidized by the *next* molecule down the hill. The whole thing might be thought of as a kind of downhill electron bucket brigade. Molecules that serve to transfer electrons from one molecule to another in ATP formation are known as **electron carriers.** The thing that makes their role a little complicated is that many of the electrons they accept are bound up originally in hydrogen atoms. You may remember from Chapter 3 that a hydrogen atom amounts to one proton and one electron. In transferring a hydrogen atom, then, a molecule is transferring a single electron (bound to a proton), which means a redox reaction has taken place.

Redox through Intermediates: NAD

The most important electron carrier in energy transfer is a molecule known as **nicotinamide adenine dinucleotide,** or **NAD,** which can be thought of as a city cab that can exist in two states: loaded with passengers or empty. And like a cab, it can switch very easily between those two states. The passengers that NAD picks up and drops off are electrons (**Figure 7.3**).

The "empty" state that NAD comes in is ionic: NAD^+. Remembering the discussion about ions, you

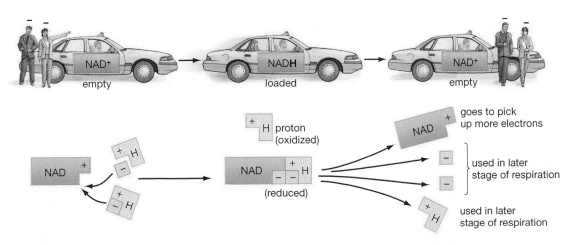

1. NAD^+ within a cell, along with two hydrogen atoms that are part of the food that is supplying energy for the body.

2. NAD^+ is reduced to NAD by accepting an electron from a hydrogen atom. It also picks up another hydrogen atom to become NADH.

3. NADH carries the electrons to a later stage of respiration then drops them off, becoming oxidized to its original form, NAD^+.

Figure 7.3
The Electron Carrier NAD^+

In its unloaded form (NAD^+) and its loaded form (NADH), this molecule is a critical player in energy transfer, picking up energetic electrons from food and transferring them to later stages of respiration.

can see that NAD⁺ is positively charged, meaning that it has fewer electrons than protons. In a redox reaction, what NAD⁺ does is pick up, in effect, one hydrogen atom (an electron and a proton) and one solo electron (from a second hydrogen atom). The isolated electron that NAD⁺ picks up turns it from positively charged to neutral: $NAD^+ \rightarrow NAD$; the whole hydrogen atom takes it from NAD to NADH. Keeping an eye on redox reactions here, NAD⁺ has become NADH by oxidizing a substance—by accepting electrons from it.

So much for half of NAD's role: picking up passengers. *Now*, as NADH, it is loaded with these passengers. It can proceed down the energy hill to donate them to molecules that have a greater potential to accept electrons than it does. Having dropped its passengers off with such a molecule, it returns to being the empty NAD⁺ and is ready for another pickup. Through this process, NADH transfers energy from one molecule to another.

How Does NAD Do Its Job?

The molecule that NAD⁺ is oxidizing is the starting glucose molecule (or actually derivatives of it). To carry out its oxidizing role, NAD⁺ obviously needs to be brought together with the glucose derivatives. What have you been looking at that brings substances together in this way? Enzymes! One of the things you'll be seeing, therefore, is NAD⁺ and glucose derivatives brought together by enzymes, at which point NAD⁺ accepts electrons from these derivatives, later to hand them off to another molecule. Electron transfer through intermediate molecules such as NAD⁺ provides the energy for most of the ATP produced. Thus, when looking at the diagrams in this chapter that outline respiration, you'll see:

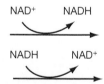

What these drawings indicate is the electron carrier shifting between its empty state (NAD⁺) and its loaded state (NADH) or vice versa.

BioFlix™

Cellular Respiration

SO FAR . . .

1. The essence of energy transfer in animals is that electrons derived from _____ run energetically downhill to power the uphill process by which a third _____ is put onto the body's energy-dispensing molecule _____.

2. A substance that loses one or more electrons to another is said to have undergone _____, while the substance that received the electrons in this reaction has undergone _____. The entire, coupled reaction is called a _____ reaction.

3. The electrons derived from food are transferred to the later stages of energy harvesting by molecules known as _____, the most important of which is one called _____ in its "empty" form and _____ in its "loaded" or reduced form.

7.2 The Three Stages of Cellular Respiration

All the energy players are finally in place: glucose, redox reactions, electron carriers, enzymes, and the rest. In terms of a molecular formula, the big picture on respiration looks like this:

$$C_6H_{12}O_6 + 6O_2 + 36ADP + 36P \rightarrow$$
$$6CO_2 + 6H_2O + 36ATP$$

The starting molecule on the first row is glucose, which is food, storing chemical energy. You can also see, next to it, the oxygen ($6O_2$) that is needed as the final electron acceptor. Then there is ADP, the two-phosphate molecule; and inorganic phosphate molecules (the 36P), which are pushed on ADP to make it ATP. The *products* of this reaction, on the second row, are carbon dioxide ($6CO_2$) and water ($6H_2O$) as by-products and energetic ATP molecules. How *much* ATP does the breakdown of one molecule of glucose yield? The answer is contained in the formula: a maximum of 36 molecules.

Although many separate steps are involved in actually getting energy from glucose to ATP, respiration can be divided into three main phases. These are known as *glycolysis*, the *Krebs cycle*, and the *electron transport chain*.

In overview, energy harvesting through these three phases goes like this: We get some ATP yield in glycolysis and the Krebs cycle, and glycolysis is useful in providing small amounts of ATP in quick bursts. But for most organisms, the main function of glycolysis and the Krebs cycle is the transfer of electrons to electron carriers such as NAD⁺. Bearing their electron cargo, these carriers then move to the third phase of energy harvesting, the electron transport chain (ETC). Here, the electron carriers are themselves oxidized, and the resulting movement of their electrons through the ETC provides the main harvest of ATP. Indeed, about 32 of the approximately 36 molecules of ATP that are netted per glucose molecule are

(a) In metaphorical terms

Just as the video games in some arcades can use only tokens (rather than money) to make them function, so our bodies can use only ATP (rather than food) as a direct source of energy. The energy contained in food—glucose in the example—is transferred to ATP in three major steps: glycolysis, the Krebs cycle, and the electron transport chain. Though glycolysis and the Krebs cycle contribute only small amounts of ATP directly, they also contribute electrons (on the left of the token machine) that help bring about the large yield of ATP in the electron transport chain. Our energy-transfer mechanisms are not quite as efficient as the arcade machine makes them appear. At each stage of the conversion process, some of the original energy contained in the glucose is lost to heat.

(b) In schematic terms

36 ATP maximum per glucose molecule

As with the arcade machine, the starting point in this example is a single molecule of glucose, which again yields ATP in three major sets of steps: glycolysis, the Krebs cycle, and the electron transport chain (ETC). These steps can yield a maximum of about 36 molecules of ATP: 2 in glycolysis, 2 in the Krebs cycle, and 32 in the ETC. As noted, however, glycolysis and the Krebs cycle also yield electrons that move to the ETC, aiding in its ATP production. These electrons get to the ETC via the electron carriers NADH and $FADH_2$, shown on the left. Oxygen is consumed in energy harvesting, while water and carbon dioxide are produced in it. Glycolysis takes place in the cytosol of the cell, but the Krebs cycle and the ETC take place in cellular organelles, called mitochondria, that lie within the cytosol.

obtained in the ETC. If you look at **Figure 7.4** you can see two representations of the three stages of energy extraction.

Glycolysis: First to Evolve, Less Efficient

The division among the three energy-harvesting phases is in one sense a division of evolutionary history. For most organisms, energy harvesting's first phase, glycolysis, could be likened to a nineteenth-century steam engine working side by side with a state-of-the-art electric turbine. By itself, glycolysis produces only two ATP molecules per glucose molecule, which is pretty

small in comparison to the 36 ATP molecules likely to come from all three phases. And glycolysis doesn't even yield many electrons compared to energy harvesting's second phase, the Krebs (or citric acid) cycle. Yet, glycolysis takes place in all living things—at the very least, as the first phase in energy harvesting—and for certain primitive one-celled organisms it can be the *only* phase in energy harvesting.

All of this points to glycolysis as a more ancient form of energy harvesting than the other two phases. It existed first, and then at some later time the processes we now call the Krebs cycle and the ETC developed during the course of evolution. The critical factor in this change was the use of oxygen in energy

Figure 7.4
Overview of Energy Harvesting

harvesting—specifically the use of oxygen in the ETC. Because the products of glycolysis feed ultimately into the ETC, the entire three-stage energy-harvesting process is referred to as oxygen-dependent or *aerobic* energy transfer. Taken as a whole, the aerobic harvesting of energy is known as **cellular respiration.**

The separation between glycolysis and the other two phases is also a physical separation. In eukaryotic cells such as ours, glycolysis takes place in the watery material that lies outside the cell's nucleus—the cytosol—while the Krebs cycle and the ETC take place within tiny organelles, called mitochondria, that are immersed in the cytosol. Let's start now to look at all three phases of cellular respiration.

7.3 First Stage of Respiration: Glycolysis

Glycolysis, the first stage of energy harvesting, means "sugar splitting," which is appropriate because our starting molecule is the simple sugar glucose. Briefly, here is what happens during glycolysis. First, this one molecule of glucose has to be prepared, in a sense, for energy release. ATP actually has to be used, rather than synthesized, in two of the first steps of glycolysis, so that the relatively stable glucose can be put into the form of a less-stable sugar. This sugar is then split in half. The two molecules formed have three carbons each (whereas the starting glucose had six). Once this split is accomplished, the steps of glycolysis take place in duplicate; it is like taking one long piece of cloth, dividing it in two, and then proceeding to do the same things to both of the resulting pieces. **Figure 7.5** sets forth the individual steps of glycolysis.

Now, what are the results of these steps? Glycolysis accomplishes three valuable things in energy harvesting: It yields two ATP molecules, it yields two energized molecules of NADH, and it results in two molecules of pyruvic acid. These pyruvic acid molecules are the derivatives of the original glucose molecule. Now *they* are the molecules that will be oxidized—that will have electrons removed from them—in the next stage of energy harvesting. Keeping our eye on the ball here, we have some net ATP through glycolysis, some traveling electrons that will help make more ATP in the ETC, and a derivative of the original glucose molecule (pyruvic acid) that will now move to the next stage of energy harvesting, where more energy will be extracted from it.

Before continuing on to this next stage, you may wish to read more about what might be called the consequences of glycolysis. Even oxygen-using organisms such as ourselves rely on glycolysis when short bursts of energy are needed. And, as noted, for some organisms glycolysis is the end of the line in energy harvesting. You can read about this in "When Energy Harvesting Ends at Glycolysis" on page 130. Glycolysis

fits into a special place in providing energy for human exercise; you can read about this in "Energy and Exercise" on page 136.

You can read about this in "When Energy Harvesting Ends at Glycolysis" on page 130.

SO FAR . . .

1. The three main stages of oxygen-dependent or aerobic energy harvesting are _____, the _____ cycle, and the _____. The first of these takes place in the cell's _____, while the second and third take place in the cellular organelles called _____.

2. While the first two of these stages do yield some ATP, their most important contribution to energy harvesting is the channeling off of the _____ used to bring about the large harvest of ATP in _____.

3. Glycolysis nets two of energy harvesting's end-product molecules, _____, it yields two "loaded" molecules of the electron carrier _____, and it results in two molecules of the substrate _____, which are the downstream derivatives of the starting molecule of glucose.

7.4 Second Stage of Respiration: The Krebs Cycle

Since glycolysis yielded only 2 of the 36 molecules of ATP that eventually are harvested, the glucose derivative that resulted from glycolysis, pyruvic acid, still clearly has a lot of energy left in it. Some of this energy will be harvested in the second stage of cellular respiration, the **Krebs cycle.** This stage is named for the German-English biochemist Hans Krebs, who in the 1930s used the flight muscles of pigeons to find out how aerobic respiration works. Because the first product of the Krebs cycle is citric acid, the cycle is sometimes referred to as the **citric acid cycle.** The ATP yield in this cycle is once again a paltry 2 molecules, but the Krebs cycle serves to set the stage for the big harvest of ATP in the ETC by stripping our molecules of pyruvic acid of their energetic electrons and sending them to the ETC, as you'll see.

Site of Action Moves from the Cytosol to the Mitochondria

Glycolysis yielded its two molecules of pyruvic acid in the cytosol, but the site of energy harvesting quickly shifts, with the pyruvic acid, to the new site of energy transfer, the mitochondria. These organelles are where

Steps in glycolysis

1. Delivered by the bloodstream, glucose enters a cell and immediately has a phosphate group from ATP attached to it. Because this process, called phosphorylation, attaches the phosphate to the sixth carbon of glucose, it now goes under the name glucose-6-phosphate. Note that one molecule of ATP has been *used* in this step.

   ATP ledger now reads: -1 ATP

2. Glucose 6-phosphate is rearranged to become a molecule called fructose-6-phosphate.

3. Another molecule of ATP is used to add a second phosphate to fructose-6-phosphate, which now becomes fructose-1,6-diphosphate.

   ATP ledger now reads: -2 ATP

4. The single, six-carbon sugar fructose-1,6-diphosphate now becomes two molecules of a 3-carbon sugar, glyceraldehyde-3-phosphate, each with a phosphate group attached. From here on out, glycolysis happens in duplicate: What happens to one of the glyceraldehyde molecules happens to the other.

5. An enzyme brings together glyceraldehyde-3-phosphate, the electron carrier NAD$^+$, and a phosphate group. The glyceraldehyde-3-phosphate molecule is oxidized by NAD$^+$, which in its new form, NADH, moves to the electron transport chain bearing its electron cargo. The oxidation of NAD$^+$ is energetic enough that it allows the phosphate group to become attached to the main molecule, now called 1,3-diphosphoglyceric acid. Because everything is happening in duplicate, two NADH molecules are produced.

6. 1,3-diphosphoglyceric acid loses one of its phosphate groups, thus becoming 3-phosphoglyceric acid. The reaction is energetic enough to push this phosphate group onto an ADP molecule, yielding ATP. Because of duplication, two ATP are produced.

   ATP ledger now reads: 0 ATP

7. In two reactions, 3-phosphoglyceric acid becomes phosphoenolpyruvic acid, which generates more ATP as it transfers its phosphate group to ADP. Two more ATP molecules are produced. The phosphate transfer turns phosphoenolpyruvic acid into pyruvic acid—the derivative of the original glucose that now will enter the Krebs cycle.

   ATP ledger now reads: +2 ATP

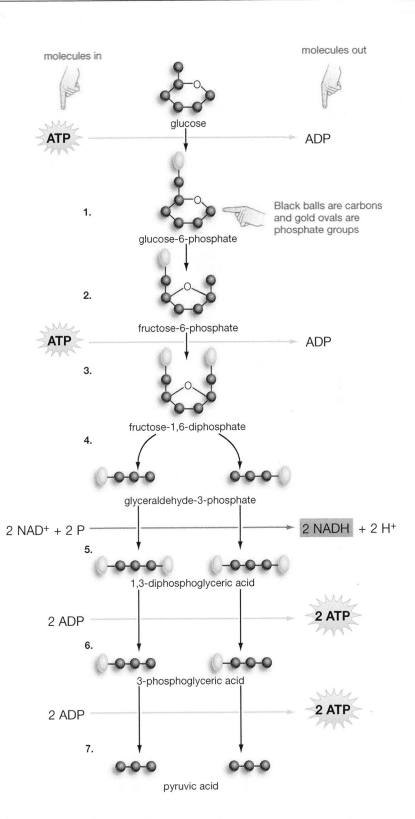

molecules in

molecules out

ATP ⟶ ADP
glucose

1. glucose-6-phosphate

Black balls are carbons and gold ovals are phosphate groups

2. fructose-6-phosphate

ATP ⟶ ADP

3. fructose-1,6-diphosphate

4. glyceraldehyde-3-phosphate

2 NAD$^+$ + 2 P ⟶ 2 NADH + 2 H$^+$

5. 1,3-diphosphoglyceric acid

2 ADP ⟶ **2 ATP**

6. 3-phosphoglyceric acid

2 ADP ⟶ **2 ATP**

7. pyruvic acid

Figure 7.5
Glycolysis

In glycolysis, the single glucose molecule is transformed in a series of steps into two molecules of a substance called pyruvic acid. These two molecules then move on to the next stage of cellular respiration (the Krebs cycle). Glycolysis also produces two molecules of electron-carrying NADH, which move to the electron transport chain. Although two molecules of ATP are used in the early stages of glycolysis, four are produced in the later stages, for a net production of two ATP.

ESSAY

When Energy Harvesting Ends at Glycolysis, Wine Can Be the Result

For yeasts, alcohol is simply a by-product of the fermentation they carry out.

Yeast Inside, Performing Fermentation
This man is inspecting wine that is fermenting in a barrel. The alcohol in the wine is a by-product of the glycolysis carried out by yeast in an oxygenless environment.

For some bacteria—and even sometimes for people—energy harvesting ends with the set of steps called glycolysis rather than proceeding on through the Krebs cycle and oxygen-dependent electron transport chain (ETC). When this happens, organisms need a way to recycle their energy transfer molecules in a way that doesn't depend on oxygen. The NADH they produced in glycolysis needs to lose its added electrons and become NAD^+ again, so it can be reused in glycolysis. The solution to this dilemma is a kind of electron dumping, the products of which turn out to be some of the most familiar substances in the world.

Fermentation in Yeast

Yeasts provide a good example of the way in which this works because yeasts are busy single-celled fungi that can live by glycolysis alone, or that can go through aerobic respiration. Say, then, that yeasts are working away on sugar, going through glycolysis, but doing so in an oxygenless environment. Recall that the final "substrate" product of glycolysis is two molecules of a substance called pyruvic acid. In yeasts, the pyruvic acid they end up with is converted to a molecule called acetaldehyde, and *it* takes on the electrons from NADH, meaning the recycling problem is now solved. Having taken on NADH's electrons, though, acetaldehyde now is converted to something very familiar: ethanol, better known as drinking alcohol.

Human beings *put* yeasts in environments in which this will happen, of course,

because this is how we make wine and beer. Imagine yeast cells inside a dark, airless wine cask, working away on burgundy grape juice, harvesting energy from the grape juice sugars, but in so doing turning out pyruvic acid, which is turned into alcohol. This continues until the alcohol content of the wine reaches a level (about 14 percent) at which the yeast can no longer survive in it. This whole process is known as *alcoholic fermentation*, the process by which yeasts produce alcohol as a by-product of glycolysis they perform in an oxygenless environment.

For yeasts, alcohol is simply a waste by-product of the glycolysis they employ in *anaerobic* energy conversion, meaning conversion in an oxygenless environment. The same is true of the carbon dioxide that also results from their conversion of pyruvic acid. Here again, humans have found great use for the refuse of nature. Put the right yeast into dough, and its continuing fermentation produces the CO_2 that causes bread to rise and become "light" because of the air holes now in it. (And the alcohol? It evaporates.)

Fermentation in Animals

Alcoholic fermentation is the process that fungi (and occasionally plants) employ to sustain glycolysis in the absence of oxygen. But animals take a different tack, because in them the product of glycolysis, pyruvic acid, accepts the electrons from NADH. In this process, pyruvic acid is turned into another substance: *lactic acid*. Thus, the

kind of fermentation that animals (and certain bacteria) carry out is called *lactate fermentation*. Have you ever experienced the muscle "burn" that comes with, for example, climbing several flights of stairs? If so, you have experienced a buildup of lactic acid in your muscles.

But why should this happen? Why should glycolysis ever end in lactate fermentation for us, when, unlike yeast, we always have access to oxygen? The problem turns out not to be a matter of oxygen access, but a matter of oxygen *delivery*. During a quick burst of energy use, oxygen cannot be delivered into our muscle cells fast enough to accommodate the big increase in our energy expenditure. When a muscle's capacity for aerobic energy transfer has reached its limit, it turns to glycolysis and lactate fermentation to supply more ATP. Note, however, that glycolysis and lactate fermentation are limited, short-term means of supplying energy in animals such as ourselves. These processes do not supply enough energy to sustain us for long; their role is to supply enough energy to meet our needs until such time as oxygen-aided energy transfer can ramp itself up.

Figure 7.6
Energy Transfer in the Mitochondria
Mitochondria are organelles, or "tiny organs," that exist within cells. They are the location for the second and third sets of steps in cellular respiration, the Krebs cycle and the electron transport chain, respectively.

cell

outer membrane

inner membrane

Mitochondrion

glycolysis

H^+ H^+ H^+ H^+

H^+ H^+ H^+

H^+ H^+

H^+

outer membrane

outer compartment

Krebs cycle

H^+

H^+

H^+

electron transport chain

e^- O_2

H^+

H_2O

inner membrane

inner compartment

cytosol

all the action takes place from here on out, so now would be a good time to look at **Figure 7.6** and examine their structure. You can see that mitochondria have both an inner and an outer membrane. The Krebs cycle reactions take place to the interior of the inner membrane—in an area known as the inner compartment—while the reactions of the ETC take place *within* the inner membrane.

Between Glycolysis and the Krebs Cycle, an Intermediate Step

There actually is a transition step in respiration between glycolysis and the Krebs cycle. In it, the three-carbon pyruvic acid molecule combines with a substance called coenzyme A, thus forming the substrate acetyl coen-

zyme A (acetyl CoA). One outcome of this reaction is that acetyl CoA enters the Krebs cycle as the derivative of the original glucose molecule. There are, however, two other products of this reaction. One is a carbon dioxide molecule that, like others you'll be seeing in the Krebs cycle, eventually diffuses out of the cell and into the bloodstream. This is conceptually an important point because *this* is the source of the carbon dioxide that we exhale with each breath. This CO_2 is officially a by-product of cellular respiration, but we could think of it as a waste product—a kind of exhaust that comes from the burning of food. The third product of this reaction is one more molecule of NADH, which finds its way to the ETC. This reaction takes place twice for each glucose molecule, as you can see in **Figure 7.7**, on the next page.

Into the Krebs Cycle

Acetyl CoA now enters the Krebs cycle. The reason this is a *cycle* becomes clear when you look at **Figure 7.8**. You can see that, in the first step of the cycle, acetyl CoA combines with a substance called oxaloacetic acid to produce citric acid. If you look over at about 11 o'clock on the circle, however, you can see that the last step in the cycle is the *synthesis* of oxaloacetic acid. Thus, a substance that's necessary for this chain of events to take place is itself a product of the chain.

Stroll around the circle now to see how the Krebs cycle functions in a little more detail. In essence, what's happening is that, as the entering acetyl CoA molecule is transformed into these various molecules, it is oxidized by electron carriers, with the resulting electrons moving on to the ETC. To look at this another way, the cycle starts with an energetic compound, citric acid, that is methodically stripped of electrons (and hence energy). Accordingly, ATP is also derived from this process, while CO_2 is a by-product. The only major player that's unfamiliar here is the FAD–$FADH_2$ that can be seen taking part in a redox reaction at about 8 o'clock. It is simply another electron carrier, similar to NAD^+/NADH.

In counting the Krebs cycle's yield of both ATP and electron carriers (NADHs and so on), note that *two* turns around this cycle result from the original glucose molecule (because it provided two molecules of the starting acetyl CoA). This means a total yield of 6 NADH, 2 $FADH_2$, and 2 ATP from Krebs for each glucose molecule.

Figure 7.7

Transition between Glycolysis and the Krebs Cycle

The pyruvic acid product of glycolysis does not enter directly into the Krebs cycle. Rather, it must first be transformed into acetyl coenzyme A. The consequences of this reaction are the production of CO_2, which diffuses into the bloodstream, and the production of an NADH molecule, which continues onto the electron transport chain.

SO FAR ...

1. In aerobic respiration, the pyruvic acid that is the product of glycolysis is converted to the molecule _____, which is the substrate that is transferred to the Krebs cycle.

2. In the Krebs cycle, the starting substrate is methodically stripped of _____, which then are transferred to the _____. Some ATP is produced in the cycle, as is the by-product _____.

3. Electrons are transferred to two different electron carriers in the Krebs cycle. One of these is the _____ carrier seen in glycolysis; the other is the carrier _____.

7.5 Third Stage of Respiration: The Electron Transport Chain

Having moved through the Krebs cycle, you've reached the final event in cellular respiration: the production of 34 more ATP molecules through the work of the **electron transport chain (ETC),** the third stage of aerobic energy harvesting. Glycolysis took place in the cytosol, and the Krebs cycle took place in the inner compartment of the mitochondria. Now, however, the action shifts to the mitochondrial inner membrane, the site of the ETC (**Figure 7.9**, on page 134). The "links" in this transport chain are a series of molecules. You've been looking for some time now at how NADH and $FADH_2$ carry off the electrons derived from glycolysis and the Krebs cycle. This is the destination of these electron carriers and their cargo.

Upon reaching the mitochondrial inner membrane, the electron carriers donate electrons and hydrogen ions to the ETC. Again, this is a trip down the energy hill, only *NADH* is now the molecule whose electrons exist at a higher energy level. Thus, when NADH runs into the appropriate enzyme in the ETC, NADH is oxidized, donating its electrons and proton to the ETC. This process then is simply repeated down the whole ETC, each carrier donating electrons to the next electron carrier in line. A carrier is reduced by receiving these electrons; donating them to the next carrier, it then returns to an oxidized state. Each carrier thus alternates between oxidized and reduced states.

Looking at Figure 7.9, you can see the carriers in the ETC: There are three large enzyme complexes with two smaller mobile molecules that link them. When NADH arrives at the inner membrane, it bumps into the ETC's first carrier and donates electrons to it; this carrier then donates these electrons to the next carrier, and so on down the line to the last electron acceptor, which is oxygen in the inner compartment (note the "$\left(\frac{1}{2}O_2\right)$," which will be explained shortly).

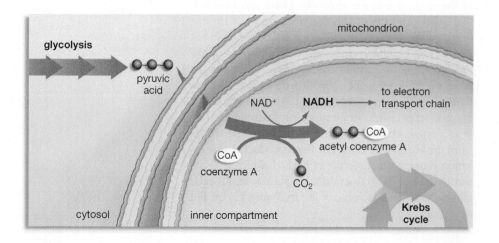

glycolysis

pyruvic acid

mitochondrion

NAD^+ **NADH** → to electron transport chain

CoA

acetyl coenzyme A

CoA

coenzyme A

CO_2

cytosol   inner compartment   **Krebs cycle**

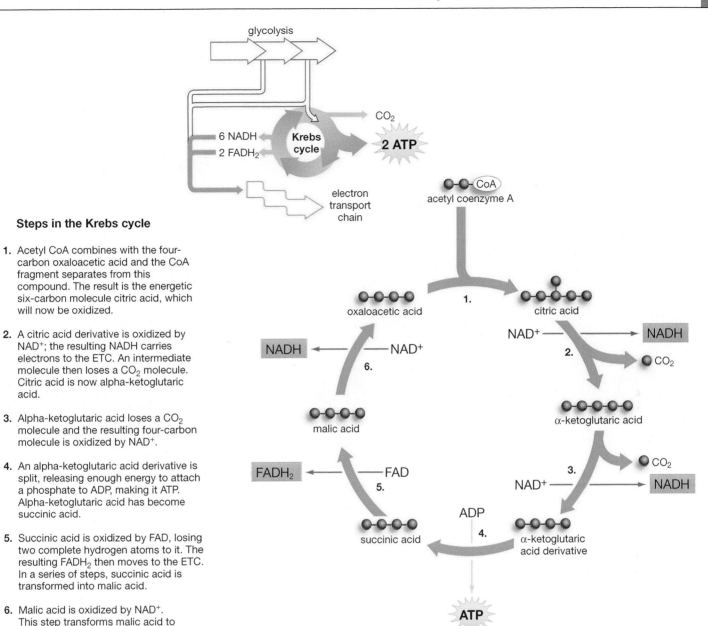

Steps in the Krebs cycle

1. Acetyl CoA combines with the four-carbon oxaloacetic acid and the CoA fragment separates from this compound. The result is the energetic six-carbon molecule citric acid, which will now be oxidized.

2. A citric acid derivative is oxidized by NAD^+; the resulting NADH carries electrons to the ETC. An intermediate molecule then loses a CO_2 molecule. Citric acid is now alpha-ketoglutaric acid.

3. Alpha-ketoglutaric acid loses a CO_2 molecule and the resulting four-carbon molecule is oxidized by NAD^+.

4. An alpha-ketoglutaric acid derivative is split, releasing enough energy to attach a phosphate to ADP, making it ATP. Alpha-ketoglutaric acid has become succinic acid.

5. Succinic acid is oxidized by FAD, losing two complete hydrogen atoms to it. The resulting $FADH_2$ then moves to the ETC. In a series of steps, succinic acid is transformed into malic acid.

6. Malic acid is oxidized by NAD^+. This step transforms malic acid to oxaloacetic acid—the molecule that enters the first step of the Krebs cycle.

Figure 7.8
The Krebs Cycle

The Krebs cycle is the major source of electrons that are transported to the electron transport chain by the carriers NADH and $FADH_2$. For each molecule of acetyl coenzyme A that enters the cycle, three NADH molecules, one $FADH_2$, and one ATP are produced. Because two acetyl CoA molecules enter per molecule of glucose, the yield per glucose is six NADH, two $FADH_2$, and two ATP.

Where's the ATP?

At this point, you may be tapping your foot, waiting for this promised harvest of ATP to appear. So far, all that's taken place is a transfer of electrons in the ETC. Well, note what happens in the first ETC enzyme complex. The movement of electrons through it releases enough energy to power the movement of *hydrogen ions* (H^+ ions) through the complex, pushing them from the inner compartment into the outer compartment. (The fall of the electrons causes the enzyme complex to change its shape in a way that facilitates the passage of H^+ ions through it and into the outer compartment.) By the time the electrons have completed their movement through the ETC, this pumping of H^+ ions will occur with the two other large enzyme complexes. Critically, these H^+ ions are being pumped *against* their concentration and electrical gradients. Put another way, the ions are being pumped up the energy hill with energy supplied by the *downhill* fall of electrons through the ETC.

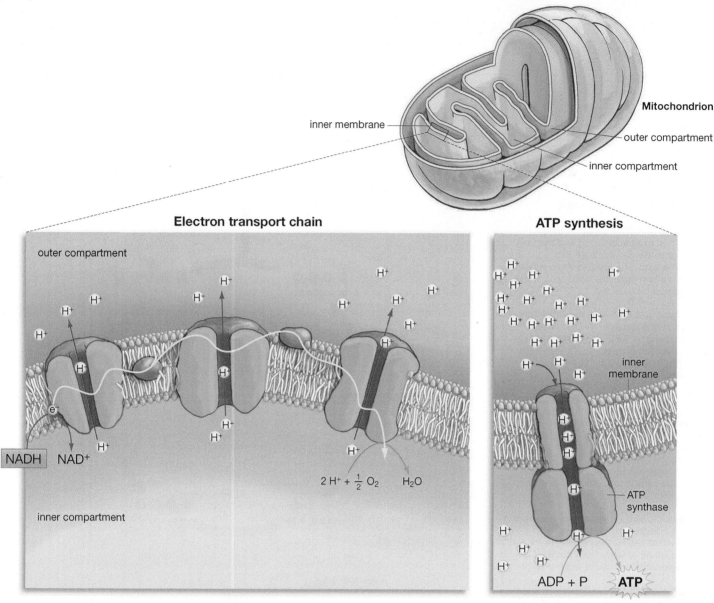

Figure 7.9
The Electron Transport Chain (ETC)

The movement of electrons through the ETC powers the process that provides the bulk of the ATP yield in respiration. The electrons carried by NADH and $FADH_2$ are released into the ETC and transported along its chain of molecules. The movement of electrons along the chain releases enough energy to power the pumping of hydrogen ions (H^+) across the membrane into the outer compartment of the mitochondrion. It is the subsequent energetic "fall" of the H^+ ions back into the inner compartment that drives the synthesis of ATP molecules by the enzyme ATP synthase.

Here's where the ATP is produced at last. The H^+ ions that have been pumped into the outer compartment now move back down their concentration and energy gradients, into the inner compartment, through a special enzyme called ATP synthase. This remarkable enzyme is driven by the H^+ ions flowing through it, which cause part of the enzyme to rotate (as fast as 100 revolutions per second). We could think of it as being something like a waterwheel, except that its movement is driven not by water, but by the movement of H^+ ions that are passing through it, on their way back into the inner com-

partment. It is this energetic spinning that puts a third phosphate group (P) onto ADP, thus making ATP. **ATP synthase** can thus be defined as an enzyme that functions in cellular respiration by bringing together ADP and inorganic phosphate molecules to produce ATP.

The basic mechanism here—the pumping of hydrogen ions powering the synthesis of ATP—was first proposed in 1961 by British biochemist Peter Mitchell, who won the Nobel Prize in 1978 for his contribution to bioenergetics. Lest we pass by it too quickly, note that in this mechanism, we can see the essence of aerobic respiration. In the links of the ETC, the downhill drop of electrons derived from food has powered the uphill synthesis of the molecule that supplies the energy for the vast majority of our activities.

The Reduction of Oxygen, the Production of Water

The story of the breakdown of glucose—the saga of *one molecule's* transformation!—is nearly complete. The only unfinished business lies at the end of the ETC. As noted earlier, oxygen is the final acceptor of the electrons that move through the ETC. In the mitochondrial inner compartment, a single oxygen atom $\left(\frac{1}{2}O_2\right)$ accepts two electrons from the last enzyme complex in the ETC and two H^+ ions. These then come together to produce H_2O: water, which is like CO_2 in that it's a by-product of cellular respiration.

This process for dealing with the electrons that made their way through respiration may sound like some minor housekeeping detail, but it's not. The electrons that are donated *to* the ETC by NADH and $FADH_2$ must be taken *from* the ETC somehow. To understand why, imagine a factory that makes, say, refrigerators. Now imagine that these refrigerators move down an assembly line on metal platforms, but that the platforms are suddenly allowed to start piling up at the end of the assembly line. Once this pile grows large enough, nothing can come off the end of the assembly line—indeed, the whole thing grinds to a halt. Just so, the body has an assembly line that results in both a product (ATP) and some materials that are used in manufacturing it (our de-energized electrons). Should these electrons not be taken away by oxygen, they would remain in place in the ETC—in its last enzyme complex. Should this happen, the complex would cease to accept electrons from the *previous* complex up the chain, and this process would continue until the whole assembly line would be "backed up" all the way to glycolysis. Some organisms (such as yeast) can get by with just the small amount of ATP that glycolysis provides, but this is not the case for large organisms such as ourselves. We must have the larger amount of energy provided by aerobic energy transfer. And ground zero for a *lack* of energy transfer in us is the brain, which has cells that are voracious users of energy. Five minutes without oxygen is enough to put a human being into the condition known as a persistent vegetative state. We need to breathe because the energy assembly line will only keep moving if the electrons that are part of it are taken away by oxygen.

Bountiful Harvest: ATP Accounting

Let's think for a moment about what might be called the ATP accounting in our story. In the ETC, each NADH molecule will be responsible for the production of three molecules of ATP. And how many NADH are coming? Ten: two produced in glycolysis, two from pyruvic acid conversion, and six from the Krebs cycle. Each $FADH_2$ carrier joins the ETC a little later than does NADH and as such is responsible for roughly two ATP. And how many $FADH_2$ are coming? Two, both of them produced in the Krebs cycle. When we put the $FADH_2$ and NADH output together, we find that 34 ATP are produced in the ETC as a result of the electrons brought by these carriers. Given this, think about what a mighty energy extractor the ETC is: 34 ATP compared to two in glycolysis. Imagine one car that got 34 miles to the gallon compared to another that got two. Our final accounting on ATP yield is the 34 from the ETC, plus the two from glycolysis, plus two from the Krebs cycle, yielding 38 in all. From this, we need to subtract two ATP that are spent transporting the NADH produced in glycolysis into the mitochondria. The final result is thus a maximum of 36 net ATP per molecule of glucose from all the steps of aerobic respiration.

7.6 Other Foods, Other Respiratory Pathways

By looking at aerobic respiration as it applies to glucose, which served as our starting food molecule, you've been able to go through the whole respiratory chain, but there are many kinds of nutrients besides glucose—for example, fats, proteins, and other sugars. All these can provide energy by being oxidized within the chain of reactions you've just gone over. However, none of them proceeds through the chain in exactly the same way as glucose. Instead, various nutrients can be channeled into the cell respiration chain in different ways.

To give one example of how this channeling of nutrients works, consider the possible fates of triglycerides. As you learned in Chapter 3, triglycerides are fats made of a three-carbon glycerol "head" and three long hydrocarbon chains that look like tines on a fork. Imagine that a given cell needs energy from fat. The question is, how do triglycerides go through aerobic respiration, as opposed to glucose?

The first thing that happens is that a triglyceride molecule is split by enzymes into its constituent parts of fatty acids and glycerol. Glycerol is then converted into glyceraldehyde phosphate. This formidable name may not ring a bell, but if you look back at step 4 in Figure 7.5, you'll see that it's one of the downstream derivatives of glucose in glycolysis. To put this another way, glycerol does not first get converted to glucose and then march through all of the steps of glycolysis. Instead, it joins the glycolytic pathway several steps down from glucose and

Energy and Exercise

One minute we're sleeping, the next we're looking for our running shoes, and 10 minutes after that we're bounding down the road trying to cover three miles at a faster pace than yesterday. Coming to the steep hill at the end of our run, we go all out—charging to the top of it, slowing only after we start going downhill, breathless and spent. How can the human body cope with a range of energy demands that runs from sleeping to sprinting? Its secret is having a kind of energy trio at its service, with each member of the group specializing in delivering energy in particular situations.

The essence of any kind of exercise is the contraction of muscles, and the only energy molecule that can power the contraction of skeletal muscle is ATP. You have seen that the human body uses a three-stage process to produce ATP: glycolysis, the Krebs cycle, and the electron transport chain (ETC). As a whole, this system is dependent on oxygen, but glycolysis is not directly dependent on it. For brief periods

of time, we can produce a good deal of the ATP we need through a glycolysis that is decoupled from the Krebs cycle and the ETC. Oxygen-independent glycolysis can thus be thought of as the first member of the body's energy trio, while *aerobic* or oxygen-using energy transfer can be thought of as the second member. Our cells also have a capacity to *store* small amounts of ATP, however, and they can also stockpile another molecule, phosphocreatine (PCr), that acts as a reservoir of phosphate groups that can be used to produce ATP. This stored ATP/PCr is the third member of the energy ensemble. Let's now see how all three players would work together in the course of a bike ride, starting out at a fairly brisk pace.

With the first turns of the pedals, bike riders bump up their body's energy demands tremendously. In their cycling, they could easily burn up 10 times the calories they would while in a resting state. (As a point of comparison, in doing housework a person typically burns up

about three times the calories he or she does while at rest.)

So, how do muscle cells accommodate such large increases in their need for ATP? In the first few seconds, the small reservoirs of ATP/PCr take the lead role, with a proportionately smaller contribution from glycolysis and a smaller contribution yet from aerobic metabolism. These differences reflect the time it takes for each of these systems to get going. You've seen how many steps there are in glycolysis and how many *more* steps there are in the Krebs cycle and ETC. By comparison, the output of ATP from stored ATP/PCr is instantaneous. Remember, though, that the ATP/PCr reservoir is small. A person who had to depend solely on it for a full-ahead sprint would have only enough energy to last about six seconds. On a longer bike ride, glycolysis and ATP/PCr are contributing roughly equal amounts of ATP within 10 seconds. Within 30 seconds, glycolysis has greatly eclipsed PCr as an energy provider.

At about this same 30-second mark, the third player, aerobic respiration, is supplying only about 20 percent of the ATP, but its contribution is growing fast. In **Figure 1**, you can see how the aerobic contribution to ATP yield grows over the

Figure 7.10
Many Respiratory Pathways

Glucose is not the only starting material for cellular respiration. Other carbohydrates, proteins, and fats can also be used as fuel for cellular respiration. These reactants enter the process at different stages.

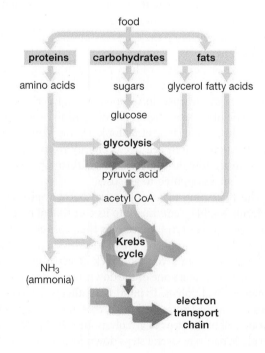

is then converted to pyruvic acid. Then, as pyruvic acid, it goes through the Krebs cycle and ETC, producing ATP. And the fatty acids? They are converted to acetyl CoA, which you may remember is the substrate that enters the Krebs cycle, yielding energy by becoming oxidized there. In **Figure 7.10**, you can see a summary of the way foods are broken down through various respiratory pathways.

On to Photosynthesis

This long walk through cellular respiration has illustrated how living things harvest energy from food. Recall, however, that almost all living things have one source to thank for this food: the sun's energy, which plants capture and then lock up in a sugar they produce. This capture of energy takes place through a process that has a beautiful symmetry with the cellular respiration you've just looked at. The process in question is called photosynthesis.

course of a long, strenuous workout. At the start, oxygen-dependent respiration is supplying less than 10 percent of our ATP, but 10 minutes into the workout it is delivering 85 percent.

You might think that this would be the final division of ATP contributions among the three players, but the amounts they supply can vary over time, depending on the intensity of the activity. **Figure 2**

shows how this would work in an actual professional-level bicycle race. Going along at a steady state in "pack" riding, you can see the overriding contribution of aerobic metabolism. In the final sprint, however, stores of ATP/PCr—replenished during the pack riding—are fully used, with the contribution of glycolysis increasing as well. In stretches of difficult hill climbing, meanwhile, glycolysis is fully used.

Of course, lots of sports have no aerobic component to them. The energy for a sport like football is supplied almost entirely by stored ATP/PCr. Even in a competition as long as a 400-meter sprint—about once around a regulation track—about 70 percent of the energy comes from a combination of ATP/PCr and glycolysis.

Duration of maximal exercise

	Seconds			Minutes					
	10	30	60	2	4	10	30	60	120
Percent anaerobic	90	80	70	50	35	15	5	2	1
Percent aerobic	10	20	30	50	65	85	95	98	99

Figure 1
Different Contributions over Time

Relative contributions of anaerobic and aerobic respiration to exercise during the duration of a workout. "Anaerobic" here means a combination of glycolysis and stored ATP/PCr release.

(Adapted from P. O. Astrand and K. Rodahl, *Textbook of Work Physiology*. New York: McGraw Hill Book Company, © 1977.)

Figure 2
Different Activities, Different Energy Stores

Energy-harvesting processes used at different stages in a bicycle race.

(Adapted from J. T. Kearney, "Training the Olympic Athletes." *Scientific American*, June 1996, p. 54.)

SO FAR . . .

1. In the electron transport chain (ETC), the electron carriers NADH and $FADH_2$ _____ electrons to a series of enzyme complexes located within the inner _____ of the mitochondria. The energetic downhill drop of this electron transfer powers the movement of _____ into the outer compartment of the mitochondria.

2. The physical movement of _____ back into the inner compartment through the enzyme _____ is a downhill energetic drop that powers the process by which _____ are added to ADP, thus yielding _____.

3. The electrons picked up at various stages of energy harvesting by NADH and $FADH_2$ must be accepted by _____ at the end of the ETC if energy transfer is to continue.

7 REVIEW

Go to the Study Area at www.masteringbiology.com for practice quizzes, myeBook, BioFlix™ 3-D animations, MP3 Tutor Sessions, videos, current events, and more.

Summary

7.1 Energizing ATP

- The molecule ATP dispenses the energy for most of the activities carried out by living things. To produce ATP, a third phosphate group must be added to ADP, a process that in animals is powered by the energetic fall of electrons derived from food. (p. 124)

- Electron transfer in the production of ATP works through redox reactions, in which one substance loses electrons to another. The substance that loses electrons in a redox reaction is said to have been oxidized; the substance that gains electrons is said to have been reduced. (p. 124)

- Electrons are carried between one part of the energy-harvesting process and another by electron carriers, the most important of which is NAD. In its "empty" state, this molecule exists as NAD$^+$. Through a redox reaction, it picks up one hydrogen atom and another single electron from food, thus becoming NADH, a form it will retain until it drops off its energetic electrons (and a proton) in a later stage of the energy-harvesting process. (p. 125)

7.2 The Three Stages of Cellular Respiration

- The three principal stages of harvesting energy from food are glycolysis, the Krebs cycle, and the electron transport chain (ETC). Collectively, this three-stage, oxygen-dependent process is known as cellular respiration. For most organisms, glycolysis serves as a primary means of energy extraction only in certain limited situations, but it must take place for the Krebs cycle and ETC processes to go forward. (p. 126)

- Glycolysis is carried out in the cell's cytosol while the Krebs cycle and the ETC

take place in the organelles called mitochondria, which lie within the cytosol. Glycolysis yields 2 net molecules of ATP per molecule of glucose, as does the Krebs cycle, while the ETC yields a maximum of 32 ATP molecules. Glycolysis and the Krebs cycle are critical to the ETC, however, in that they yield electrons that are utilized in it. (p. 126)

BioFlix

Cellular Respiration

7.3 First Stage of Respiration: Glycolysis

- When glycolysis begins with a single molecule of glucose, the products are two molecules of NADH (which move to the ETC, bearing their energetic electrons) and two molecules of ATP (which are ready to be used). Glycolysis also produces two molecules of pyruvic acid—the derivatives of the original glucose molecule—which move on to the Krebs cycle. (p. 128)

7.4 Second Stage of Respiration: The Krebs Cycle

- In the transition between glycolysis and the Krebs cycle, each pyruvic acid molecule that was produced in glycolysis combines with coenzyme A, thus forming acetyl CoA, which enters the Krebs cycle. Carbon dioxide (which diffuses to the bloodstream) is another product of this reaction, as is one more molecule of NADH (which moves to the ETC). (p. 131)

- In the Krebs (or citric acid) cycle, the derivatives of the original glucose molecule are oxidized, thus yielding more energetic electrons that are transported by NADH and the electron carrier FADH$_2$ to the ETC. The net energy yield of the Krebs cycle is six molecules of NADH, two molecules of FADH$_2$, and two molecules of ATP per molecule of glucose. (p. 132)

7.5 Third Stage of Respiration: The Electron Transport Chain

- The ETC is a series of molecules located within the mitochondrial inner membrane. On reaching the ETC, NADH and FADH$_2$ are oxidized by molecules in the chain. Each carrier in the chain is then reduced by accepting electrons from the carrier that came before it. The last electron acceptor in the ETC is oxygen. (p. 132)

- The movement of electrons through the ETC releases enough energy to power the movement of hydrogen ions through the three ETC protein complexes, moving them from the mitochondrion's inner compartment to its outer compartment. The movement of these ions down their concentration and charge gradients, back into the inner compartment through an enzyme called ATP synthase, drives the synthesis of ATP from ADP and phosphate. In the inner compartment, oxygen accepts hydrogen ions and electrons from the ETC, forming water. If oxygen is not present to accept the ETC electrons, the energy-harvesting process downstream from glycolysis comes to a halt. (p. 133)

7.6 Other Foods, Other Respiratory Pathways

- Different nutrients and their derivatives can be channeled through different pathways in cellular respiration in accordance with the needs of an organism. (p. 135)

Key Terms

Understanding the Basics

Multiple-Choice Questions

(Answers are in the back of the book.)

1. You need energy to think, to keep your heart beating, to play a sport, and to study this book. This energy is directly dispensed by _____, which is produced in the process of cellular respiration.
   a. enzymes
   b. ATP
   c. NAD^+
   d. vitamins
   e. proteins

2. Energy transfer in living things works through redox reactions, in which one substance is _____ by another substance, thereby _____.
   a. oxidized ... losing electrons to it
   b. transported ... becoming more energetic
   c. digested ... becoming more energetic
   d. reduced ... losing electrons to it
   e. oxidized ... gaining electrons from it

3. _____ and _____ are important not so much for the ATP produced in them, but for their _____.
   a. Glycolysis ... the Krebs cycle ... yield of electrons transported to the ETC
   b. Glycolysis ... the ETC ... yield of electrons transported to the cytosol
   c. Redox reactions ... fatty acid breakdown ... yield of calories
   d. The Krebs cycle ... the ETC ... numerous redox reactions
   e. The Krebs cycle ... the ETC ... fatty acid breakdown

4. The carbon dioxide we exhale with each breath is produced in _____ and in _____. This CO_2 can be thought of as a(n) _____ of cellular respiration.
   a. glycolysis ... the ETC ... waste product
   b. glycolysis ... the ETC ... ultimate product
   c. the formation of acetyl CoA ... the Krebs cycle ... waste product
   d. glycolysis ... the Krebs cycle ... intermediate product
   e. Krebs cycle ... the reduction of water ... intermediate product

5. At most, how many net molecules of ATP can be produced per glucose molecule in cellular respiration?
   a. 2
   b. 8
   c. 24
   d. 36
   e. 72

6. Where does the Krebs cycle occur in this model of a mitochondrion?

   a. A
   b. B
   c. C
   d. D
   e. none of these

7. When NADH passes its electrons to the ETC, it is
   a. electrolyzed.
   b. polarized.
   c. reduced.
   d. oxidized.
   e. deformed.

8. We need to breathe because we need
   a. both atmospheric nitrogen and the oxygen for energy transformation.
   b. oxygen to donate electrons to NAD+.
   c. nitrogen to donate phosphate groups to oxygen.
   d. oxygen to act as the final acceptor of electrons in the ETC.
   e. oxygen to donate phosphate groups to ADP, making it ATP.

Brief Review

(Answers are in the back of the book.)

1. Living things need ATP to power most of the processes that go on within them. In essence, how does cellular respiration yield this ATP?

2. Where do you expect people would have more mitochondria: their skin cells or their muscle cells? Why?

3. In the ETC, what is physically moved across the inner membrane—and energetically moved to a higher state—to drive the attachment of phosphate groups to ADP?

4. Where does the energy come from that powers this movement across the inner membrane in the ETC?

5. Most of the ATP we use is produced in the ETC. So, when we have to run across the street to avoid traffic, does the ATP we are using come primarily from the ETC?

Applying Your Knowledge

1. In Madeleine L'Engle's children's novel *A Wrinkle in Time*, the mitochondria in one of the characters start to die. Describe what would happen to people who lost their mitochondria and explain why it would happen.

2. Most of the heat in the human body is generated within mitochondria. Why should this be?

3. The food we eat is broken down in our digestive tract, but where are most of the calories in this food actually "burned"?

The Green World's Gift:

Photosynthesis

Plants use the sun's energy to make their own food—and ours.

Energy from the sun helps produce the food that sustains nearly all living things.

On a summer's evening, out by a pond as the sun is going down, nature tunes up her symphony. The crickets bring their chirping to the fore, while frogs chime in with their own countermelody. Silently, something else is changing as the last light fades: The green world is shutting down. Microscopic pores that dot the undersides of leaves are closing

up, ceasing to be openings for the carbon dioxide that flows in and the water vapor that flows out during the day. The green world is alive at night, but it is only fully active during the day, when a special talent that it has is set in motion by the warm rays of the sun.

8.1 Photosynthesis and Energy

The green world's special talent is called photosynthesis, and the wonder of it can perhaps best be appreciated by imagining what life would be like if we humans possessed it. The bone and muscle within us—and the energy to make them work—come from the foods we eat: carbohydrates, fats, and proteins. Imagine, though, having the ability to flourish simply by spending time in the sun and having access to three things: water, small amounts of minerals, and carbon dioxide. In this condition, we would not *eat* carbohydrates in the usual forms (bread, sugar, potatoes). Rather, we would transform the simple gas carbon dioxide *into* carbohydrates using nothing more than water, minerals, and sunlight. Carbohydrates produced in this way are as useful as any food; they can be stored away as starches, used to provide ATP for energy needs, or transformed to make proteins. This, then, is what plants do: *They make their own food.* They use the energy provided by the sun to take a simple gas, carbon dioxide, join it to a carbohydrate (a sugar), and then *energize* that sugar, thus transforming it into food. In this activity, they are joined by a variety of other photosynthesizing organisms (**Figure 8.1**).

From Plants, a Great Bounty for Animals

The process of photosynthesis is not only good for plants; it's good for other living things, including animals, since most of the living world ultimately depends on photosynthesis for food. Try naming something you eat that isn't a plant or doesn't itself eat plants to survive, and you will come up with a very short list indeed.

Food, however, is only half the bounty that plants provide. A by-product of photosynthesis—a kind of castoff from the work of plants—is oxygen. As part of photosynthesis, plants break water molecules apart. In doing so, they use electrons and protons from H_2O, but they leave behind oxygen molecules (O_2). This is the oxygen that exists in our atmosphere; it is the oxygen that we breathe in every minute of every day or suffer the mortal consequences.

With this, you can step back and begin to view the largest picture of them all with respect to energy flow in living things. It is a great pathway in which energy comes from the sun and then, in photosynthesis, is stored in plants in the chemical bonds of the carbohydrates they produce. Thus stored—in such forms as wheat grains or grass leaves—these carbohydrates

Figure 8.1
Three Types of Photosynthesizers

Photosynthesis is carried out not only by familiar plants, such as these sunflowers **(a)**, but also by algae, such as this giant kelp **(b)**, and by some bacteria, such as these cyanobacteria **(c)**.

(a) Sunflowers (plants)   **(b)** Giant kelp (algae)   **(c)** Cyanobacteria (bacteria)

Figure 8.2
Energy flows through the living world in two great phases. The first of these is photosynthesis, in which the sun's energy is captured by plants and then stored within them. The second is cellular respiration, in which this stored energy is extracted and then transferred to ATP, which in turn powers most of the activities that organisms undertake.

The process of cellular respiration converts the energy stored in carbohydrates to ATP, the most important energy-transfer molecule in living things.

ATP ⟶ Powers many chemical reactions

Figure 8.3
The Electromagnetic Spectrum

Sunlight is composed of rays of many different wavelengths, but we can see only those in the visible light range (represented by the color spectrum). When the light of the sun shines on a green leaf, it is primarily the sun's green rays that are reflected, while frequencies in other ranges are absorbed; frequencies in the red and blue ranges drive photosynthesis most strongly.

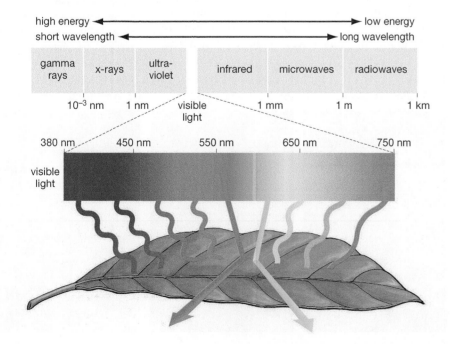

can be broken down and used, either by the plants themselves or by the organisms that eat them. The breakdown of this food ends with the "cellular respiration" covered last chapter that provides ATP. If you look at **Figure 8.2**, you can see this whole process displayed in graphic form.

Note that photosynthesis and cellular respiration are trips up and down the energy hill that became so familiar in Chapter 7. In respiration, the trip was down the hill, meaning from more stored energy (in food) to less, as the food was broken down to produce ATP. Photosynthesis is a trip up the energy hill. Here, electrons are removed from water, boosted to a more energetic state by the power of sunlight, and then brought together with a sugar and carbon dioxide, resulting in an energy-rich sugar—food in the form of a carbohydrate. The story of how this carbohydrate production is accomplished is the subject of this chapter. To encapsulate this story in a definition, **photosynthesis** is the process by which certain groups

of organisms capture energy from sunlight and convert this solar energy into chemical energy that is initially stored in a carbohydrate.

We could think of this process in terms of a kind of recipe—a formula that shows us what "ingredients" go into photosynthesis and what products come out.

sunlight energy

$$6CO_2 + 6H_2O \rightarrow C_6H_{12}O_6 + 6O_2$$

Over on the left, you can see six molecules of carbon dioxide ($6CO_2$) and six molecules of water ($6H_2O$) as starting ingredients (or "reactants"), and then on the right is a molecule of glucose ($C_6H_{12}O_6$) and six molecules of oxygen ($6O_2$) as products. Intervening in the middle, and driving the whole process, is the energy contained in the rays of the sun.

8.2 The Components of Photosynthesis

We can think of photosynthesis as starting with the absorption of sunlight by leaves. *Absorption* here means just what it sounds like: Light is taken in by the leaves. Actually, leaves capture only a *portion* of the light that falls on them. The sunlight that makes it to the Earth's surface is composed of a spectrum of energetic rays (measured by their "wavelengths") that range from very short ultraviolet rays, through visible light rays, to the longer and less-energetic infrared rays. (In **Figure 8.3** you can see that these wavelengths are, in turn, part of a larger range of electromagnetic radiation.) Photosynthesis is driven by part of the *visible light* spectrum—mainly by blue and red light of certain wavelengths. Tune a laser to emit blue light of a certain wavelength, shine this beam on a plant, and the plant will absorb a great deal of this light. Tune the laser to emit *green* light, on the other hand, and the plant will reflect most of this light. This is why plants are green: They strongly reflect the green portion of the visible light spectrum.

Where Does Photosynthesis Occur?

So, where is this light absorption occurring within plants? To answer this question, you need to know something about the primary playing fields of photosynthesis: leaves.

If you look at the idealized leaf in **Figure 8.4**, you can see that it can be likened to a kind of cellular sandwich, with one layer of outer (or epidermal) cells at the top, another layer of epidermal cells at the bottom, and several layers of mesophyll cells in between. Take time now to read through Figure 8.4's drawings and captions; as you do, you'll go from the leaf's layers of cells, then into the cells themselves, and then into the tiny structures *within* the cells—the organelles called chloroplasts—that are the actual sites of photosynthesis.

Here is some detail on the structures seen in Figure 8.4. The **stomata** seen in the figure are the microscopic pores, mentioned at the start of the chapter, that open during the day to let carbon dioxide pass

Figure 8.4
Site of
Photosynthesis

1. Leaf

The primary site of photosynthesis in plants, leaves have a two-part structure: a petiole (or stalk) and a blade (normally thought of as the leaf).

2. Leaf cross section

In cross section, leaves have a sandwich-like structure, with epidermal layers at top and bottom and mesophyll cells in between. Most photosynthesis is performed within mesophyll cells. Leaf epidermis is pocked with a large number of microscopic openings, called stomata, that allow carbon dioxide to pass in and water vapor to pass out.

3. Mesophyll cell

A single mesophyll cell within a leaf contains all the component parts of plant cells in general, including the organelles—called chloroplasts—that are the actual sites of photosynthesis.

4. Chloroplast

Each chloroplast has an outer membrane at its periphery; then an inner membrane; then a liquid material, called the stroma, that has immersed within it a network of membranes, the thylakoids. These thylakoids sometimes stack on one another to create a granum.

5. Granum

Electrons used in photosynthesis will come from water contained in the thylakoid compartment, and all the steps of photosynthesis will take place either within the thylakoid membrane, or in the stroma that surrounds the thylakoids.

petiole

blade

epidermis

mesophyll cells

epidermis

stomata

nucleus

chloroplast

cell wall

vacuole

thylakoids

stroma

granum

inner membrane

outer membrane

Energy from sunlight is absorbed by pigments in the thylakoid membrane.

thylakoid

thylakoid membrane

thylakoid compartment

into leaves and water vapor pass out of them. There is no shortage of stomata for this work; a given square centimeter of plant leaf may contain from a thousand to a hundred thousand of them.

Going down a couple of levels, **chloroplasts** can be defined as the organelles within plant and algae cells that are the sites of photosynthesis. Anywhere from one to several hundred of these oblong structures might exist within a given leaf cell, each one capable of carrying out photosynthesis on its own. As Figure 8.4 shows, chloroplasts present another example of something you've seen before—membranes within membranes. The chloroplast has outer and inner membranes at its periphery. Inside them, in the interior of the chloroplast, there is a network of chloroplast membranes, active in photosynthesis, called **thylakoids.** (These thylakoids often stack on top of one another like so many pancakes, creating structures called *grana*.) Thylakoids are immersed in the liquid material of the chloroplast, the **stroma.** Keep your eye on the thylakoid membranes and on the stroma because all the steps of photosynthesis occur in one of these two places.

The thylakoid membranes are, in fact, the place where photosynthesis starts, with the absorption of sunlight we just talked about. Any compound that strongly absorbs certain visible wavelengths of sunlight is called a *pigment*. Thylakoid membranes contain a pigment, called **chlorophyll a,** that can be defined as the primary pigment active in plant photosynthesis. Chlorophyll *a* is then aided by several substances known as *accessory pigments*, which do just what their name implies: They aid chlorophyll *a* in absorbing energetic rays from the sun, after which they pass the absorbed energy along.

The Two Essential Stages in Photosynthesis

Keeping these structures and concepts in mind, you can now begin tracing the steps of photosynthesis. It is helpful to divide photosynthesis into two main stages. In the first stage (the *photo* of photosynthesis), the power of sunlight will do two things—strip water of electrons and then boost these electrons to a higher energy level. Thus boosted, the electrons are passed along through a series of electron carriers similar to those introduced in Chapter 7. All of this takes place in the thylakoid membranes. This first stage of photosynthesis ends when the original, energized electrons get attached to a mobile electron carrier, called NADP$^+$, that transports them to the second set of reactions. In this second stage (the *synthesis* of photosynthesis), the electrons come together with carbon dioxide and a sugar. The attachment of the electrons and CO_2 to this sugar produces a high-energy sugar—meaning food. This second stage takes place in the stroma of the chloroplast.

The steps in the first stage of photosynthesis obviously depend directly on sunlight. Thus, these steps are sometimes referred to as the *light reactions*. Meanwhile, the second set of steps is referred to as the *Calvin cycle*, in honor of Melvin Calvin, the scientist who first revealed their details. You will be following both sets of steps as they occur in time—that is, from the collection of sunlight to the synthesis of carbohydrates.

The Working Units of the Light Reactions

Looking first at the light reactions, we see that they take place within a set of working units. Each of these units is a **photosystem**—an organized complex of molecules within a thylakoid membrane that, in photosynthesis, collects solar energy and transforms it into chemical energy. If you look at **Figure 8.5**, you can see the components that make up a photosystem. First, there is a group of a few hundred pigment molecules that serve to absorb the sunlight. The majority of these molecules—most of the chlorophyll *a* and all of the accessory pigments—serve only as "antennae" that absorb energy from the sun and pass it on. At the center of the antennae system, however, there is a **reaction center**—a pair of special chlorophyll *a* molecules and associated compounds that first receive the solar energy from photosystem pigments

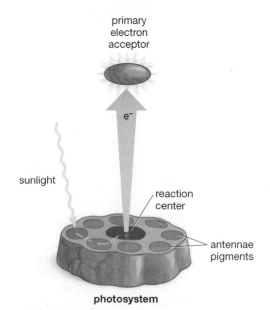

Figure 8.5
The Working Units of Photosynthesis
Photosystems are multipart units that bring together electrons derived from water and energy derived from the sun. Hundreds of antennae pigments absorb sunlight and transfer solar energy to the photosystem's reaction center. This energy gives a boost to an electron within the reaction center in two ways: It physically moves the electron to the center's primary electron acceptor, and it moves the electron up the energy hill to a more energetic state.

and then transform this solar energy into chemical energy. As you can see in Figure 8.5, the reaction center includes a molecule that could be thought of as the first recipient of the absorbed solar energy, the *primary electron acceptor*.

You could conceptualize photosynthesis as beginning when sunlight is absorbed by any of the hundreds of antennae pigment molecules in a photosystem unit. The absorbed energy is then passed on to the pair of chlorophyll *a* molecules in a reaction center. As a result, electrons from this pair are "moved" in a couple of ways, one physical and one metaphorical. Physically, these electrons are transferred to the primary electron acceptor. You also could think of the initial "distance traveled" by the electrons in a metaphorical way, however: as a movement up the energy hill. The energy from sunlight is pumping the electrons up the hill in photosynthesis.

Energy Transfer through Redox Reactions

How can electrons be transferred from one molecule to another? Recall from Chapter 7 that some substances have a tendency to *lose* electrons to other substances, and that any time one substance loses (or "donates") electrons to another, it is said to have been oxidized. Meanwhile, the substance that gained elec-

trons is said to have been reduced. These two reactions always happen together; if one substance is oxidized, another must be reduced. This kind of reduction-oxidation reaction has a shorter name: a *redox reaction*.

Many of the photosynthetic steps you will be seeing are redox reactions. Indeed, you have already seen one. The movement of electrons within the reaction center—from the chlorophyll *a* molecules to the primary electron acceptor—is a redox reaction. The chlorophyll molecules were oxidized by the primary electron acceptor, meaning they lost electrons to it. What happens in the light reactions is a continuation of this energy transfer: Electrons are passed on by means of one electron carrier oxidizing another.

As electrons physically move through the light reactions in this way, they are also moving both up and down the energy hill—they are becoming first more and then less energetic. If you look at **Figure 8.6**, you can trace their movement up and down the energy hill as they make their journey through the electron transport chain you can see there. With energy supplied by the sun, electrons are pumped up a couple of formidable energy gradients (in photosystems II and I) only to come partway back down them as they "seek" their lowest energy state. Critically, they are releasing energy as they fall—just as a boulder releases energy by rolling downhill.

Figure 8.6
Collecting Solar Energy, Boosting Electrons
The solar energy gathered by photosystems II and I is used to energize electrons that exist within the photosystems' reaction centers. Energetically, the electrons are boosted up, and then move down, two energy hills. Physically, they first move to primary electron acceptors and then down electron transport chains until they are at last taken up by $NADP^+$ to form NADPH. The NADPH molecules then transfer the electrons to the Calvin cycle, in which they are used to make sugars.

SO FAR . . .

1. In photosynthesis, the power of the sun is used to boost the energy of _____ that are derived from water and bring them together with both a low-energy sugar and _____ from the atmosphere, thus producing an energy-rich _____, meaning food.

2. In plants, photosynthesis takes place within the organelles called _____, which are found most abundantly in certain cells that make up the interior portions of _____. Pigments within the membranes of these organelles, in particular a pigment called _____, serve to absorb sunlight, which provides the energy that drives photosynthesis.

3. Photosynthesis can be divided into two major sets of steps. In the first set, known as the _____, absorbed solar energy moves electrons derived from water in two ways: (a) physically to a molecule called a _____ and (b) metaphorically to a higher _____.

8.3 Stage 1: The Light Reactions

With these components and processes in mind, let's trace the steps of the light reactions (Figure 8.6). The first step is that solar energy, collected by photosystem II's antennae molecules, arrives at the reaction center. This energy then gives a boost to an electron in the reaction center in the two ways noted: The electron *physically* moves to another part of the reaction center complex, the primary electron acceptor, and is also pumped up the energy hill. With this activity, the reaction center chlorophyll has *lost* an electron. That loss leaves an energy "hole" in this chlorophyll, making it an oxidizing agent. With the energy provided by this imbalance, a special enzyme in the reaction center splits water molecules that lie within the thylakoid compartment. These water molecules are now being oxidized, which means *they* are losing electrons. The electrons travel to the reaction center, where they will be the next electrons in line for an energy boost.

A Chain of Redox Reactions and Another Boost from the Sun

By following Figure 8.6 in a general way, you can see what happens next to electrons that are boosted in photosystem II. After arriving at the primary electron acceptor, they fall back down the energy hill as they are transferred through a series of electron transport chain molecules, each oxidizing its predecessor. At the bottom of this hill, they arrive at photosystem I, which includes a slightly different kind of reaction center. This center is also receiving solar energy and uses it to boost electrons to a higher energy state. From this energetic state, electrons are transferred down the second energy hill—until they are received by the electron carrier $NADP^+$, which is very much like the electron carrier NAD^+ reviewed in Chapter 7. In accepting electrons, $NADP^+$ becomes reduced to NADPH, an electron carrier that ferries the electrons into the next stage of photosynthesis. This second stage is the Calvin cycle, which will yield the high-energy sugar that is the essential product of photosynthesis.

The Physical Movement of Electrons in the Light Reactions

In this movement up and down the energy hill, the electrons have moved physically through the chloroplast. As **Figure 8.7** shows, they started out in the water of the thylakoid compartment, moved into and then through the thylakoid membrane—handed off at each step by the various electron transport molecules—and then finally ended up in the stroma, attached to NADPH.

What Makes the Light Reactions So Important?

The steps just reviewed are the essence of the light reactions. To make sure you don't miss the forest for the trees, let's be clear about two momentous things that have taken place within these steps: the splitting of water and the transformation of solar energy to chemical energy.

The Splitting of Water: Electrons and Oxygen

The first notable event takes place near the start of these reactions: the splitting of water. Critically, this reaction provides the traveling electrons whose path you've just followed. But it also provides something else: the oxygen that today accounts for 21 percent of the Earth's atmosphere. In the water splitting that goes on in photosynthesis, hydrogen atoms are removed from H_2O, while the oxygen is left behind. When two liberated oxygen atoms come together in the thylakoid compartment, the result is O_2—the form of oxygen that exists in our atmosphere. *Here* is where we get the substance that is the breath of life itself for most species, all of it contributed by living things. Given its importance, it is no small irony that oxygen is, in another sense, a kind of green-world refuse—leftovers from the process by which plants strip water of the electrons they use to carry out photosynthesis.

chloroplast

sunlight

photosystem II

sunlight

photosystem I

e⁻

2 H₂O

4 H⁺ + O₂

electron
transport chain

electron
transport chain

NADPH

to Calvin
cycle

thylakoid compartment

thylakoid
membrane

stroma

Figure 8.7
The Light Reactions
The light reactions take place within the thylakoid membranes in the chloroplasts. Electrons are donated by water molecules located in the thylakoid compartments. Powered by the sun's energy, these electrons are passed along the electron transport chain embedded in the thylakoid membrane and end up stored in NADPH in the stroma. An additional product of the splitting of water molecules is individual oxygen atoms, which quickly combine into the O₂ form. This is the atmospheric oxygen that we breathe.

The Transformation of Solar Energy to Chemical Energy

The second major feat that takes place during light reactions is the transformation of solar energy to chemical energy. When the energy of sunlight moves to a chlorophyll molecule in a reaction center, it boosts an electron there from what is known as a ground state to an excited state. Thus far, this has been described as a movement up a metaphorical energy hill. In physical terms, however, this electron is moving farther out from the nucleus of an atom. To appreciate what's special about photosynthesis, consider what the *common* fates are for such excited electrons. One is for the electrons to drop back down to the original (and more stable) state, in the process releasing as *heat* the energy they have absorbed. This is the process by which black objects get hot on sunny days. Another possible fate is for falling electrons to release part of their energy as light in the process known as fluorescence.

In photosynthesis, however, the energized electrons are *transferred to a different molecule*—the initial electron acceptors of photosystems II and I. They don't fall back to their ground state, releasing relatively useless heat or light in the process. They are passed on in a redox reaction. This is the bridge to life as we know it.

Without this step, the energy of the sun merely makes the Earth warmer. With it, the green world grows profusely; it captures some of the sun's energy and with it builds trunks and grains and leaves. Electrons are taken from water, boosted to a higher energy state by the sun, and then transferred to molecules that have the ability to *store* the energy they've received, rather than letting it dissipate as heat. When looked at globally, this set of chemical reactions has enormous consequences. By one reckoning, photosynthesis produces up to 155 billion tons of material each year—about 25 tons for every person on Earth.

Production of ATP

It's also important to note that a primary function of the fall of electrons between photosystems II and I is a release of energy that is used for the production of ATP. Put together through a process similar to the one you looked at last chapter, this ATP will be used to power the reactions that are coming up in the second stage of photosynthesis. Thus, the sun's power is providing energy that is put into *two* forms in the light reactions: ATP and the energetic electrons that are channeled into NADPH. Looking at the big picture, you can see that the *photo* of photosynthesis is an energy-capturing operation.

8.4 Stage 2: The Calvin Cycle

BioFlix™

Photosynthesis

In the second stage of photosynthesis, the energy captured in the light reactions will be *used*. It will power a process by which carbon dioxide taken in from the atmosphere will be joined to a sugar, with the resulting product energized, thus creating a high-energy carbohydrate. To see how this happens, let's begin by taking stock of where the light reactions left off. The short answer is, in the stroma. That's where NADP$^+$ has become NADPH by accepting the energized electrons pouring out from photosystem I. There's also ATP in the stroma, another product of the light reactions.

Figure 8.8
The Calvin Cycle
CO_2, ATP, and electrons (contained in hydrogen atoms) from NADPH are the input into the Calvin cycle, while a sugar (G3P) is its output.

Energized Sugar Comes from a Cycle of Reactions

Even with the right ingredients, however, it takes more than one step to go from carbon dioxide and a low-energy sugar to a sugar that has enough energy in its chemical bonds to serve as food. What's required is a set of chemical reactions that make up a cycle. This is the **Calvin cycle,** or the C_3 cycle, the set of steps in photosynthesis in which energetic electrons are brought together with carbon dioxide and a sugar to produce an energetic carbohydrate. The highlights of this cycle are set forth in **Figure 8.8**. This is the *synthesis* of photosynthesis: a bringing together of elements.

The first steps of this cycle can be thought of as a process of **fixation**—of a gas being incorporated into an organic molecule. Specifically, carbon dioxide, which comes in through the stomata on the leaves of the plant, is being fixed into the starting sugar, which is called RuBP. (From the time plants are embryos, they have small amounts of this sugar in them as a legacy from their parent plants.) This is a terrifically important step for it is the way life builds itself up with materials that lie *outside* of life. Note that carbon is being taken in from the atmosphere and then made part of a living thing—a plant.

The next reactions in the cycle are the energizing steps of the process (which you can see in section 2 of the cycle). Here is where our low-energy sugar receives the energetic products of the light reactions.

1. **Carbon fixation.** An enzyme called rubisco brings together three molecules of CO_2 with three molecules of the sugar RuBP. In this reaction, one carbon from each CO_2 molecule is being added to the five-carbon RuBP, and this is being done three times. The three resulting six-carbon molecules are immediately split into six three-carbon molecules named 3-PGA (3-phosphoglyceric acid).

2. **Energizing the sugar.** In two separate reactions, six ATP molecules react with six 3-PGA, in each case transferring a phosphate onto the 3-PGA. The six 3-PGA derivatives oxidize (gain electrons from) six NADPH molecules; in so doing, they are transformed into the energy-rich sugar G3P (glyceraldehyde 3-phosphate).

3. **Exit of product.** One molecule of G3P exits as the output of the Calvin cycle. This molecule, the product of photosynthesis, can be used for energy or transformed into materials that make up the plant.

4. **Regeneration of RuBP.** In several reactions, five molecules of G3P are transformed into three molecules of RuBP, which enter the cycle.

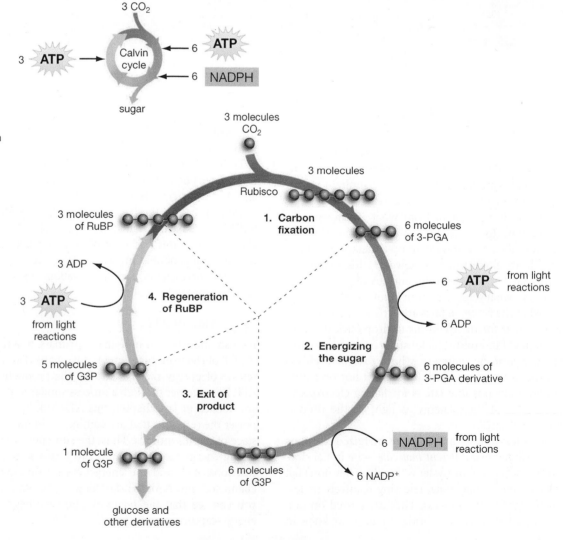

The RuBP derivatives first interact with ATP and then receive energetic electrons from NADPH—the electrons that came originally from water and that were boosted up the energy hills by sunlight. With this, a relatively low-energy sugar has been energized—it has been moved up the energy hill—from which position it can now serve as food. The energized sugar that is produced, called G3P, is the essential product of photosynthesis. One molecule of it is netted with each turn of the Calvin cycle, as you can see in section 3. The remainder of the cycle can be thought of as a preparation of molecules for another trip around the cycle. In section 4, several reactions are carried out that result in the formation of more RuBP, which then enters the cycle again.

The Ultimate Product of Photosynthesis

The importance of photosynthesis becomes clear only with an understanding of what G3P can give rise to once it exits the Calvin cycle. This sugar has something in common with steel coming out of a factory in that it can be turned into many things. Put two molecules of G3P together, and you get the more familiar six-carbon sugar glucose. In turn, many molecules of glucose can come together to form the large storage molecules known as starches, familiar to us in such forms as potatoes or wheat grains. Beyond this, sugar is used to make proteins, which are then used as structural components of the plant or as enzymes. And sugar can be broken down, of course, to provide more of the ATP that powers a plant's activities. Given all this, if we ask what the *ultimate* product of photosynthesis is, the answer turns out to be: *the whole plant.* If you look at **Figure 8.9**, you can see a summary of the process of photosynthesis.

Figure 8.9

Summary of Photosynthesis in the Chloroplasts of Plant Cells

In the light reactions, which take place in the thylakoids of chloroplasts, solar energy is converted to chemical energy that is stored temporarily in the molecules ATP and NADPH. Water is required for these reactions and oxygen is a by-product. In the Calvin cycle, which takes place in the stroma of chloroplasts, the energy stored in ATP and NADPH is used to produce a high-energy sugar (G3P). Carbon dioxide is required for the cycle's reactions.

8.5 Photorespiration and the C₄ Pathway

You have now gone through the basic process of photosynthesis. It's necessary, however, to say something about what might be called a glitch in this process and then to note a mechanism that evolved within one group of plants that allows them to avoid the problem.

The glitch is called *photorespiration,* and it takes place within the Calvin cycle you just went over. Recall that this cycle begins with carbon dioxide (from the atmosphere) being joined to a low-energy sugar (from the plant). What is it that brings these two compounds together? Readers of the last few chapters will not be surprised to learn that it is an enzyme—a massive one called rubisco. Unfortunately, this molecular worker turns out to be something like the giant in "Jack and the Beanstalk": extremely powerful but slow moving and prone to making errors.

Extremely powerful? Rubisco is the bridge between the living world and the non-living world. It is the molecule that allows plants to capture, from the atmosphere, the carbon atoms that are the building blocks for all living things. One of the problems with the way it works, however, is its speed—or lack of it. Whereas an average enzyme can catalyze 1,000 reactions per second, rubisco can manage only three.

ESSAY

Using Photosynthesis to Fight Global Warming

How important can one of nature's processes be to one of society's issues? Really important. Just ask the scientists, economists, and political leaders from Boston to Bangalore who today are struggling to get a better handle on the process of photosynthesis as a means of combating the critical societal issue of global warming.

How are the two things related? Remember that global warming's root cause is a buildup of so-called greenhouse gases in the atmosphere, with the most important of these gases being carbon dioxide (CO_2). Now recall that plants and other photosynthesizing organisms take CO_2 *out* of the atmosphere and use it to build themselves up. Not all of the carbon they take in serves this function; indeed, much of the carbon they capture will quickly be returned to the atmosphere when the plants burn up some of their food stores, thus producing CO_2 as a waste product. Even allowing for this, however, trees and other photosynthesizers constitute what is known as a carbon sink: On balance they *remove* CO_2 from the atmosphere. Meanwhile, entities such as coal-fired power plants are so-called carbon sources—they *add* CO_2 to the atmosphere.

Given this, what happens when you cut down trees on a large scale, often burning them in the bargain? You get what you can see in **Figure 1**: an enormous quantity of human-generated greenhouse gases, second in size only to the quantity of gases society generates by burning fossil fuels. Trees that are merely cut down will start to decay, slowly releasing the carbon within them as CO_2. Trees that are burned, meanwhile, will release this CO_2 immediately. And of course trees that cease to exist will also cease to serve as carbon sinks. This part of the problem is less pronounced in the tropics, where mature trees are thought to return about as much CO_2 to the atmosphere as they take from it. But in so-called temperate and boreal forests—think of the eastern United States and north-central Canada—trees serve as significant carbon sinks, locking away an additional 1.5 billion tons of carbon each year, according to a recent analysis.

Given all this, one way to reduce global warming is, of course, to reduce global deforestation. This is one of the reasons we hear so much about tropical rainforests: They lock up an enormous amount of carbon and, among all the world's forests, they are being cut and burned at the highest rate. In 2005 alone, Brazil's Amazon

Figure 1
Big Contributor to Global Warming
Deforestation produces about 17 percent of all human-generated greenhouse gases. Only the burning of fossil fuels puts a greater amount of CO_2 into the atmosphere.
(Adapted from *Climate Change 2007: Synthesis Report,* Intergovernmental Panel on Climate Change, Figure 2.1.)

This snail's pace has consequences. Because rubisco works so slowly, every plant must have a lot of it. As a result, it is easily the world's most abundant protein; at least 11 pounds of it exist for every person on Earth.

Slow pace is one thing, but it turns out that rubisco has a problem in even binding with the right substance: It can bind to *oxygen* as well as to carbon dioxide; indeed, it does this all the time. In C_3 photosynthesis, rubisco may fix up to one molecule of O_2 for every three of the carbon dioxide it incorporates. Worse, when this happens, some of the CO_2 that *has* been fixed by a plant is released by it. It is as if a carpenter building a house took boards that were stored inside and began throwing them out the window.

Photorespiration is especially likely to take place when temperatures rise, because heat prompts the stomata on leaves to close to preserve water. The effect of closed stomata, however, is that both water and *oxygen* are kept inside plant cells—remember that plants produce oxygen during photosynthesis—while CO_2 from the atmosphere is kept out of them. The result, understandably, is that rubisco binds rainforest lost 7,200 square miles of forest—an area about the size of Massachusetts—through the logging practice known as clear-cutting.

Harmful as this kind of deforestation is, even halting it altogether wouldn't be enough to stop global warming. Instead, society is going to have to find many ways to cut down on carbon sources while channeling material into carbon sinks. Most of the ideas we hear about today have to do with sources—specifically with reducing society's use of fossil fuels. But scientists and public policy makers are also thinking about carbon sinks, which essentially means they are thinking about photosynthesis. They are asking, for example, whether it would be possible to increase photosynthesis worldwide by focusing on the portion of it carried out on the world's oceans. As it turns out, ocean-dwelling algae (and certain types of bacteria that float alongside them) undertake slightly more than half of the world's photosynthesis already. But algae often cannot flourish in the open ocean because these waters are deficient in iron, which is a basic nutrient. One idea to combat global warming, therefore, has been to fertilize the oceans with iron in the way that agricultural fields are fertilized with nitrogen. With this addition to the ocean environment, the idea goes, the algae would flourish and then would sink to the bottom of the ocean as they die, carrying with them the carbon they've taken in while alive.

This idea has come in for some sharp criticism; among other things, it appears doubtful that a significant proportion of algae in a so-called algal bloom actually sink after they die—something that would have to happen if the carbon these organisms capture is to be kept out of the atmosphere. But this idea is representative of the kind of proposals that have gotten increased attention as the world scrambles to figure out what it's going to do about global warming.

A related set of ideas has to do not with increasing photosynthesis per se, but rather with locking up the *products* of photosynthesis so that they don't decay, thus releasing CO_2. For example, a project currently underway in California's San Joaquin Delta, northeast of San Francisco, seeks to demonstrate the potential of "carbon-capture" farming, which in this case would mean paying farmers to "grow" marshlands of the sort that flourished throughout the delta before it was drained for farming, back in the nineteenth century. The idea is to slightly submerge the land once again and then grow marsh grasses and cattails on it. Such plants can quickly build up into a peat soil that has the benefit of *not* decaying because, as it accumulates in depth—by as much as 4 inches per year—it will be kept submerged. A pilot project has shown that this process can lock up or "sequester" as much as 25 metric tons of CO_2 per acre per year. Project directors calculate that if this savings were applied to all 321,000 acres of suitable land in the California delta, the effect would be the equivalent of transforming all of California's SUV's into gas-sipping small hybrids.

A question that follows from this, of course, is how delta farmers are going to profit from producing carbon sinks rather than agricultural crops, but the answer actually is not hard to envision. One of the general strategies to combat global warming is the development of government-run cap-and-trade systems, in which industries that emit CO_2 in the course of their business (such as electric utilities) would be allowed to offset these emissions by purchasing carbon "credits" from businesses whose work reduces atmospheric CO_2—in this case, California farmers.

To make a dent in global warming, carbon-capture farming would, of course, have to be ramped up to an enormous scale. But such farming is just one of the carbon-capture ideas that have been put on the table. How about burying old or dead trees below ground, so that they won't decay? How about putting photosynthesizing bacteria right at the source of coal-plant emissions, where they would soak up CO_2 and other greenhouse gases? Both these ideas have been proposed by serious scientists, and the latter idea currently is undergoing pilot-project testing. Only time will tell whether either proposal will work, of course, but note that both involve photosynthesis. This process of nature is by far the most powerful mechanism ever developed for first capturing and then locking up atmospheric carbon. Given this, it makes sense that a world that has an atmospheric carbon problem would be looking to photosynthesis for answers.

frequently with oxygen. The problem with this is that oxygen cannot serve as a building block for plant growth; only carbon can do that. Thus, when rubisco fails to bind with CO_2, plant growth is undercut. With all this in mind, here is a definition of **photorespiration:** a process in which the enzyme rubisco reduces carbon fixation in photosynthesis by binding with oxygen instead of with carbon dioxide. Meanwhile, **rubisco** can be defined as an enzyme that allows organisms to incorporate atmospheric carbon dioxide into their own sugars during the process of photosynthesis.

Evolution, however, produced an adaptation that allows some warm-climate plant species to lessen the photorespiration problem. It is a mechanism that uses a special carbon-fixing "front-end" and then a carbon-dioxide shuttle into the Calvin cycle. The so-called C_4 plants that make use of this mechanism don't initially use rubisco to fix carbon dioxide. Rather, they employ a different enzyme that will not bind with oxygen. The immediate product of this reaction is a four-carbon molecule (hence the C_4 cycle's name). A derivative of that molecule moves to a special group of cells and releases the CO_2 that will

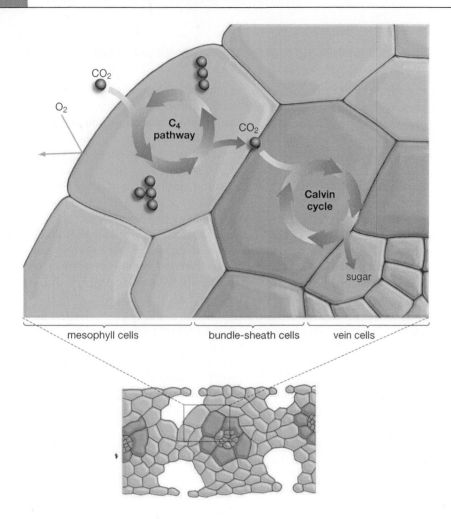

mesophyll cells   bundle-sheath cells   vein cells

Figure 8.10
C_4 Photosynthesis

Photorespiration occurs when the C_3 enzyme rubisco binds to oxygen rather than to carbon dioxide (thereby undercutting the production of sugar). C_4 plants contain a different enzyme in their mesophyll cells that binds to carbon dioxide but not to oxygen. Then the carbon dioxide is escorted into special bundle-sheath cells, where rubisco can bind to it, thus initiating the Calvin cycle.

then bind to rubisco and go through the Calvin cycle. These special cells are wrapped around leaf veins and are hence named the bundle-sheath cells (**Figure 8.10**). What the C_4 system provides—even at times when little CO_2 may be coming in through the stomata—is a relatively high concentration of CO_2 where it's needed: in the cells where the Calvin cycle takes place. We can thus define **C_4 photosynthesis** as a form of photosynthesis in which carbon dioxide is first fixed to a four-carbon molecule and then transferred to special cells in which the Calvin cycle is undertaken, bundle-sheath cells.

Lest all this seem like a purely theoretical issue, consider the fact that an international consortium of plant researchers is hard at work today trying to develop a C_4 version of the world's most important food crop, rice (**Figure 8.11**). The perceived need for such a plant is straightforward: Asia's population is expected to grow by 50 percent in the next 40–50 years, but the region's rice yields haven't changed appreciably in the last 30 years. Researchers calculate that these yields could be boosted by up to 50 percent if they could alter rice in such a way that it could carry out C_4 photosynthesis, rather than the C_3 variety it undertakes now. The goal is to develop a C_4 plant through a combination of bioengineering and old-fashioned plant breeding.

8.6 CAM Photosynthesis

When plants live in climates that are not just warm but *dry*, a large part of their survival comes down to retaining water. Photosynthesis, however, works against water retention because, as you have seen, when CO_2 can pass in, water vapor can pass out. Evolution produced a third form of photosynthesis, however, that minimizes this problem for the dry-weather plants known as succulents. These plants *close* their stomata during the day and then open them at night. They then carry out C_4 metabolism at night, but only up to a point. They fix carbon dioxide into an initial four-carbon molecule and then stand pat. The CO_2 stays "banked" in them, awaiting the energy of the next day's sun, which will power the production of the ATP they need to carry out the Calvin cycle. This is **CAM photosynthesis,** defined as a form of photosynthesis, undertaken by plants in hot, dry climates, in which carbon fixation takes place at night and the Calvin cycle occurs during the day. This process gets the job done for cactus, pineapple, orchid, and some mint family plants, among others. As you may have guessed, CAM is an acronym; it stands for crassulacean acid metabolism. The succulent plant family Crassulaceae (which includes

Figure 8.11
Producing a Better Rice Plant

A consortium called the International Rice Institute, headquartered in the Philippines, is leading the effort to develop a C_4 rice plant as a means of increasing rice production worldwide. In the photo, an IRI worker is inspecting one of the institute's experimental varieties of rice.

jade plants) was the first group of plants in which CAM metabolism was discovered. The three methods of photosynthesis we've looked at—C_3, C_4, and CAM—are summarized in **Table 8.1**.

On to Genetics

In the last three chapters, we've been looking at energy as it flows from the sun to plants and then on to the rest of the living world. In this journey, energy acts as a great enabler of life—as the essential force that allows life to exist in the first place and that, on a daily basis, allows flowers to open and birds to fly. Having learned something about how energy underlies life, however, it's now time to see what life does with its energy. Initially, we'll be interested in an activity that is undertaken on a grand scale within the confines of life: the amazing ability living things have of producing more living things. Two parents produce a son, but what exactly did the parents pass on that resulted in the color of this child's hair or the shape of his nose? And what are the chances that he might inherit a physical malady that afflicted his grandfather but that did not affect either of his parents? There's a branch of biology that seeks to answer questions such as these; it's called genetics, and it's the next stop in our tour of the living world.

SO FAR ...

1. The enzyme rubisco brings together the _____ (from the plant) and _____ (from the atmosphere), creating the product that moves through the Calvin cycle. Unfortunately, rubisco also has an affinity for binding with _____, a process known as _____.

2. An evolutionary adaptation to this process, found in plants that thrive in _____ climates, is _____ photosynthesis, in which carbon dioxide is first fixed to a four-carbon molecule and then transferred into cells that carry out the Calvin cycle.

3. Plants that exist in climates that are both warm and dry employ a variation on photosynthesis, _____ photosynthesis, in which carbon dioxide is brought into the plant only _____, while the Calvin cycle is carried out only _____.

Table 8.1

Three Modes of Photosynthesis

	C_3	C_4	CAM
Used by:	Majority of plants	Corn, sugarcane (warm environments)	Cactus, pineapple, orchid (dry environments)
Benefits:	Efficient use of ATP	Less photorespiration	Less water loss
Problems:	Photorespiration	Uses up more ATP	Uses up more ATP; hard to "bank" enough CO_2
How It Works			

Go to the Study Area at www.masteringbiology.com for practice quizzes, myeBook, BioFlix™ 3-D animations, MP3 Tutor Sessions, videos, current events, and more.

CHAPTER

8 REVIEW

Summary

8.1 Photosynthesis and Energy

- The sugar produced in photosynthesis is the source of food for most living things. Photosynthesis also is responsible for the atmospheric oxygen used by living things in cellular respiration. (p. 141)

8.2 The Components of Photosynthesis

- In plants and algae, photosynthesis takes place in the organelles called chloroplasts, which exist in abundance in the mesophyll cells of plant leaves. The energy for photosynthesis comes mostly from blue and red wavelengths of visible sunlight that are absorbed by pigments in the chloroplasts. Plant leaves contain microscopic pores called stomata that can open and close, letting carbon dioxide in and water vapor out. (p. 142)

- In the first stage of photosynthesis (the light reactions), electrons derived from water are energetically boosted by the power of sunlight. These electrons are passed through a series of electron carriers, ending up as part of NADPH, which carries them to the second stage of photosynthesis (the Calvin cycle), in which electrons are brought together with carbon dioxide and sugar to produce a high-energy sugar. (p. 144)

8.3 Stage 1: The Light Reactions

- In the light reactions, photosynthesis works by absorbing and transmitting solar energy through a pair of molecular complexes, photosystems II and I. (p. 146)

- In these reactions, water is split, yielding both the electrons that move through the light reactions and the oxygen that organisms breathe. The derived electrons are given an energy boost by solar energy

and are transferred to the initial electron acceptor. The energetic fall of electrons through the electron transport chain between photosystems II and I also releases energy that produces the ATP that powers the second stage of photosynthesis. (p. 146)

8.4 Stage 2: The Calvin Cycle

- In the Calvin or C_3 cycle, carbon dioxide is brought together with the sugar RuBP. The resulting compound is energized with the addition of electrons supplied by the light reactions. The result is the essential product of photosynthesis, the high-energy sugar G3P, which can be used for energy or for plant growth. (p. 148)

BioFlix™

Photosynthesis

8.5 Photorespiration and the C_4 Pathway

- In C_3 plants, the enzyme rubisco frequently binds with oxygen rather than with carbon dioxide—a process called photorespiration that undercuts photosynthesis and that occurs with greater frequency in warm-weather climates. (p. 149)

- In some warm-weather plants, a form of photosynthesis called C_4 photosynthesis evolved that employs an enzyme that binds with carbon dioxide but not with oxygen. The carbon dioxide is then shuttled to special bundle-sheath cells and released, after which it moves into the Calvin cycle. (p. 151)

8.6 CAM Photosynthesis

- Many dry-weather plants employ CAM photosynthesis, in which the plant's stomata open only at night, letting in and fixing CO_2, which is then "banked" until sunrise, when the sun will supply the energy needed to power the Calvin cycle. (p. 152)

Key Terms

Understanding the Basics

Multiple-Choice Questions
(**Answers are in the back of the book.**)

1. In photosynthesis, energy from the sun is being _____ while in the cellular respiration looked at in Chapter 7, energy is being _____ .
   a. turned into light ... turned solely into heat
   b. entirely lost to heat ... stored as ADP
   c. stored in carbohydrates ... released from storage in food
   d. absorbed as green light ... stored in carbohydrates
   e. spent as carbohydrates ... stored as carbohydrates

2. Stomata are the _____ on leaves that serve not only to let water vapor out but to let ____ in.
   a. proteins ... oxygen
   b. cilia ... oxygen
   c. outer cell layers ... sunlight

d. stems ... carbon dioxide

e. pores ... carbon dioxide

3. Two important products of the light reactions in photosynthesis are:
a. electrons, oxygen.
b. electrons, carbon dioxide.
c. chloroplasts, carbon dioxide.
d. rubisco, oxygen.
e. rubisco, carbon dioxide.

4. Suppose you become a biologist. On a bright summer day, while studying the rate of photosynthesis in a desert plant, you discover that its stomata are closed, yet it is producing ATP. This plant must be carrying out:
a. photorespiration.
b. the C₃ cycle.
c. the C₄ pathway.
d. CAM photosynthesis.
e. CO_2 uptake.

5. Most plant photosynthesis occurs in the _____ of leaves.
a. upper epidermal cells
b. lower epidermal cells
c. petioles
d. stomata
e. mesophyll cells

6. The essential product of photosynthesis is:
a. ATP.
b. the enzyme rubisco.
c. the sugar G3P.
d. plant structural proteins.
e. carbon dioxide

7. The electrons boosted to a higher energy level in photosystem II are derived from the splitting of _____, which results in the release of the by-product _____.
a. carbon dioxide ... ATP
b. water ... oxygen
c. NADPH ... carbon dioxide
d. ATP ... carbon dioxide
e. rubisco ... oxygen

8. The enzyme rubisco is important because:
a. it aids in splitting water molecules, thus yielding oxygen.
b. it powers the light reactions through use of ATP.
c. it brings together carbon dioxide from the atmosphere with the plant's own sugar.
d. it is photosystem II's primary electron acceptor.
e. it is photosystem I's primary electron acceptor.

Brief Review

(Answers are in the back of the book.)

1. Since plants capture energy through photosynthesis, do they need to carry out cellular respiration as well? Why or why not?

2. Sunlight reaching Earth is composed of a spectrum of energetic rays. Describe the rays that make up this spectrum. Which portion of the spectrum drives photosynthesis?

3. What are the component parts of a photosystem?

4. Which plant would you expect to grow more rapidly in a warm-weather climate—a C₃ plant or a C₄ plant? Explain your answer.

5. The text notes that the fall of electrons between photosystems II and I provides energy used to produce ATP. What is this ATP used for?

Applying Your Knowledge

1. Rubisco has been called the most important protein on Earth. Why should it be regarded as so important?

2. In the mid-seventeenth century, Dutch scientist Jan Baptista van Helmont struggled to understand where plants get the material that allows them to grow larger. He planted a willow tree of a given weight in a fixed quantity of soil and then, five years later, weighed both the willow and the soil. He found that the tree had gained 164 pounds during the period but that the soil had lost very little weight. His conclusion was that the willow's weight gain came solely from the water it absorbed through its roots. If you could be transported back to van Helmont's time, what would you tell him about the source of the willow's weight gain?

9

The Links in Life's Chain:
Genetics and Cell Division

Life depends on information that is stored in DNA. This information is duplicated and then apportioned every time a cell divides.

How do living things grow and reproduce? Through cell division. Here, one human cell is about to become two through this tightly choreographed process.

Everyone knows how one generation of living things gives rise to another, at least in a general sense. But the details of how this works are not apparent just by looking at Earth's creatures. A brief sexual encounter takes place, and the next thing we know there are new kittens, chicks, or babies. Only the encounter and the newborns are obvious; what comes in between is mysterious.

The problem, of course, is that most of the component parts of reproduction are hidden away and, in any event, are so small that the process is completely invisible to the naked eye. Given this, it's no wonder that for centuries human beings wondered what it was that one generation passed on, so that the next generation could be formed.

A similar kind of puzzlement existed over a related question: What is the mechanism that controls the development of a living thing as it goes from being a microscopic cell to being a human baby in full cry? For that matter, how is it that the adult body is able to build muscle or repair a minor wound? What, in short, is the mechanism that controls day-to-day physical functioning?

how living things develop and then function each day, the answer is: largely through the information provided by the genes in the genome.

To understand what this latter role means in practice, let's think about what happens when you eat something—say, a candy bar. The result of doing this is that you'll get a surge of simple sugar coursing through your veins; this is blood-sugar that needs to move into your cells to satisfy their energy needs. Now, this sugar will move into these cells largely through the action of the protein insulin, which helps create channels in cells through which nutrients can pass. But as you can imagine, none of us has a huge supply of ready-made insulin stored within us, just waiting for our blood-sugar surges. Instead, this protein has to be produced *as needed*—whenever we have a surplus of

Figure 9.1
Passing on Genetic Information
Half of each person's genome comes from the father and half from the mother.

9.1 **An Introduction to Genetics**

It took roughly a century of hard-won scientific advances for these questions to be answered. In the end, it turned out that a single substance is central to the reproduction of living things, their development from single cells, and their day-to-day functioning. This substance is deoxyribonucleic acid, a long, vanishingly thin molecule known everywhere today by its acronym, DNA.

DNA contains what is known as an organism's **genome:** the complete collection of that organism's genetic information. This information exists in units called genes that lie along DNA's famous double helix.

But how is it that this one molecule can undertake all the tasks just described? Well, if we ask what it is that humans *pass on* in reproduction, the answer turns out to be: half of a father's genome and half of a mother's genome, with both these halves coming together in a fertilized egg to produce a whole, new genome (**Figure 9.1**). With respect to the question of blood-sugar in circulation. And the way this insulin gets produced is that the body's protein-producing machinery will go to a strand of DNA to retrieve one tiny bit of the information that is stored along it: the information on how to put together insulin.

This story deepens with recognition of the fact that insulin is only one protein among thousands that will be put together in a typical cell. And as it turns out, the information for the production of *all* of these proteins is contained in DNA. To grasp the importance of this, it's helpful to remember something first noted in Chapter 3: that proteins are the living world's most active and versatile molecules, serving not only as structural building blocks of life but as the chemically active workers that carry out most of life's essential tasks. Thus, there are proteins that form cartilage and hair; there are communication proteins that help form the receptors on cells; there are hormonal proteins and transport proteins. And then there are enzymes, the catalyst proteins that speed up—or in practical terms, *enable*—chemical reactions in living things. Without these proteins, almost nothing could get done in the body; with them, a dazzling set of chemical reactions takes place every second in every living thing. In sum, it's difficult to overstate how important proteins are to life, and the way proteins get produced is through the information contained in DNA.

Figure 9.2
Information-Bearing DNA Molecule

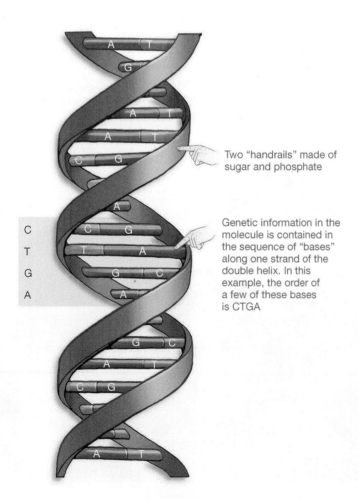

Two "handrails" made of sugar and phosphate

Genetic information in the molecule is contained in the sequence of "bases" along one strand of the double helix. In this example, the order of a few of these bases is CTGA

But what is the actual linkage here? That is, how does the information in DNA bring about the production of a protein? In Chapter 14, you'll get the details of this process, but for now let's just look at the essentials of the story. Imagine you are a telegraph operator in the Old West, and your "key" starts tapping frantically. You leap forward in your chair, listening for the sound of short and long bursts on the key, and you begin writing down the letters these sounds stand for. Here's the message you get:

.—.. ——— —.—. —.—   — ....— ..—. .

which means:

L   o   c   k   t   h   e   s   a   f   e

You walk over and do just that. There is thus a code here, Morse code, that has resulted in some action. In DNA there is likewise a code, but instead of a code specified in short or long sounds, it is a code specified in chemical substances. There are four of these substances, and they lie along the double helix. They are the "bases" adenine, thymine, guanine, and cytosine, abbreviated A, T, G, C, respectively.

A particular sequence of these bases—usually thousands of letters long—contains information that can be acted on, just as the Morse code did. Only the action here is the production of a particular protein. One series of A's, T's, C's, and G's contains the information for the production of one protein, but a *different* sequence of A's, T's, G's, and C's specifies a different protein. These separate sequences of bases are separate genes.

You saw in Chapter 3 that proteins are composed of building blocks called amino acids. The base sequence that makes up a gene, then, is like a message that says, "Give me this amino acid, now this one, then this one, . . . " and so on for hundreds of amino acids until a protein is created that folds up and gets busy on some task. This task can be one small part of *forming* a human being—as in embryonic development—or of *maintaining* one, as in an adult. One generation gives rise to another by passing on this entire complement of information.

The Architecture of DNA

It is the architecture of the DNA molecule that makes this protein production process possible. Look at the general scheme of it pictured in **Figure 9.2**. As you can see, DNA looks something like an open, spiral staircase, the handrails of which are a repeating series of sugar (deoxyribose) and phosphate molecules. Meanwhile, the messages you've just been reading about are contained in the steps of the staircase in the order in which the bases A, T, C, and G are placed along the helix. As you can see, these bases extend inward from both of the DNA rails. The order in which the bases occur along the rails is extremely varied. It is this order that "encodes" the information for the production of proteins.

The Path of Protein Synthesis

Look now at **Figure 9.3** and see the path that is followed in protein production or "synthesis." The DNA you have been reading about is contained in the nucleus of the cell. The first step in synthesis is that a stretch of it unwinds there, and its message—the order of a string of bases—is copied onto a molecule called messenger RNA (mRNA). This length of mRNA then exits from the cell nucleus. Its destination is a molecular workbench in the cell's cytoplasm, a structure called a ribosome. It is here that both message (the mRNA sequence) and raw materials (amino acids) come together to make the product (a protein). The mRNA sequence is "read" within the ribosome, and as this happens a chain of amino acids is put together in the ribosome in the order specified by the mRNA sequence. When the chain is finished and folded up, a protein has come into existence.

Genetics as Information Management

The story you have been reading about is that of **genetics,** meaning the study of physical inheritance among living things. In reflecting on this story, the first thing to note is that it concerns the storage, duplication, and transfer of *information.* True, it is information encoded in chemical form, but that shouldn't bother us. Information comes in lots of forms; there are the familiar words on a page, but there are also bar graphs, smoke signals, or a baby's smile.

To grasp the fact of genetics as molecular information, think back to Chapter 6, where you looked at a particular protein, an enzyme called lactase that helps break up milk sugar (lactose) into its components of glucose and galactose. In line with what you've seen so far, there is a gene that prompts the production of lactase. This gene's message is copied onto a length of mRNA, which then migrates to a ribosome in the cytoplasm. Lactase is put together there, amino acid by amino acid, and once synthesized, it folds up and gets busy clipping lactose molecules.

Now, consider the role of the gene in this process. It didn't do the lactose clipping; it didn't even migrate to the cytoplasm to be involved in the synthesis of lactase. In this case, its role was more like that of a ... cookbook recipe. It specified this amino acid, then that amino acid, and eventually lactase was produced.

From One Gene to a Collection

Now, in considering not just one gene, but rather the entire *collection* of genes in a living thing—its genome, in other words—it is easy to see that we are dealing with a vast *library* of information. The size of such a collection can vary, but to give you some idea, the human genome is estimated to include 20,000–25,000

genes. We generally think that information comes to us after birth and from outside the body, but in fact we are born with a volume of information that has been amassed, edited, and passed down to us over 3.8 billion years of evolution.

The amazing thing about such collections is that there is not just one copy of them in living things; there may be trillions. Most cells within an organism contain a complete copy of that organism's genome. A given type of cell puts to use (or "expresses") only some parts of this genome, while another type of cell uses other parts; but this is merely a way of saying that different genes are active in different cells. This is what distinguishes a liver cell, say, from a bone cell. These cells do different things and, accordingly, need to synthesize different proteins. But *both* kinds of cells have within them the whole genomic library; they merely put different parts of it to use.

Cells duplicate, of course. One cell divides to become two, the two divide to become four, and so on. Given this, if each cell in the body is to have its own copy of the genome, then each time a cell duplicates, the genome that lies within that cell must duplicate as well, prior to the actual cell division. This is just what happens, in a process we'll look at now.

Figure 9.3
The Path of Protein Synthesis

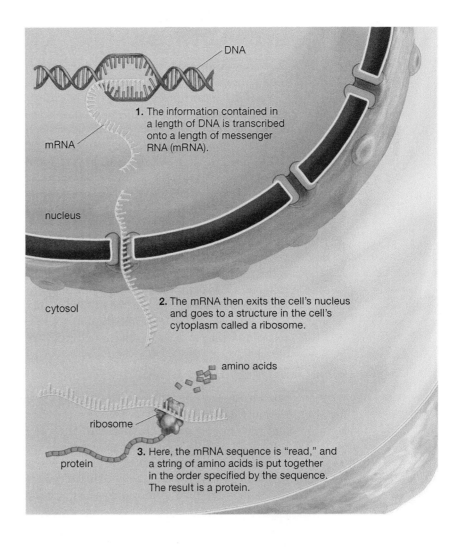

1. The information contained in a length of DNA is transcribed onto a length of messenger RNA (mRNA).

DNA

mRNA

nucleus

cytosol

2. The mRNA then exits the cell's nucleus and goes to a structure in the cell's cytoplasm called a ribosome.

amino acids

ribosome

protein

3. Here, the mRNA sequence is "read," and a string of amino acids is put together in the order specified by the sequence. The result is a protein.

SO FAR . . .

1. Genes contain information for the production of _____. The building blocks of genes are a set of four _____ whose symbols are _____, _____, _____, and _____.

2. Proteins are made up of a set of building blocks called _____. In any given protein, the order of these building blocks is specified by the order of the _____ that make up a _____.

3. Proteins are produced by means of information encoded in DNA being copied onto a molecule called _____, which then ferries the information to a structure called a _____. At this structure, _____ are linked to one another in the order specified by the _____, thus resulting in a _____.

9.2 An Introduction to Cell Division

How does a baby grow, or a plant develop, or a wound heal? Always through cell division. As noted in Chapter 4, with the possible exception of viruses, life exists only inside cells. Further, we know that cells come only from other cells. And the *way* cells come from cells is by dividing. To understand the continuity in life, then, we need to have some understanding of how cells divide.

The sheer numbers involved in this process are mind-boggling. In your body, as many as 25 million cell divisions are taking place each second. It is likely that every one of these divisions serves to maintain your body in some way, yet there are instances in which cells divide excessively. How does the disease we call cancer take hold? Always through the *unrestrained* division of cells. As you can see in "When the Cell Cycle Runs Amok" on page 168, cancer is intimately related to basic processes of cellular division.

Why Do Cells Divide?

But why should cells divide at all? That is, why don't they just stay as they are? One answer is that cells die and need to be replaced. Beyond this, cells can only grow so large before they become too large—past a certain size, they can't function. (See "The Size of Cells" on page 68.) The solution to this dilemma is to divide and start small again. Moreover, more cells may

be needed at one point in life than in another. To take one example, the material that makes up human bones is secreted by cells. A growing teenager needs to add more of this bone material than does a mature adult. So, where is the teenager going to get this additional material? From additional cells—produced through cell division. None of this is to say that *every* cell divides. Most human brain cells are formed in the first three months of embryonic existence and then live for decades, with relatively few of them ever dividing again. Much the same is true of the leaf cells in plants; they divide only when the leaf is very small, then grow for a time, and then function at this mature size for as long as the leaf lives. At the other extreme, cells located in human bone marrow never *stop* dividing as they produce red blood cells (each one of which only lives for about two months). The output here is staggering: About 180 million new red blood cells are produced inside us each minute through cell division.

"Cell division" actually may be a somewhat misleading term if it is taken to mean a simple separation of cellular material, akin to a candy bar being split between two friends. Indeed, a splitting does occur in cell division, but certain parts of the cell must *duplicate* before this happens. Then, the duplicated material is parceled out with fine precision, half of it going to one "daughter" cell and half to the other.

What's being duplicated and apportioned is DNA. Because a cell's full complement of DNA contains such critical information, it would not do for a cell to be left with 50 or 75 percent of this information; rather, it needs the whole thing—no more and no less.

With this in mind, here is the big picture on cell division. First, there is a duplication of DNA; then there is the movement of two precisely matched quantities of DNA to opposite sides of the "parent" cell; finally, there is the splitting of the parent cell into two daughter cells. The duplication of DNA is known as *replication,* the apportioning of it into two identical quantities is known as *mitosis,* and the splitting of the cellular material is known as *cytokinesis* (**Figure 9.4**). The goal for the remainder of this chapter is to learn a little bit about replication and a good deal more about mitosis and cytokinesis.

The Replication of DNA

So how does the first part of cell division work—the DNA replication? If you look at **Figure 9.5**, you can see a simplified representation of the DNA molecule shown in Figure 9.2. Notice that the strands of the double helix have started to unwind, which is an initial step in DNA replication (Figure 9.5, step 1). Each of the two resulting single strands then serves as a template or pattern on which a new strand is created

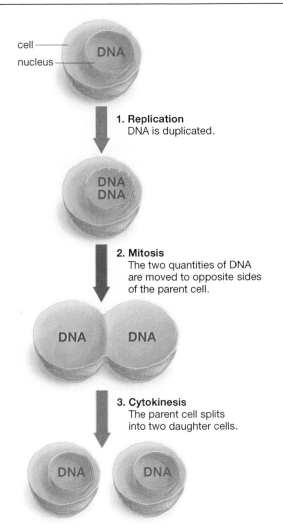

Figure 9.4
Overview of Cell Division

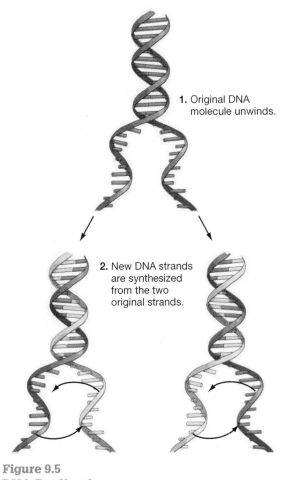

1. Original DNA molecule unwinds.

2. New DNA strands are synthesized from the two original strands.

Figure 9.5
DNA Replication

(1) A DNA molecule unwinds.

(2) Each of the single strands of the original molecule (in red) serves as a template or pattern for the creation of a second DNA strand (in blue).

(Figure 9.5, step 2). Earlier, DNA structure was compared to a spiral staircase. Now, think of that staircase as splitting right down the middle of its steps (where the A and T or the G and C bases meet). Then, a new *half*-staircase is created that bonds with one of the old DNA strands; a second half-staircase is likewise created that bonds with the *second* original strand. (These new strands are the blue ones in Figure 9.5, step 2.) How does this happen? Free-floating DNA bases will bond, one base at a time, with bases on the original strand. This process continues down the line until two strands have been created, each composed of one "old" half-strand and one "new" half-strand. This replication process, which doubles the cell's DNA content, takes place in advance of the cell dividing.

In Chapter 13, you will metaphorically walk along the rungs of the double helix to grasp the details of this doubling of DNA strands. Right now, however, you'll be considering DNA on a larger scale, as it comes packaged.

9.3 DNA in Chromosomes

You have thus far conceptualized each cell's DNA as spiraling out in *one* long double helix, but it does not, in fact, take this form. Rather, the DNA in each cell comes divided and packaged into individual units of DNA called **chromosomes.** Different organisms have different numbers of chromosomes; human cells have 46, for example, while onion cells have 16. The chromosomes of eukaryotic organisms, such as ourselves, amount to DNA "packages" in several senses. They consist not only of DNA itself but of proteins around which DNA is wrapped. The result is **chromatin:** a molecular complex, composed of DNA and associated proteins, that makes up the chromosomes of eukaryotic organisms. Thus, a number of chromosomes, composed of chromatin, exist in a cell's nucleus, detached but in close physical proximity to one another, and the *collection* of chromosomes makes up nearly the entire complement of a cell's DNA.

(a) DNA is packaged in units called chromosomes

DNA wraps around protein to make chromatin

Chromatin folds up to make chromosomes

DNA

chromatin

duplicated chromosome

cell

(b) DNA replication at two levels

Figure 9.6
Chromosomes and DNA Replication

(a) The DNA molecule is bound up with proteins, with the resulting combination known as chromatin. This chromatin then makes up structures called chromosomes.

(b) When DNA replicates, the result is two copies of the original DNA molecule. At the chromosomal level, the result of this replication is a single chromosome in duplicated state. The chromosome is composed of two sister chromatids—the two copies of the original DNA molecule. An unduplicated chromosome doesn't actually have the well-defined shape of the chromosome in the figure. It's shown this way merely for purposes of comparison with the duplicated chromosome.

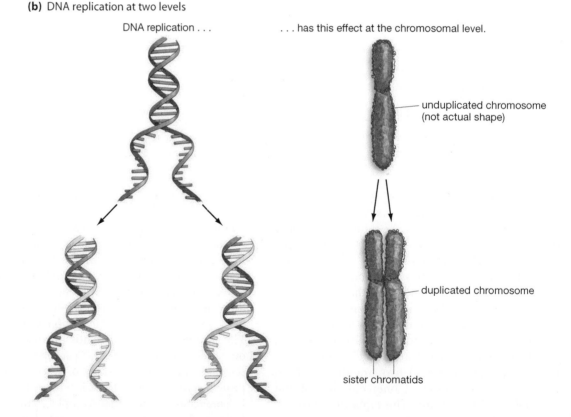

DNA replication . . .

. . . has this effect at the chromosomal level.

unduplicated chromosome (not actual shape)

duplicated chromosome

sister chromatids

If you look at **Figure 9.6a**, you can see how to think about the double helix being packaged into chromosomes. **Figure 9.6b** shows you how to relate the "staircase-splitting" DNA replication just described to what this means at the chromosomal level. When we say that DNA is replicating, this is another way of saying that the chromosomes that DNA helps make up are *duplicating*. Once that has happened, the result is chromosomes in "duplicated state," which means individual chromosomes, each of which is made up of two sister chromatids. Each chromatid is one of the newly replicated DNA double helices plus its associated proteins, as you can see in Figure 9.6b. More formally, a **chromatid** is one of the two identical strands of chromatin that make up a chromosome in its duplicated state. (It probably goes without saying that despite their name, sister chromatids are neither siblings nor females.)

Matched Pairs of Chromosomes

Chromosomes are detached from one another, but that does not mean they are completely different from one another. In eukaryotes, in fact, chromosomes tend to come in *pairs* that are close, but not exact, matches. The 46 chromosomes we have come to us as 23 chromosomes from *each parent*. Critically, with one exception that you'll soon get to, these are 23 matched pairs of chromosomes, each chromosome from the mother matching with one from the father.

What is a "matched pair" of chromosomes? Well, we have a chromosome 1 that we inherit from our mother, and it contains a set of genes very similar to those that lie on the chromosome 1 we inherit from our father. And the way the genes on these two chromosomes are similar is that they code for the same types of proteins. For example, human chromosome 1 contains a gene that codes for a protein, called F5, that helps blood to clot following an injury. For our purposes, the important thing is that the *F5* gene exists on *both* the maternal and paternal copies of chromosome 1. Indeed, if we were to look at all the roughly 4,200 genes found on chromosome 1 we would find this same symmetry: A given gene found on *pa*ternal chromosome 1 will almost certainly have a counterpart on *ma*ternal chromosome 1. This pattern then continues for the genes found on chromosome 2, chromosome 3, and so forth. It's easy to see, then, that the paternal and maternal copies of a given chromosome are the same in function; any two chromosomes that share this quality are said to be **homologous chromosomes.**

It's important to note, however, that homologous chromosomes are not *exactly* alike, because there can be variations on the genes found on the members of any homologous pair. If a given paternal chromosome has a gene that codes for, say, hair color, then it's a safe bet that the matching maternal chromosome will likewise have a gene that codes for hair color. But a gene on the paternal chromosome may help code for red hair, while the gene on the matching maternal chromosome may help code for blond hair. Nevertheless, both chromosomes have genes that code for hair color, as well as for thousands of other traits, and as such are said to be homologous.

X and Y Chromosomes

The one exception to the matched-pairs rule in human chromosomes is the so-called sex chromosomes of males. Human females have the 23 pairs of homolo-

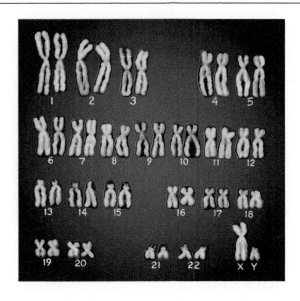

Figure 9.7
A Karyotype Displays a Full Set of Chromosomes
One member of each chromosome pair comes from the individual's father and the other member from the mother. Each paired set of chromosomes is said to be "homologous," meaning the same in function. (The two chromosomes over the number 1 are a homologous pair, as are the two over number 2, and so forth.)

gous chromosomes mentioned before; 22 of these are pairs of *autosomes,* or non-sex chromosomes, but one is a pair of homologous X chromosomes that, when present, means a growing embryo will be a female. Males, on the other hand, have the 22 pairs of homologous autosomes and one X chromosome; but then they also have one *Y* chromosome that, when present, means a growing embryo will be a male.

This whole scheme can be set forth in a visual display called a **karyotype,** meaning a pictorial arrangement of a complete set of human chromosomes. If you look at **Figure 9.7**, you can see an example of a karyotype, with its 46 chromosomes arranged in order, 22 of them matched pairs. In this case, one pair, at lower right, has one X chromosome and one Y chromosome, meaning this is a male.

The chromosomes in Figure 9.7 are in the duplicated state noted earlier, each of them being composed of two sister chromatids. For the sake of clarity, it would be nice to see a picture of some *un*duplicated chromosomes, but we have no pictures that are the counterpart to Figure 9.7. This is because chromosomes take on an easily discernible shape only after they duplicate, prior to cell division. As cell division approaches, the DNA–protein complex changes its form; it tightens up, condensing mightily to produce well-defined chromosomes (**Figure 9.8b**, on the next page). After cell division is complete, the cell's chromosomes return to their relatively formless state, shown in **Figure 9.8a**.

Why this change in form? This condensing before cell division has the same effect as you taking all your scattered belongings and packing them into boxes just before moving from one apartment to another. Remember that DNA is packing up to leave as well, in this case for life in a successor cell. Were it not to tighten into its duplicated chromosomal form, its elongated fibers would get tangled up in the move.

Figure 9.8
DNA Can Be Arranged in Two Ways
(a) Replication occurs when the chromosomes are in a relatively formless state. In this state, the chromatin that makes up the chromosomes has yet to condense into its compact arrangement.
(b) Mitosis occurs after chromatin condenses into the easily discernible shapes of duplicated chromosomes. The micrograph is of color-enhanced duplicated human chromosomes.

(a) DNA in uncondensed form

(b) DNA condensed into duplicated chromosomes

SO FAR ...

1. For any cell to divide, the DNA it contains must first double or _____ so that both of the daughter cells that are produced will have their own complement of DNA. To look at this process another way, prior to cell division each of the chromosomes in a cell must _____.

2. Chromosomes are composed of both DNA and its associated _____. In duplicated state, each chromosome is composed of two identical _____.

3. In human beings (and many other organisms) chromosomes come in pairs that are said to be _____, meaning the same in function. The pairs rule is seen in women, who have a pair of chromosomes that confer female gender, the _____ chromosomes. Meanwhile, men have one _____ chromosome (like women) but one _____ chromosome, which confers the male gender.

Chromosome Duplication as a Part of Cell Division

With the chromosomes duplicated, you are now ready to look at the process by which they will split up. Before following this path, though, recognize that this separation occurs within the larger process that we are following: the division of the cell as a whole. As you saw in Chapter 5, there are many more things inside a cell than its complement of chromosomes. There are mitochondria, lysosomes, ribosomes, and so forth and the cytosol in which they are immersed. Together, these things lie in the cell's cytoplasm—the area *outside* the nucleus, as opposed to chromosomes, which lie *inside* the nucleus. With cell division, half of the cytoplasmic material goes to one daughter cell and

half to the other. It is helpful, then, to conceptualize cell division as having two separable components. **Mitosis** is the separation of a cell's duplicated chromosomes prior to cytokinesis. **Cytokinesis** is the physical separation of one cell into two daughter cells. These two processes are part of the big picture of cell division sketched earlier, which now can be stated in a slightly different way. First, chromosomes duplicate; then chromosomes separate and move to opposite sides of the parent cell (mitosis); then the parent cell splits into two daughter cells (cytokinesis).

The Cell Cycle

If you look at **Figure 9.9**, you can see how all these processes are linked over time. The figure illustrates the **cell cycle:** the repeating pattern of growth, genetic duplication, and division seen in most cells. There are two main phases in this cycle. First, there is **interphase:** that portion of the cell cycle in which the cell simultaneously carries out its work and, in preparation for division, duplicates its chromosomes. Second, there is **mitotic phase** (or M phase): that portion of the cell cycle that includes both mitosis and cytokinesis.

Interphase and M phase are in turn subdivided into smaller phases. In interphase, first there is G_1, standing for "gap-one." What goes on here are normal cell operations and cell growth. The cell then enters the S or "synthesis" phase, which is the synthesis of DNA, resulting in the duplication of the chromosomes. When this ends, interphase's gap-two or G_2 period begins, during which there is more cytoplasmic growth and a preparation for cell division. Because DNA synthesis is stopped in G_2 as well as G_1, the word *gap* in G_1 and G_2 can be thought of as a gap in DNA synthesis.

The length of the cell cycle varies greatly from one type of cell to another. In a typical animal cell, the total cell-cycle length averages about 24 hours. Within this cycle, mitotic phase takes up only about 30 minutes. Within interphase, an animal cell spends roughly 12 hours in G_1, 6 hours in S, and 6 hours in G_2. Some cells divide only rarely, while others—such as most

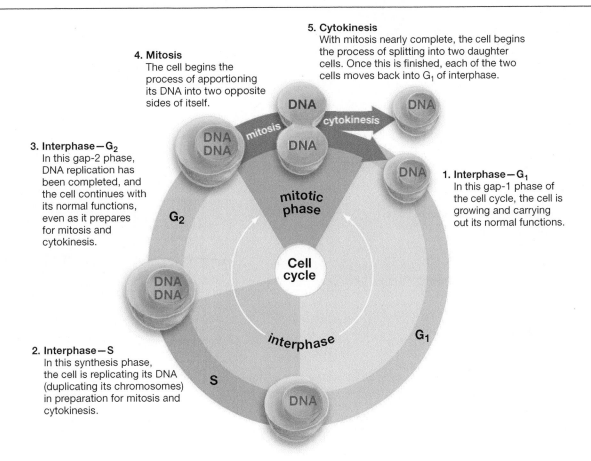

4. Mitosis
The cell begins the process of apportioning its DNA into two opposite sides of itself.

5. Cytokinesis
With mitosis nearly complete, the cell begins the process of splitting into two daughter cells. Once this is finished, each of the two cells moves back into G_1 of interphase.

mitosis

cytokinesis

DNA

DNA
DNA

DNA

DNA

DNA

3. Interphase—G_2
In this gap-2 phase, DNA replication has been completed, and the cell continues with its normal functions, even as it prepares for mitosis and cytokinesis.

G_2

mitotic phase

1. Interphase—G_1
In this gap-1 phase of the cell cycle, the cell is growing and carrying out its normal functions.

Cell cycle

2. Interphase—S
In this synthesis phase, the cell is replicating its DNA (duplicating its chromosomes) in preparation for mitosis and cytokinesis.

DNA
DNA

S

interphase

G_1

DNA

Figure 9.9
The Cell Cycle

The three main stages of cell division—DNA replication, mitosis, and cytokinesis—can be seen here in the context of a complete cell cycle. This cycle traditionally is divided into two main phases, interphase and mitotic (or M) phase, which are in turn divided into other phases.

nerve cells—don't divide at all. We could think of these cells as existing in an extended G_1 phase. But to distinguish them from cells that are simply moving through G_1, they are said to be in G_0 phase.

9.4 Mitosis and Cytokinesis

It is the second main phase of the cell cycle, mitotic phase, that is the focus of the rest of this chapter. Now the concern is not with how a cell manages its general functions, or with how it replicates its DNA, but with how it *divides*—how it carries out both mitosis and cytokinesis. Mitosis turns out to have four phases: prophase, metaphase, anaphase, and telophase. We'll now look at these phases in order, after which we'll review cytokinesis.

The Phases of Mitosis

Prophase

The beginning of mitosis marks the end of the cell's interphase (**Figure 9.10**, on the next page). The starting state is that the cell's DNA, which was replicated during the S phase, has just begun to pack itself into well-defined chromosomes. When we can finally *see* such chromosomes with a microscope, we can say that mitosis has begun, with prophase. Now the packing job continues; before it is done, the DNA will have coiled and condensed into one eight-thousandth of its

S-phase length. When this is over in human beings, there are 46 well-defined chromosomes in the nucleus in duplicated state (meaning they are composed of 92 chromatids). Meanwhile, the nuclear envelope—the double membrane surrounding the nucleus—begins to break up.

While this is going on, big changes are taking place outside the nucleus. Recall from Chapter 4 the structures called **microtubules:** protein fibers that are part of the cell's cytoskeleton or internal fiber network. In some of their roles, microtubules can be compared to tent poles that can shorten or lengthen as need be. Throughout mitosis, microtubules stretch the cell as a whole and physically move the cell's chromosomes around.

In an interphase cell there exists, just outside the nucleus, a **centrosome:** a cellular structure that acts as an organizing center for the assembly of microtubules. This centrosome duplicates, so that now there are two microtubule organizing centers. Now, in prophase, these two centrosomes start to move apart. Where are they going? To the poles. From here on out, it is convenient to think of mitosis and cytokinesis in terms of a global metaphor: The centrosomes migrate to the cellular poles, while the chromosomes first align, and then separate, along a cellular equator called the metaphase plate. Unlike microtubules or the centrosome, the **metaphase plate** is not a physical structure but instead is a plane located midway between

BioFlix™

Mitosis

pair of centrosomes

nucleus

replicated, uncondensed DNA

spindle fibers (microtubules)

chromosomes (each a pair of sister chromatids joined together)

mitotic spindle

metaphase plate

End of interphase

DNA has already duplicated back in S phase. Centrosome has doubled.

Prophase

Mitosis begins: Chromosomes take shape; the two centrosomes begin to move toward the cellular poles, sprouting microtubules as they go

Metaphase

Attachment and alignment: Microtubules attach to sister chromatids and align them at the metaphase plate.

Figure 9.10 Mitosis and Cytokinesis

The micrographs at the bottom of the figure are pictures of mitosis and cytokinesis in a whitefish embryo.

the poles of a dividing cell. As the centrosomes move apart, they begin sprouting microtubules in all directions. One variety of them forms a football-shaped cage around the nuclear material, while a second variety attaches to the chromosomes themselves. Taken together, the microtubules active in cell division are known as the **mitotic spindle.**

Metaphase

By the time metaphase begins, the nuclear envelope has disappeared completely, and the microtubules

that were growing toward the chromosomes now *attach* to them. Through a lively back-and-forth movement, the microtubules align the chromosomes at the equator. With this, each chromatid now faces the pole *opposite* that of its sister chromatid, and each chromatid is attached to its respective pole by perhaps 30 microtubules.

Anaphase

At last the genetic material divides. As you may have guessed, this is a parting of sisters. The sister

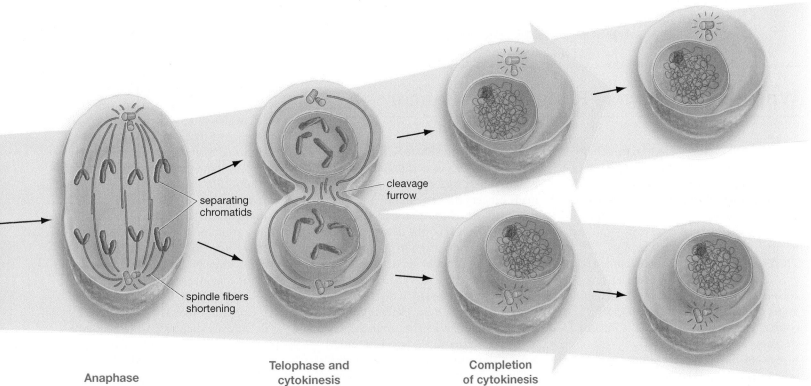

Anaphase

Separation:
Sister chromatids are moved to opposite poles in the cell, each chromatid now becoming a full-fledged chromosome.

Telophase and cytokinesis

Exit from mitosis:
Chromosomes decondense; nuclear envelopes form around the two separate complements of chromosomes. Cleavage furrow begins to form.

Completion of cytokinesis

One cell becomes two:
The cell membrane pinches together completely; membranes on either side fuse together, creating two cells.

Beginning of interphase

These two cells now enter the G$_1$ phase of interphase.

chromatids are pulled apart, each now becoming a full-fledged chromosome. All 46 chromatid pairs divide at the same time, and each member of a chromatid pair moves toward its respective pole, pulled by a shortening of the microtubules to which it is attached.

Telophase

Telophase represents a return to things as they were before mitosis started. The newly independent chromosomes, having arrived at their respective poles,

now unwind and lose their clearly defined shape. New nuclear membranes are forming. When this work is complete, there are two finished daughter nuclei lying in one elongating cell. Even as this is going on, though, something else is taking place that will result in this one cell becoming two.

Cytokinesis

Cytokinesis actually began back in anaphase and is well under way by the time of telophase. It works

ESSAY

When the Cell Cycle Runs Amok: Cancer

The cell cycle reviewed in this chapter is, in one sense, a common natural process: Cells grow; they duplicate their chromosomes; these chromosomes separate; one cell divides into two. This goes on like clockwork, millions of times a second in each one of us. Then one day we learn that an aunt, a grandfather, or a friend is experiencing an *unrestrained* division of cells. Things aren't explained to us in this way, of course. We are simply told that someone we know has cancer.

At root, all cancers are failures of the cell cycle. Put another way, all cancers represent a failure of cells to limit their multiplication in the cell cycle. What is liver cancer, for example? It is a damaging multiplication of liver cells. First one, then two, then four, then eight liver cells move repeatedly through the cell cycle, and as their numbers increase, they destroy the liver's working tissues. Given that cancer manifests in this way, it's not surprising that a large portion of modern cancer research is *cell-cycle* research. The logic here is simple: To the extent that uncontrolled cell division can be stopped, cancer can be stopped.

In recent years, cell-cycle research has brought about a remarkable change in the kinds of treatments that are being developed for cancer. For decades, the basic idea behind cancer treatment was to kill as many cancer cells as possible, either by removing these cells from the body altogether (in surgery) or by destroying them with radiation or drugs. In contrast, nearly all the cancer drugs being developed today are intended not to kill cancerous cells. Instead, they are intended to disrupt the process by which these cells multiply. The idea is that, just as a light can be switched off by disrupting an electrical circuit, so cell division can be switched off by disrupting a *molecular* circuit—the chain of chemical reactions that keeps a cancerous cell moving constantly through cell division. The new breed of cancer treatments that are built on this idea are called targeted therapies.

To get a feel for what this approach means in practice, consider the first targeted therapy ever developed: a drug called Gleevec, which is aimed at combating a form of cancer, called chronic myeloid leukemia (CML), that results in an uncontrolled proliferation of certain types of white blood cells. In the 1990s, the researcher most responsible for Gleevec's use in CML treatment, Oregon Health and Sciences University Professor Brian Druker, began to focus on the process by which CML cells come to their out-of-control state. Druker knew that CML begins in a single white blood cell when two of its chromosomes undergo an unusual form of segment-swapping with one another. When a segment from chromosome A fuses with a segment of chromosome B in this process, the result is that information from both chromosomes combines to create a mutant gene—a gene that does not exist in any normal white blood cell. Of course, this mutant gene (dubbed *BCR-ABL*) then results in a protein that is capable of carrying out some task in the white blood cell. Unfortunately, what the BCR-ABL protein does is flip a molecular switch; through it, the white blood cell starts multiplying more rapidly, even as it and its daughter cells start undergoing further destabilizing changes that ultimately result in full-blown leukemia.

Druker's key insight into stopping CML was to look very carefully at the BCR-ABL protein, which you can see represented in **Figure 1**. He realized that BCR-ABL is powered into activity following its binding with the energy-transfer molecule ATP. So, he wondered, what would happen if the ATP binding site on the BCR-ABL protein became unavailable—what would happen if this binding site became *occupied* by another molecule? The substance he eventually hit upon that takes on this occupying role

**Figure 9.11
Cytokinesis in Animals**

Cytokinesis in animal cells begins with an indentation of the cell surface, a cleavage furrow, shown here in a dividing frog egg.

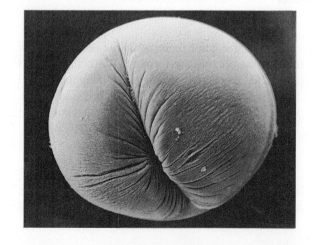

through the tightening of a cellular waistband that is composed of two sets of protein filaments working together. These filaments—the same type that allow your muscles to contract—form a *contractile ring* that narrows along the cellular equator (**Figure 9.11**). An indentation of the cell's surface (called a cleavage furrow) results from the ring's contraction; consequently, the fibers in the mitotic spindle are pushed closer and closer together, eventually forming one thick pole that is destined to break.

The dividing cell now assumes an hourglass shape; as the contractile ring continues to pinch in, one cell becomes two by means of something you looked at in Chapter 4: membrane fusion. The membranes on each

Figure 1
Blocking Cancer's Progress
The drug Gleevec is a so-called targeted therapy for cancer in that it blocks a molecular signaling pathway that sustains a particular cancer, chronic myeloid leukemia, which affects white blood cells. Gleevec binds to a site on the mutant protein BCR-ABL, thus preventing the energy-dispensing molecule ATP from binding to the site. With this, BCR-ABL is deprived of the energy it needs to carry out its reactions and can no longer keep the cell moving through the process of cell division.

was the drug that became Gleevec, which had been developed in the 1990s by the pharmaceutical firm Ciba-Geigy. (For more on the development of Gleevec, see "How Science and Business Take on Cancer," on page 12).

As it turned out, the effect of Gleevec was revolutionary—in two ways. First, this drug turned CML from an invariably deadly form of cancer into a chronic, manageable illness. Eight-five to 90 percent of CML patients now survive at least five years and it appears that the vast majority of these patients will never die from CML. Second, Gleevec was proof-positive of the potential of targeted therapy. It showed that disrupting the circuitry of a given form of cancer could upend that cancer altogether. Since Gleevec's debut, two other notable targeted therapy drugs have been brought to market: Herceptin, which works against certain forms of breast cancer; and Avastin, which is aimed at denying cancer tumors the blood supply they need to keep growing. Neither drug has had the dramatic effect of Gleevec, but it would have been unreasonable to expect every targeted therapy drug to yield Gleevec's startling results.

A broader measure of Gleevec's impact, however, comes not from looking at cancer drugs currently in use, but from looking at cancer drugs currently in development. Almost all the drugs that are in the research pipelines of pharmaceutical firms today are forms of targeted therapy. Rather than being intended to kill cancer cells outright, these drugs are intended to disrupt the specific molecular pathways of particular cancers. A change such as this may ultimately result in a completely different way of thinking about cancer. Whereas cancer researchers have traditionally defined different forms of cancer by their anatomical sites of origin—liver cancer, lung cancer, and so forth—they are today defining cancers more and more by the molecular pathways that sustain them. Only time will tell what will come of this sweeping change in the fight against cancer, but the results so far have been promising.

half of the hourglass circle toward each other and then fuse. With this, the two cells become separate. Mitosis and cytokinesis are over, and the two daughter cells slip back into the relative quiet of interphase.

SO FAR...

1. Cell division has two separable components: Mitosis is the movement of a cell's _____ into opposite parts of the cell, while cytokinesis is the physical separation of one cell into two _____.

2. Mitosis and cytokinesis take place in the relatively short _____ phase of the cell cycle. Meanwhile, a typical cell spends most of its time in the cycle's _____, carrying out its normal function and duplicating its chromosomes in preparation for division.

3. In mitosis, the apportioning of DNA comes about through the separation of _____, each of which then becomes a fully functional _____ in one of the newly formed daughter cells.

9.5 Cell Division in Plants and Bacteria

Having looked at cell division as it takes place in animal cells, we'll now look at some variations on the process, as seen in plant cells and in bacteria.

Plant Cells

Plant cells carry out most of the steps of mitosis just as animal cells do. In the splitting of cytokinesis, however, plant cells must deal with something that animal cells don't have: the cell wall (see page 84 in Chapter 4). The way animal cells carry out cytokinesis—pinching the plasma membrane inward via the contractile ring—wouldn't work with plant cells because their thick cell wall lies *outside* the plasma membrane.

The plant cell's solution is to grow a new cell wall and plasma membrane that run roughly down the middle of the parent cell. If you look at **Figure 9.12**, you can see how this works. A series of membrane-lined vesicles begins to accumulate near the metaphase plate; the vesicles then begin to fuse together; eventually, they will form a flat *cell plate* that runs from one side of the parent cell to the other. The membrane portion of the cell plate then fuses with the original plasma membrane of the parent cell, and the result is two new adjacent plasma membranes that split the parent cell in two. Meanwhile, the material enclosed *inside* the cell-plate membrane is the foundation for the new cell-wall segments of the daughter cells.

Prokaryotes: Bacteria and Archaea

It's also important to recognize that some cells have fundamentally different ways of replicating. The cells of prokaryotes—the bacteria and archaea you looked at in Chapter 4—are a case in point.

If you look at **Figure 9.13**, you can see how cell division works among the prokaryotes. Bacteria are single-celled and have a single, circular chromosome. Bacterial cells do not, however, have their chromosome sequestered inside a nucleus, for the simple reason that they have no nucleus. Instead, their lone chromosome is attached to their plasma membrane.

A bacterial cell begins its division by duplicating its chromosome. As the daughter chromosomes are completed, however, they attach to *different sites* on the plasma membrane. The cell then begins developing an outgrowth of its plasma membrane and cell wall in between these attachment sites. This outgrowth, called a septum, begins growing from opposite sides of the cell. When the two septum extensions join in the middle, they divide the one cell into two (**Figure 9.14**). This process is very different from the eukaryotic mitosis and cytokinesis you looked at. As such, prokaryotic cell division goes under an entirely different name: **binary fission.** The simplicity of binary fission makes for a short cell cycle. Remember how the animal cells we looked at took about 24 hours to go through a cycle? Bacteria can complete their cycle in as little as 20 minutes.

On to Meiosis

The cell division reviewed in this chapter concerns "somatic" cells—the kind that form bone, muscle, nerve, and many other sorts of tissue. Given a distribution this wide, you might well ask: What kind of cells are *not* somatic? The answer is only one kind—the kind that forms the basis for each succeeding generation of sexually reproducing living things. The division of these cells, through a process known as meiosis, is the subject of Chapter 10.

Figure 9.12
Cytokinesis in Plants

cell wall

vesicles

plasma membrane

two daughter cells

1. Membrane-lined vesicles accumulate near the metaphase plate. The vesicles contain precursors to the cell wall.

2. Vesicles fuse together, forming a cell plate that grows toward the parent cell wall.

3. The newly formed plasma membrane and cell wall fuse with the parent plasma membrane and cell wall, forming two distinct daughter cells.

Figure 9.13
Binary Fission in
Bacteria

cell wall

chromosome

cell membrane

parental
bacterial
cell

two
daughter
cells

1. Bacterial cell starts with a single, circular chromosome attached to its plasma membrane.

2. The chromosome replicates and the daughter chromosomes attach to different sites on the plasma membrane.

3. The cell membrane and wall grow an extension between the attachment points of the two chromosomes.

4. The cell wall and membrane join together in the middle, resulting in two new cells.

SO FAR...

1. Owing to their cell walls, plant cells cannot carry out _____ in the same way that animal cells do. Thus, plant cells build a new _____ and _____ that run roughly down the middle of the parent cell, creating two daughter cells that then separate.

2. Bacterial cells are prokaryotes, meaning their cells have no _____. In cell division, a bacterial cell's single chromosome duplicates and the resulting daughter chromosomes attach to different sites on the _____, after which the cell divides in two. This process is known as _____.

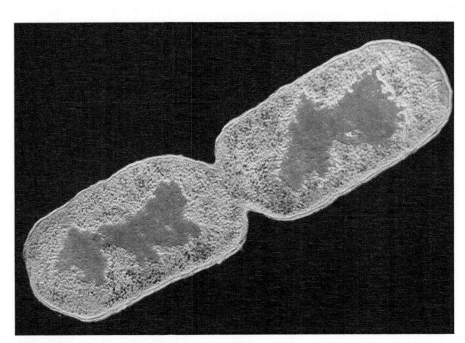

Figure 9.14
Cell Division for a Resident of the Human Gut
An *Escherichia coli* (*E. coli*) bacterium in a late phase of cell division.

CHAPTER 9 REVIEW

Go to the Study Area at www.masteringbiology.com for practice quizzes, myeBook, BioFlix™ 3-D animations, MP3 Tutor Sessions, videos, current events, and more.

Summary

9.1 An Introduction to Genetics

- DNA contains the information for the production of proteins, which carry out a wide variety of tasks in living things. (p. 157)

- The information in DNA is encoded in chemical substances called bases, laid out along the DNA double helix in four varieties: adenine (A), thymine (T), guanine (G), and cytosine (C). One series of bases contains information for the production of one protein; a different series of bases specifies a different protein. Each series of protein-specifying bases is known as a gene. (p. 158)

- In protein synthesis, a sequence of DNA bases is copied onto the molecule messenger RNA (mRNA). This molecule moves out of the cell's nucleus to a ribosome, located in the cell's cytoplasm, where the mRNA sequence is brought together with amino acids. As the mRNA sequence is "read" within the ribosome, a chain of amino acids is linked together in the ribosome in the order specified by the mRNA sequence. The result is a chain of amino acids that folds into a protein. (p. 159)

9.2 An Introduction to Cell Division

- Cell division includes the duplication of DNA (replication); the apportioning of the copied DNA into two quantities in a parent cell (mitosis); and the physical splitting of this parent cell into two daughter cells (cytokinesis). In DNA replication, the two strands of the double helix unwind, after which each single strand serves as a template for construction of a second, complementary strand. (p. 160)

9.3 DNA in Chromosomes

- DNA comes packaged in units called chromosomes, which are composed of DNA and its associated proteins. Chromosomes exist in an unduplicated state until DNA replicates, before cell division. DNA replication results in chromosomes that are in duplicated state, meaning one chromosome composed of two identical sister chromatids. (p. 161)

- Chromosomes in human beings (and many other species) come in matched pairs, with one member of each pair inherited from the mother and father, respectively. Such homologous chromosomes have closely matched sets of genes, although many of these are not identical. Human beings have 46 chromosomes—22 matched pairs plus either a matched pair of X chromosomes (in females) or an X and a Y chromosome (in males). (p. 163)

- The cell cycle has two main phases: (1) interphase, in which the cell carries out its work, grows, and duplicates its chromosomes in preparation for division; and (2) mitotic phase, in which the duplicated chromosomes separate (mitosis) and the cell splits in two (cytokinesis). (p. 164)

9.4 Mitosis and Cytokinesis

- There are four stages in mitosis: prophase, metaphase, anaphase, and telophase. Duplicated chromosomes line up along the metaphase plate, with sister chromatids on opposite sides of the plate. Attached to fibers called microtubules, the sister chromatids are pulled apart, to opposite poles of the parent cell. Once cell division is complete, a pair of sister chromatids that once formed a single chromosome will reside in separate daughter cells, with each sister chromatid now functioning as a full-fledged chromosome. (p. 165)

- In cytokinesis in animal cells, a ring of protein filaments tightens at the middle of

a dividing cell. Membranes being pinched together then fuse, resulting in two daughter cells. (p. 167)

BioFlix™

Mitosis

9.5 Cell Division in Plants and Bacteria

- In cytokinesis in plant cells, the cells grow new cell walls and plasma membranes near the metaphase plate, thus dividing the parent cell into two. (p. 170)

- In cell division in prokaryotes, cells double their single, circular chromosome, with the two resulting chromosomes attaching to different sites on the plasma membrane. Then an outgrowth of plasma membrane and cell wall, called a septum, begins growing from opposite sides of the cell, between the two chromosomes. When the two septum extensions join, they divide the one cell into two. (p. 170)

Key Terms

binary fission   170
cell cycle   164
centrosome   165
chromatid   163
chromatin   161
chromosome   161
cytokinesis   164
genetics   159
genome   157
homologous chromosomes   163
interphase   164
karyotype   163
metaphase plate   165
microtubule   165
mitosis   164
mitotic phase   164
mitotic spindle   166

Understanding the Basics

Multiple-Choice Questions

(Answers are in the back of the book.)

1. Proteins serve in living things as:
   a. hormones.
   b. enzymes.
   c. cell receptors.
   d. structural building blocks.
   e. all of the above.

2. The four bases found along the DNA double-helix are:
   a. adenine, thymine, guanine, and cytosol.
   b. adenine, thyroxine, glucose, and cytosine.
   c. adrenaline, thymine, glucosamine, and uracil.
   d. adenine, thymine, guanine, and cytosine.
   e. none of the above.

3. A gene can be described as:
   a. a protein that contains enough information to carry out a task.
   b. a hormone that prompts some action inside a cell.
   c. a series of DNA bases that transfer energy within a cell.
   d. a series of DNA bases that contain information for production of a protein.
   e. a protein that delivers information to a ribosome.

4. The human genome contains:
   a. 23 pairs of chromosomes.
   b. 48 chromosomes.
   c. as many as 25,000 genes.
   d. b and c, above.
   e. a and c, above.

5. Prophase has begun when:
   a. well-defined chromosomes are distinguishable.
   b. a cleavage furrow has formed.
   c. chromosomes have aligned along the metaphase plate.
   d. chromosomes have duplicated.
   e. sister chromatids have separated.

6. If a cell is not dividing, and has not yet replicated its DNA (duplicated its chromosomes), what phase of the cell cycle would it be in?
   a. gap-two (G_2) phase
   b. synthesis (S) phase
   c. gap-one (G1) phase
   d. prophase
   e. mitotic phase

7. The average length of the cell cycle in animal cells is about:
   a. 16 hours.
   b. 24 hours.
   c. 30 minutes.
   d. 2 hours.
   e. 12 hours.

8. The cell cycle is linked to cancer because cancer always entails:
   a. too much time spent in S phase.
   b. a slow-down in mitosis.
   c. unrestrained cell division.
   d. a misalignment of chromosomes.
   e. not enough time spent in M phase.

Brief Review

(Answers are in the back of the book.)

1. In what way does DNA help form and then maintain our bodies?

2. The drawing below shows a cell in a phase of mitosis. What phase is shown? How many chromatids are present in this stage? What is the total number of chromosomes each daughter cell will have?

3. How do mitosis and cytokinesis differ?

4. Name the four phases of mitosis and describe the major events occurring in each phase.

5. Compared to animal cells, what additional cell structure must plant cells deal with when they are undergoing cytokinesis? Given this difference, how do plant cells carry out cytokinesis?

6. In what way are the 23 pairs of human chromosomes "matched" pairs of chromosomes?

7. The protein synthesis pathway—DNA → mRNA → protein—is a very important concept in biology. Within this framework:
   a. What are the information-bearing "building blocks" of DNA?
   b. Where is DNA located in the cell?
   c. What does the "m" in mRNA stand for?
   d. Using this knowledge, what is the function of mRNA, and where is it used?
   e. What are the building blocks of proteins?
   f. Where does protein formation occur?

Applying Your Knowledge

1. Why is it accurate to think of each human being as the owner of a library of ancient information?

2. People who are born with the condition called Down syndrome generally have three copies of a certain chromosome (chromosome 21), rather than the usual two copies. What can you deduce from this regarding the proteins produced by a person with Down syndrome?

3. The tools of computer science are today being applied to the genomes of living things thanks to the happy coincidence that the information in both computers and genomes exists in digital form. In computers, digital information is expressed as a series of 0's and 1's. What is the digital form that a genome's information comes in?

10

Preparing for Sexual Reproduction:

Meiosis

One special kind of cell division yields the sex cells that give rise to succeeding generations and serves as the foundation for much of the diversity seen in the living world.

Animals, fungi, plants. How did the living world become so diverse? In part, through the process of meiosis.

A real-life couple—let's call them Jack Fennington and Jill Kent—combine their last names when they get married and thus become Jack and Jill Fennington-Kent. Now, what would happen if the Fennington-Kent's children were to continue in this tradition? Their daughter, Susie, might marry, say, Ralph Reeson-Dodd, which would make her Susie Fennington-Kent-Reeson-Dodd. If *Susie's* daughter, Alicia, were to keep this up, she might be fated to become Alicia Fennington-Kent-Reeson-Dodd-Garcia-Lee-Minderbinder-Green, and so on.

This growing chain of names illustrates a kind of problem that living things have managed to address in carrying out reproduction. *Reproduction* in this context does not mean the mitotic cell division you looked at in Chapter 9. Reproduction here means *sexual* reproduction, in which specialized reproductive cells come together to produce offspring. The cells described in Chapter 9—the ones that undergo mitosis—are known as *somatic* cells, which in animals means all the cells in the organism except for one type. What type is this? Sex cells; cells called *gametes*. These are reproductive cells, known more commonly as eggs and sperm.

Eggs and sperm are not commonly thought of as cells, but that's just what they are, complete with plasma membranes, nuclei, chromosomes, and all the rest (though sperm eventually lose much of this material). Eggs and sperm are special cells, however, in that they are not destined to divide like somatic cells and thus make more eggs and sperm. Rather, they will *fuse*—sperm fertilizing egg—to make a zygote, which can develop into a whole organism. It is sperm and egg that take part in sexual reproduction and that thus bear some relation to the Fennington-Kent problem.

Here's how it plays out in humans. Human somatic cells, as you have seen, have 23 pairs of chromosomes, or 46 chromosomes in all. If an egg and sperm each brought 46 chromosomes to their *union*, the result would be a zygote with 92 chromosomes. The next generation down would presumably have 184 chromosomes, the next after that 368, and so on. This would be about as functional as having Fennington-Kent-Reeson-Dodd-Garcia-Lee-Minderbinder-Green as a last name.

10.1 An Overview of Meiosis

How do chromosomes avoid the problem of doubling with each generation? In sexual reproduction, chromosome union is preceded by chromosome *reduction*. The reduction comes in the cells that give rise to sperm and egg. When these cells divide, the result is sperm or egg cells that have only *half* the usual, somatic number of chromosomes. Human sperm or eggs, in other words, have only 23 chromosomes in them. (Not the 23 *pairs* of chromosomes that somatic cells have, mind you; 23 chromosomes.) Each 23-chromosome sperm can then unite with a 23-chromosome egg to produce a 46-chromosome zygote that can develop into a new human being. In each generation, then, there is first a halving of chromosome number (when egg and sperm cells are produced), followed by a coming together of these two halves (when sperm and egg unite). This basic pattern holds true for sexual reproduction in all eukaryotes.

Now here are a few terms that will be helpful in understanding this process. The kind of cell division that results in the halving of chromosome number is called *meiosis,* in contrast with *mitosis,* which you looked at in Chapter 9. In mitosis, there is no halving of chromosome number; just a duplication of chromosomes and then a division of these chromosomes into each of two daughter cells.

In animals, cells that are produced in meiosis—thus getting the half-number of chromosomes—are always reproductive cells, the term for which is **gametes,** as we've seen. Such reduced-chromosome cells are said to be in the haploid state, the term *haploid* meaning "single number." When egg and sperm unite, however, it marks a return to the *diploid,* or "double-number" state of cellular existence, meaning 46 chromosomes in human beings. (More formally, **haploid** means possessing a single set of chromosomes, while **diploid** means possessing two sets of chromosomes.) **Meiosis** can thus be defined as a process in which a single diploid cell divides to produce four haploid reproductive cells. Diploid cells are also sometimes referred to as **2n** cells (the "2" here standing for a doubled number of chromosomes), while haploid cells are said to be **n.** Thus, eggs and sperm are n, while the diploid cells that give rise to them are 2n.

In what follows, we will be looking at meiosis as it occurs in human beings; toward the end of the chapter, we'll go over some variations on reproduction in other kinds of organisms.

10.2 The Steps in Meiosis

How does the chromosomal halving we've been talking about take place? Let's go over the process of meiosis and see. **Figure 10.1** shows meiosis, in a stripped-down form, as compared to the mitosis described in Chapter 9. Two essential differences between the two processes can be seen in the figure. First, you may remember that the formula for mitosis was: duplicate once, divide once. Duplicate the chromosomes once, then divide the original cell once. With meiosis, on the other hand, the formula is: duplicate once, divide *twice*. Meiosis includes one chromosome duplication followed by two cellular divisions, which means the process produces four cells (instead of the two that come about in mitosis). The other big difference you can see is that the first of the meiotic divisions is a separation of homologous chromo*somes*, not the separation of chroma*tids* that you saw in mitosis. The subsequent meiotic division is, however, just like mitotic division: It separates the chromatids that make up the homologous chromosomes.

But what is this term *homologous*? You may remember from Chapter 9 that homologous chromosomes are chromosomes that are the same in function (and hence size). These chromosomes do similar things, which is to say they have genes on them that code for similar proteins. We have a chromosome 1 that we inherit from our mother, and it is homologous to the chromosome 1 we inherit from our father. Likewise, we inherit a chromosome 2 from our mother that is homologous with chromosome 2 from our father, and so forth for 23 pairs. The lone exception to this pairs rule is that the X and Y chromosomes males have are not homologous with one another.

The steps of meiosis are separated into two multistep stages, called meiosis I and meiosis II. The big picture here is that, in meiosis I, homologous chromosomes are positioned close together, on opposite sides of the cellular equator called the metaphase plate. Then these chromosomes will move apart into opposite parts of the cell—parts that will become different daughter cells. In meiosis II, the chroma*tids* of these now-separated chromosomes will, in turn, separate into different daughter cells. Let's walk through the steps of meiosis now, as illustrated in **Figure 10.2** on pages 178–179. These steps will reveal a process that not only divides up genetic material but provides for a great deal of the diversity that exists among living things.

Meiosis I

Prophase I

Meiosis I begins, in prophase I, with the same appearance of 46 identifiable chromosomes that you observed in mitosis. The first big difference between meiosis and mitosis also appears in prophase I. It is that, in meiosis, *homologous chromosomes pair up*. In mitosis, 46 individual chromosomes condensed, but did not pair up in any way. In meiosis, however, each pair of homologous chromosomes link up as they condense. Maternal chromosome 5, for example, aligns with *p*aternal chromosome 5, maternal chromosome 6 with paternal 6, and so on. When two homologous chromosomes have paired up in this way, they are called a **tetrad** (which you can see illustrated in Figure 10.3).

A critical bit of part-swapping then takes place between the non-sister chromatids of the paired chromosomes. This process is called *crossing over* (or *recombination*), and you'll be looking at it in detail later. Once this crossing over has finished, the homologous chromosomes begin to separate from one another, although they remain in alignment.

Metaphase I

Still existing as tetrads, the homologous chromosomes, attached to microtubules, are moved to the metaphase plate, via a lengthening and shortening of the microtubules; in this step of meiosis, the maternal member of a given pair lies on one side of the plate and the paternal member on the other. A critical point about this, however, is that the alignment adopted by any one pair of chromosomes bears no relation to the alignment adopted by any other pair. It may be, for example, that paternal chromosome 5 will line up on what we might call side A of the metaphase plate; if so, then maternal chromosome 5 ends up on side B. Shift to chromosome 6, however, and things could just as easily be reversed: The *maternal* chromosome might end up on side A and the paternal on side B. It is thus a throw of the dice regarding which side of the plate a given chromosome lines up on. More important, it is this chance event that determines which *cell* a chromosome joins because each side of the plate becomes a separate cell once cell division is finished (something you can see illustrated in Figure 10.4). As you will see, this randomness is critical in the shuffling of genetic material.

Anaphase I

In anaphase I, the paired, homologous chromosomes now begin to move away from each other, toward their respective poles, pulled through the disassembly of the

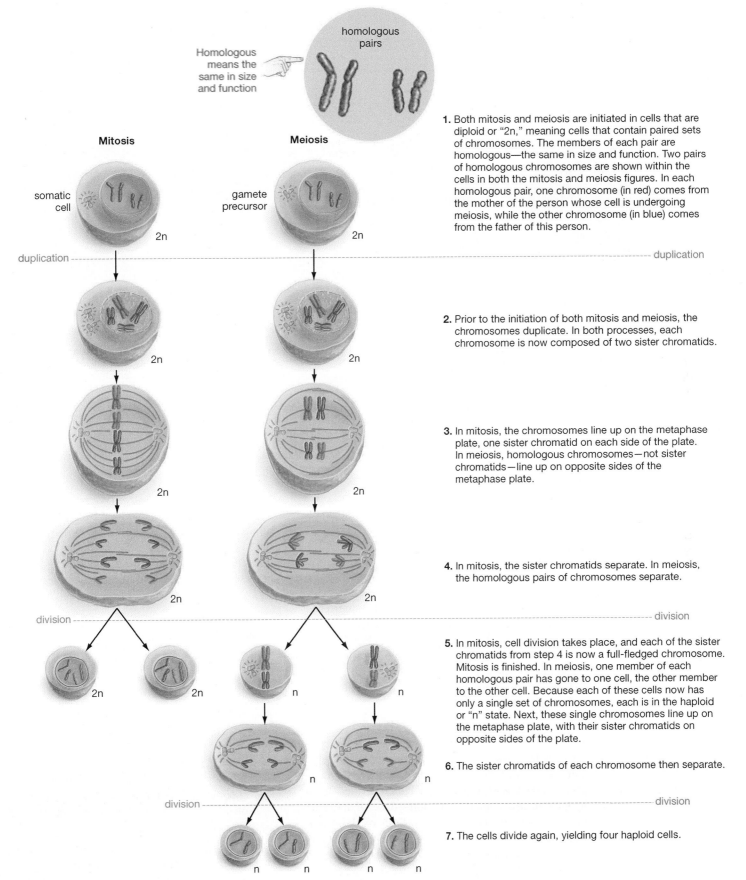

1. Both mitosis and meiosis are initiated in cells that are diploid or "2n," meaning cells that contain paired sets of chromosomes. The members of each pair are homologous—the same in size and function. Two pairs of homologous chromosomes are shown within the cells in both the mitosis and meiosis figures. In each homologous pair, one chromosome (in red) comes from the mother of the person whose cell is undergoing meiosis, while the other chromosome (in blue) comes from the father of this person.

2. Prior to the initiation of both mitosis and meiosis, the chromosomes duplicate. In both processes, each chromosome is now composed of two sister chromatids.

3. In mitosis, the chromosomes line up on the metaphase plate, one sister chromatid on each side of the plate. In meiosis, homologous chromosomes—not sister chromatids—line up on opposite sides of the metaphase plate.

4. In mitosis, the sister chromatids separate. In meiosis, the homologous pairs of chromosomes separate.

5. In mitosis, cell division takes place, and each of the sister chromatids from step 4 is now a full-fledged chromosome. Mitosis is finished. In meiosis, one member of each homologous pair has gone to one cell, the other member to the other cell. Because each of these cells now has only a single set of chromosomes, each is in the haploid or "n" state. Next, these single chromosomes line up on the metaphase plate, with their sister chromatids on opposite sides of the plate.

6. The sister chromatids of each chromosome then separate.

7. The cells divide again, yielding four haploid cells.

Figure 10.1
Meiosis Compared to Mitosis

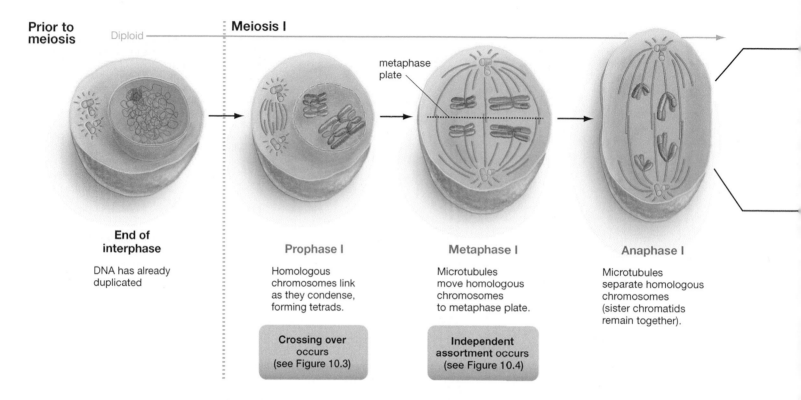

Prior to meiosis

Diploid ———— **Meiosis I** ————————————————————————→

metaphase plate

End of interphase

DNA has already duplicated

Prophase I

Homologous chromosomes link as they condense, forming tetrads.

Crossing over occurs (see Figure 10.3)

Metaphase I

Microtubules move homologous chromosomes to metaphase plate.

Independent assortment occurs (see Figure 10.4)

Anaphase I

Microtubules separate homologous chromosomes (sister chromatids remain together).

**Figure 10.2
The Steps of Meiosis**

BioFlix

Meiosis

microtubule spindles they are attached to. Although homologous chromosomes have now separated, the sister chromatids that make them up are still together.

Telophase I

With chromosome movement toward the poles completed, the original cell now undergoes cytokinesis, dividing into two completely separate daughter cells. With this, there are two haploid cells, whereas in the beginning there was one diploid cell. (Why are the cells now haploid? Meiosis I moved one set of chromosomes to one cell and the second set to another cell. Therefore, each cell now has only one set of chromosomes, meaning each is haploid.)

Meiosis II

There is little pause for interphase between meiosis I and meiosis II; little time for the daughter cells to regroup and carry on regular metabolic activities. What happens instead is another division—or set of divisions, because there are now two cells. Each of these cells now has 23 duplicated chromosomes in it. After a very brief prophase II, these chromosomes line up at a new metaphase plate, with sister chromatids on opposite sides of each plate (metaphase II in the figure). What happens next is the same thing that happened in mitosis. The *sister chromatids* now separate, moving toward

opposite poles; with this, they assume the role of full-fledged chromosomes (anaphase II). Once this separation is completed, cytokinesis occurs. Where once there were two cells, now there are four (telophase II). The difference between this process and mitosis is that each of these cells has 23 chromosomes in it instead of 46.

SO FAR . . .

1. Meiosis is the process by which the reproductive cells commonly known as _____ and _____ are formed. This takes place by means of one ____ cell, meaning a cell with a paired set of chromosomes, giving rise to four _____ cells, meaning cells that each have a single set of chromosomes.

2. Meiosis I involves a separation not of sister chromatids, as in mitosis, but a separation of _____. Meiosis II involves a separation of _____.

3. In human beings, meiosis starts with a single cell that contains _____ chromosomes and ends with four cells, each of which contains _____ chromosomes.

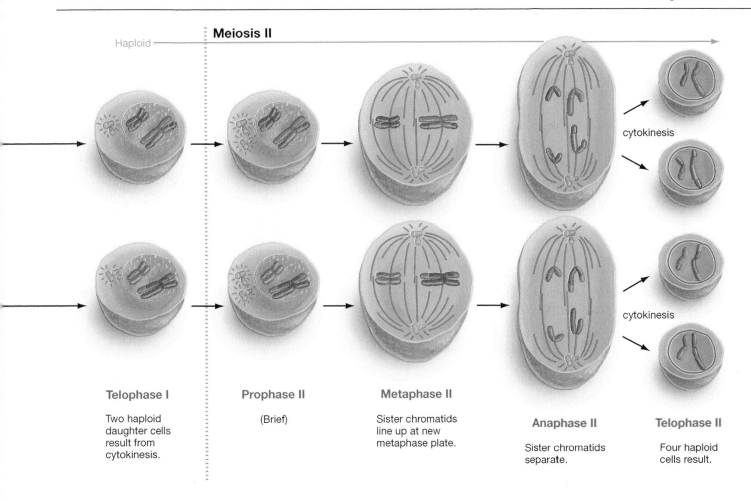

Meiosis II

Haploid

Telophase I

Two haploid daughter cells result from cytokinesis.

Prophase II

(Brief)

Metaphase II

Sister chromatids line up at new metaphase plate.

cytokinesis

Anaphase II

Sister chromatids separate.

cytokinesis

Telophase II

Four haploid cells result.

10.3 The Significance of Meiosis

You have now examined the mechanics of meiosis, but what are the effects of this process? First, the "Fennington-Kent" problem noted at the beginning of the chapter has been solved. There will be no 92-chromosome zygotes because egg and sperm will each bring only 23 chromosomes to their union, thus yielding a combined 46 chromosomes in human somatic cells. Just as notable, however, are two kinds of diversity that meiosis brings about. The first of these is genetic diversity in offspring; the second is a large-scale diversity in the natural world.

Genetic Diversity through Crossing Over

What is genetic diversity? Recall that, back in prophase I of meiosis, the homologous chromosome pairs aligned for a time and then engaged in something called crossing over (or recombination). In this, there is an exchange of *parts* of chromosomes prior to their lining up at the metaphase plate.

Look at **Figure 10.3** to see how this important process works. In the first stage of meiosis I, there is a physical breaking of non-sister chromatids and

then a "reunion" of these reciprocal chromosomal sections onto new chromatid partners. With this, what had been a "maternal" chromosome now has a portion of the paternal chromosome within it, and vice versa. Formally, then, **crossing over** can be defined as a process, occurring during meiosis, in which

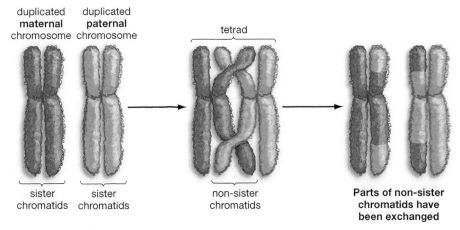

duplicated **maternal** chromosome

duplicated **paternal** chromosome

tetrad

sister chromatids

sister chromatids

non-sister chromatids

Parts of non-sister chromatids have been exchanged

Figure 10.3
Crossing Over and Genetic Diversity

In this process, which occurs in prophase I of meiosis, two homologous chromosomes join with each other, thus forming a tetrad, after which non-sister chromatids from each chromosome exchange reciprocal portions of themselves. In this way, genetic material from maternal and paternal sources is shuffled during the formation of gametes.

homologous chromosomes exchange reciprocal portions of themselves.

The linkage between crossing over and genetic diversity probably is apparent; the ability of reciprocal lengths of DNA to be exchanged between chromosomes provides a means by which the genetic deck can be reshuffled prior to the formation of gametes. This is so because of what you saw in Chapter 9 about homologous chromosomes: While the genetic information on any two will be similar, it will not be identical. A gene on one chromosome may code for red hair color, but the gene on its homologous chromosome may code for blond hair color. In crossing over, such genetic variants are being swapped between chromosomes.

Genetic Diversity through Independent Assortment

Another way that meiosis ensures genetic diversity is a crucial event that took place in metaphase I (right after crossing over). It is the random alignment or *independent assortment* of chromosomes at the metaphase plate, which you can see illustrated in **Figure 10.4**. Recall that the alignment of any one pair of homologous chromosomes along the plate bears no relation to the alignment of any other homologous pair. If you looked at, say, chromosome 5, the paternal member of the pair might line up on "side A" of the metaphase plate, meaning maternal chromosome 5 will be on side B. Shift to chromosome 6, however, and things could just as easily be reversed. This random alignment of chromosomes then leads to a random

separation of them because a chromosome that lines up on *side* A of the plate will end up in *cell* A, while a chromosome that lines up on side B will end up in cell B. **Independent assortment** can thus be defined as the random distribution of homologous chromosome pairs during meiosis. If we wonder how traits from a mother and father can get "mixed up" in their children, independent assortment joins crossing over in providing an answer. Indeed, for complex creatures such as humans, independent assortment ensures that, with the exception of identical twins, offspring produced through sexual reproduction will not just be diverse; each offspring will be *unique*—no other offspring will be exactly like it in genetic terms. The sheer number of ways in which chromosomes can line up in independent assortment makes this a mathematical certainty. Think about it: We have two locations for any chromosome (side A or side B of the metaphase plate), and we have 23 chromosomes. This means there are 2^{23} different ways that chromosomes could line up in meiosis, which is to say nearly 8.4 million different ways. The egg from your mother that produced you may have been, say, variation 1,527,000 in this range, while the egg that produced your brother or sister may have been variation 4,573,000.

Why does this matter? Remember that there are genes on these chromosomes, and that the genes on any given paternal chromosome may differ somewhat from those on its matched maternal chromosome. Which chromosome the offspring gets thus makes a difference—in eye color, height, or any of thousands of other characteristics. Given this, each of us is very much affected by the way paternal and

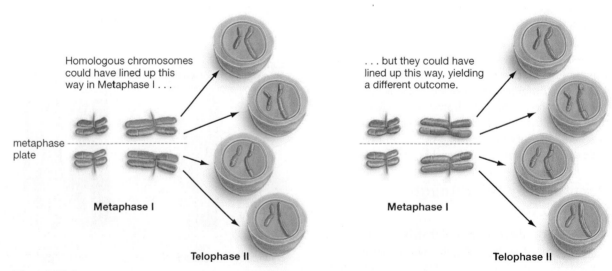

metaphase plate

Homologous chromosomes could have lined up this way in Metaphase I . . .

Metaphase I

Telophase II

. . . but they could have lined up this way, yielding a different outcome.

Metaphase I

Telophase II

Figure 10.4
Independent Assortment and Genetic Diversity

In this process, which occurs in metaphase I of meiosis, homologous pairs of chromosomes align on opposite sides of a cell's metaphase plate. Critically, the alignment that each pair assumes at the plate—maternal chromosome on one side, paternal on the other—is a random event. The alignment that any one pair assumes does not affect the alignment of any other pair. This independent assortment of homologous chromosomes is a second means by which meiosis produces genetic diversity in gametes—and hence in offspring.

maternal chromosomes happened to line up in two very special meioses: those that produced the egg cell and the sperm cell that gave rise to us.

When we add independent assortment to crossing over, it's easy to see why separate children from the same parents can come out looking so different—from each other as well as from the parents themselves (**Figure 10.5**). Overall, meiosis generates genetic *diversity,* while its counterpart, mitosis, does not. Mitosis makes genetically exact copies of cells; it *retains* the qualities that cells have from one generation to the next. Meiosis mixes genetic elements each time it produces reproductive cells and thus brings about genetic variation in succeeding generations.

Diversity in the Living World

This genetic variation has an importance way beyond that of making siblings look different from each other. It turns out that this diversity is responsible, in significant part, for the fantastically diverse natural world around us. Think of it: two-foot ferns, 100-yard redwood trees, bats, bees, whales, mushrooms. How did the natural world come to be such a remarkably diverse place? The short answer is that evolution is spurred on by the *differences* in offspring that meiosis brings about. Let's see why.

Three frog siblings survive to reproductive age from a clutch of eggs laid by a female and fertilized by a male. Thanks to crossing over and independent assortment, one of these frogs may end up having, say, a darker coloration than all the other frogs of its species in its area. In the formation of the eggs and sperm that led to this frog, chromosome parts were swapped (in crossing over), and chromosomes lined up (in independent assortment) in such a way that this frog was the darkest frog possible among all the frogs in its population. Further, it happens that, because of shifting rain patterns in this frog's habitat, this dark coloration is starting to be useful for evading predators. This frog will thus survive to have more offspring of its own than do other frogs around it. By being selected for survival in this way—by undergoing what is called natural selection—this frog may have started its population down the road to having a darker coloration.

Now, it's easy to see that coloration is only one of a countless number of traits that could be selected for in this way. Taller height in a tree? Diving stamina in a dolphin? Meiosis and sexual reproduction would lead the way to these traits by producing, in one generation after another, *this* tree that grew a little taller or *that* dolphin that dove a little deeper. Just as General Motors provides an array of models for consumers to choose from each year, meiosis and sexual reproduction provide an array of models for *nature* to choose from each generation.

To put a finer point on this, consider an alternative to meiosis and sexual reproduction. Bacteria are single-celled organisms that possess a single, circular chromosome. As you saw in Chapter 9, bacteria divide through the process of binary fission, one bacterium becoming two in the course of cell division. As it turns out, that's it for bacteria as far as reproduction goes. There is no chromosomal part swapping or independent assortment of chromosomes in reproduction. And there is no fusion of two gametes from separate organisms, as occurs with eggs and sperm. Instead, there is just an exact duplication of the bacterial chromosome and a splitting of one bacterial cell into two. In general, then, every "daughter" bacterial cell is a genetic replica of its parent cell—a clone of it. What this means is that differences among bacteria are not a built-in feature of their reproduction. Instead, such differences as come to pass are dependent on their DNA mutating (which is rare) or on a form of gene transfer they are capable of (which is intermittent). Natural selection simply does not have as much to choose from in asexually reproducing organisms such as bacteria. Where is the equivalent of our darker-colored frog in a group of bacterial cells descended in a line? How could an equivalent difference come about, given that each bacterium is a clone of its predecessor?

What evidence do we have that sexual reproduction makes a practical difference? Well, consider that bacteria and their fellow single-celled organisms, the archaea, came into existence perhaps 3.8 billion years ago. Then, for 1.8 billion years after that, the living world consisted of nothing *but* bacteria and archaea—it took that long for anything else to evolve from them. We are not sure when sexual reproduction got going, but we have some evidence that it was taking place by 1.2 billion years ago. So, in the last 1.2 billion years, all the fish and birds and trees and fungi and flowers that we see before us developed through

Figure 10.5
Ensuring Variety

The shuffling of genetic material that occurs during meiosis is the primary reason that children look different from their parents and from each other.

sexual reproduction, whereas in the 1.8 billion years after bacteria and archaea got going, they changed very little in physical form. Although other factors contributed to the ramping up of diversity on Earth, meiosis and sexual reproduction were key players in it. The British geneticist J. B. S. Haldane is said to have remarked that "Evolution could roll on fairly efficiently without sex but such a world would be a dull one to live in." How did the living world come to be such a diverse place? In part through the very small-scale process you've been looking at, meiosis.

10.4 Meiosis and Sex Outcome

Let us think now about what meiosis means in relation to passing on sex to offspring. How do humans, in particular, come to be male or female? In humans, there is one exception to the rule that chromosomes come in homologous pairs. Human females do indeed have 23 pairs of matched chromosomes, including 22 pairs of "autosomes" and one matched pair of **sex chromosomes,** meaning the chromosomes that determine what sex an individual will be. The sex chromosomes in females are called X chromosomes, and each female possesses two of them. In males, conversely, there are 22 autosome pairs, one X sex chromosome, and then one Y sex chromosome. It is this Y chromosome that leads to the male sex. (**Figure 10.6** illustrates the differences in the X and Y sizes.)

In meiosis I in a female, the female's two X chromosomes, being homologous, line up together at the metaphase plate. Then, these chromosomes separate, each of them going to different cells (**Figure 10.7**). In males, the non-homologous X and Y chromosomes line up as if they were homologues. Then one resulting

cell gets an X chromosome, while the other gets the Y chromosome.

Sex determination is then simple. Each of the eggs produced by a female bears a single X chromosome. If this egg is fertilized by a sperm bearing an X chromosome, the resulting child will be a female. If, however, the egg is fertilized by a sperm bearing a Y chromosome, the child will be a male.

Because females don't have Y chromosomes to pass on, it follows that the Y chromosome that any male has must come from his father. Meanwhile, the single X chromosome that any male has must come from his mother. Females, conversely, carry one X chromosome from their mother and one from their father.

SO FAR . . .

1. Two features of meiosis ensure that each generation of sexually reproducing organisms will differ from its parents genetically. In one of these features, crossing over, _____ exchange reciprocal portions of themselves. In the other feature, independent assortment, there is a random distribution of _____ at the metaphase plate.

2. The reason that crossing over and independent assortment ensure genetic diversity is that any two members of a pair of homologous chromosomes _____ in the genetic information they carry.

3. In human beings, any fertilized egg that carries two _____ chromosomes will be a female; fertilized eggs destined to become males, meanwhile, carry one _____ chromosome (donated by the mother) and one _____ chromosome (donated by the father).

10.5 Gamete Formation in Humans

You've seen that, through meiosis, a single diploid cell gives rise to four haploid gametes. But what are the diploid cells that go through meiosis? As you might expect, there is a whole sequence of actions involved in the process by which egg and sperm are produced—a process known as *gamete formation*. In humans, the starting female cells in gamete formation are known as **oogonia,** while the starting male cells are **spermatogonia.** These are diploid cells that give rise to two other sets of diploid cells, the **primary oocytes** and **primary spermatocytes.** These, then, are the cells that undergo meiosis, yielding haploid egg and sperm cells.

Figure 10.6
The X and the Y

The human X chromosome can be seen on the left, while the human Y chromosome is on the right. The difference in size between them is in part a reflection of the difference in the number of genes each of them contains. The Y chromosome only has only 78, while the X has about 1,500.

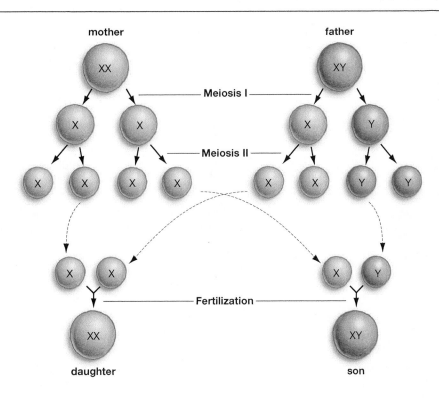

1. Early in meiosis I, the mother's two X chromosomes line up at the metaphase plate (XX). Meanwhile, in the father's meiosis, his X and Y chromosomes line up (XY).

2. The X-X and X-Y pairs then separate into different cells.

3. The chromatids that made up the duplicated chromosomes separate, yielding individual eggs and sperm.

4. Should an X-bearing sperm from the male fertilize the egg, the child will be a girl; should a Y-bearing sperm from the male fertilize the egg, the child will be a boy.

Sperm Formation

The starting cells in male gamete formation, the spermatogonia, exist in the male testes. Each time a spermatogonium divides, it gives rise to two cells, of course, but there's a twist to this. One of the cells that's produced will be a primary spermatocyte that will in turn give rise to a sperm cell. But the *other* cell will be another spermatogonium. Thus, spermatogonia are sperm-producing "factories" that generate not only sperm but more factories as well (**Figure 10.8**, on the next page). It is this self-generating ability that qualifies spermatogonia as "stem" cells and that allows males to *keep* producing sperm throughout their lives, beginning at puberty.

The primary spermatocytes that come from spermatogonia go through meiosis I and thus produce the haploid *secondary spermatocytes*. Meiosis II then ensues, and the result is four haploid *spermatids*. These are not yet the familiar, tadpole-like sperm; those come only after spermatids develop further, a process that takes about three weeks. (You can read more about this in Chapter 33, beginning on page 639.) There is thus an assembly-line quality to sperm production. Once a male reaches puberty, he starts producing sperm in this manner, with each sperm moving right through the entire process in a matter of weeks, and the process continuing until the male dies. As you'll see, female egg production takes a much different route.

What is the nature of the sperm produced? A given sperm cell must, of course, fully develop its best-known feature, its tail-like flagellum (which in the human body is found *only* on sperm cells). It turns out that each flagellum is composed of the microtubules you have been

seeing so much of in cell division. Moving the flagellum in a whip-like motion, microtubules serve to propel the sperm on their journey (**Figure 10.9**, on page 185). Because this journey is difficult—only a tiny fraction of the sperm that start it will complete it—and because sperm contribute nothing but their set of chromosomes to a fertilized egg, sperm have no use for most of the cellular organelles reviewed back in Chapter 4: lysosomes, the Golgi complex, and so forth. In consequence, sperm lose all these structures and more as they develop. By the time a given sperm is mature, it amounts to little more than a haploid set of chromosomes in front, a collection of "engines" (mitochondria) in the middle, and a propeller (the flagellum) in the back. About 250 million sperm are produced within a male each day, and about that number will be released with each ejaculation. Sperm that are not released will age and eventually are destroyed by the body's immune system.

Egg Formation: Stem Cells in Females?

The need of male sperm to become stripped-down, mobile DNA packages stands in contrast to the needs of female ova or eggs, which must have rich resources of nutrients and building materials to sustain life once they have been fertilized. This difference in function is reflected in size: The volume of an egg is 200,000 times the volume of a sperm. (Figure 10.9 allows you to get an idea of this difference.) Accordingly, eggs are created in a process that maximizes cell content, at least for the fraction of eggs that move fully through development.

Egg formation begins with the cells of the female called the *oogonia*. These cells are very different from

Figure 10.7
Sex Outcome in Human Reproduction

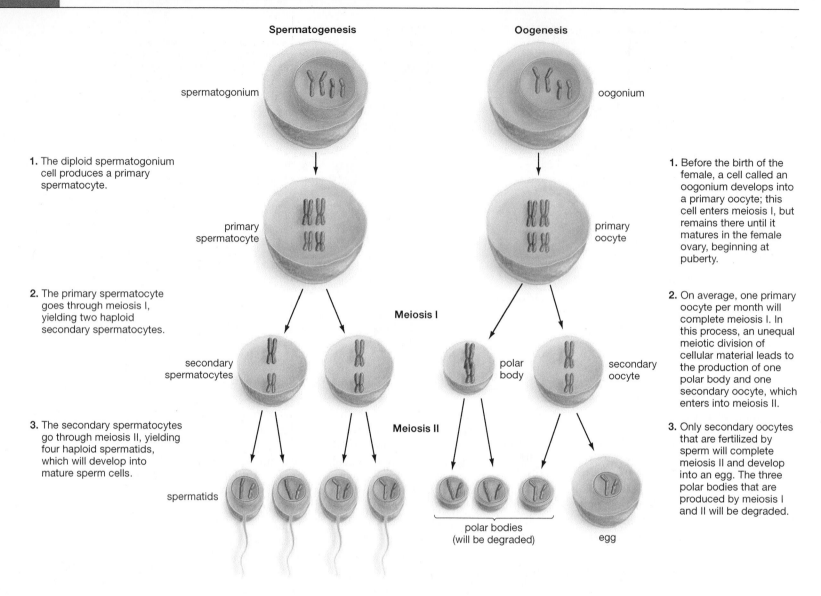

Spermatogenesis

spermatogonium

1. The diploid spermatogonium cell produces a primary spermatocyte.

primary spermatocyte

2. The primary spermatocyte goes through meiosis I, yielding two haploid secondary spermatocytes.

secondary spermatocytes

Meiosis I

3. The secondary spermatocytes go through meiosis II, yielding four haploid spermatids, which will develop into mature sperm cells.

Meiosis II

spermatids

Oogenesis

oogonium

1. Before the birth of the female, a cell called an oogonium develops into a primary oocyte; this cell enters meiosis I, but remains there until it matures in the female ovary, beginning at puberty.

primary oocyte

2. On average, one primary oocyte per month will complete meiosis I. In this process, an unequal meiotic division of cellular material leads to the production of one polar body and one secondary oocyte, which enters into meiosis II.

polar body

secondary oocyte

3. Only secondary oocytes that are fertilized by sperm will complete meiosis II and develop into an egg. The three polar bodies that are produced by meiosis I and II will be degraded.

polar bodies (will be degraded)

egg

Figure 10.8
Sperm and Egg Formation in Humans

their counterpart cells in males (the spermatogonia). How? They are produced in large numbers only up to the seventh month of fetal life, and it's possible that none are created after birth. Put another way, these cells seem to be produced only while a female is a fetus. Further, of the millions produced, most die before the female is born. Some survive to become the generation of cells, the primary oocytes, that enter meiosis.

Under this view, as you can see, adult females have no reproductive stem cells—cells that have the ability to keep on producing more of themselves in the way that spermatogonia do. Oogonia appear to exist only up until birth, and until quite recently, scientists were confident that no other variety of reproductive stem cell existed in adult females. This in turn was thought to be the primary reason that women lose the ability to reproduce in middle age: They run out of eggs, in part because they have no stem cells that are capable of giving rise to new eggs.

All this seemed well understood until 2004, when researchers from Harvard claimed that, in adult female

mice, they had detected the presence of reproductive stem cells. This report rocked the world of *human* reproductive research because of its implications. Imagine if such cells could be found or coaxed into development in human females. Fertility might be prolonged for older women or enhanced for women of any age. At present, therefore, the reproductive research community has an important question before it: Do adult female mammals possess reproductive stem cells? Despite much research in the last few years, no one can say with certainty whether they do or not. Only more research will provide an answer.

Egg Formation: From Oogonia to Eggs

Setting aside the question of reproductive stem cells, the path by which most eggs are produced in women is well understood. It starts with the oogonia we just talked about—the cells that are produced largely, or perhaps entirely, prior to the birth of the female.

Figure 10.9
The Products of Gamete Formation
A human egg surrounded by much smaller human sperm.

These cells give rise to the next generation of cells, the primary oocytes, which are the cells that enter into meiosis I (Figure 10.8). Amazingly enough, meiosis I is where these oocytes *stay*—for years. Imagine a collection of oocytes in the female ovaries (which are walnut-sized structures just right and left of center in the female pelvic area). Once puberty begins, each oocyte is theoretically capable of maturing into an egg, but an average of only *one* oocyte per month actually starts this maturation process. Which oocyte is this? The one released from the ovary each month in the process called ovulation. All the other oocytes in the ovaries halt their meiosis in prophase of meiosis I. Their chromosomes are duplicated, and they have completed crossing over, but they have not yet lined up at the metaphase plate. And this is where things stay for most of the oocytes a female possesses. Only the one oocyte per month that is expelled from the ovary will complete meiosis I and thus enter into meiosis II. Even this meiosis is "arrested," however, until this oocyte is fertilized by a sperm. It is the union with a sperm that prompts the completion of meiosis II. Thus, an oocyte that came into being when a female was a fetus might remain suspended in the cell cycle for years or even decades. Of the millions of oocytes originally created, only a few hundred will mature even through metaphase of meiosis I during a woman's lifetime.

How do certain oocytes get "selected" to mature through metaphase I—how do they get selected to be ovulated, in other words? This occurs in connection with an intricate interplay that involves their surrounding tissue, hormones, and the happenstance of timing. You'll read more about this process in Chapter 33.

One Egg, Several Polar Bodies

For the few oocytes selected, the process of going through meiosis I and II means proceeding from one diploid cell to four haploid cells. In this process, however, almost all the cytoplasm from the original diploid cell will be shunted to *one* of the four daughter cells, thus preferentially building up its stores of nutrients and other cytoplasmic material. This happens in two rounds: meiosis I and meiosis II. When cytokinesis comes in meiosis I, one daughter cell gets almost all the cytoplasm, while the second daughter cell gets almost none. This same thing happens in meiosis II. The result? One richly endowed haploid oocyte and two, or perhaps three, very small haploid **polar bodies:** non-functional cells produced during meiosis in females (Figure 10.8). (Only two polar bodies and the oocyte will be the end result if the polar body produced in meiosis I does not continue through meiosis II, which often happens.) The oocyte has a chance at taking part in producing offspring, but the polar bodies are bound for oblivion rather than a shot at immortality. They will eventually degrade into their constituent substances.

10.6 Life Cycles: Humans and Other Organisms

The process of the formation of the human gametes called egg and sperm is followed, as you have seen, by the union of these gametes. In humans, the oocyte that is expelled from the ovary makes a slow trip down the female's uterine (or Fallopian) tube, during which time it may encounter a traveling sperm. If it does, the result will be a fertilized egg (or zygote), which then may develop into a whole human being. One of the things that will eventually occur in this new human being is the development of another group of eggs or sperm through the process of meiosis. Thus, do we see a **life cycle:** the repeating series of steps that occur in the reproduction of an organism. You have looked at the human life cycle, but it's important to recognize that it amounts to only one life cycle among many that exist.

Not All Reproduction Is Sexual

As noted earlier, human reproduction is **sexual reproduction:** the union of two reproductive cells to create a new organism. In many other species, there is **asexual reproduction** or reproduction that does not involve sex. Asexual reproduction actually is seen in a vast array of organisms. In fact, mammals are the only grouping of living things that never carries out asexual reproduction. Admittedly, asexual reproduction is rare in creatures as complex as birds, fish, and reptiles, but it does happen. In the American southwestern desert, for example, there are a few species of whiptail lizard that are entirely female

Figure 10.10
All-Female Species

Pictured is a whiptail lizard, *Aspidoscelis uniparens,* that reproduces solely through partheno-genesis. Because the eggs these lizards produce are not fertilized by males, they contain only one set of chromosomes, passed on by the mother. Hatchlings develop from these haploid eggs, however, and as a consequence the hatchlings themselves are haploid and genetically identical to the mother. The end result is a species that is entirely female.

Other forms of asexual reproduction also are possible. In fact, you've already been introduced to one of them. Recall that a bacterial cell engages in a form of asexual reproduction, called *binary fission,* in which it duplicates its single chromosome and then divides in two. Beyond this, anyone who has ever seen a cutting taken from a plant knows that a snipped-off stem or branch will, when properly planted, sprout its own roots and grow into an independent plant, complete with the ability to take part in sexual reproduction. This process is called *vegetative reproduction,* and it has a counterpart in the animal world. Cut the arm and part of a central disk from a sea star, for example, and, through *regeneration,* this severed limb will grow into a whole, multi-armed sea star (**Figure 10.11**).

As we go through the branching tree of life, from more complex creatures to less complex ones, asexual reproduction becomes more common. By the time we reach bacteria, it is the only form of reproduction that exists. Note that all forms of asexual reproduction produce offspring that are genetically identical to their parents. There is no mixing and matching of chromosomes from different parents in these asexual processes; just a cloning of one genetically identical individual from its parent.

(**Figure 10.10**). The female whiptail lays haploid eggs, but they are never fertilized. Instead, they develop into haploid clones of her through regular mitotic cell division. This method of reproduction (called *parthenogenesis*) also results in "drone" male honey-bees. Those eggs that a queen bee chooses not to fertilize (with stored-up sperm) develop into drones through parthenogenesis.

Variations in Sexual Reproduction

Within the framework of sexual reproduction, as you can imagine, there are many variations. For example, separate gametes need not come from separate organisms. Some animals, such as tapeworms, are hermaphrodites, meaning they have both male and female reproductive parts. In some cases, hermaphrodites

Figure 10.11
Regenerating the Whole from a Part

A sea star off the coast of Papua New Guinea has regenerated a body and other arms from a piece of one arm and part of its central disk.

fertilize themselves, but generally they are fertilized by another member of their species. Most plants contain both male and female parts, and some plants "self-fertilize"—their sperm can fertilize their eggs—as with a famous pea plant you will be looking at in Chapter 11.

On to Patterns of Inheritance

Our tour of cell division over the last couple of chapters has yielded a look not only at how one cell becomes two, but at how chromosomes operate within this process. Given the paired nature of chromosomes and their precisely ordered activity during meiosis, it stands to reason that there would be some predictability or pattern to the passing on of traits. This is the case, as it turns out. And the person who first recognized this pattern was a monk who worked in nineteenth-century Europe in an obscurity he did not deserve.

SO FAR . . .

1. Spermatogonia are regarded as _____ cells because they can produce not only a specialized variety of cell (the spermatocyte) but also more spermatogonia. Meanwhile, it is possible that the female counterpart to spermatogonia, the oogonia, are produced in females only _____.

2. The function of eggs as rich sources of nutrients and cellular materials results in oogenesis producing not four cells but one viable cell and several _____.

3. Each organism produced through asexual reproduction is genetically _____ to its parent.

Go to the Study Area at www.masteringbiology.com for practice quizzes, myeBook, BioFlix™ 3-D animations, MP3 Tutor Sessions, videos, current events, and more.

CHAPTER 10 REVIEW

Summary

10.1 An Overview of Meiosis

- In humans, nearly all cells have paired sets of chromosomes, meaning these cells are diploid. In meiosis, a single diploid cell divides to produce four haploid cells—cells that contain a single set of chromosomes. (p. 175)

- The haploid cells produced through meiosis are called gametes, which are the reproductive cells of many organisms. Female gametes are eggs; male gametes are sperm. When the haploid sperm and haploid egg fuse, a diploid fertilized egg is produced, setting into development a new generation of organism. (p. 175)

10.2 The Steps in Meiosis

- There are two primary stages to meiosis. In meiosis I, chromosome duplication is followed by a pairing of homologous chromosomes with one another, during

which time they exchange reciprocal sections of themselves. Homologous chromosome pairs then line up on opposite sides of the metaphase plate. These homologous pairs are then separated, each of them becoming part of a separate daughter cell. In meiosis II, the sister chromatids of the duplicated chromosomes are separated into separate daughter cells. (p. 176)

BioFlix™

Meiosis

10.3 The Significance of Meiosis

- Meiosis generates genetic diversity among offspring in two ways. In prophase I of meiosis, homologous chromosomes pair with each other and, in the process called crossing over, exchange reciprocal segments of themselves. Then in metaphase I of meiosis, there is an independent assortment of maternal and paternal

chromosome pairs on either side of the metaphase plate. This chance alignment determines which daughter cell each chromosome will end up in. (p. 179)

- Thanks to the differences it ensures among offspring, meiosis is responsible to a significant extent for the diversity of lifeforms seen today in the living world. By contrast, asexual reproduction, as seen in bacteria and other organisms, produces organisms that are exact genetic copies of the parent. (p. 181)

10.4 Meiosis and Sex Outcome

- Human females have 23 matched pairs of chromosomes—22 pairs of autosomes and one pair of sex-determining X chromosomes. Human males have 22 autosome pairs, one X chromosome, and one sex-determining Y chromosome. Each egg that a female produces has a single X chromosome in it. Each sperm that a male produces has either an X or a

Y chromosome within it. If a sperm with a Y chromosome fertilizes an egg, the offspring will be male. If a sperm with an X chromosome fertilizes the egg, the offspring will be female. (p. 182)

10.5 Gamete Formation in Humans

- Male gamete formation begins with cells called spermatogonia, which are stem cells in that they give rise not only to diploid primary spermatocytes but also to more spermatogonia. Primary spermatocytes then go through meiosis, producing haploid secondary spermatocytes, which in turn give rise to the spermatids that develop into mature sperm cells. (p. 182)

- Female gamete formation begins with cells called oogonia, most or all of which are produced prior to the birth of the female. These give rise to primary oocytes—the cells that will go through meiosis I, producing haploid oocytes. Only the primary oocyte released each month during ovulation completes meiosis I. Only those ovulated oocytes that are fertilized by sperm complete meiosis II. Only one of the four cells produced in meiosis will receive enough cytoplasmic material during cell division to be able to develop into a haploid egg; the other cells are destined to become non-functional polar bodies. (p. 184)

10.6 Life Cycles: Humans and Other Organisms

- Asexual reproduction can take several forms. Bacteria reproduce through binary fission, in which a given bacterial cell replicates its single chromosome and then divides in two. Plants can engage in vegetative reproduction; other organisms, such as worms and sea stars, can carry out regeneration. (p. 185)

Key Terms

n   176
2n   176
asexual reproduction   185
crossing over   179
diploid   176
gamete   175
haploid   175
independent assortment   180

life cycle   185
meiosis   176
oogonia   182
polar body   185
primary oocyte   182
primary spermatocyte   182
sex chromosome   182
sexual reproduction   185
spermatogonia   182
tetrad   176

Understanding the Basics

Multiple-Choice Questions

(Answers are in the back of the book.)

1. With respect to chromosomes, meiosis involves:
   a. no duplications, 1 reduction.
   b. 1 duplication, 2 reductions.
   c. 2 duplications, 1 reductions.
   d. 2 duplications, 2 reductions.
   e. none of the above.

2. Independent assortment occurs during:
   a. prophase I.
   b. anaphase II.
   c. metaphase I.
   d. metaphase II.
   e. both c and d.

3. Which of the following statements is not true regarding egg formation in humans?
   a. Oogonia are not produced until the eleventh or twelfth year.
   b. At the completion of division, one oocyte and two or three polar bodies exist.
   c. In both meiosis I and II, cytoplasmic material will be preferentially shunted to one cell.
   d. Oocyte maturation occurs in approximately a 28-day cycle.
   e. Each egg contains 23 chromosomes.

4. What are the two sources of genetic diversity in meiosis?
   a. binary fission and regeneration
   b. crossing over and independent assortment
   c. oogenesis and crossing over
   d. spermatogenesis and oogenesis
   e. vegetative reproduction and regeneration

5. Meiosis and sexual reproduction have fostered diversity in the natural world because they:
   a. are so accurate in copying genetic information.
   b. are nearly certain to produce differences among offspring.
   c. are such ancient processes.
   d. produce genetic replicas, one generation after another.
   e. are used by such a wide range of organisms.

6. Eggs are relatively large because they _____; sperm are relatively small because they _____.
   a. must contain spare sets of chromosomes … function through mobility
   b. must contain room for the growing zygote … have only one set of chromosomes
   c. must contain room for the sperm … have a short life-span
   d. must contain nutrients for the zygote … function through mobility
   e. exist in a harsh environment … exist in a nurturing environment

7. In prophase I of meiosis:
   a. maternal chromosome 1 joins with maternal chromosome 2.
   b. maternal chromosomes exchange genetic material with other maternal chromosomes.
   c. paternal chromosomes exchange genetic material with other paternal chromosomes.
   d. homologous chromosomes exchange genetic material.
   e. Both c and d are correct.

8. At the completion of meiosis I, each human cell going through the process contains:
   a. 23 chromosomes, 46 chromatids.
   b. 46 chromosomes, 46 chromatids.
   c. 46 chromosomes, 92 chromatids.
   d. 23 chromosomes, 23 chromatids.
   e. none of the above.

9. Asexual reproduction is _____ and always results in _____.
   a. found in only a few types of organisms … offspring that are different from parents
   b. found in all types of organisms … offspring that are sometimes genetically identical to parents

c. reproduction that results from a fusion of two reproductive cells ... twice as many offspring as parents

d. found more commonly in simple organisms than in complex ones ... offspring that are genetically identical to parents

e. found in only a few mammals and birds ... offspring that are different from parents

Brief Review

(Answers are in the back of the book.)

1. Describe the essential differences between mitosis and meiosis.

2. Does chromosome reduction take place during meiosis I or II?

3. Why are men able to keep producing sperm throughout their lifetime, from puberty forward?

4. How does cytokinesis in the production of the eggs that females produce differ from cytokinesis in regular mitotic cell division?

5. Define and distinguish between somatic cells and gametes.

6. A diploid organism has four chromosomes. Name the phases of mitosis or meiosis shown in the following figures.

7. In what ways does meiosis ensure genetic diversity in offspring?

8. When human egg and sperm come together, how many chromosomes does each kind of gamete have? What is the genetic makeup of the resulting zygote?

Applying Your Knowledge

1. Ultimately, is it the paternal or maternal gamete that delivers the sex-determining chromosome? Describe the process.

2. Mammals have now been cloned by scientists (think of Dolly the sheep). Suppose that half the world's human births were achieved through cloning. How would our world be different?

3. All the bananas we eat come from trees that are produced through "cuttings"—a stem from an existing tree is planted in the ground, resulting in a new tree. Thus, each tree is a clone of another. Why would growers find it advantageous to produce an enormous series of identical clones, rather than using trees that reproduce sexually?

11

The First Geneticist:

Mendel and His Discoveries

A straightforward set of rules governs the way living things pass on many of their traits. Gregor Mendel was the first person to understand what those rules are.

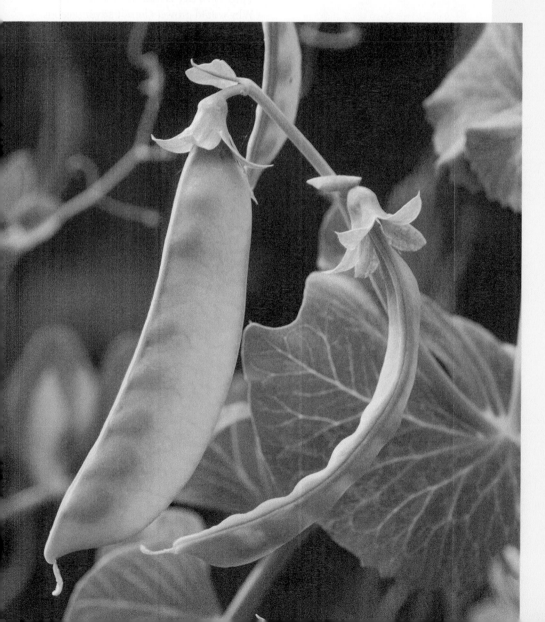

By experimenting with generations of garden peas such as these, Gregor Mendel became the first person to understand some of the basic rules of genetics.

In the Czech Republic, in the oldest part of the city of Brno, stands the former Monastery of St. Thomas. Now a research center, St. Thomas has a small, fenced-in garden that sits just outside its historic living quarters. At one end of the garden stands an ivy-covered tablet, inscribed with a few simple words: "Prelate Gregor Mendel made his experiments for his law here." Visitors to the garden can cast their eyes upward and see the rooms that Gregor Johann Mendel lived in while carrying out his work in the years between 1856 and 1863 (Figure 11.1). Mendel labored during this time on a species of common peas, *Pisum sativum*, using tweezers and an artist's paintbrush as his tools. Like many scientific discoverers, Mendel looked at ordinary objects; and as with many scientists, his work was tedious and exacting. Nevertheless, the distance from what Mendel did to what Mendel learned is the distance from the ordinary to the historic.

Coming to adulthood in the mid-nineteenth century, Mendel knew nothing of the elements of genetics we have reviewed so far. Chromosomes and the genes that lie along them had not even been discovered when he was working with his peas; little knowledge existed of meiosis or mitosis, to say nothing of DNA. And as it happened, Mendel himself played no direct role in discovering any of these things. Yet, this unassuming monk, the son of eastern European peasant farmers, generally is accorded the title of the father of genetics. What contribution earned him this honor?

Figure 11.1
Austrian Monk and Naturalist Gregor Mendel

11.1 Mendel and the Black Box

Mendel's achievement was to comprehend what was going on inside what might be called the "black box" of genetics without ever being able to look inside that box himself. Science is filled with so-called black-box problems, in which researchers know what goes *into* a given process and what comes *out*. It is what is going on in between—in the black box—that is a mystery. In the case of genetics, what lies inside the black box is DNA, chromosomes, meiosis, and so forth—all the component parts of genetics, in other words, and the way they work together. Because of the timing of his birth, Mendel had no knowledge of any of these things. Until Mendel, however, nobody had looked carefully at even the starting and ending points of this black-box problem: at what went in and what came out. Mendel's original pea plants represented the input side to the black box of genetics, while the offspring he got from breeding these plants represented the output. By looking carefully at generations of parents and offspring—at both sides of the box, in a sense—Mendel was able to infer something about what had to be going on within. As you will see, his main inferences were correct: (1) that the basic units of genetics are material elements; (2) that these elements come in pairs; (3) that these elements (today called genes) can retain their character through many generations; and (4) that gene pairs *separate* during the formation of gametes.

These insights may sound familiar because all of them were approached from another direction in Chapters 9 and 10. Here are the lessons you went over then:

1. Genes are material elements—lengths of DNA.

2. In human beings, genes come in pairs, residing in pairs of homologous chromosomes.

3. Chromosomes make copies of themselves, thus giving the genes that lie along them the ability to be passed on intact through generations.

4. In meiosis, homologous chromosomes line up next to each other and then separate, with each member of a pair ending up in a different egg or sperm cell.

By observing generations of pea plants and applying mathematics to his observations, Mendel inferred

that something like this had to be happening in reproduction. Because Mendel was the first to perceive a set of principles that govern inheritance, we date our knowledge of genetics from him.

11.2 The Experimental Subjects: *Pisum sativum*

Beginning work in his monastery garden after a period of scientific study in Vienna, Mendel picked the pea plant *Pisum sativum* as the species on which he would carry out his experiments. If you look at **Figure 11.2**, you can see something of the life cycle of this garden pea. Note that what we think of as peas in a pod are seeds in this plant's ovary. Each of these seeds begins as an unfertilized egg, just as a human baby begins as a maternal egg that is unfertilized. Sperm-bearing pollen, landing on the plant's stigma, then set in motion the fertilization of the eggs.

Importantly, *Pisum* plants can *self*-pollinate. The anthers of a given flower release pollen grains that land on that flower's stigma. Each seed that develops

Figure 11.2
Life Cycle of the Pea Plant

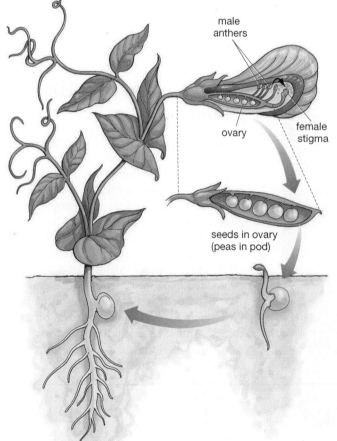

male anthers

ovary

female stigma

seeds in ovary (peas in pod)

1. **Self-pollination.** Pollen from the male anthers of a plant falls on the female stigma of that same plant.

2. **Fertilization.** Sperm from the pollen fertilize the plant's eggs, which lie inside the ovary. These eggs will develop into seeds in the ovary (peas in a pod), which represent a new plant generation. Each seed is fertilized separately.

3. **Germination.** Each seed can be planted and grown into a separate plant.

4. **Development.** Seedlings develop into mature seed plants, capable of producing their own offspring.

from the resulting fertilizations can then be planted in the ground and give rise to a new generation of plant. The way to think of the seeds in a pod is as multiple offspring from multiple fertilizations—one pollen grain fertilizes this seed, another pollen grain fertilizes another. This is why, as you'll see, seeds that are in the same pod can have different characteristics.

Although the pea plants can self-pollinate, they can also **cross-pollinate**—one plant can pollinate another. Indeed, Mendel could accomplish such cross-pollination through his own efforts, by going to work with his tweezers and paintbrushes, as shown in **Figure 11.3**.

In directing pollination, Mendel could control for certain attributes in his pea plants—qualities now referred to as *characters*. If you look at **Table 11.1**, on the next page, you can see that Mendel looked at seven characters in all—such things as stem length, seed color, and seed shape. Note that each of these characters comes in two varieties. There are yellow or green seeds, for example, and purple or white flowers. Such character variations are known as *traits*. Mendel referred to

each of these variations as being either a "dominant" or a "recessive" trait, as the table shows. For now, you can think of a recessive trait as one that tends to remain hidden in certain generations of pea plants. A dominant trait, meanwhile, can be thought of as a trait that tends to appear in those same generations. You'll get a formal definition of dominant and recessive later.

Phenotype and Genotype

Now, let's put these traits in another context. Taken together, traits represent what are called **phenotypes.** Broadly speaking, a phenotype is a physiological feature, bodily characteristic, or behavior of an organism. In the context of our look at *Pisum sativum*, phenotype means the plant's visible physical characteristics. Purple flowers are one phenotype, white flowers another; yellow seeds are one phenotype, green seeds another. Meanwhile, any phenotype is in significant part determined by an organism's underlying **genotype,** meaning its genetic makeup.

**Figure 11.3
How to Cross-Pollinate
Pea Plants**

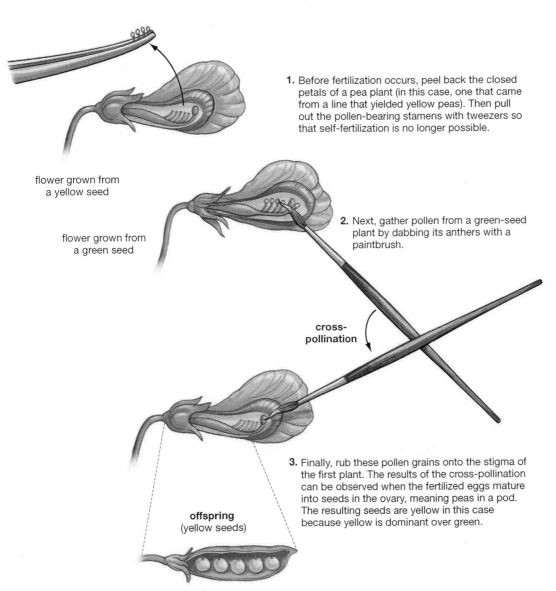

1. Before fertilization occurs, peel back the closed petals of a pea plant (in this case, one that came from a line that yielded yellow peas). Then pull out the pollen-bearing stamens with tweezers so that self-fertilization is no longer possible.

flower grown from
a yellow seed

flower grown from
a green seed

2. Next, gather pollen from a green-seed plant by dabbing its anthers with a paintbrush.

cross-
pollination

3. Finally, rub these pollen grains onto the stigma of the first plant. The results of the cross-pollination can be observed when the fertilized eggs mature into seeds in the ovary, meaning peas in a pod. The resulting seeds are yellow in this case because yellow is dominant over green.

offspring
(yellow seeds)

11.3 Starting the Experiments: Yellow and Green Peas

Mendel began by making sure that his starting plants "bred true" for the phenotypes under study. That is, he assured himself that, for example, all of his purple-flowered plants would produce nothing but generations of purple offspring if they self-pollinated.

Table 11.1

Pea-Plant Characters Studied by Mendel

Character Studied	Dominant Trait	Recessive Trait
Seed shape	smooth	wrinkled
Seed color	yellow	green
Pod shape	inflated	wrinkled
Pod color	green	yellow
Flower color	purple	white
Flower position	on stem	at tip
Stem length	tall	dwarf

Parental, F_1, and F_2 Generations

The **parental generation** in such experiments is often referred to in shorthand as the **P** generation. Meanwhile, the offspring of the parental generation are known as the **first filial generation,** the word *filial* indicating a son or a daughter. The shorthand for first filial is F_1. The F_x form can be used for any succeeding generation. You will be seeing a lot of the second filial, or F_2 generation, for example.

So, how did Mendel proceed with his plants? Let's start with just one example. Mendel took, for his P generation, some plants from a line that bred true for yellow seeds and other plants from a line that bred true for green seeds. Then he took pollen from one variety of the plants and fertilized the other variety, as seen in Figure 11.3. The plants fertilized in this way then produced their own seeds—every one of which was yellow. (Remember that although these seeds were developing within the pods of the parental generation, they represented the new generation—the F_1 generation.) Getting all yellow seeds was an interesting result in itself. Because each seed in a pea-plant pod is fertilized separately, it can be the case that a given pod will contain both yellow and green seeds. (Other pea characters can be variable within a pod as well, as you can see in **Figure 11.4**.) Yet, all the seeds in this generation were yellow, indicating that yellow was a dominant trait and green a recessive one.

Having viewed these results, Mendel then planted his F_1 seeds and let plants grow from them. These plants were then allowed to *self*-pollinate—sperm from a given plant fertilized the eggs from that same plant, so that instead of "crossing" one plant with another, Mendel was crossing a plant with itself. What he got from this self-pollination, in the F_2 generation, was 6,022 yellow seeds and 2,001 green seeds.

Some of these peas have a smooth texture, while others are wrinkled

Figure 11.4
Variation within a Pea Pod
Since each garden pea is fertilized separately, individual peas within a pod can have different character traits.

The Power of Counting

In counting the seeds, Mendel was taking a giant step forward. Why? Experimenters before Mendel had gotten the kind of results he had. What they did not do, however, was undertake a careful *counting* of their results and then analyze the results in terms of proportions.

Looking at the specific results, two things stand out. First, green seeds disappeared in F_1, but came back in F_2. Recall that there was not a green seed to be found in the F_1 generation pods, but in F_2, there are 2,001 of them. Second, green seeds came back in F_2 as *one-fourth* of the seeds as a whole. The F_2 generation isn't divided 50/50, half yellow and half green; instead, there are roughly 3 yellow seeds for every 1 green seed—or to put it another way, a 3:1 ratio of yellow to green seeds. As it turned out, Mendel got the same result with each of the seven characters he was studying, as you can see in **Table 11.2**. Note that the 3:1 ratio is a proportion of dominant to recessive traits—more yellow seeds than green, more purple flowers than white. It was *solely* the dominant traits that appeared in the F_1 generation, but in the F_2 generation the dominants are simply appearing in greater proportion than the recessives.

Interpreting the F_1 and F_2 Results

What did Mendel learn from these results? For one thing, he saw that inheritance for his peas was not a matter of the "blending" of their characteristics. For example, the flower colors purple and white were retained as just that. No intermediate phenotypes—say, lavender flowers—resulted from the cross in any generation. This finding ran contrary to the notion, popular in Mendel's time, that two given traits would blend into a homogeneous third entity, as coffee and milk will blend together.

Beyond this finding, it was apparent that, dominance notwithstanding, plants could retain the *potential* for recessive phenotypes, even though those phenotypes might not appear in a given generation. Mendel's F_1 plants had no green seeds, but in F_2 the green seeds were back. It was reasonable to assume, therefore, that the yellow-seed F_1 plants retained a green-seed *element*, which got expressed only in the F_2 generation. Finally, because his phenotypes came in pairs, it was reasonable for Mendel to hypothesize that the elements likewise came in pairs.

If you think Mendel's *pairs of elements* sound suspiciously like the "pairs of genes" on homologous chromosomes we've seen before, you are right. However, it's time to start referring to these "matched pairs of genes" in scientific terminology. It is more accurate to think of matched pairs of genes as alternative forms of a single gene. The proper name for an alternative form of a gene is an **allele.** Thus, the pea

plant had a single gene for seed color that came in two alleles—one of which coded for yellow seeds, the other of which coded for green seeds. These alleles resided on separate homologous chromosomes.

Table 11.2

Ratios of Dominant to Recessive in Mendel's Plants

Dominant Trait	Recessive Trait	Ratio of Dominant to Recessive in F2 Generation
Smooth seed	Wrinkled seed	2.96:1 (5,474 smooth, 1,850 wrinkled)
Yellow seed	Green seed	3.01:1 (6,022 yellow, 2,001 green)
Inflated pod	Wrinkled pod	2.95:1 (822 inflated, 299 wrinkled)
Green pod	Yellow pod	2.82:1 (428 green, 152 yellow)
Purple flower	White flower	3.14:1 (705 purple, 224 white)
Flower on stem	Flower at tip	3.14:1 (651 along stem, 207 at tip)
Tall stem	Dwarf stem	2.84:1 (787 tall plants, 277 dwarfs)
	Average ratio, all traits	3:1

11.4 Another Generation

Having seen recessive phenotypes reappear in F_2, Mendel decided to extend his breeding. In his next experiment, he took a set of F_2 generation seeds—all of them yellow—planted them, and let the plants they grew into self-pollinate. Then, he looked at the color of the F_3 seeds contained in the pods of these plants. What he found was that, of 519 plants grown, 166 yielded only yellow seeds, while the remaining 353 plants had a mixture of yellow and green seeds in the pods, in the familiar 3:1 ratio. But when he similarly took F_2 green seeds, planted them, and let them self-pollinate, these plants produced nothing but green seeds.

What could have caused these results? The answer was the underlying elements Mendel had hit upon, meaning the alleles for the color gene. When he planted his yellow seeds, some of them yielded all-yellow offspring, but others yielded mixed (green and yellow) offspring. He reasoned that there must be *two kinds* of yellow plants: those that were "pure" yellow (the 166 that yielded solely yellow seeds) and those that were "mixed" yellow (the 353 that produced both yellow and green seeds). Pure yellow had nothing but yellow alleles within and would produce nothing but yellow seeds when self-pollinated. Meanwhile, the mixed yellow would have one yellow and one green allele within and thus would produce pods that contained seeds of both colors. Finally, the green seeds had nothing but green alleles and thus produced nothing but green seeds.

(a) P generation crosses

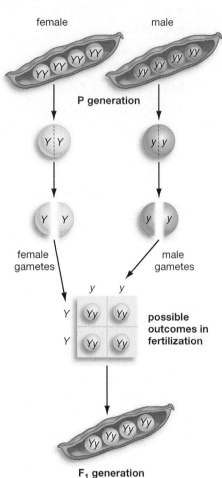

1. Female gametes are being provided by a plant that has the dominant, yellow alleles (*YY*); male gametes are being provided by a plant that has the recessive, green alleles (*yy*).

2. The cells of the pea plants that give rise to gametes start to go through meiosis.

3. The two alleles for pea color, which lie on separate homologous chromosomes, separate in meiosis, yielding gametes that each bear a single allele for seed color. In the female, each gamete bears a *Y* allele; in the male, each bears a *y* allele.

4. The Punnett square shows the possible combinations that can result when the male and female gametes come together in the moment of fertilization. (If you have trouble reading the Punnett square, see Figure 11.5b). The single possible outcome in this fertilization is a mixed genotype, *Yy*.

5. Because *Y* (yellow) is dominant over *y* (green), the result is that all the offspring in the F₁ generation are yellow because they all contain a *Y* allele.

(b) How to read a Punnett square

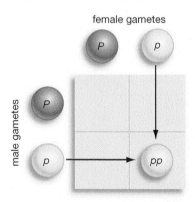

1. A *p* gamete from the male combines with a *p* gamete from the female to produce an offspring of *pp* genotype (and white color).

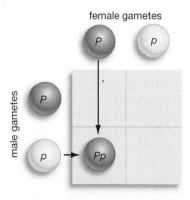

2. A *p* gamete from the male combines with a *P* gamete from the female to produce an offspring of *Pp* genotype (and purple color).

Figure 11.5
Visualizing Mendel's Results

(a) Mendel's P Generation Crosses

(b) Examples of Punnett Squares

SO FAR . . .

1. A physical characteristic, such as the height of a person or the color of one of Mendel's peas, represents a _____ in these organisms, which is in large part based on their genetic makeup or _____.

2. In Mendel's experiments, the first generation of plants that he got, from crossing parental generation plants, exhibited only _____ traits, while the next generation of plants, which resulted from self-pollination of plants, exhibited both _____ and _____ traits, in a 3:1 ratio.

3. Genes come in alternative forms known as _____, which reside on separate _____.

Mendel's Generations in Pictures

Let's now make these points clearer by reviewing all three generations of experiments schematically.

The F₁ Generation

To start out, it will be helpful to introduce a common, shorthand method of denoting alleles. Let us refer to dominant and recessive alleles by uppercase and lowercase letters, with uppercase used for dominant types and lowercase used for recessive types. Thus, a "pure" yellow-seeded plant, having *two* yellow alleles, would be symbolized as *YY*. Meanwhile, pure green-seeded plants are *yy*, while mixed seeds are *Yy*. Let us say, just as an example, that female gametes are being supplied by a plant that is *YY*, while male gametes are coming from a plant that is *yy*. In meiosis, as you've seen, homologous chromosomes separate. This happens in the pea plants, meaning that each of these plants will contribute *one member* of its gene pair to its respective gametes—the *YY* female contributing a *Y* gamete, and the *yy* male contributing a *y* gamete. When these gametes fuse in the moment of fertilization, the result is a *Yy* hybrid in the F₁ generation. If you look at **Figure 11.5**, you will be introduced to a time-honored way to represent such outcomes, the Punnett square, and see Mendel's F₁ results symbolized as well.

Note that, because *Y* is dominant, all the seeds in the F₁ offspring pods will have a yellow *phenotype*, even though every one of these seeds contains a mixed *genotype*. (Every one is *Yy*.) It takes only one *Y* allele for a seed to be yellow; for a seed to be green, then, it must have two *y* alleles.

The F₂ Generation

Next come the F₁ crosses that yielded the F₂ generation. The starting point here is the F₁ seeds, which are all of the mixed *Yy* type, as you can see in **Figure 11.6**.

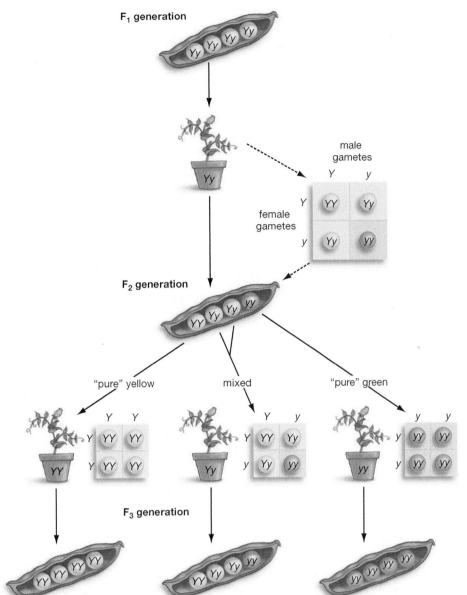

F₁ generation

male gametes

female gametes

F₂ generation

"pure" yellow   mixed   "pure" green

F₃ generation

1. From the F₁ to the F₂ generation

The starting point is the F₁ generation, a set of seeds that all have the *Yy* genotype. These seeds are planted and the plants go through meiosis, yielding the gametes shown around the Punnett square. When these gametes come together in self-fertilization, the possibilities include *YY* and *yy* combinations, as well as the *Yy* combination seen in the F₁ generation. The existence of *yy* individuals is the reason green seeds reappear in the F₂ generation. Because *Y* is dominant, the green phenotype could not appear in seeds that had even a single *Y* allele.

2. From the F₂ to the F₃ generation

With three starting genotypes (*YY, Yy, yy*) the F₂ generation yields plants that have these three genotypes, though there are more F₂ plants of "mixed" genotype than of either "pure" genotype.

Figure 11.6
From the F₁ to the F₃ Generation

Meiosis then occurs in the gamete precursors, which results in a separation of these alleles: Half the gametes now contain *Y* alleles and the other half *y*. You can see from the figure why this cross can now give us back the green-seed phenotype, on average in a 1:3 proportion with yellow seeds. Note that there are twice as many mixed-genotype seeds (*Yy*) as either variety of pure seed (*YY* or *yy*). Important mathematical principles underlie this outcome. You can read more about them in "Proportions and Their Causes" on page 198.

The F₃ Generation

Finally, in Figure 11.6, you can see why Mendel got the results he did when he went from F₂ to F₃. Recall that when Mendel planted and self-fertilized his *yellow* F₂ seeds, he got 519 plants, of which 166 produced nothing but yellow seeds. Now you can see why: These were not only phenotypically yellow; they were "pure" yellow in terms of genotype (*YY*). Mendel also got 353

plants that produced both yellow and green seeds. This is because the seeds these plants grew from were of mixed genotype (*Yy*); in reproduction, their offspring would be of both pure (*YY, yy*) and mixed (*Yy*) genotype. Finally, when Mendel planted and self-fertilized *green* F₂ seeds, all the plants that resulted from these seeds bred true for green seeds because all of them began as *yy*. Figure 11.7 illustrates how the three genotypes discussed here yield only the two phenotypes of yellow or green.

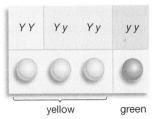

| YY | Yy | Yy | yy | **Three genotypes yield ...** |

two phenotypes.

yellow   green

Figure 11.7
Three Genotypes Yield Two Phenotypes
The two alleles for seed color (*Y* = yellow and *y* = green) can result in three genotypes (*YY, Yy, yy*), but these can yield only two phenotypes (yellow and green).

Proportions and Their Causes: The Rules of Multiplication and Addition

What are the odds of tossing up two coins and having both come up heads?

To be a good songwriter, a person needs to be both a good musical composer and a good lyricist. Of all the people who decide to take up songwriting, say that 1 in 10 is a good composer and that 1 in 10 is a good lyricist. Now, what is the probability that a person who takes up songwriting will be *both* a good composer and a good lyricist? The answer to this question turns out to have relevance to all kinds of questions in our world, including the results that Gregor Mendel got.

When Mendel examined the F_2 pods that contained the F_3 seeds, he found that there were many more pods that had mixed seed colors within (yellow and green) than pods with seeds that were either all yellow or all green. It was the F_1 meiosis that set the stage for this outcome, as you can see here:

The Punnett square provides an intuitive visual sense of why things turned out

the way they did. Meiosis in the F_1 plants produced twice as many mixed F_2 seeds (Yy) as either type of "pure" seeds (YY or yy). It's even more helpful, however, to understand a principle that underlies this outcome. A simple coin-tossing example can illustrate what is at work. Suppose that you are going to throw two coins in the air—a nickel and a dime. What is the likelihood that *both* coins will come up heads? There is only one way to get this result:

1. Nickel = heads; dime = heads

Now, consider tossing the two coins and specifying a *mixed* result. There are *two* ways that this condition can be satisfied:

1. Nickel = heads; dime = tails
2. Dime = heads; nickel = tails

The seeds are in the same situation. What is the likelihood of getting a "pure" yellow seed? As you can see by looking again at the Punnett square, there is only one way to get this: female Y, male Y. Now consider specifying a mixed result. There are two ways to get this: female y, male Y; and female Y, male y.

The Rule of Multiplication

To state a principle that can be applied to any situation, let's look at this concept in a

more formal way. What are the odds of tossing up one coin and getting heads? Fifty/fifty, right? This means a 50 percent chance, which equals 0.5. Now, what are the odds of tossing up two coins and having both come up heads? A principle called the **rule of multiplication** comes into play here. It states that the probability of any two events happening is the product of their respective probabilities. In this case, the probability for each head coming up is 0.5, so the equation is $0.5 \times 0.5 = 0.25$, or a 25 percent probability of two heads.

The Rule of Addition

Now, what is the probability of getting one coin that comes up heads and one that comes up tails—when either of them can be heads or tails? When an outcome can occur in two or more *different* ways, as is the case here, the probability of this happening is the *sum* of the respective probabilities. This principle is known as the **rule of addition.** The probability of nickel = heads, dime = tails is the same 0.25 probability you saw in the rule of multiplication, but the probability of nickel = tails, dime = heads is also 0.25. The probability that *either* of these outcomes will take place is thus $0.25 + 0.25 = 0.50$, or 50 percent.

All this gives us a way to figure the songwriter probability—or any set of independent probabilities. Remember the stipulation that 1 in 10 aspiring songwriters is a good composer and 1 in 10 is a good lyricist. Thus, under the rule of multiplication, $0.10 \times 0.10 = 0.01$, meaning 1 in 100 is likely to be good at both composing and lyric writing.

The Law of Segregation

For inheritance to work this way, Mendel saw something we noted earlier: that, although plant cells may contain two copies (alleles) of a gene relating to a given character, these copies must *separate* in gamete formation. How else could two Yy parents ever give rise to yy (or YY) progeny unless the Yy elements could first separate (in the parents) and then recombine in different ways (in the offspring)? Thus did Mendel derive his insight, sometimes called Mendel's First Law or the **Law**

of Segregation: Differing characters in organisms result from two genetic elements (alleles) that separate in gamete formation, such that each gamete gets only one of the two alleles. As noted, the physical basis for this law, which Mendel knew nothing of, is the separation of homologous chromosomes during meiosis.

Homozygous and Heterozygous Conditions

It's time to add a couple more terms to the concepts you have been considering. There is scientific terminology for the genotypically "pure" and "mixed" organisms noted earlier. An organism that has two identical alleles of a gene for a given character is said to be **homozygous** for that character (as with *YY* or *yy*). An organism that has differing alleles for a character is said to be **heterozygous** for that character (as with *Yy*). You often see homozygous used in combination with the terms dominant and recessive. For example, a *yy* plant is a *homozygous recessive*, while a *YY* is a *homozygous dominant* (**Figure 11.8**). Knowledge of these terms puts you in a position to understand the formal definitions of dominant and recessive promised earlier. **Dominant** is a term used to designate an allele that is expressed in the heterozygous condition. In a heterozygous pea plant (*Yy*), the yellow allele (*Y*) is expressed, meaning it is dominant over the green allele (*y*). **Recessive** is a term used to designate an allele that is not expressed in the heterozygous condition. The green allele (*y*) is recessive because it is not expressed when it exists heterozygously with the yellow allele (*Yy*).

11.5 Crosses Involving Two Characters

Thus far, the subject has been how pea plants come to differ in *one* of their characters, seed color. When people breed organisms for a single difference such as this, looking to see how the offspring will come out, the procedure is known as a **monohybrid cross.** Mendel, however, went on to ask: What happens if you breed organisms for *two* characters? What happens, in other words, if you undertake what is known as **dihybrid cross**? The question Mendel was seeking to answer in carrying out his dihybrid crosses was: Do given characters travel together in heredity, or do they travel separately? If you get one character passed on to a plant, do you necessarily get the other?

Crosses for Seed Color and Seed Shape

One dihybrid cross that Mendel performed involved, for its first character, the yellow and green seeds you've become so familiar with. In addition, this cross involved a second character of these seeds: their shape, which can be smooth or wrinkled (as you saw in Figure 11.4). It's clear that yellow color is dominant to green, and as Table 11.1 shows, smooth seed shape is dominant to wrinkled. We have been denoting the alleles for seed color as *Y* for yellow and *y* for green. In the same fashion, let us now denote seed-shape alleles as *S* for smooth and *s* for wrinkled.

You can see, in **Figure 11.9a** on the next page, what the phenotypic outcomes were for these crosses from the P to F$_1$ generations. In the F$_1$ generation, all the seeds were smooth and yellow. When the F$_1$s were self-

pollinated, however, the F$_2$ phenotypes that resulted came out as 315 smooth yellow seeds; 108 smooth green seeds; 101 wrinkled yellow seeds; and 32 wrinkled green seeds. These numbers work out to a 9:3:3:1 ratio, meaning 9 parts smooth yellow; 3 parts smooth green; 3 parts wrinkled yellow; and 1 part wrinkled green.

A Hidden, Underlying Ratio

For Mendel, these imposing figures represented another opportunity to perceive something about how the black box of genetics operated. He realized early on that this ratio might be a composite, hiding an underlying reality for each of the *single* characters he was studying. Think for a second, as Mendel did, of only one of these characters, the color of the seeds. Here, the result is:

315 (smooth) yellow seeds   108 (smooth) green seeds
101 (wrinkled) yellow   32 (wrinkled) green
416 yellow seeds   140 green seeds

This equals a yellow:green ratio of about 3:1. In other words, the familiar 3:1 ratio in the F$_2$ generation still holds. It held as well when Mendel looked only at seed *shape*. This suggested something to Mendel that turned out to be another of his major insights: that characters—in this case, seed shape and seed color—are transmitted *independently* of one another. When these two characters were being crossed at the same time, the results for each were the same as when they were crossed as single characters in the

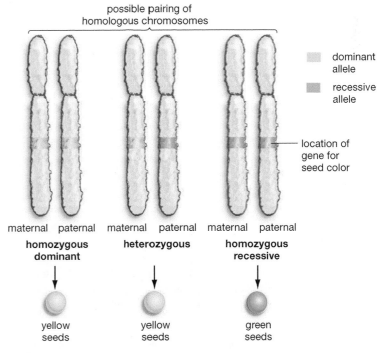

possible pairing of homologous chromosomes

dominant allele

recessive allele

location of gene for seed color

maternal paternal   maternal paternal   maternal paternal
homozygous dominant   **heterozygous**   **homozygous recessive**

yellow seeds   yellow seeds   green seeds

Figure 11.8
Chromosomes and Phenotypes

The figure shows how alleles on chromosomes yielded the pea-color phenotypes that Mendel observed.

earlier experiments. Thus, one character's transmission did not appear to affect the other's.

Understanding the 9:3:3:1 Ratio

Still, what's the basis of the formidable 9:3:3:1 ratio that Mendel got in his dihybrid cross, with its mixture of wrinkled yellows, smooth greens, and so forth? This is simply a more complex example of the kind of outcomes you saw earlier with the aid of the Punnett square. If you look at the square in **Figure 11.9b** and start adding up internal squares *by phenotype*, Mendel's 9:3:3:1 ratio starts making sense. You can see, for example, where the 1 in the ratio comes from: There is only 1 part wrinkled green seeds because it is only the *sy* (pollen) and *sy* (egg) combination that yields this phenotype. Likewise, you will get three parts wrinkled yellow seeds by adding up the three possible male and female gamete combinations that could bring this about.

The Law of Independent Assortment

This outcome could only come about, however, if Mendel's fundamental insight about dihybrid crosses was correct: that characters were being transmitted independently of one another. If one character had affected another's transmission, these ratios would have been very different. This insight of Mendel's is now known as Mendel's Second Law, or the **Law of Independent Assortment.** It states that during gamete formation, gene pairs assort independently of one another.

Independent Assortment and Chromosomes

Now recall that the underlying physical basis for this law was set forth in Chapter 10: In meiosis, pairs of homologous chromosomes *assort independently* from one another at the metaphase plate. It may be, for example, that paternal chromosome 5 will line up on side A of

Figure 11.9
Phenotype Ratios in a
Dihybrid Cross

(a) Results of Mendel's dihybrid cross

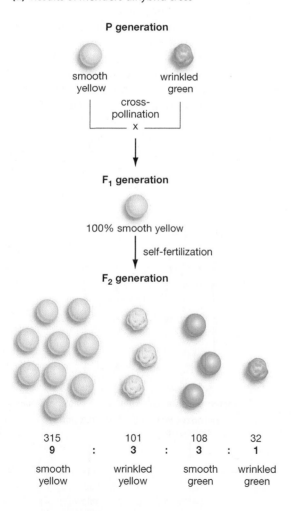

In one of his dihybrid crosses, Mendel cross-bred plants that had smooth yellow seeds with those that had green wrinkled seeds. The result was a generation of plants that all had smooth yellow seeds. When these plants self-fertilized, the result was an F₂ generation that had the phenotypes shown in a 9:3:3:1 ratio.

(b) Why Mendel got these results

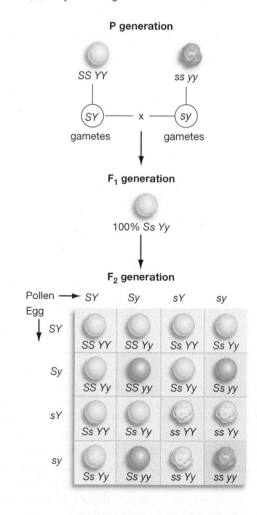

The Punnett square demonstrates why Mendel got the 9:3:3:1 phenotypic ratio in his dihybrid cross. Nine combinations yield smooth yellow seeds, 3 yield smooth green seeds, 3 yield wrinkled yellow seeds, while only 1 results in a wrinkled green seed.

the metaphase plate; if so, then maternal chromosome 5 ends up on side B. For chromosome 6, however, things could just as easily be reversed: The *maternal* chromosome might end up on side A and the paternal on side B (Figure 10.4, page 180). The genes for Mendel's seed color exist on the plant's chromosome 1, while the genes for seed shape exist on its chromosome 7. Because these are separate chromosomes, they assort independently at the metaphase plate, meaning they are passed on independently to future generations.

11.6 Reception of Mendel's Ideas

When Mendel finished his experiments, he delivered two lectures on them to a local scientific society in 1865. It would be nice to report that the society members' jaws dropped open once Mendel let them in on how inheritance worked in the living world, but no such thing happened. His findings were ultimately published in a scientific journal that was distributed in Germany, Austria, the United States, and England. Mendel even took it upon himself to get 40 reprints of his paper, thereafter sending some out to various scientists in an effort to spark some exchange on his findings—all to no avail. His work sank nearly without a trace, finally to be rediscovered in 1900, 16 years after his death.

This poor early reception notwithstanding, Mendel's insights have stood the test of time. For certain kinds of phenotypes, his rules of inheritance are extremely reliable. To this day, biologists will begin an observation by noting that "Mendelian rules tell us that . . . " or "Mendelian inheritance operates here." Even allowing that he had intellectual predecessors, the fact is that Mendel did not just add to the discipline of genetics—he founded it.

SO FAR . . .

1. Mendel's law of segregation states that differing traits in organisms result from two differing _____ that _____ in gamete formation, such that each gamete gets only one of the two.

2. Homozygous refers to an organism that has two _____ alleles for a character, while heterozygous refers to an organism that has two _____ alleles for the character.

3. An allele that is expressed in the heterozygous condition is said to be _____, while an allele that is not expressed in the heterozygous condition is said to be _____.

11.7 Incomplete Dominance and Codominance

Mendel knew as well as anyone that the rules he discovered did not apply in all instances of inheritance. In his peas, crossing white- and purple-flowered plants resulted in an F_1 generation in which all flowers were purple. In some other species, however, the results are different. Crossing a true-breeding red-flowered *snapdragon* with a true-breeding white-flowered snapdragon produces neither red- nor white-flowered F_1 snapdragons, but *pink* snapdragons (Figure 11.10 on the next page). This might seem to indicate that inheritance can indeed work through the blending of genetic traits—a notion that Mendel's work had quashed. Blending is not taking place, however. When breeding is continued through the F_2 generation, red and white flowers come back, along with the pink, in a ratio of 1 part red, 2 parts pink, 1 part white. This 1:2:1 ratio demonstrates that red and white alleles have not irretrievably blended into pink but rather have come together in F_1, only to separate out again in F_2. Still, how can the pink F_1 snapdragons be explained?

Incomplete Dominance

First, think about what genes do: They contain information regarding the production of proteins. In the case of colors, such proteins can bring about the formation of pigments. This is the case with the snapdragons; they have a gene for color, and one of the alleles of this gene brings about the production of red pigment. Meanwhile, the second allele of this gene is nonfunctional—it brings about the production of no pigment at all. Two of the red alleles, then, yield a red color, while one red allele produces only enough pigment to yield a pink color. Neither the red nor the white allele, therefore, is completely dominant; each is thus said to have **incomplete dominance,** meaning a genetic condition in which the heterozygote phenotype is intermediate between either of the homozygous phenotypes.

Codominance

The notion of genes as protein-producing entities can help us steer through another variation on Mendelian inheritance, this one having great importance for variety in the living world. When people speak of blood "types," what they mean is types of "glycolipids"—lipid molecules with carbohydrate chains attached—that extend from the surface of red blood cells. These surface extensions come in many different varieties, the two most important of which are designated A and B

Blood types are completely under genetic control, with a single gene that lies on chromosome 9 determining what blood type a person will have—A, B,

AB, or O. There are two copies of this gene in each individual because there are two copies of chromosome 9 in each individual—one inherited from the mother, the other inherited from the father. Thus, there exists the possibility for *alleles*, or gene variants, in each individual. One of these alleles codes for a protein that modifies surface extensions into the A form, while the other codes for a protein that modifies the extensions into the type B form.

Now, a single person could have two alleles that code for type A extensions, or a person could have both alleles coding for type B extensions. In the first case, a person would have type A blood and in the second type B blood. However, a person could have one allele that codes for the type A extensions *and* one that codes for type B, in which case that person would have type AB blood. Finally, a person could

have two alleles that are inactive—that code for neither extension—and would thus have type O blood, as **Table 11.3** shows.

What's new in this case is, first, another aspect of the idea of dominance in alleles. In the blood types, *both* the A and B alleles produce proteins that modify the cell-surface extensions; each allele thus has an independent effect on phenotype. People who are heterozygous for these alleles thus do not get a phenotype that, like pink flowers, lies halfway between A and B. They get both the A and B versions of the molecules on the surface of their blood cells. Alleles that have this kind of effect result in **codominance:** a condition in which two alleles of a given gene have different phenotypic effects, with both effects manifesting in organisms that are heterozygous for the gene.

Figure 11.10
How Red and White Yield Pink: Incomplete Dominance in Snapdragons

RR
red

rr
white

P generation

1. The starting plants are a snapdragon homozygous for red color (*RR*) and snapdragon homozygous for white color (*rr*).

Rr
100% pink

F₁ generation

2. When these plants are crossed, the resulting *Rr* genotype yields only enough pigment to produce a flower that is pink—the only phenotype in the F₁ generation.

sperm
R   *r*

egg
R

RR   *Rr*

r

Rr   *rr*

F₂ generation

3. In the F₂ generation, alleles combine to produce red, pink, and white phenotypes.

1 : 2 : 1
red   pink   white

Table 11.3		

Human Blood Types

This blood type (phenotype) . . .	. . . has these surface glycolipids . . .	. . . and is produced by these genotypes
A		AA or AO
B		BB or BO
AB		AB
O	(no surface glycolipids)	OO

The familiar ABO human blood-typing system refers to glycolipid molecules that extend from the surface of red blood cells. People whose blood is "type A" have A extensions on their blood cells. It is also possible to have only B extensions (and be type B); to have both A and B extensions (and be type AB); or to have none of these extensions (and be type O). Note that a person whose genotype is AO is phenotypically type A; likewise, a person whose genotype is BO is phenotypically type B.

Dominant and Recessive Alleles

All this gets us to an important point, which is the relationship between dominant and recessive alleles. In common speech, the word *dominance* is used all the time to mean "bringing another under submission by means of superior power." Alleles, however, are not locked in a power struggle with one another. Alleles contain information for the production of proteins. Such proteins (or lack of them) can create dominant phenotypes (smooth peas), incompletely dominant phenotypes (pink snapdragons), or codominant phenotypes (AB blood). "Dominance," then, just refers to the ways in which a given allele is expressed. As you've seen, a recessive allele is not *eliminated* by being paired with a dominant allele—it simply isn't expressed in a given generation. When this generation gives rise to another, the recessive allele will be passed on intact, at which point it may be expressed. When the pea plant's recessive green allele was passed on, for example, it was expressed when brought together with another green allele. This has relevance for traits more familiar to us. People seem to have an idea that human blond hair, to give one example, eventually will cease to exist because the alleles for it are recessive to those for dark hair. The alleles for blond hair are, however, not disappearing. To the extent that alleles for it come together in reproduction, there will always be blond-haired people, as you can see in **Figure 11.11**.

SO FAR ...

1. Incomplete dominance, such as that of the pink snapdragon, exists when a _____ phenotype is intermediate between that of either of the _____ phenotypes.

2. Codominance exists when alleles have _____ effects on a phenotype, with both effects manifesting in organisms that are _____ for a codominant gene.

3. A recessive allele is not eliminated when paired with a dominant allele in a single individual; it simply is not _____. It may have phenotypic effects in a later generation, however, if paired with _____.

11.8 Multiple Alleles and Polygenic Inheritance

ABO blood types have one more lesson for us. In Mendel's seed shapes, we saw two phenotypic variants: smooth and wrinkled. In blood types, we saw four: A, B, AB, and O. As you know, no one person can have more than *two* alleles for a given gene. As a result, a person may be, say, A and B, but he or she cannot be A, B, and O. It is thus only in a *population* of humans that the full range of ABO alleles can be found. And therein lies the lesson: In a population, alleles can come not just in two, but in many variants.

When three or more alleles of the same gene exist in a population, they are known as **multiple alleles.** Such alleles are important in and of themselves for they can bring diversity to traits that are governed by single genes (such as human blood types). Their more general significance comes, however, in connection with traits that are controlled not by one gene, but by many. Recall that seed texture in Mendel's peas was governed by a single gene (which had smooth and wrinkled allelic variants). This situation is, however, the exception rather than the rule in the living world. Most traits are governed by many genes. The human traits of height, weight, eye color, and skin color are each controlled by several genes. In the wider living world, the color of a wheat grain, the length of an ear of corn, and the amount of milk a cow gives are all controlled by many genes acting together. The term for such genetic

Figure 11.11

Alleles Are Retained Across Generations

The fraternal Hodgson twins, Kian on the left and Remee on the right, were born one minute apart in 2005 to English parents Kylie Hodgson (at far left) and Remi Horder. Both parents are biracial, from mixed-race, black-white unions, a circumstance that set the stage for the unusual genetic outcome in their twins. Kian happened to inherit alleles, passed on from both of her black grandparents, that produced her darker skin, black hair, and brown eyes, while Remee inherited alleles, passed on from both of her white grandparents, that led to lighter skin, blond hair, and blue eyes.

influence is **polygenic inheritance,** meaning the inheritance of a genetic character that is determined by the interaction of multiple genes, with each gene having a small additive effect on the character.

When we have many genes contributing some small increment to a trait, the result is what you see in **Figure 11.12**. Human beings don't come in two heights, or three or four; they display what is known as a "continuous variation" in height, each person being just barely taller or shorter than the next. Continuous variation also holds true for human skin color. Human beings don't really have "black" or "white" skin. Instead, they have skin that comes in a range of hues, in which one color shades imperceptibly into another. Likewise, trees of a given species come in a range of heights, and the beaks of birds come in a range of lengths. Polygenic inheritance creates this fine-grained diversity.

Now, note something else about Figure 11.12a. Most of the students fall in the middle range of heights in the group. Put another way, there are fewer tall or short students than there are students of medium height. This height distribution means that the group as a whole takes on a kind of shape—a bell shape. This is, in fact, the famous **bell curve,** meaning a distribution of values that is symmetrical around the average. Most biological traits manifest in this way. Look, for example, at the beak depths in a group of Darwin's finches in Figure 11.12b. Graphs like this just confirm what we know intuitively—that traits in living things tend to cluster around the middle of a range of values, rather than at the extreme ends of the range.

In polygenic inheritance, with its many genes and alleles, gene interactions are so complex that predictions about phenotype are a matter of *probability*, not certainty. Human height is largely under genetic control, and there are means of trying to predict the height of children based on the height of their parents. (The starting point generally is to add together the height of the parents and divide the result by two.) All that such predictions can do, however, is specify that if parents are of a given height, then there is a certain probability that their children will fall into a given range of heights. Think how different this is from the situation with Mendel's peas. There, you could confidently predict that a given cross would yield, say, all green peas.

11.9 Genes and Environment

Scientists work awfully hard at trying to determine the probabilities for certain polygenic outcomes—those related to disease. In carrying out this work, they are essentially doing what Mendel did: observing traits in a parental generation and then observing traits in the parents' offspring. Such work is the basis for the warnings we sometimes hear about how much a person's risk for a particular cancer goes up if that person has a relative who has contracted the disease. (To learn more about how science is working to predict disease susceptibility on the basis of genotype, see "Scanning DNA for Disease Markers" on page 206.) With polygenic illnesses such as cancer, however, it is difficult to

(a) Continuous variation in human height

(b) The bell curve

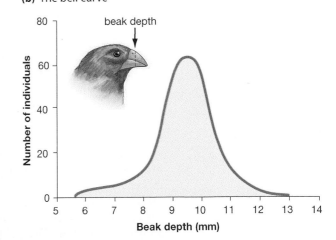

Figure 11.12
Continuous Variation and the Bell Curve

(a) Human heights exist in a range, with no fixed increments between heights of individuals. Such "continuous variation" results from polygenic inheritance, in which each of several genes contributes a small additive effect to a character. University of Connecticut students in the picture have been arranged by height to show how continuous variation works in this one human trait. Note that the group as a whole takes on the shape of a bell. The students' heights are distributed in a pattern that creates a bell curve.

(b) A bell curve can also be seen in this graph, which plots the average beak depth of a population of Darwin's finches from the Galapagos Islands. Note how most of the finches had beak depths that fell within a middle range of values for the trait.

ESSAY

Scanning Genomes for Disease Markers

Should an individual's genetic information ever become public information?

Since genes underlie the traits seen in healthy people—their height, their skin color, and so forth—it's not surprising that they also can play a part in producing the traits seen in unhealthy people: weak hearts, failing eyesight, bad kidneys. Scientists have been trying to decipher the linkage between genetic makeup and disease since the early twentieth century, but from that time until very recently they had to deal with a critical missing piece of information: They didn't know what the genetic makeup of any human being was. This state of affairs changed dramatically in 2003 with the completion of the Human Genome Project, which revealed the order of the 3 billion A's, T's, G's, and C's that make up the full complement of human DNA. The hope at the time was that, with this information in hand, scientists would be able to look at the genomes of, say, cancer patients and pinpoint the ways in which their genetic

makeup had made them susceptible to their disease.

This kind of detective work has borne some fruit in recent years, but the yield has not been nearly what scientists had hoped for. Now, however, a Harvard biologist named George Church has proposed tackling the problem by taking what might be called a Wikipedia approach to genes and disease. His idea is to sequence the genomes of 100,000 average citizens, get detailed physical profiles of each of these people, and then make all this information freely available on the Web. Straightforward as this idea may sound, in the time since it was announced, it has sparked a vigorous debate on a societal issue: Should an individual's genetic information ever become public information?

The scientific impetus behind Church's Personal Genome Project (PGP) is that, even with the human genome sequence in

hand, medical researchers today have inadequate information to use when looking for linkages between genetic makeup and disease. At present, when researchers want to look for such connections, they get DNA samples from disease victims and then sequence a number of target regions in their genome—that is, regions that seem to have a reasonable chance of playing a part in their illness. Then they look for single-letter differences between these regions and the same regions in a comparable group of healthy individuals. In such a case, one small part of the result might look like so:

Standard genome: AATCGCGGAC
Patient's genome: AATCTCGGAC

The difference between the two genomes, called a single nucleotide polymorphism, or SNP, is likely to be one of many such differences between patients and healthy individuals. Because major diseases are almost always *polygenic* diseases—that is, afflictions in which many genes play a role—the question then becomes: With what frequency do given *sets* of SNPs show up in patients when compared to healthy individuals? The problem thus far has been that almost no clear associations have emerged between SNP patterns and major diseases; scientists have

separate the genetic factors from what are called "environmental" factors. What's an environmental factor? Any external influence that is favorable or unfavorable for the development of a trait in an organism. Smoking, for example, is an environmental factor that influences development of lung cancer. Indeed, smoking is responsible for about 90 percent of all lung cancer cases. Even so, only a minority of smokers ever contract lung cancer. Why do some smokers get this disease while others are spared? A large part of the answer is genetic susceptibility: The genetic makeup of some individuals makes them more susceptible to the environmental influence of smoking. Thus, we can see genes and environment working together to create the outcome of lung cancer. As it turns out, this is almost always the case in nature. For polygenic traits—which is to say, most traits—it is rare for genes to be the sole determining factor.

A clear example of how genes and environment work together can be seen in **Figure 11.13**, which shows a picture of the most popular species of hydrangea flower, *Hydrangea macrophylla*. Any gardener could start with a blue hydrangea, like the one in the picture on the right, take a "cutting" from it, do a little preparatory work, plant the cutting in the ground, and get a whole new hydrangea plant as a result. For our purposes, the important point is that this second plant is a clone of the first. It is not produced by mixing eggs and sperm; it is an exact genetic replica of the first plant. It can, however, be a plant with *pink* flowers instead of blue if some garden lime is mixed into its surrounding soil. It's possible, therefore, to have two hydrangea plants with the exact same genotype but with very different phenotypes—pink or blue flowers. The message here is one of genetic limitation. Genotype specifies been unable to say that a given set of SNP differences is related in any meaningful way to a given condition. To get a feel for what this means in practice, consider a recent test for this kind of inquiry that involved not disease but the character of human height, which is known to be 80 to 90 percent under genetic control. After looking at SNP patterns in more than 30,000 individuals, scientists then looked at how tall each individual was and found that no set of SNPs among them could account for more than 5 percent of the variance seen in their heights. Thus, while we know that genes have a huge effect on height, we don't know *where* this control lies within the genome.

Enter George Church, who believes that the answer to this issue may lie in giving scientists around the world access to two kinds of information that they don't have now: DNA sequence data on a large number of complete human genomes—rather than just individual regions of the genome—and physical profiles of the people whose genomes have been sequenced. In short, Church's Personal Genome Project is aimed at providing researchers not just with genotypic information on a huge group of people, but with *phenotypic* information on them as well—their height, weight, blood pres-

sure, cholesterol levels, allergies they suffer from, their mood states, even their television-watching habits. Once all this information is up on the Web, researchers around the world will have an enormous database to tap into in looking for connections between genetic makeup and disease.

Despite this potential, the initial phases of PGP created quite a stir because, as may be apparent, the project is a large-scale experiment in turning private information into public information. At present, only two people in the world have made their genomes public (scientists James Watson and Craig Venter). Now Church is proposing to go public with the genotypes and phenotypes of 100,000 people. These volunteers will be given numerical identities on the PGP website, but the project is careful to warn prospective participants that no level of confidentiality can be assured for any of them over the long run. So, suppose that a SNP pattern is discovered for, say, Alzheimer's disease and that 1,000 PGP volunteers share in this pattern. At present, federal law forbids employers and health insurance companies from discriminating on the basis of genetic makeup, but life insurance and long-term care insurance companies are not

restricted in this way. So, wouldn't it be reasonable to assume that these companies would begin trying to figure out if anyone who comes to them seeking insurance is one of the 1,000 PGP volunteers who shares in the Alzheimer's SNP pattern? Beyond this, what about the close relatives of PGP volunteers—their siblings, parents, and children? How much genetic privacy can they have if a genetic profile very similar to theirs has been made public on the Web?

Church is the first to admit that, because something like PGP has never been tried, no one is sure how the privacy issues it raises will play out. As such, he and his team have taken a cautious approach in the project's early phases. PGP's first 10 volunteers were required to have a high level of knowledge regarding genetics and they were encouraged to consult with close relatives before taking part. Even when the project ramps up to a larger scale, volunteers will be required to demonstrate a fair amount of familiarity with genetics. Despite misgivings about such privacy concerns, however, the PGP experiment has, you might say, opened for business. Anyone who wants to be part of it can learn more by going to personalgenomes.org.

Figure 11.13
Flower Color Is Affected by Environment

Both the blue hydrangeas on the right and pink hydrangeas on the left are from the same species (*Hydrangea macrophylla*), yet they have different coloration because of different chemical conditions in their soil. (The soil the blue plants are in is more acidic than the soil the pink plants are in.) This is but one example of how genes and environment work together to produce the traits we see in living things.

only so much about phenotype. Protein products that bring about a blue plant in one environment will bring about a pink plant in another. Across the natural world, things generally work this way. Most genes do not come with an unvarying ability to bring about an effect. Rather, genes and environment work together to create the phenotypes we see in living things.

On to the Chromosome

This completes the survey of Mendel's work and the variations on his ideas of inheritance. As you have seen, Mendel's findings lay dormant for some decades in the nineteenth century. What sent scientists scurrying back to his reports were experiments on those tiny entities you have looked at in detail before: chromosomes, the subject of the next chapter.

SO FAR . . .

1. The usual case in nature is that a given character in an organism is influenced by _____ genes. To put this another way, the character is produced through _____ inheritance. True or false: This form of inheritance tends to produce fixed increments of difference between organisms.

2. When we measure the traits found in living things, we find that they tend to be distributed in a form known as the _____, which can be defined as a range of values that is symmetrical around the _____.

3. The hydrangea example in the book shows that the same genes can produce different phenotypes depending on _____ influences that act on an organism.

<table>
<tr><td>C H A P T E R</td><td>11</td><td>REVIEW</td></tr>
</table>

Go to the Study Area at www.masteringbiology.com for practice quizzes, myeBook, BioFlix™ 3-D animations, MP3 Tutor Sessions, videos, current events, and more.

Mastering BIOLOGY

Summary

11.1 Mendel and the Black Box

- Gregor Mendel was the first person to comprehend the most basic principles of genetics. (p. 191)

11.2 The Experimental Subjects: *Pisum sativum*

- Mendel experimented by breeding pea plants (*Pisum sativum*) that possessed a set of seven attributes called characters, each of which came in two forms, referred to as traits, one of them dominant, the other recessive. In his experiments, he bred generations of pea plants and observed the frequencies with which given traits showed up in each generation. (p. 192)

- A phenotype is any physiological feature, bodily characteristic, or behavior of an or-

ganism. Phenotypes in any organism are determined in significant part by that organism's genotype, meaning its genetic makeup. (p. 193)

11.3 Starting the Experiments: Yellow and Green Peas

- Mendel realized that it was possible for organisms to have identical phenotypes, such as yellow seeds, but differing underlying genotypes. (p. 195)

- Mendel discovered that the basic units of genetics are material elements that come in pairs. These elements, today called genes, come in alternative forms called alleles. One allele for a given gene resides on one chromosome, while the other allele for the gene resides on a second chromosome that is homologous to the first. Mendel demonstrated that genes retain their character through many generations rather than being "blended" together. (p. 195)

11.4 Another Generation

- Mendel realized that alleles separate during the formation of gametes. Although Mendel did not know it, the physical basis for this is that the alleles he was observing resided on homologous chromosomes, which always separate in meiosis. An organism that has two identical alleles for a given character is said to be homozygous for that character. An organism that has differing alleles for a character is said to be heterozygous for that character. Dominant means expressed in the heterozygous condition. Recessive means not expressed in the heterozygous condition. (p. 195)

11.5 Crosses Involving Two Characters

- Mendel observed that the genes for the characters he studied were passed on independently of one another. This was so because the genes for these characters resided on separate, non-homologous chromosomes. The physical basis for what he found is the independent assortment of chromosome pairs during meiosis. (p. 199)

11.6 Reception of Mendel's Ideas

- During Mendel's lifetime, almost no one recognized the significance of his discoveries. (p. 201)

11.7 Incomplete Dominance and Codominance

- Incomplete dominance operates when neither allele for a given gene is completely dominant, with the result that a heterozygous genotype will yield an intermediate phenotype. (p. 201)

- In some instances, differing alleles of the same gene will have independent effects in a single organism. In such a situation, neither allele is dominant; each has a separate phenotypic effect, meaning that each is said to be codominant. (p. 201)

11.8 Multiple Alleles and Polygenic Inheritance

- While in many species an individual can have no more than two alleles for a given gene, within a population there can be many allelic variants of a single gene. Most traits in living things are governed not by one gene but by many, with each of these genes often having several allelic variants. Inheritance of such traits is known as polygenic inheritance, a situation in which each gene has a small additive effect on a trait. (p. 204)

- Polygenic inheritance tends to produce continuous variation in phenotypes, in which there are no fixed increments of difference between individuals. (p. 204)

- The traits produced in polygenic inheritance tend to manifest in bell-curve distributions, in which most individuals display middle-range, rather than extreme, trait values. Gene interactions and gene–environment interactions are so complex in polygenic inheritance that predictions about phenotypes are a matter of probability. (p. 205)

11.9 Genes and Environment

- The effects of genes can vary greatly in accordance with the environment in which the genes are expressed. (p. 205)

Key Terms

allele   195

bell curve   205

codominance   202

cross-pollinate   193

dihybrid cross   199

dominant   199

first filial generation (F_1)   194

genotype   193

heterozygous   199

homozygous   199

incomplete dominance   201

Law of Independent Assortment   200

Law of Segregation   198

monohybrid cross   199

multiple alleles   204

parental generation (P)   194

phenotype   193

polygenic inheritance   205

recessive   199

rule of addition   198

rule of multiplication   198

Understanding the Basics

Multiple-Choice Questions

(Answers are in the back of the book.)

1. The first filial generation, or F_1 results when:
   a. two P generation organisms are crossed.
   b. the progeny of a P generation is crossed.
   c. a P generation is crossed with an F_2 organism.
   d. an F_3 organism is crossed with an F_2 organism.
   e. both a and d.

2. When Mendel crossed pure-bred yellow peas with pure-bred green peas, the F_1 generation contained:
   a. all yellow peas.
   b. all green peas.
   c. green and yellow peas.
   d. green, wrinkled peas.
   e. both b and d.

3. If a cross is made between a pure-breeding green, smooth (*yySS*) plant and a pure-breeding yellow, wrinkled (*YYss*) plant, what is the result?
   a. all green, wrinkled peas
   b. all yellow, wrinkled peas
   c. all yellow, smooth peas
   d. yellow wrinkled; green wrinkled
   e. none of the above

4. Mendel's first law states that:
   a. during the formation of gametes, gene pairs demonstrate independent assortment.
   b. during the formation of gametes, genetic elements (alleles) segregate from each other.
   c. the probability of any two events happening is the product of their respective probabilities.
   d. if an organism is pure-breeding for any trait, it will display incomplete dominance.
   e. Mendel did not write any laws regarding genetics.

5. A trait whose phenotype in the heterozygous condition is an intermediate of the two homozygous conditions (that is, heterozygous pink flowers, homozygous red flowers, homozygous white flowers) demonstrates:
   a. polygenic inheritance.
   b. incomplete dominance.
   c. intermediate dominance.
   d. codominance.
   e. multiple alleles.

6. Mendel's second law states that:
   a. no organism can have more than two alleles for a given character.
   b. no two organisms can ever be genetically identical.
   c. organisms will tend to be heterozygous for most traits, rather than homozygous.
   d. the way one gene pair assorts during gamete formation will affect the way other gene pairs assort.
   e. gene pairs assort independently of one another during gamete formation.

7. Which of the following is true about polygenic inheritance? (More than one answer may be correct.)
   a. It is the rule rather than the exception in living things.
   b. Its outcomes are always predictable.
   c. It is never seen in human beings.
   d. It produces phenotypes that grade smoothly into one another.
   e. It always produces heterozygous individuals.

8. Which of the following is true regarding the effects of genes and environment on phenotypic variation?
   a. Gene expression will always be greatest in the native environment.
   b. Gene expression is not affected by a change in environment.
   c. Phenotypes are based only on environmental influences.
   d. Environment may easily affect genotype, not phenotype.
   e. The phenotypes of genetically identical organisms may vary in different environments.

Brief Review

(Answers are in the back of the book.)

1. What are the differences between:
   a. phenotype and genotype?
   b. dominant and recessive?
   c. codominance and incomplete dominance?

2. True or false: When Mendel conducted his genetic research, neither DNA nor chromosomes had been discovered.

3. How many alleles is an individual human being likely to possess for any given gene? Name the source of each allele.

4. In a case of Mendelian genetics where one gene affects one trait, how many different genotypes may bring about a dominant phenotype (for example, yellow pea color)?

5. If a heterozygous yellow-seed pea plant is crossed with a homozygous green-seed pea plant, approximately what percentage of the progeny peas would be expected to be yellow?

6. What term is now given to Mendel's element of inheritance?

7. Name and describe the two laws that are credited to Mendel and his research.

8. Using the symbols A, a, B, and b, what Mendelian crosses would be expected to result in the following phenotypic ratios?
   a. 1:1
   b. 3:1
   c. 1:1:1:1
   d. 9:3:3:1

Applying Your Knowledge

1. Stands of aspen trees often are a series of genetically identical individuals, with each succeeding tree growing from the severed shoot of another tree. Using what you've learned of genetics in this chapter, would you expect one aspen tree in a stand to differ greatly from another in its phenotype? Would you expect each to look exactly like the next in terms of phenotype?

2. The ABO blood-typing system mentioned in the text has great practical significance because the human immune system will attack cells displaying blood-cell surface molecules that it recognizes as "foreign"—that is, molecules that a person does not have on his or her own blood cells. Given this, what is the "universal donor" blood type? What is the "universal recipient" type?

3. If, as the text states, the effects of genes can be expected to vary in accordance with the environment in which these genes work, would you expect this phenomenon to be applicable to human genes, such as those that help produce such traits as height, weight, or introversion and extroversion?

Genetics Problems

(Answers are in the back of the book.)

One of Mendel's many monohybrid (single-character) crosses was between a true-breeding (homozygous) parent bearing purple flowers and a true-breeding (homozygous) parent bearing white flowers. All the offspring had purple flowers. When these offspring were allowed to self-fertilize, Mendel observed that their offspring occurred in the ratio of about three purple-flowered plants to one white-flowered plant. The allele deter-mining purple flowers is symbolized P, and the allele determining white flowers is symbolized p. Use this information to answer the following questions:

1. What are the genotypes of the parents?
   a. PP; pp
   b. PP; Pp
   c. Pp; Pp
   d. pp; pp

2. Which generation has only purple-flowered plants?
   a. P
   b. F_1
   c. F_2
   d. F_3

3. Which generation tells you which of the traits is dominant?
   a. P
   b. F_1
   c. F_2
   d. F_3

4. How many phenotypes are present in the F_2 generation?
   a. 1
   b. 2
   c. 3

5. How many different genotypes are present in the F_2 generation?
   a. 1
   b. 2
   c. 3

6. Mendel allowed the white-flowered F_2 plants to self-fertilize. What proportion of these F_2 plants produced only white-flowered offspring?
   a. none
   b. $\frac{1}{4}$
   c. $\frac{1}{3}$
   d. $\frac{3}{4}$
   e. all

7. Mendel allowed the purple-flowered F_2 plants to self-fertilize. What proportion of these F_2 plants produced only purple-flowered offspring?
   a. none
   b. $\frac{1}{4}$
   c. $\frac{1}{3}$
   d. $\frac{3}{4}$
   e. all

8. If a heterozygous purple-flowered pea plant is crossed with a homozygous white-flowered plant, what proportion of offspring will be white-flowered?
   a. none
   b. $\frac{1}{4}$
   c. $\frac{1}{2}$
   d. $\frac{3}{4}$
   e. all

9. Given what you know about the alleles that determine purple and white color in pea flowers, why is it possible to have a purple-flowered heterozygote but not a white-flowered heterozygote?

10. In considering flower color in pea plants, we are dealing with _____ gene(s) and _____ allele(s).
    a. 1; 1
    b. 1; 2
    c. 1; 4
    d. 2; 1
    e. 2; 2

11. The next three questions require you to apply rules of probability.
    a. In a toss of two coins, what is the chance of obtaining two heads?
       (1) 0
       (2) 12.5 percent
       (3) 25 percent
       (4) 50 percent
       (5) 75 percent
    b. What rule of probability was used to determine the chance of obtaining two heads?
    c. Now, use this rule to solve the following problem. In a cross between two purple-flowered heterozygotes, 75 percent of their offspring are expected to be purple flowered. In a cross between two heterozygotes with yellow-colored seeds, 25 percent of their offspring are expected to be green. If two purple-flowered, yellow-seeded individuals, each heterozygous for both genes, are crossed, what proportion of their offspring is expected to be purple-flowered with green seeds?

12. By observing flower color in snapdragons, is it possible to unambiguously determine the genotype? Is the same true for flower color in peas? Why or why not?

13. If the alleles for snapdragon flower color were codominant instead of incompletely dominant, a possible phenotype for a heterozygous individual would be:
    a. pure red flowers.
    b. pure pink flowers.
    c. pure white flowers.
    d. a mosaic pattern of red and white regions on flowers.

14. If two individuals with AB blood type marry, what proportion of their children are expected to have AB blood type?
    a. none
    b. 0.25
    c. 0.50
    d. 0.75
    e. all

12

Units of Heredity:
Chromosomes and Inheritance

Chromosomes are critical players in the process by which living things pass on traits. Some of our worst diseases result from chromosomes that have failed to function properly.

Chromosomes are units of heredity composed of DNA and proteins. Pictured is a partial set of human chromosomes in their well-defined duplicated state.

The condition known as Down syndrome is almost always caused by the inheritance of an extra chromosome. But how can a parent who does not have an extra chromosome pass one on to a son or daughter? The gene that causes sickle-cell anemia also seems to provide some protection against malaria. How can it have both effects? The chromosomal makeup of women offers them a kind of protection against being color-blind. Why should this be so?

From these questions, it may be apparent that chromosomes and the genes on them are centrally involved in issues of human health. You saw last chapter that chromosomal activity lies at the root of several of the genetic principles that Gregor Mendel uncovered. Mendel's "pairs of elements," which separate in reproduction, had as their physical basis the pairs of homologous chromosomes—one inherited from the male, one from the female—that first pair up and then separate from one another in meiosis. The differing traits that Mendel investigated so thoroughly, such as yellow or green peas in a pod, had as their physical basis the pairs of *alleles* or differing forms of a gene that lie on homologous chromosomes.

But there are aspects of chromosomal functioning that Mendel's work scarcely touched on. For one, there is the issue of sex chromosomes. As noted in Chapter 10, the sex of human beings is determined by their chromosomal makeup. Human females have two X chromosomes, while human males have one X and one Y chromosome. Apart from determining sex, what part do these special chromosomes play in heredity? Next, how do the terms *dominant* and *recessive* that you looked at last chapter play out with respect to human disease? And how can genetically based diseases be traced through generations of a family? Finally, you saw in Chapter 10 that a critical step in meiosis is the *crossing over* (or recombination) that occurs early in it. In this process, homologous chromosomes first intertwine and then swap pieces of themselves, after which they separate in meiosis. But what happens when chromosomes fail to properly carry out this part swapping or the separation that follows? The short answer is that such mistakes are responsible for a number of the afflictions that affect human beings, including Down syndrome.

So, in this chapter you will look at sex chromosomes, dominant and recessive disease genes, tracing diseases through generations, and diseases caused by chromosomal mistakes. All the disorders that will be reviewed are transmitted through so-called Mendelian inheritance, meaning they are all disorders in which a single gene or chromosome means the difference between sickness and health. In contrast, many widespread diseases, such as heart disease and cancer, are polygenic—they are based on many genes working in concert, with a given set of genes only predisposing a person toward sickness or health, rather than ensuring it. Let's start now with sex and heredity.

12.1 X-Linked Inheritance in Humans

Minor cuts are simply an irritation to most of us, but for people suffering from the condition known as hemophilia, such cuts can be life-threatening. Hemophilia is a failure of blood to clot properly. A group of proteins interact to make blood clot, but about 80 percent of hemophiliacs lack a functioning version of just one of these proteins (called factor VIII). Genes contain the information for the production of proteins, of course, so at root hemophilia is a genetic disease—a faulty gene is causing the faulty factor VIII protein. This same process is at work in a couple of other well-known afflictions: the disease called Duchenne muscular dystrophy and a far less serious condition, red-green color blindness. These disorders have more in common than being genetically based, however. All of them are known as *X-linked* disorders because the genes that cause them lie on the X chromosome. As it turns out, X-linked disorders claim more male victims than female. Why should this be so? A look at color blindness can provide the answer.

Figure 12.1
Typical Test for Red-
Green Color Blindness
If you do not see two numbers (3 and 8) inside the large
circle, you may have this
recessive trait.

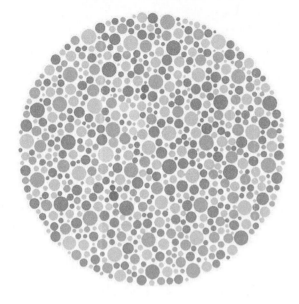

The Genetics of Color Vision

Despite its name, "color blindness" almost never means a *total* inability to perceive color. Rather, it most often means an inability to distinguish among certain shades of red and green (**Figure 12.1**). To understand how color vision can malfunction in this way, it's important to understand how it commonly works. When light enters our eyes, it travels to the back of them and lands on a group of cells (called cones) that have within them molecules called pigments. A pigment is simply a substance that strongly absorbs a given color of light. The pigments in cone cells turn out to be molecules composed of two main parts, one of which is a protein called opsin. Because genes code for proteins, it's easy to see how color blindness is genetically based: We have genes that are coding for the protein portions of our light-absorbing pigments. More specifically, we

have a gene that codes for blue-absorbing pigment, and it lies on chromosome 7; then we have genes that code for both red- and green-absorbing pigments, and they lie very close to one another on the X chromosome. A red-green color-blind person, then, is one in whom these X-located genes fail to code for the proper pigment proteins.

Alleles and Recessive Disorders

In the normal case, as you've seen, a given gene comes in two variant forms, or *alleles,* in each person. One allele for a gene might reside on, say, the chromosome 1 we inherit from our mother; if so, the second allele for this gene will reside on the chromosome 1 we inherit from our father. There is therefore a kind of backup system in human genetics: Genes come in pairs of alleles that lie on separate, homologous chromosomes. If one allele for a given trait is defective, there will usually exist a second, functional allele for that same trait on a homologous chromosome.

This genetic structure usually works fine when a condition is a so-called **recessive disorder,** meaning a genetic disorder that will not exist in the presence of a functional allele. In such a condition, a person does not have to have *two* functional alleles; a single "good" allele will do. Red-green color blindness turns out to be a recessive disorder: A person who has even one functional allele for red pigment and one functional allele for green pigment will not be color-blind. So, why do men suffer more from this condition than women? Because men have no backup: They have only one allele for red pigment and one allele for green pigment because they have only one *X chromosome* (and one Y). Meanwhile, women have two X chromosomes. If the pigment alleles are defective on one of their chromosomes, the alleles on their other X chromosome will still provide them with full color vision.

Given this, think about the interesting way that color blindness is passed along. Say there is a mother who is not color-blind herself but who is heterozygous for the trait. That is, she has functional color alleles on one of her X chromosomes but dysfunctional alleles on her other X chromosome. Should her son happen to inherit this second X chromosome, he will be color-blind because the X chromosome he got from his mother is his *only* X chromosome (**Figure 12.2**). Meanwhile, a daughter who inherited this chromosome would likely be protected by her second X chromosome—the one she got from her father. Not surprisingly, then, more males are color-blind than females. About 8 percent of the male population has some degree of color blindness, while for females the figure is about half a percent. Women enjoy a similar protection in connection with other X-linked disorders, such as hemophilia and muscular dystrophy. (For more on the way hemophilia can be passed down through generations, see Figure 12.6 on page 219.)

Figure 12.2
The Value of Having
Two X Chromosomes

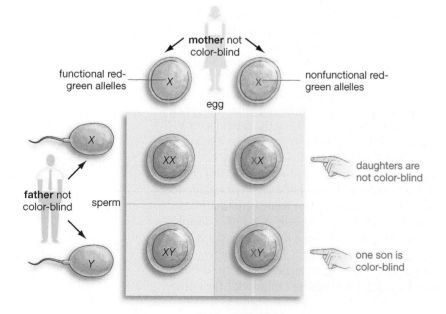

mother not
color-blind

functional red-
green allelles — X   X — nonfunctional red-
green allelles

egg

sperm   daughters are
not color-blind

father not
color-blind   one son is
color-blind

12.2 Autosomal Genetic Disorders

Recessive Disorders

The X and Y chromosomes are, of course, only two of the chromosomes in the human collection, and any chromosome can have a malfunctioning gene on it. The chromosomes other than the X and Y chromosomes are called *autosomes*. A recessive dysfunction related to an autosome is thus known as an **autosomal recessive disorder.** (For a list of all the disorders you'll be looking at and more, see **Table 12.1.**)

Sickle-Cell Anemia

A well-known example of an autosomal recessive disorder is sickle-cell anemia, which affects populations derived from several areas on the globe, including Africa. In the United States it is, of course, most widely known as a disease affecting African Americans. The "sickle" in the name comes from the curved shape that is taken on by the red blood cells of its victims. Red blood cells carry oxygen to all parts of the body; in their normal shape, they look a little like doughnuts with incomplete holes. When they take on a sickle shape, however, red cells clog up capillaries, resulting in decreased oxygen supplies to various parts of the body (**Figure 12.3**). In the United States, the average life expectancy for men with the condition is 42 years; for women, it is 48 years.

The question is, what causes a red blood cell to take on this lethal, sickled shape? There is a protein, called hemoglobin, that carries the oxygen within red blood cells. The vast majority of people in the world have one form of hemoglobin, called hemoglobin A, but sickle-cell anemia sufferers have another form of this protein, hemoglobin S, which coalesces into crystals that distort the cell.

Now, how is sickle-cell anemia passed from parents to offspring? Because it is a recessive condition, any child who gets it must inherit *two* alleles for it—one allele from the mother, one from the father, each of them coding for the hemoglobin S protein. This means, of course, that both parents must themselves have at least one hemoglobin S allele; both parents must be at least heterozygous for the trait. In this situation, the laws governing inheritance of this disorder are simply those of Mendel's monohybrid cross: A child of these two parents has a 25 percent chance of inheriting the disorder. You can look at the Punnett square in **Figure 12.4a** on the next page to see how this works out.

It's important to note the status of the parents in this example. They are heterozygous for a recessive debilitation, meaning they do not suffer from the condition themselves because they are protected by their single "good" allele. Each of them is, however, a **carrier** for the condition: a person who does not suffer from a recessive genetic debilitation but who carries an allele for it that can be passed along to offspring. In this respect, they are just like the mother in the color blindness example.

Table 12.1

Selected Examples of Human Genetic Disorders

Type	Name of Condition	Effects
X-linked recessive disorders	Hemophilia	Faulty blood clotting
	Duchenne muscular dystrophy	Wasting of muscles
	Red-green color blindness	Inability to distinguish shades of red from green
Autosomal recessive disorders	Albinism	No pigmentation in skin
	Sickle-cell anemia	Anemia, intense pain, infections
	Cystic fibrosis	Impaired lung function, lung infections
	Phenylketonuria	Mental retardation
	Tay-Sachs disease	Nervous system degeneration in infants
	Werner syndrome	Premature aging
Autosomal dominant disorders	Huntington disease	Brain tissue degeneration
	Marfan syndrome	Ruptured blood vessels
	Polydactyly	Extra fingers or toes
Aberrations in chromosome number	Down syndrome	Mental retardation, shortened life span
	Turner syndrome	Sterility, short stature
	Klinefelter syndrome	Dysfunctional testicles, feminized features
Aberrations in chromosome structure	Cri-du-chat syndrome	Mental retardation, malformed larynx
	Fragile-X syndrome	Mental retardation, facial deformities

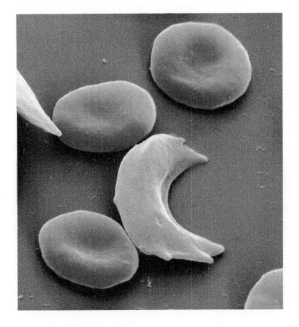

Figure 12.3 Healthy Cells, Sickled Cell

Three normal red blood cells flank a single sickled cell.

Figure 12.4
Transmission of
Recessive and
Dominant Disorders

(a) Sickle-cell anemia: transmission of a recessive disorder.

Sickle-cell anemia is a recessive autosomal disorder; both the mother and father must carry at least one allele for the trait in order for a son or a daughter to be a sickle-cell victim. When both parents have one sickle-cell allele, there is a 25% chance that any given offspring will inherit the condition.

 25% probability of inheriting the disorder

(b) Huntington disease: transmission of a dominant disorder.

50% probability of inheriting the disorder

In Huntington disease, if only a single parent has a Huntington allele there is a 50% chance that a son or daughter will inherit the condition.

Malaria Protection: Hemoglobin S as a Useful Protein

Sickle-cell anemia offers another lesson in connection with the notion of hemoglobin S as a "faulty" protein. It is in fact quite a functional protein in certain circumstances, namely, when it appears heterozygously (with hemoglobin A) in people who live in regions where malaria is common. The most severe form of malaria is caused by a single-celled parasite that is transmitted into human beings by the *Anopheles* mosquito. Traveling through the bloodstream, these parasites invade and ultimately destroy red blood cells. For reasons we still don't understand, having hemoglobin

S in one's system makes red blood cells resistant to invasion. Thus, it is likely that hemoglobin S became as widespread as it is because of its value in resisting malaria. The price of this resistance, however, is that some offspring are not heterozygous for hemoglobin S. They are homozygous for it, meaning they have sickle-cell anemia.

Dominant Disorders

Although sickle-cell anemia is an autosomal disorder and red-green color blindness an X-linked disorder, both are recessive disorders. That is, a person with even a single properly functioning allele will not suffer from them. However, there are also **dominant disorders:** genetic conditions in which a single faulty allele can cause damage, even when a second, functional allele exists. This leads to the concept of an **autosomal dominant disorder,** simply meaning a dominant genetic disorder caused by a faulty allele that lies on an autosomal chromosome. There is, for example, an autosomal dominant disorder called Huntington disease. Affecting about 30,000 Americans, it results in both mental impairment and uncontrollable spastic movements called *chorea*. Perhaps its most famous victim was the American folksinger Woody Guthrie. Like most Huntington sufferers, Guthrie did not begin to show symptoms of the disease until well into adulthood—*after* he had children, who then may have had the disease passed along to them. You can look at the Punnett square in **Figure 12.4b** to see how the inheritance pattern of an autosomal dominant disease such as Huntington differs from that of an autosomal recessive illness. Because a parent need only pass on a single Huntington allele for a son or daughter to suffer from the condition, the chances of any given offspring getting the disease from a single affected parent are one out of two.

SO FAR . . .

1. A recessive genetic disorder is one that will not exist in the presence of a _____, while a dominant disorder is one in which a _____ can cause trouble, even in the presence of a _____.

2. True or false: A woman who has only one X chromosome containing dysfunctional alleles for red-green color vision is not color-blind.

3. To inherit an autosomal recessive disorder, both parents of an offspring must be at least _____ for the condition, meaning each parent must have at least _____.

12.3 Tracking Traits with Pedigrees

Confronted with a medical condition, such as Huntington, that is running through a family, scientists find it helpful to construct a medical **pedigree,** defined as a familial history intended to track genetic conditions. Normally set forth as diagrams, medical pedigrees do more than give a family history of disease. They can be used to ascertain whether a condition is dominant or recessive, and X-linked or autosomal. This can help establish probabilities for *future* inheritance of the condition—something that can be very helpful for couples thinking of having a child.

If you look at **Figure 12.5**, you can see a simple pedigree for albinism: a lack of skin pigmentation, which is known to be an autosomal recessive condition. In the figure, you can see some of the standard symbols used in pedigrees. A circle is used for a female and a square for a male. Parents are indicated by a horizontal line connecting a male and a female, while a vertical line between the parents leads to a lower row that denotes the parents' offspring. This second row—a horizontal line of siblings—has an order to it: oldest child on the left, youngest on the right. A circle or square that is filled in indicates a family member who has the condition (in this case, albinism), while a symbol that is half filled in indicates a person known to be heterozygous for a recessive condition (a carrier). One of the strengths of a pedigree is that it can sometimes tell researchers which persons are heterozygous carriers of a recessive condition. Remember that a carrier does not display *symptoms* of the condition. So, how can a pedigree reveal this?

Take a look at Figure 12.5. The only thing that would be apparent from actually seeing any of the people in the pedigree is that two of them—a female in generation II and a male in generation III—have the condition of albinism. But a little knowledge of Mendelian genetics also allows some other deductions. If the condition had been dominant, then it would have manifested itself in at least one of the parents on the left in generation I. Because this was not the case, it is fair to deduce that this is a recessive

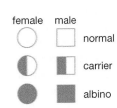

Figure 12.5
A Hypothetical Pedigree for Albinism through Three Generations

condition. The fact that it is recessive, however, means that *both* parents in generation I had to be carriers for the allele—both have to be heterozygous for the condition, which is why their symbols can be half shaded in. Things are less clear with the parents on the right in generation I. One of their sons did not manifest the condition himself but went on to have a son who did. From this, we know that the son in generation II had to have been heterozygous for the condition. But, from which parent did this son get his albinism allele? Either, or both, of his parents in generation I could have been heterozygous for the condition and yet between them, only have passed along a single albinism allele.

This mixture of certainty and uncertainty leads to the genotype labeling you see in the figure, with *A* representing the dominant "normal" allele and lowercase *a* representing the recessive albinism allele. We know, for example, that both parents on the left in generation I had to be *Aa*, but all we can say for sure about the parents on the right in the same generation is that at least one of them was a carrier. As you can imagine, pedigrees can get much more elaborate than this one. To see how a trait can be tracked through many generations, look at **Figure 12.6.**

12.4 Aberrations in Chromosomal Sets: Polyploidy

All of the maladies you've looked at so far have resulted from dysfunctional genes that exist among a standard array of chromosomes. In humans, this array is 22 pairs of autosomes and either an XX combination (in females) or an XY combination (in males). Meanwhile, Mendel's peas had seven pairs of chromosomes, and the common fruit fly has four pairs. Whatever the *number* of chromosomes, note the similarity in all these species: Their chromosomes come in pairs, or to put it another way, they all have two *sets* of chromosomes, meaning the organisms that possess them are diploid.

In many situations, however, organisms end up with more than two sets of chromosomes. This is called **polyploidy,** a condition in which one or more entire sets of chromosomes has been added to the genome of a diploid organism.

You may wonder how a human being could end up with more than two sets of chromosomes. After all, in meiosis, sperm and egg end up with just one set of chromosomes in them. When they later fuse, in the moment of conception, the result is then two sets of chromosomes in the fertilized egg. But what if *two* sperm manage to fuse with one egg? The result is a fertilized egg with three sets of chromosomes, and the

outcome is polyploidy. Normally, an egg lets in only one sperm, and it blocks the others hovering about with a kind of chemical gate-slamming mechanism. (For more on this, see page 644 in Chapter 33.) But occasionally, more than one sperm manages to make it in. Human polyploidy can also get started before fertilization, when meiosis malfunctions and gives a single egg or sperm two sets of chromosomes, meaning that there will be three sets in total when egg and sperm fuse.

Polyploidy actually is tolerated well in some organisms. Indeed, it has come about countless times in plant species and generally gives rise to perfectly robust plants. In human beings, however, polyploidy is a disaster. Perhaps only 1 percent of human embryos with the condition will survive to birth, and none of these babies lives long. Concerns about chromosome number in living persons, then, center not on addition or deletion of whole sets of chromosomes, but rather on the gain or loss of *individual* chromosomes.

12.5 Incorrect Chromosome Number: Aneuploidy

The condition called **aneuploidy** is one in which an organism has either more or fewer chromosomes than normally exist in its species' full set. This usually means that an organism has gained or lost a *single* chromosome, although more complex patterns are possible, as you'll see. Among human genetic malfunctions, aneuploidy is unusual in that it occurs quite commonly and yet goes largely unrecognized. This is so because aneuploidy occurs most often not in fully formed human beings but in embryos. A would-be mother may know only that she is having a hard time getting pregnant. What she may not know is that she actually *has* been pregnant—perhaps several times—but that aneuploidy has doomed the embryo in each case. Doomed it in what way? The most common outcome of aneuploidy is a pregnancy that ends in miscarriage. Many of these miscarriages happen so early in a pregnancy that a woman never realizes she was pregnant; the microscopic embryo may simply be part of material that is discharged, perhaps with the woman's next menstrual period. Even when a miscarriage is recognized as such, tests can seldom be run that can identify aneuploidy as the cause. But by undertaking careful examinations of thousands of pregnancies, scientists have concluded that aneuploidy is responsible for about 30 percent of miscarriages. And how common is miscarriage? In the best study conducted to date, scientists found that it takes place in 31 percent of pregnancies. A small proportion of embryos do manage to survive aneuploidy, but even in these instances there are consequences. Down syndrome is one of the outcomes of aneuploidy.

Three Lessons from a Royal Pedigree

○ female   ◖ carrier of hemophilia allele

□ male   ■ hemophiliac

Generations

the labels in black are referred to in the text ☞

British Royal Family

Prussian Royal Family   **Russian Royal Family**

1. The luck of the draw can mean good luck down through generations.

The hemophilia allele almost certainly arose as a mutation in either Queen Victoria or in one of her parents. Whichever the case, the Queen was undoubtedly a carrier for the allele. For Britain's royal family, the key event was that King Edward VII (toward the left in generation II) did not inherit the hemophilia allele from his mother, but instead inherited her second "good" allele. With this, the British Royal House—right down through today's princes William and Harry—avoided hemophilia, barring its introduction through marriage.

2. The luck of the draw can mean bad luck down through generations.

Queen Victoria's daughter Alice (in generation II) did inherit the hemophilia allele and this chance event had momentous consequences. Though she herself was only a carrier, she had one son, Friedrich, who was hemophiliac (dying at age 3); and two daughters who, as carriers, went on to pass the allele along. One of these daughters, Alexandra, became the czarina of Russia after marrying Czar Nicholas II. The couple had a male child, Alexis, who inherited his mother's hemophilia allele—now passed down through at least three generations—and was thus a hemophiliac. So precarious was Alexis' condition that his mother turned to a semiliterate monk, Rasputin, as a means of trying to care for him. Anger with Rasputin among the Russian populace may have played a part in bringing down the Russian Royal House in the revolutions of 1917. Neither Alexis nor his sisters lived long enough to have children, since they and their parents were murdered by communist revolutionaries in 1918. We know the genetic status of Alexis' sisters, however, thanks to a 2009 analysis carried out on the remains of members of the royal family. Among the four sisters, only one was a carrier for the hemophilia allele—most likely Anastasia, to judge by anthropological evidence.

3. X-linked inherited traits tend to "skip" a generation.

Victoria had one son—Leopold, in generation II—who was hemophiliac by reason of inheriting his mother's faulty allele. Note, however, that among Leopold's offspring, there are no hemophiliacs. The next hemophiliac is found one generation further down, in Rupert, in generation IV. Why should things work this way? Remember that the gene for hemophilia is on the X chromosome and that every male must get his lone X chromosome from his mother. Thus, Leopold's son, Charles, was not at risk of being hemophiliac because Charles' single X chromosome came from his mother. However, Leopold's daughter, Alice, carried two X chromosomes—one "good" chromosome from her mother and the faulty X chromosome from Leopold. She then passed on Leopold's chromosome to one of her sons (Rupert), though not to the other (Maurice). The luck of the draw was on display again.

Figure 12.6
A Pedigree for Hemophilia in Europe's Royal Families

Hemophilia is a rare, recessive genetic disorder, but it managed to affect a large portion of Europe's royal family members in the nineteenth and twentieth centuries after being passed on to them from England's Queen Victoria. As the main text notes, hemophilia usually is caused by a particular variant form of a gene (an allele) that leads to a faulty form of a blood-clotting protein called Factor VIII. In the case of Queen Victoria and her descendants, however, a mutated allele that leads to a closely related protein, called Factor IX, was responsible. Since the genes for factors VIII and IX reside on the X chromosome, hemophilia is a condition that is much more likely to affect men than women. The pedigree shown here for hemophilia among Europe's royal families has been greatly simplified; in most of the British royal family, for example, only the heirs to the throne and their spouses are shown.

Aneuploidy's Main Cause: Nondisjunction

What brings about the harmful condition of aneuploidy? The cause usually is a phenomenon known as **nondisjunction,** which simply means a failure of homologous chromosomes or sister chromatids to separate during cell division. If you look at Figure 12.7 you can see how this can work during the meiotic cell division we looked at in Chapter 10. Note that it can occur either in meiosis I or in meiosis II. In meiosis I, two homologous chromosomes, on the opposite side of the metaphase plate, can be pulled to the *same* side of a dividing cell, producing daughter cells with imbalanced numbers of chromosomes. Conversely, nondisjunction can take place in meiosis II by means of sister chromatids going to the same daughter cell after failing to "disjoin" (hence the cumbersome term *nondisjunction*). Such actions then produce an egg or sperm that has 24 or 22 chromosomes instead of the standard haploid number of 23; after union with a normal egg or sperm, this results in an embryo that has either 47 or 45 chromosomes instead of the standard 46.

The effect of this is that the embryo has a genetic imbalance—one that perhaps can be made clear by an analogy. Imagine that while baking chocolate chip cookies, you decided to increase the amount of flour called for in the recipe. This change might be of little consequence if you increased all the other ingredients in the same proportion. If, however, you increased nothing but the flour, the final product would be hard and flavorless because the ingredients in it would be unbalanced. An added chromosome has this same effect: It unbalances the proportions of *biological* ingredients (the proteins) that help produce and maintain a living thing.

Figure 12.7
A Mistake in Meiosis Brings about an Abnormal Chromosome Count
Nondisjunction can occur in either meiosis I or meiosis II, when either chromosomes or chromatids fail to separate properly. When it occurs in meiosis I, 100 percent of the resulting gametes will be abnormal; when it takes place in meiosis II, only 50 percent will be abnormal.

SO FAR ...

1. A medical pedigree is used to identify _____ disorders that are passed along in _____.

2. Aneuploidy exists when an organism has more or fewer _____ than normally exist in its species' _____.

3. The most common cause of meiotic aneuploidy is a failure of homologous chromosomes or sister chromatids to _____, which leads to one daughter cell having _____, while the other daughter cell has _____.

The Consequences of Aneuploidy

As noted, embryos with the wrong number of chromosomes are not likely to survive. Setting aside meiotic aneuploidies that affect the X and Y chromosomes, *all* such aneuploidies result in miscarriage except for those that give an embryo an additional chromosome 13, 18, or 21. It is the gain of an additional chromosome 21 that causes the most well-known outcome of aneuploidy in human beings.

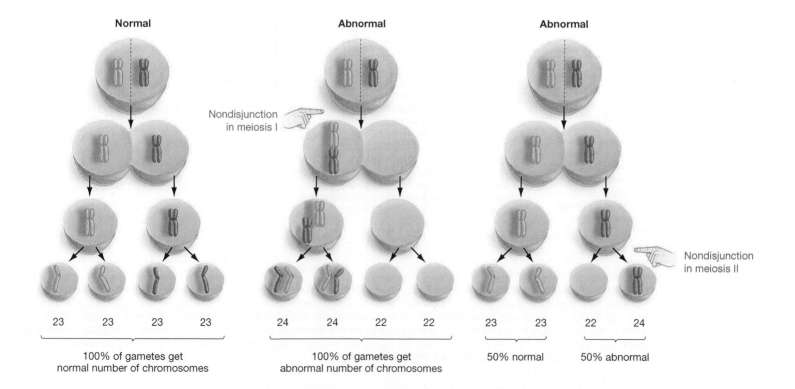

Normal	Abnormal	Abnormal

Nondisjunction in meiosis I

Nondisjunction in meiosis II

23 23 23 23	24 24 22 22	23 23 22 24
100% of gametes get normal number of chromosomes	100% of gametes get abnormal number of chromosomes	50% normal 50% abnormal

Down syndrome is, in some 95 percent of cases, a condition in which a person has three copies of chromosome 21 rather than the standard two. Ninety percent of these cases come about because of nondisjunction in egg formation, with the remaining 10 percent caused by nondisjunction in sperm formation. Seen in about 0.1 percent of all live births, Down syndrome results in an array of effects: smallish, oval heads; IQs that are well below normal; infertility in males; short stature; and reduced life span in both sexes.

It is well known that when women pass the age of about 35, their risk of giving birth to a Down syndrome child increases dramatically (**Figure 12.8**). Nevertheless, most Down syndrome children are born to mothers under the age of 35 for the simple reason that younger mothers give birth to most children. As such, in 2007 the American College of Obstetricians and Gynecologists recommended that all pregnant women, regardless of age, undertake Down syndrome screening, whereas previously the group recommended such testing only for women 35 or older.

Scientists are not certain why a mother's age should figure so prominently in Down syndrome, although several hypotheses have been put forward to account for this. Most scientists agree that one piece of the puzzle is something you saw in Chapter 10: In egg development, the process of meiosis generally stretches on for decades. Any given egg that develops in a woman starts meiosis I before the woman is born, but may not complete this meiosis until she is, say, in her thirties. In the intervening decades, this egg's cellular machinery has aged, perhaps to the point that it can no longer separate its chromosomes or chromatids properly.

Beginning in the late 1960s, it became possible to test developing fetuses for genetic abnormalities. In recent years, however, reproductive technology has moved beyond testing. Prospective parents can now choose, from a group of embryos they have created, embryos that do not have any recognizable genetic defects. You can read more about this in "PGD: Screening for a Healthy Child" on page 222.

Abnormal Numbers of Sex Chromosomes

Aneuploidy can affect not only autosomes but sex chromosomes as well, meaning the two X chromosomes that females have and the X and Y chromosomes that males have. Embryos often survive sex chromosome aneuploidies, but the result, once again, is usually debilitations. An example is Turner syndrome, which produces people who are phenotypically female, but who have only one X chromosome. Such females, then, have only 45 chromosomes, rather than the usual 46. Their state is sometimes referred to as XO, the "O" signifying the missing X chromosome. The absence of a second sex chromosome causes a range of afflictions. Females with Turner syndrome have ovaries that don't develop properly (which causes sterility), they are generally short, and they often have brown spots (called nevi) over their bodies.

(a) Maternal age and Down syndrome risk

Mother's age	Chances of giving birth to a child with Down syndrome
20	1 in 1925
25	1 in 1205
30	1 in 885
35	1 in 365
40	1 in 110
45	1 in 32

(b) Karyotype of a person with Down syndrome

Figure 12.8
Down Syndrome

(a) The risk of giving birth to a Down syndrome child increases dramatically past maternal age 35. Despite this, most Down syndrome children are born to women under the age of 35 because younger women give birth to most children.

(b) A karyotype is a visual display of an entire set of chromosomes. Pictured is a karyotype of a person with Down syndrome. Note the three chromosomes above the number 21. The karyotype shows that this person is a male, as indicated by the Y chromosome.

PGD: Screening for a Healthy Child

"Is the baby OK?" In a life full of questions, it's possible that none carries more weight than this one. In most cases, the answer will be reassuring, but in some it will be devastating. Small wonder, then, that scientists constantly are trying to perfect ways to know in advance whether a newborn will be healthy. You have seen that a large number of debilitating human conditions have genetic causes. Further, you know that nearly every kind of cell in a person's body contains a complete copy of that person's genome, or set of genes. Therefore, to check on someone's genetic well-being, all that is necessary is to have access to a small collection of that person's cells. Such cells exist, of course, in embryos as well as in newborn babies and adults. Thus, it's not hard to see what the procedure would be for prenatal genetic testing: Gather embryonic cells and examine their DNA and chromosomes.

This kind of testing has been going on, in ever-more-refined forms, since the late 1960s. From that time until recently, however, most prospective parents who got bad news from a genetic test had two choices: abort the fetus or bring a child with an incurable condition into the world. Now, an ever-growing number of reproductive clinics are providing a third choice. Parents who are willing to undertake so-called in vitro fertilization—fertilization of the mother's eggs in a laboratory—can have each one of the early-stage embryos that results from this process tested for genetic trouble. Of this initial group of embryos, only those found to be genetically healthy are candidates to

be inserted back into the mother. The hope is that at least one of them will implant in the mother's uterus and result in a child.

Right now, some clinics allow parents to use PGD to choose the sex of their child.

This process, called preimplantation genetic diagnosis or PGD, can be used by couples who have no known genetic risk factors but who are simply having a hard time conceiving a child. As the main text notes, a significant proportion of human embryos have genetic defects (such as aneuploidy). Moreover, some couples may be particularly prone to producing such embryos, which generally are lost in miscarriages. PGD allows couples to screen their embryos for genetic problems before implantation in the uterus, thus greatly upping their chances of bringing a child to term.

PGD can also be used, however, in connection with couples who are *likely* to produce a child with genetic defects. In an extreme example, imagine a prospective father who knows he is fated to fall victim to Huntington disease because he has been found to carry the defective Huntington allele. Since Huntington is a dominant disorder, his odds of passing the disease along to one of his children are one in two. With PGD, only those embryos without the harmful allele would be selected for implantation.

Of course, more conventional means of genetic screening, such as amniocentesis, can provide information about conditions

such as Huntington, but there is a difference. In amniocentesis, cells are obtained from an embryo that has been developing in a mother's uterus for a minimum of 14 weeks. By the time the results of amniocentesis are in, more than four months of a nine-month pregnancy may have elapsed. Most prospective parents would make a distinction between aborting a four-month-old fetus on the one hand or not implanting a four-day-old embryo on the other. Of course, not everyone feels this way. For some people, all embryos represent human life; therefore, producing an embryo and then not using it amounts to taking a human life. In PGD, most embryos have two fates: Those that are not implanted are eventually destroyed. (However, a small number of "embryo adoptions" are now taking place, in which preserved embryos from fertility clinics are, with the biological parents' consent, implanted in an adoptive mother and then brought to term.)

Beyond this issue, PGD also raises another ethical question: What limits should be placed on choosing from among embryos? Right now, some clinics allow parents to use PGD to choose the *sex* of their child. If this seems disturbing, consider that, with our expanding knowledge of genetics, it may be possible in the future to select for a tall or muscular child. Prospective parents who would never abort a fetus to get such an outcome might not object to choosing from among embryos to get it, particularly since more embryos must be produced than will be used. Parents may think: Since a selection process is going to take place anyway (for healthy genes), why not select for things like height as well?

Such questions become less abstract with a little knowledge of how PGD works. Many of its steps are those that occur with any in vitro fertilization (IVF). The starting point for IVF is to administer to the prospective mother a group of hormones that stimulate maturation of a large group of eggs in her ovaries. (These eggs are the oocytes you looked at in Chapter 10.) Anywhere from a week to two weeks later, a physician uses a needle attached to an ultrasound guide to remove the mature eggs from the ovaries. Although numbers vary, it would not be uncommon for 10 or 12 eggs to be recovered in this process. The husband then provides sperm to fertilize the eggs, with this fertilization taking place in a laboratory.

Three days after fertilization, each egg has divided into an eight-cell embryo. If you look at **Figure 1a**, you can see what comes next: Using a tiny hollow tube called a pipette, a physician gently suctions one of these cells away from the others. (Embryonic cells are so undifferentiated at this point that the loss of any one of them does not interfere with development of the others into a child.) The cell that is removed provides the DNA for testing. If you look at **Figure 1b**, you can see the results of one of the tests. Recall that children born with Down syndrome generally have a third copy of chromosome 21. It is possible to *test* for a third chromosome 21 by preparing a length of DNA whose "bases" will latch onto the unique set of DNA bases that exist on chromosome 21. Moreover, these lengths of "homing" DNA are fluorescent—they light up. The result is what you see in the figure: The prepared DNA has latched onto three chromosome 21's in these embryonic cells; they have revealed that, had this embryo been implanted in

the mother, the result would have been a child with Down syndrome.

By use of this test and others, embryos produced through IVF are ranked according

to their health. Parents then choose from among them, selecting perhaps three or four that will be transferred back into the mother by a physician.

(a)

(b)

Figure 1

(a) Removing a Cell for Testing

A human embryo at the eight-cell stage (center) being manipulated to have one of its cells removed for preimplantation genetic diagnosis. A pipette at left holds the embryo, while a smaller pipette at right gently suctions off one cell from it. The cell's genetic material is then checked for abnormalities. If this embryo is determined to be normal, it may be inserted into the mother's uterus, where it can develop into a baby.

(b) Down Syndrome Diagnosed

Genetic testing of this embryo has revealed that each of its cells has three copies of chromosome 21, indicated by the pink areas in the nuclei of the cells. Such an embryo would develop into a child with Down syndrome. The pink areas represent fluorescently labeled DNA that has bound or "hybridized" with regions of DNA specific to chromosome 21.

Turner syndrome results from a loss of a chromosome, but all manner of sex chromosome *additions* can also take place. There are, for example, XXY men who, while phenotypically male in most respects, tend to have a number of feminine features: some breast development, a more feminine figure, and lack of facial hair. When coupled with other characteristics (such as tall stature and dysfunctional testicles), the result is a condition called Klinefelter syndrome.

Aneuploidy and Cancer

We've thus far looked at varying conditions that can result when aneuploidy takes place in meiosis, which is to say the cell divisions that produce eggs or sperm. But it's also possible for aneuploidy to take place in *mitosis,* meaning regular cell division in nonsex or "somatic" cells. As one cell divides into two, a given chromatid can fail to migrate properly, and one resulting daughter cell ends up with one chromosome too many, while the other ends up with one chromosome too few.

Now, note that this kind of aneuploid event might take place in a child, a teenager, or an adult. If so, the only cells affected would be the "line" of cells that stem from the original two cells that underwent aneuploidy. Put another way, not every cell in the body would be affected, as is the case with meiotic aneuploidy; only the daughter cells of the original aneuploid cells would have the wrong number of chromosomes. You might think: Well, this is bound to be less serious than aneuploidy resulting from meiosis; and in general, this is the case. Most aneuploid cells resulting from mitosis will die, but a few can survive. Indeed, mitotic aneuploidy is often seen in a destructive kind of cell found in the body, the cancer cell.

Researchers have known about aneuploidy in cancer cells for decades. Today, it's clear that almost all cancer cells have undergone aneuploidy—that is, almost all cancerous cells have the wrong number of chromosomes in them. But for many years, it was assumed that such aneuploidies were the *result* of a cancer in progress rather than the *cause* of it. In recent years, however, this idea has been turned on its head. Some prominent cancer researchers believe that aneuploidy is a cause of cancer. To be sure, this idea differs from the leading hypothesis about cancer: that it results from a series of mutations to individual genes. The problem with this idea is that, despite decades of research, no one has yet identified a series of mutations that will predictably cause any of the most serious forms of cancer. Meanwhile, it has been demonstrated that, at the least, aneuploidy can occur before the very earliest stages of some forms of cancer. The question is whether it is the triggering event in these cancers (**Figure 12.9**). Only more research will answer this question. For now, don't be surprised if you start see-

Figure 12.9
Aneuploidy before Cancer

In this karyotype of a cell taken from a young girl, aneuploidy can be seen to exist in a complex form. Note that the cell has the standard two copies of chromosomes 1 through 4, but then three copies of chromosome 5, only one copy of chromosome 6, and so on. This aneuploidy was present in the girl during embryonic development, meaning it was present prior to the time she developed a form of childhood cancer (called an embryonal rhabdomyosarcoma). Evidence of this sort has convinced some researchers that aneuploidy can be a cause of cancer.
(Karyotype courtesy of Dr. Sandra Hanks and Dr. Nazneen Rahman.)

ing newspaper stories about aneuploidy and cancer. We're certain that the cellular mistake of aneuploidy has devastating consequences every day. The question is whether cancer is one of them.

12.6 Structural Aberrations in Chromosomes

Aberrations can occur *within* a given chromosome, sometimes resulting from interactions *between* chromosomes. A frequent cause of such change is that pieces of chromosomes can break off from the main chromosomal body. Such a chromosomal fragment may then be lost to further genetic activity, or it may rejoin a chromosome—either the one it came from or another—sometimes to harmful effect. These structural aberrations may come about spontaneously, but they may also be caused by exposure to such agents as radiation, viruses, and chemicals.

Deletions

A chromosomal **deletion** occurs when a chromosome fragment breaks off and then does not rejoin any chromosome. Such an event might take place during meiosis in a healthy parent, who then could pass along a complement of 23 chromosomes, one chromosome of which would be missing a segment. If the deleted piece were large enough, the zygote

(a) Cri-du-chat syndrome

(b) Cri-du-chat karyotype

Chromosome with portion deleted

Figure 12.10
Chromosomal Deletion

(a) A 5-year-old boy affected by cri-du-chat syndrome, which results from a chromosomal deletion. Note the small head and low-set ears.

(b) Karyotype of a person with cri-du-chat syndrome. Note, in chromosome 5, that the chromosome on the right is shorter than the chromosome on the left because of loss of a chromosomal section.

would likely not survive. You can see how critical even a portion of a chromosome is by looking at children who suffer from a rare condition called *cri-du-chat* ("cry of the cat") syndrome, which results from the deletion of the far end of the "short arm" of chromosome 5. If you look at **Figure 12.10**, you can see a chromosome set that shows you this deletion. Children born with the cri-du-chat condition exhibit a host of maladies, among them mental retardation and an improperly constructed larynx that early in life produces sounds akin to those of a cat.

Inversions and Translocations

When a chromosome fragment rejoins the chromosome it came from, it may do so with its orientation "flipped," so that the fragment's chemical sequence is out of order. This is an **inversion**: a chromosomal abnormality that comes about when a chromosomal fragment that rejoins a chromosome does so with an inverted orientation (**Figure 12.11**). A **translocation** is a chromosomal abnormality that occurs when two chromosomes that are not homologous exchange pieces, leaving both with improper gene sequences, which can have phenotypic effects.

Duplications

There is, of course, a perfectly normal process of chromosomal part swapping—crossing over. But consider what might happen if two homologous chromosomes exchanged *unequal* pieces of themselves in crossing over. One would lose genetic material, while the other would gain it. Because these are homologous (meaning paired) chromosomes, the fragment added to the latter chromosome would duplicate some of the material it already has. This is but one of the ways in which genetic duplication can take place. Such duplication is something of a double-edged sword. For individuals, it

Figure 12.11
Chromosomal
Structural Changes

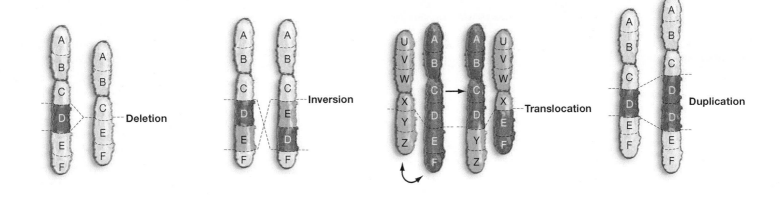

Deletion

Inversion

Translocation

Duplication

THE PROCESS OF SCIENCE

Thomas Hunt Morgan: Using Fruit Flies to Look More Deeply into Genetics

Gregor Mendel used pea plants in his work, but generations of researchers after him have employed a common fruit fly, *Drosophila melanogaster*, in trying to unravel the secrets of genetics. One of the earliest *Drosophila* workers was a Kentuckian named Thomas Hunt Morgan, who greatly deepened our understanding of heredity with work he began in 1908 in his lab at Columbia University.

The *Drosophila* fly has a lot going for it as an experimental subject: It is small, it has unusually large chromosomes, and it has what is known as a short generation time. Whereas Mendel got one or two generations of pea plants a year, Morgan got one generation of *Drosophila* every 12 days or so. In practical terms, this meant that Morgan's group had to wait at most a month to see the results of their experiments.

Lessons from a Mutation: White-Eyed Flies

Morgan's path to discovery began with a chance event. One day he looked into one of the empty milk bottles in which he kept his flies and saw something strange: Among numerous normal or "wild-type" *Drosophila* with red eyes was a single male

The importance of Morgan's insight was that he had linked a particular trait to a particular chromosome, which was a first.

with white eyes (**Figure 1**). Morgan correctly assumed that the variation he saw had come about because of a spontaneous genetic change or "mutation" in the fly. He then crossed his white-eyed male with females that he knew bred true for red eyes

and got all red-eyed flies in the F_1 generation. No surprise there; it simply looked as though red eyes were the same type of dominant trait that Mendel had seen in, for example, his yellow peas. Indeed, when Morgan went on to breed the F_1 generation—those that had mixed red and white alleles—he got a 3:1 red-to-white ratio in the F_2 generation. The strange thing was that every white-eyed fly was a *male*. Why should that be?

As it turns out, sex chromosomes exist in *Drosophila* as they do in human beings: Females have two X chromosomes, while

males have one X and one Y. Doing further experiments on these flies, Morgan eventually decided that the gene for eye color had to lie on a *particular* chromosome: the X chromosome. Why? Any fly that was white-eyed had to have only white-eyed alleles (because white was recessive). Normally, of course, this would mean *two* white-eyed alleles, but there was an exception: Males could be white-eyed if they had but a single white allele—because they have only a *single X chromosome*. You can look at **Figure 2** to see how this plays out schematically. The importance of Morgan's insight was not that he had grasped something about eye color in the fly. It was that he had linked a particular trait to a particular chromosome, which was a first.

When Genes Separate: Recombination

Continuing with *Drosophila* breeding work, Morgan and his colleagues soon were finding all kinds of mutations in the flies. There was, for example, a mutation

(a) Eye of red-eyed *Drosophila*

(b) Eye of white-eyed *Drosophila*

Figure 1
The Mutation Morgan Saw

for "miniature" wings, as opposed to full ones. This trait followed the rules described earlier for the white-eyed mutation and accordingly was deemed to be an X-linked characteristic. Not surprisingly, the white-eyed and miniature-winged mutations tended to be transmitted *together* when both of these mutations were bred for because the genes for both of them lay on the same chromosome. The question was, though, did genes on the same chromosome *always* travel together? Surprisingly, the answer was no. For example, miniature wings were usually passed on together with white eyes, but not always. Sometimes, one trait would appear in an offspring, but the other would not. Since genes for these traits were on one chromosome, how did they get separated from one another?

A paper published in Europe in 1909 gave Morgan a clue. Viewing cells under a microscope, F. A. Janssens had observed chromosomes entwining with each other during an early phase of meiosis. Given this and his own data, Morgan made a creative leap. He suggested that chromosomes can swap parts with each other during their meiotic intertwining. Sound at all familiar? Remember, in the Chapter 10 review of meiosis, the discussion of the phenomenon known as crossing over? Here, with Morgan, is the insight that led to this now-established tenet of science. Appropriately enough, insights such as these won Morgan a Nobel Prize in 1934.

Figure 2
Why All Morgan's White-Eyed F₂'s Were Males

The F₂ female flies that inherited one white-eyed X-chromosome allele also inherited a second red-eyed X allele, making them red-eyed. However, the males inheriting the white-eyed allele had no second X chromosome. Instead, they inherited a Y chromosome—which has no genes on it for eye color—leaving them white-eyed.

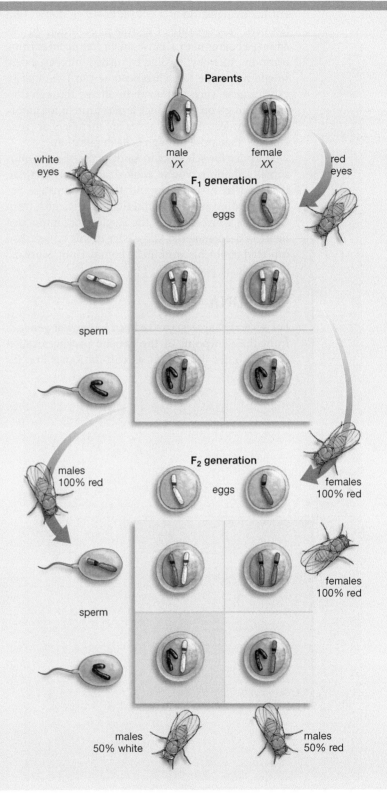

may have no effect at all, although large duplications can have negative effects, such as mental retardation. For the living world as a whole, however, duplication has been vital because of its role in evolution. Just as adding a bedroom to a house might free up an existing bedroom, such that it could be turned into, say, a den, so adding a gene to a chromosome can "free up" an existing gene, such that it can be altered through mutation and go on to produce a new protein for an organism. At least half our genes are members of "gene families" that arose through gene duplication.

In order for scientists to understand the chromosomal afflictions you've looked at in this chapter, they had to first understand the basic linkage between chromosomes and inheritance. A scientist from Columbia University was the single most important figure in deepening our knowledge of this subject. You can read about his work in "Thomas Hunt Morgan" beginning on page 226.

On to DNA

For several chapters, you've been looking at genetics from the viewpoint of the genetic packages called chromosomes. Important as chromosomes are, it's probably been apparent that the real genetic control lies with the units that help make them up: the DNA sequences we call genes. As you've seen, it is genes that make pea-plant flowers purple or white—and that give a person Huntington disease or not. It's time to explore just what these genes are and how they operate.

SO FAR . . .

1. Which of the following can be a result of aneuploidy: (a) miscarriage, (b) Down syndrome, (c) Turner syndrome?

2. The aneuploidy that exists in cancerous cells develops during the process of _____, rather than _____, and thus is not seen in every cell in the body, but only in a _____ of cells.

3. Chromosomal aberrations include deletions, in which a person is missing a _____ of a _____.

12 REVIEW

Go to the Study Area at www.masteringbiology.com to practice quizzes, myeBook, BioFlix™ 3-D animations, MP3 Tutor Sessions, videos, current events, and more.

Mastering
BIOLOGY

Summary

12.1 X-Linked Inheritance in Humans

- X-linked genetic conditions stem from dysfunctional alleles located on the X chromosome. Men are more likely to suffer from these conditions because men have only a single X chromosome. A woman with a dysfunctional allele on one of her X chromosomes usually will be protected by a second functional allele that lies on her second X chromosome. (p. 213)

- Recessive genetic conditions are those that will not exist in the presence of a single functional allele. Persons who do not suffer from recessive genetic conditions may still possess an allele for them, which they can pass on to their offspring. Such carriers are heterozygous for the condition—the alleles they have for the trait differ, one being functional, the other being dysfunctional. (p. 214)

12.2 Autosomal Genetic Disorders

- Autosomal genetic disorders involve neither the X nor the Y chromosome. Any person who suffers from a recessive autosomal disorder must be homozygous for the alleles that cause the disorder. (p. 215)

- Dominant disorders are those in which a single allele can bring about the condition, regardless of whether a person also has a normal allele. (p. 216)

12.3 Tracking Traits with Pedigrees

- In tracking inherited diseases, scientists often construct medical pedigrees, which are genetic familial histories that normally take the form of diagrams. (p. 217)

12.4 Aberrations in Chromosomal Sets: Polyploidy

- Many species have diploid or paired sets of chromosomes. In human beings, this means 46 chromosomes in all: 22 pairs of autosomes and either an XX chromosome pair (for females) or an XY pair (for males). The state of having more than two sets of chromosomes is called polyploidy. Many plants are polyploid, but the condition is fatal for human beings. (p. 218)

12.5 Incorrect Chromosome Number: Aneuploidy

- In aneuploidy, an organism has either more or fewer chromosomes than normally exist in its species' full set. Aneuploidy is responsible for a large proportion of the miscarriages that occur in human pregnancies. A small proportion of embryos survive aneuploidy, but the children who result from these embryos are born with such conditions as Down syndrome. (p. 218)

- The cause of meiotic aneuploidy usually is nondisjunction, in which homologous chromosomes or sister chromatids fail to separate correctly, leading to eggs or sperm that have one too many or one too few chromosomes. (p. 220)

- Aneuploidy can come about in regular cell division (mitosis) as well as in meiosis. A number of cancer researchers believe that mitotic aneuploidy can be a cause of cancer rather than an effect of it. (p. 224)

12.6 Structural Aberrations in Chromosomes

- Harmful aberrations can occur within chromosomes, with many coming about because of mistakes in chromosomal interactions. Chromosomal aberrations include deletions, inversions, translocations, and duplications. (p. 224)

Key Terms

aneuploidy   218
autosomal dominant disorder   217
autosomal recessive disorder   215
carrier   215
deletion   224
dominant disorder   217
Down syndrome   221
inversion   225
nondisjunction   220
pedigree   217
polyploidy   218
recessive disorder   214
translocation   225

Understanding the Basics

Multiple-Choice Questions

(Answers are in the back of the book.)

1. Examples of sex-linked genetic diseases include:
   a. sickle-cell anemia, red-green color blindness, and polyploidy.
   b. Duchenne muscular dystrophy, Down syndrome, and red-green color blindness.
   c. hemophilia, red-green color blindness, and Duchenne muscular dystrophy.
   d. Huntington disease, hemophilia, and Klinefelter syndrome.
   e. Down syndrome, cri-du-chat, and hemophilia.

2. Healthy individuals least likely to suffer from malaria are those who:
   a. are heterozygous for hemoglobin (one hemoglobin A, one hemoglobin S).
   b. are homozygous for hemoglobin S alleles.

c. are hemophiliacs.

d. are homozygous for hemoglobin A alleles.

e. both a and c.

3. Inheritance of an autosomal dominant disorder differs from inheritance of an autosomal recessive disorder in that:

a. a dominant disorder may be passed on only if both parents are affected.

b. a dominant disorder is evident only if the offspring is homozygous for the allele.

c. a dominant disorder is more often seen in females.

d. a dominant disorder may be passed on even if only one parent is affected.

e. both b and d.

4. An individual having 44 autosomes and one X chromosome would be classified as:

a. polyploid.

b. aneuploid.

c. having Klinefelter syndrome.

d. having Turner syndrome.

e. both b and d.

5. A human embryo with 69 chromosomes would:

a. die in the womb or shortly after birth.

b. be considered polyploid.

c. have fewer problems than a plant with the same condition.

d. both a and b.

e. all of the above

6. A carrier is a person who:

a. suffers from a recessive disorder.

b. is heterozygous for a recessive disorder.

c. is homozygous for a recessive disorder.

d. does not suffer from a recessive disorder but possesses an allele for it.

e. b and d.

7. Which of the following statements is *not* true regarding Down syndrome?

a. Affected individuals usually have three copies of chromosome 21.

b. The condition is usually caused by nondisjunction in egg formation.

c. Most Down syndrome children are born to women 35 years of age or older.

d. Approximately 0.1 percent of all live births are children with Down syndrome.

e. The physical characteristics associated with the disorder include mental retardation, male infertility, short stature, and reduced life span.

8. Which of the following diseases usually is not evident until well into adulthood?

a. Huntington disease

b. Down syndrome

c. cri-du-chat

d. Turner syndrome

e. none of the above

Brief Review

(Answers are in the back of the book.)

1. In sex-linked diseases, which gender is more frequently affected—male or female? Why?

2. How can the serious genetic defect known as aneuploidy be both widespread and relatively unrecognized?

3. The text notes the possibility that some forms of human cancer may result from aneuploidy. What is the fundamental difference between an aneuploidy that might lead to cancer and one that results in Down syndrome?

4. Compare and contrast the four chromosome structural aberrations discussed in this chapter: deletions, inversions, translocations, and duplications.

5. Given the following situations, answer accordingly:

a. A human cell with 47 chromosomes has probably undergone _____.

b. Two sperm manage to fuse with a single egg, producing an embryo. The result would be _____.

6. Why would a person with Klinefelter syndrome exhibit both male and female features?

7. Certain genotypes may be advantageous in specific situations. Give an example of a heterozygous genotype that is advantageous over either homozygous genotype. Why is this the case?

Applying Your Knowledge

1. In the United States, 8 percent of African Americans are carriers for the sickle-cell allele, while in central Africa the figure is 20 percent. What could account for this difference?

2. The text notes that the technique known as preimplantation genetic diagnosis (PGD) allows prospective parents to screen embryos not only for serious genetic defects such as Down syndrome but for traits that may be regarded as more or less desirable, such as male or female gender. What limits, if any, should be placed on parents' ability to choose from among embryos for traits such as this?

3. Thinking back to what you learned in Chapter 10 about how sperm are produced, why is it that the cells that give rise to sperm undergo nondisjunction less frequently than the cells that give rise to eggs?

Genetics Problems

(Answers are in the back of the book.)

1. A man who is a carrier for sickle-cell anemia, a recessive genetic disease, marries a woman who is not a carrier. What proportion of their children is expected to be afflicted with sickle-cell anemia?

2. Hemophilia is an X-linked recessive disease that prevents blood clotting. If a woman who is a carrier for hemophilia marries a man who is not a carrier, what proportion of their sons are expected to have hemophilia? What is the chance that their first child will have hemophilia? (Assume that the sex of this child is unknown until birth.)

Consider the following pedigree for a human autosomal trait. (Note that in pedigrees, generations are indicated by Roman numerals and individuals within a generation are numbered from left to right with Arabic numerals.)

3. Is the allele that determines this trait dominant or recessive? Explain your reasoning.

4. Using symbols *A* and *a* for the dominant and recessive alleles, respectively, what is the genotype of the affected male in the second generation (individual II-3)?

5. What is the genotype of this individual's mate?

6. If female III-2 marries a heterozygous man, what proportion of their children is expected to have this trait?

7. Consider the following pedigree, which assumes a fantasy gene for ear shape. In answering the questions below about it, use the symbol *P* for the regular allele or *p* for a pointy-shaped allele if this is an autosomal trait; or X^+ for the regular allele or X^p for the pointy allele if this is an X-linked trait.

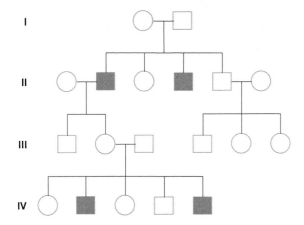

This pedigree indicates the trait is most likely inherited as an:
   a. autosomal dominant.
   b. autosomal recessive.
   c. X-linked dominant.
   d. X-linked recessive.

8. What is the genotype of individual I-1?

9. If a woman who is a carrier for this trait married individual III-1, what proportion of their children is expected to show this trait? What proportion of their sons is expected to show this trait?

10. Construct a pedigree to answer the following question: Red-green color blindness is an X-linked recessive trait. A woman who has a color-blind mother and a father with normal color vision marries a man with normal vision. This couple has a son. What is the chance that the son is color-blind?

11. Neurofibromatosis is a genetic disorder associated with an allele of one autosomal gene. Individuals with neurofibromatosis have uneven skin pigmentation and skin tumors. A man with neurofibromatosis marries a woman who does not carry the allele for this disorder. The couple has five children, three of whom have neurofibromatosis. The most likely explanation for this outcome is that neurofibromatosis is a _____ trait and that the man is _____.
   a. recessive; homozygous recessive
   b. recessive; heterozygous

   c. dominant; homozygous dominant
   d. dominant; heterozygous
   e. a and b are both possible explanations.

12. Hyperphosphatemia, a disease that causes a form of rickets (abnormal bone growth and development), is inherited as an X-linked dominant trait. A woman who is heterozygous for the disease allele marries a man who has a normal allele. What proportion of their sons will have hyperphosphatemia? What proportion of their daughters will have hyperphosphatemia? If hyperphosphatemia were an X-linked recessive trait, how would your answer differ?

Passing on Life's Information:

DNA Structure and Replication

DNA serves as a storehouse of information for living things. Scientists could not understand how DNA's information could be passed on from one generation to the next until they understood how all its component parts fit together.

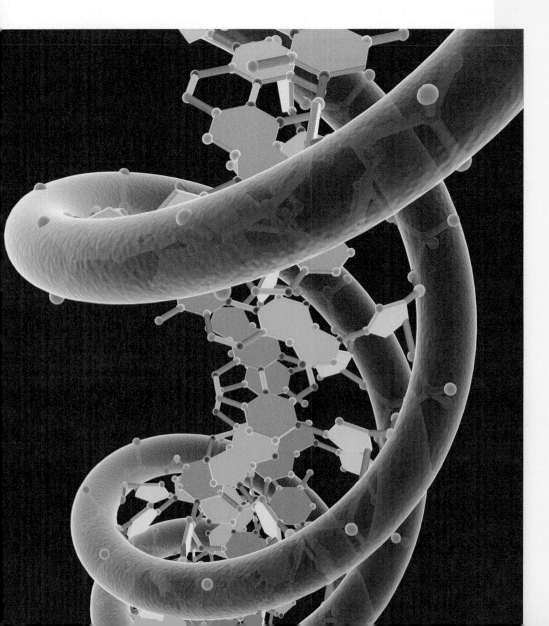

Life is able to build on itself thanks to the structure of DNA, shown here in a computer-generated model.

figure by S and P). The "steps" lying between these handrails are composed of DNA's bases. As the figure shows, each of the bases amounts to a *half*-stairstep, if you will. Each extends inward from one handrail of the double helix and is then joined to a base extending inward from the other handrail of the DNA molecule. (The bases are linked via hydrogen bonds, symbolized by the dotted lines in the figure.)

The figure shows some examples of one base being paired with another. At the bottom, for example, an A base on the left is paired with a T base on the right. Go two sets of nucleotides up, and a G on the left is being paired with a C on the right. This turns out to be one of the fundamental rules about DNA structure. If you viewed a billion DNA *base pairs*, as they're called, you would find the same thing: A always pairing with T, and G always pairing with C, across the helix. (Any two bases that can pair together in this way are said to be *complementary*; thus, A is complementary to T, and G is complementary to C. Likewise, you can have complementary chains of DNA.)

The Structure of DNA Gives Away the Secret of Replication

It was this structure of DNA that suggested the answer to one of the great questions of genetics: How is genetic information passed on? To put this another way, how does a cell make a copy of its own DNA? As you've seen, a full complement of our DNA is contained in nearly every cell in our body. Yet cells divide, and each pair of daughter cells contains exactly the same complement of DNA as did the parent cell they came from. This means that genetic information is passed on by means of DNA being copied, with one copy of this molecule ending up in one daughter cell and a second copy in the other. Indeed, such copying extends to the formation of egg and sperm cells, meaning this is the way genetic information is passed on from one *generation* to the next. But how could this work?

The structure Watson and Crick discovered suggested a way. We've observed that A must always pair with T, and G with C, across the two strands of the double helix. This rule, Watson and Crick saw, meant that each single strand of DNA could serve as a *template* for the synthesis of a new single strand (**Figure 13.6**). Each A on an old strand would specify the place for a T on the new, each G on the old a place for a C on the new, and so forth. All that was required was for the two old strands to separate—splitting the stairsteps right down the middle—and for new strands to be put together that were complementary to the old.

DNA Structure and Protein Production

The second thing DNA structure suggested was a partial answer to another great question of genetics: How

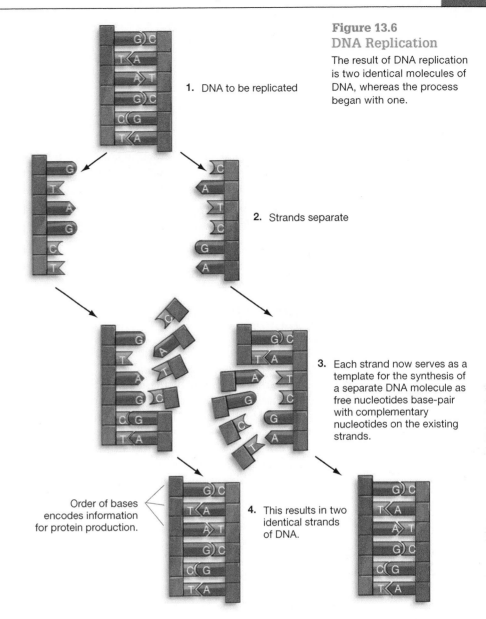

Figure 13.6
DNA Replication
The result of DNA replication is two identical molecules of DNA, whereas the process began with one.

1. DNA to be replicated

2. Strands separate

3. Each strand now serves as a template for the synthesis of a separate DNA molecule as free nucleotides base-pair with complementary nucleotides on the existing strands.

Order of bases encodes information for protein production.

4. This results in two identical strands of DNA.

could DNA be versatile enough to specify the dazzling array of proteins that all living things produce? The handrails of DNA's double helix are monotonous—phosphate, sugar, phosphate, sugar. But the bases can be laid out along these handrails in an extremely varied manner. A has to pair with T and G with C *across* the helix; but *along* the handrails, the bases can come in any order. Look at the top drawing in Figure 13.6 to see the order this hypothetical group of bases comes in; starting from the bottom right, A-G-C-T-A-C. Strung together by the thousands, such bases can specify a particular protein, just as in Morse code a series of short and long clicks can specify a particular word. And thanks to the variability of DNA's bases along the handrails, an enormous number of proteins can be specified. Next chapter, we'll look at the process by which cells start with the information contained in DNA and end up with completed proteins.

SO FAR...

1. James Watson and Francis Crick discovered the _____.

2. The key to DNA replication is that each _____ base on an original strand of DNA serves as a template for the addition of a T base on the new strand, while each _____ on the original strand serves as a template for the addition of a G base.

3. A particular sequence of DNA _____ can specify a particular _____.

Figure 13.7
How Life Builds on Itself
Each newly synthesized DNA molecule is a combination of the old and the new. An existing DNA molecule unwinds, and each of the resulting single strands (the old, in red) serves as a template for a complementary strand that will be formed through base pairing (the new, in blue).

The Building Blocks of DNA Replication

You have already looked briefly at the process by which DNA is copied or "replicated," but we now need to review some of the details of this process. The basic steps here are straightforward. The essential building block of DNA is the unit called the **nucleotide,** which can be seen in the highlighted portion of Figure 13.5. Every nucleotide contains one sugar and one phosphate group. What differentiates one nucleotide from another is the base that is attached to it; in this case the base is A, but as you can see, others have T, C, or G.

Figure 13.6 shows the process of DNA replication in overview. Note that the first thing that happens is that the joined strands of the double helix unwind, separating from one another. The nucleotides on each of the single strands are then paired with free-floating nucleotides that line up in new, complementary strands. Because *both* strands of the original double helix are being paired with new strands, the end product is two double helices, where before there was one. This is important because each of these strands is destined to serve in separate cells—the daughter cells that are produced from a single parent cell during the process of cell division.

You can see in Figure 13.6 that the addition of nucleotides moves in differing directions on the two strands. This is so because of something you can see in Figure 13.5: The two strands of the double helix have opposite orientations. Note that the sugars of the right-hand strand, for example, are upside down relative to the sugars of the left-hand strand. (If the strands were people, we would think of them lying head to *foot*, relative to each other.) Because new nucleotides can be added to only one end of a DNA strand, the nucleotides are added in different directions.

Something Old, Something New

It's worth drawing a little finer point on one aspect of this process: Each resulting double helix is a combination of the old and the new. Each has one "parental" strand of DNA and one newly synthesized complementary strand (**Figure 13.7**). This combination is conceptually important because this is how life builds on itself. We think of life as a process in which the old gives rise to the new, but here we can see how this is accomplished. The old *specifies* the new, even as it is joining with it, in a newly synthesized strand of DNA. If we ask why life has such remarkable continuity—why it is that one generation of living thing tends gives rise to another that is so much like it—we find that this process is largely responsible. Through it, what is old will be passed on largely intact to what is new.

As noted, each instance of DNA replication comes in the service of producing something new: the two daughter cells that arise from a single parent cell during the process of cell division. As such, each pair of newly formed double helices is destined to part company. As part of the mitosis we looked at in Chapter 9, each of the new strands of DNA is moved to opposite sides of a dividing parent cell. Once this cell splits into two, the separation of the helices is complete; each strand now resides in a separate daughter cell and each now serves as an independently functioning segment of DNA. At the chromosomal level, each newly replicated helix is, when joined by appropriate proteins,

BioFlix

DNA Replication

one of the sister chromatids you've seen so much of in the last few chapters.

Enzymes Facilitate Replication

The DNA replication that sets all this in motion may sound simple in overview, but in fact its details are enormously complicated. As you might imagine, such a process could not proceed without enzymes to catalyze it. To name just two groups of them, there are enzymes called helicases that unwind the double helix, separating its two strands to make the bases on them available for base pairing. There is also another group of enzymes, collectively known as **DNA polymerases,** that move along each strand of the double helix, joining together nucleotides as they are added—one by one—to form the new, complementary strands of DNA.

Editing Out Mistakes

The base pairing that takes place in replication goes on millions of times in a given stretch of DNA: Free-standing A's are aligned with complementary T's, while C's are aligned with G's. When the entire human genome is considered, 3.2 *billion* base pairs must be aligned in this way, not just once, but twice. (The human genome is 3.2 billion base pairs long, but each human cell contains two copies of each chromosome.) The amazing thing about this copying is how few mismatches are produced in it by the time it's completed. The error rate in human replication—the rate at which the *wrong* bases have been brought together—might be only one in every billion bases by the end of replication. Yet *during* replication, such a mistake might be made once in every 100,000 bases. Obviously, to start with a given number of mistakes but to end up with far fewer, the cell's genetic machinery has to be capable of correcting its errors.

This happens partly through the services of the versatile DNA polymerases, which are able to perform a kind of DNA editing: They remove a mismatched nucleotide and replace it with a proper one. Interestingly enough, this happens through a kind of backspacing. Normally, the DNA polymerases are moving along a DNA chain, linking together recently arrived nucleotides. When an error is detected, however, they stop, move "backward," remove the incorrect nucleotide, put in the correct one, and then move forward again.

13.4 **Mutations**

With this consideration of alterations in DNA structure, you have arrived at an important concept: that of a **mutation,** which can be defined as a permanent alteration of a DNA base sequence. Such alterations come about because the cell's various DNA error-correcting mechanisms are not foolproof; they do not correct all the mistakes that occur. For the balance of this chapter, we'll focus on these genetic mistakes, which have a powerful effect both on human health and on evolution.

DNA's makeup can be altered in many ways. A slight change in the chemical form of a base might, for example, cause a G to link up across the helix with a T (instead of with its normal partner, C), as you can see in **Figure 13.8**. Then, in a subsequent round of DNA replication, the cell might "repair" this error in such a way that a permanent mistake is introduced: An A-T pair now exists, whereas the original sequence had a G-C pair. Permanent mistakes like these are called **point mutations,** meaning a mutation of a single base pair in the genome. Such mutations stand in contrast to the kind of whole-chromosome aberrations pre-

Starting DNA   **Incorrect base pairing**   **Mutation**

Point mutation

**Figure 13.8
One Route to a
Mutation**

1. In replicating a cell's DNA, mistakes are sometimes made, such that one base can be paired with another base that is not complementary to it (G with T in this case).

2. The next time a cell replicates its DNA, the replication repair mechanism may "fix" this error in such a way that a permanent alteration in the DNA sequence results. The original G will be replaced, instead of the wrongly added T. The result is an A-T base pair, whereas the cell started with a G-C base pair.

sented in Chapter 12, although these also qualify as mutations under some definitions.

In what way are mutations "permanent"? Think of how DNA replication works. Before any cell can divide, it must first make a copy of its complement of DNA. Should this DNA contain an uncorrected mistake, it too will be copied—again and again, actually, with each succeeding cell division. Most mutations have no noticeable effect on an organism, and as you'll see, mutations are vital to the process of evolution. But the concept of mutation is quite rightly fearful to us because, in relatively rare instances, mutations can have disastrous effects.

Cancer and Huntington Mutations

A cancerous growth is a line of cells that has undergone a special kind of mutation—one that causes the affected cells to proliferate wildly. As an example, the skin cancer known as melanoma causes skin cells called melanocytes to start dividing very rapidly. For our purposes, the question is: How does this process get going? In 2002, British scientists looked at numerous lines of melanoma cells that had been taken from cancer patients. They found that 59 percent of these cells contained a mutation in a gene called *BRAF*. This gene, like all others, amounts to a sequence of DNA bases—a sequence of C's, T's, A's, and G's. When the British scientists looked at how the *BRAF* gene had actually mutated, they found that in 92 percent of cases, there had been a single change: an A had been substituted for a T at *BRAF*'s 1,796th base. What they found, in other words, was a point mutation, nearly 2,000 bases within the sequence of bases that makes up the *BRAF* gene. And the effect of this mutation? It produces a protein that is a slightly altered version of the normal BRAF protein. This protein is altered enough, however, that it keeps melanocytes moving through the cell-division cycle, causing them to multiply wildly.

Cell proliferation is not the only kind of trouble mutations can bring about. Chapter 12 introduced Huntington disease, which causes spastic movements, severe dementia, and ultimately death among its victims. In all people, there is a gene, called *IT15*, that has within it a number of repeats of a particular "triplet" of bases, CAG. People with 34 or fewer CAG repeats in their *IT15* gene are fine; they will suffer no illness at all from the gene. People with 35–39 CAG repeats, however, may develop Huntington, although this is not a certainty. Meanwhile, people who have more than 40 repeats definitely will develop the disease, and the more repeats they have, the younger they will be when its symptoms first appear. Unlike the case with cancer, however, the Huntington mutation does not cause cells to multiply wildly. Instead, the mutated *IT15* gene creates a faulty protein called huntingtin, which cannot be broken down by nerve cells and ends up

building up inside them, eventually killing them. Because Huntington is caused by a repeating group of three nucleotides, it is referred to as a "trinucleotide repeat" disease. At least eight other diseases of the nervous system fall into this category.

Heritable and Nonheritable Mutations

Though Huntington disease and melanoma are both caused by mutations, there is an important distinction to be made between them. Most mutations come about in the body's **somatic cells,** which is to say cells that do not become eggs or sperm. This is the case with the mutations that bring about melanoma. Conversely, some mutations arise in **germ-line cells,** meaning the cells that do become eggs or sperm. This is the case with the Huntington mutation. The important point here is that germ-line cell mutations are *heritable*—they can be passed on from one generation to the next, in the ways reviewed in Chapter 12. In contrast, although a line of melanoma cells may be quite harmful, it is separate from the line of cells that gives rise to eggs or sperm. For this reason, melanoma cannot be passed on from one generation to the next.

What Causes Mutations?

A critical question, of course, is what causes DNA to mutate? One answer is so-called environmental insults. The chemicals in cigarette smoke are powerful *mutagens,* meaning substances that can mutate DNA. So is the ultraviolet light that comes from the sun. To look at the latter example in a little more detail, ultraviolet light is a form of radiation that can link adjacent T's together in a single strand of DNA; sometimes it even causes both strands of the DNA helix to break. When this latter damage takes place in a cell, one of three things can happen. First, enzymes can successfully repair the damage. Second, the cell will recognize that this damage *cannot* be repaired, in which case it may either stop dividing (in the process known as cellular senescence) or commit suicide (in the process known as apoptosis). Third, the cell will undertake none of these responses to its DNA alteration but will simply keep on dividing. In this instance, the erroneous "spelling" in the cell's DNA will be copied over and over as this original cell gives rise to two cells, which then give rise to four, and so on. In short, a mutation is being passed on in a line of cells.

Not all mutations are caused by environmental influences. Mutations happen simply as random, spontaneous events. The collision of water molecules with DNA can remove nucleotide bases or alter them in such a way that their base-pairing properties are changed. The very process of eating and breathing produces so-called free radicals that can damage DNA. And the DNA replication machinery itself may introduce errors, irrespective of any outside influences.

Once such errors occur, it is understandable that some of them will go uncorrected simply because of the size of the replication operation. As noted, every time a human cell divides, 3.2 billion bases have to be copied twice. And some 25 million cells are dividing each second in human beings. The surprise, therefore, is not that mistakes happen, but that so *few* of them happen, and that fewer still become permanent. (Recall the one-in-a-billion error rate in DNA replication that was observed earlier.) After learning about the kinds of effects mutations can have on organisms, however, you can understand why this error rate is so low: Life as we know it could not exist with a high error rate, at least in the portions of genome that code for proteins. Remember that within 3.2 billion A's, T's, G's, and C's, the substitution of a single A for a single T can help bring about melanoma. How could life exist if such mistakes were common?

Mutations and Evolutionary Adaptation

While it's true that, for individuals, mutations can have a negative effect, for the living world as a whole mutations have been vitally important because of a role they play in evolution. It turns out that germ-line mutations are the only means by which completely new genetic information can be added to a species' genome. Without mutations, organisms can shuffle *existing* genetic information in myriad ways. (Think of meiosis, with its chromosomal part swapping and random alignment of chromosome pairs). But no amount of genetic recombination could have produced, for example, the eyes that some living things possess. To go from no eyes to eyes, there had to have been some mutations along the line—some accidental reorderings of DNA sequences that either produced entirely new proteins or that altered the production of

existing proteins in beneficial ways. Modifications such as these are vital to living things given their struggle to get along in environments that are constantly changing. (Temperatures shift; streams dry up.) When environments change, species either change with them or become extinct. And the primary way major changes come about in species is through mutations. You'll be looking at this topic again in the evolution unit of this book. For now, however, isn't it interesting to ponder the fact that the living world adapts partly through its mistakes?

On to Protein Production

Back in Chapter 9, you saw that since antiquity, human beings have speculated about how one generation of living things can give rise to another—about *how* it is that life goes on. The detailed answer to this question turned out to be the something-old, something-new quality of DNA replication: parental DNA strands serve as templates for new strands, with the result that the qualities of one generation can be passed along to the next. Splendid as this function is, it is only one of the two great tasks carried out by our genetic machinery. You have just reviewed the process by which genetic information is replicated; now we'll look at the process by which this information is used. How can a stretch of DNA bring about the production of a protein? You'll see in the chapter coming up.

SO FAR . . .

1. In DNA replication, both of the strands of the double helix serve as templates for _____.

2. The _____ are a group of enzymes that add nucleotides to a replicating DNA chain.

3. A permanent alteration in a DNA base sequence is known as a _____.

CHAPTER

13 REVIEW

Go to the Study Area at www.masteringbiology.com for practice quizzes, myeBook, BioFlix™ 3-D animations, MP3 Tutor Sessions, videos, current events, and more.

Mastering
BIOLOGY

Summary

13.1 The Form and Function of Genes

- In trying to decipher the structure of DNA, scientists were performing work in molecular biology, defined as the investigation of life at the level of its individual molecules. (p. 233)

13.2 Watson and Crick: The Double Helix

- James Watson and Francis Crick discovered the chemical structure of DNA in 1953, which ushered in a new era in biology because it allowed researchers to understand some of the most fundamental processes in genetics. (p. 234)

- Watson and Crick's research was aided by the work of others, including Rosalind Franklin, who was using X-ray diffraction to learn about DNA's structure. (p. 234)

13.3 The Components of DNA and Their Arrangement

- The DNA molecule is composed of building blocks called nucleotides, each of which consists of one sugar (deoxyribose), one phosphate group, and one of four bases: adenine, guanine, thymine, or cytosine (A, G, T, or C). The sugar and phosphate groups are linked in a chain that forms the "handrails" of the DNA double helix. Bases then extend inward and are joined to each other in the middle by hydrogen bonds. A always pairs with T across the helix; G always pairs with C. (p. 236)

- DNA is copied by means of each strand of DNA serving as a template for the synthesis of a new, complementary strand. The DNA double helix first divides down the middle. Each A on an original strand then specifies a place for a T in a new strand,

while each G specifies a place for a C, and so forth. Because both strands of the original double helix are being paired with new strands in this process, the end product is two double helices. (p. 237)

- DNA can encode the information for the huge number of proteins used by living things because the sequence of bases along DNA's handrails can be laid out in an extremely varied manner. A collection of bases in one order encodes the information for one protein, while a different sequence of bases encodes the information for a different protein. (p. 237)

- Each double helix produced in replication is a combination of one parental strand of DNA and one newly synthesized complementary strand. This is how life builds on itself. Each instance of DNA replication occurs prior to the division of one parent cell into two daughter cells. When this division is complete, each of the newly formed helices will reside in separate daughter cells. (p. 238)

- Enzymes called DNA polymerases move along the double helix in DNA replication, bonding together new nucleotides in complementary DNA strands. (p. 239)

BioFlix™

DNA Replication

13.4 Mutations

- The error rate in DNA replication is very low, partly because repair enzymes are able to correct replication mistakes. When such mistakes are made and then not corrected, the result is a mutation: a permanent alteration of a DNA base sequence. (p. 239)

- Most mutations have no noticeable effect on an organism, but when mutations do have an effect, it is generally negative. Cancers result from a line of cells that have undergone types of mutations that cause them to proliferate wildly. (p. 240)

- Mutations that come about in the body's germ-line cells, meaning cells that become eggs or sperm, can be passed from one generation to another. Most mutations, however, come about in the body's somatic cells, which are cells that do not give rise to eggs or sperm, and these mutations cannot be passed on. (p. 240)

- Mutagens, such as cigarette smoke or ultraviolet light, can mutate DNA. Spontaneous events that are brought about by normal cellular processes can also lead to mutations. (p. 240)

- Mutations are important to evolution because they are the only means through which completely new genetic information can be added to a species' genome. Mutations can, in rare instances, either produce new proteins or alter the production of existing proteins in ways that are beneficial. (p. 241)

Key Terms

DNA polymerase   239
germ-line cell   240
molecular biology   234
mutation   239
nucleotide   238
point mutation   239
somatic cell   240

Understanding the Basics

Multiple-Choice Questions

(Answers are in the back of the book.)

1. James Watson and Francis Crick:
   a. proved that DNA contains information for the production of proteins.

b. elucidated the nature of genetic mutations.

c. discovered DNA.

d. proved that chromosomes were made partly of DNA.

e. discovered the structure of DNA.

2. The type of biological study that was exemplified through the discovery of DNA structure is called:

a. detailed biology.

b. component biology.

c. microscopic biology.

d. elemental biology.

e. molecular biology.

3. The components of the DNA handrails are _____ and _____.

a. nucleotides, phosphates

b. sugars, nucleotides

c. sugars, bases

d. sugars, phosphates

e. none of the above

4. Which of the following combinations is an example of a nucleotide?

a. sugar + phosphate + adenine

b. sugar + phosphate + guanine

c. sugar + phosphate + thymine

d. sugar + phosphate + cytosine

e. all of the above

5. Which of the following DNA sequences contains a mismatched base pair?

a. TCAA

a. AGTT

b. CAGC

b. GTCG

c. GATA

c. CTCT

d. AATT

d. TTAA

e. GACG

e. CTGC

6. DNA polymerases work to:

a. unwind the double helix during replication.

b. cause mutations in DNA.

c. join together nucleotides in a growing, complementary DNA strand.

d. correct errors in DNA base sequences during replication.

e. both c and d.

7. Watson and Crick made their momentous discovery about DNA in _____.

a. 1943

b. 1953

c. 1921

d. 1973

e. 1962

8. How are the base pairs of the DNA double helix linked together?

a. phosphate bonds

b. hydrogen bonds

c. carbon-carbon bonds

d. sugar bonds

e. basic bonds

Brief Review

(Answers are in the back of the book.)

1. How does the phrase "something old, something new" describe the method of DNA replication employed by the cell?

2. What two fundamental questions of genetics did the discovery of the structure of DNA help answer?

3. True or False: DNA polymerases can correct errors made in DNA replication.

4. What is a mutation? Are all mutations harmful?

5. What is the nature of the Huntington disease mutation, and what is its effect at a cellular level?

Applying Your Knowledge

1. Given the following DNA sequence, determine the complementary strand that would be added in replication:

ATTGCATGATAGCC

2. Would you expect cancer to arise more often in types of cells that divide frequently (such as skin cells) or in types of cells that divide rarely or not at all (such as nerve cells in the brain)? Explain your reasoning.

3. The Huntington disease referred to in the main text sends all of its victims into dementia, physical immobility, and ultimately death, but usually does not start doing so until the person is at least 35. Imagine yourself as the adolescent child of a parent who has started to manifest Huntington symptoms. Your chances of inheriting this incurable condition are one out of two, but you have thus far shown no symptoms of it. The question is: Do you get yourself tested to see if you inherited the harmful Huntington allele? Do you find out for sure whether you will, or will not, have this illness, or do you live with uncertainty? Assuming you've arrived at an answer, consider it now in the context of the conclusion that most people in this situation come to: Ninety-five percent of such people decline to be tested.

How Proteins Are Made:

Genetic Transcription, Translation, and Regulation

Like workers using a set of blueprints to construct a house, cells use the information contained in DNA to construct proteins. Each cell can finely tune its production of proteins in accordance with its needs.

Two kinds of structural proteins have been stained to be visible in these mouse cells: actin (in blue) and microtubules (in yellow).

The scientific advance that was reviewed in Chapter 13, the discovery of the structure of DNA in 1953, bears some comparison to the birth of Napoleon: Both events had momentous consequences, but not for a while. Only slowly did the discoveries come that, in time, were seen as hinging on James Watson and Francis Crick's work. So significant were these

advances, however, that the years between 1953 and 1966 are now regarded by some scholars as a kind of golden age of genetics—a time when basic findings about this field came fast and furious, such that by the mid-1960s scientists had at last grasped the essentials of how the genetic machinery works.

These discoveries were made in connection with both of the two great tasks of genetics: on the one hand, the copying or "replication" of DNA that you reviewed in Chapter 13; on the other, the means by which DNA's genetic information brings about the production of proteins. The first task has to do with how genetic information is passed on, the second with how genetic information is used. This second task is the subject of this chapter.

14.1 The Structure of Proteins

Because you'll be dealing extensively with proteins here, now may be a good time to review some basic information about them. As you saw in Chapter 3, proteins fit into the "building blocks" model of biological molecules. The blocks in this case are amino acids. String a number of these together, and you have a **polypeptide** chain, which then folds up in a specific three-dimensional manner, resulting in a protein. Proteins are likely to be made of hundreds of amino acids strung together, often in several linked polypeptide chains.

Though there are hundreds of thousands of different proteins, each one of them is put together from a starting set of a mere 20 amino acids. If you wonder how such diversity can proceed from such simplicity, think of the English language, which has thousands of words but only 26 letters in its alphabet. It is the *order* in which letters occur that determines whether, for

example, "cat" or "act" is spelled out; just so, it is the order of amino acids that determines which protein is synthesized.

If you look at **Figure 14.1a** on the next page, you can see the chemical structure of two amino acids, glycine (gly) and isoleucine (ile). If you look at **Figure 14.1b**, you can see that these two amino acids are the first two that occur in one of the two polypeptide chains that make up the unusually small protein we call insulin. **Figure 14.1c** then shows a three-dimensional representation of insulin—the folded-up form this protein assumes before taking on its function of moving blood sugar into cells. A list of all 20 primary amino acids and their three-letter abbreviations can be found in **Table 14.1**.

For our purposes, the question is: How do the chains of amino acids that make up a protein come into being? How do gly, ile, val, and so forth come to be strung together in a specific order to create this protein? You know from what you've studied so far that genes can be thought of as "recipes" for proteins, and that these recipes are set forth as a series of chemical "bases"—the A's, T's, C's, and G's that lie along a DNA strand. How, then, do we get from *this* series of DNA bases to *that* series of amino acids—to a protein? Let's find out.

14.2 Protein Synthesis in Overview

In overview, the process of protein synthesis can be described fairly simply. In eukaryotic organisms such as ourselves, the DNA just referred to is contained in the nucleus of the cell. The first step is that a stretch of DNA unwinds there, and its message—the order of a string of A's, T's, C's, and G's—is copied onto a molecule called messenger RNA (mRNA). This

Table 14.1	
Amino Acids	
Alanine	ala
Arginine	arg
Asparagine	asn
Aspartic Acid	asp
Cysteine	cys
Glutamic Acid	glu
Glutamine	gln
Glycine	gly
Histidine	his
Isoleucine	ile
Leucine	leu
Lysine	lys
Methionine	met
Phenylalanine	phe
Proline	pro
Serine	ser
Threonine	thr
Tryptophan	trp
Tyrosine	tyr
Valine	val

glycine **(gly)**

isoleucine **(ile)**

(a) Amino acids
The building blocks of proteins are amino acids such as glycine and isoleucine, which differ only in their side-chain composition (light colored squares).

(b) Polypeptide chain
These amino acids are strung together to form polypeptide chains. Pictured is one of the two polypeptide chains that make up the unusually small protein insulin.

(c) Protein
Polypeptide chains function as proteins only when folded into their proper three-dimensional shape, as shown here for insulin. Note the position of the glycine and isoleucine amino acids in one of the insulin polypeptide chains (colored light green).

Figure 14.1
The Structure of Proteins

length of mRNA then exits from the cell nucleus (**Figure 14.2**).

The destination of this mRNA is a molecular workbench in the cell's cytoplasm, a structure called a ribosome. More formally, a **ribosome** is an organelle, located in the cell's cytoplasm, that is the site of protein synthesis. At the ribosome, both the recipe (the mRNA sequence) and the raw materials (amino acids) come together to make the product (a protein). As the mRNA sequence is "read" within the ribosome, something grows from it: a chain of amino acids that have been linked together in the ribosome in the order specified by the mRNA sequence. When the chain is finished and folded up, a protein has come into existence. And how do amino acids get to the ribosomes? They are brought there by a second type of RNA, transfer RNA (tRNA).

As may be apparent from this account, protein synthesis divides neatly into two sets of steps. The first set is called **transcription:** the process by which the genetic information encoded in DNA is copied onto

messenger RNA. The second set is called **translation:** the process by which information encoded in messenger RNA is used to assemble a protein at a ribosome. Let's now look in more detail now at both of these processes, starting with transcription.

SO FAR ...

1. Though there are hundreds of thousands of proteins active in living things, all of them are put together from a starting set of 20 of the building blocks known as _____.

2. The information for building proteins that is encoded in DNA is passed on first to _____, which then migrates to an organelle called a _____, where the protein is put together.

14.3 A Closer Look at Transcription

From what's been reviewed so far, you can see that a key player in transcription (and translation) is RNA, whose full name is ribonucleic acid. As it turns out, RNA is structurally very similar to DNA. For one thing, RNA has the sugar and phosphate "handrail" components you saw in DNA last chapter. Then, in both molecules, this two-part structure is joined to a third element, a base, as you can see in **Figure 14.3**.

There are, however, differences between DNA and RNA. One is that RNA usually is single stranded, whereas DNA is structured in two strands that form its famous double helix. Beyond this, recall that any given DNA building block or "nucleotide" has one of four bases: adenine, guanine, cytosine, or thymine (A, G, C, or T). RNA uses the first three of these, but then uses uracil (U) instead of the thymine (T) found in DNA.

Passing on the Message: Base Pairing Again

Given the chemical similarity between DNA and RNA, it's not hard to see how DNA's genetic message can be passed on to messenger RNA: Base pairing is at work again. Recall from Chapter 13 how DNA is replicated. The double helix is unwound, after which bases along the now-single DNA strands are paired up with complementary DNA bases. Every T on a single DNA strand is

Transcription

1. In transcription, a section of DNA unwinds and nucleotides on it form base pairs with nucleotides of messenger RNA, creating an mRNA chain.

2. This segment of mRNA then leaves the cell nucleus, headed for a ribosome in the cell's cytoplasm, where translation takes place.

Translation

3. Joining the mRNA chain at the ribosome are amino acids, brought there by transfer RNA molecules. The length of messenger RNA is then "read" within the ribosome. The result? A chain of amino acids is linked together in the order specified by the mRNA sequence.

4. When the chain is finished and folded up, a protein has come into existence.

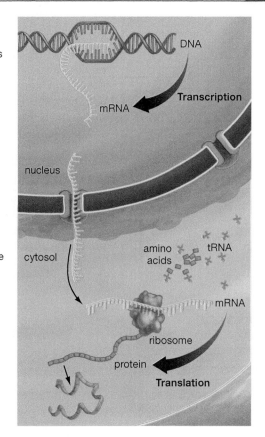

Figure 14.2
The Two Major Stages of Protein Synthesis

(a) Comparison of RNA and DNA nucleotides

(b) Comparison of RNA and DNA three-dimensional structure

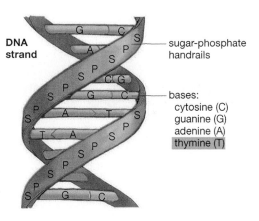

Figure 14.3
RNA and DNA Compared

(a) Each building-block nucleotide of both DNA and RNA is composed of a phosphate group, a sugar—ribose in RNA, deoxyribose in DNA—and one of four bases. RNA and DNA both use the bases adenine, guanine, and cytosine (A, G, and C), but RNA uses the base uracil (U) instead of the thymine (T) that DNA uses.

(b) Both RNA and DNA amount to linked chains of these nucleotides. The "handrails" of both RNA and DNA are composed of the sugar molecule of one nucleotide linked to the phosphate molecule of the next nucleotide (thus the S-P-S-P labeling). The "stairsteps" stemming from the handrails are formed by the bases of the nucleotides.

paired with a free-floating A, and every C is linked with a G, thus yielding a complementary DNA *chain*. Because of RNA's similarity to DNA, the bases RNA has can also form base pairs with DNA. The twist to this RNA–DNA base pairing is that each A on a DNA strand links up with a U on the RNA strand, instead of the T that would be A's partner in DNA-to-DNA base pairing.

You can see how transcription works by looking at **Figure 14.4**. It will come as no surprise to you that an enzyme is critically involved in this process. **RNA polymerase,** as this complex of enzymes is known, actually undertakes two critical tasks: It unwinds the DNA sequence and then strings together a series of RNA nucleotides that is complementary to it, thus producing an initial RNA chain.

In organisms such as ourselves (the eukaryotes), this initial chain is not actually the finished messenger

RNA we've been talking about. Instead, it is an RNA chain called a *primary transcript* that must undergo some modification or "editing" before it qualifies as messenger RNA. You can read more about this editing in section 14.5, on genetic regulation. For now, we'll set it aside and follow the fate of a completed mRNA chain. Before leaving the subject of mRNA, however, here's a more formal definition of it: **Messenger RNA (mRNA)** is a type of RNA that encodes, and carries to ribosomes, information for the synthesis of proteins.

A Triplet Code

Thus far, we have been looking at what might be called the flow of genetic information (from DNA to mRNA). A separate issue in protein synthesis, however, has to do with the linkage between DNA and

Figure 14.4

Transcription Works through Base Pairing

Thanks to their chemical similarity, DNA and RNA can engage in base pairing, and this base pairing is how RNA transcripts are synthesized.

1. RNA polymerase unwinds a region of the DNA double helix.

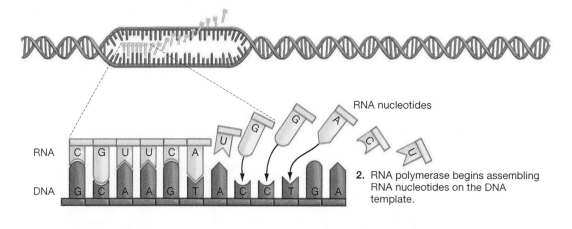

RNA nucleotides

2. RNA polymerase begins assembling RNA nucleotides on the DNA template.

3. The completed portion of the RNA transcript separates from the DNA. Meanwhile, RNA polymerase unwinds more of the untranscribed region of the DNA.

4. The RNA transcript is released from the DNA, and the DNA is rewound into its original form. Transcription is completed.

RNA on the one hand and amino acids on the other. The question here is: How many DNA bases does it take to code for an amino acid? As **Figure 14.5** shows, the answer is three. Each three bases in a DNA sequence pair with three mRNA bases, but each group of three mRNA bases then codes for a *single* amino acid. Each coding triplet of mRNA bases is known, appropriately enough, as a **codon.**

A question that follows is this: If you have a given three mRNA bases, *which* amino acid do they specify? In Morse code, the sounds . — . (short-long-short) code for the letter *R*. But if we know that a given mRNA codon has the base sequence UCC, what *amino acid* does this code for? Today, we know that the answer is serine (ser), but at one time this was not clear. Indeed, it took years for scientists to figure out all the linkages between codons and amino acids. When this work was completed, the result was the **genetic code,** which can be defined as the inventory of linkages between nucleotide triplets and the amino acids they code for. If you look at "The Importance of the Genetic Code" on page 254, you can learn more about the significance of this inventory.

14.4 **A Closer Look at Translation**

With a length of RNA having first been transcribed from a length of DNA and having then moved to a ribosome as mRNA, many of the players are in place for translation—the second stage of protein production.

The Triplet Code

What's also needed, however, are the building blocks of proteins, amino acids. As noted, they are brought to ribosomes by a second form of RNA, called transfer RNA (or tRNA).

The Nature of tRNA

If you look at **Figure 14.6**, you can see why tRNA is aptly placed within the translation phase of protein synthesis. When, in everyday speech, we think of a *translator,* we think of someone who can communicate in *two* languages. Transfer RNA effectively does

Figure 14.5
Triplet Code

Each triplet of DNA bases codes for a triplet of mRNA bases (a codon), but it takes a complete codon to code for a single amino acid.

1. tRNA and amino acids float freely in cytoplasm.

2. tRNA links to an amino acid and transfers it to the ribosome.

3. tRNA links to the appropriate mRNA codon at the ribosome.

4. A polypeptide chain is produced.

mRNA

ribosome

Figure 14.6
Bridging Molecule

Transfer RNA (tRNA) molecules link up with amino acids on the one hand and mRNA codons on the other, thus forming a chemical bridge between the two kinds of molecules in protein synthesis. They also transfer amino acids to ribosomes, as shown in the steps of the figure.

Figure 14.7
The Structure of Transfer RNA

In this two-dimensional model of transfer RNA, one end of the tRNA molecule can be seen binding to a specific amino acid (arg), while the other end binds to its counterpart mRNA codon (CGA).

this. One end of each tRNA molecule links with a specific *amino* acid, which it finds floating free in the cytoplasm. Then, transferring this amino acid to the ribosome, this tRNA molecule binds with a *nucleic* acid—a codon on the mRNA that is moving through the ribosome. Thus, tRNA is binding with two very different kinds of molecules—amino acids on the one

Figure 14.8
The Structure of Ribosomes

hand, nucleic acids on the other—thereby serving as a translator between them. **Transfer RNA (tRNA)** can be defined as a form of RNA that, in protein synthesis, binds with amino acids, transfers them to ribosomes, and then binds with messenger RNA.

Figure 14.7 provides a more detailed look at how transfer RNA carries out this function. You can see that it binds with an mRNA codon by means of three bases it possesses, called an **anticodon.** At its other end (the 12 o'clock position in the figure), there is an attachment site for the amino acid. The linkage between amino acids and tRNA molecules is specific enough that any tRNA that binds to an mRNA codon will be carrying an appropriate amino acid.

The Structure of Ribosomes

You've now been introduced to almost all the players that will be active in protein synthesis at the ribosome. But what is the structure of the ribosome itself? If you look at **Figure 14.8**, you can begin to get an idea. Note that ribosomes are composed of two "subunits"—one larger than the other—both made of a mixture of proteins and yet another type of RNA, **ribosomal RNA (rRNA).** The two subunits may float apart from one another in the cytoplasm until prompted to come together by the process of translation. You can see that when the subunits have been joined, there exist three binding sites (which are convenient to think of as slots), one of them an "E" site, the next a "P" site, and the third an "A" site. You'll be looking at their roles shortly. **Table 14.2** sets forth the three types of RNA reviewed so far that are active in protein synthesis.

The Steps of Translation

With all the players introduced, let's see how translation works. To keep things simple, we'll follow the

(a) Large and small ribosomal units

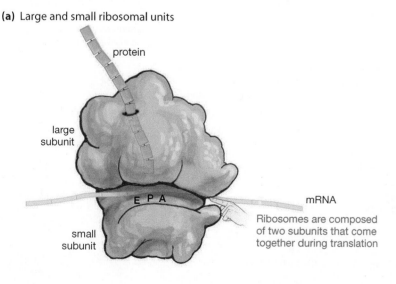

Ribosomes are composed of two subunits that come together during translation

(b) Binding sites in the ribosome

A simplified cross section of the ribosome illustrates the E, P, and A sites where tRNA molecules bind during translation process as it occurs in prokaryotes. Our starting point is an mRNA transcript that is ready to begin binding with a ribosome. Meanwhile, nearby tRNA molecules have linked to their appropriate amino acids.

mRNA Binds to Ribosome, First tRNA Arrives

In this first step, the mRNA chain arrives at the ribosome and binds to the ribosome's small subunit (**Figure 14.9**). The mRNA codon AUG is the usual "start" codon for a polypeptide chain. Next, a tRNA molecule with the appropriate anticodon sequence (UAC) binds to this AUG codon. This tRNA arrives bearing its appropriate amino acid, which is methionine (met).

Polypeptide Chain Is Elongated

Following this, the large ribosomal subunit becomes part of the ribosome, providing the ribosome's A, P, and E binding sites (**Figure 14.10** on the next page). Next, amino acids will start to be joined together in a chain. As you can see, this elongation process begins with a second incoming tRNA molecule binding to an mRNA codon in the A site. Because it's a CUG codon that has moved into the site, a tRNA with a GAC anticodon binds to it. This tRNA comes bearing the amino acid leucine (leu). Now here's how we get the chain: The met amino acid attached to the tRNA in the P site bonds with the leu amino acid attached to the tRNA in the A site. In this process, the bond is broken between met and its original tRNA.

Once this occurs, a kind of molecular musical chairs ensues: The ribosome effectively shifts one codon to the right. With this, the tRNA that had been in the P site is relocated to the E site. What does the E stand for? Exit. The tRNA in this site bears no amino acid now; soon, it will be ejected from the ribosome altogether. Meanwhile, the tRNA that had been in the A site moves to the P site, and a new codon shifts into the now-vacated A site. You can see

what comes next: A tRNA binds with this new codon in the A site. Soon, the growing polypeptide chain will bind with this tRNA's amino acid, and the process will continue.

Termination of the Growing Chain

There are three separate codons that don't code for any amino acid but that instead act as stop signals for polypeptide synthesis. Any time one of these "termination" codons moves into the ribosome's A site, it doesn't bind with an incoming tRNA but instead brings about a severing of the linkage between the P-site tRNA and the polypeptide chain. Indeed, the whole translation apparatus comes apart at this

*Bio***Flix**

Protein Synthesis

Type of RNA	Function	Functions in
Messenger RNA (mRNA)	Carries DNA sequence information to ribosomes	Nucleus, migrates to ribosomes in cytoplasm
Transfer RNA (tRNA)	Provides linkage between mRNA and amino acids; transfers amino acids to ribosomes	Cytoplasm
Ribosomal RNA (rRNA)	Structural component of ribosomes	Cytoplasm

Table 14.2

Types of RNA

First step of translation

1. A messenger RNA transcript binds to the small subunit of a ribosome as the first transfer RNA is arriving. The mRNA codon AUG is the "start" sequence for most polypeptide chains. The tRNA, with its methionine (met) amino acid attached, then binds this AUG codon.

start codon

met

UAC
AUG

mRNA

met

Figure 14.9
How Translation Begins

In this initial step in translation, a messenger RNA chain binds to the small unit of a ribosome, setting the stage for the arrival of the first transfer RNA, which binds with its complementary codon in the mRNA chain.

Translation continues

2. The large ribosomal subunit joins the ribosome, as a second tRNA arrives, bearing a leucine (leu) amino acid. The second tRNA binds to the mRNA chain, within the ribosome's A site.

3. A bond is formed between the newly arrived leu amino acid and the met amino acid, thus forming a polypeptide chain. The ribosome now effectively shifts one codon to the right, relocating the original P site tRNA to the E site, the A site tRNA to the P site, and moving a new mRNA codon into the A site.

4. The E site tRNA leaves the ribosome, even as a new tRNA binds with the A site mRNA codon, and the process of elongation continues.

Figure 14.10
Next Steps of Translation

point, with the polypeptide chain being released to fold up and be processed as a protein. Translation has been completed.

Speed of the Process; Movement through Several Ribosomes

How fast does this process go? Eukaryotic ribosomes can string together up to 4 amino acids per second, which means that an average-sized protein of about 400 amino acids can be completed in less than 2 minutes. Note, however, that mRNA sequences often are read not by one ribosome but by many. As you can see in **Figure 14.11**, several ribosomes—perhaps scores of them— might move over a given mRNA transcript, with the result that identical polypeptide chains grow out of each

ribosome. This greatly increases the number of proteins that can be put together in a given period of time.

SO FAR ...

1. DNA passes on its information to messenger RNA by means of _____.

2. Each three _____ bases code for three _____ bases, which code for one _____.

3. A transfer RNA molecule attaches to an _____ on one end and a _____ on the other.

(a)

(b)

Figure 14.11
Mass Production

(a) An mRNA transcript can be translated by many ribosomes at once, resulting in the production of many copies of the same protein.

(b) A micrograph of this process in operation.

14.5 **Genetic Regulation**

From what you've read so far, you might have gotten the impression that transcription never ends for genes—that all genes are constantly being transcribed, thus bringing about a constant production of the proteins they code for. But a genome that worked like this would be like a restaurant that ceaselessly turned out every dish on its menu, no matter how many customers it had. Life is complex, which means that organisms need to finely tune their production of proteins. To look at but one example of this, after we eat a meal, one of the proteins that comes into play is a hormonal protein, called CCK, that prompts our pancreas to release enzymes that break down the food we've consumed. Now, in a person who hasn't eaten in awhile, the gene for the CCK protein is transcribed only at very low levels. After a person consumes a meal high in proteins and fats, however, the story changes. Now transcription of the CCK gene proceeds at high levels, with the result that much greater quantities of the CCK protein start being produced. In short, the activity of the CCK gene is *regulated*—something that is true of all genes. The protein production you've been reading about operates through a system of genetic regulation that turns out to be very important. Indeed, cutting-edge research conducted over the past decade has begun to suggest that it is the regulation of genes, rather than genes themselves, that has been the most important factor in making human beings as complex as they are and in producing the fantastic diversity we see today in the living world. We'll now go over some of the highlights of genetic regulation, but before we do, we need to look a little more closely at the entity that gets regulated, the **human genome,** defined here as the full complement of DNA found in the nucleus of each human cell.

Our Genome Contains More than Genes

At one time, scientists thought that genes in the human genome sat right beside each other like pearls on a string. Beginning in the 1970s, however, scientists began to realize that the genome contains large segments of DNA that do not code for proteins. Indeed, over time it became apparent that, in all eukaryotic organisms, it is the *coding* sections of the genome that are few and far between. Completion of the Human Genome Project in 2003 revealed that less than 2 percent of the human genome codes for proteins. To gain some perspective on this number, consider that although the DNA in any of our cells would stretch to about 6 feet in length if uncoiled, less than 1 inch of this length is protein-coding sequence.

So, what is the rest of this DNA doing in our genome? When scientists first began to investigate this question, they thought that most non-coding DNA served no function at all. This seemed reasonable since, at the time, long stretches of human DNA were known to have come about through a kind of genetic invasion: During the course of evolution, *viruses* were able to insert their DNA into our genome through a cut-and-paste operation. This would have resulted only in some small additions to the genome but for the fact that some inserted viral sequences could make copies of themselves—copies that *also* got spliced into the genome, along with some internally derived sequences that had this same capability. The ultimate effect of this was big: Some 45 percent of the DNA in our genome seems to have been produced through this copy-and-splice process. Scientists in the early days of DNA sequencing were aware of the origins of this DNA and thus reasonably assumed it amounted to "junk DNA," which is to say DNA that

ESSAY

The Importance of the Genetic Code

Like scholars trying to extract meaning from an ancient written language, biologists in the early 1960s were trying to extract meaning from an ancient molecular language. They knew that triplets of mRNA bases were coding for amino acids, but what was the linkage? If you had a given RNA triplet, *which* amino acid did it code for? Although it took them the better part of a decade to find out, eventually they succeeded. If you look at Figure 1, you can see a summation of their work—the genetic code in its entirety. Let's look a little closer at this code to understand its nature and significance.

One of the notable things about the code is that not every mRNA triplet in it codes for an amino acid. Note, in Figure 1, that three mRNA codons specify "stop" codes that bring an end to the synthesis of a polypeptide chain. One triplet (AUG) specifies a special amino acid, methionine (met), which serves as the starting amino acid for most polypeptide chains. Note also that the genetic code is redundant. The

amino acid phenylalanine (phe), for example, is coded for not only by the UUU triplet but by UUC as well. Indeed, almost all the amino acids are coded for by more than one mRNA codon. Leucine (leu) and serine (ser) are coded for by six.

What is the importance of knowing this code? For one thing, it gives scientists a powerful tool. If they know one "end" of a genetic chain, they are instantly given insight into the other. Knowing something about a DNA sequence means knowing something about a protein sequence—and vice versa. If you know, for example, that a protein has a tryptophan (trp) amino acid at one point in its sequence, you know that a UGG triplet has to exist at a corresponding point in the *messenger RNA* sequence for this protein. This then tells you to look for an ACC sequence at this point in the DNA sequence for the protein.

Apart from providing these kinds of practical linkages, the cracking of the genetic code also had the effect of revealing how unified life is at the genetic level. As

biologists looked among various species at the linkages between DNA sequences and amino acids, they found that, with only a few exceptions, the genetic code is universal in all living things. This means that the base triplet CAC codes for the amino acid histidine, whether this coding is going on in a bacterium or in a human being.

This insight turned out to be important in two ways. First, it is evidence that all life on Earth is derived from a single ancestor. How else can we explain all of life's diverse organisms sharing this very specific code? Such a complex molecular linkage—this triplet equals that amino acid—is extremely unlikely to have evolved *more* than once. What seems likely is that it came to be employed in an ancient common ancestor, after which it was passed on to all of this organism's descendants—every creature that has subsequently lived on Earth. Note, then, that this code has been passed on from one generation to the next, and from one evolving species to the next, for billions of years. We humans share in an informational linkage that stretches back billions of years and runs through all the contemporary living world.

Apart from this, the universality of the genetic code has a very practical consequence. It means that genes from one organism can function in another. This has both good and bad consequences for human beings. First the bad: Viruses that cause diseases ranging from colds to AIDS can "hijack" the human cellular machinery precisely because their genes function in human cells. (The human cellular machinery will put together proteins whether these proteins are called for by human or viral DNA.) Now the good news: Using biotechnology processes you'll be learning about in Chapter 15, human beings can today use viruses and bacteria to manufacture all kinds of products, including medicines such as human insulin and human growth hormone. In these cases, human genes are being put to work inside microorganisms. This transferability of genes from one species to another has, as its basis, the universality of the genetic code.

Figure 1
The Genetic Code Dictionary
If we know what a given mRNA codon is, how can we find out what amino acid it codes for? This dictionary of the genetic code offers a way. Say you want to confirm that the codon CGU codes for the amino acid arginine (arg). Looking that up here, C is the first base (go to the C row along the "first base" line), G is the second base (go to the G column under the "second base" line), and U is the third (go to the codon parallel with the U in the "third base" line).

did neither harm nor good to human beings but that simply resided in the human genome like an uninvited house guest.

A good deal of non-coding DNA may yet turn out to be junk DNA in this sense, but as we'll see, we now have reason to wonder whether any of the 3.2 billion base-pairs in our genome deserves this label. What has been clear for decades, however, is that some of our non-coding DNA does serve a set of vital functions—a set of regulatory functions that we'll now turn to.

Promoters, Enhancers, and Proteins That Bind Them

When organisms develop as embryos, there are genes in them that control the development of their mid-body or "thoracic" structures, such as the vertebrae that make up their backbones. One of these genes, called *Hoxc8*, is nearly identical in creatures as diverse as chickens, mice, and snakes. Yet, as you can see in **Figure 14.12**, a chicken has 7 vertebrae, while a mouse has 13. So the same developmental gene is at work in these two animals, yet it is yielding very different outcomes in them. If we ask what accounts for this, the answer is that the mouse *Hoxc8* is being *transcribed* more than the chicken *Hoxc8*. More transcription means the mouse has more of the protein that *Hoxc8* codes for; this in turn means a broader distribution of this protein in the mouse embryo, and the result is more vertebrae in the mouse.

But why would *Hoxc8* get transcribed more in a mouse than a chicken? You may recall that for any gene to be transcribed, an enzyme complex called RNA polymerase has to go down the line on the gene's sequence, pairing up its DNA bases with complementary RNA bases. But this is not an all-or-nothing proposition. RNA polymerase is *more or less* likely to get busy transcribing a gene depending on how it is chemically positioned on a DNA sequence that lies just "upstream" from the gene. This is the "promoter" sequence that you can see in the figure—our first example of non-coding DNA. For transcription to take place in any gene, a multipart protein complex must bind with the promoter sequence to help RNA polymerase align with it.

The question then becomes: What factors stand to facilitate or impede this alignment? If you look just upstream from the promoter in the figure, you can see a facilitating factor: a sequence called an enhancer. This, too, is a sequence of DNA, but like the promoter, it does not code for anything. Its sole role is to serve as a binding site for proteins that help get RNA polymerase positioned at the promoter. Now, remember that the *Hoxc8* gene is nearly identical in lots of animals. But this is not true of the *Hoxc8* enhancer; its sequence differs markedly from chickens, to mice, to snakes. Accordingly, the mouse's enhancer binds with a different set of aligning proteins than does the chicken's. And these mouse proteins more strongly induce transcription than do the chicken's. The result is more *Hoxc8* transcription in the mouse and ultimately more vertebrae in it.

So, note what's at work here. First, there are two stretches of DNA—the promoter and enhancer

Figure 14.12
Genetic Regulation in Action

(a) For transcription of any gene to begin, RNA polymerase must be aligned at a sequence of DNA called the promoter, which lies just upstream from a given gene—in this case the *Hoxc8* gene. A multipart protein complex, seen here surrounding RNA polymerase, is active in getting a base level of transcription going. Another DNA sequence, called an enhancer, can facilitate transcription by acting as a binding site for other proteins that can interact with the promoter-site protein complex.

(b) The enhancer in the mouse has a different DNA sequence than that of the enhancer in the chicken—a sequence that binds a different set of proteins. These proteins interact with the promoter sequence proteins in such a way as to better align RNA polymerase at the promoter. The result is increased transcription of the *Hoxc8* gene in the mouse.

(a) Chicken

enhancer proteins

enhancer promoter low transcription rate

DNA *Hoxc8* gene

RNA polymerase

7 thoracic vertebrae

transcription complex

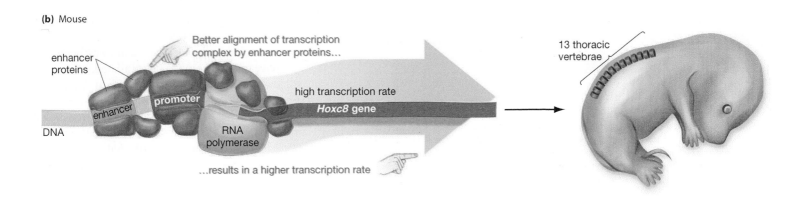

(b) Mouse

Better alignment of transcription complex by enhancer proteins...

enhancer proteins

enhancer promoter high transcription rate

DNA *Hoxc8* gene

RNA polymerase

13 thoracic vertebrae

...results in a higher transcription rate

sequences—that do not code for protein but that do serve a regulatory function (facilitating transcription by RNA polymerase). Second, note what it is that's binding to these regulatory sequences: proteins. One multipart protein complex binds to the promoter sequence (getting a base-level of transcription going), while another complex binds to the enhancer sequence (increasing the rate of transcription). Now, where did these proteins come from? They were produced through transcription and translation, just like any other protein. Thus, DNA codes for proteins that then *feed back* on DNA itself, controlling its transcription. (Appropriately enough, these DNA-binding proteins are called transcription factors.) With this,

1. A length of micro-RNA is transcribed from DNA.

2. Following processing, the micro-RNA binds to a protein complex in the cytoplasm.

3. A messenger RNA (mRNA) arrives at the micro-RNA-protein complex.

4. mRNA binds to the micro-RNA through base pairing.

5. The mRNA is cut in two by the Slicer enzyme within the protein complex.

Figure 14.13
Micro-RNAs and Gene-Silencing

Genes can be silenced through the activity of micro-RNAs—short sequences of RNA that are produced through transcription but that do not code for proteins. Following transcription, each micro-RNA undergoes some processing and then moves to a special protein complex in the cell's cytoplasm. There it binds to a recently produced messenger RNA transcript via complementary base pairing, after which the messenger RNA is cut in two by an enzyme within the complex called Slicer.

you can begin to see what lies at the root of genetic regulation: The whole system is *self*-regulating. DNA brings forth proteins and some of these proteins then go on to control the transcription of DNA.

Finally, notice that it is not necessary to have a change in the sequence of a gene to have a change in the effect of that gene. The mouse and the chicken have the same *Hoxc8* gene; where they differ is in their segments of regulatory DNA for this gene. Over evolutionary time, mutations worked to make the *Hoxc8* regulatory segments different in the two species. So when we think of mutation working hand-in-hand with evolution to channel species in different directions, it's not necessarily a mutation of *genes* that we're talking about; it may be a mutation of regulatory DNA. Indeed, most of the scientists who look at evolution by studying the embryonic development of animals have become convinced that regulatory mutations have been far more important than gene mutations in bringing about the differences we see among animals. Why? Because mutations to regulatory sequences allow an organism to *fine-tune* its use of a protein (as with *Hoxc8*), whereas mutations to protein coding sequences are likely to result in the *elimination* of a protein—often a disastrous event for an organism, since so many proteins serve a vital function.

A Second Form of Regulation: Micro-RNAs

The message "DNA makes RNA makes protein" has come through loud and clear in this chapter, but this message actually needs a little modification. DNA does indeed code for RNA, but not all RNA then goes on to code for protein. As it turns out, some of the RNA that results from transcription ends up serving a bricks-and-mortar function: Once it's produced, it goes on to help make up ribosomes or transfer RNA. But transcription also produces non-coding RNA sequences that are *regulatory*. A collective name for one variety of these sequences is *micro-RNAs*—"micro" because they are only 20 to 22 bases long. So far, about 500 human micro-RNA sequences have been discovered, and one estimate holds that twice that many may actually exist. Almost all of the micro-RNAs identified to date have the effect of reducing the production of specific proteins, and the most common means by which they do this is well known: They interfere with *messenger* RNAs, either by targeting them for destruction or by locking them away before they can move to a ribosome to be translated.

How would this work? If you look at **Figure 14.13**, you can see one example. A length of micro-RNA comes into being through transcription, goes through some processing, and then moves to the cell's cytoplasm, where it's cleaved to a short form that is enclosed in a protein complex that includes an enzyme named Slicer. Each micro-RNA has a base sequence that is

Saccharomyces cerevisiae (baker's yeast)	*Drosophila melanogaster* (fruit fly)	*Caenorhabditis elegans* (roundworm)	*Arabidopsis thaliana* (mustard plant)
Estimated number of genes: 6,034	13,061	19,099	25,000

complementary to a messenger RNA that has recently been produced through transcription. As you might guess, base pairing brings the micro-RNA and mRNA sequences together, at which point Slicer cuts the messenger RNA in two. The result? Decreased production of the protein that the messenger RNA coded for.

Now, it may seem strange that our genome would first produce messenger RNAs that it then goes on to destroy, but in some instances it may be cost-effective to "silence" genes after they have been transcribed rather than to stop their transcription altogether. If we ask how important this gene silencing is, the answer seems to be: very important. In animal studies conducted to date, scientists have found micro-RNAs operating in every organ system they have examined—in the eyes, the lungs, the liver, and the pancreas, for example. And in 2007, several teams of scientists used genetic engineering to produce groups of mice that *lacked* some of their normal micro-RNAs. The result was one group of mice that could not fight off infections and another group that died young because they developed holes in their hearts. You might think that any part of the genetic operation that is this critical would have been well understood for decades. In fact, however, the existence of micro-RNAs was completely unknown to scientists until the late 1990s. Since that time, so many roles have been discovered for them that some scientists have become convinced they are active in regulating all the major metabolic processes in the body.

A Third Form of Regulation: Alternative Splicing

When the first stage of the Human Genome Project was completed in 2000, biologists got a surprise: The human genome was shown to contain far fewer genes than the 100,000 that had been the standard estimate for years. The teams that sequenced the genome first came up with an estimate of about 30,000 human genes and then, three years later, produced the estimate that still stands today—between 20,000 and 25,000 genes. These figures actually were surprising in two ways: We learned from them not only that we have fewer genes than previously imagined but that some rather humble organisms have nearly as many genes as we do. You can see some comparisons in **Figure 14.14**. Note that we humans—with our vision, speech, and 10 trillion cells—have, at most, 6,000 more genes than the microscopic roundworm *Caenorhabditis elegans*, which is eyeless, speechless, and made up of 959 cells. So how are we able to do so much more with our 25,000 genes than the roundworm does with its 19,000? Part of the explanation lies in a third form of genetic regulation.

Remember how, back in this chapter's section on transcription, we noted that the initial length of RNA that is transcribed from DNA—the primary transcript—has to undergo some editing before it becomes messenger RNA? **Figure 14.15** presents the classic view of how this editing takes place. As you can

Figure 14.14
Not as Much Difference as We Thought

Genome sequencing has revealed that the human genome probably contains about 20,000–25,000 genes. This is, at most, about 6,000 more genes than the tiny roundworm *C. elegans* has and about 12,000 more than the *Drosophila* fruit fly has.

Figure 14.15
Editing Out Non-coding Sequences

In eukaryotes, lengths of DNA that are transcribed contain sequences that code for amino acids as well as sequences that do not code for them. Both kinds of sequences are copied onto RNA primary transcripts. Once this is done, however, the non-coding sequences (called introns) are removed by enzymes through the editing process shown, while the coding sequences (called exons) are spliced back together. The result is a messenger RNA molecule.

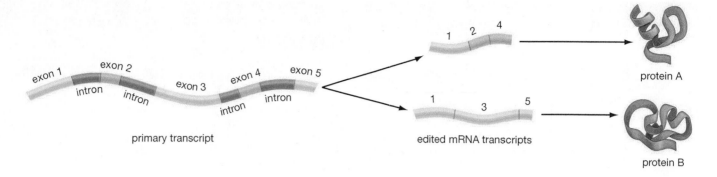

primary transcript

edited mRNA transcripts

protein A

protein B

Figure 14.16
Alternative Splicing

In the figure, a single primary transcript, containing five exons or protein-coding portions, has been transcribed from a single gene. The human genetic machinery can then splice these exons together in alternative ways to yield different proteins— A or B in the figure.

see, the primary transcript has some sequences cut out of it, after which the sequences that remain are spliced back together. The sequences that are cut out are called introns (for *intervening* sequences), while the sequences that are retained are called exons (because most of them are *expressed* as proteins). It is the exons that code for protein, in other words, while the introns are not coding for protein. Given the exons' seemingly more important role, you might think that a gene would mostly be made up of them, but the reverse is true: Introns account for more than 90 percent of the length of the average human gene.

Note that, in the classic view, all the introns are edited out, while all the exons are retained. But if you look at **Figure 14.16**, you can see that many genes are more versatile than this in that their primary transcripts can be edited in different ways. Each of these alternative edits then yields a different messenger RNA, and each of these mRNAs can yield a different protein.

What's at work here is another form of genetic regulation, this one known as **alternative splicing,** a process in which a single primary transcript can be edited in different ways to yield multiple messenger RNAs. This is one of the ways we do so much with our relatively small number of genes. Thanks to alternative splicing, our 20,000–25,000 genes don't produce 20,000–25,000 proteins; they produce more than 90,000 proteins. Under one estimate, 94 percent of human genes undergo alternative splicing, whereas for the *C. elegans* roundworm, the figure is about 10 percent.

The Importance of Genetic Regulation

The three forms of genetic regulation we've looked at may at first just seem to be a fine-tuning of the basic transcription and translation process, but we have reason to believe that regulation is much more important than this. To look at the examples we've just gone over, what gives mice more vertebrae than chickens? What has been the most important genetic factor in producing the various forms of animals seen in the world? What is a critical factor in making human beings more complex than roundworms? In every case, the answer is genetic regulation.

To extend this notion, what makes for complexity when we look across the living world at *many* different kinds of organisms? **Figure 14.17** gives you some idea. What seems to go hand-in-hand with complexity is the proportion of an organism's genome that does *not* code for proteins—the proportion of its genome that potentially is involved in genetic regulation. And here, we humans really do shine. Remember how more than 98 percent of our DNA is non-coding? This is the highest percentage we know of in any organism.

The obvious implication of all this is that the gene—defined here as a sequence of DNA that codes for protein—seems to be just one player in the genetic operation rather than the central player in it. The reason it's necessary to ask whether this is true, however, is that many of the elements of regulation we've just gone over sit right at the cutting edge of contemporary genetics research. The basic process of protein production we looked at earlier—DNA makes RNA makes protein—has been understood

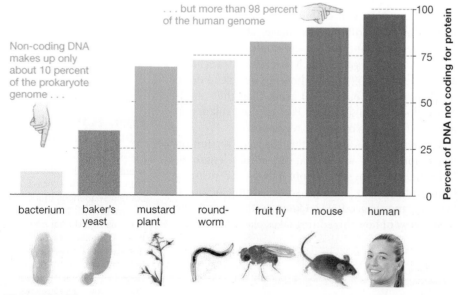

. . . but more than 98 percent of the human genome

Non-coding DNA makes up only about 10 percent of the prokaryote genome . . .

Percent of DNA not coding for protein

bacterium | baker's yeast | mustard plant | round-worm | fruit fly | mouse | human

Figure 14.17
What Makes for Complexity in Living Things?

The seven categories of living things in the figure are arranged from least complex on the left to most complex on the right. Note that complexity in these organisms increases in accordance with the proportion of DNA in their genomes that does not code for proteins.

(Adapted with permission from "Increasing Biological Complexity Is Positively Correlated with the Relative Genome-wide Expansion of Non-Protein-Coding DNA Sequences," Ryan J. Taft and John S. Mattick, *Genome Biology,* 5:1, 23, 2003.)

for decades, at least in outline. We are only beginning to comprehend, however, the nature of microRNAs and some of the non-coding portions of the genome. There are researchers who feel that these component parts of genetics are important enough that we have, in essence, *mis*understood the genetic operation for decades. While the jury is still out on this issue, what is clear is that recent discoveries about regulation and non-coding DNA are forcing biologists to ask fundamental questions about genetics. How does our genetic machinery really work? The hope is that research will soon be providing some answers.

14.6 Genetics and Life

The 20,000–25,000 genes that human beings have are contained in a genome that is about 3.2 billion base pairs long. To make this large number a little less abstract, consider the following exercise. If we took the base sequence of the human genome and simply arrayed the single-letter symbols for the bases on a printed page, going like this:

AATCCGTTTGGAGAAACGGCCCTATTG
GCAGCAAGGCTCTCGGGTCGTCAACG
CGTATTAAACATATTTCAAGGCTCTA ...

it would take about 1,000 telephone books, each of them 1,000 pages long, merely to record it all. We're talking, then, about an unbroken series of these base symbols that goes on for a million pages. That is one measure of the size of the human genome. Simply maintaining this genome—making sure that it is passed on from one cell and generation to another—requires that all of these 3.2 billion bases be faithfully copied each time a cell divides. (They have to be copied twice, actually, because we have two copies of each chromosome.) When we start thinking about *using* this genome—about producing proteins from it—all the layers of genetic regulation just sketched out come into play. Genes help bring about proteins; some of these proteins feed back on other genes and control their production of other proteins; RNA sequences get spliced in different ways, yielding different proteins, and so forth.

The obvious message here is that the human genetic operation is unimaginably complex. But it turns out that humans are only marginally special in this regard. If we were to walk through the genetic operation of even a humble bacterium, you would see that its complexity is stunning, too. What's important to recognize is that this complexity is necessary because it *enables life.* Living things must obtain energy, they must grow, they must respond constantly to their environment, they must reproduce, and they must coordinate all these activities. Only an incredibly sophisticated system of information storage and use could allow a self-contained entity to do all these things. And genetics is exactly such a system. With each twitch of a muscle or swig of a soft drink, information repositories called genes are opened or closed within us, setting in motion the delivery of the tiny working entities called proteins—or stopping delivery of them, if that's what is called for.

Most of the universe is made up of relatively simple, inanimate objects. But we living things are different. We get to inherit and then use an enormous library of information that was amassed by our ancestors over a period of 3.8 billion years. And this endowment has made us complex, capable, and conscious to a greater degree than anything else we know of in the universe. Looked at one way, you might say that all living things are born rich.

Biotechnology Is Next

If each gene in a genome is something like a book in a library, think what the effect would be if organisms could, in effect, check books out of each other's libraries. Actually, you don't have to imagine what this would be like; it's happening right now with great frequency. Soybeans in the fields of Indiana and Iowa have the genes of bacteria spliced into their genomes. And human genes have been spliced into the genomes of bacteria so that these one-celled creatures can turn out human medicines. Moreover, we are now able to read individual letters in our own genetic library with an efficiency that lets us catch criminals on the basis of flakes of dandruff they leave at crime scenes. This may sound fanciful, but it's not. It's biotechnology, the subject of Chapter 15.

SO FAR ...

1. A central feature of genetic regulation is that proteins called transcription factors bind to non-coding _____, thus regulating the _____ of genes.

2. Small lengths of RNA called _____ have the effect of "silencing" genes in the genome by means of targeting their _____ for destruction or otherwise interfering with them.

3. In eukaryotic organisms such as ourselves, the RNA chains, called primary transcripts, that code for proteins must undergo _____ on their way to becoming _____. The segments of the primary transcripts that are removed in this process are called _____, while the segments that are retained are called _____.

Go to the Study Area at www.masteringbiology.com for practice quizzes, myeBook, BioFlix™ 3-D animations, MP3 Tutor Sessions, videos, current events, and more.

Mastering
BIOLOGY

CHAPTER

14 REVIEW

Summary

14.1 The Structure of Proteins

- Proteins are composed of building blocks called amino acids. A string of amino acids is called a polypeptide chain, which when folded into a three-dimensional shape is a protein. Hundreds of thousands of proteins are put together from a starting set of 20 amino acids. The order in which the amino acids are linked in a polypeptide chain determines which protein will be produced. Proteins often are composed of two or more linked polypeptide chains. (p. 245)

14.2 Protein Synthesis in Overview

- There are two principal stages in protein synthesis: transcription, during which the information encoded in DNA is copied onto a length of messenger RNA (mRNA); and translation, during which amino acids brought to a ribosome by transfer RNA (tRNA) molecules are linked together within the ribosome in the order specified by the mRNA sequence. (p. 245)

14.3 A Closer Look at Transcription

- The information in DNA is transferred to mRNA through complementary base pairing. The enzyme RNA polymerase unwinds the DNA sequence to be transcribed and then strings together a chain of RNA nucleotides that is complementary to it. In all eukaryotes, the initial RNA chain transcribed from a DNA sequence is the primary transcript, which must undergo editing before becoming an mRNA chain. (p. 247)

- Each three coding bases of DNA pair with three RNA bases, but each group of three mRNA bases then codes for a single

amino acid. Each triplet of mRNA bases that codes for an amino acid is called a codon. The genetic code is the inventory of linkages between base triplets and the amino acids they code for. (p. 248)

14.4 A Closer Look at Translation

- Transfer RNA serves as a bridging molecule in protein synthesis thanks to its ability to bind with both amino acids and nucleic acids (in the form of mRNA). A given tRNA molecule binds with a specific amino acid in the cell's cytoplasm and then transfers that amino acid to a ribosome in which an mRNA transcript is being "read." There, another portion of the tRNA molecule, an anticodon, binds with the appropriate codon in the mRNA chain. (p. 249)

- Ribosomes, the "workbenches" of protein synthesis, are composed of proteins and ribosomal RNA (rRNA). Each bears A, P, and E binding sites, which tRNA molecules occupy, thus facilitating the synthesis of a polypeptide chain. (p. 250)

- In translation, a succession of tRNA molecules arrive at a ribosome, bound to their appropriate amino acids, and then bind to their appropriate codon in the mRNA transcript. As this proceeds, a succession of amino acids is linked together into a polypeptide chain. (p. 251)

BioFlix™

Protein Synthesis

14.5 Genetic Regulation

- Protein production is carefully regulated in living things in that genes are transcribed in accordance with the needs of an organism. (p. 253)

- Less than 2 percent of the DNA in the human genome codes for proteins.

Some non-coding segments of DNA may be "junk" that never had a function, but scientists are increasingly skeptical that any human DNA fits this description. (p. 253)

- All gene transcription requires that RNA polymerase be properly aligned at a non-coding promoter DNA sequence that lies just "upstream" from a gene sequence. There often is also a non-coding enhancer sequence that lies at some distance from the promoter sequence. Proteins called transcription factors bind to both the promoter and enhancer sequences, thus facilitating the alignment of RNA polymerase at the promoter. Transcription factors are produced through normal transcription and translation. (p. 255)

- DNA codes for several different forms of RNA, but of these, only mRNA then goes on to code for proteins. DNA also codes for several varieties of regulatory RNA, one of which is micro-RNA, most of the known sequences of which reduce the production of particular proteins, often by targeting their mRNAs for destruction. (p. 256)

- In all eukaryotes, the RNA primary transcript undergoes editing in which some sequences (called introns) are cut out and the remaining sequences (called exons) are spliced back together. The result is a completed mRNA chain. Introns do not code for protein, but most exons do. (p. 257)

- Some relatively simple organisms have nearly as many genes as human beings do. Human beings are much more complex than these organisms, however, thanks in part to alternative splicing, in which a primary transcript is edited in different ways, thus yielding different mRNA chains, which in turn result in different proteins. (p. 257)

- Many researchers believe that the regulation of genes is the most important factor in bringing about the differences among organisms. There seems to be little relation between the number of genes an organism has and its complexity. The complexity of organisms does seem to correlate with the proportion of their DNA that does not code for protein. (p. 258)

14.6 Genetics and Life

- Life is made possible by the fantastic ability of genetic systems to store, use, and pass on information. (p. 259)

Key Terms

alternative splicing	258
anticodon	250
codon	249
genetic code	249
human genome	253
messenger RNA (mRNA)	248
polypeptide	245
ribosomal RNA (rRNA)	250
ribosome	246
RNA polymerase	248
transcription	246
transfer RNA (tRNA)	250
translation	246

Understanding the Basics

Multiple-Choice Questions

(Answers are in the back of the book.)

1. A chain of _____ results in a polypeptide chain that folds up into a _____.
   a. RNA bases ... transcript
   b. amino acids ... gene
   c. proteins ... ribosome
   d. DNA bases ... gene
   e. amino acids ... protein

2. The genetic code is an inventory of which _____ specify(ies) which _____.
   a. three mRNA bases ... amino acid
   b. mRNA base ... amino acid
   c. amino acids ... proteins
   d. polypeptide chain ... protein
   e. three DNA bases ... three mRNA bases

3. The "t" of tRNA stands for:
   a. tripartite
   b. teleporting
   c. transfer
   d. tracking
   e. transcribing

4. Which of the following statements is true regarding ribosomes?
   a. They are composed of two separate units, each made of rRNA combined with protein.
   b. They are used to translate the mRNA sequence into a protein composed of amino acids.
   c. They have three different tRNA binding sites
   d. all of the above
   e. a and b only

5. Why can transfer RNA be referred to as a "bridging" molecule?
   a. It forms a chemical bridge between DNA and messenger RNA.
   b. It creates the linkage between the base pairs of the double helix.
   c. It links species through evolution.
   d. It links ribosomes together.
   e. It binds to both amino acids and messenger RNA.

6. A typical eukaryote protein might be _____ amino acids long and could be produced in less than _____ in translation.
   a. 50 ... 5 minutes
   b. 50,000 ... 5 hours
   c. 5 ... 5 seconds
   d. 400 ... 2 minutes
   e. 4,000 ... 4 minutes

7. In one form of genetic regulation, proteins called transcription factors bind to _____, thus facilitating the work of _____.
   a. ribosomes ... transfer RNA
   b. messenger RNA ... ribosomes
   c. non-coding DNA sequences ... RNA polymerase
   d. coding DNA sequences ... RNA polymerase
   e. transfer RNA ... ribosomes

8. An intron is a sequence of _____ RNA that is _____ a primary transcript, while an exon is a sequence of _____ RNA that is _____ a primary transcript.
   a. non-coding ... cut out of ... coding ... left in
   b. transfer ... cut out of ... non-coding ... left in
   c. coding ... left in ... non-coding ... cut out of
   d. transfer ... left in ... transfer ... cut out of
   e. non-coding ... left in ... coding ... left in

Brief Review

(Answers are in the back of the book.)

1. What two great tasks are carried out by the genetic machinery of living things?

2. What are the three types of RNA that are used by a cell any time a protein is produced? What do their abbreviations stand for? What are their functions?

3. Define transcription and translation.

4. During transcription, DNA neither unwinds itself nor pairs its own bases with complementary RNA bases. How are these tasks accomplished?

5. How many DNA bases does it take to code for an RNA codon? How many amino acids does an RNA codon code for?

6. Describe one means by which the genetic operation is self-regulating.

7. What recent research results have given scientists reason to doubt the importance of genes relative to the importance of the regulation of genes?

Applying Your Knowledge

1. Given the following sequence of mRNA, what would the resulting amino acid sequence be?

   AUGAAACGGGGACCAAUGGAUAACUAA

2. If you were a scientist and you found that a given gene was being transcribed, and yet the protein coded for by the gene was not being produced, what would you suspect might be at work?

3. Whether the subject is living things, businesses, or music, do complexity and regulation always go hand in hand?

15

The Future Isn't What It Used to Be:

Biotechnology

By manipulating the information contained in DNA, scientists are raising hopes—and some fears—on a grand scale.

Is it possible to produce an artificial spider's thread? Scientists have done it by splicing genes into bacteria—just one of the marvels made possible through biotechnology.

The little mouse that can be seen in **Figure 15.1** looked typical enough to anyone who saw it after it was born in 2008. It was active, it fed normally, and it even went on to father a litter of healthy offspring. Admittedly, it was produced through cloning, but that in itself wasn't particularly surprising—since the mid-1990s, lots of animals have been produced through cloning. This mouse was different, however, in that it was a clone of a mouse that had been dead for 16 years. To be sure, the body of this "donor" mouse had been kept in a deep freeze for all those years, but outside of this, nothing special had been done to preserve its cells or its DNA. Teruhiko Wakayama and his colleagues in Kobe, Japan, simply thawed out the frozen mouse, isolated some of its DNA, and used a double-round of cloning procedures to produce the mouse in the photo and three more like it.

As you might imagine, the point of this work was not to give the world a few more mice. Instead, Wakayama and his colleagues wanted to know whether it was possible to use tissue that had been frozen to "resurrect" members of a given species. The potential value of this work stemmed from the fact that a growing number of Earth's animals—the Siberian tiger, the white rhino, the mountain gorilla—are teetering on the brink of extinction. Given this, Wakayama reasoned, society may wish to develop a means of bringing such species back *after* all their living members are gone. This kind of resurrection would only be thought of as a last-ditch means of preserving a species—as a procedure that might be employed should all other conservation efforts fail. But in a world where numerous species now have a tenuous grasp on existence, research such as this ultimately could provide society with one last card to play.

As it happened, the very month Wakayama's results were published, society was abuzz with talk of another kind of animal resurrection, this time of a species that *has* gone extinct—a long time ago. Researchers from Pennsylvania State University succeeded in sequencing nearly 3 billion bases of DNA extracted from a Siberian wooly mammoth that died nearly 20,000 years ago. And the scientists who accomplished this feat believe they'll eventually be able to get an accurate reading of the entire 4 billion bases of woolly mammoth DNA. It was a short step from this to wondering whether mammoths could be brought back to life through a combination of genetic engineering and cloning. As it turns out, though, there is a long list of hurdles standing in the way of achieving this resurrection—no one is going to be producing a live woolly mammoth anytime soon. Yet Pennsylvania State researcher Stephan C. Schuster now believes this feat is at least theoretically possible, whereas in the period before his team's sequencing accomplishment, he regarded the idea as "science fiction."

But isn't this the way with science and living organisms these days—things that once were pure fantasy now have actually been done or at least seem conceivable? In one instance after another, scientists working in the field known as biotechnology have been upsetting our notions of what is possible and what is impossible. We may assume that all animals must have both a biological mother and father, but the cloned mice noted earlier arguably had neither. We may assume that humans and sheep are fundamentally separate entities, but scientists have been adding human "stem" cells to sheep fetuses, thus producing sheep that have mostly human liver tissues. Even the simple bacterium routinely has human genes spliced into it, which allows it to turn out human proteins for medical use. Meanwhile, if you have

Figure 15.1
A Live Mouse from Dead Tissue

The brown mouse in the photo is one of four cloned in 2008 from a mouse that died 16 years earlier. In the intervening years, the cloned mouse's tissues were kept frozen.

eaten anything made from soybeans recently, you probably have eaten food from a plant that was bioengineered. And if a criminal in your town leaves so much as six or seven skin cells on the steering wheel of a car, chances are police will be able to get a DNA profile of him, which would be bad news for him if a DNA profile of him already exists in a police database.

Taken together, achievements such as these amount to a revolution; but like all revolutions, this one seems to be inspiring both hope and fear in equal measure. For many people, the idea of bringing an animal species back from the dead doesn't mean we're living in a world that is better controlled; it means we're living in a world that is out of control. Forget about the "promise" of biotechnology, this view goes; just put the genie back in the bottle. On the other hand, who wouldn't want better medicines or cheaper foods?

In thinking about such questions, it's helpful to view biotechnology not as a monolithic entity, but rather as a collection of separate *capabilities.* There is the capability to clone, the capability to splice genes into organisms, and so forth. The purpose of this chapter is to provide you with a basic understanding of some of these capabilities. Once you see what's at work in them, you'll be in a better position to make judgments about the degree to which biotechnology holds promise or peril.

15.1 What Is Biotechnology?

The term *biotechnology* is familiar to most of us, but what does it really mean? **Biotechnology** can be defined as the use of technology to control biological processes as a means of meeting societal needs. One biological process that can be controlled is the way a cell copies its DNA every time it divides. In the 1980s, a California scientist realized there was a way to use technology to exploit this natural copying, such that a tiny DNA sample could rapidly be copied over and over, thus yielding a relatively large DNA sample. One result of this *polymerase chain reaction* or PCR process is the ability police have to get DNA "matches" in criminal cases on the basis of tiny flecks of human tissue. Like other biotech processes we'll be looking at, PCR is a marriage of both biology and technology. By the time you finish this chapter, you'll see why biotechnology is such an appropriate term.

Because biotechnology is so varied, any account of it has to be limited to a few examples chosen from among thousands that exist. In this chapter, we will consider four aspects of biotechnology:

- Transgenic biotechnology—the splicing of DNA from one species into another
- Reproductive cloning—the production of mammals through cloning
- Cell reprogramming—the production of needed cell types through the reprogramming of genomes

- Forensic biotechnology—the use of biotechnology to establish identities (of criminals, of crime victims, and so forth)

Let's start now by reviewing an area of biotechnology in which genes are moved from one organism to another.

15.2 Transgenic Biotechnology

Human beings grow to their full height under the influence of human growth hormone (HGH), which normally is secreted by the human pituitary gland. HGH's role in promoting growth is, of course, most important during childhood and adolescence. A faulty pituitary gland can greatly reduce the amount of HGH young people have in their system, leaving them abnormally short. For years, the only way to get HGH was to laboriously extract it from the pituitaries of dead human beings, a practice that not only yielded too little HGH to go around but that also turned out to be unsafe.

Enter biotechnology, which in the mid-1980s produced synthetic HGH in the following way. Using collections of human cells, the gene for HGH was snipped out of the human genome and inserted into the *Escherichia coli* bacterium. Each bacterium that took on the HGH gene began transcribing and then translating this gene, which is to say turning out a small quantity of HGH protein. These bacteria were then grown in vats by the billions. The result? Collectible quantities of HGH, clinically indistinguishable from that produced in human pituitary glands, manufactured by a biotech firm, and shipped to pharmacies worldwide.

Note that in this process, a gene was taken from one species (a human being) and spliced into another species (a bacterium). With this, the bacterium became a **transgenic organism:** an organism whose genome has stably incorporated one or more genes from another species. This same phenomenon is repeated time and time again in biotechnology. The goats you can see in **Figure 15.2** are transgenic—they have incorporated a human gene into their genome. But how is this possible? How do you cut DNA out of one genome and paste it into another? To get an answer, we'll take a walking tour of some basic biotech processes. As a starting point, imagine that, as with human growth hormone, the goal is to produce quantities of a hypothetical human protein through the use of a living organism.

A Biotech Tool: Restriction Enzymes

In the early 1970s, it became possible for scientists to cut genomes at particular places, with the discovery of **restriction enzymes.** These are enzymes, occurring naturally in bacteria, that are used in biotechnology to cut DNA into desired fragments. (In nature, bacteria use them to cut up the DNA of invading viruses.) In isolating restriction enzymes, scientists found that many of them had a wonderful property: They didn't

Figure 15.2
Transgenic Animals
A firm called GTC Biotherapeutics has specialized in splicing human DNA into the genomes of goats. The result is goat's milk that contains therapeutic human proteins, among them a protein called antithrombin that prevents the formation of blood clots.

just cut DNA randomly; they cut it at very specific places. Here is how it works with an actual restriction enzyme called *Bam*HI. The two strands of DNA's double helix are complementary, as we've seen, and they also happen to run in opposite directions. Thus, the sequence GGATCC would look like **Figure 15.3** if we were viewing both strands of the helix.

Now, the *Bam*HI restriction enzyme will move along the double helix, leaving the DNA alone until it comes to this series of six bases, known as its recognition sequence, and here it will make identical cuts on both strands of the DNA molecule, always between adjacent G nucleotides. When another *Bam*HI mole-

cule encounters another GGATCC sequence, it also makes cuts, which effectively is like making a second cut in a piece of rope, giving us rope *fragments*. *Bam*HI's recognition sequence may be GGATCC, but another restriction enzyme will have a different recognition sequence and will make its cuts between a different pair of bases. Indeed, several thousand restriction enzymes have been identified so far, which cut in hundreds of different places

Note that with *Bam*HI each of the resulting DNA fragments has one strand that protrudes. Restriction enzymes that make this kind of cut are particularly valuable for they produce "sticky ends" of DNA, so named because they have the potential to *stick to* other complementary DNA sequences. In the fragment on the lower left in Figure 15.3, for example, the protruding sequence CTAG could now easily form a base pair with any piece of DNA whose sequence is the complementary GATC. So great is the need for restriction enzymes that they can now be ordered from biochemical suppliers, much as a person might order a set of socket wrenches from a hardware store.

Another Tool of Biotech: Plasmids

From our look at manufacturing human growth hormone, recall that the human gene for HGH was inserted into *E. coli* bacteria, which then started turning out quantities of this protein. The question is, how did this human gene get into a bacterium? Several methods of transfer are available, but for now let's focus on a specific kind of DNA delivery vehicle. As it turns out, bacteria have small DNA-bearing units that lie *outside* their single chromosome. These are the **plasmids,** extra-chromosomal rings of bacterial DNA that can be as little as 1,000 base pairs in length

1. A portion of a DNA strand, highlighted here, has the recognition sequence GGATCC.

2. A restriction enzyme moves along the DNA strand until it reaches the recognition sequence and makes a cut between adjacent G nucleotides.

3. A second restriction enzyme makes another cut in the strand at the same recognition sequence, resulting in a DNA fragment.

Figure 15.3
The Work of Restriction Enzymes

(**Figure 15.4**). Plasmids can replicate independently of the bacterial chromosome, but just as important for biotech's purposes, they can *move into* bacterial cells.

How do plasmids do this? Bacteria are capable of taking up DNA from their surroundings, after which this DNA will function—that is, code for proteins—inside the bacterial cells. Appropriately enough, this process is known as **transformation:** a cell's incorporation of genetic material from outside its boundary. Some bacterial cells are naturally adept at transformation, while others, such as *E. coli*, can be induced to perform it by means of chemical treatment. Critically, plasmid DNA can be taken in via transformation and continue to function, as plasmid DNA, inside the bacteria.

Using Biotech's Tools: Getting Human Genes into Plasmids

At this point, you know about a couple of tools in the biotech tool kit: restriction enzymes and the transformation process involving plasmids. Let's now see how they work together. As you can see in **Figure 15.5**, the process starts with a gene of interest in the human genome. The first step is to use restriction enzymes on this human DNA. Knowing, say, the starting and ending sequence of the gene of interest, a restriction enzyme is selected that allows part of the genome to be cut into a manageable fragment including this sequence of interest, preferably in a sticky-ended form.

Here's where the beauty of restriction enzymes really comes into play. If the same restriction enzyme is now used on the DNA of isolated *plasmids,* the result is complementary sticky ends of plasmid and human DNA. In other words, these segments of human and plasmid DNA, through sticky-ended base pairing, fit together like puzzle pieces.

When the DNA fragments are mixed with the "cut" plasmids, that's just what happens: Human and plasmid DNA form base pairs, and the human DNA is incorporated into the plasmid circle. With this, a segment of DNA that was once part of the human genome has now been *re-combined* with a different stretch of DNA (the plasmid sequence). This process gives us the term **recombinant DNA,** defined as two or more segments of DNA that have been combined by humans into a sequence that does not exist in nature.

Getting the Plasmids Back inside Cells, Turning out Protein

To this point, what has been done is to produce a collection of independent plasmids having a human gene as part of their makeup. Remember, though, the goal is to turn out quantities of whatever protein the human gene is coding for. To do this requires a vast quantity of plasmids working away, which means working away *back inside* bacterial cells, and it's here that transformation comes into play. If the plasmids are put into a medium containing specially treated bacterial cells, a few of these cells will take up plasmids through transformation (at which point these cells have become transgenic, as noted earlier). Once this happens, the plasmids start *replicating* along with the bacterial cells themselves. As one bacterial cell becomes two, two become four, and so on, the plasmids are replicating away as well (Figure 15.5). And as the cell count reaches into the billions, collectible quantities of the protein begin to be turned out via instructions from the human gene inserted into the plasmid DNA.

A Plasmid Is One Kind of Cloning Vector

In this example, plasmids were the vehicle that served to take on some foreign DNA and then to ferry it into working bacterial cells. Note, however, that plasmids are only one vehicle among several that can be used. Collectively, such vehicles are known as **cloning vectors,** meaning self-replicating agents that serve to transfer and replicate genetic material. Next to plasmids, the most common cloning vector is a type of virus that infects bacteria—a bacteriophage.

Real-World Transgenic Biotechnology

The example we just went over concerned a hypothetical medicine, but lots of actual medicines are being produced through biotechnology today. By one industry count, more than 250 biotechnology drugs and vaccines have been approved by the U.S. Food and Drug Administration. We've already touched on one biotech medicine: the human growth hormone that is produced inside the *E. coli* bacterium. As it turns out, *E. coli* is something of a workhorse in medical biotech. Human insulin and several kinds of cancer-fighting compounds are also produced through it.

E. coli and its fellow bacteria are not the only transgenic "bio-factories" used in medical biotech-

Figure 15.4
Transfer Agent

Plasmids are small rings of bacterial DNA that are not a part of the bacterial chromosome. They can exist outside bacterial cells and then be taken up by these cells. This artificially colored micrograph shows a type of plasmid, from *E. coli* bacteria, that is commonly used in genetic engineering.

bacterium

bacterial chromosome

plasmid

Figure 15.5
How to Use Bacteria
to Produce a Needed
Human Protein

human cell containing
gene of interest

bacterium

DNA

protein
synthesis

human protein
of interest

bacterial
chromosome

plasmid

Use same restriction
enzyme to snip
plasmid.

1. Use restriction enzymes
to snip gene of interest
from the isolated human
genome.

recombinant DNA

2. Insert gene into plasmid
(complementary sticky ends
will fit together).

transformation

3. Transfer the plasmid
back into bacterial cell.

replication

4. Let bacterial cells
replicate. Harvest and
purify the human protein
produced by the plasmids
inside the bacterial cells.

bacterial
clones

nology, however. Yeast, hamster cells, and even mammals are used in this way as well. Goats of the type pictured in Figure 15.2 produce several kinds of human proteins in their milk, including one called antithrombin that prevents the formation of blood clots. You might wonder why large, expensive goats would be used to turn out proteins when small, inexpensive bacteria are available. The answer is that lactating goats naturally produce a tremendous amount of protein. A single goat can produce as much antithrombin in a year as can be derived from 90,000 human blood donations. You also might wonder how a human gene can be spliced into a goat genome. The answer is, through the splicing of a human gene into a single goat cell and then a cloning of an adult goat from that cell.

Genetically Modified Food Crops

Animals are not the only kind of transgenic organisms. You may have heard of genetically modified, or "GM," food crops. It won't surprise you to hear that all of these crops are transgenic. If you look at **Figure 15.6** on the next page, you can see a transgenic rice that has been dubbed "golden rice" because of its ability to produce its own beta carotene, which the human body converts to vitamin A. Conventional rice does not contain beta carotene, and this fact has health consequences. The World Health Organization estimates that half a million children go blind each year from vitamin A deficiency and that one to two million children die from it. The hope is that golden rice can help alleviate this problem (though this is a hope that has existed for a long time now). Golden rice actually is transgenic in more ways

Figure 15.6
A More Nutritious Rice
Grains of the genetically engineered "golden rice" stand out next to grains of ordinary rice. The rice has a golden color because it is able to produce its own beta carotene, which the human body converts into vitamin A.

than one: Genes from both a bacterium and a daffodil have been spliced into it.

Though the public seems scarcely aware of it, several other transgenic food crops are in full commercial production right now. Indeed, in the United States, 92 percent of all soybeans, 86 percent of all cotton, and 80 percent of all corn crops currently are genetically modified, though only for a couple of limited purposes. One of these is to allow the crops to resist insects; the other is to allow them to tolerate the chemical weed killers known as herbicides. So, why is biotechnology's role in agriculture so limited? Stay tuned.

SO FAR . . .

1. A transgenic organism is one whose genome has stably incorporated one or more _____ from _____.

2. DNA is cut into useful fragments through use of the molecular scissors known as _____.

3. The plasmids noted in the text had _____ DNA spliced into them as a first step in using them to turn out a human _____.

15.3 Reproductive Cloning

The concept of *cloning* has come up a couple of times so far. Thanks mostly to movies, this word has taken on some sinister implications, as if biological cloning were inherently a Frankenstein-like procedure. But it need be no more threatening than the process of making copies of a single gene. To **clone** simply means "to make an exact genetic copy of." An individual clone is one of these exact genetic copies. Thus, in the biotech

world, the gene for human growth hormone is cloned by means of being snipped out of the human genome and then copied within bacterial cells. A collection of such cells can be thought of as a single clone because all of them are genetically identical. (One bacterium splits into two, and both "daughter" cells are genetic replicas of the parent cell.)

Cloning can involve not just bacteria, however, but larger organisms as well. Human beings actually have been making clones for centuries, although by low-tech rather than high-tech means. Some "cuttings" taken from a plant and put into soil can grow into a whole new plant. When this happens, there is no mixing of eggs and sperm from two different plants. The new plant comes entirely from one individual—the original plant—and thus meets the definition of a clone in that it is an exact genetic copy of another entity.

All this said, in recent years biotechnology has greatly expanded the range of what can be cloned. The potential for such cloning appears to be very broad indeed—something that has inspired both great optimism and great concern. Biotechnology has now joined with various reproductive technologies to produce clones not just of genes or cells or plants but of mammals, with the starting cells for these mammals coming from adult mammals. Though we've mentioned a couple of these cloned animals already, the most famous one by far is Dolly the sheep, cloned by researcher Ian Wilmut and his colleagues in Scotland in 1997 (**Figure 15.7**). Dolly and similar animals are products of **reproductive cloning:** cloning intended to

Figure 15.7
Revolutionary Sheep
Dolly, the first mammal ever cloned from an adult mammal, is shown here as a young sheep with her surrogate mother.

produce adult mammals of a defined genotype. Powerful in its own right, this procedure gains added potential when combined with the basic biotech processes you've been reviewing.

Reproductive Cloning: How Dolly Was Cloned

Dolly, who died in 2003, was a clone as that term is defined: She was, to a first approximation, an exact genetic replica—in this case, of another sheep. Here's how she was produced (**Figure 15.8**). A cell was taken from the udder of a six-year-old adult sheep and cultured in the laboratory, meaning that the original cell divided into many "daughter" cells. While this was going on, researchers took an *egg* from a second sheep and removed its nucleus, meaning they removed all its nuclear DNA. Then they placed the udder cell (which had DNA) next to the egg cell (which did not have DNA) and applied a small electric current to the egg. This had two effects: It caused the two cells to fuse into one, and it mimicked the stimulation normally provided when a *sperm* cell fuses with an egg. With this, the udder cell DNA began to be reprogrammed. As a result of this reprogramming, the fused cell started to develop as an embryo. (Though the egg cell had its DNA removed, it still contained all kinds of egg-cell proteins whose normal function is to trigger development of an embryo. It was these factors still in the egg that reprogrammed the donor-cell DNA.) After the embryo had developed to a certain point, the researchers implanted it in a third sheep, which served as a surrogate mother. The result, 21 weeks later, was the lamb Dolly, who went on to give birth to two sets of her own lambs.

Every cell in Dolly had DNA in its nucleus that was an exact copy of the DNA in the six-year-old donor sheep. Thus, Dolly was a clone of that sheep. There was no second parent contributing chromosomes to Dolly, no mixing of genetic material at the moment of conception—just a copying of one individual from another. The procedure through which she was cloned is known today as **somatic cell nuclear transfer (SCNT):** a means of cloning mammals through fusion of one somatic (non-sex) cell with an egg cell whose nucleus has been removed (an "enucleated" egg cell).

Cloning and Recombinant DNA

Once Dolly was born, science was off to the races in terms of producing clones of mammals. To date, horses, mules, cows, pigs, cats, mice, goats, and dogs are among the animals that have been cloned, almost all of them through SCNT. But to what end? That is, what use do scientists have for these animals? Actually, we've already talked about one use. Remember the cloned goats we looked at earlier—the transgenic ones able to produce human proteins in their milk? They are intended to serve as living factories for

human medicines. (Indeed, this is the role Ian Wilmut and his colleagues envisioned for cloned animals before they ever produced Dolly.) Along other lines, scientists have now produced cloned pigs whose tissues have been engineered to contain high levels of heart-healthy omega-3 fats.

In both these examples, we can see something that is true of reproductive cloning in general: So far, it's

Figure 15.8
How Dolly Was Cloned

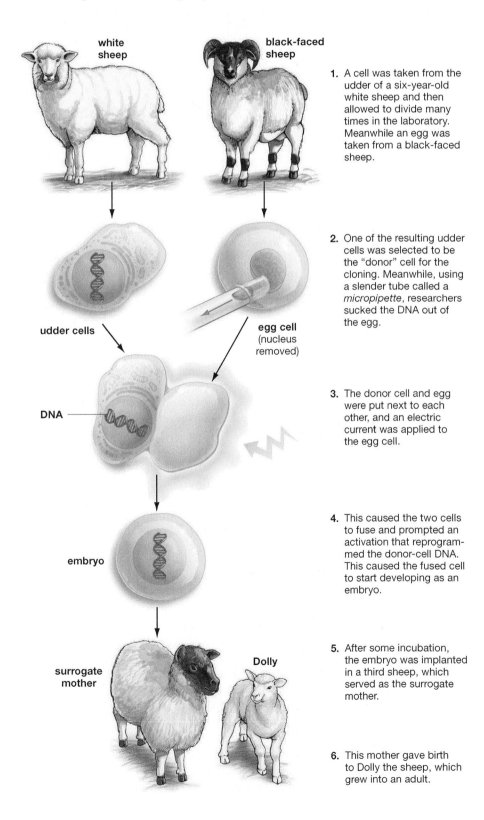

1. A cell was taken from the udder of a six-year-old white sheep and then allowed to divide many times in the laboratory. Meanwhile an egg was taken from a black-faced sheep.

2. One of the resulting udder cells was selected to be the "donor" cell for the cloning. Meanwhile, using a slender tube called a *micropipette*, researchers sucked the DNA out of the egg.

3. The donor cell and egg were put next to each other, and an electric current was applied to the egg cell.

4. This caused the two cells to fuse and prompted an activation that reprogrammed the donor-cell DNA. This caused the fused cell to start developing as an embryo.

5. After some incubation, the embryo was implanted in a third sheep, which served as the surrogate mother.

6. This mother gave birth to Dolly the sheep, which grew into an adult.

envisioned not so much as a means of producing genetic copies of normal animals; rather, it's seen as a means of producing genetically *altered* animals that can serve some special purpose. It is true that for a hefty fee (at least $140,000 at present), you can get a clone of your favorite dog. And, as noted earlier, scientists are looking into cloning as a means of preserving endangered species. But by and large, cloning today is thought of as a means of producing animals whose genomes have been manipulated to bring about special traits (such as producing human proteins). Scientists know how to make single cells genetically capable of bringing about such traits. What cloning does is provide a way to go from an altered single cell to a full-grown animal.

Human Cloning

Reproductive cloning may interest scientists because of its potential to yield products such as medicines, but it has captured the attention of the average person because it raises the possibility of *human* cloning. Despite some grandiose claims to the contrary, we have no reason to believe that a human being has ever been cloned so far. But this does not mean that the feat is technically impossible or that it will never be attempted.

The prospect of a human clone is so dizzying that it's worthwhile to think about what such a person would represent in biological terms. He or she would be a genetic replica of the person who provided the donor cell with the DNA in it. One helpful way to think of this person's biological status is in terms of a more familiar concept: that of an identical twin. As it happens, identical twins also are genetic replicas of one another. Early in a human pregnancy, separate cells from a single embryo can start forming as two separate embryos, and the result is identical twins. Cloning is a *different* means of producing genetically identical individuals, but the critical point is that a donor and a clone would be no more alike than two identical twins.

The parallels between twins and clones end there, however, because the donor-DNA cell for a clone can come from so many different sources. It could, for example, come from a person of any age—an 80-year-old, an 8-year-old; it could even come from a fetus. Indeed, the donor cell used in cloning need not even come from a living person. In 2001, an American couple sought help in cloning their son, who had died in a hospital operation at the age of 10 months. How could this boy be cloned? Through the use of cells that were taken from him while he was alive and then frozen. It was these cells that the parents proposed to use as the donor-DNA cells in cloning the boy (which was never attempted).

Given possibilities such as these, the prospect of a human clone has the power to stun us—generally to repulse us, to judge by news reports. And scientists are no different than average citizens in their aversion to the idea of human cloning. But does this mean that no scientist in the world would be willing to undertake the procedure? Actually, several have already announced that they are willing to carry it out, despite the fact that cloning today remains a largely *experimental* procedure that often results in animals that have serious physical defects. As Ian Wilmut has written with cloning expert Rudolf Jaenisch:

> Newborn clones often display respiratory distress and circulatory problems, the most common causes of neonatal death. Even apparently healthy survivors may suffer from immune dysfunction, or kidney or brain malformation, which can contribute to death later.

With possibilities such as these in mind, would anyone actually attempt to clone a human being? Only time will tell.

SO FAR . . .

1. To "clone" means to make an exact _____.

2. Reproductive cloning is cloning intended to produce _____ of a defined genotype.

3. Dolly was a clone of the sheep who _____.

15.4 Cell Reprogramming

In one way, human cells are like human beings: They start off with the potential to be lots of things, but eventually most of them commit themselves to being just one thing. This course of events takes place during human "development," meaning the process by which an embryo becomes a fully formed human being. Early in this process, cells need to be adaptable enough to go down different developmental pathways. Why? Because the embryo is developing in so many basic ways. For example, it needs to create both muscle cells and bone cells. Fortunately, there is a type of embryonic cell that is flexible enough to give rise to either type of cell. As time goes on, however, more and more tissues become fully specialized, which means there is less and less need for cells that are developmentally flexible. By the time humans reach adulthood, specialization has almost completely won out over flexibility. The vast majority of cells in our bodies have undergone what is known as *commitment*: a developmental process that results in cells whose roles are completely determined. Almost all your muscle cells, for example, are committed in that they can be nothing but muscle cells and can give rise to nothing but muscle cells.

The problem with this sequence of events is that the tissues of fully developed human beings can become damaged. They break down or become diseased; they are injured in car accidents or fires. And many damaged tissues will not regenerate themselves. A person whose spinal cord is damaged does not generate a new spinal cord. Thus, for medicine, the question for decades has been: Could we use developmental processes to generate new tissues? One obvious way to go about this would be to harness the power of the cells that, in nature, generate new kinds of tissue—early embryonic cells. For most of the past 10 years, one variety of these cells, *embryonic stem cells* (ESCs), seemed to hold the most promise to generate needed human tissues. All this changed in 2007, however, with the announcement by two teams of scientists that they had been able to transform ordinary adult skin cells into cells that have all the developmental power of ESCs. These induced pluripotent stem cells (iPS cells) thus join ESCs in having the potential to generate needed human tissues.

As we'll see, the commonality between ESCs and iPS cells is that they represent two forms of *cell reprogramming*: ESCs are being reprogrammed to yield desired cell types and ordinary adult cells are being reprogrammed to yield iPS cells that then go on to yield desired cell types. The challenge now before scientists is to use both forms of reprogramming to generate large quantities of very specialized cells—those that can take on specific tasks after being introduced into diseased or damaged human bodies. Let's take a look now at some of the ways scientists are attempting to do this, first in connection with ESCs.

Embryonic Stem Cells

A **stem cell** can be defined as any cell that can give rise to more cells of its kind, along with at least one variety of specialized cell. At different stages of life, human bodies possess different kinds of stem cells, but we'll limit our consideration here to a single variety of stem cell—one that in nature exists only in the first few weeks of human life.

When human sperm and egg come together, they create a fertilized egg (an embryo) that has begun to undergo cell division. If we go forward about five days from the first division, the embryo has developed into a hollowed-out, fluid-filled ball of 100–150 cells—a **blastocyst.** One section of the blastocyst becomes the placenta that will help nurture a growing embryo, while another section, called the inner cell mass, constitutes the embryo itself (**Figure 15.9**). It is the cells of this latter section that interest us, for these are **embryonic stem cells (ESCs),** which can be defined as cells from the blastocyst stage of a human embryo that are capable of giving rise to all the types of cells in the adult body.

Given a developmental power this extensive, you might wonder why the medical potential of ESCs wasn't realized years ago. The answer is that it was only in 1998 that scientist James Thomson of the University of Wisconsin, Madison, succeeded in *culturing* ESCs—that is, in getting them to go through cell division outside of embryos, in laboratory containers. Only with this advance could scientists begin to work with ESCs, channeling groups of them down different developmental pathways—toward becoming nerve or heart cells, for example.

So far, the high-water mark of this channeling has been the development of cells that can produce a type of nervous system tissue, called myelin, that normally wraps around cells called neurons. In victims of spinal cord injuries, this myelin wrapping often is destroyed at the site of injury, and there is no natural way for it to be regenerated. The good news for spinal cord patients is that, in 2005, researchers in California coaxed human ESCs into becoming myelin-producing nerve cells. Better yet, when these cells were injected into the spinal cords of rats whose spinal cords had been damaged, the new cells started producing a myelin covering around spinal cord neurons in the damaged area. The result? Rats who had been paraplegic—who had lost control of their hind legs—regained enough function in them to do a kind of impaired walking, rather than dragging themselves along with their front legs.

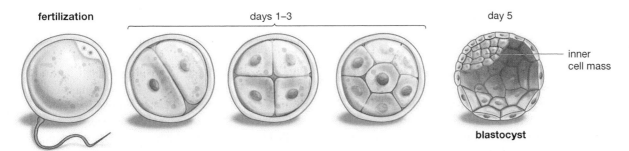

fertilization **days 1–3** **day 5**

inner cell mass

blastocyst

Figure 15.9
Cells with a Great Ability to Specialize
Human development starts with the fertilization of egg by sperm, after which the resulting embryo proceeds through several days of cell division. By day 5, it has developed into a hollow ball of 100–150 cells called a blastocyst. In nature, one segment of the blastocyst, the inner cell mass, develops into the baby.

At the moment, the pharmaceutical company that financed this research is preparing to proceed with the first human trials of this regeneration procedure.

In ESC work of this sort, the cell reprogramming noted earlier takes place when scientists coax ESCs down a desired developmental pathway. Without this guidance, ESCs would only produce more of themselves. By adding the right chemical compounds to a culture of ESCs, however, scientists get more ESCs along with cells of the desired type. The ability of ESCs to generate more of themselves is important in itself, however, for it is this ability that allows ESCs to *keep on* producing specialized cells in large numbers. In the myelin-regeneration experiments noted above, scientists had to inject a pea-size volume of about 1.5 million nerve cells into the spinal cord of each rat—a volume that would have been impossible to produce had each ESC been generating nothing but nerve cells.

This regenerative capacity of ESCs is then linked to a second ability they have, which is their power to produce many different *types* of cells (something that's not surprising, given that, in nature, they end up giving rise to every kind of cell in the body). Thus far, researchers have managed to coax ESCs into producing nerve cells, heart cells, immune cells, blood cells, and more.

Given strengths such as these, you might think the future of ESCs in medicine would be assured, but this is not the case. For one thing, a number of basic questions about these cells have to be answered before they can be used in connection with most human illnesses. Once cells derived from ESCs have been implanted, can we be sure they won't then differentiate further—into other types of specialized cells? Can implanted cells be counted on to stay where they are needed, rather than "migrating" to other areas? Serious as such questions are, they may actually end up playing a minor role in deciding whether ESCs have a future in medicine. A bigger threat to them at the moment is that their role might be usurped by a different kind of stem cell—one whose discovery was driven in part by a moral issue surrounding ESCs.

The Fight over Embryonic Stem Cells

To state the obvious, human embryonic stem cells come from human embryos—from collections of cells that have the potential to become fully formed human beings. Where do researchers get the embryos that are the source of ESCs? Almost always from fertility clinics, which each year discard thousands of excess embryos that have been produced for in vitro fertilizations. (A couple undergoing fertility treatments generally will produce more embryos than they need to bring about a pregnancy. With the couple's consent, excess embryos that would have been discarded are used instead in scientific research.) When scientists extract stem cells from these early stage embryos, however, the embryos are destroyed, and this is a matter of great concern to many people. For them, the destruction of an embryo is a destruction of human life. In contrast, many people feel that an embryo in the blastocyst stage represents only a *potential* human life. And others hold that, no matter what one's view of this issue, society has a greater responsibility toward impaired children and adults than it does toward embryos.

Deeply held beliefs such as these eventually resulted in a national political decision: In 2001, then-President George Bush decided that the federal government—the country's largest single source of biological research funds—would severely restrict funding for research on embryonic stem cells. (Only those genetically identical "lines" of stem cells in existence at the time the president made his decision were eligible for federal funding.) Apart from limiting funding for ESC research, this decision greatly disrupted ongoing ESC research. Single research labs that got both private and federal funding had to maintain clear lines of separation—often a physical separation—between their federally funded and privately funded research operations. After 2001, then, the scientific community had a great impetus to develop stem cells that were not derived from human embryos. Eventually, two groups of scientists succeeded in doing exactly this.

Induced Pluripotent Stem Cells

In December 2007, scientific teams led by Shinya Yamanaka of Kyoto University in Japan and James Thomson of the University of Wisconsin, Madison, announced that, by inserting just four developmental genes into ordinary adult skin cells, they had been able to produce cells that have all the generative potential of ESCs (**Figure 15.10**). These are the **induced pluripotent stem cells (iPS cells)** noted earlier: cells that have been induced into a state of pluripotency through the introduction of genes from outside their genome. (A "pluripotent" cell is simply one that is capable of giving rise to all the types of cells in the body. Thus, both iPS cells and ESCs are pluripotent.)

In the years since iPS cells were unveiled, they have lived up to their initial billing—they do seem to have all the developmental power of ESCs without carrying any of the moral baggage associated with ESCs. Because iPS cells are derived from ordinary cells, the sources for them can be small samples of tissue taken harmlessly from a person of any age. Indeed, cells called keratinocytes, which are abundant in hair, have turned out to be particularly easy to reprogram into iPS cells, which means that iPS cell lines can be initiated by means of plucking out a single human hair.

The ordinary origins of iPS cells may end up giving them another substantial advantage over ESCs: an ability to help produce *personalized* lines of specialized cells. To understand this, think first about any specialized cells that might be produced through ESCs. Having been derived originally from an embryo, and then placed into the body of a patient, such cells are likely to be regarded as invading *foreign* cells by the patient's immune system, meaning these cells would set off an immune system attack. Thus, transplanted cells derived from ESCs could be "rejected" by a body in the same way a transplanted kidney can be. Conversely, iPS cells that give rise to specialized cells could come originally from … patients themselves! Patients could donate some of their own cells; these cells would be reprogrammed into iPS cells; and the iPS cells would go on to yield the specialized cells that would be implanted. In short, patients would be able to generate their own therapeutic cells.

Patient-specific cells of this sort would require such an enormous research expenditure for each patient served that no one thinks they will become a reality anytime soon. But a kind of half-way measure might be possible. In organ transplantation today, doctors try to match donated organs with organ recipients in accordance with whether both organ and recipient have an immune system compatibility. Specifically, doctors look to see if the cells of both the organ and the recipient have, on their surface, similar sets of immune system proteins—proteins called HLA markers. With iPS cells, it may become possible to produce *banks* of cells that are specialized not just for cell type but for HLA type as well. The result would be collections of readily available cells that could be counted on not to set off severe immune reactions.

Disease treatments such as these lie off in the future, but iPS cells are proving invaluable to medical scientists right now as a means of *learning* about human disease. Consider, for example, an inherited disease called spinal muscular atrophy (SMA) that can cause death in children. As SMA researcher Michael Sendtner wrote recently in the journal *Nature,* prior to the advent of iPS cells, anyone who studied SMA ran up against two powerful obstacles. First, this disease exists only in humans, which means it can't be studied in lab animals such as mice. Second, the cells that SMA most strongly affects—cells called spinal motor neurons—cannot be isolated and cultured. But as other researchers have found, it's possible to take common cells called fibroblasts from an SMA patient, reprogram those cells into iPS cells, and then coax the iPS cells into producing stable lines of the needed spinal motor neurons. Critically, each of these neurons has the genetic makeup of the SMA victim—meaning, the genetic makeup that causes SMA. Since spinal motor neurons are developing from iPS cells in this procedure, it becomes possible to trace the way SMA develops *over time* in the neurons. Beyond this, it becomes possible to see how the neurons

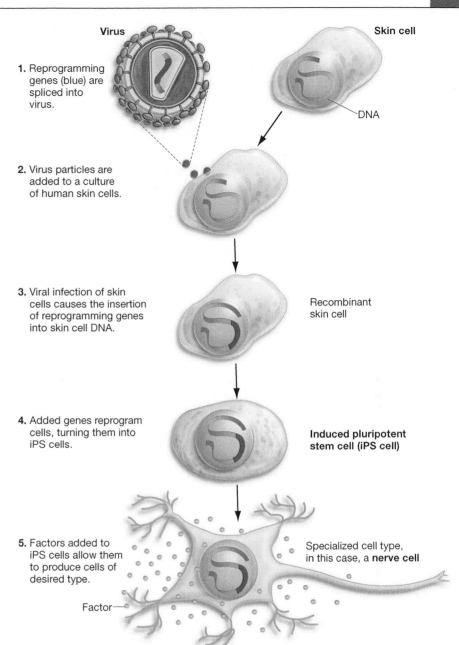

Figure 15.10
A New Kind of Stem Cell
How induced pluripotent stem cells are produced and used.

respond to various drugs that are applied to them—drugs that may eventually serve as treatments for the disease. In short, iPS cells have made it possible to produce what some researchers have called "diseases in a dish." So promising is this avenue of research that scores of disease-specific iPS cell lines are now in development.

Research advances such as these have provided scientists with a great sense of optimism about iPS cells. To be sure, any treatments these cells might provide are years away—at present, scientists are merely investigating the details of their developmental power

ESSAY

Biotechnology Gets Personal: Reading Your Genome

Though it was grand in impact, the Human Genome Project, completed in 2003, did have a name that was a bit misleading, in that there is no single, standard human genome. Instead, each of us has a personal genome—a sequence of 3.2 billion A's, T's, G's, and C's that is unique to us (except for those of us who have an identical twin). If we could line up the genomes of any two unrelated individuals, we'd find about three million differences between them, which is to say three million places at which their bases do not line up. Scientists have long known that genomic variation leads to variation in disease susceptibility—one person responds to a modest weight gain by becoming diabetic while another does not; one person develops lung cancer from smoking while another does not. What's different today is that, thanks to modern DNA sequencing and analysis, scientists have a hope of *identifying* the genetic variations that leave people susceptible to these conditions. Such work is aimed at ushering in an era of personal genomics, meaning a time in which meaningful information can be extracted from each person's genome.

The personal genomics era may actually be with us now, in the sense that scientists have already identified some genetic variations that modestly raise or lower a person's chances of contracting diseases such as Type 2 diabetes and rheumatoid arthritis. Indeed, the budding ability of scientists to make associations of this sort has sparked the development of a *commercial* aspect to personal genomics. At present, for a fee of as little as $399, commercial genotyping firms will obtain a sample of your DNA, analyze it, and provide you with the most up-to-date information they have on how any genetic variants you possess correlate with predispositions toward sickness or health.

In carrying out this work, the genotyping firms are not sequencing the entire genomes of any of their customers—that task would be far too expensive to carry out at present. Instead, they are scanning customers' genomes for what are called single-nucleotide polymorphisms, or SNPs (pronounced "snips"). At a given point in the genome, for example, individual A may have the sequence CCGTC while individual B has the sequence CCGTA. The final letter in these sequences constitutes a SNP, assuming that the least common variant of this letter is found in at least 1 percent of the population. About 10 million SNPs are thought to exist in the human genome. Some of these occur within sequences of DNA that code for proteins and thus stand to be able to *alter* proteins, but most lie outside of protein-coding regions. Even these latter SNPs, however, can serve as so-called markers for disease and can thus provide valuable information. Suppose, for example, that researchers find that a particular group of eight SNPs occurs at a higher frequency in the genomes of asthma sufferers than in the genomes of individuals without asthma. It's not necessary to know whether these SNPs are doing anything to cause asthma; all that's necessary to know is that a person's odds of being asthmatic are raised by possessing this particular group of SNPs.

The challenge to commercial genotyping firms is to stay current on what science has revealed about associations such as these, after which they can inform customers about their *personal* associations. How does a given customer's SNP lineup for, say, Parkinson's disease compare with a lineup seen in Parkinson's victims?

The ability of private firms to provide clients with this kind of information is a testament to how far personal genomics has come in recent years. Nevertheless, a key question for consumers today is whether they stand to get much *useful* information from an analysis of their SNP patterns. If there's a consensus among experts about this today, it seems to be that consumers don't stand to benefit greatly from peering inside their own genomes in this way, for the simple reason that science has not yet learned enough about the links between SNPs and disease. Consider, for example, what Harvard psychologist Steven Pinker learned in 2008 when he had his genome analyzed by a commercial genotyping firm. As he wrote in the *New York Times Magazine*:

The two biggest pieces of news I got about my disease risks were a 12.6 percent chance of getting prostate cancer before I turn 80 compared with the average risk for white men of 17.8 percent, and a 26.8 percent chance of getting Type 2 diabetes compared with the average risk of 21.9 percent. Most of the other outcomes involved even smaller departures from the norm. For a blessedly average person like me, it is completely unclear what to do with these odds. A one-in-four chance of developing diabetes should make any prudent person watch his weight and other risk factors. But then so should a one-in-five chance.

This said, personal genomics is a rapidly changing field, and what is true today may not be true tomorrow. Scientific work aimed at identifying the genetic variations that predispose people to disease or health is proceeding at a rapid pace. Should this work bear fruit, then commercial genotyping operations would presumably have customers flocking to them, for the simple reason that they'll have so much useful information to offer.

ACGGCTAAAATCGCTTAATTGGCCGCGCTATCGATGCTAGGGTAGCCTAGTTAAAAGATAGATCGAGATTA while looking for any safety risks they might pose. Thus far, however, iPS cells have shown a remarkable set of strengths. In one test after another, they have put the power of cell reprogramming on full display.

SO FAR ...

1. Embryonic stem cells (ESCs) are derived from embryos when they are in the blastocyst stage, which occurs about (a) 5 days (b) 5 weeks (c) 5 months following conception.

2. Induced pluripotent stem cells (iPS cells) are like ESCs in that they seemingly can give rise to _____ human cell types, yet they are unlike ESCs in that they are derived from _____ cells.

3. iPS cells could in theory solve the problem of the rejection of transplanted tissue because, through such cells, transplanted tissue might be generated from a patient's _____.

15.5 Forensic Biotechnology

After New York's World Trade Center (WTC) was destroyed on September 11, 2001, public officials had to undertake the grim task of trying to identify all the victims of the attack to provide some sense of closure to the victims' loved ones. In the weeks and months following the attack, therefore, officials collected samples of DNA not only from WTC victims but from the toothbrushes and razors of persons who were missing since the tragedy and hence *presumed* to be victims. They also collected DNA from relatives of these presumed victims. With this DNA database in hand, workers then made an effort to match one kind of DNA with another—to match the DNA found on a toothbrush, for example, with the DNA from a WTC victim.

High-profile cases such as these are the most visible manifestation of a huge change that has come about in the way society identifies persons—criminals, biological fathers, and victims, most notably. In the criminal arena, the most highly valued type of physical evidence today is not fingerprints; it is tiny bits of human tissue from which DNA can be extracted. But how do police use DNA to get a "match" in a criminal case? Let's find out.

The essence of "forensic DNA typing," as it is known, is to get two sets of physical samples—first, a sample left by a crime's perpetrator in such forms as blood or semen; and second, a blood sample from a suspect. By comparing the DNA patterns of both samples, forensic scientists can establish odds of whether the suspect was present at the crime scene. If he or she was, but had no good reason to be there, this is strong evidence that the suspect committed the crime.

Another way of gathering DNA evidence is to use a victim's blood sample and test it against, for example, blood found on a suspect's clothing.

The Use of PCR

When forensic DNA typing first came into use in the 1980s, a significant limitation on it was that relatively *large* samples of human tissue had to be obtained to get enough DNA to work with; blood samples, for example, had to be about the size of a quarter. Eventually, however, this problem was all but eliminated by something called the **polymerase chain reaction (PCR):** a technique for quickly producing many copies of a specific segment of DNA. Thanks to PCR, if a criminal so much as licks an envelope and leaves it behind, police can retrieve enough DNA to get a match.

The PCR process is very simple in outline. Four kinds of materials are mixed together to carry it out. The first of these is a quantity of DNA itself. Then, there is a collection of DNA nucleotides and DNA polymerase (which, remember, goes down the line on single-stranded DNA, affixing nucleotides to available bases). Finally, there are two DNA "primer" sequences— short sequences of single-stranded DNA that act as signals to DNA polymerase, saying "start adding nucleotides here."

The first step in the process is that the starting quantity of DNA is heated until the two strands of DNA's double helix separate, resulting in two single strands of DNA (**Figure 15.11**, on the next page). As the heated DNA mixture cools, primers will attach to each of the now-separate strands of DNA. Then the DNA polymerases go down the line, starting from the primers, linking nucleotides to the template DNA and thus producing strands that are complementary to the original strands. The result is two double-stranded lengths of DNA, both identical to the original double strand. In short, the DNA sample has been doubled in one copying "cycle." Then the entire process of heating and cooling is repeated. Since each copying cycle takes only 1–3 minutes, by the time 90 minutes have passed, millions of copies can be created. Moreover, thanks to the specificity of primers, the sequence that is copied can be limited to a small sequence of interest within the larger genome. So useful is PCR that it is employed in countless facets of biological research. We are focusing here on one specific use for PCR, but it has so many applications that in 1993, its inventor, Kary Mullis, was awarded the Nobel Prize in Chemistry for his achievement.

Finding Individual Patterns

Once PCR has done its job, the police have enough DNA to begin looking for the individual patterns within it—one set of patterns found in the crime-scene DNA, one set of patterns seen in the suspect's DNA. But what are these patterns that each of us

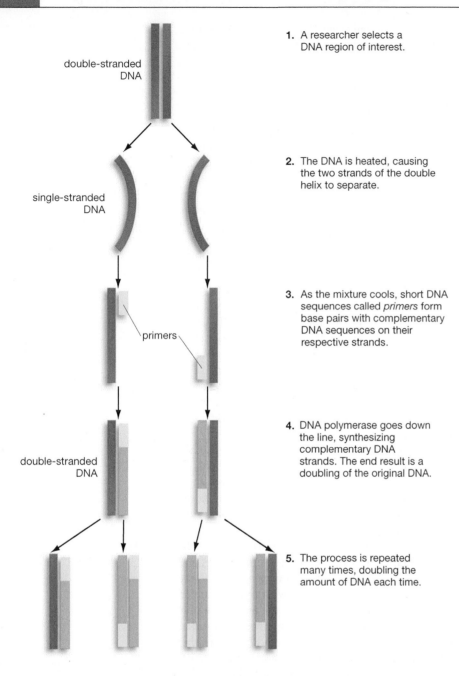

1. A researcher selects a DNA region of interest.

2. The DNA is heated, causing the two strands of the double helix to separate.

3. As the mixture cools, short DNA sequences called *primers* form base pairs with complementary DNA sequences on their respective strands.

4. DNA polymerase goes down the line, synthesizing complementary DNA strands. The end result is a doubling of the original DNA.

5. The process is repeated many times, doubling the amount of DNA each time.

Figure 15.11
DNA Copying Machine

The polymerase chain reaction (PCR) makes copies of a given length of DNA very quickly.

carries? Human genomes are filled with short sequences of DNA that are repeated over and over, from 3 to 50 times, like this:

TCATTCATTCATTCATTCAT

This TCAT example is not hypothetical. It is an actual short tandem repeat (or STR) that police departments use in today's DNA typing. The usefulness of STRs is that, at a given location in the genome, one person will have one number of tandem repeats, while another person is likely to have a different number of repeats, like so:

Individual 1: TCAT TCAT TCAT TCAT
Individual 2: TCAT TCAT TCAT TCAT TCAT TCAT

Now, the chances are small that two unrelated individuals will have an identical number of repeats at even one location in the genome. But modern forensic DNA typing looks at STR repeats at 13 different locations. Imagine yourself, then, as a forensic investigator who is reviewing both DNA from a crime scene and DNA from a suspect in the crime. At genomic location 1, the STR patterns are:

Crime scene: TCAT TCAT TCAT TCAT
Suspect: TCAT TCAT TCAT TCAT

So, you have a match at this one location. If the STR patterns continue to line up this way at the other 12 locations, then what once was just probable becomes certain. Your suspect was certainly at the crime scene because the odds of any two unrelated people having identical STR patterns at 13 locations are astronomically small.

It's important to recognize that this kind of DNA evidence can be used to prove innocence as well as guilt. DNA testing regularly exonerates not only suspects but people who have been *convicted* of crimes. In the past 20 years, more than 200 prisoners who were jailed for various offenses have been freed on the basis of DNA testing. If you look at the essay "Reading DNA Profiles," you can see the means by which STR patterns are visualized in today's criminal cases.

Beyond matching a known suspect to a crime scene or victim, forensic DNA typing has another power. Increasingly, it is allowing police to make so-called *cold hits*. All 50 states now require criminals convicted of violent crimes to provide DNA samples. Capitalizing on this, the FBI has put together a national database of the DNA profiles of these criminals. Given this, imagine a situation in which a crime is committed, and no suspect was identified, but in which a DNA sample was retrieved. A DNA profile will be produced from this sample—a profile that can be matched against all those that are stored in a DNA database. If the profile from the crime scene matches a criminal's stored profile, that in itself is sufficient evidence to make an arrest. And this is happening all the time—cold hits result in hundreds of arrests across the nation each year.

SO FAR . . .

1. PCR has been described as a copying machine for _____.

2. In forensic biotechnology, the value of PCR is that it allows the establishment of identities based on _____ samples of DNA.

3. The DNA of every individual contains groups of _____ whose number can be used to establish the identity of that individual.

Reading DNA Profiles

What does a forensic DNA profile look like? Law enforcement agencies use the kind of imaging you can see below. The upper profile was produced from DNA taken from a crime scene, while the lower profile was produced from DNA obtained from a suspect in the crime. The short tandem repeat, or STR, patterns that differ from one person to another are represented by the peaks that run across the rows in both figures. Each peak, or set of two peaks, represents one location in the genome—a location whose STR pattern was examined. In the upper figure's first row, the peak labeled 16 indicates that the person who left DNA at the crime scene had 16 repeats at this location. The

nearby 17 then indicates that this person had 17 repeats at this same location, but on his second, homologous chromosome. Meanwhile, the 24 that can be seen farther to the right represents the number of repeats at a different location in the genome. In this case, the person had 24 repeats on both chromosomes—he was homozygous for repeats at this location.

The scale running across the top of the figure indicates the number of DNA base pairs in the lengths of DNA that were examined at each location. Thus, the 16 repeats at the first peak were found in a section of DNA that was about 125 base pairs long. The height of each peak has no bearing on identity but simply reflects the

quantity of DNA that was derived, through the PCR process, for each location. The X and Y peaks on the second row represent a section of the genome that differs between men and women. Had a woman's DNA been found at the crime scene, there would have been no Y peak.

A quick look at both the upper and lower figures reveals that the STR patterns in them match up perfectly. The obvious implication is that the suspect was at the crime scene. Indeed, the odds that the crime-scene DNA came from anyone *other* than the suspect are infinitesimally small. What are the chances that a person selected at random from a general population would have the same STR profile as the one found in the crime-scene DNA? The odds of this occurring range from 1 in 4.6 trillion for the U.S. Caucasian population to 1 in 36 trillion for the U.S. southwestern Hispanic population.

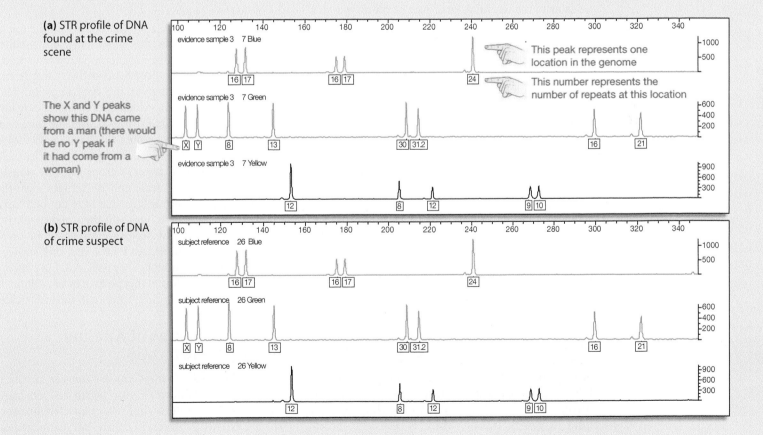

(a) STR profile of DNA found at the crime scene

The X and Y peaks show this DNA came from a man (there would be no Y peak if it had come from a woman)

(b) STR profile of DNA of crime suspect

15.6 Controversies in Biotechnology

Genetically Modified Crops

You may recall the biotech crops we looked at earlier—the ones that are transgenic, in that they have one or more genes from another species spliced into them. Worldwide, tens of millions of acres have been planted with these genetically modified, or GM, crops. It turns out, however, that almost all this acreage is devoted to just *four* crops: cotton, corn, soybeans, and canola. Moreover, GM crops have not been modified to make their ultimate products—food or clothing—preferable to consumers in some way. Instead, all four GM crops have been modified to be preferable to *farmers,* either by being resistant to pests or tolerant of herbicides. (One of the latter crops is "Roundup-ready" soybeans, whose seeds contain a bacterial gene that allows them to tolerate the herbicide Roundup.) You might think that the list of GM crops will certainly be getting longer in the future, but this may not be the case. Consider that in 1999 about 120 GM fruits and vegetables were being field-tested in the United States, but that by 2003 this number had dropped to about 20.

So, why are there so few GM crops, either in the fields or in the works? A large part of the answer can be summed up in two words: consumer resistance. Worldwide, a significant number of consumers have become persuaded that biotech foods are dangerous, and the effect of this has been a continued shelving of plans for biotech crops. In 2004, for example, the Monsanto Corporation gave up on a program it had started seven years earlier aimed at producing GM wheat. The company worried that few American or Canadian farmers would plant the wheat because they feared resistance to it from European and Japanese consumers. Such resistance, the farmers thought, might effectively put a "do not import" label on all U.S. and Canadian wheat, whether genetically modified or not. This same chain of reasoning is operating in connection with other GM foods.

And what is the basis for consumer fears about GM foods? Nothing that has occurred so far. In 2004, the National Academy of Sciences published a report whose central conclusion is still valid: "To date, no adverse health effects attributed to genetic engineering have been documented in the human population." The report went on to note that food crops actually have been "genetically modified" for centuries, although this has come about through the low-tech means of breeding different plant strains with each other. This form of genetic mixing, which is relatively uncontrolled, stands in contrast to the biotech variety, in which a small number of identifiable genes are inserted into (or removed from) a plant's genome. Yet it is biotech crops that have encountered resistance as "frankenfoods," while plants produced through conventional means can be changed without notice.

Resistance to GM crops is based on more than the fear of their health effects, however. The other great concern about them has to do with environmental effects. If you look at **Figure 15.12**, you can see a case in point in this battle. Pictured are two sets of cotton plants, one set genetically modified, the other not. The modified plants contain genes from a bacterium, called *Bacillus thuringiensis,* that is found naturally in the soil and that produces proteins toxic to a number of insects. Collectively, these proteins constitute a natural insecticide known as Bt, which has been sprayed on crops for years, mostly by "organic" farmers, meaning those who do not use human-made fertilizers, pesticides, or herbicides. Enter biotechnology firms, which in the 1990s spliced Bt genes into crop plants, with the result that these plants—corn, cotton, and potatoes—now produce their own insecticide. The results have in some ways been an environmentalist's dream. In one survey conducted in the American Southeast, farmers who planted Bt cotton reduced the amount of chemical insecticides they applied to their fields by 72 percent. They did this, moreover, while increasing cotton yields by more than 11 percent.

Despite such benefits, we can also see, in the use of Bt seeds, the qualities that make environmentalists uneasy about GM crops in general. Those few insects that survive in Bt-enhanced fields are likely to give rise to populations resistant to the natural toxin. This raises the prospect of a valued natural insecticide losing its effectiveness against insects over the long run. So alarming is this possibility that the U.S. Environmental Protection Agency requires that at least 20 percent of any given farmer's crops must be non-Bt plants. The idea is to create non-Bt "refuges" near the Bt fields that will harbor bugs that have not built up a resistance to Bt. These bugs will then mate with Bt-resistant bugs, thus helping to ensure that Bt resistance does not spread. And how has this strategy worked so far? Seemingly very well. A USDA survey completed in 2003 found that pests in or near Bt fields had developed little or no resistance to the insecticide.

The Ethical Issue of Altering Living Things

Disputes over GM crops involve mostly practical questions—do GM crops pose health and environmental hazards or not?—but some biotech controversies are essentially ethical in nature. We've touched on one of these ethical controversies already, which is the

Figure 15.12
**Built-in Resistance
to Pests**
The cotton plants on the left
have had genes spliced into
them from the bacterium
Bacillus thuringiensis. These
genes code for proteins that
function as a pesticide.
Meanwhile, the cotton plants
on the right are not transgenic in this way—they have
not had genes from another
organism spliced into them.
Both stands of cotton were
under equal attack from insects, but the Bt-enhanced
plants fared much better.

use of human embryonic stem cells to produce needed human tissues. A more general ethical objection to biotech research, however, has to do with the question of altering living things—of altering nature, if you like.

Of course, human beings have been altering nature for centuries through such means as the plant breeding we talked about. But for an example that is a little more relevant, consider one of our favorite pets, the dog. The fantastic variety in dog breeds that we see today has mostly come about in the past 400 years, and this has happened almost entirely as a result of the human practice of selectively breeding one kind of dog with another. So is this inherently unethical? If your answer is no, then what about producing a sheep whose liver tissue is mostly made of human cells? Is there some ethical line that is crossed when we go from mixing different breeds of an animal to mixing different species of animal? (The animal that results from this mixing is "chimeric" in scientific parlance.) If the answer to this is no, then what about injecting immature human brain cells into the brain of a monkey? This has been done already, as a means of conducting Parkinson's disease research, and the monkeys have, to outside observers' eyes, remained "all monkey." But is there a point at which this becomes unethical? Perhaps the point at which a monkey might develop the first glimmer of human consciousness?

The possibilities that biotech has opened up for chimeric animals drives home the point that we have entered a new era in altering nature. Given biotech's power, however, it isn't necessary to consider chimeras to confront the kind of "altering" dilemmas that might eventually be upon us. Suppose you could alter a chicken's own genes so that you could create an animal that could lay eggs but that had no eyes or legs. (This would make these chickens easier to control, which would in turn bring the price of eggs down.) Suppose further that these animals suffered no apparent discomfort as a result of this manipulation. If you could do such a thing, would you?

On to Evolution

In touring the strands of DNA's double helix, you've had many occasions to see how this microscopic molecule can profoundly affect our macroscopic world. DNA replicates, it mutates, it is passed on from one generation to the next. And some organisms will have more *success* in passing on their DNA—in reproducing, in other words—than will others. This last fact has been critical in bringing about the huge variety of life-forms that Earth houses, from bacteria to bats to trees. Over billions of years, genetics has interacted with Earth's myriad environments to produce the grand story of life. That story is called evolution, and it is the subject of the next four chapters.

CHAPTER 15 REVIEW

Go to the Study Area at www.masteringbiology.com for practice quizzes, myeBook, BioFlix™ 3-D animations, MP3 Tutor Sessions, videos, current events, and more.

Mastering
BIOLOGY

Summary

15.1 What Is Biotechnology?

- Biotechnology is the use of technology to control biological processes as a means of meeting societal needs. (p. 264)

15.2 Transgenic Biotechnology

- A transgenic organism is one whose genome has stably incorporated one or more genes from another species. (p. 264)

- Restriction enzymes are proteins derived from bacteria that can cut DNA in specific places. Plasmids are small, extra-chromosomal rings of bacterial DNA that can exist outside of bacterial cells and that can move into these cells through the process of transformation. (p. 264)

- Human DNA can be inserted into plasmid rings. Scientists use the same restriction enzyme to cut both the human DNA of interest and the plasmids. Complementary "sticky ends" of the fragmented human and plasmid DNA will then bind together, splicing the human DNA into the plasmid, producing recombinant DNA. (p. 266)

- Plasmids with human DNA spliced into them can then be taken up into bacterial cells through transformation. As these cells replicate, the plasmid DNA inside them replicates as well. Because the plasmids are producing the protein coded for by the human DNA that has been spliced into them, the result is production of a quantity of the human protein of interest. (p. 266)

- Transgenic organisms that are used to produce a number of medicines and vaccines include bacteria, yeast, hamster cells, and mammals such as goats. Transgenic food crops are planted in abundance today in the United States. (p. 266)

15.3 Reproductive Cloning

- A clone is a genetically identical copy of a biological entity. Genes can be cloned, as can cells, and clones of plants exist in the form of plants grown from "cuttings." Reproductive cloning is the process of making adult clones of mammals of a defined genotype. Today in reproductive cloning of mammals, an egg cell has its nucleus removed and is fused with an adult cell containing a nucleus and, therefore, DNA. The fused cell then starts to develop as an embryo and is implanted in a surrogate mother. This process is called so-matic cell nuclear transfer (SCNT). (p. 268)

- Reproductive cloning can work in tandem with various recombinant DNA processes to produce adult mammals possessing de-sired traits. A cell can be made transgenic for such a trait and then used as the donor DNA cell in producing an adult mammal with the trait. (p. 269)

- No human being has been cloned to date, but the possibility of such cloning cannot be ruled out. A human clone would be ge-netically identical to the person who pro-vided the donor DNA cell. (p. 270)

15.4 Cell Reprogramming

- Two promising methods now exist for gen-erating human cells that are needed to treat victims of accident or disease: production through embryonic stem cells and produc-tion through induced pluripotent stem cells. Both methods employ the reprogramming of cells to yield desired cell types. (p. 270)

- Stem cells are cells that have a continuing capacity to produce more cells of their own type, along with at least one type of special-ized daughter cell. One source of human stem cells is the blastocyst. Cells from the inner cell mass of the blastocyst are embry-onic stem cells (ESCs): cells that can give rise to all the different cell types in the adult human body. Scientists harvest ESCs from blastocysts and then induce the ESCs to produce needed cell types. (p. 271)

- In 2007, two research teams developed a type of human stem cell that is not derived from an embryo: the induced pluripotent stem cell (iPS cell), which was first pro-duced by means of splicing four develop-mental genes into the genomes of ordinary adult skin cells. iPS cells appear to have all the developmental power of ESCs; they hold promise of reducing problems of tissue rejection in medical transplantation proce-dures; and they are being widely used as a means of studying human disease. (p. 272)

15.5 Forensic Biotechnology

- Identities of criminals, biological fathers, and disaster victims often are established through the use of forensic DNA typing. (p. 275)

- The polymerase chain reaction is a tech-nique for quickly producing many copies of a segment of DNA. It is useful in situa-tions, such as crime investigations, in which a large amount of DNA is needed for analysis, yet the starting quantity of DNA is small. (p. 275)

- Forensic DNA typing usually works through comparisons of short tandem repeat patterns that are found in all human genomes. (p. 275)

15.6 Controversies in Biotechnology

- Opponents of genetically modified crops are concerned about their effect on human health and the environment. There is no ev-idence so far that these crops have had detri-mental effects, but consumer resistance to the crops has sharply limited both the types being planted and being developed. (p. 278)

- Some biotech controversies are essentially ethical in nature. One general controversy has to do with the question of what level of constraint society ought to impose on the modification of living things. (p. 278)

Key Terms

biotechnology   264

blastocyst   271

clone   268

Understanding the Basics

Multiple-Choice Questions

(Answers are in the back of the book.)

1. How is biotechnology defined?
   a. the study of technical biology
   b. the use of biology to control technological processes as a means of meeting societal needs
   c. the use of technology to control biological processes as a means of meeting societal needs
   d. the technological process of cloning genes
   e. the commercialization of biological research results

2. Researchers who work with DNA are able to cut it into desired lengths through the use of:
   a. transformation.
   b. cloning.
   c. RNA.
   d. restriction enzymes.
   e. DNA polymerase.

3. In transgenic biotechnology involving bacteria, which sequence of events would be followed in the process of harvesting a protein of interest?
   a. Replicate host bacterial cells; isolate gene that codes for protein; splice gene into plasmids; harvest protein of interest; transform plasmids into bacteria.
   b. Transform plasmids into bacteria; isolate gene that codes for protein; replicate host bacterial cells; splice gene into plasmids; harvest protein of interest.

   c. Harvest protein of interest; isolate gene that codes for protein; splice gene into plasmids; replicate host bacterial cells; transform plasmids into bacteria.
   d. Isolate gene that codes for protein; splice gene into plasmids; replicate host bacterial cells; transform plasmids into bacteria; harvest protein of interest.
   e. Isolate gene that codes for protein; splice gene into plasmids; transform plasmids into bacteria; replicate host bacterial cells; harvest protein of interest.

4. Which of the following is an example of a transgenic organism?
   a. *E. coli* bacterium with a human gene inserted
   b. Dolly the sheep
   c. rice with bacterium and daffodil genes inserted
   d. all of the above
   e. a and c only

5. What is a clone?
   a. an exact genetic copy of a gene or an entire living thing
   b. a cell that can take up plasmids
   c. a segment of DNA of a specified length
   d. an offspring produced by test-tube fertilization
   e. a segment of DNA that can prime the polymerase chain reaction

6. Dolly the sheep was cloned by means of:
   a. applying an electric current to an egg and sperm in a laboratory.
   b. taking an embryo from one sheep and implanting it in another.
   c. taking a cell from an adult sheep and fusing it with a sheep egg that had its DNA removed.
   d. inserting new genes into an existing mammary cell.
   e. getting sperm to fuse with egg outside a living sheep.

7. As a means of producing large quantities of cells needed for the regeneration of human tissues, medical scientists are utilizing:
   a. somatic cell nuclear transfer, plasmids, and gene splicing.
   b. gene splicing, polymerase chain reaction, and transgenic organisms.
   c. embryonic stem cells and induced pluripotent stem cells.
   d. somatic cell nuclear transfer, embryonic stem cells, and induced pluripotent stem cells.
   e. gene splicing, cloned cells, and transgenic organisms.

8. Criminal investigators who want to make copies of a DNA sample from a crime do so through:
   a. the polymerase chain reaction.
   b. transformation.
   c. cloning vectors.
   d. DNA sequencing.
   e. iPS cells.

Brief Review

(Answers are in the back of the book.)

1. Why is it useful to have organisms such as bacteria turning out human proteins?

2. Why are restriction enzymes that cut DNA to produce sticky ends useful? If the following piece of DNA were cut with *Bam*HI, what would the fragment sequences be?

   ATCGGATCCTCCG
   TAGCCTAGGAGGC

3. Why did Dolly the sheep end up looking like the sheep that "donated" the udder cell rather than the sheep that donated the egg?

4. Why is the polymerase chain reaction (PCR) so valuable?

5. Name two advantages that induced pluripotent stem cells (iPS cells) seem to have relative to embryonic stem cells (ESCs).

Applying Your Knowledge

1. One of the motives put forth for human cloning is that people want to replace children or other loved ones who have died. To what extent could a clone of a loved one be a replacement for that person? If the technique had then been available, should doctors in the nineteenth century have preserved the DNA of Abraham Lincoln for cloning?

2. Should society demand that there be no risks to genetically modified foods before it allows them to be developed? Does any significant technology have no risks associated with it?

3. What limits, if any, should be put on the ability of human beings to modify the genomes of other living things? Should human beings be free to carry out any modification that does not harm an organism?

An Introduction to Evolution:

Charles Darwin, Evolutionary Thought, and the Evidence for Evolution

Charles Darwin is the person most responsible for deepening our understanding of how life evolved on Earth. Evidence uncovered from his time to ours has confirmed his insights.

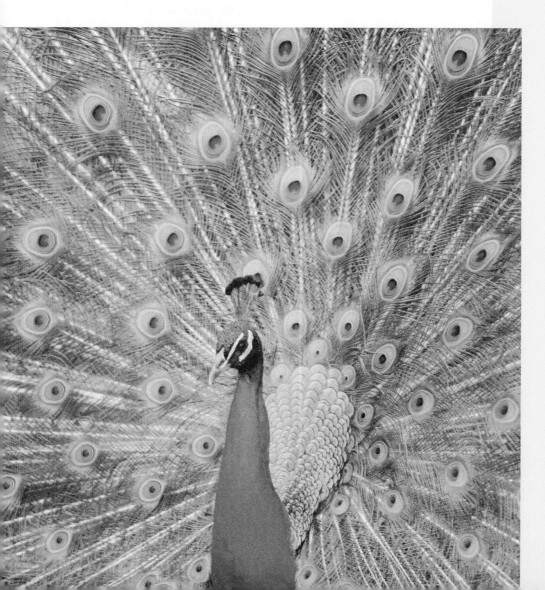

The theory of evolution explains countless features of the natural world, including the dazzling plumage of the peacock *(Pavo cristatus)*.

Standing in a coastal redwood grove in California, we see trees stretching hundreds of feet into the air and wonder: Why are they so tall? Watching a nature program on television, we observe the exquisite plumage of the male peacock but are puzzled that such a *cumbersome* display could exist on a creature that has to be wary of predators. Leafing through a book, we discover that the color vision of honeybees is most sensitive to the colors that exist in the very flowering plants they pollinate. We wonder: Can this be an accident?

For as long as humans have existed, people have asked questions like these. Yet for most of human history, even the most informed individuals had no way to make sense of the variations that nature presented. Why does the redwood have its height or the peacock its plumage? Through the middle of the nineteenth century, the answer was likely to be either a shrug of the shoulders or a statement such as: "The creator gave unique forms to living things for reasons we can't understand."

Jumping ahead to our own time, modern-day biologists would give different answers to these questions. Their replies would go something like this:

- Redwoods (and trees in general) are so tall because, over millions of years, they have been in competition with one another for the resource of sunlight. Individual trees that had the genetic capacity to grow tall got the sunlight, flourished, and thus left relatively many offspring, which made for taller trees in successive generations.

- Extravagant plumage exists on male peacocks because it is attractive to *female* peacocks when they are choosing mating partners. Such finery is indeed cumbersome and carries a price (in lack of mobility), but this price is outweighed by the value of the feathers. Over time, the peacock ancestors with more attractive plumage mated more often and thus sired more offspring than peacocks with less-impressive plumage. This made for successive generations of peacocks with more elaborate plumage.

- It is not an accident that honeybee eyesight is most sensitive to the colors that exist in the flowering plants they pollinate. Both bees and flowering plants flourish because of their interactions with one another—bees get food, and flowers get pollinated. It is likely that flower color, or bee vision, or both, became modified over time in ways that maximized this interaction.

Comparing contemporary answers such as these to that single nineteenth-century answer, you might well ask: What is it that came *in between,* so that we no longer must simply stand in puzzled wonderment before the diversity of nature?

16.1 Evolution and Its Core Principles

What intervened was a set of intellectual breakthroughs in the mid-nineteenth century that today go under the heading of the *theory of evolution.* Two principles lie at the core of this theory.

Common Descent with Modification

One of these principles has been labeled **common descent with modification.** It holds that particular groups, or species, of living things can undergo modification in successive generations, with such change sometimes resulting in the formation of new, separate species—one species separating into two, these two then separating further. If you had a diagram of this "branching" of species and then looked at it from top to bottom, what you'd see is a reduction of all these branches into one, meaning that all living things on Earth ultimately are descended from a single, ancient ancestor. Evolution itself can have several definitions. In this chapter, we will think of it as synonymous with common descent with modification. In Chapter 17, you'll get a more technical definition of it.

Natural Selection

Common descent with modification is joined to a second evolutionary principle, **natural selection:** The process through which traits that confer a reproductive advantage to individual organisms grow more common in populations of organisms over successive generations. In the redwood example, the genetically based trait of increased tallness conferred a reproductive advantage: It allowed taller trees to capture more sunlight and hence to leave more offspring than shorter trees. The offspring of these taller trees would likewise tend to inherit the genetic capacity to grow tall, meaning they, too, would leave more offspring than other trees of *their* generation. In this way, the trait of tallness was becoming increasingly common in this population of trees from one generation to the next. Put another way, this population of trees was *evolving* in the direction of greater tallness by means of a process in which taller trees were selected to leave more offspring than shorter trees. As you will see, of all the processes that shape evolution, none is as important as natural selection.

The Importance of Evolution as a Concept

Evolution is not just important to biology; it is *central* to it. If biology were a house, evolution's principles would be the mortar binding its stones together. Why? Because all life on Earth has been shaped by evolution's key principles: natural selection and common descent with modification. This is easy to see once you think about any given organism. Take your pick: a fish, a tree, a human being? *All* of them evolved from ancestors, all of them ultimately evolved from a common ancestor, and natural selection was the primary process that shaped their evolution.

Given this, the theory of evolution provides a means for us to understand nature in all its buzzing, blooming complexity. It allows us to understand not just things that are familiar to us, such as the forms of the redwoods and peacocks, but all manner of new natural phenomena that come our way. When physicians observe that strains of infectious bacteria are becoming resistant to antibiotics, they don't have to ask: How could this happen? General evolutionary principles tell them that organisms evolve, that bacteria are capable of evolving very quickly (because they can produce many generations a day), and that antibiotic resistance is simply an evolutionary adaptation to the human use of antibiotics.

Evolution Affects Human Perspectives Regarding Life

So far-reaching is the theory of evolution that its importance stretches beyond the domain of biology and into the realm of basic human assumptions about the world. Once persuasive evidence for the theory had been amassed, it meant that human beings could no longer view themselves as something *separate* from all other living things. Common descent with modification tells us that we are descended from ancestors, just like other organisms. Thus, we sit not on a pedestal, viewing the rest of nature beneath us, but rather on one ordinary branch of an immense evolutionary tree.

Beyond this, evolution meant the end of the idea of a *fixed* living world in which, for example, birds have always been birds and whales have always been whales. Birds are the descendants of dinosaurs, while whales are the descendants of medium-sized mammals that walked on land (**Figure 16.1**). Life-forms only appear to be fixed to us because human life is so short relative to the time frames in which species undergo change.

Finally, in evolution human beings are confronted with the fact that, through natural selection, life has been shaped by a process that has no mind and no goals. Like a river that digs a canyon, natural selection shapes, but it does not design; it has no more "intentions" than does the wind. Trees that received more sunlight left more offspring, and thus trees grew taller over time. This is not a "decision" on the part of nature; it is an outcome of an impersonal process. And if evolution has no consciousness, it follows that it can have no morals. This force that has so powerfully shaped the natural world is neither cruel nor kind, but simply indifferent.

Figure 16.1
From Land to Water
Whales, such as this breaching humpback, are warm-blooded, air-breathing mammals. How can we explain such classic mammalian traits in creatures who live solely in water? Whales are the descendants of four-legged land-dwelling mammals who made a gradual transition from land to water over a very long period—about eight million years, beginning about 50 million years ago. Their closest living relative is the hippopotamus.

SO FAR . . .

1. The principle of common descent with modification holds that groups of living things can undergo modifications that,

over time, can lead to the formation of new _____ and that all living things on Earth are descended from a _____.

2. The principle of natural selection holds that some traits will confer a _____ to individual organisms and that these traits will accordingly become more _____ over time in a population of organisms.

3. Evolutionary theory supports the idea that humans are _____ other organisms and thus are not _____ from other living things.

16.2 Charles Darwin and the Theory of Evolution

How did such a far-reaching theory come into existence? Thinking back to this book's unit on genetics, you may recall that the basic principles of that field were developed over the course of about a century by a large number of scientists. In contrast, a single person—nineteenth-century British naturalist Charles Darwin—is credited with bringing together the essentials of the theory of evolution (**Figure 16.2**).

Darwin's Contribution

Darwin's contribution was two-fold. First, he developed existing ideas about descent with modification while providing a large body of evidence in support of them. Second, he was the first person to perceive natural selection as the primary driving force behind descent with modification.

To be sure, the study of evolution has been refined and expanded since Darwin. And it should be noted that before Darwin had ever published anything on his theory, a contemporary of his, fellow Englishman Alfred Russel Wallace, independently arrived at his insight about the importance of natural selection to evolution. (This makes Wallace the co-discoverer of this principle.) Yet, there is universal agreement that it is Charles Darwin who deserves primary credit for providing us with the core ideas that exist in evolutionary biology even today.

Darwin's Journey of Discovery

Darwin was born on February 12, 1809, in the country town of Shrewsbury, England. He was the son of a prosperous physician, Robert Darwin, and his wife, Susannah Wedgwood Darwin, who died when Charles was 8. Young Charles seemed destined to follow in his father's footsteps as a doctor, being sent away to the University of Edinburgh at age 16 for medical training. But he found medical school boring, and his medical

Figure 16.2 Scientist of Great Insight

Charles Darwin, late in his life.

(Painting by John Collier, 1883. London, National Portrait Gallery. ©Archiv/Photo Researchers.)

career came to a halt when, in the days before anesthesia, he found it unbearable to watch surgery being performed on children. His father then decided that he should study for the ministry. At the age of 20, Darwin set off for Cambridge University to spend 3 years that he later recalled as "the most joyous in my happy life." Darwin's happiness came in part from the fact that theology at Cambridge took a backseat to what had been his true passion since childhood: the study of nature. From his early years, he had collected rock, animal, and plant specimens and was an avid reader of nature books. His studies at Cambridge did yield a divinity degree, but they also gave Darwin a solid background in what we would today call life science and Earth science.

An Offer to Join the Voyage of the Beagle

Darwin's training, and the contacts he made at school, came together in one of the most fateful first-job

Thus did Darwin spend time on a research vessel—almost 5 years in all—beginning in England two days after Christmas 1831 and ending back there in October 1836. Just 22 when he left, he was prone to seasickness; he had to share a 10-by-15-foot room with two other officers; he was not a traveler by nature; and the journey was dangerous (three of the *Beagle*'s officers died of illness during it). Yet Darwin was happy because of the work he was doing: looking, listening, collecting, and thinking about it all. Here he is writing about a part of coastal Brazil:

> A most paradoxical mixture of sound and silence pervades the shady parts of the wood. The noise from the insects is so loud that it may be heard even in a vessel anchored several hundred feet from the shore; yet within the recesses of the forest a universal silence appears to reign. To a person fond of natural history such a day as this brings with it a deeper pleasure than he can ever hope to experience again.

Figure 16.3
What the *Beagle* Looked Like

A reconstruction of the *HMS Beagle,* sailing off the coast of Tierra del Fuego in South America.

offers ever extended to a recent college graduate. One of Darwin's Cambridge professors arranged to have him be the resident naturalist aboard the *HMS Beagle,* a ship that was to undertake a survey of coastal areas around the world (**Figure 16.3**). In **Figure 16.4** you can trace the *Beagle*'s journey. In addition to numerous stops on the east coast of South America (the ship's primary survey site), the *Beagle* also stopped briefly at the remote Galapagos Islands, about 600 miles west of Ecuador—a visit you'll learn more about later.

16.3 Evolutionary Thinking before Darwin

Darwin beheld these sights and sounds during a period in the nineteenth century in which change was in the air with respect to ideas about life on Earth.

Charles Lyell and Geology

The single book Darwin took with him when he boarded the *Beagle* was the first volume of Charles Lyell's *Principles of Geology,* published in 1830 and bearing a message that even Lyell's fellow scientists

Figure 16.4
Journey into History

The main mission of *HMS Beagle*'s 5-year voyage of 1831–1836 was to chart some of the commercially promising waters of South America. Darwin observed nature and collected specimens throughout the ship's journey, but for purposes of the theory of evolution, the ship's most important stops came in 1835 on the Galapagos Islands, west of South America.

Figure 16.5
Earth's Life-Forms Change over Time
Animals known as ammonites swam in Earth's oceans from about 400 million years ago to 65 million years ago. Pictured are ammonite fossils dating from 150 million years ago that were unearthed in sediments that are now part of Great Britain's coastline. Ammonites became extinct at the time Earth's dinosaurs did, but they are closely related to such living animals as octopus and squid.

found hard to accept: that geological forces *still operating* could account for the changes geologists could see in the Earth's surface. (As Darwin put it, "that long lines of inland cliffs had been formed, the great valleys excavated, by the agencies which we still see at work.") Under this view, Earth had not been put into final form at a moment of creation, but rather was steadily undergoing change. If such a thing were possible for the Earth itself, why not for the creatures that lived on it (**Figure 16.5**)?

Jean-Baptiste de Lamarck and Evolution

An idea along this line *had* been proposed, by the French naturalist Jean-Baptiste de Lamarck, in a book published in 1809. Lamarck believed that organisms changed form over generations through what has been termed the inheritance of acquired characteristics. Ducks or frogs did not originally have webbed feet, he said, but in the act of swimming they stretched out their toes to move more rapidly through the water. In time, membranes grew between their toes, effectively becoming webbing; critically, this characteristic was passed along to their offspring (**Figure 16.6**). Over time, he believed, an animal would acquire enough changes that one species would diverge into two, with this branching extending all the way to human beings. In his work, Lamarck lent support to a *means* of evolution that we know today is false. (Animals don't acquire and then pass along traits such as webbed feet in accordance with their activities.) Yet, note what Lamarck

got right: that organisms can evolve; that one kind of organism can be ancestral to a different kind of organism.

Georges Cuvier and Extinction

Another French scientist, Georges Cuvier, in examining the fossil-laden rocks of the Paris Basin early in the nineteenth century, provided conclusive evidence of the extinction of species on Earth. This was a radical notion at the time because many Christians believed that the creator would never allow one of his creatures to perish. (One amateur fossil collector who believed this was Thomas Jefferson.) This much about extinction Cuvier got right. However, seeing in his rock layers seeming "breaks" in the sequence of animal forms—a layer of simple forms would be followed by a layer of more complex forms as he went from older to newer layers—he held that there had been a series of catastrophes, such as floods, that wiped out life in given areas, after which the creator had carried out *new* acts of creation, bringing more complex life-forms into being with each act.

If you were to survey a broad swath of scientific thought leading up to Darwin, you'd repeatedly find what you've seen with Lamarck and Cuvier: a given scientist getting things partly right and partly wrong (which is almost always the way in science). The result was a rich mix of scientific findings and fanciful speculation that existed in Darwin's world as he boarded the *Beagle*. He himself believed at the time that species were fixed entities; that they did not change over time.

16.4 Darwin's Insights Following the *Beagle*'s Voyage

Darwin observed and collected wherever he went, but the most important stop on his journey took place nearly 4 years into it, when the *Beagle* stopped for a

Figure 16.6
The Duck's Feet
Jean-Baptiste de Lamarck proposed that new species evolve through a branching evolution, which is correct. He also proposed, however, that one of the forces driving this evolution is the inheritance of acquired characteristics, which does not take place in the form he imagined. Under Lamarck's view, common at the time, a duck got its webbed feet because of activities it carried out during its lifetime, and this change was then passed on to its offspring.

Figure 16.7
The Galapagos Islands
Galapagos is Spanish for *tortoise.* A part of Ecuador, the islands are still an important site of evolutionary research. Here a giant tortoise (*Geochelone nigra*) moves through the Alcedo Volcano area on the Galapagos island of Isabela.

scant five weeks at the remote series of volcanic outcroppings called the Galapagos Islands (**Figure 16.7**). There, in the dry landscape, amid broken pieces of black lava, he saw strange iguanas and tortoises and mockingbirds that varied from one island to another. He shot and preserved several of these mockingbird "varieties" for transport back home, along with a number of small birds that he took to be blackbirds, wrens, warblers, and finches.

Perceiving Common Descent with Modification

Arriving back in England in October of 1836, Darwin soon donated a good deal of his *Beagle* collection to

the Zoological Society of London. If there was a single most important flash of insight for him regarding descent with modification, it came when one of the society's bird experts gave him an initial report on the birds he had collected on the Galapagos. Three of the mockingbirds were not just the "varieties" that Darwin had thought; they were separate species, as judged by the standards of the day. Beyond that, the small birds he had believed to be blackbirds, finches, wrens, and warblers were all finches—separate species of finches, each of them found nowhere but the Galapagos (**Figure 16.8**).

With this, Darwin began to see a pattern: The Galapagos finches were related to an ancestral species that could be found on the mainland of South America, hundreds of miles to the east. Members of that ancestral species had come by air to the Galapagos and then, fanning out to separate islands, had diverged over time into separate species. Thus it was with Galapagos tortoises and iguanas and cactus plants as well; they had common mainland ancestors, but on these islands had diverged into separate species. Darwin began to perceive the infinite branching that exists in evolution.

Perceiving Natural Selection

But what drives this branching? In England and set on a career as gentleman naturalist, Darwin married and settled in London for a time before moving to a small village south of London, where he would live out his days (**Figure 16.9**). Two years after his homecoming, inspiration on evolution's key process came to him not from looking at nature, but from reading a book on human population and food supply—*An Essay on the Principle of Population,* by T. R. Malthus. As Darwin later wrote in his autobiography:

Figure 16.8
Three of Darwin's Finches
Thirteen species of finch evolved on the Galapagos Islands, all of them descendants of a single species of finch native to South America. Shown, left to right, are *Geospiza fuliginosa, G. fortis,* and *G. magnirostris.*

Figure 16.9
Where *On the Origin of Species* Was Written

In this study in his house in rural England, Charles Darwin conducted scientific research and wrote his groundbreaking work, *On the Origin of Species by Means of Natural Selection.*

I happened to read for amusement Malthus on Population, and being well prepared to appreciate the struggle for existence which everywhere goes on . . . it at once struck me that under these circumstances favourable variations would tend to be preserved and unfavourable ones to be destroyed.

Thus did natural selection occur to Darwin as the driving force behind evolution. Organisms that had "favorable variations" were preserved (they lived and left many offspring), while those that had unfavorable variations were destroyed (they left fewer offspring or none at all). As a result, over generations, organisms evolved in the direction of the favorable variations.

You might think that, with two major insights in place—common descent with modification and its link to natural selection—Darwin would have rushed to inform the world of them. In fact, more than 20 years were to elapse between his reading of Malthus and the 1859 publication of his great book, *On the Origin of Species by Means of Natural Selection.* In between, though incapacitated much of the time with a mysterious illness, Darwin published on geology, bred pigeons, and spent 8 years studying the variations in barnacles—activities that each had relevance to his theory and that yet constituted a kind of holding pattern for him as he contemplated informing the world of a theory that he knew would be controversial. Darwin finally got to work on what he thought would be his "big species book" in 1856.

16.5 Alfred Russel Wallace

Two years after Darwin began this labor, half a world away and unbeknownst to him, a fellow English naturalist lay in a malaria-induced delirium on an Indonesian island. Alfred Russel Wallace made a living collecting bird and butterfly specimens from the then-exotic lands of South America and Southeast Asia, selling his finds to museums and collectors. He had thought long and hard (and even published) about how species originate. Now, shivering with malarial fever in a hut in the tropical heat, with the question on his mind again, Wallace came on the very insight that had come to Darwin 20 years earlier: Natural selection is the process that shapes evolution. Recovering from his illness, Wallace wrote out his ideas over the next few days and sent them to a scientific hero of his in England—Charles Darwin! He asked Darwin to read his manuscript and submit it to a journal if Darwin thought it worthy.

Darwin was stunned as he faced the prospect of another man being the first to bring to the world an insight he thought was his alone. Nevertheless, he would not allow himself to be underhanded with the younger scientist. He informed some of his scientist friends about his plight, and (without informing Wallace) they arranged for both Wallace's paper and some of Darwin's letters, sketching out his ideas, to be presented at a meeting of a scientific society in London on July 1, 1858. The readings before the scientific society turned out to have little immediate effect, but they did prod Darwin into working on what would become *On the Origin of Species,* published some 16 months later. This event had a great effect. Indeed, it set off a thunderclap whose reverberations can still be heard today.

16.6 Darwin: Accepted, Doubted, and Vindicated

Sparking both scorn and praise, Darwin's ideas were fiercely debated in the years after 1859. At least within scientific circles, however, it did not take long for common descent with modification to be accepted. Fifteen years or so after *On the Origin of Species* was published, almost all naturalists had become convinced of it, and it's not hard to see why. With evolution as a framework, so many things that had previously seemed curious, or even bizarre, now made sense.

For example, years before *Origin* was published, scientists had known that, at a certain point in their

Figure 16.10
Different Embryos,
Same Structure

(Adapted from M. K. Richardson, 1997.)

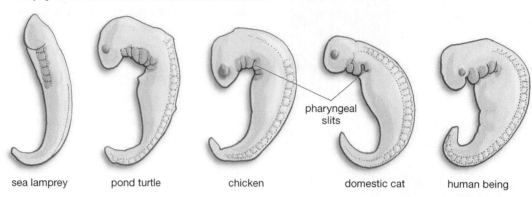

Pharyngeal slits exist in these five vertebrate animals . . .

pharyngeal
slits

sea lamprey   pond turtle   chicken   domestic cat   human being

. . . evidence that all five evolved from a common ancestor.

embryonic development, organisms as diverse as fish, chickens, and humans all have structures known as pharyngeal slits (**Figure 16.10**). In fish, these structures go on to be *gill* slits; in humans, they develop into the eustachian tubes, among other things. The question was: Why would land-dwelling and sea-dwelling animals share this common structure in embryonic life? For that matter, why would organisms as different as a human and a chicken share this structure? With evolution, the answer became clear. All of them shared a common vertebrate *ancestor,* which had the slits. The vertebrate ancestral line had branched out into various species, yet elements of the common ancestor persisted in these different species in their embryonic stage.

You might think that this would leave open the question of why organisms should differ more as adults than as embryos, but Darwin's theory made sense of this, too. Remember that natural selection is the primary process that brings about the differences that we see among species. Now consider one trait that natural selection stands to operate on in all animal species—the trait of movement or "locomotion." If you think about it, *adult* animals must deal with the issue of movement all the time, but embryonic animals never deal with it (because they don't move). Hence, for millions of years, natural selection was channeling the adult forms of vertebrate species in different ways with respect to their means of movement (fins, legs, wings). But this channeling was going on *only* in the adult forms. Likewise, natural selection was only affecting adults with respect to such traits as mating and the means of obtaining food. (Embryos don't mate, and food is delivered to them.) Hence, natural selection was driving differences in the adult forms of animals more than it was driving differences in embryonic forms. The result? Early embryos of various species could retain the ancestral vertebrate form more than adults could.

In bringing together countless loose ends such as this, evolution became the mortar that unified the study of the living world. (It's interesting to think of

biologists from this period as readers who start going over a detective novel a *second* time, saying, "Of course!" and "Why didn't I see that?") Given this, scientists had little trouble accepting the *fact* of evolution—that is, the occurrence of common descent with modification. But the primary process that Darwin said was driving evolution, natural selection, was not embraced so quickly. Indeed, the twentieth century would be almost halfway over before it was generally accepted.

The Controversy over Natural Selection

The essential stumbling block for the theory of evolution by natural selection was this: It asserted that traits can vary in ways that confer reproductive advantages on given individuals and that these variations can be passed on from one generation to the next. With the trees considered earlier, the trait was height, and the variation that conferred a reproductive advantage was greater height. In a given environment, therefore, added height represents a *difference* that allows some members of the species to leave more offspring than others, leading eventually to a taller species over all. But in the middle of the nineteenth century, no one could imagine how such differences could reliably be passed down over many generations. Even scientists of the time could not understand this because they had no grasp of the field that we today call genetics.

Coming to an Understanding of Genetics

Thinking back to the genetics section of this book, recall, from Chapter 11, that a trait such as tree height is likely to be governed by many genes working in tandem, with each of these genes coding for a protein that has some small, additive effect on height. Indeed, such multi-gene, or "polygenic," inheritance is at work with most of the traits in living things. (See "Multiple Alleles and Polygenic Inheritance" in Chapter 11, page

204.) A tree's "height genes" will be shuffled in countless ways when tree egg and sperm are formed and when they fuse in fertilization. As a result, gene combinations that yield particularly tall trees will come together in certain instances. In addition, outright mutations—alterations in genetic information—can take place, showing up as new physical traits, one of them being a taller tree. Most important for our purposes, whatever the genetic information is, it *persists*; it is passed on largely intact from one generation to another in the small informational packets we call genes. The result is small physical differences that can be reliably passed on from one generation to the next.

Darwin could not have imagined a better mechanism for carrying out natural selection as he had envisioned it. The problem was that neither he nor anyone else in his time knew that things worked like this. Most nineteenth-century scientists believed that inheritance worked through a "blending" process akin to mixing different-colored paints. If you blend red and blue paint, for example, you get something that lies halfway between them, purple. Under such a system, differences in traits would not be preserved over time; they would be averaged into oblivion. Blending would work to make groups of organisms the same, not to allow differences among them. How could natural selection work if there were no persistent differences to select from?

The vindication of natural selection required, first, a demonstration (by Gregor Mendel) that inheritance doesn't work by blending. Rather, it works through the transmission of the stable genetic units we now call genes. Then, in the early part of the twentieth century, came the demonstration that, through polygenic inheritance, genes could account for very small physical differences that arise within a given population. Trees come in a *range* of heights, with the differences in this range governed by the combinations of individual genes described earlier.

Darwin Triumphant: The Modern Synthesis

Advances in genetics such as this were later joined to other types of evolutionary research, such that in the period roughly from 1937 to 1950 there took place what is known as the **modern synthesis**: the convergence of several lines of biological research into a unified evolutionary theory. Taxonomists reported on how species are distributed throughout the world. Mathematical geneticists provided guidance on how evolution *could* work, given the shifting around of genes among organisms. Paleontologists studied evolution in the fossil record. Critically, these different types of scientists were involved in a process of mutual education with one another; the findings of geneticists, for example, were now known to taxonomists, and vice versa. The upshot was a greatly deepened understanding of how evolution

works—an understanding that provided conclusive evidence for Darwin's assertions about the importance of natural selection. The architect of evolutionary theory had been vindicated nearly 100 years after publishing his great work. (For another example of natural selection's importance, see "An Evolving Ability to Drink Milk" on page 294.)

SO FAR . . .

1. True or false: Charles Darwin was the first person to perceive common descent with modification.

2. The co-discoverer of natural selection was _____.

3. Following the publication of *On the Origin of Species*, the evolutionary principle of _____ was quickly accepted by most scientists, but the importance of _____ would not be accepted by most authorities until midway through the twentieth century.

16.7 Opposition to the Theory of Evolution

So, why are Darwin's essential insights so widely believed to be correct? We'll now review some of the evidence for these insights, but first a word about why a look at this evidence is desirable. When you studied cells in this book, you did not review the "evidence for cells." Nor did you go over the "evidence for energy transfer" when studying cellular respiration, nor the "evidence for lipids" when studying biological molecules. What makes evolution different from these topics?

The False Notion of a Scientific Controversy

Evolution has an unusual status among major biological subdisciplines in that, almost alone among them, its findings are regularly challenged as being unproven or simply wrong. For anyone unfamiliar with biology, these attacks make it appear that the theory of evolution is not a body of knowledge, solidly grounded in evidence, but rather a kind of scientific guess about the history of life on Earth.

What Is a Theory?

Several factors are critical in allowing the appearance of a "scientific debate" on the validity of the theory of evolution, when in fact none exists. The first of these has to do with a simple misunderstanding regarding terminology. You saw in Chapter 1 that, to the average person, the word *theory* implies an idea that certainly is unproven and that may be pure speculation. In science, however, a theory is a general set of principles, supported by evidence, that explains some aspect of the natural world. Accordingly, we have Isaac Newton's theory of gravitation, Albert Einstein's general theory of relativity, and many others. Lots of principles go into making up the theory of evolution, some of them on surer footing than others. Over time, however, some of these principles have achieved the status of established fact—we are as sure of them as we are sure that the Earth is round. Among these principles are the fact that evolution has indeed taken place and the fact that this has occurred over billions of years.

The Nature of Historical Evidence

A second factor that provides an opening for the opponents of evolution is the nature of the evidence for it. If you were called on to provide the "evidence for cells" referred to earlier, a look through a microscope at some actual cells might be enough to stop this "debate" in its tracks. Conversely, one of evolution's most important manifestations—radical transformations of life-forms—can never be observed in this way because these transformations take place over vast expanses of time. Asking to "see" the equivalent of a dinosaur evolving into a bird before you'll believe it is like asking to see the European colonization of North America before you'll acknowledge it.

Evolution is taking place right now, all around us, but the evidence for evolution is historical evidence to a degree that is not true of, say, the study of genetics or of photosynthesis. Any ancient historical record is fragmentary, and evolution's historical record is ancient indeed. The fossils that scientists analyze are what remain from hundreds of millions of years of weathering and decay. Such an incomplete record leaves room for a great deal of interpretation among scientists—far more than is the case in purely experimental science. This interpretation has to do, however, with the *details* of evolution, not with its core principles. It has to do with what group descended from what other, with the rate at which evolution has proceeded, or with the role that pure chance has played in evolution. It does not have to do with *whether* evolution has occurred.

16.8 The Evidence for Evolution

So, what makes scientists so sure about the core principles of evolution? In any search for truth, we are more comfortable when lines of evidence are internally consistent and then go on to agree with *other* lines of evidence. The evidence for evolution satisfies both criteria. If we were to find even a single glaring inconsistency within or between lines of evidence, the whole body of evolutionary theory would be called into question. But no such inconsistencies have turned up yet, and scientists have been looking for them for 150 years.

Radiometric Dating

One claim of evolutionary theory, as you have seen, is that evolution proceeds at a leisurely pace, with billions of years having elapsed between the appearance of life and the present. Yet how do we know that Earth isn't, say, 46,000 years old, as opposed to the 4.6 billion that scientists believe it to be? The conceptual bedrock on which we have determined the age of the Earth and its organisms is **radiometric dating,** a technique for determining the age of objects by measuring the decay of the radioactive elements they contain. As volcanic rocks are formed, various elements in their surroundings are incorporated into them. Some of these elements are radioactive, meaning they emit energetic rays or particles and "decay" in the process.

With such decay, one element can be transformed into another, the most famous example being uranium-238, which becomes lead-206 through a long series of transformations. The critical thing is that this transformation proceeds at a fixed *rate*; it is as steady as the most accurate clock imaginable. It takes 4.5 billion years for half a given amount of uranium-238 to decay into lead-206 (hence the term *half-life*). When such a transformation takes place in a cooled rock, the original or "parent" element is trapped within the rock, as is the "daughter" element, and the atoms of both elements can be counted. Therefore, comparing the proportion of a parent element to the daughter element in a rock sample provides a date for the rock with a fair amount of precision. There are now more than 40 different radiometric dating techniques used, each of them employing a different radioactive isotope. Some of these isotopes have very long half-lives (as with uranium-238), but some have relatively short half-lives. (See Chapter 2, page 26, for information on an isotope with a very short half-life, carbon-14.) Given the range of such "radiometric clocks," scientists have been able to date objects from nearly the formation of the Earth to the present, although there are some gaps in the picture.

Fossils

Today, one line of evidence for evolution is the similarity of fossil types by sedimentary layers. Looking at the same geologic layers of sediment worldwide, scientists find similar types of fossils, with a general movement toward more complex organisms as they go up through the newer strata. Chapter 1 noted that scientific claims must be *falsifiable*—they must be open to being proved false with the discovery of new

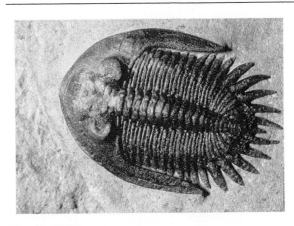

Figure 16.11
Ancient Organism, Now Extinct
Shown is a fossilized trilobite, a kind of arthropod that became extinct long before the animals known as primates came to exist. This fossilized trilobite dates from about 370 million years ago and was found in present-day Morocco.

evidence. The fossil record presents a falsifiable claim. For example, creatures called trilobites (**Figure 16.11**) had a long run on Earth, existing in the ancient oceans from about 500 million years ago until some 245 million years ago, when they became extinct. By contrast, the evolutionary lineage that humans are part of, the primates, *began* no more than 81 million years ago. If scientists were to find, in a single fossil bed, fossils of trilobites existing side by side with those of early primates, our whole notion of evolutionary sequences would be called into question. No such incompatible pairing has happened, however, and the strong betting is it won't. Given this, the line of fossil evidence is internally consistent—but there's more. When we compare fossil placement with the dates we

get from radiometric dating, we get excellent agreement *between* these two lines of evidence. We don't find trilobites embedded in sediments that turn out to be 81 million years old.

Morphology and Vestigial Characters

Morphology is the study of the physical forms that organisms take. In comparative morphology, some classic evidence for evolution is seen in the similar forelimb structures found in a very diverse group of mammals—in a whale, a cat, a bat, and a gorilla, as seen in **Figure 16.12**. Look at what exists in each case: one upper bone, joined to two intermediate bones, joined to five digits. Evolutionary biologists postulate that the four mammals evolved from a common ancestor, adapting this 1-2-5 structure over time in accordance with their environments. Such features are said to be **homologous,** meaning the same in structure owing to inheritance from a common ancestor.

Along similar lines, if you look in detailed human anatomy textbooks, you'll see listings for the muscles of the human head. One of these, for example, is a muscle that retracts the tongue (the hyoglossus) and another is a muscle that helps us swallow (the aryepiglottic). In any such list, however, you'll also find the auricular muscles—three of them, which lie on each side of the head. And what do these muscles do? *They wiggle our ears.* That's it; no other natural use has ever been found for them. And, of course, in most people, they are useless for even this. Now, muscles are tissues that are specialized to do one thing—contract—and relative to fat tissue, they burn up a lot of energy. Given this, we have to ask: Why do we humans have auricular muscles? If we imagine that our bodies were designed, then wouldn't it be strange

whale   cat

bat   gorilla

Figure 16.12
Four Animals, One Forelimb Structure

Whales, cats, bats, and gorillas are all descendants of a common ancestor. As a result, the bones in the forelimbs of these diverse organisms are very similar despite wide differences in function. Four sets of homologous bones are color-coded for comparison. Note that in each case there is one upper bone, joined to two intermediate bones, joined to five digits.

ESSAY

An Evolving Ability to Drink Milk

Anyone who thinks that the effects of evolution lie strictly off in the past might consider asking themselves the following question: How would you feel about having a glass of milk right now? If the answer is you'd feel fine about it, then that puts you in the company of hundreds of millions of adults worldwide who would feel the same way. Meanwhile, for nearly 100 percent of adults in China, and for nearly that percentage of adults in parts of Africa, the idea of drinking a glass of milk is about as appealing as the idea of acquiring a low-grade food poisoning, because both things can have the same effect: abdominal pain, bloating, and gas. Within the United States, at least 30 million adults are averse to milk: Some 75 percent of adult African Americans and 90 percent of adult Asian Americans cannot digest it. Conversely, no more than 5 percent of adults of Northern European descent have a problem with it.

So, why should human beings have such differing reactions to a healthy food? The answer is that, for tens of thousands of years, *no* adult human beings appear to have had an ability to digest milk. Then, in the last 7,000 years, a human cultural change—the initiation of animal herding—worked hand-in-hand with the evolutionary forces of mutation and natural selection to produce select groups of people who could digest milk throughout their lives. It's possible that all of the people in the world today who can digest milk as adults are descended from members of these original groups.

Human beings of any age who digest milk do so by producing an enzyme, called lactase, that breaks down the milk sugar lactose when it enters the small intestines.

Virtually all human *infants* can break down the lactose in milk—something that's not surprising, given that through most of human history, all human infants were nurtured on milk from their mothers. When early childhood ends, however, a majority of the world's people stop producing the lactase enzyme. The gene for lactase, called *LCT,* ceases to be transcribed in them, which means it effectively shuts down. Individuals in whom this takes place become lactose-intolerant; any lactose that enters their small intestines simply stays in the digestive tract for a time, drawing in water while feeding bacteria—conditions that lead to bloat, gas, and discomfort. The fact that the *LCT* gene shuts down in most people actually is not surprising, however, since for most of human history an *active LCT* gene would have been useless in adults. This is so because, for the first 190,000 years of human history, humans had no source of milk other than mothers' milk. The default position for the human lactase gene was to shut down after early childhood because *after* early childhood most humans consumed no milk at all.

In some parts of the world, however, the human nutritional environment began to change considerably beginning about 10,000 years ago, when people first domesticated herd animals. The cattle, sheep, goats, and camels that human beings brought under control would eventually serve as rich sources of milk in the human diet. Of course, such milk initially had a limited value because of adult lactose intolerance, but this was about to change. Research conducted in the last 10 years has shown that the ability of adults to digest

milk arose separately in at least three places—Northern Europe, the Middle East, and Eastern Africa—and that this occurred through the same mechanism in each case: an accidental mutation to human DNA followed by rounds of natural selection that spread the ability to digest milk through ever-expanding proportions of the human population.

In 2002, Leena Peltonen and her colleagues in Helsinki, Finland, lifted the curtain on the Northern European part of this story. An analysis Peltonen conducted of nine extended Finnish families revealed a mutation to the DNA of some family members that correlated perfectly with their ability to digest milk. Exactly 13,910 bases "upstream" from the lactase *LCT* gene, the C base found in most human beings mutated into a T base in the ancestors of these Northern Europeans. This small change made all the difference, for it allowed the binding of a protein to the DNA of these Europeans that kept their transcription of the lactase gene going, even after they passed childhood. Thus, anyone who inherited this "T_13910" mutation effectively inherited a lifelong ability to digest milk.

The discovery of this European mutation deepened a question that University of Maryland, College Park, researcher Sarah Tishkoff had been asking herself since the late 1990s: What accounts for the "lactase persistence" seen in the cattle-herding tribal populations of East Africa? (**Figure 1**) Sequencing of the DNA of some lactase-persistent East Africans made clear that they didn't share the T_13910 mutation seen in Europeans. To find out what did account for their ability to digest lactose, Tishkoff and her colleagues spent long stretches of time over a period of 3 years driving around East Africa in a Land Rover, obtaining DNA samples from 470 Africans

---

for a designer to put in place these sets of costly, specialized, and useless structures? Against this, evolutionary theory makes sense of their presence.

What we think of as our ears are really our outer ears, or "pinna." Almost all mammals have pinna, but these usually are *mobile* pinna. The common house cat

swivels its pinna up to 180 degrees as a means of homing in on sounds of predators or prey. We don't have this swiveling ability, however, and neither do any of the other "anthropoid" primates, which is to say monkeys and apes. Now, note that primates are among the latest evolving mammals. So, a likely explanation for human

Figure 1
From a Human Cultural Practice, an Evolving Human Ability
A Masai tribesman in Kenya tends to a herd of cattle. The diet of most Masai consists largely of meat and milk derived from the cows and goats they raise. The East African region that is home to the Masai is one of three in the world in which human adults first acquired the ability to digest milk.

while testing them for their ability to digest lactose. In 2007, Tishkoff let the world in on what this work revealed: The ancestors of Africans in Kenya and Tanzania developed a mutation to their DNA that, while different from the European mutation, nevertheless had the same effect; it drove lifelong transcription of the *LCT* gene. One year after this discovery was announced, the Peltonen group in Finland added a third chapter to the human lactase story. DNA testing of modern-day Saudi Arabians revealed that their ancestors had experienced two mutations—completely separate from the European and African mutations—that now are widespread in the Middle East and that account for the ability of many Middle Eastern residents to digest milk in adulthood.

Modern DNA analysis is so powerful that it allows researchers to assign rough dates to the appearance of mutations such

as these. Peltonen's group estimated that one of the two Middle Eastern lactase mutations first appeared about 4,100 years ago, though this event could have taken place about 2,100 years to either side of this date. Meanwhile, the African mutation is thought to have appeared sometime between 3,000 and 7,000 years ago, and the Northern European mutation is thought to have arisen about 7,000 years ago. Taking a step back from these dates, note, first, how well they correlate with the initiation of animal herding 10,000 years ago. Second, notice how *recently* lactase persistence arose within the context of the 200,000 years that human beings have existed as a species. If human existence were an hour long, the ability of any adult humans to digest milk would have come about only in the last two minutes of that hour. We might marvel at the fact that such a large share of humanity has become lactase-persistent in this

relatively short period of time, but a little reflection on the mechanism that brought this change about, natural selection, makes clear that a rapid spread of lactase persistence was all but inevitable.

Imagine two girls born, say, 6,000 years ago in what is now Finland. Life in this region is precarious for everyone; the winters are long and food is scarce even in warm months. The Northern European lactase mutation appeared about 1,000 years prior to the birth of these girls, which means that only some Northern Europeans now possess this genetic variant. Imagine that one of the girls we're considering has inherited this variant but the other hasn't. This means that from the age of, say, 4, one of these girls can obtain nourishment from cow or goat's milk while the other cannot. Given this, which of these girls is more likely to *survive* into adulthood? The answer, of course, is the girl with the lactase mutation. The milk that she consumes will provide her, all year round, with precious calories and calcium. In the environment in which she's growing up, this girl has been *selected* to survive by virtue of her genetic makeup. And with this survival comes an increased likelihood that she will go on to have children of her own—children who themselves will have a reproductive advantage, assuming that they too have the lactase-persistence mutation.

When this process is repeated in one generation after another, the result is the rapid spread of a trait through a population. Today in parts of Northern Europe, 98 percent of the population is believed to be lactase-persistent. In 7,000 years, then, lactase persistence evolved from a 0 percent prevalence to a 98 percent prevalence in this one part of the world. How strong a force is evolution through natural selection? Well, how would you feel about having a glass of milk?

auricular muscles is that they are *vestiges* of our mammalian evolutionary history. Such muscles had a real function in our mammalian ancestors: They moved the pinna of these animals. In the anthropoid primates, however, moveable pinna became less useful for some reason (the three-dimensional vision we have?) and

over time these muscles fell into their current, functionless state.

Auricular muscles are one example among many of a **vestigial character,** meaning a structure in an organism whose original function has been lost during the course of evolution. The ostrich is a bird and it has wings, but it cannot fly. Ostrich wings do have several modern-day functions; they help balance the bird as it runs, for example. But, like muscles, wings are structures *specialized* for something—lifting animals off the ground. So is it reasonable to assume that a designer fashioned wings for the ostrich just to help it with balance? To paraphrase chemist Douglas Theobald, this would be like designing a computer keyboard that is meant to be used in hammering tacks. Evolution has a different explanation: The ostrich came from birds that could fly, but its own line *evolved* into a flightless condition. Looked at one way, the wings of the ostrich and the auricular muscles of human beings are like calling cards left by our ancestors; they tell us where we came from.

Evidence from Gene Modification

In the genetics unit, you saw that every living thing on Earth employs DNA and uses an almost identical "genetic code" (*this* triplet of DNA bases specifies *that* amino acid). At the very least, this means there is a unity running through all earthly life; it is also consistent with the idea that all life on Earth ultimately had a single starting point—the single common ancestor mentioned earlier.

In recent decades, molecular biology has also provided another check on what scientists have long believed to be true about evolutionary relationships—about which species are more closely related and about how long it's been since they've shared a common ancestor. All genes amount to a sequence of A, T, G, and C bases along DNA's double helix. And there are some genes that do very similar things in different organisms. There is, for example, a gene called *hedgehog* that helps regulate embryonic development in the *Drosophila* fruit fly and a gene called *sonic hedgehog* that helps regulate embryonic development in mice. Though the *hedgehog* and *sonic hedgehog* genes are similar, we would not expect them to be identical. This is so because gene base sequences change over time through the process of mutation. If the *rate* of this change is constant, then mutations are like a molecular clock that's ticking: With the passage of a given amount of time, you get a set number of mutations. Given this, the longer it has been since two organisms shared a common ancestor, the greater the number of base differences we should see in the sequence of genes like *hedgehog* and *sonic hedgehog*.

To better understand this last point, it may be helpful to think in terms of something more familiar: natural language. The European settlers of Australia were predominantly English. Once the Australians and the English became fundamentally separate, however, their manner of speaking began to evolve independently. For example, we could think of the word *outback* as a "mutation" in Australian speech.

Meanwhile, England would be developing its own "mutations," meaning words not used in Australia. And the longer the Australians went on being separate from the English, the greater the number of such differences we would see between the two languages. Just so, the longer it has been since two species went down separate evolutionary lines, the greater the number of base differences we would see in similar genes they have, as measured by the different mutations each has acquired.

This gene-modification hypothesis has been put to the test in connection with a gene that codes for an enzyme called cytochrome *c* oxidase, which exists in organisms as different as humans, moths, and yeasts. Going into this experiment, evolutionary theory predicted that there should be fewer DNA base-pair differences between the cytochrome *c* oxidase genes of, say, a human and a duck than between a human and a moth because all the *other* evidence we had told us that humans and ducks share a more recent common ancestor than do humans and moths. In **Figure 16.13** you can see that evolutionary theory was fully borne out by the DNA sequencing. There are 17 sequence differences between a human and a duck but 36 between a human and a moth. Indeed, all the differences between the species pictured fall into line with evolutionary theory. Thus, we have another confirmation for evolution between lines of evidence—between DNA sequencing *and* the fossil record *and* radiometric dating *and* comparative morphology.

Experimental Evidence

Finally, much evidence for evolution has been provided in recent years by experiment and observation. At first glance, this may seem rather improbable because, as you've seen, evolutionary change can often be perceived only over long stretches of time. Scientists have devised clever ways to catch evolution in the act, however.

Consider the experiments of John Endler, who believed that the male guppies he was studying were being pulled in two directions by natural selection. On the one hand, those that were larger and had brighter coloration were chosen more often by females for mating. On the other, these very characteristics made the males more vulnerable to predators. Endler saw that he could test natural selection by putting some guppies in a predator-free environment. In only a few generations, brighter coloration and larger tails evolved in the males. When Endler then reintroduced predators into this population, things went the other way: Over several generations, smaller tails and less-brilliant colors evolved in the males. Both of these outcomes are precisely what evolutionary theory would predict. In both instances, the physical

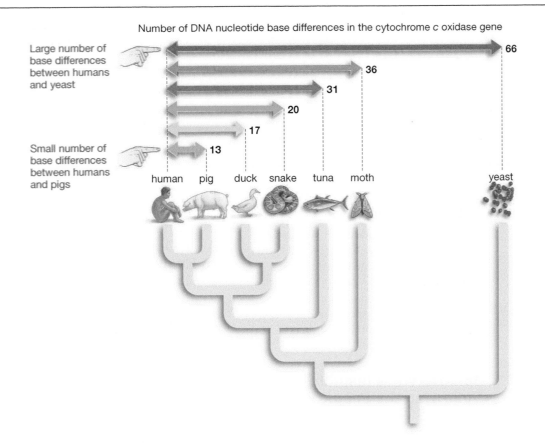

Number of DNA nucleotide base differences in the cytochrome *c* oxidase gene

Large number of base differences between humans and yeast

Small number of base differences between humans and pigs

66
36
31
20
17
13

human   pig   duck   snake   tuna   moth   yeast

Figure 16.13
Using Molecules to Track Evolution

Diverse organisms—such as yeast, moths, and pigs—all have a gene that codes for an enzyme called cytochrome *c* oxidase. Over time, however, the cytochrome *c* oxidase genes have undergone mutations that have altered the sequence of their DNA "building blocks," called bases. The longer it has been since any two species shared a common ancestor, the more differences there should be in their cytochrome *c* oxidase bases. There are 13 differences between the bases found in the human cytochrome *c* oxidase gene and the one found in pigs, but there are 66 differences between the human and yeast genes.

(Data from Whitfield, Philip. 1993. From *So Simple a Beginning: The Book of Evolution.* New York: Macmillan: Maxwell Macmillan International.)

characteristics of the guppies were modified in directions that maximized their reproductive success—more mates with the brighter colors in the predator-free environment, and a longer life (and hence more reproduction) with the drab coloration in the predator-laden environment.

On to How Evolution Works

Given the abundance of evidence for evolution, biologists long ago stopped asking whether it occurred. For decades the really interesting questions have been: Through what means has evolution proceeded? At what pace? In what direction, if any? These are the questions we'll look at in the next three chapters.

SO FAR...

1. The age of the Earth has been established through the use of _____, in which scientists test for the _____ of parent and daughter elements in a given sample of rock or other material.

2. _____ features are features in different species that are the same in structure owing to inheritance from a _____.

3. The auricular muscles of human beings and the wings of ostriches are examples of _____ characters.

16 REVIEW

Go to the Study Area at www.masteringbiology.com for practice quizzes, myeBook, BioFlixTM 3-D animations, MP3 Tutor Sessions, videos, current events, and more.

Mastering
BIOLOGY

Summary

16.1 Evolution and Its Core Principles

- A key principle within the theory of evolution is common descent with modification: the process by which species of living things can undergo modification over time, with such change sometimes resulting in the formation of new species. All species have descended from other species and all living things descend ultimately from a single, common ancestor. (p. 283)

- A second key principle in the theory of evolution is natural selection: the process through which traits that confer a reproductive advantage to individual organisms grow more common in populations of organisms over successive generations. (p. 284)

- With an understanding of the theory of evolution, human beings have become aware that (1) we are descended from other varieties of living things and that (2) species are not fixed entities, but instead are constantly undergoing modification. (p. 284)

16.2 Charles Darwin and the Theory of Evolution

- Charles Darwin deserves primary credit for the theory of evolution. He developed existing ideas about descent with modification while providing much evidence in support of them. And he was the first to perceive natural selection as the primary process that drives evolution. Darwin's insights were inspired by the research he carried out during a 5-year voyage he took around the world on the ship *HMS Beagle*, beginning in 1831. (p. 285)

16.3 Evolutionary Thinking before Darwin

- Some of Darwin's ideas can be traced to the work of Lyell, de Lamarck, and Cuvier, who respectively noted the dynamic geological nature of the Earth, the possibility of descent with modification, and the extinction of some species on Earth and the appearance of others within different time frames. (p. 286)

16.4 Darwin's Insights Following the *Beagle*'s Voyage

- Darwin understood descent with modification for several years before he comprehended that natural selection was the most important process driving it. (p. 287)

16.5 Alfred Russel Wallace

- English naturalist Alfred Russel Wallace is the co-discoverer of natural selection as the principal process underlying evolution. (p. 289)

16.6 Darwin: Accepted, Doubted, and Vindicated

- Descent with modification was accepted by most scientists not long after publication of Darwin's *On the Origin of Species by Means of Natural Selection* in 1859 because the principle explained so many facets of the living world. (p. 289)

- That natural selection is the most important process underlying evolution was not generally accepted until the middle of the twentieth century, when the modern synthesis in the theory of evolution brought together lines of evidence from genetics, the fossil record, and the distri-bution of organisms throughout the world. (p. 290)

16.7 Opposition to the Theory of Evolution

- One factor leading to the appearance of a scientific debate over evolution is confusion about the meaning of the word *theory*, which in everyday speech can mean an idea that is pure speculation but that in science means a general set of principles, supported by evidence, that explains some aspect of the natural world. (p. 291)

16.8 The Evidence for Evolution

- Six lines of evidence that are consistent with the theory of evolution are (1) radiometric dating, (2) the fossil record, (3) the common occurrence of homologous physical structures in different organisms, (4) the existence of vestigial characters in various organisms, (5) variations found in the DNA sequences of various organisms, and (6) experimental demonstrations of evolution. (p. 292)

Key Terms

common descent with modification 283
homologous 293
modern synthesis 291
morphology 293
natural selection 284
radiometric dating 292
vestigial character 295

Understanding the Basics

Multiple-Choice Questions

(Answers are in the back of the book.)

1. In science, a theory is:
   a. an untested hypothesis.
   b. a general set of principles, supported by evidence, that explains some aspect of the natural world.
   c. speculation about the natural world, based on general knowledge of a field.
   d. an observation.
   e. the first idea proposed to explain some aspect of the natural world.

2. Which of the following are central ideas in the theory of evolution by natural selection? (List all that apply.)
   a. Organisms vary in traits that affect their reproduction.
   b. Descent with modification occurs over generations.
   c. Evolution has a goal.
   d. Traits that confer a reproductive advantage will become more common in populations over time.
   e. Traits that are acquired during the life of an individual contribute to evolution.

3. Which of the following observations provide evidence for evolution? (List all that apply.)
   a. Monkey and trilobite fossils are never found in the same fossil beds.
   b. Athletic training can produce an increase in muscle mass.
   c. DNA sequences of genes shared by various species vary in accordance with predictions about how closely related those species are.
   d. The genetic code is nearly universal.
   e. Species whose adult forms look very different may have similar features in embryonic life.

4. During the formulation of his theory of evolution by natural selection, Darwin brought together ideas and results from several disciplines. Match the person with the phrase that describes his work.
   a. Lyell — Evidence of extinction of species
   b. Wallace — One form of organism can evolve into another
   c. Lamarck — Natural selection as a mechanism underlying evolution
   d. Cuvier — Geological forces observable today caused changes in Earth

5. Some of the following structures are homologous with each other. Which ones are they, and which two do not belong to this group?
   a. whale flipper
   b. insect leg
   c. bat wing
   d. cat forelimb
   e. octopus tentacles

6. Discoveries in the field of _____ provided key evidence needed for natural selection to be widely accepted as the mechanism of evolution (select one).
   a. radiometric dating
   b. fossils
   c. genetics
   d. DNA sequencing
   e. medicine

7. Important implications of the theory of evolution by natural selection include (select all that apply):
   a. All organisms, including humans, are descended from a common ancestor.
   b. The biological world is constantly evolving.
   c. Nature designs things intentionally.
   d. Traits found in organisms are the outcomes of a goal-less process.
   e. Humans occupy one ordinary branch on an enormous tree of life.

8. John Endler performed an experiment involving guppies in which he demonstrated evolution driven by natural selection that worked through a predator–prey relationship. Which of the following are true statements about the results of his experiments? (Select all that are correct.)
   a. Males with longer tails and brighter coloration were more frequently eaten by predator fish.
   b. Females preferred to mate with dull-colored males.
   c. When males were put in a predator-free environment, brighter coloration and larger tails evolved in them.
   d. In the predator-free environment, the average brightness of females increased.
   e. When predators were reintroduced, duller coloration and smaller tails evolved in the males.

Brief Review

(Answers are in the back of the book.)

1. What is homology, and why does it provide evidence for evolution?

2. How does the evidence presented in Figure 16.13 on page 297 support the conclusion that humans are more closely related to pigs than to yeast?

3. Describe two examples in which agreement among different lines of evidence provides evidence for evolution.

4. What is one observation that Darwin made in the Galapagos that influenced his thinking about evolution, and why was it important? Would he have been as likely to formulate his theory had he not had the opportunity to sail on the *Beagle*? Why or why not?

5. What major tenet of Darwin's theory of evolution was accepted by almost all scientists within Darwin's lifetime? What major tenet of his theory did not gain acceptance until midway through the twentieth century?

Applying Your Knowledge

1. Using evolutionary principles, explain why large ears might be expected to evolve in a terrestrial plant eater such as a rabbit or deer but not in an aquatic mammal such as a seal.

2. Explain the evolutionary steps by which bacteria may become resistant to antibiotics, using the core requirements for evolution by natural selection.

3. Critics of the theory of evolution say it leaves no room for human purpose since the theory asserts that human beings evolved through a process—natural selection—that has no goals or intentions. Does the theory undercut the idea of purpose in human life?

The Means of Evolution:

Microevolution

What is it that evolves? The essential unit that does so is the population. Pictured is part of a migrating population of snow geese (*Anser caerulescens*).

When people hear the word *evolution,* what generally comes to mind is the grand sweep of evolution: the story of how microorganisms were the first life-forms; of how dinosaurs came and went; of how human beings arose as newcomers on the planet. It is quite a story, to be sure, but to fully appreciate it, the place to look initially is not at evolution's outcomes, but rather at its processes. *How* do generations of organisms become modified over time? That's the subject of this chapter. When you understand it, you'll be in a position to comprehend evolution on its grander scale.

17.1 What Is It That Evolves?

In approaching this topic, the first question to be answered is: What is it that evolves? If you think about it, it's pretty clear that it is not individual organisms. A tree may inherit a mix of genes that makes it slightly taller than other trees, but if this tree is considered in isolation, it is simply one slightly taller tree. If **it** were to die without leaving any offspring, nothing could be said to have evolved because no persistent quality (added height) has been passed on to any group of organisms.

In Chapter 16 you were introduced to the idea of a **species,** which can briefly be defined as a group of organisms that can successfully interbreed with one another in nature but that don't successfully interbreed with members of other such groups. You might think that it is species—such as horses or American elm trees—that evolve. Indeed, scientists often speak this way when they refer, for example, to a species of amphibious mammal having evolved into today's whales. But this is a kind of shorthand whose inaccuracy becomes apparent when species are considered as they live in the real world.

Populations Evolve

Think of a hypothetical species of frog living in, say, equatorial Africa in a single expanse of tropical forest. Suppose that a drought persists for years, drying up the forest such that this single lush range is now broken up into two ranges separated by an expanse of barren terrain (**Figure 17.1**). When the separation occurs, there is still only a single species of frog, but that species is now divided into two *populations* that

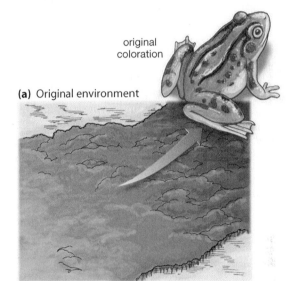

original coloration

(a) Original environment

(b) Altered environment

lighter coloration

population B

expanse of barren terrain

darker coloration

population A

Figure 17.1
Evolution within Populations

(a) A hypothetical species of frog lives and interbreeds in one expanse of tropical forest.

(b) After several years of drought, the forest has been divided by an expanse of barren terrain. The single frog population has thus been divided into two populations, separated by the barren terrain. The two frog populations now have different environmental pressures, such as the kinds of predators each faces, and they no longer interbreed; after many generations their coloration diverges as they adapt to the different pressures.

are geographically isolated and hence no longer inter-breeding. Each population now faces the natural selection pressures of its *own* environment—environments that may differ greatly even though they are nearly adjacent. One area may get more sun, while the other has a larger population of frog predators, for example. Thus, each population stands to be modified individually over time—to evolve. What is it that evolves? The essential unit that does so is a **population,** which can be defined as all the members of a species that live in a defined geographic region at a given time.

The question then becomes: What is the process by which populations evolve? In the population of frogs that has more predators, a darker coloration may evolve over many generations. But how does this darker coloration come about? Through genes. A given frog is unable to change its spots, but over many generations, a *population* of frogs can have its spots changed through the shuffling, addition, and deletion of genetic material.

Gene Pools and Evolution

Recall from Chapter 11 that the genetic makeup of any organism is its **genotype**—and that a genotype provides an underlying basis for an organism's **phenotype,** meaning any observable traits that an organism has, including its physical characteristics and behavior. Many genes are likely to be involved in producing a phenotype such as coloration. In sexually reproducing organisms, *each* of these coloration genes will likely come in variant forms, called **alleles,** with each offspring inheriting one allele for each gene from its

father and one from its mother (**Figure 17.2**). Although both alleles help code for coloration, one may result in slightly lighter or darker coloration than the other.

Genes don't just come in two allelic variants, however; they can come in many. In most species, no one organism can possess more than two alleles of a given gene, but a *population* of organisms can possess many allelic variants of each gene (which is one reason human beings don't just come in one or two colors, but in a continuous range of colors).

When the concept of a population is put together with that of genes and their alleles, the result is the concept of the **gene pool:** all the alleles that exist in a population. This gene pool is very important to the story of evolution, because all evolutionary change ultimately is based on it. If evolution were a card game, the gene pool would be its deck of cards. Individual cards (alleles) are endlessly shuffled and dealt into different "hands" (the genotypes that individuals inherit), with the strength of any given hand dependent on what game is being played. (Survival in a drought? Survival against a new set of predators?)

17.2 Evolution as a Change in the Frequency of Alleles

Thinking of genes in terms of a gene pool gives us a new perspective on what evolution is at root: a change in the frequency of alleles in a population. This may sound a little abstract until you consider the frog coloration example. A frog inherits, from its mother and father, a darker coloration that allows it to evade predators slightly more successfully than other frogs of its generation. It thus lives longer and leaves more offspring than the other frogs. It is successful in this way because of the advantageous set of alleles it inherited. Because this frog is more successful at breeding, its alleles are being passed on to the *next* generation of frogs in greater numbers than the alternative alleles carried by less-successful frogs. As such, this frog's alleles have increased in frequency in the frog population—and this population is now slightly darker in coloration as a result. Put another way, through a change in its allele frequencies, the frog population has evolved in the direction of a slightly darker coloration. In looking at any example of evolution in a population over time, you would find this kind of change in allele frequency as its basis, assuming a stable environment.

With this perspective in mind, you're ready for a definition of **microevolution:** a change of allele frequencies in a population over a relatively short period of time. Why the *micro* in microevolution? Because evolution *within* a population is evolution at its smallest scale. This concept of microevolution allows you to understand the formal definition of evolution

Figure 17.2
Genetic Basis of Evolution

Many genes can produce a trait such as body coloration, and each gene often has many alleles or variants. Each individual in a population, however, can possess only two alleles for each gene, one allele inherited from its mother and one inherited from its father. The two frogs in the figure both have maternal and paternal copies of chromosome 3 that house genes for coloration. The chromosomes of the two frogs may differ, however, in the allelic variants they have of these genes. The frog with dark coloration may possess alleles a_1 and a_2, while the light-colored frog may possess alleles a_2 and a_4 of this same gene.

maternal chromosome 3 · paternal chromosome 3 · maternal chromosome 3 · paternal chromosome 3

a_1 a_2
alleles

a_2 a_4
alleles

dark coloration

light coloration

promised to you last chapter. **Evolution** can be defined as any genetically based phenotypic change in a population of organisms over successive generations. Taking a step back, the large-scale patterns produced by microevolution eventually become visible, as with the evolution of, say, mammals from reptiles. This is **macroevolution,** defined as evolution that results in the formation of new species or other large groupings of living things.

SO FAR . . .

1. The essential unit that evolves in nature is the _____, which can be defined as all the members of a _____ living in a specific geographic region at a given time.

2. Genes come in variant forms called _____. A gene pool is defined as all the _____ that exist in a _____.

3. Microevolution is defined as a change in _____ in a population over a relatively short period of time.

17.3 Five Agents of Microevolution

So, what is it that causes microevolution? Put another way, what causes the frequency of alleles to change in a population? In the frog-coloration example, a familiar process was at work: natural selection. The frog's coloration allowed the frog to evade predators, thus helping the frog to live and produce more offspring than did other frogs. This particular coloration was thus *selected* for greater transmission to future generations. From a microevolutionary perspective, this selection brought about a change in allele frequencies in the population: Thanks to the frog's greater reproductive success, the alleles it possessed increased relative to other sets of alleles.

Natural selection is not the only process that can change allele frequencies, however. There are five "agents" of microevolution, meaning forces that can alter allele frequencies in populations. These are mutation, gene flow, genetic drift, sexual selection, and natural selection. You can see these processes summarized in **Table 17.1**. (For a review of how scientists tell whether one of these processes is actually at work changing allele frequencies, see "Detecting Evolution: The Hardy-Weinberg Principle," on page 314.) We'll now look at each of these agents of change in turn.

Table 17.1

Agents of Change: Five Forces That Can Bring about Change in Allele Frequencies in a Population

Agent	Description
Mutation	Alteration in an organism's DNA; generally has no effect or a harmful effect. But beneficial or "adaptive" mutations are indispensable to evolution.
Gene flow	The movement of alleles from one population to another. Occurs when individuals move between populations or when one population of a species joins another, assuming the second population has different allele frequencies than the first.
Genetic drift	Chance alteration of gene frequencies in a population. Most strongly affects small populations. Can occur when populations are reduced to small numbers (the bottleneck effect) or when a few individuals from a population migrate to a new, isolated location and start a new population (the founder effect).
Sexual selection	Occurs when some members of a population mate more often than other members.
Natural selection	Some individuals will be more successful than others in surviving and hence reproducing, owing to traits that give them a better "fit" with their environment. The alleles of those who reproduce more will increase in frequency in a population.

Mutations: Alterations in the Makeup of DNA

As you saw in the genetics unit, a mutation is any permanent alteration in an organism's DNA. Some of these accidental alterations are *heritable,* meaning they can be passed on to future generations. Mutations can be as small as a change in a single base pair in the DNA chain (a point mutation) or as large as the addition or deletion of a whole chromosome or parts of it. Whatever the case, a mutation is a change in the informational set an organism possesses (**Figure 17.3**). Looked at one way, it is a change in one or more alleles.

The rate of mutation is very low in most organisms; during cell division in humans, it might be just one DNA base pair per billion. And of the mutations that do arise, very few are beneficial or "adaptive." Most do nothing, and many are harmful to organisms. So mutations usually are not working to *further* survival and reproduction, as the frog-coloration alleles did. Given this, any trait produced by a mutation is not likely to become more common over successive generations. The upshot is that mutations are not likely to account for much of the change in allele frequency that is observed in any population.

But a few mutations occur that *are* adaptive. These genetic alterations are something like creative thinkers in a society: They are rare but very important. Such mutations are the only means by which new genetic information comes into being—by which new proteins are produced that can modify the form or capabilities of an organism. The evolution of eyes or wings had to involve mutations. No amount of shuffling of existing genes could get the living world from no eyes to eyes. Of course, no mutation can bring about a feature such as eyes in a single step; such changes are the result of many mutations, followed by rounds of genetic shuffling and natural selection, generally over millions of years.

Gene Flow: When One Population Joins Another

Allele frequencies in a population can also change with the mating that can occur after the arrival of members from a *different* population. This is the second microevolutionary agent, **gene flow,** meaning the movement of genes from one population to another. Such movement takes place through **migration,** which is the movement of individuals from one population into the territory of another. Some populations of a species may truly be isolated, such as those on remote islands, but migration and the gene flow that goes with it are the rule rather than the exception in nature. It may seem at first glance that migration would be limited to animal species, but this isn't so. Mature plants may not move, but plant seeds and pollen do; they are carried to often-distant locations by wind, sea currents, and animals (**Figure 17.4**). Of course, for a migrating population to alter allele frequencies of another population, its gene pool must be different from that of the population it is joining.

Genetic Drift: The Instability of Small Populations

To an extent that may surprise you, evolution turns out to be a matter of chance. You can almost see the dice rolling in the third microevolutionary agent, genetic drift. Imagine a hypothetical population of 10,000 individuals. An allele in this gene pool is carried by 1 out of 10 of them, meaning that 1,000 individuals carry it. Now imagine that some disease sweeps over the population, killing half of it. Say that this allele had nothing to do with the disease, so the illness might be expected to decimate the allele carriers in rough accordance with their proportion in the population. If this were the case, 5,000 individuals in

Figure 17.3
Basis of New Genetic Information

A mutation is any permanent alteration in an organism's DNA. Examples of mutations include:

(a) point mutations, in which the nucleotide sequence is incorrect, and

(b) deletions, in which part of a chromosome is missing.

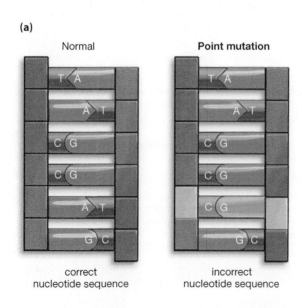

(a)

Normal / **Point mutation**

correct nucleotide sequence / incorrect nucleotide sequence

(b)

Normal / **Deletion**

complete chromosome 5 / incomplete chromosome 5

the population would survive, and 1 in 10—or about 500 of them—could be expected to be carriers of this allele. Let us say, however, that just by chance, *550* of the allele carriers were killed, thus leaving the surviving population of 5,000 with only 450 allele carriers. In that scenario, the frequency of the allele in this population would drop from 10 percent to 9 percent (**Figure 17.5a**).

Now for the critical step. Imagine the same allele, with the same 1-in-10 frequency, only now in a population of *10*. There is now but a single carrier of the allele, and that individual may not be one of the 5 members of the population to survive the disease. In this case, the frequency of this allele drops from 10 percent to zero (**Figure 17.5b**). It can be replaced only by a mutation (which is extremely unlikely) or by migration from another population. Assuming that neither happens, no matter how this population grows in the future, in genetic terms it will be a different population than the original in that it lost this allele. The allele might be helpful or harmful, but its adaptive value doesn't matter. It has been eliminated strictly through chance. This is an example of **genetic drift:** the chance alteration of allele frequencies in a population, with such alterations having the greatest impact on small populations. It is true that some genetic drift has taken place in the larger population, but consider how small the effect is. The allele simply went from a 10 percent to a 9 percent frequency, with no loss of allele. Chance events can have much greater effects on small populations than on large ones.

Genetic drift can have large effects on small populations through two common scenarios: Populations can be greatly reduced through disease or natural catastrophe, or a small subset of a population can migrate elsewhere and start a new population. The first of these scenarios is called the *bottleneck effect;*

(a) Hawaiian silversword   **(b)** Tarweeds in California

Figure 17.4
Migration in Plants

Brought about by volcanic eruptions, the Hawaiian Islands have always been surrounded by the Pacific Ocean. Therefore, all the plant species existing on the islands today are descended from species that were introduced to the islands through one means or another—human activity, wind currents, water currents, or animal dispersal of seeds and pollen.

(a) Hawaiian silverswords are derived from
(b) a lineage of California plants commonly known as tarweeds.

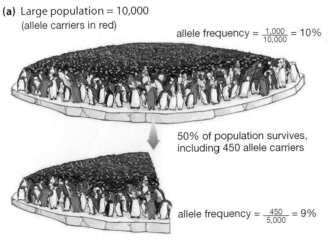

(a) Large population = 10,000
(allele carriers in red)

allele frequency = $\frac{1,000}{10,000}$ = 10%

50% of population survives, including 450 allele carriers

allele frequency = $\frac{450}{5,000}$ = 9%

**little change in allele frequency
(no alleles lost)**

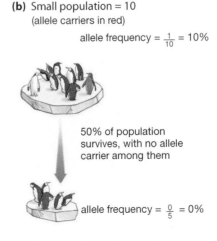

(b) Small population = 10
(allele carriers in red)

allele frequency = $\frac{1}{10}$ = 10%

50% of population survives, with no allele carrier among them

allele frequency = $\frac{0}{5}$ = 0%

**dramatic change in allele frequency
(potential to lose one allele)**

Figure 17.5
Genetic Drift

(a) In a hypothetical population of 10,000 individuals, 1 in 10 carries a given allele. The population loses half its members to a disease, including 550 individuals who carried the allele. The frequency of the allele in the population thus drops from 10 percent to 9 percent.

(b) A population of 10 with the same allele frequency likewise loses half its members to a disease. Because the one member of the population who carried the allele is not a survivor, the frequency of the allele in the population drops from 10 percent to zero.

BioFlix™

Mechanisms of Evolution

the second is called the *founder effect*. Let's have a look at both of them in turn.

The Bottleneck Effect and Genetic Drift

The **bottleneck effect** can be defined as a change in allele frequencies in a population due to chance following a sharp reduction in the population's size. Real populations, or even species, can go through dramatic reductions in numbers. For example, northern elephant seals, which can be found off the Pacific coast of North America, were prized for the oil their blubber yielded and thus were hunted so heavily that, by the 1890s, fewer than 50 animals remained. Thanks to species protection measures, the seals' numbers have rebounded somewhat in recent decades. But genetically, all the members of this species are very similar today because they all descended from the few seals that made it through the nineteenth-century bottleneck. What occurs in these reductions is a "sampling" of the original population—the "sample" being those who survived the devastation (**Figure 17.6**).

The reason allele frequencies change in such an event has to do with the nature of probability and sample size. Imagine a box filled with M&Ms candies, with equal numbers of red, green, and yellow M&Ms inside. You close your eyes and grab a handful of M&Ms and pull out 12. With such a small sample, you might get, say, 6 reds, 4 greens, and 2 yellows, rather than the 4 of each kind that would be expected from probability. If you pulled out *120* M&Ms, conversely, your reds, greens, and yellows would be much more likely to approach the 40 of each kind that would be expected. In just such a way, a small sample of *alleles* is likely to yield a gene pool that's different from the distribution found in the larger population.

The Founder Effect and Genetic Drift

Genetic drift can also result from the **founder effect,** which is simply a way of stating that when a small subpopulation *migrates* to a new area to start a new population, it is likely to bring with it only a portion of the original population's gene pool. This is another kind of sampling of the gene pool, in other words, but in this case it's caused by the migration of a few individuals rather than the survival of only a few. This sample of the gene pool now becomes the founding gene pool of a new population. As such, it can have a great effect; whichever genes exist in it become the genetic set that is passed on to all future generations as long as this population stays isolated.

The genetic drift that comes with the founder effect can be seen most clearly when a founding population brings with it the alleles for rare genetic diseases. There is, for example, a very rare genetic affliction of the eyes called *cornea plana* that results in a misshapen cornea—the first structure of the eye through which light passes. The result can be impaired close-range vision and a general clouding of eyesight. Cornea plana is known to affect only 113 people worldwide. The strange thing is that 78 of these people are in Finland, most of them in an area in northern Finland. Current research indicates that about 400 years ago, a small population arrived in this isolated area, with at least one member of this population carrying the recessive allele that causes this affliction. Since then, this allele has continued to profoundly affect subsequent generations in the area. This will always be the case if the descendants of a founder population stay relatively isolated over time—that is, if the descendants breed mostly among themselves.

Figure 17.6
The Bottleneck Effect
Northern elephant seals were hunted so heavily by humans that by the 1890s, fewer than 50 animals remained. The population has grown from the few survivors (represented here by the three seals in the second frame), but the resulting genetic diversity of this population is very low. (Seal coloration for illustrative purposes only.)

"bottleneck" only allows a few individuals through

Original population, original allele frequency.

Hunting of seals in late 1800s greatly reduced population size.

Surviving population had different allele frequency and little genetic diversity.

This different allele frequency is reflected in today's population.

From this and the earlier examples, you may have perceived by now that there is an inherent value in genetic diversity; you can read about this in "The Price of Inbreeding," on page 308.

Sexual Selection: When Mating Is Uneven across a Population

You've now looked at mutation, gene flow, and genetic drift as agents of change with respect to allele frequencies in a population. Now let's look at a fourth agent, **sexual selection,** defined as a form of natural selection that produces differential reproductive success based on differential success in obtaining mating partners. In practice, this is mating based on *phenotype,* which you may recall is any observable trait in an organism, including differences in appearance and behavior. It is the appearance of particularly nice plumage on a male peacock that makes female peacocks choose it for mating, rather than another male, while it is the behavior of strutting and chest-swelling in a male sage grouse that causes a succession of female grouse to mate with it rather than nearby competitors (**Figure 17.7**). It's easy to see that if one male mates four times as much as the average male of his generation, his alleles stand to increase proportionately in the next generation.

Differential mating success among members of one sex in a species often is based on choices made by members of the opposite sex in that species. It generally is females who are doing the choosing in these situations. Differential mating success can also, however, be based on differences in combative abilities that give individuals of one sex (generally males) greater access to members of the opposite sex. Sexual selection is a form of natural selection in that some alleles—those that help bring about attractiveness, for example—are being preferentially selected for transmission to future generations. But while natural selection has to do with differential survival and reproductive capacity (and hence reproduction), sexual selection has to do with differential *mating* (and hence reproduction).

Natural Selection: Evolution's Adaptive Mechanism

You've already gone over a good deal about natural selection in this review of evolution, but it's time now to look at it as the last agent of change in microevolution. First, what is meant by natural selection? Here is a short definition: **Natural selection** is a process through which traits that confer a reproductive advantage to individual organisms grow more common in populations of organisms over successive generations. In our frog example, the trait of darker coloration conferred a reproductive advantage to an individual frog, in that this coloration helped this frog evade predators—

something that allowed the frog to live longer and leave more offspring than other frogs of its generation. The fact that this frog's more numerous offspring *likewise* bore the darker coloration meant that this trait was becoming more common in this population of frogs. And to the extent that darker coloration continued to carry a reproductive advantage, in one frog generation after another, then this trait would continue to become more common in the frog population over time. Through a process of being selected for transmission, then, a darker coloration was evolving within this population of frogs.

A key concept in natural selection is that of **adaptation,** meaning a modification in the form, physical functioning, or behavior of organisms in a population over generations in response to environmental change. Environmental change may come to a population (through streams drying up or new predators arriving, for example), or a population may come to environmental change (through migration). Either way, natural selection is a process through which populations can adapt to new environmental conditions. Indeed, among the five agents of microevolution, natural selection is the *only* process that consistently works to adapt populations to their environment. Genetic drift is random; it could as easily make an adaptive trait less common in a population. Although mutations can have an adaptive effect, they more often have no effect or even a negative effect. Gene flow doesn't necessarily bring in genes that are better suited to a given environment. And sexual selection has to do with the ways mating partners are selected, not with matching individuals to environment.

Natural selection is, however, constantly working to modify populations in accordance with the

Figure 17.7
Sexual Selection

Individuals in some species choose their mates based on appearance or behavior. Female sage grouse (*Centrocercus urophasianus*) prefer to mate with males who put on superior courtship displays—physical demonstrations that include sounds, a kind of strutting, and a puffing up of their chests. Here a male grouse takes part in such a display by inflating two air sacs on his chest.

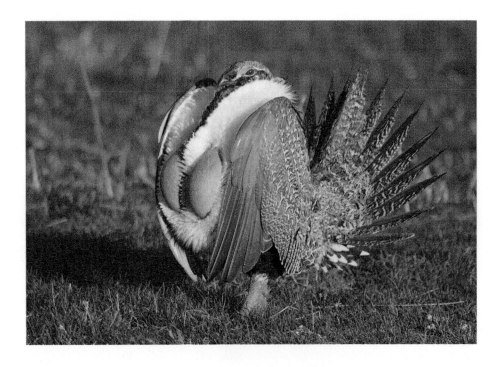

ESSAY

The Price of Inbreeding

" Marry afar" is advice given by the pygmy men of Africa, by which they mean, "marry a woman who lives far from your home." The pygmies point to the hunting rights a man acquires in distant territory by marrying a woman from a remote region, but there is another benefit to this practice as well: It helps ensure genetic diversity

Inbreeding brings together the recessive alleles that are required for many genetic diseases.

among the pygmies. When pygmies from remote locations marry, it cuts down on the chances of *inbreeding*, meaning mating in which close relatives produce offspring. Inbreeding can have harmful effects not only in humans but in any species.

What are these effects? Well, consider what has happened in the United States with "purebred" dogs (**Figure 1**), which is to say dogs that over many generations have been bred solely with members of

their own breed (cocker spaniels mating only with cocker spaniels, and so forth). In the mid-1990s it was estimated that up to one-fourth of all U.S. purebred dogs had some sort of serious genetic defect—ranging from improper joint formation, to heart defects, to deafness. We also have a good deal of experimental evidence from other animals on the

effect of inbreeding. In one instance, a group of white-footed mice that had been inbred and then let out into the natural environment survived at only 56 percent the rate of a group of genetically diverse mice. In humans, meanwhile, evidence of

the harm that can come when husbands and wives come from the same isolated community can be found in some of the Amish and Mennonite groups of Pennsylvania and Ohio, which for generations have been plagued by numerous cases of genetic conditions that are either exceedingly rare in society in general or that are not found at all in it. There is, for example, a condition called Amish Lethal Microcephaly that results in infants with very small brains and a life expectancy of between five and six months. In the 40 years

Figure 1
Result of Generations of Controlled Breeding

environments around them. As such, it is regarded as the most important agent in having shaped the natural world—in having given zebras their stripes and flowers their fragrance. Because it is so important, we'll now look at it in a little more detail.

SO FAR . . .

1. What the agents of microevolution all have in common is that each of them can alter _____ in a population.

2. Genetic drift is a _____ alteration of _____ in a population that has its greatest effect on _____ populations.

3. In sexual selection, differential reproductive success comes about because of differential success in obtaining _____.

17.4 Natural Selection and Evolutionary Fitness

Even the strongest supporters of natural selection as a shaping force would not maintain that it has the effect of producing perfect organisms. The concept of "fitness" is helpful here, if only to clear up some misconceptions. To a biologist, **fitness** means the success of an organism in passing on its genes to offspring *relative to* other members of its population at a particular time. An organism cannot be deemed "fit," even if it has 1,000 offspring. It can only have *more or less* fitness relative to other members of its population (who might have 900 or 1,100 offspring). This has to do, once again, with allele frequencies in a gene pool. No matter how many offspring an individual has, its allele frequencies will increase in a population only if it has *more* offspring than other members of its generation. Thus, fitness is a measure of impact on allele frequencies in a population.

This concept then gets us to the notion of "survival of the fittest" and the misunderstandings that arise that ended in 2005, at least 61 infants from 33 Pennsylvania Amish families were born with this condition, whereas outside this community not a single case of the condition has ever been documented.

But why should reproduction within a limited community cause such trouble? As you've seen, every organism has a whole series of genes, most of which come in variant forms, or alleles. In any individual, one allele for a given gene will be inherited from the father and one from the mother. In all organisms, a very small proportion of these alleles is potentially harmful or even lethal. But in most instances, such alleles are recessive. *One* defective allele is not enough to cause trouble because the second differs from it and provides sufficient information for the organism to function properly. Only an individual who has two copies of the defective allele—an individual who is homozygous for it—would suffer from the condition. Meanwhile, an individual who has one "good" and one harmful allele would have no trouble.

So how do these biological facts play out in inbreeding? Imagine two seals, brother and sister, that have mated together because their population has been so reduced.

Imagine that their mother had a recessive allele that brings about a heart defect and that this allele occurs in only 1 of every 100 seals. There is a 1-in-2 chance that the mother will pass this allele on to any one of her offspring, and let's say it happened with the male and female here: Both brother and sister have inherited a single defective allele. When *they* mate, the chance that either of them will pass along the defective allele to their offspring is likewise 1 in 2. More important, however, the chance that *both* of them will pass the allele along—producing an offspring with two defective alleles—is 1 in 4. If, on the other hand, the brother had mated with an unrelated member of the population, the chances of this union passing along two copies of this defective allele are 1 in 400.* Why the difference? Because the unrelated female had only a 1-in-100 chance of having the allele in the first place.

The essence of this lesson, as you may have realized, is that inbreeding has brought together rare, identical alleles— the recessive alleles that are required for many genetic diseases. Random breeding, meanwhile, tends to keep such alleles apart. It tends to preserve genetic diversity, to put it another way.

You might think from this that there are no uses for genetic *similarity*, but consider what human beings have been doing for centuries with dog breeding. Cocker spaniels did not come about by accident. Dogs that had cocker spaniel features were bred together for many generations, ultimately giving us today's dog. It was the *novel features* of the spaniel that people wanted, and novel features are often the result of recessive alleles coming together. While the breeding done to produce American cocker spaniels has resulted in dogs with cute, floppy ears, the unintended effect of this practice is a breed that is also prone to ear infections and a "rage syndrome" that can result in unprovoked aggression, even against familiar humans. In short, inbreeding produces a range of "novel features," some of which are desirable, but others of which are more aptly referred to as genetic defects.

* Remembering the rule of multiplication from Chapter 11, to calculate the odds of passing on two defective alleles in the random mating example, take the son's chances of passing along the allele (1 in 2, or 50 percent, or 0.5) × 0.01 (the chance of his female partner *having* the allele) × 0.5 (the chance of her passing the allele along). This works out to 0.0025, which equals 1 in 400. For the brother-and-sister mating, the figures are 0.5 (the chance of the brother passing it along) × 0.5 (the chance of the sister passing it along), which equals 0.25—or 1 in 4.

from it. The phrase can be taken to imply the existence of superior beings; that is, organisms that are simply "better" than their counterparts, with images of being faster, more muscular, or smarter coming to mind. In fact, however, evolutionary fitness tells us nothing about organisms being *generally* superior, and it certainly tells us nothing about the value of any particular capacity, be it brawn or brain. All it tells us about are organisms who are better than others in their population at passing along their genes in a given environment at a given time. An accurate phrase, as others have pointed out, would not be "survival of the fittest," but rather "survival of those who fit—for now." Let's look at a real-life example of natural selection to see why this is true.

Galapagos Finches: The Studies of Peter and Rosemary Grant

When Charles Darwin stopped at the Galapagos Islands in 1835, some of the animal varieties he collected were various species of finches. Over the years,

biologists kept coming back to "Darwin's finches" because of the very qualities Darwin found in them: They seemed to present a textbook case of evolution, with their 14 species having evolved from a single ancestral species on the South American mainland. Yet for more than 100 years after Darwin, it was a puzzle for scientists to figure out how Darwin's posited mechanism of evolution, natural selection, could have been at work with the finches. This changed beginning in the 1970s, when the husband-and-wife team of Peter and Rosemary Grant began a painstakingly detailed study of the birds.

Natural selection in the finches came into sharp focus in 1977, when a tiny Galapagos island, Daphne Major, suffered a severe drought. Rain that normally begins in January and lasts through July scarcely came at all that year. This was a disaster for the island's two species of finches; in January 1977 there were 1,300 of them, but by December the number had plunged to fewer than 300. Daphne's medium-size ground finch, *Geospiza fortis*, lost 85 percent of its population in this calamity. The staple of this

Figure 17.8
A Product of Evolution on the Galapagos

A male of the finch species *Geospiza fortis,* which is native to the Galapagos Islands.

difference were the survivors able to get into large, tough seeds and make it through the catastrophe, eventually to reproduce (**Figure 17.9**).

This is natural selection in action, but there is more to be learned from the Grant study, which is to say *evolution* made visible. The Grant team knew that beak depth had a high "heritability" in the finches, meaning that beak depth is largely under genetic control. As it turned out, the offspring of the drought survivors had beaks that were 4 to 5 percent deeper than the average of the population before the drought. In other words, natural selection had preferentially preserved those alleles from the starting population that brought about deeper beaks, and the result was a population that evolved in this direction.

But the Grant study yielded one more lesson. In 1984–1985 there was pressure in the opposite direction: Few large seeds and an abundance of small seeds provided an advantage to smaller birds, and it was these birds that survived this event in disproportionate numbers.

bird's diet is plant seeds. When times get tough, as in the drought, the size and shape of *G. fortis* beaks—their beak "morphology"—begins to define what one bird can eat as opposed to another (**Figure 17.8**). In *G. fortis,* larger body size and deeper beaks turned out to make all the difference between life and death in the drought of 1977. Measuring the beaks of *G. fortis* that survived the drought, the Grant team found they were larger than the beaks of the population before the drought by an average of some 6 percent. This was a difference of about half a millimeter, or roughly two-hundredths of an inch; by such a

Lessons from *G. fortis*

So, where is the "fittest" bird in all this? There isn't any. Evolution among the finches was not marching toward some generally superior bird. Different traits were simply favored under different environmental conditions. Second, there is no evolutionary movement toward combativeness or general intelligence here. Survival had to do with size—and not necessarily *larger* size at that. Looking around in nature, it's true that some showcase species, such as lions and mountain gorillas, gain success in reproduction by being aggressive. And it's true that our own

Figure 17.9
Who Survives in a Drought?

Peter and Rosemary Grant observed that individuals of the finch species *Geospiza fortis* who survived an island drought in 1977 had a greater average beak depth than individuals surveyed before the drought, in 1976. The offspring of the survivors likewise had a larger average beak size than did the population before the drought. Thus, evolution through natural selection was observed in just a few years on the island.

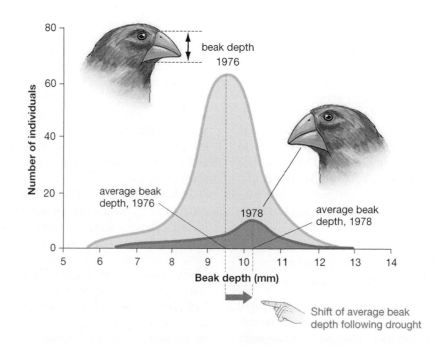

species owes such success as it has had to intelligence. But in most instances, it is not brawn or brain that make the difference; it is something as seemingly benign as beak depth and its fit with the environment.

Finally, consider how imperfect natural selection is at the genetic level. Suppose the smaller *G. fortis* that disproportionately died off in 1977 also disproportionately carried an allele that would have aided just slightly in, say, long-distance flying. In the long run this might have been an adaptive trait, but it wouldn't matter. The flight allele would have been reduced in frequency in the population (as the smaller birds died off) because flight distance didn't matter in 1977; beak depth did. Evolution operates on the phenotypes of whole organisms, not individual genes. As such, it does not work to spread *all* adaptive traits more broadly. Instead, the destiny of each trait is tied to the constellation of traits the organism possesses. Genes are "team players," in other words, that can only do as well as the team they came with.

17.5 Three Modes of Natural Selection

In what directions can natural selection push evolution? As noted in Chapter 11, a character such as human height is under the control of many different genes and is thus **polygenic.** Such polygenic characters tend to be "continuously variable." There are not one or two or three human heights, but an innumerable number of them in a range. (See "Multiple Alleles and Polygenic Inheritance" on page 204.) When natural selection operates on characters that are polygenic and continuously variable, it can proceed in any of three ways. The essential question here is: Does natural selection favor what is average in a given character or what is extreme (**Figure 17.10**)?

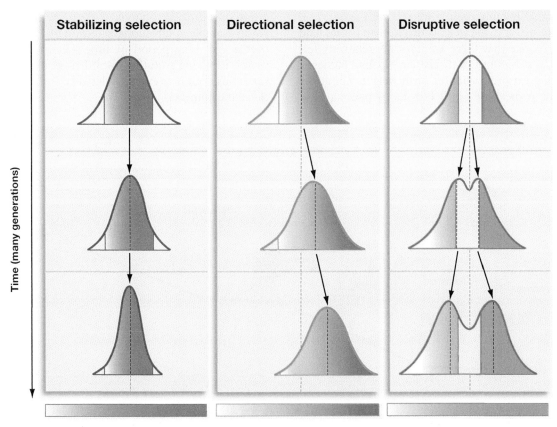

Figure 17.10
Three Modes of Natural Selection

Range of a particular characteristic (in this instance, lightness or darkness of coloration)

In stabilizing selection, individuals that possess extreme values of a characteristic are selected against and die or fail to reproduce. Over succeeding generations, an increasing proportion of the population becomes average in coloration.

In directional selection, one of the extremes of a characteristic is better suited to the environment, meaning that individuals at the other extreme are selected against. Over succeeding generations, the coloration of the population moves in a directon–in this case toward darker coloration.

In disruptive selection, individuals with average coloration are selected against and die. Over succeeding generations, part of the population becomes lighter, while part becomes darker, meaning the range of color variation in the population has increased.

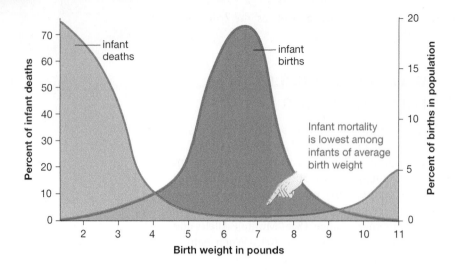

Figure 17.11
Stabilizing Selection: Human Birth Weights and Infant Mortality

Note that infant deaths are more prevalent at the upper and lower extremes of infant birth weights.

Stabilizing Selection

In **stabilizing selection,** intermediate forms of a given character are favored over extreme forms. An example of this is human birth weights. In **Figure 17.11**, you can see, first, the weights that human babies tend to be. Notice that there are not only relatively few 3-pound babies but relatively few 9-pound babies as well. A great proportion of birth weights fall at the average or mean of a little less than 7 pounds. Now

look at the infant mortality curve. Infant deaths are highest at both extremes of birth weight; low-birth-weight babies *and* high-birth-weight babies are more at risk than are average-birth-weight babies (although low birth weight poses the greater risk). Put another way, the children most likely to survive (and reproduce) are those carrying alleles for intermediate birth weights. Thus, natural selection is making intermediate weights even more common. Through it, birth weights are not moving toward the extremes of higher or lower weights; they are being stabilized at intermediate levels. Stabilizing selection is assumed to be the most common type of selection operating in the natural world. This should not be surprising because most organisms are well adapted to their environments.

Directional Selection

When natural selection moves a character toward *one* of its extremes, **directional selection** is in operation—the mode in which we most commonly think of evolution operating. If you look at **Figure 17.12**, you can see an example of directional selection that took place over a very long period of time—about 4 million years—involving evolution toward larger brain size in some close, but now extinct, relatives of ours, a group called the hominins.

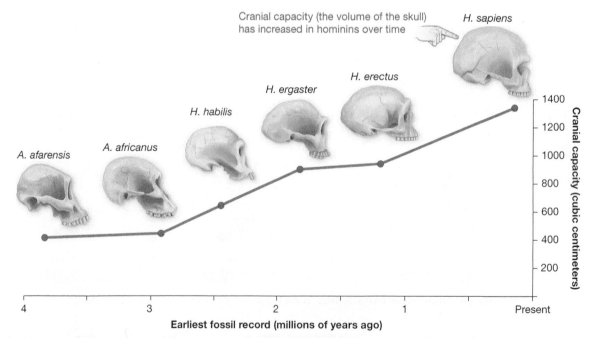

Figure 17.12
Directional Selection: Evolving toward Increased Brain Size

Modern humans are part of an evolutionary group, called the hominins, that includes all the upright-walking or "bipedal" primate species. Cranial capacity is a measure of the volume of brain tissue that can fit inside a skull. Directional selection for cranial capacity can clearly be seen in the ever-increasing capacities of this group of hominins (all of whom are now extinct, except for ourselves). The line in the figure does not trace ancestry, but merely shows the trend toward increased brain size. Going from left to right, the full names of the species shown are *Australopithecus afarensis, Australopithecus africanus, Homo habilis, Homo ergaster, Homo erectus,* and *Homo sapiens* (ourselves).

Disruptive Selection

When natural selection moves a character toward *both* of its extremes, the result is **disruptive selection,** which appears to occur much less frequently in nature than the other two modes of natural selection. This mode of selection is visible in the beaks of yet another kind of finch. A species of these birds found in West Africa (*Pyrenestes ostrinus*) has a beak that comes in only two sizes. Thomas Bates Smith, who has studied the birds, has observed that if human height followed this pattern, there would be some Americans who are 4 to 5 feet tall and some who are 6 to 7 feet tall, but no one who is 5 to 6 feet tall (**Figure 17.13**).

The environmental condition that leads to this mode of selection in the finches is, once again, diet.

Figure 17.13
Disruptive Selection: Evolution That Favors Extremes in Two Directions

Finches of the species *Pyrenestes ostrinus,* found in West Africa. Birds of this species have beaks that come in two distinct sizes—large and small.

When food gets scarce, large-billed birds specialize in cracking a very hard seed, while small-billed birds begin feeding on several soft varieties of seed, with each type of bird being able to out-compete the other for its special variety. Given how these birds have evolved, it's probably safe to assume that a bird with an intermediate-size bill would get less food than one with a bill of either extreme type. Bill size seems to be under the control of a single genetic factor in these birds, so that bills are able to come out either large or small. This genotype was presumably shaped by natural selection over generations, such that any alleles for intermediate-size bills were weeded out.

On to the Origin of Species

Stabilizing selection does what it says: It stabilizes given traits in a population, thereby preserving the similarity this population has with other populations in its species that likewise are undergoing stabilizing selection. However, both disruptive and directional selection can serve as the basis for speciation—for bringing about the transformation of a single species into two or more *different* species. How is it, though, that such speciation works? And how do we classify the huge number of species that are the outcome of evolution's myriad branchings? These are the subjects of the next chapter.

> ## SO FAR. . .
>
> 1. True or false: If an insect has 1,000 offspring, we can label it as "fit" in an evolutionary sense.
>
> 2. In stabilizing selection, forms that are _____ are favored over forms that are _____.
>
> 3. We normally think of evolution working through _____, in which a character moves toward _____.

Detecting Evolution: The Hardy-Weinberg Principle

Possible genotypes in the population

How can scientists tell when evolution is taking place? As you've seen, evolution always entails a change in allele frequencies in a population. And there are five primary "agents" of allele frequency change—processes such as genetic drift and natural selection. So, how can scientists tell when one of these agents actually is at work? They can employ a procedure—a kind of test—devised early in the twentieth century by a British mathematician, Godfrey Hardy, and a German physician, Wilhelm Weinberg. Working independently, Hardy and Weinberg arrived at an insight, now called the *Hardy-Weinberg principle*, that today is used routinely not just in evolutionary biology, but in fields like public health as well.

The starting point for the Hardy-Weinberg principle is its assertion that allele frequencies will *not* change unless one of the five agents is at work. A population whose alleles are not being altered by one of the agents is said to be at *Hardy-Weinberg equilibrium*—a state in which the population's allele frequencies remain constant from one generation to the next. Let's walk through an example now that shows how a population at Hardy-Weinberg equilibrium stays the same. Along the way, you'll see the kinds of insights that are made possible by the Hardy-Weinberg principle.

Imagine a hypothetical species of plant whose flowers come in two colors, red and white, and say that we are looking at a population of 100 of these individuals. Further, we know from breeding these plants that red results from a dominant allele for a gene, while white results from a recessive allele for that gene. In the tradition of

Mendel, we signify the red allele as *R* and white as *r*. Finally, we have sampled this population's DNA and found that *R* has a frequency of 78 percent, while *r* has a frequency of 22 percent. What does "frequency" mean in this context? It means that if we looked at the gametes of these plants—their eggs and sperm—78 percent of them would contain a dominant *R* allele while 22 percent would contain a recessive *r* allele. Now, keep your eye on this 78:22 allele frequency because that is what we are primarily interested in. The essential question is: When we look at the *next* generation of plants, will the allele frequencies in it remain 78:22?

To see what happens in the next generation, we need to calculate the *genotypes* of our starting generation. What is a genotype in this context? Each egg or sperm may contain only *one* allele for a gene—in this case *R* or *r*—but in diploid organisms such as flowering plants, egg and sperm fuse in fertilization, thus bringing alleles together to create an organism that has *two* alleles for each gene—one from the male, one from the female. In this context, then, genotype means the combination of *R* and *r* alleles that an individual possesses. Now, what possible combinations could a given individual have? An easy way to visualize them is to return once again to the Punnett squares that were used in Chapter 11. Imagine, in the parental generation, a male and female that are both heterozygous for the color gene—

each of them has one *R* allele and one *r* allele. In this case, our Punnett square looks like the one you can see above.

So, the possible genotypes in the next generation are *RR, Rr,* or *rr.* (Further, note that because the *r* allele is recessive, only the *rr* genotype yields white flowers, signified by the white flower in the square.) But how do we calculate the genotype frequencies that will come about from this range of possibilities? How do we calculate what percentage of the population will have the *RR* genotype, for example, based on the allele frequencies we started with? The heart of the Hardy-Weinberg principle, the Hardy-Weinberg equation, allows us to do this. To generalize beyond the case of our red- or white-flowered plants, let's use a couple of conventional symbols in the equation: *p* will stand for the frequency of the more common *R* allele, and *q* will stand for the frequency of the less common *r* allele. The Hardy-Weinberg equation then looks like this:

The Hardy-Weinberg equation ...	p^2	+	$2pq$	+	q^2
Applied to this example means ...	R^2	+	$2Rr$	+	r^2
And this yields the ...	frequency of the *RR* genotype	+	frequency of the *Rr* genotype	+	frequency of the *rr* genotype

This formula says: If we take the frequency of the R allele and square it (R^2), we will get the frequency of the RR genotype in the population. Well, we know that the frequency of the R allele in the population is 0.78, so this means 0.78×0.78, which equals 0.6084. This is another way of saying that 60.84 percent of the population should have the genotype RR. Next, doubling $R \times r$ (2Rr) yields the genotype frequency of individuals that are heterozygous for the gene, meaning the plants that are the Rr genotype. This works out to 34.32 percent of the population. Finally, taking r times itself (r^2) yields the frequency of the rr genotype, which works out to be 4.84 percent of the population.

Although this formula has allowed us to work out genotype frequencies for the population, we have, in a sense, merely taken Mr. Hardy and Mr. Weinberg's word that things work like this. A question you may be asking yourself at this point is: Why do these particular mathematical steps reveal this information? Why, for example, should squaring the percentage of R alleles in the population tell us what the percentage of RR genotypes is in this population? To grasp the logic that's at work, it's important to understand that the Hardy-Weinberg equation deals with probabilities. It starts with a set of allele frequencies in a population and then says, given these, what are the probabilities of getting various genotypes? The particular steps that the formula uses to answer this question can perhaps best be understood by looking at a more familiar set of probabilities, those that come with flipping a coin.

When we flip a coin, what is the probability that heads or tails will come up? Fifty–fifty, or 0.5, right? Now, what are the chances that when we flip two coins, *both* will come up heads? The answer is contained in something covered in Chapter 11, the rule of multiplication (see page 198). This rule states that the probability of any two events happening is the *product* of their respective probabilities. In the case of our coin toss, this means the respective probabilities of each of our tosses, 0.5×0.5, which equals 0.25—so we have a 25 percent chance of getting two heads.

Now, it's important to recognize that the 50/50 odds that exist in coin tossing actually stem from an initial set of *frequencies*. There are heads, which have a frequency of 0.5 in our population of coins, and there are tails, which likewise have a 0.5 frequency. But there are other frequencies besides 0.5—and other probability exercises to run besides flipping coins. In our *flowering plant* population, we have frequencies of *alleles*. These are 0.78 for R and 0.22 for r. If the probability of getting one R allele is 0.78, then the rule of multiplication tells us that the probability of getting two R alleles in an organism is 0.78×0.78, or to put it another way, 0.78^2. This last number is simply a specific value for p^2 in the Hardy-Weinberg equation of $p^2 + 2pq + q^2$. You can easily see that the rr genotype frequency is similarly derived from q^2, which in this case means 0.22^2.

But what about the middle term in the equation, the 2pq that gives us the percentage of Rr genotypes in the plant population? Look at the Punnett square again; you can see that there are *two* ways a plant could end up with the Rr genotype—male R and female r or female R and male r. When an outcome can occur in two or more different ways, something called the rule of addition comes into play. It states that the probability of a given outcome is the *sum* of its respective probabilities. In this case, the probability of getting one R and one r is 0.78×0.22. But this same probability can happen in two different ways (Rr and rR), so the formula for it is $(0.78 \times 0.22) + (0.78 \times 0.22)$, which can be stated as $2 \times (0.78 \times 0.22)$. With this, we can see the basis of the whole equation, which plays out this way in our example: The Hardy-Weinberg equation of $p^2 + 2pq + q^2$ in this case means $0.78 \times 0.78 + 2 \times (0.78 \times 0.22) + 0.22 \times 0.22$. Doing the calculations on this yields the answers: $0.6084 + 0.3432 + 0.0484$, which provides us with our final probabilities: 60.84 percent of the population is likely to be RR, 34.32 percent Rr, and 4.84 percent rr.

Now we have only one more step to go, which is to calculate expected allele frequencies in the *second* generation based on the first-generation genotype frequen-

cies that we got. This is just a matter of unpacking, we might say, the genotype frequencies. To calculate what the R allele frequencies will be, we start by dividing the 0.3432 Rr genotype in half—yielding 0.1716—because half the alleles in this genotype are, by definition, R (and the other half r). Then we add to this number all of the 0.6084 alleles in the RR genotype because all these alleles are R. To get the frequency of r alleles, we take the 0.1716 figure and add to it the 0.0484 figure for the rr genotype. Thus:

$$R = 0.6084 + 0.1716 = 0.78$$

$$r = 0.0484 + 0.1716 = 0.22$$

Hopefully, these last two figures look familiar, because they are, in fact, the allele frequencies we started with in the first generation. Thus the Hardy-Weinberg equation has demonstrated that allele frequencies do not change from one generation to the next simply as a matter of reproduction.

To grasp the importance of this lack of change, imagine that you are a geneticist who has sampled a human population for the frequency of an allele suspected of contributing to disease in young adults. With your allele frequencies in hand, you run your Hardy-Weinberg equation to get the genotype frequencies for this population. Then you sample the population for its *actual* genotype frequencies and find that they don't match the Hardy-Weinberg prediction. You discover that there are fewer people in the population with the homozygous recessive (qq) genotype frequency than predicted by Hardy-Weinberg. This means that at least one of the agents noted earlier has to be at work—one of them must be disturbing Hardy-Weinberg equilibrium. Among the possibilities is that the agent at work is natural selection. The qq genotype may in fact contribute to people dying younger and hence having fewer children. This could be why there are fewer people with this genotype in the population than predicted by the formula. The Hardy-Weinberg principle, then, provides scientists with insights not just about evolution, but about public health as well.

17

REVIEW

Go to the Study Area at www.masteringbiology.com for practice quizzes, myeBook, BioFlix™ 3-D animations, MP3 Tutor Sessions, videos, current events, and more.

Mastering BIOLOGY

Summary

17.1 What Is It That Evolves?

- The smallest unit that evolves is a population, defined as all the members of a single species living in a defined area at one time. (p. 301)

- Genes exist in variant forms called alleles. In most species, no individual will possess more than two alleles for a given gene—one allele coming from the individual's father, the other allele coming from the mother. A population, however, is likely to possess many different alleles for a given gene. The total of all alleles in a population is that population's gene pool. (p. 302)

17.2 Evolution as a Change in the Frequency of Alleles

- If a set of alleles increases in frequency from one generation to the next within a population, the phenotypes, or observable characteristics, produced by those alleles will be exhibited to a greater extent within the population. Through this, a population can be said to have evolved. Evolution at this level is referred to as microevolution: a change of allele frequencies within a population over a relatively short time. Macroevolution is evolution on a larger scale, which results in the formation of new species or other large groupings of living things. (p. 302)

17.3 Five Agents of Microevolution

- Five evolutionary forces can produce changes in allele frequencies within a population: mutation, gene flow, genetic drift, sexual selection, and natural selection. (p. 303)

- A mutation is any permanent alteration in an organism's DNA; some mutations are heritable. Mutations appear infrequently

and most either have no effect or are harmful; rare adaptive mutations are vital to evolution, however, because they are the only means by which entirely new genetic information comes into being. (p. 304)

- Gene flow, the movement of genes from one population to another, takes place through migration. (p. 304)

- Genetic drift is the chance alteration of allele frequencies in a population. It has its greatest effects on small populations via two common scenarios: the bottleneck effect, a change in allele frequencies due to chance during a sharp reduction in a population's size; and the founder effect, a change in frequencies brought about when a small subpopulation migrates to a new area, thus founding a new population that possesses only a portion of the original population's gene pool. (p. 304)

- Sexual selection occurs when differences in reproductive success arise because of differential success in mating. (p. 307)

- Natural selection is a process through which traits that confer a reproductive advantage to individual organisms grow more common in populations over successive generations. A given organism that has a trait that provides it with a reproductive advantage will leave more offspring than other members of its generation. This trait will then be seen with greater frequency in the succeeding generation. (p. 307)

- Natural selection is the only agent of microevolution that consistently works to adapt populations of organisms to their environments; as such, it is regarded as the most powerful force underlying evolution. (p. 307)

BioFlix™

Mechanisms of Evolution

17.4 Natural Selection and Evolutionary Fitness

- The phrase "survival of the fittest" is misleading because it implies that evolution works to produce beings who would be superior in any environment. Evolutionary fitness refers only to the relative reproductive success of individuals in a given environment at a given time. Fitness can change within an individual's lifetime in accordance with changes in the surrounding environment. (p. 308)

17.5 Three Modes of Natural Selection

- Natural selection has three modes: stabilizing selection, directional selection, and disruptive selection. Stabilizing selection moves a given character in a population toward an intermediate form and hence tends to preserve the status quo; directional selection moves a given character toward one of its extreme forms; and disruptive selection moves a given character toward two extreme forms. (p. 311)

Key Terms

adaptation 307

allele 302

bottleneck effect 306

directional selection 312

disruptive selection 313

evolution 303

fitness 308

founder effect 306

gene flow 304

gene pool 302

genetic drift 305

genotype 302

macroevolution 303

microevolution 302

Understanding the Basics

Multiple-Choice Questions

(Answers are in the back of the book.)

1. In most populations of living things, each individual has __ copies of each gene, which may be the same or different allelic variants. A population may have _____ allelic variants for a given gene.
   a. 1, 2
   b. 2, 4
   c. 2, many
   d. 1, many
   e. 2, 2

2. Match the terms with their meanings:
   a. gene pool   a variant form of a gene
   b. allele   the set of all alleles in a population
   c. allele frequency the genetic makeup of an organism
   d. genotype   exchange of genes between populations
   e. gene flow   the relative representation of a given form of a gene in a population

3. Which of the following statements is true of microevolution? (Select all that apply.)
   a. It is a change in allele frequency within populations.
   b. It is caused by inheritance of characters acquired during the life of an organism.
   c. It is only seen when some allelic variants cause individuals to have increased reproductive success.
   d. It always leads to adaptation.
   e. It is caused only by natural selection.

4. Agents of allele frequency change in populations include (select all that apply):
   a. genetic drift.
   b. meiosis.
   c. mutation.
   d. segregation.
   e. natural selection.

5. Agents that consistently produce adaptive evolution (adaptation) include (select all that apply):
   a. genetic drift.
   b. mutation.
   c. meiosis.
   d. natural selection.
   e. gene flow.

6. Mutations are (select all that apply):
   a. generally beneficial.
   b. sometimes heritable
   c. always caused by changes in single base pairs of DNA.
   d. the ultimate source of new genetic information.
   e. prone to occur with great frequency.

7. Match the agent of microevolution to its description:
   a. mutation   chance alterations of allele frequencies, having the greatest effect on small populations
   b. gene flow   a process through which traits that confer a reproductive advantage to individuals are seen with greater frequency in succeeding generations of a population
   c. natural selection movement of alleles between populations by migration
   d. genetic drift   genetic drift brought about by migration of a subpopulation
   e. founder effect   changes in the genetic material

8. Finches in the Galapagos experienced _____ selection on beak depth following a drought; the African finch *P. ostrinus* experienced _____ selection on beak size because it eats either very small, soft seeds or much larger, hard seeds.
   a. stabilizing, directional
   b. sexual, disruptive
   c. directional, disruptive
   d. disruptive, directional
   e. stabilizing, disruptive

Brief Review

(Answers are in the back of the book.)

1. Explain the statement "Individuals are selected, populations evolve."

2. What is a gene pool, and why do changes in gene pools lie at the root of evolution?

3. What are the five causes of allele frequency changes (microevolution), and how does each work?

4. Why is evolutionary fitness always a measure of relative reproduction in a population?

5. Why is natural selection the only agent of evolution that consistently produces adaptation?

6. Is the evolutionary fitness of an individual expected to be the same or different in different environments? How did the Grants' study of beak depth of finches after the drought and then again in 1984–1985 provide a real example of this?

Applying Your Knowledge

1. What common misconceptions about nature result from the phrase "survival of the fittest," as opposed to the phrase that accurately describes what happens in nature, "survival of those who fit—for now"?

2. Explain why genetic drift may be important when captive populations of animals or plants are started with just a few individuals.

3. Two moth populations of the same species use different host plants. A green color has evolved in a population that rests on leaves—a color that allows these moths to escape predation by blending in with the leaves. Members of the other population rest on tree trunks and are brown in color. The colors of these moths are genetically determined by different alleles of the same gene. List some consequences of a migration of moths leading to gene flow between these two populations.

18

The Outcomes of Evolution:
Macroevolution

New species come about when populations of existing species cease to breed with one another. Each new species that arises constitutes another branch on life's family tree. Scientists are trying hard to figure out what this tree looks like.

Male and female little green bee-eaters (*Merops orientalis*) engage in a courtship ritual in which the male feeds the female. Such rituals are one of the mechanisms that help produce new species.

How many types of living things are there on Earth? How many varieties of life-forms are there that we can recognize as being fundamentally different from one another? It may surprise you to learn that we haven't the foggiest idea. The lowest estimate is about 3 million species, but higher-end estimates often come in at 10 to 15 million, and the highest of them all is 100 million. Scientists simply have been unable to catalogue the vast diversity that exists on our planet. In 250 years of watching, digging, netting, and bagging, they have identified about 1.8 million species—a large number, to be sure, but only a fraction of the species that actually exist, even if our lowest estimates are correct.

Since no one knows how many species there are, let's suppose that there are "only" 3 million on Earth. Isn't this number staggering? This seems particularly true given its starting point. A single type of organism arose perhaps 3.8 billion years ago, branched into two types of organisms, and then the process continued—branches forming on branches—until at least 3 million different types of living things came to exist on Earth. Now here's the real surprise: These are just the *survivors*. The fossil record indicates that more than 99 percent of all species that have ever lived on Earth are now extinct. Branching indeed.

The questions to be answered in this chapter are: How does this branching work? How do we go from the microevolutionary mechanisms explored in Chapter 17 to the actual divergence of one species into two? And how do we classify the creatures that result from this branching?

18.1 What Is a Species?

The category of life that's been mentioned so far, the species, has a great importance not only to biology but to society in general. If we allow that some bacteria are harmful to human beings while others are helpful, that some varieties of mosquitoes transmit malaria while others do not, that some species of birds are endangered while others are not, then it follows that there must be some means of distinguishing one of these groupings from another (**Figure 18.1**).

(a) Endangered species

(b) Not endangered

Figure 18.1
Separate Entities

The concept of a species can have very practical effects.

(a) This bird is a northern spotted owl (*Strix occidentalis*), which is an endangered species, protected by federal law.

(b) This bird is a barred owl (*Strix varia*), which is not endangered.

The whole notion of knowing something about the natural world begins to break down if we can't say *which* grouping it is that is endangered or harmful.

Over the centuries, human beings have devised various ways of defining the groups now called species. But in science today, the most commonly accepted definition stems from what is known as the **biological species concept,** which uses breeding among organisms to make classifications. We actually looked at a version of the biological species concept in Chapter 17. Here it is again, as formulated by the evolutionary biologist Ernst Mayr:

> Species are groups of actually or potentially interbreeding natural populations which are reproductively isolated from other such groups.

Note that the breeding Mayr talks about can be real or potential. Two populations of finch may be separated from one another by geography, but if, on being reunited in the wild, they begin breeding again, they are a single species. Note also that Mayr stipulates that species are groups of *natural* populations. This is important because breeding may take place in captivity that would not in nature. No one doubts that lions and tigers are separate species, yet they will mate in zoos, producing little tiglons or ligers, depending on whether the father was a tiger or a lion (**Figure 18.2**). In natural surroundings, however, they apparently have never interbred, even when their ranges overlapped centuries ago.

You might think that, with the biological species concept in hand, scientists would be able to study any organism and, by discerning its breeding activity, pronounce it to be a member of this species or that. Nature is so vast and varied, however, that this doesn't always work. We can't look at the breeding activity of

single-celled bacteria or archaea, for example, because they don't *have* any breeding activity; they multiply instead by simple cell division. To complicate matters further, different varieties of these microbes transfer genes among themselves (a phenomenon that can be appreciated if you imagine, say, an adult mouse being able to exchange genes with an adult squirrel). Given this, if one bacterial "species" exchanges a substantial number of genes with another, do we even have two distinct species? Microbiologists define bacterial and archaeal species today by sequencing their DNA or RNA and looking for identifying patterns among these sequences, but most specialists would say that, so far, we do not have a satisfactory means of placing bacteria and archaea into clearly defined species categories.

Given this limitation, the biological species concept applies only to organisms who reproduce *sexually*—that is, to organisms who reproduce by means of generating individual reproductive cells, such as sperm and eggs, that come together to produce a new generation of organism. Almost all the plants and animals with which we're familiar reproduce this way, as do many fungi and even a good number of the generally microscopic organisms called protists. Even among these sexual reproducers, however, there are "separate" species that sometimes interbreed in nature, producing so-called hybrid offspring as a result. Such mixing between species happens more in the plant world than the animal, but it does take place in both. If species are supposedly "reproductively isolated" from one another, then what are we to make of these crossings? (Ernst Mayr pointed out that it is *populations* in his concept that are reproductively isolated, not individuals, and that whole populations do tend to stay within their species confines.)

Despite these difficulties, the biological species concept provides a meaningful way of defining a

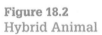

Figure 18.2
Hybrid Animal
Pictured is a liger—a big cat whose father was a lion and whose mother was a tiger. These animals are produced only in captivity, never in nature.

fundamental category of Earth's living things. This is so because the concept is rooted in a critical activity of organisms: their mating, which controls the flow of genes among them. As you saw last chapter, it is the flow of genes across generations that lies at the root of microevolution. Let's look now at how the flow of genes between populations controls **speciation,** which we can define as the development of new species through evolution.

18.2 How Do New Species Arise?

When we begin to think about speciation, it's helpful to recall the gene variants or alleles reviewed in Chapter 17. As you saw in that chapter, evolution within a population means a change in that population's allele frequencies. Let's shift now, however, to thinking about *two* populations of a single species—say, a species of bird in which one population has become separated from another by means of having flown to a nearby location. To the extent that these two populations continue to breed with one another, with individuals moving between the locations, each population will *share* in whatever allele frequency changes are going on with the other population. Hence, the two populations will evolve together, remaining a single species. A critical step would come, however, if migration should *stop* between the two populations. Through the various agents of change we looked at last chapter—natural selection, genetic drift, and so forth—each population would continue to undergo allele frequency changes. But now neither population would be sharing these changes with the other. And, over time, such genetic changes may bring about alterations in form and behavior. Coloration or bill lengths may change; feeding habits may be transformed; mating preferences may be modified. After enough time, should the two populations find themselves geographically reunited, they may no longer freely interbreed. At that point, they are separate species. Speciation has occurred.

The critical change here came when the two populations quit interbreeding. For scientists, the key question thus becomes: Why would this happen? What could drastically reduce interbreeding, and hence gene flow, between two populations of the same species?

The Role of Geographic Separation: Allopatric Speciation

In the preceding example, a very clear factor set the stage for reduced gene flow between the bird populations: They were separated geographically. And geographical separation turns out to be the most important starting point in speciation.

Populations can become separated in lots of ways. On a large scale, glaciers can move into new territory, cutting a previously undivided population into two. Rivers can change course, with the result that what was a single population on one side of the river may now be two populations on different sides of it. On a smaller scale, a pond may partially dry up, leaving a strip of exposed land between what are now two ponds with separate populations. Such environmental changes are not the only ways that populations can be separated, however. Part of a population might *migrate* to a remote area, as did the bird population, and in time be cut off from its larger population. For a real-life example of how migration can help bring about speciation, see **Figure 18.3.**

1. The original population started in the north and migrated southward.

2. The population split to the east and west of the Central Valley. Then two populations began to evolve independently.

3. Evolution of eastern population.

4. Evolution of western population.

Central Valley

5. The east and west populations came back together in Southern California, but could no longer interbreed (or produced infertile hybrid offspring).

Figure 18.3
Speciation in Action

Millions of years ago, the salamander *Ensatina eschscholtzii* began migrating southward from the Pacific Northwest. When it reached the Central Valley of California—an uninhabitable territory for it—populations branched west (to the coastal range) and east (to the foothills of the Sierra Nevada). Over time, the populations took on different colorations as they moved southward. By the time the two populations were united in Southern California, they differed enough, genetically and physically, that they either did not interbreed or produced infertile hybrid offspring when they did. (Salamanders are falsely colored in the drawing for illustrative purposes.)

Figure 18.4
Geographical
Separation—Leading
to Speciation?

These two varieties of squirrel had a common ancestor
that at one time lived in a single range of territory. Then
the Grand Canyon was
carved out of land in northern
Arizona, leaving populations
of this species separated
from one another, about
10,000 years ago. In the area
of the Grand Canyon, **(a)** the
Abert's squirrel lives only on
the canyon's south rim, while
(b) the Kaibab squirrel lives
on the north rim. It's unclear
whether these two varieties
of squirrel would be reproductively isolated if reunited
today—that is, whether they
are now separate species—
but the geographical separation they have experienced is
the first step on the way to
allopatric speciation.

(a) Abert's squirrel, south rim of Grand Canyon

(b) Kaibab squirrel, north rim of Grand Canyon

When geographical barriers divide a population and
the resulting populations then go on to become separate species, what has occurred is **allopatric speciation.**
Allopatric literally means "of other countries" (**Figure
18.4**). Look along the banks on either side of the Rio
Juruá in western Brazil and you will find small monkeys, called tamarins, that differ genetically from one
another in accordance with how wide the river is at any
given point. Where it is widest, the members of this
species do not interbreed, while at the narrow headwa-
ters they do. Are the non-breeding populations on their
way to becoming separate species? Perhaps, but only if
gene flow is drastically reduced between them for a
very long time.

Reproductive Isolating Mechanisms

While geographical separation is the most important
factor in getting speciation going, it cannot bring
about speciation by itself. Following geographical
separation, two populations of the same species must
then undergo physical or behavioral changes that will
keep them from interbreeding should they ever be
reunited. Allopatric speciation thus operates through a
one–two process: first the geographic separation, then
the development of differing characteristics in the two
resulting populations. These are characteristics that will
isolate them from each other in terms of reproduction.

Thus arises the concept of **reproductive isolating
mechanisms,** which can be defined as any factor that,
in nature, prevents interbreeding between individuals
of the same species or of closely related species. Geographic separation is itself a reproductive isolating
mechanism because it is a factor that prevents interbreeding. But because the mountains or rivers that are
the actual barriers to interbreeding are outside of or
extrinsic to the organisms in question, geographic
separation is called an **extrinsic isolating mechanism.**
For allopatric speciation to take place, what also must
occur is the second in the one–two series of events:
the evolution of *internal* characteristics that keep organisms from interbreeding. Such characteristics are
referred to as **intrinsic isolating mechanisms:** evolved
differences in anatomy, physiology, or behavior that

prevent interbreeding between individuals of the
same species or of closely related species.

Six Intrinsic Reproductive Isolating Mechanisms

So, what are these intrinsic isolating mechanisms? A
list of the most important ones is presented in **Table
18.1.** An easy way to remember them is to think about
what sequence of events would be required for fertile
offspring to be produced in any sexually reproducing
organism. First, organisms that live in the same area
must encounter one another; if they don't, the "ecological isolation" mechanism is in place. If they do encounter one another, they must then mate in the same
time frame; if they don't, then temporal isolation is in
place, and so on.

Ecological Isolation

Two closely related species of animals may overlap in
their ranges and yet feed, mate, and grow in separate
areas, which are called *habitats*. If they use different
habitats, this means they may rarely meet up. If so,
gene flow will be greatly restricted between them.
Lions and tigers *can* interbreed, but they never have
in nature, even when their ranges overlapped in
the past. One reason for this is their largely separate

habitats: Lions prefer the open grasslands, tigers the deep forests.

Temporal Isolation

Even when two populations share the same habitat, if they do not mate within the same time frame, gene flow will be limited between them. Two populations of the same species of flowering plant may begin releasing pollen at slightly different times of the year. Should their reproductive periods cease to overlap altogether, gene flow would be cut off between them.

Behavioral Isolation

Even when populations are in contact and breed at the same time, they must choose to mate with one another for interbreeding to occur. Such choice is often based on specific courtship and mating displays, which can be thought of as passwords between members of the same species. Birds must hear the proper song, spiders must perform the proper dance, and fiddler crabs must wave their claws in the proper way for mating to occur.

Mechanical Isolation

Reproductive organs may come to differ in size, shape, or some other feature, such that organisms of the same or closely related species can no longer mate. Different species of alpine butterfly look very similar, but their genital organs are different enough that one species cannot mate with another.

Gametic Isolation

Even if mating occurs, offspring may not result if there are incompatibilities between sperm and egg or between sperm and the female reproductive tract. In plants, the sperm borne by pollen may be unable to reach the egg lying within the plant's ovary. In animals, sperm may be killed by the chemical nature of a given reproductive tract or may be unable to bind with receptors on the egg.

There is one special form of gametic isolation, called *polyploidy,* that is very important in plants and that may have played a part in giving rise to the vertebrate evolutionary line that we humans are part of. You can read about it in "New Species through Genetic Accidents: Polyploidy" on page 326.

Hybrid Inviability or Infertility

Even if offspring result, they may develop poorly—they may be stunted or malformed in some way—or they may be *infertile,* meaning unable to bear offspring of their own. A well-known example of such infertility is the mule, which is the infertile offspring of a female horse and a male donkey (**Figure 18.5** on the next page).

Sympatric Speciation

Thus far, you have looked at the development of intrinsic reproductive isolating mechanisms strictly as a second step in speciation—one that follows a

Table 18.1		
Reproductive Isolating Mechanisms		
Extrinsic isolating mechanism		**Geographic isolation** Individuals of two populations cannot interbreed if they live in different places (the first step in allopatric speciation).
Intrinsic isolating mechanisms		**Ecological isolation** Even if they live in the same place, they can't mate if they don't come in contact with one another.
		Temporal isolation Even if they come in contact, they can't mate if they breed at different times.
		Behavioral isolation Even if they breed at the same time, they will not mate if they are not attracted to one another.
		Mechanical isolation Even if they attract one another, they cannot mate if they are not physically compatible.
		Gametic isolation Even if they are physically compatible, an embryo will not form if the egg and sperm do not fuse properly.
		Hybrid inviability or infertility Even if fertilization occurs successfully, the offspring may not survive, or if it survives, may not reproduce (e.g., mule).

geographic separation of populations. As it happens, however, intrinsic reproductive isolating mechanisms can develop between two populations in the *absence* of any geographic separation of them. If these isolating mechanisms reduce interbreeding between the populations sufficiently, speciation can take place. What occurs in this situation is not allopatric speciation, however; it is **sympatric speciation,** which can be defined as any speciation that does not involve geographic separation. (*Sympatric* literally means "of the same country.")

Sympatric speciation has been a contentious subject in biology for decades. Scientists have long recognized one of its forms: the polyploidy reviewed in "New Species through Genetic Accidents." But for years, most biologists were skeptical that it existed in

Figure 18.5
Mules Are Infertile Hybrids

Even though mules cannot themselves reproduce, humans frequently cross horses and donkeys to produce them to take advantage of their exceptional strength and endurance. Chromosomal incompatibilities between horses and donkeys leave the mules sterile.

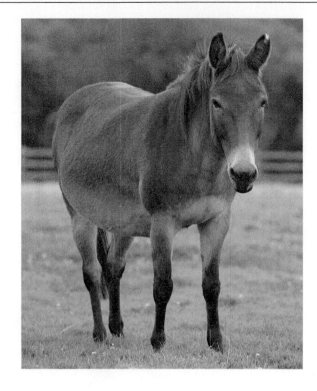

any other form. Over the past decade, however, new evidence has convinced most experts that sympatric speciation has operated in a number of instances. No one claims that it has the importance of allopatric speciation, but for most biologists today, the key question about sympatric speciation is not whether it has taken place but how frequently it has occurred.

Sympatric Speciation in a Fruit Fly

To see how sympatric speciation works, consider one of its best-studied examples, a species of fruit fly named *Rhagoletis pomonella*. Prior to the European colonization of North America, *R. pomonella* existed solely on the small, red fruit of hawthorn trees (**Figure 18.6**). The

Figure 18.6
A Species Undergoing Sympatric Speciation?

The fruit-fly species *Rhagoletis pomonella*, pictured here on the skin of a green apple, may be undergoing speciation.

Europeans brought *apple* trees with them, however, and by 1862 some *R. pomonella* had moved over to them. It seemed to at least one mid-nineteenth-century observer, however, that with the introduction of apples there had arisen separate varieties of the flies—what are sometimes called apple flies and haw flies—with each variety courting, mating, and laying eggs almost exclusively on its own type of tree. A modern researcher named Guy Bush led the way in investigating whether this was the case, and the answer turned out to be yes. The two varieties of flies are separated from each other in all these ways. In one study of them, only 6 percent of the apple and haw flies interbred with one another. The apple and haw *R. pomonella* are not separate species yet, but they certainly give indication of being in transition to that status.

For our purposes, the first thing to note is that this separation has not come about because of *geographic* division. The apple and hawthorn trees that the two varieties of flies live on may scarcely be separated in space at all. Given this, how did this single species move toward becoming two separate species? Bush offers a likely scenario, based on a critical difference between the hosts the two species live on. Apples tend to ripen in August and September, while hawthorn fruit ripens in September and October. In the summer, all fruit flies emerge as adults after wintering underground as larvae, after which they fly to their host tree to mate and lay eggs in the fruit.

Bush believes that about 150 years ago (when hawthorns were hosts to all the flies), some individuals in a population of *R. pomonella* experienced either a mutation or perhaps a chance combination of rare existing alleles. In either event, this change did two things: It caused these flies to emerge slightly *earlier* from their underground state than did most flies, and it drew these flies to the smell of *apples* as well as hawthorns. Because apples mature slightly earlier than the hawthorn fruit, these flies had a suitable host waiting for them. More important, these flies would have bred *among themselves* to a high degree. Recall that the other flies were emerging later, and the adult fly only lives for about a month. Thus, the variant alleles were passed on to a selected population in the next generation. Today, the apple *R. pomonella* flies indisputably do emerge earlier than the hawthorn flies. This is one of the things that ensures reproductive isolation between the two groups; their periods of mating don't fully overlap.

Such a lack of overlapping mating periods may sound familiar because it is one of the intrinsic reproductive isolating mechanisms you looked at earlier. (It is temporal isolation.) You also can see ecological isolation in operation with these flies. Although the two types of flies live in the same area, they meet up with relatively little frequency because they have different habitats (hawthorn vs. apple trees). In short, these populations have developed intrinsic reproductive isolating mechanisms without ever having been separated from one another geographically. They are headed toward speciation, but in this case it is sympatric speciation.

SO FAR . . .

1. Name as many intrinsic isolating mechanisms as you can.

2. The mule provides an example of the intrinsic isolating mechanism of hybrid _____.

3. Sympatric speciation is speciation that does not involve _____.

18.3 Adaptive Radiation and the Pace of Speciation

The Hawaiian Islands are places of such lush natural diversity that it can be a surprise to learn that they harbor no native species of reptiles or amphibians and only one native variety of land mammal: the bat. On the other hand, Hawaii is home to more than 500 native species of the fruit flies known as drosophilids—a number so large it represents a quarter of all the drosophilid species found in the world (**Figure 18.7**). This story becomes more puzzling with knowledge that genetic analysis has revealed that every one of these 500 species evolved from a single drosophilid species that made it to the islands millions of years ago. Hence we have mystery: A small geographic area has been home to a tremendous amount of speciation within one group of living things. What can explain this kind of speciation? A phenomenon known as adaptive radiation, which turns out to have had a far-reaching importance in the diversification of Earth's organisms.

New Environments and Speciation

As most people know, Hawaii's islands were formed by volcanic activity. The oldest of the islands, Kauai, arose through this activity about 5 million years ago, while the youngest island, Hawaii, formed about 375,000 years ago. If you've ever seen a landscape recently coated by lava, you know the meaning of the word *barren*. Each Hawaiian island originally was barren in this way, which meant that, for a brief time, each island was sterile, with no life on it. Very quickly, however, life did come to the islands, with bacteria, fungi, plant seeds, and tiny animals landing on them, all being borne by ocean currents, wind, or migrating animals. In time, numerous large plant species became established.

By the time the drosophilid flies arrived, it's likely they encountered two things that were critical to their speciation: an environment that *had* plenty of food and habitat but that *lacked* any flies of the drosophilid variety. To understand the importance of these factors, imagine that you are a graphic artist, working in a big city with lots of other graphic artists, most of whom specialize in this or that (magazines, Internet websites, etc.). Now you and a few other graphic artists move to a new city in which there are few graphic artists but a good number of *possibilities* for graphic arts work. You would thus be able to specialize fairly easily—filling a *niche* or working role in this new environment—because many of these niches would not yet have been taken. Just so did the drosophilids rush in to fill previously unoccupied niches on the Hawaiian Islands—this mating environment, this food source, this place on the forest floor for laying eggs.

Such a situation is ripe with possibilities for change (meaning speciation) because, while niches are in flux, there is a good deal of shaping of species to environment through natural selection. But more of this occurred on Hawaii because this niche-filling was taking place on separate *islands*. These islands represented a geographic barrier to interbreeding, and you know what follows from this: allopatric speciation.

Taking a step back from these steps, we can see that the drosophilid species of Hawaii proliferated through

---

(a) *Drosophila plantibia*

(b) *Drosophila cyrtoloma*

Figure 18.7
Two of Many

The Hawaiian islands are home to more than 500 species of the flies known as drosophilids. Pictured are two varieties of these flies, *Drosophila plantibia,* on the left, and *D. cyrtoloma* on the right. Both flies live in rainforest habitats on the island of Maui.

ESSAY

New Species through Genetic Accidents: Polyploidy

In this chapter so far, speciation has been portrayed as something that takes place over many generations. But plants have a means of speciating in a single generation. It is called *polyploidy,* and it is very important in the plant world, as it is thought to have figured in the evolutionary history of more than 70 percent of all flowering plants. Beyond this, polyploidy may have had great importance in the evolution of animals. Evolutionary biologists currently are debating whether a polyploidy "event" helped speed the rise of animals with backbones—the vertebrates, such as ourselves. As you'll see, whenever polyploidy comes about, it helps speed up evolution.

How does polyploidy work? Here is one of the ways. From the genetics unit, you may recall that human beings have 23 pairs of chromosomes, *Drosophila* flies 4 pairs, and Mendel's peas 7. Whatever the *number* of chromosomes, the commonality among all these species is that their chromosomes come in *pairs,* which is the general rule for species that reproduce sexually (**Figure 1**).

As noted at the start of the chapter, plants are more adept than animals at producing "hybrids," with the gametes from two separate species coming together to create an offspring. Often these offspring are sterile, however, because when it comes time for them to produce *their* gametes (eggs and sperm) the sets of chromosomes they inherited from their different parental species may not "pair up" correctly in meiosis owing to differences in chromosome number or structure.

Now comes the accident. Suppose that, back when it was first created as a single-celled zygote, the hybrid offspring carried out the usual practice of doubling its chromosome number in preparing for its initial cell division. Now, however, the cell fails to actually divide; whereas it was supposed to put half its complement of chromosomes into one daughter cell and half

Did polyploidy speed the evolution of our own vertebrate line?

into another, it doesn't do this. It doubles the chromosomes but keeps them all in one cell. Equipped with *twice* the usual number of chromosomes, this single cell then proceeds to undergo regular cell division, meaning that every cell in the plant that follows will have this doubled number of chromosomes. Critically, this plant will have doubled both its *sets* of chromosomes—the set it got from parental species A and the set it got from species B. If you double a set, by definition every member of that set now has a partner to pair with in gamete formation. Thus, the roadblock to a hybrid producing offspring has been removed; the chromosomes can all pair up.

This pairing up yields eggs and sperm that can then come together and fuse

thanks to another capability of plants. Recall that many plants can *self-fertilize.* A single plant contains male gametes that can fertilize that same plant's female gametes. Thus, the plant with the doubled set of chromosomes can fertilize itself, theoretically beginning an unending line of fertile offspring. This line of organisms is "reproductively isolated" from either of its parental species because it has a different number of chromosomes than either parental species. With reproductive isolation, we have a *separate* species, and with self-fertilization, we have a species that can perpetuate itself.

A multiplication of the normal two sets of chromosomes to some other set number is known as **polyploidy**; here we have speciation by polyploidy, which is one type of sympatric speciation. The importance of this in the plant world is immense. Many of our most important food crops are polyploid, including oats, wheat, cotton, potatoes, and coffee. Indeed, the type of polyploid speciation we've looked at—which begins with a hybrid offspring—often produces bigger, healthier plants. As a result, breeders have developed ways to artificially induce polyploidy.

But what about animals? The self-fertilization that some plants are capable of does not exist among more complex animals. As a result, polyploidy that can be maintained over generations is extremely rare in the animal kingdom. But in the course of hundreds of millions of

---

adaptive radiation: the rapid evolution of many species from a single species that has been introduced to a new environment. Though this mode of speciation can be perceived most readily on islands, it has an importance that goes way beyond the emergence of limited groups of living things in small geographical areas. Indeed, a number of experts in speciation believe that much of the diversity we see in the living world has come about through episodes of adaptive radia-

tion. The basic factors in play with the Hawaiian drosophilids stand to have been repeated, in less extreme form, with one species after another over the long course of Earth's evolutionary history. All that's necessary for an adaptive radiation to take place anywhere is that a given environment present a species with a set of unfilled niches. Critically, species can come to such environments, through migration, but such environments can also come to species, through years of evolution, it clearly has been maintained several times. An extremely important polyploidy event may have occurred about 500 million years ago, just as vertebrate animals were evolving from invertebrates. A controversial hypothesis holds that this event doubled the chromosomal set of our invertebrate ancestors, thus greatly accelerating the pace of their evolution.

How can polyploidy speed up evolution? Think of it this way: If you added an extra room to a house, that would give you the flexibility to transform, say, an existing bedroom into a den. Now, if you add genes to a genome, as polyploidy does, that provides the *genome* with a kind of flexibility: the flexibility to have one kind of gene transformed into another. Where once an organism would have but two copies of a given gene—one allele from each parent—with polyploidy it has four. With this change, members of one pair of these alleles can mutate without causing harm to the organism because the *other* pair of alleles can carry out their function all by themselves. And in a few cases, alleles that mutate will produce new proteins that can help transform an organism—that can help it evolve down different lines. Polyploidy, then, provides for a tremendous increase in the genetic capacity to evolve. And it provides this capacity in a single generation.

1. gamete formation

2. fertilization

3. doubling of chromosomes without dividing

4. gamete formation

5. self-fertilization

New species has arisen through polyploidy

Figure 1
Polyploidy in Wheat
Two different species of wheat exist in nature, with slightly different "genomes" or complements of DNA.

1. Gametes (eggs and sperm) are formed in the different species.

2. These gametes fuse, in fertilization, to form a zygote—a single cell that will develop into a new plant. Such a mixed-species or "hybrid" zygote generally develops into a sterile plant because its chromosomes cannot pair up correctly when the plant produces its own gametes during meiosis.

3. In this case, however, the zygote doubles its chromosomes in preparation for cell division, but then fails to divide. With this doubling, each chromosome now has a compatible homologous chromosome to pair with during meiosis. This is the polyploidy event.

4. Gamete formation then takes place in the plant.

5. These gametes from the same plant then fuse because this is a self-fertilizing plant. With this, a new generation of wheat plant has been produced—one that is a different species from either parent generation because each of the parent species has two pairs of chromosomes, while this new hybrid species has four pairs.

such means as climate change. Either way, the result is a changing relationship between environment and species. When this occurs, speciation becomes much more likely.

To get a sense of how this process can play out on a large scale, look at **Figure 18.8** on the next page, which traces speciation in the evolutionary group we ourselves are part of, mammals. Note that mammalian speciation did not take place in a steady way over time, but instead came about in two waves, the first and most dramatic of which ran from 100 million to 85 million years ago. What occurred to spark this diversification is unknown. Mammals may have come into new environments, bringing with them traits, such as warm-bloodedness, that were *novel* traits within those environments. Conversely, it's possible that new environments came to mammals, in the form of, for example, the cooling temperatures of the period. A third

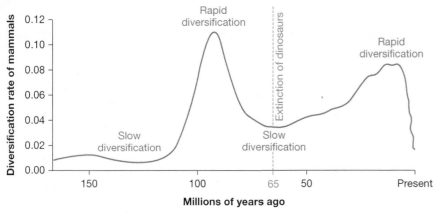

Figure 18.8
The Diversification of Mammals

Mammals evolved from reptiles beginning about 220 million years ago but did not diversify in a steady way from that time forward. Instead, as the figure shows, mammals appear to have undergone two bursts of speciation, the first of them beginning about 100 million years ago, and the second beginning about 50 million years ago. Speciation that follows a trajectory such as this is likely to have come about through a series of adaptive radiations. Contrary to the long-held hypothesis that mammalian diversification was unleashed by the extinction of the dinosaurs 65 million years ago, the first round of mammalian diversification occurred long before the extinction of the dinosaurs, while the second round took place long after.

(Adapted with permission from: Bininda-Emonds, Olaf R.P. et al., "The Delayed Rise of Present-Day Mammals," *Nature:* 29 March 2007, 446:507–512.)

Figure 18.9
Speedy Speciation

Through sympatric specia-tion, the fish on the right, *Amphilophus zaliosus,* evolved from the fish on the left, *A. citrinellus*, within less than 10,000 years in a rela-tively small lake in Nicaragua. The two species are kept separate by both ecological and behavioral isolating mechanisms. Ecologically, *A. zaliosus* is a surface-feeder, while *A. citrinellus* is a bottom-feeder. Behaviorally, differences in courtship signals keep the two species from mating, even when males and females from the two species come together in nature or in the laboratory.

possibility is that niches were opened up to mammals by means of other kinds of animals dying out. What-ever the case, the assumption is that an altered "fit" between mammals and their environments brought about the same phenomenon as occurred with the drosophilids in Hawaii: Mammals diversified rapidly as they adapted to fill new environmental niches. When this process was repeated over and over again, the result was the emergence of the fantastically diverse group of mammals we see today—from whales to bats to bears to ourselves.

The Pace of Speciation

So, how long does speciation take? Setting aside the instantaneous speciation that can come about through polyploidy, it can occur in as little as a few thousand years or as many as several million. If you look at **Figure 18.9**, you can see an example from the speedy side of this spectrum. Pictured are two species

(a) *Amphilophus citrinellus*

(b) *Amphilophus zaliosus*

of fish from a small lake in Nicaragua, Lake Apoyo. The species on the right (*Amphilophus zaliosus*) evolved from the species on the left (*Amphilophus citrinellus*) in a sympatric speciation that certainly took no more than 10,000 years and may have taken as few as 2,000. (One of the ways we know who evolved from whom is that *A. citrinellus* is widespread in the region, while *A. zaliosus* exists nowhere in the world except Lake Apoyo.) On the other end of the spectrum, species within a group of freshwater fish called the characins—which include piranhas and many aquarium fish—have been shown to take up to 9 million years to speciate. In between these extremes, there are species that appear to have taken hundreds of thousands of years to give rise to sister species.

18.4 The Categorization of Earth's Living Things

This chapter began by noting the importance of the species concept—of being able to say that this organ-ism is fundamentally separate from that. To have a species concept means that there has to be some means of *naming* separate species. You have probably noticed that most of the species considered in this chapter have been referred to by their scientific names; you didn't just look at a fruit fly, but rather at *Rhagoletis pomonella*. To the average person, such names may be regarded as evidence that scientists are awfully exacting—or just plain fussy. Why the two names? Why the Latin? Can't we just say fruit fly?

To take these questions one at a time, scientists can't just say "fruit fly" for the same reason a person can't say "the guy in the white shirt" while trying to identify a player at a tennis tournament. There are lots of guys in white shirts at tennis tournaments, and there are lots of different kinds of flies in the world. It is important to be able to say *which* fly we are talking about. The importance of this can be seen with *Rhagoletis pomonella* itself, which is a major pest in the apple industry. Tell some apple growers that you have spotted flies on their apples, and you may get a shrug of the shoulders; tell them you have spotted *R. pomonella,* and you may get a very different reaction.

The Latin that is used stems from the fact that this naming convention was standardized by the Swedish scientist Carl von Linné in the eighteenth century, at a time when Latin was still used in the Western world in scientific naming. (In fact, Linné is better known by the Latinized form of his name—Carolus Linnaeus.) Linnaeus recognized the confu-sion that can result from having several common names for the same creature and thus devoted himself to giving specific names to some 4,200 species of ani-mals and 7,700 species of plants—all that were known to exist in his time. Many of the names he conferred are still in use today.

The fact that there are two parts to scientific names—a **binomial nomenclature**—points to the central question of groupings of organisms on Earth. Consider the domestic cat, which has the scientific name *Felis domestica*. The first part of this name specifies a genus—*Felis* in this case—which is to say a group of closely related but still separate species. Meanwhile, the second, "specific," part of this name designates a *particular* member of the *Felis* genus. Together, these two names constitute the name of a species: *Felis domestica*. The practical importance of making genus names a part of species names is that, if we know that two organisms are part of the same genus, then to know something about one of the organisms is to know a good deal about the other. There are six species of small cat within the *Felis* genus, for example, and all of these species share a very similar set of physical characteristics.

Taxonomic Classification and the Degree of Relatedness

But what is the basis for placing organisms in a category such as genus? Modern science classifies organisms largely—although not entirely—in accordance with how closely they are *related*. In this context, "related" has the same meaning as it does when the subject is extended human families. If people have the same mother, they are more closely related than if they shared only a common *grandmother*, which in turn makes them more closely related than if they had only a common great-great grandmother, and so on.

In the same way, species can be thought of as being related. Domestic dogs (*Canis familiaris*) are very closely related to gray wolves (*Canis lupus*), with all dogs being descended from these wolves. Indeed, by some reckonings dogs and gray wolves are the same species (*Canis lupus*) because they will interbreed in nature. Such differences as exist between them are the product of a mere 15,000 years or so of the human domestication of dogs. It may be, then, that 15,000 years ago there was but one species (the gray wolf) that gave rise to both today's wolf and today's dog—a close relation indeed.

Domestic dogs are also related, however, to domestic cats; if we look far back enough in time, we can find a single group of animals that gave rise to both the dog and cat lines. This does not mean going back 10,000 years, however; it means going back perhaps 60 million years. So there is a big difference in how closely related dogs and wolves are as opposed to dogs and cats. Establishing such *degrees* of relatedness is the most important task of the scientific classification system. There is a field of biology, called **systematics,**

that is concerned with the diversity and relatedness of organisms; part of what systematists do is try to establish the truth about who is more closely related to whom. They study the evolutionary history of groups of organisms.

Setting aside for the moment the difficulty in *determining* what such evolutionary histories are, there obviously is a tremendous cataloguing job here, in light of the number of living and extinct species mentioned earlier. Given this diversity, a method of classifying organisms, called a *taxonomic system,* is employed to classify every species of living thing on Earth. There are eight basic categories in use in the modern taxonomic system: species, genus, family, order, class, phylum, kingdom, and domain. The organisms in any of these categories make up a grouping of living things, a **taxon.**

A Taxonomic Example: The Common House Cat

If you look at **Figure 18.10**, you can see how this taxonomic system works in connection with the domestic cat. As noted, this cat is only one species in a genus

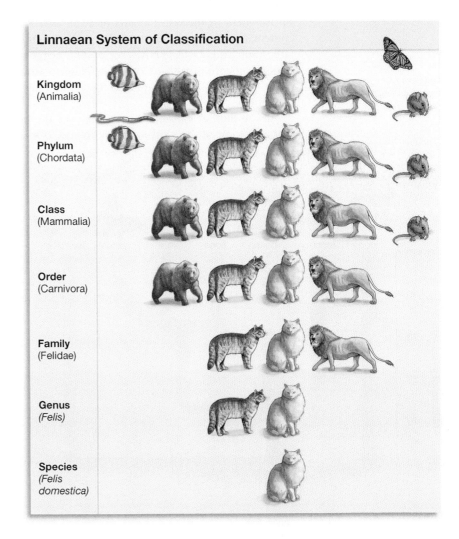

Figure 18.10 Classifying Living Things

The classification of the house cat, *Felis domestica,* based on the Linnaean system.

Linnaean System of Classification

Kingdom (Animalia)

Phylum (Chordata)

Class (Mammalia)

Order (Carnivora)

Family (Felidae)

Genus (Felis)

Species (Felis domestica)

(*Felis*) that has six living species in it. The genus then is a small part of a family (Felidae) that has 17 other genera in it (panthers, snow leopards, and others). The family is then part of an order (Carnivora) that includes not only big and small "cats" but other carnivores, such as bears and dogs. On up the taxa we go, with each taxon being more inclusive than the one beneath it until we get to the highest category in this figure, the kingdom Animalia, which includes all animals. (In Chapter 19, you'll look at the "supercategory" above kingdom, called domain, but for simplicity's sake, kingdom is the highest level taxon considered here.)

Constructing Evolutionary Histories

So how do systematists go about putting organisms into these various groups? What evidence do they use in constructing their evolutionary histories? They rely on radiometric dating, the fossil record, DNA sequence comparisons—all the things reviewed in Chapter 16 that are used to chart the history of life on Earth. In practice, there has been a revolution in this field in the last 20 years or so in that most systematics work today is molecular work—scientists are comparing DNA, RNA, and protein sequences among modern organisms and using patterns among these sequences to make judgments about lines of descent.

If you look at **Figure 18.11**, you can see the outcome of some of this work, an evolutionary "tree" for

one group of organisms, in this case one of the major groups of mammalian carnivores. You can see that the tree is "rooted," about 60 million years ago, with an ancestral carnivore whose lineage split two ways: to dogs on the one hand and everything else on the other. One interesting facet of this evolutionary history is how closely related bears are to the aquatic carnivores. All such histories are hypotheses about evolutionary relationships, with each such hypothesis known as a **phylogeny.**

Obscuring the Trail of Evidence: Convergent Evolution

One of the things that makes the interpretation of evolutionary evidence difficult is that similar features may arise *independently* in several evolutionary lines. A bedrock of systematic classification is the existence of **homologies,** which can be defined as common structures in different species that result from a shared ancestry. In Chapter 16, a strong homology was noted in forelimb structure that exists in organisms as different as a gorilla, a bat, and a whale. If you look at **Figure 18.12**, you can see the gorilla and the bat again.

Now, however, consider an extinct group, the litopterns, that once lived in what is now Argentina. Like the modern-day horse, they roamed on open grasslands. Over the course of evolutionary time, they developed legs that were extraordinarily similar to the horse's, right down to having an undivided hoof. In fact, litopterns are only very distantly related to the horse, but the leg similarities were enough to convince one nineteenth-century expert that he had found in litopterns the ancestor to the modern horse.

What is exhibited in the legs of the litoptern and horse is an **analogy**: a feature in different organisms that is the same in function and superficial appearance. When nature has shaped two separate evolutionary lines in analogous ways, what has occurred is **convergent evolution.** (Both the litoptern and horse lines converged in their development of similar legs.) But analogous features have nothing to do with common descent; they merely show that the same kinds of environmental pressures lead to the same kinds of physical features. (There are only so many leg structures that work well for grass-eating mammals that roam over long distances, so it's not surprising that natural selection would have channeled two separate evolutionary lines toward a similar leg shape.) The problem is that analogy can be confused with homology; analogies can make us think that species share common ancestry when in fact they don't. (Convergent evolution can take place *within* a species—indeed, it has in our own species in the relatively recent past, as you can see in "Converging on an Ability to Drink Milk" on page 332.)

Figure 18.11
A Family Tree for a Selected Group of Mammalian Carnivores

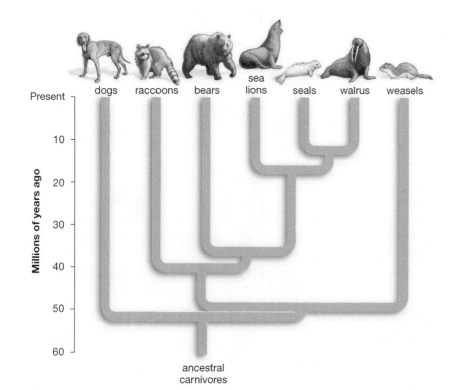

(a) Homology: Common structures in different organisms that result from common ancestry

bat

bones of wing   bones of arm

gorilla

(b) Analogy: Characters of similar function and superficial structure that have *not* arisen from common ancestry

litoptern

horse

one-toed foot   one-toed foot

Figure 18.12

(a) Bats and gorillas have the same bone composition in their forelimbs—one upper bone, joined to two intermediate bones, joined to five digits—because they share a common ancestor. Of course, these forelimbs are used today for very different functions.

(b) Horses and the extinct litopterns have long legs and one-toed feet that serve the same function, but these features were derived independently in the two creatures—in separate lines of descent.

SO FAR . . .

1. Adaptive radiation is the rapid emergence of many species from a single species that has been introduced to _____.

2. Living things are classified largely in accordance with degrees of _____.

3. All species are referred to by a two-part name, the first part of which is a species' _____.

18.5 Classical Taxonomy and Cladistics

Given difficulties such as convergent evolution and a less-than-perfect fossil record, systematists over the years have been driven to devise several method-

ologies for producing phylogenies. The essential question they have asked is: What means of *interpreting* the evidence will give us the most accurate picture of how Earth's living and extinct organisms are related?

One of the methodologies for interpreting evidence actually predates the field of systematics and most of the techniques used in it. Handed down from the time of Darwin, this methodology is sometimes called *classical taxonomy* (or descriptive taxonomy). In thinking about animals in Earth's family tree, classical taxonomists would look first and foremost at the physical form or morphology of the animals in question, as preserved in the fossil record, and compare it to the morphology of modern animals. Skull shape, "dentition" (teeth patterns), limb structure, and much more would be considered. They would also look at *where* the ancient forms existed compared to modern forms. More recently, they have been using molecular techniques, such as comparing DNA or protein sequences

ESSAY

Converging on an Ability to Drink Milk

Convergent evolution may sound like an exotic concept with little relevance to everyday life, but we human beings have experienced an important convergent evolution of our own: The human ability to digest milk throughout life evolved at least three separate times over the past 7,000 years—once in East Africa, once in Northern Europe, and once in the Middle East. In each case, this ability originated by means of a mutation that occurred within a population of humans who had begun to domesticate milk-yielding animals such as cows or camels (**Figure 1**). Each of these populations experienced a different mutation, but all of the mutations resulted in alleles that had the same effect: They allowed individuals to keep producing an enzyme called lactase once past infancy, a change that gave these individuals a lifelong ability to digest the lactose in milk. Once these alleles appeared, they spread through each of the three local populations and then spread to ever-larger groups of people, such that today a substantial minority of human adults can digest milk. In keeping with the geographic

Figure 1
An Ability that Evolved Several Times
The ability to digest milk throughout life has evolved at least three times in the human species over the last 7,000 years. In each case, the ability arose in a geographical region in which human beings had begun to domesticate herd animals. One such region was the Middle East, where camels were domesticated. Here a man drinks milk provided by his camels near Suweibah, Kuwait.

origins of "lactase persistence," however, most people of East Asian, West African, or Hispanic ancestry cannot digest milk following childhood.

It's actually not surprising that lactase persistence should have evolved several times in the course of human history, given the tremendous advantage this trait would have provided to humans who, thousands of years ago, lived in groups in which food in general was scarce but milk from animals was available. Anyone who inherited an allele for lactase persistence was effectively granted a tremendous survival and reproduction advantage compared to someone whose ability to digest milk ended in childhood. The result was that lactase-persistent individuals left more offspring, which meant that lactase persistence quickly became prevalent in populations that possessed the allele for it. In short, natural selection acted very strongly to spread lactase persistence, which is why this trait traveled so far in a time span that, in evolutionary terms, was the mere blink of an eye. (For more on human milk digestion, see "An Evolving Ability to Digest Milk" on page 294.)

in different living species to determine the relatedness among them. In essence, classical taxonomists would look at how many similarities one group has with another and, on that basis, try to judge relatedness among them. The word *judge* is used advisedly here because, at the end of the day in the classical system, subjective judgments usually need to be made about who is more closely related to whom. It is a matter of weighing one piece of evidence against another, but who's to say which piece of evidence is more important?

Another System for Interpreting the Evidence: Cladistics

The subjectivity inherent in classical taxonomy helped bring about the formation of another system for establishing relatedness. Developed in the 1950s by the German biologist Willi Henning, it is called **cladistics** (from the Greek *klados*, meaning "branch"). In prac-

tice, cladistics has become the core of most phylogenetic work going on today.

In **Figure 18.13** you can see a **cladogram,** which is an evolutionary tree constructed within the cladistic system. Note that there is a very simple branched line and that no time scale is attached to it, as was the case with the evolutionary tree of carnivores. Cladistics concerns itself first with lines of descent—with the *order* of branching events. Once this order has been established, efforts can be made to fix events in time, but that is a secondary concern. First and foremost, this cladogram is a proposed answer to the question: Among the animals lizard, deer, lion, and seal, which two groups of animals have the most recent common ancestor? Then, which other two have the *next* most recent common ancestor, and so on. By extension, the question is: Who is more closely related to whom? Note that these questions are being asked about only four of the five animals listed. You'll get to the role of the hagfish in a moment.

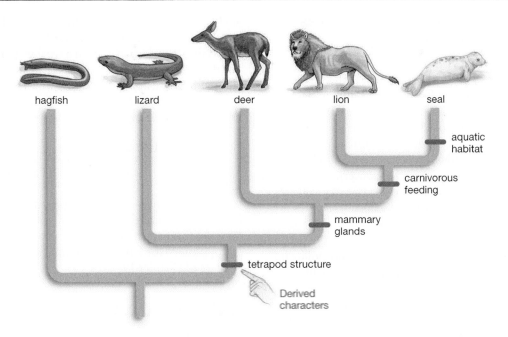

Figure 18.13
A Simple Cladogram

Among the lizard, deer, lion, and seal, which two are most closely related? The tentative answer displayed in this cladogram is the lion and the seal. The basis for this assertion is the number of unique or "shared derived" characters these two creatures have compared to any other two organisms under consideration. (They share three characters: tetrapod structure, mammary glands, and carnivorous feeding.) Such a system pays no attention to superficial similarities among organisms. Like fish, seals swim in the water, but they share far more derived characters with lions than they do with fish—enough to persuade scientists that seals have returned to the water in relatively recent times, following a period in which their ancestors lived on land.

Shared Ancestral and Derived Characters

The starting point for cladistic analysis is the difference between so-called ancestral characters and derived characters. If you look at any group of species (any taxon), its **ancestral characters** are those that existed in an ancestor common to them all. There are about 50,000 species of animals on Earth that possess a dorsal vertebral column (better known as a backbone). The ancestor to all fishes, reptiles, and mammals had such a feature, which makes the vertebral column an ancestral character for all these groups. On the other hand, only *some* vertebrates then went on to become animals that have four limbs (and are thus tetrapods). The tetrapod feature is thus a **derived character** of the vertebrate state; it is a character *unique* to taxa descended from a common ancestor.

In Figure 18.13, you can see a continuation of this process of ever-more selective grouping in that only some mammals are carnivorous feeders, and only some members of this taxon are aquatic mammalian carnivores. The presumption in cladistics is that shared derived characters are evidence of common ancestry and that the *more* derived characters any two organisms share, the more recently they will have shared a common ancestor compared to other organisms under study. At its most fundamental level, cladistics becomes a matter of counting shared derived characters. Seals and lions share three derived characters (tetrapod

structure, mammary glands, and carnivorous feeding), while the lizard has only one derived character that it shares with all the other animals in Figure 18.13 (tetrapod structure). Cladistics infers from this that the lion and the seal have a more recent common ancestor than do any other two groups in the cladogram—that their branching from this common line of descent came later than any other branching in the line. And the hagfish? It is a starting-point organism for the mammalian carnivores, known as an *out-group*. If we are to say that the animals under consideration have derived characters, they must be derived *compared to* some other organism—in this case, the hagfish.

The examples here employ visible, physical traits, but in practice modern cladistics relies heavily on comparisons among molecular sequences, such as the number of shared, derived base pairs in lengths of DNA or RNA. Furthermore, since cladistics often compares many species, its phylogenies cannot be produced through simple counting; instead, they are the result of multiple rounds of computer-aided calculations.

Taking a step back, the important thing to note about the cladistic method is that it has done away with one of the problems of classical taxonomy: It has removed the element of subjectivity. There is a firm rule in cladistics for inferring relatedness—the number of shared derived characters—which means that judgment need not play a part in its analyses.

Should Anything but Relatedness Matter in Classification?

Strictly speaking, cladistic analysis is not about the classification of Earth's living things. Rather, cladistics is concerned solely with establishing lines of descent. Once these are established, categories can be overlaid on them. Having looked at various cladograms, we could say that a given group constitutes a class called Reptilia, while another constitutes a class called Amphibia. But cladistics per se is not concerned with this. If the question, however, is not just one of phylogeny, but how to *categorize* Earth's organisms, then it's not clear that cladistic analysis always provides the most sensible categories.

To appreciate this point, consider the following question. Who is more closely related: dinosaurs and lizards or dinosaurs and birds? It may surprise you to learn that it is dinosaurs and birds. Birds split off from a dinosaur line within the last 200 million years or so while the split between the lizard and dinosaur lines came much earlier. Despite this, conventional taxonomy says that dinosaurs and lizards belong in one class (Reptilia) while birds belong in another (Aves; **Figure 18.14**). The assumption here is that, in classifying creatures, something should count *besides* their relatedness—in this case, the special qualities of birds (feathers, flight).

To some scientists, a categorization such as this makes no sense. Why should relatedness dictate taxonomy in some instances but not in others? Shouldn't we consis-

tently categorize organisms on the basis of relatedness? On the other hand, aren't birds different enough from lizards that they deserve to be in a separate grouping? If you think that both sides in this debate are making sensible arguments, then you understand why it is so difficult to come up with a universally accepted means of classifying Earth's living things.

On to the History of Life

The millions of species that exist on Earth today took billions of years to evolve. During that time, life went from being exclusively microscopic and single-celled to being the staggeringly diverse entity it is today. How did this happen over time? And what is the order of appearance for Earth's living things? These are the subjects of Chapter 19.

> ## SO FAR . . .
>
> 1. Cladistics determines relatedness among organisms by counting shared, derived characters: characters that are _____ to taxa descended from a _____.
>
> 2. One school of thought holds that Earth's organisms ought to be categorized in strict accordance with _____, while another holds that other factors, such as shared physical qualities, ought to be considered as well.

Figure 18.14
Are Birds Reptiles?

(a) Classical taxonomy employs three classes, Aves, Mammalia, and Reptilia, for birds, mammals, and reptiles, respectively. Thus, dinosaurs and birds are in separate classes—a recognition on the part of classical taxonomists of the unique features of birds, such as feathers.

(b) In cladistic analysis, by contrast, birds are grouped very closely with dinosaurs in recognition of the recent shared ancestry of the two taxa. The only consideration in this system of classification is who is more closely related to whom.

(a) Classical view of relationships among tetrapods

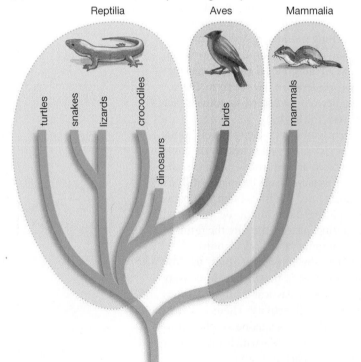

(b) Cladistic view of relationships among tetrapods

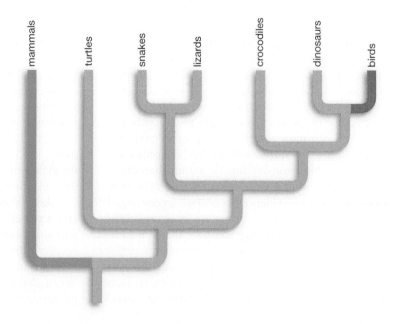

18 REVIEW

Go to the Study Area at www.masteringbiology.com to practice quizzes, myeBook, BioFlix™ 3-D animations, MP3 Tutor Sessions, videos, current events, and more.

Mastering BIOLOGY

Summary

18.1 What Is a Species?

- The biological species concept defines species as groups of actually or potentially interbreeding natural populations that are reproductively isolated from other such groups. This definition does not apply to bacteria and archaea (which reproduce through simple cell division), but does apply to all organisms that multiply through sexual reproduction. (p. 319)

18.2 How Do New Species Arise?

- Branching evolution, which occurs when a single "parent" species diverges into two species, is based on reductions in gene flow between populations of the same species. When evolution has altered the characteristics of separated populations of the same species enough that they will no longer interbreed, even if reunited, speciation has occurred. (p. 321)

- Geographic separation is the most important factor in reducing gene flow between populations of the same species. When geographic separation plays a part in the evolution of a species, allopatric speciation has occurred. (p. 321)

- Geographic separation cannot bring about speciation by itself. Following geographic separation, separate populations of the same species must develop internal characteristics, called intrinsic isolating mechanisms, that will keep them from interbreeding should they reunite. The six most important of these mechanisms are ecological, temporal, behavioral, mechanical, and gametic isolation and hybrid inviability or infertility. (p. 322)

- Speciation can occur in the absence of geographical separation, but such sympatric speciation is thought to occur much less frequently than allopatric speciation. (p. 323)

18.3 Adaptive Radiation and the Pace of Speciation

- Speciation is more likely to occur when a species comes to a new environment or a new environment comes to a species (through climate change, for example). Environmental shifts of this sort make niches available to a species, a condition that fosters the adaptation of the species to its environment through natural selection and that hence promotes the evolution of new species from it. This is known as adaptive radiation: the rapid emergence of many species from a single species that has been introduced to a new environment. Much of the living world's diversity may have been produced through episodes of adaptive radiation. (p. 325)

- Polyploidy is sympatric speciation that can give rise to a new species in a single generation. It is most important in plants, but it has occurred in animal species as well. Polyploidy speeds evolution by providing a redundancy in alleles that allows some to mutate without causing harm to the organism. (p. 326)

18.4 The Categorization of Earth's Living Things

- A binomial nomenclature is used for each of Earth's species. The first name designates the organism's genus and the second designates its species. Genus and species are categories that fit into a larger framework of taxonomy, meaning the classification of species. Going from least to most inclusive, the eight most important categories in the taxonomy of Earth's organisms are species,

genus, family, order, class, phylum, kingdom, and domain. (p. 328)

- Species that are closely related are in the same genus while species that are distantly related may only be in the same phylum or kingdom. The scientific discipline called systematics establishes degrees of relatedness among both living and extinct species. (p. 329)

- Systematists establish phylogenies, or hypotheses about evolutionary family trees, by reviewing radiometric dating, the fossil record, and DNA sequence comparisons, among other kinds of evidence. Most of the work in systematics today is molecular. (p. 330)

- Systematists look for homologous structures (common structures in different species that result from a shared ancestry). One problem with the use of these structures is that they can be confused with analogous structures (similar features that developed independently in separate lines of organisms). (p. 330)

18.5 Classical Taxonomy and Cladistics

- Classical taxonomy employs subjective judgments in deciding what weight to give one piece of evidence versus another in proposing phylogenies. An alternate methodology, cladistics, does away with this subjectivity by following a firm rule for inferring relatedness. It counts the number of shared derived characters two organisms have. (p. 331)

- Cladistics is chiefly concerned with establishing phylogenies, although the results it produces can be used to put species into taxonomic categories. Classical taxonomy holds that, in putting organisms into various categories, factors other than phylogeny ought to be taken into account. (p. 334)

Key Terms

Understanding the Basics

Multiple-Choice Questions

(Answers are in the back of the book.)

1. In the biological species concept, the factor that defines a species is:
   a. geographical separation.
   b. reproductive isolation.
   c. hybridization.
   d. cladogenesis.
   e. its behavior.

2. In allopatric speciation (select all that apply):
   a. allele frequency changes are shared between populations of the same species.
   b. populations are geographically isolated.
   c. gene flow between populations is greatly reduced because of geographic separation.

   d. populations accumulate genetic changes over time that result in physical or behavioral changes that eventually block successful inter-breeding.
   e. populations are directly adjacent.

3. Possible intrinsic reproductive isolating mechanisms include (select all that apply):
   a. mating at different times of year or times of day.
   b. geographical isolation.
   c. incompatibility between eggs and sperm that prevent fertilization.
   d. singing a different mating song than another species.
   e. producing fertile hybrids.

4. Match the reproductive isolating mechanism with the means by which it works:
   a. temporal isolation — populations utilize different habitats
   b. ecological isolation — populations employ different courtship or mating displays
   c. behavioral isolation — mating occurs at different times of day or year
   d. gametic isolation — progeny of a cross are unable to reproduce
   e. hybrid sterility — egg and sperm do not fuse

5. In ocean-dwelling creatures such as sea urchins or corals, sperm and eggs are released into the water by males and females and fertilization occurs externally. If several closely related species of coral live in the same location, what reproductive isolating mechanisms could potentially prevent interbreeding? (Select all that apply.)
   a. behavioral isolation
   b. gametic isolation
   c. temporal isolation
   d. ecological isolation
   e. hybrid infertility

6. Order the following categories into the appropriate biological hierarchy, with the least inclusive category first
   a. family
   b. species
   c. phylum
   d. genus
   e. class

7. Factors that can be problems in determining relatedness among organisms may include (select all that apply):
   a. homologous traits.
   b. analogous traits.
   c. convergent evolution.
   d. poor fossil record.
   e. shared derived traits.

8. Adaptive radiations (select all that apply):
   a. can be seen most clearly in mainland environments.
   b. are episodes of rapid speciation that occur when the "fit" between environment and species is in flux.
   c. concern the evolution of heat loss in vertebrates experiencing stressful climates.
   d. are exemplified by the Hawaiian drosophilid flies.
   e. can be seen most clearly in island environments.

Brief Review

(Answers are in the back of the book.)

1. State the biological species concept.

2. Why is gene flow central to both microevolution and the macroevolutionary process of speciation?

3. Why is the evolution of intrinsic reproductive isolation mechanisms required for two groups to be called separate species? Why isn't simple geographical isolation sufficient?

4. Describe one major difference between allopatric and sympatric speciation. What is one thing that they have in common?

5. What is convergent evolution, and why is it a problem for phylogenetic analyses?

Applying Your Knowledge

1. Living things are classified into a set of hierarchical categories. Why is this more useful to biologists than simply giving everything a one-word name (or a number) and eliminating some of the categories?

2. Populations of some kinds of organisms may be isolated by a barrier as small as a roadway, while other organisms require a much larger physical barrier to block gene flow. What features of organisms might determine how readily they become geographically isolated? What impact might these features have on how often or how rapidly speciation is likely to occur in these groups?

3. In an adaptive radiation, one species may colonize a previously empty environment, such as an island, and diversify evolutionarily into a set of closely related species that occupy a very wide range of habitats. For example, with Darwin's finches on the Galapagos Islands, one species fills the role of woodpecker by using a stick to tap on trees and dig out insects. Do you think that such a species would have been likely to evolve in an area that already had woodpeckers? Why or why not?

21

Viruses, Bacteria, Archaea, and Protists:

The Diversity of Life 1

Across its categories, life is stunningly diverse. Some of the most interesting living things are microscopic.

The single-celled microscopic algae known as diatoms possess outer cell walls, made of silica, that come in a fantastic variety of geometric forms. This color-enhanced micrograph is of the diatom *Cyclotella pseudostelligera*, which lives in both fresh and brackish water.

The smallest living thing discovered to date is a type of bacteria that measures about two-tenths of a micrometer in diameter—that is, two-tenths of one-millionth of a meter in diameter. When we turn to the biggest living thing, elephants or whales might come to mind, but it turns out that animals aren't even in the running for this title. At a maximum length of about 89 feet, the blue whale is the largest animal that has ever existed, but it's small compared to California's coastal redwood trees, which might reach a height of 330 feet. This is large indeed, but consider that a giant sea kelp once was found that was about 900 feet long. It may be, though, that in terms of size, both kelp and redwoods have to take a backseat to a life-form normally thought of as quite small. In 1992, researchers reported finding a fungus growing in Washington state that runs underground through an area of 1,500 acres and that arguably is a single organism.

Now, how about the *deepest* living things? The current record holders are bacteria that were found in the early 1990s—in a combination of oil drilling and scientific exploration—living almost 1.9 miles beneath Earth's surface. Food and water are so scarce at such depths that these bacterial cells may live in a kind of suspended animation, dividing perhaps once a year or even once a century. Turning to the highest living things, 12 species of bacteria have been found living in the Himalayas at 27,000 feet above sea level, which is just a couple thousand feet lower than the peak of Mount Everest. A species of chickweed survives in the Himalayas at more than 20,000 feet.

All kinds of life-forms—clams, tube worms, crabs—live kilometers beneath the surface of the oceans, near the "hot-water vents" that spew out water and minerals from the Earth's interior onto the ocean floor. Microbes from a group called archaea, living at these deep-sea vents, set the pace for life in a hot environment. An average, midday temperature in the Sahara Desert would be so *cold* it would end the reproduction of the archaeon *Pyrolobus fumarii,* which lives within hot-water vents at temperatures of up to 113°C, which is hotter than the temperature at which water boils. At the other extreme, the well-named bacterium *Phormidium frigidum* carries out photosynthesis in lakes in Antarctica whose temperatures sit right at the point at which water freezes.

Finally, what about the oldest living things? Humans have been known to live to 120, but this is an eyeblink compared to the lives of some plants. There is a bristlecone pine tree (*Pinus longaeva*) that has been living in the dry slopes of eastern California for 4,900 years, meaning it has been alive since the pharaohs ruled Egypt. For many years, this "Methuselah" tree was believed to be the oldest in the world, but in 2008 scientists performed carbon-14 dating on a set of spruce trees growing in the mountains of western Sweden and found that they are 8,000 years old. All trees, however, are mere youngsters compared to some microbes, which can survive in a form called spores for immensely long periods of time. In the 1990s, bacterial spores were found living within a bee that had been encased in amber for 25 to 40 million years. Even this eye-popping number did not prepare scientists for what came next, however. In 2000, researchers announced that they had found, encased within salt crystals at the bottom of a New Mexico air shaft, archaeal spores that date from 250 million years ago. These spores were revived, and billions of their offspring now exist. This claim has been controversial from the time it was made; one possibility is that the crystal sample the researchers were looking at was contaminated with modern DNA. But if true, it raises the question of whether some microbes are "effectively immortal," as one researcher has put it.

Looking at life like this—at its biggest or deepest or oldest extremes—is one way to get at its incredible diversity. But it does not begin to do justice to life's variety because life is diverse in so many ways. Honeybees do a "dance" to let their hive-mates know the location of a food supply. Corn plants, when attacked by army worms, can call in an air force: The plants release an airborne substance that attracts parasitic wasps, which then prey on the worms. Pacific salmon live for years in the ocean, only to make one arduous, upstream journey to spawn in the waters where they were born, after which they die. Look closely at almost

Figure 21.1
An Amazing Diversity in the Living World

(a) Mouse beneath the foot of an elephant

(b) A lion nudibranch moving across a giant kelp blade

(c) Fungus growing on a fallen log

(d) Water flea swimming near green algae

any creature, and you are likely to find something only slightly less dramatic (**Figure 21.1**).

21.1 Life's Categories and the Importance of Microbes

The purpose of this chapter and the three that follow is to introduce you to life as it exists across all its large-scale categories. As you may recall from Chapter 19, all living things can be placed into one of three *domains* of life. Two of these domains are Archaea and Bacteria, whose members are all single-celled and microscopic. The third domain, Eukarya, encompasses such incredible diversity that it is further divided into four separate *kingdoms*. These are the kingdoms of plants, animals, fungi, and a group of mostly microscopic organisms called protists. We will begin our tour of the living world by starting small, looking in this chapter at Domains Bacteria and Archaea and at the protists within Domain Eukarya. Then, we'll look at fungi in Chapter 22, animals in Chapter 23, and plants in Chapter 24.

Figure 21.2 shows the evolutionary relationships among all three domains of life and the kinds of organisms that are part of each domain.

Because this chapter is devoted to mostly unfamiliar *microbes*—meaning living things so small they can't be seen with the naked eye—it might be helpful to say a word at the start about their significance. Microbes are something like the foundation of a house: seldom thought of but critically important. To the extent that they cross our minds at all, we are aware of them mostly for the diseases they cause. This is an important topic—one we'll go into extensively—but thinking of microbes strictly as disease-causing organisms is like thinking of cars strictly as wreck-causing machines. Where does the oxygen we breathe come from? If your answer is "plants," that's partly correct. But the photosynthesis carried out by plants supplies less than half our oxygen; the balance comes from microscopic algae and bacteria—mostly drifters on the ocean's surface. How about the nitrogen that is indispensable to all plants and animals? Among living things, only bacteria and archaea are capable of

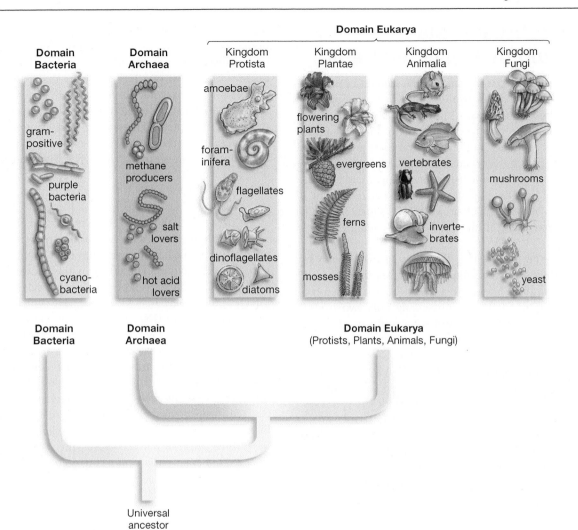

Figure 21.2
The Tree of Life
Life is presumed to have developed from a single common ancestor (represented by the base of the tree), which gave rise to the three domains of the living world: Bacteria, Archaea, and Eukarya.

taking nitrogen that exists in the air and transforming it into a form that plants can use. If there were no bacteria and archaea, there would be no plants—and consequently no land animals. And how is it that dead tree branches, orange peels, or the bones of animals are broken down and recycled into the Earth? Almost entirely through the work of bacteria and fungi. Without these organisms, Earth would long ago have become a garbage heap of dead, organic matter. Animals cannot decompose a dead tree branch, but bacteria and fungi can.

The upshot of all this is that life on Earth would grind to a halt without microbes; they are an essential underpinning to all forms of life. They come to this status in part because of the environments they live in, which is to say all environments on Earth that support life of any kind. It probably didn't escape your attention that the coldest-, hottest-, highest-, and deepest-living things were all bacteria or archaea. Wherever a plant or animal can live, microbes can be found, too.

Just as impressive is the sheer number and tonnage of these tiny organisms. A common denominator for measuring the amount of living material is something called *biomass,* defined as the total dry weight of material produced by a given organism. Each bacterium or microscopic alga has an infinitesimally small weight, of course—but then again, there are so many of them! It has been estimated that there are more bacteria living in your mouth now than the number of people who have ever lived, and there are far more bacterial cells in the human body than there are human cells (a topic we'll return to). A typical gram of fertile soil—about a quarter teaspoon's worth of material—has about 100 million bacteria living in it, and a mere drop of water near the ocean's surface contains thousands of the tiny algae called phytoplankton. All this adds up. When the calculations are done, we find that microbes probably make up more than half of Earth's biomass. Put another way, the microbes of the world outweigh all the plants, animals, and visible fungi of the world combined.

In sum, microbes matter, and not just in ways that are harmful. We'll now start to look at the portion of the living world that is made up of them. Our first stop on this tour, however, will be a category of tiny replicating entities that most biologists would say lie just outside of life, although they have a great effect on living things.

21.2 Viruses: Making a Living by Hijacking Cells

If a living thing is too small to be seen and can cause disease, most people would put it in the vague category known as "germs." But there is a fundamental distinction to be made between *two* kinds of infectious organisms. On the one hand there are bacteria, which may be very small but nevertheless are *cells,* complete with a protein-producing apparatus, a mechanism for extracting energy from the environment, a means of getting rid of waste—in short, complete with everything it takes to be a self-contained living thing.

On the other hand, there are *viruses,* which by themselves possess none of these features. Indeed, viruses can be likened to a thief who arrives at a factory he intends to rob possessing only two things: the tools to get inside and some software that will make the factory turn out items he can use. The factory being broken into is a living cell, and the software that the virus brings is its DNA or RNA, which it puts inside this "host" cell. Once this is accomplished, viruses employ different tactics, as you'll see, but in most cases the result is that viruses make more copies of themselves. Viruses are an integral part of the living world, and not all of them cause harm. But unlike the case with bacteria, it's right to think of them first and foremost in terms of the diseases they cause, not only in humans but in every variety of living thing. **Viruses** are noncellular replicating entities that must invade living cells to carry out their replication.

HIV: The AIDS Virus

If you look at **Figure 21.3a**, you can see a simplified rendering of a particular virus, the human immunodeficiency virus (HIV), which is the cause of AIDS. All viruses have two of the three large-scale structures you can see in HIV: the genetic material at the core (in HIV's case, two strands of RNA) and a protein coat, called a **capsid,** that surrounds the viral genetic material. Many viruses then go on to have a third major element—a fatty membrane, called an *envelope,* which you can see surrounding the HIV capsid. Protruding from the HIV envelope are a series of receptors, often referred to as "spikes," which are proteins capped with carbohydrate chains. These serve the critical role of binding with receptors that protrude from the target cell, thus giving the virus a way to get in.

If you look at **Figure 21.3b**, you can see how the life cycle of HIV proceeds from this initial binding. The target cell in this case is the one most commonly invaded by HIV, an immune system cell called a helper T-cell (also known as a CD-4 cell). As you can see, once HIV binds with two receptors on the T-cell's surface, the viral envelope fuses with the T-cell membrane. With this, HIV's capsid, with the genetic material enclosed, is inside the cell. Once there, the capsid disintegrates. Now two HIV enzymes that had been enclosed in the capsid get to work. If you look at Figure 21.3a, you can see these enzymes, integrase and reverse transcriptase. The reverse transcriptase gets busy first, using HIV's RNA strands as a template to produce double-stranded viral DNA. Then integrase does just what its name implies: It integrates the viral DNA into the *cell's* DNA through a cut-and-paste operation.

At this point, the viral DNA might simply stay integrated in the T-cell's DNA, causing no great harm but getting copied, along with the cell's DNA, each time the cell divides. The effect of this, however, is that every "daughter" cell of this infected cell will be infected too; each new cell will have viral DNA spliced into its own DNA. Each of these cells then has a time bomb ticking within it because at some point the HIV DNA will change course. It will no longer simply go on replicating within the cell's DNA. Instead, it will start turning out the materials necessary to make whole new copies of the virus. As you can see in the figure, virus construction takes place just inside the cell's outer membrane (helped along by a third enzyme that HIV brought with it, protease). This location is important because the cell's membrane ends up serving as the final structural part of each new viral copy or "particle." When the capsid is completed, it buds off from the cell, taking with it part of the cell's membrane, which now becomes the capsid's envelope. The completed viral particle that emerges from the cell then goes on to infect other cells.

Helper T-cells that produce new viral particles in this way may be targeted for destruction by the immune system (since they are infected cells). Beyond this, HIV receptors that have become detached from the virus can land on the surface of *un*infected helper T-cells, thus causing them to initiate a kind of cellular suicide known as programmed cell death. Once both these processes have been set in motion, the result is a greatly reduced population of helper T-cells—a potentially calamitous event since these cells are central to the body's immune system response. A person whose helper-T cell-count has dropped below a certain minimum level loses the ability to fight off everyday infections caused by bacteria, fungi, and viruses other than HIV.

Viral Diversity

In the HIV life cycle, you can see four steps that are common to most viruses: Get genetic material inside the host cell, turn out viral component parts, construct new particles from these parts, and move these particles out of the cell. HIV uses RNA as its genetic

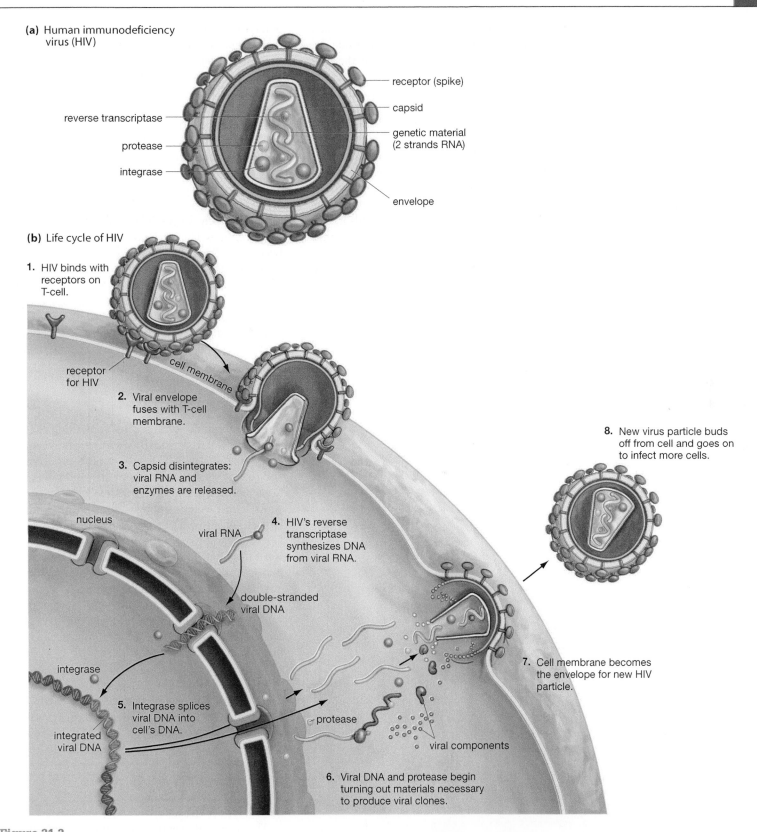

(a) Human immunodeficiency virus (HIV)

receptor (spike)

reverse transcriptase

capsid

protease

genetic material
(2 strands RNA)

integrase

envelope

(b) Life cycle of HIV

1. HIV binds with receptors on T-cell.

receptor for HIV

cell membrane

2. Viral envelope fuses with T-cell membrane.

3. Capsid disintegrates: viral RNA and enzymes are released.

nucleus

viral RNA

4. HIV's reverse transcriptase synthesizes DNA from viral RNA.

double-stranded viral DNA

integrase

5. Integrase splices viral DNA into cell's DNA.

integrated viral DNA

protease

viral components

6. Viral DNA and protease begin turning out materials necessary to produce viral clones.

7. Cell membrane becomes the envelope for new HIV particle.

8. New virus particle buds off from cell and goes on to infect more cells.

Figure 21.3
The Virus That Causes AIDS
The anatomy and life cycle of HIV, the human immunodeficiency virus.

material, but many viruses use DNA. Viruses that lack an envelope don't get their genetic material inside the cell by fusing with the cell's membrane in the way HIV does. In **Figure 21.4**, you can see a spacecraft-shaped virus called T4 that infects bacteria through an alternate means. T4 keeps its capsid outside the target cell but gets its DNA inside by injecting it through the bacterium's cell wall and membrane.

As you might be able to tell from the size of T4 compared to its target cell, viruses are very small things. Thousands of them can typically fit within a bacterial cell. Some amount to nothing but their genetic material and the capsid that surrounds it, and there are even virus-like entities, called *viroids,* that lack a capsid; they are simply small strands of infectious RNA. What viruses lack in size, however, they

make up in numbers. One researcher has calculated that a typical milliliter—a thousandth of a liter—of ocean water has 10 million virus particles in it. If so, then ocean-going viruses contain as much as 270 million metric tons of carbon, which is more than 20 times the amount of carbon contained in all the whales in the world.

In every case, viruses are not only small but *simple* things compared to the organisms they infect. First, they lack the usual machinery that cells have—a protein assembly line, a waste disposal system, and so forth. Even when we look at the one thing all of them do have, which is genetic material, they are still very simple entities. Human beings are thought to have between 20,000 and 25,000 genes, and even a primitive organism like baker's yeast has 6,000 genes. But the AIDS virus? It has nine genes. To be sure, some viruses are more complex than HIV, but in no case is a virus complex enough to replicate by itself. Because viruses can carry on scarcely any of life's basic functions by themselves, most scientists don't classify them as living things.

The Influenza Viruses

But what trouble is caused by something that isn't even alive! Apart from AIDS, viruses are responsible for polio, measles, chickenpox, rabies, herpes, rubella, and some forms of cancer, hepatitis, and pneumonia, to say nothing of common colds.

As if this weren't enough, there are the influenza viruses, which come in common forms that cause a fair amount of trouble each year—in the form of seasonal flus—but which also come in uncommon forms that can throw societies into full-blown states of alarm. In 2009, for example, countries around the world took extraordinary measures to prevent the spread of an influenza virus properly known as H1N1, but referred to in the early days of its outbreak as swine flu (**Figure 21.5**).

In the United States, about 11,700 Americans died from H1N1 from its emergence in April 2009 through mid-January 2010—a large number of deaths to be sure, but about 24,000 *fewer* deaths than typically result from seasonal flu in the United States each year. So why did H1N1 cause such widespread anxiety? Because some classes of viruses carry more potential danger than others and H1N1 was a threatening member of a very dangerous viral class—the influenza type A viruses.

The twentieth century saw three *pandemics,* or worldwide outbreaks of fatal disease, that were caused by influenza A viruses. One of these, in 1957, killed between 1 and 4 million people, while another, in 1968, killed about a million people. Both paled in comparison, however, to an outbreak that occurred in

**Figure 21.4
Another Variety
of Virus**

(a) The T4 virus looks like a spacecraft that has landed on the surface of a bacterium.

(b) A viral invader lands. An artificially colored T4 virus injects its DNA into an *Escherichia coli* bacterium (in blue).

(a)

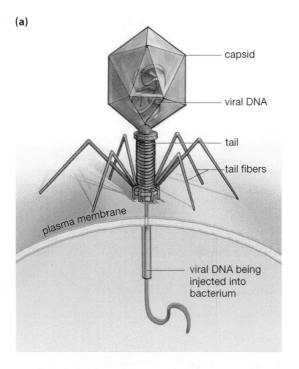

capsid

viral DNA

tail

tail fibers

plasma membrane

viral DNA being injected into bacterium

(b)

1918–1919. That pandemic is estimated to have infected a third of the people then living in the world and to have killed 50 million of them. (By way of comparison, AIDS took a quarter century to kill 25 million people.) When H1N1 first surfaced in Mexico and the United States, it was immediately recognized as an influenza A virus that shared several characteristics of the twentieth-century's killer influenzas: It contained a mixture of genes so novel that people were unlikely to have any natural immunity to it; it spread easily from one person to another; and its effects could be lethal—of the first 26 people known to have contracted it in Mexico, 7 died from it.

Given these characteristics, the initial reactions of public health officials to the H1N1 outbreak now seem understandable. Even so, we might ask how these experts managed to be taken by surprise by the appearance of a virus as potentially catastrophic as this one. The answer is that many influenza A viruses are likely to come as a surprise to experts because of the way these viruses evolve. Though all of them are assumed to originate in aquatic birds, they can move between several animal species and they can combine with each other in new ways *within* animal species. Two different viruses that commonly circulate among, say, human beings and birds will infect a population of pigs and exchange genetic sequences with one another during this infection. The result? A new virus that is different from either of the parental varieties. This process of *reassortment,* as it's called, was on full display in the evolution of the H1N1 virus. It contained two genes that came originally from an "avian" or bird influenza virus that infected swine in 1979, three genes from a swine virus that was first isolated in 1930, two genes from human and avian viruses that reassorted in swine in the 1990s, and one gene that came from humans after being transmitted to them from birds in 1968.

It would be nice to report that a mind-bogglingly complex pattern of evolution such as this is only seen in viruses like H1N1, but that's not the case. Influenza A viruses in general evolve in this way, which is why, even in their less dangerous forms, these infectious agents join the influenza B viruses in giving societies a predictable problem to deal with each year: The need for annual flu vaccinations. Last year's flu vaccine will not protect anyone against this year's viruses because this year's threat is a set of recently evolved viral "strains" or subtypes. Ultimately, society is helpless to prevent the emergence of harmful influenzas because new strains of them are generated so quickly in so many different ways. The best we can do is to keep close tabs on the animals that commonly serve as influenza hosts and to put in place containment responses that can be ramped up quickly when the time comes.

Figure 21.5
Trying to Prevent a Pandemic

An employee of the Richardson, Texas school district sprays an antimicrobial solution on the Canyon Creek Elementary School in April 2009. The school closed for several days after two of its students contracted H1N1 flu.

SO FAR . . .

1. The three domains of life are _____, _____, and Eukarya. The four kingdoms within Eukarya are composed of _____, _____, _____, and _____.

2. Microbes perform several activities that are critical to the maintenance of other life-forms on Earth. Name three of these activities.

3. In order to replicate, viruses must invade _____.

21.3 Bacteria: Masters of Every Environment

Domain Bacteria is made up entirely of the microbes called bacteria. Keeping in mind that almost all the organisms we're looking at are microbes, what separates bacteria from any of the others? Recall from Chapter 4 that if we set a bacterial cell and, say, a fungal cell side by side, anyone peering through a microscope could see a fundamental difference between the two. The fungal cell would have a large, circular-shaped structure near its center, while the bacterial cell would not. The circular structure is the fungal cell's nucleus, which contains almost all of its DNA. But bacteria are

ESSAY

Good News in the Fight Against Herpes

The first outbreak usually is the worst, but the real problem is that the first outbreak usually isn't the last. Herpes comes back, as herpes sufferers well know. A few weeks or months after the initial outbreak, everything seems fine, but then there may be a tingling—nothing that can be seen yet, but instead just a feeling. Not much later, however, it's back: the same unsightly "cold sore" on the mouth or lesions on the genitals, in the same place that the first outbreak occurred.

This sequence of events is depressingly familiar to millions of Americans. And at present, the best medical treatment available to any of them is a drug called Acyclovir, which can shorten the duration and frequency of herpes outbreaks but which cannot eliminate herpes from the body altogether. In 2008, however, researchers at Duke University made a fundamental breakthrough against herpes: They discovered the means by which the virus that causes it hides from the human immune system. With this knowledge in hand, pharmaceutical researchers began working on a drug that essentially will force the herpes virus to show itself in all its hiding places. Any virus that is flushed out in this way is vulnerable to being eradicated from the body.

The term "herpes virus" is shorthand for a pair of viruses, the *herpes simplex viruses,* which in turn are part of a group of 100 known viruses in the herpes family. (Other viruses in the family cause chicken pox, shingles, and the Epstein-Barr disease.) Herpes simplex viruses come in type 1 and type 2 varieties. The type 1 variety supposedly is "oral," while the type 2 is "genital." But either variety can end up in either location because of oral sex.

The herpes sores that can be so distressing are the result of newly formed virus particles breaking out of skin cells, thereby destroying them. Fever, swollen glands, and other symptoms often accompany these lesions, particularly in an initial infection. Within a couple of weeks or so, however, the immune system (or a drug like Acyclovir) has killed all the virus particles in and around the skin cells, and the symptoms are gone. The problem is that, by this time, the virus has also infected *nerve* cells in the area. Such nerve cells (or neurons) have long extensions of themselves called axons. With the initial infection, herpes virus particles start making a slow migration up these axons to the *body* of the nerve cells, specifically to the nucleus inside the cell body. In the case of genital herpes, this means a journey from the vagina or penis to cell bodies that sit right at the base of the spinal cord. And these cell bodies are where the virus stays—permanently. Once there, it does next to nothing; it's not causing any nerve damage or replicating. And the nerve cells it is in never divide, so it isn't passed on to a larger group of cells.

This lack of activity is, however, the essence of the problem with herpes. Most viruses are *active* inside the cells they infect; they produce viral proteins, fragments of which end up being displayed on the surfaces of infected cells. These fragments serve as signals to the immune system, conveying the message "Infected cell here; begin attack." The herpes virus, however, avoids all this by staying silent—it produces no proteins at all. It is this lack of viral productivity that the researchers from Duke figured out. They discovered that, in an infected cell, the herpes virus actually is active in one major way: It produces a length of RNA that then is processed into four *micro*-RNAs, which is to say RNAs that *prevent* the production of proteins.

Indeed, micro-RNAs often end up cutting up the messenger RNAs that are required for the production of any protein. Thus, the herpes virus silences itself inside cells; it undercuts its own production of viral proteins.

The only change in this series of events comes when the virus senses that the cell it's part of is threatened in some way—say, by the body having acquired a cold. Now the virus' production of proteins overwhelms the micro-RNA control system. The result? Newly made viral particles leave the infected cell—in a manner that one researcher has compared to rats deserting a sinking ship—and migrate back up the cell's axon and end up at the same old place in skin cells on the lips or the genitals. With this, the body has a new herpes outbreak. (Since a cold is capable of bringing this sequence of events on, you can see why herpes lesions are sometimes referred to as cold sores.) A drug like Acyclovir can kill all the virus particles in any of these outbreaks. The problem is that not all of the body's infected cells go through this cycle at the same *time;* the virus remains latent in some cells even while it has become active in others. Thus, there is no point at which the virus is showing itself in all of the body's infected cells. As a result, in any given person, the herpes virus always perseveres to break out another day—at least for now, but perhaps not in the future.

With the discovery made at Duke, pharmaceutical researchers began trying to develop a drug that will stop the production of herpes micro-RNAs. Any drug that could do this should theoretically *initiate* the production of herpes proteins. Once this happens, each infected cell could be identified as infected by the immune system and Acyclovir, and that could spell the end of herpes throughout the body. Only time will tell whether this sequence of events actually will unfold, but at the moment, promising anti-herpes compounds are being tested for safety in animals.

prokaryotes: organisms whose DNA is not contained within a cell nucleus. Only bacteria and archaea lack a nucleus. All other organisms—all plants, animals, fungi, and protists—are composed of cells that have a nucleus, which makes them **eukaryotes.** The lack of a cell nucleus is, however, just one defining feature of bacteria. Here is a list of others.

- **No membrane-bound organelles.** A nucleus is an example of an *organelle:* a highly organized structure within a cell that carries out specific cellular functions. You may remember from Chapter 4 that, in addition to a nucleus, eukaryotic cells have such organelles as mitochondria and lysosomes, which are surrounded by a membrane. Bacteria have only a single kind of organelle, the ribosome, which differs from other organelles in that it is not surrounded by a membrane.

- **Single-celled organisms with small cell size.** Bacteria often come together in groupings that have an organization to them, but each bacterial cell is a self-contained living thing—each one can live and reproduce without the aid of other cells. Most bacterial cells are also very small, relative to eukaryotic cells; thousands of them could typically fit into a single eukaryotic cell. (If you look at **Figure 21.6,** you can see a size comparison of bacteria, a T4 virus, and a protist you'll be looking at called a paramecium.)

bacteria *(E. coli)*
2 µm long

viral particles (T4)
0.2 µm long

protist *(Paramecium)*
75 µm long

Figure 21.6
Small Is a Relative Thing
The bacteria, protist, and viral particles shown in the figure are all microscopic. Nevertheless, they differ greatly among themselves in terms of size. A typical human cell might be about a third the size of the *Paramecium*.

- **Asexual reproduction.** Bacteria reproduce through a form of simple cell splitting called **binary fission:** one cell splits into two, with both "daughter" cells being genetic replicas of the parental cell. In contrast, most eukaryotes are capable of sexual reproduction, in which reproductive cells from two separate organisms come together to produce offspring (as with egg and sperm coming together in human reproduction).

If you look at **Figure 21.7,** you can see micrographs of three forms that bacterial cells commonly take: round, rod shaped, and spiral shaped. A round bacterium is known as a *coccus;* a rod-shaped bacterium is a *bacillus;* and a spiral-shaped bacterium goes under

(a) Round bacteria (cocci)

(b) Rod-shaped bacteria (bacilli)

(c) Spiral-shaped bacterium (spirochete)

Figure 21.7
Different Shapes of Bacteria

(a) The round bacterium *Staphylococcus epidermis* is a normal part of the bacteria that cover our skin.

(b) The rod-shaped bacterium *Bacillus anthracis* is the cause of the deadly disease anthrax.

(c) The spiral-shaped bacterium *Leptospira interrogans* often infects rodents, sometimes infects dogs, and occasionally infects human beings.

a variety of names, the best known of which is a *spirochete*. Different species of bacteria fit into all three groups.

Almost all bacteria have a structure called a cell wall at their periphery that is largely composed of a material called peptidoglycan. This may seem like a technical detail, but the fact that bacteria have cell walls is of great importance to humans because it represents a *difference* between bacterial cells and human cells. As you'll see, we humans have exploited this difference in our development of the medical drugs known as antibiotics.

Bacterial Numbers and Diversity

In 2006, scientists reported on a bacterial census they undertook by means of looking for bacterial DNA sequences within tiny quantities of soil from Alaska. The result? Each gram of soil contained about 4,000 different species of bacteria. Meanwhile, a comparative analysis indicated that a gram of Minnesota farm soil contained about 10,000 bacterial species. Fascinatingly, only about 20 percent of the species the researchers identified were present in the soils of *both* states. You might think that surveys such as these could give us a handle on how many bacterial species there are in total, but so far that's not the case. We really have no idea how many different kinds of bacteria there are in the world; the most we can say is that the number appears to be very large.

When we begin to examine these various types of bacteria, we find that an incredible diversity exists among them. It may seem strange to think of bacteria as "diverse," given that all of them are microscopic and single-celled. But physical form is only one kind of diversity. Imagine that only some human beings got their nutrition in the conventional way—by ingesting food—while others could make their own food by carrying out photosynthesis. Bacteria do things both ways. Imagine that only some human beings needed oxygen to live, while others could take it or leave it, and still others were poisoned by it. Bacteria fit into all three categories. Animals and plants have diverse forms, but bacteria have diverse metabolisms.

21.4 Intimate Strangers: Humans and Bacteria

In the chapter introduction, you saw how bacteria are indispensable to life in general because they can capture atmospheric nitrogen, decompose dead organic material, and so forth. As it turns out, however, bacteria may be indispensable to *human* life in an even more direct way. From the time we travel down our

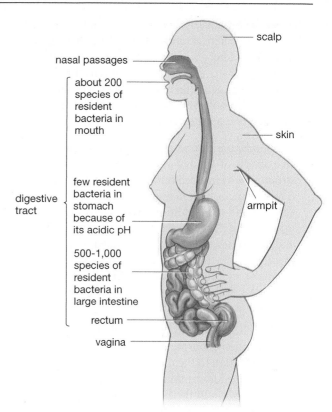

Figure 21.8
At Home in Us
We human beings live with trillions of "resident" bacteria, meaning bacteria that are always present on us or within us. Bacteria on the scalp or skin might temporarily be washed away, but they quickly return.

mother's birth canal, we enter into a lifelong interdependence with these microorganisms. If you look at **Figure 21.8**, you can see the places bacteria are found in quantity outside and inside the human body. Outside, we are covered in bacteria from head to toe, with heavy concentrations in the armpits and scalp. Inside, they exist in our nasal passages, in the vaginas of females, and most especially, in our digestive tracts. All told, perhaps 100 trillion bacterial cells live in or on the human body. Meanwhile, the number of *human* cells in a human body is only a tenth of this number—about 10 trillion cells. (So why aren't we bloated with bacterial cells? They're so small that their collective weight is only about 3 pounds.) This is not to say that bacteria are everywhere within us; most of our tissues are kept bacteria free, except for occasional invaders. But about half the contents of our colon are bacteria, as are perhaps a fourth of our feces by weight. These are not transient varieties of bacteria that come for brief periods and then are gone. They are so-called resident bacteria whose permanent home is the human body.

This account may make you feel like you've been colonized, but the relationship between us and many of the bacteria we harbor actually is one of **mutualism,** which is to say a relationship between two organisms that benefits both of them. If we could shrink ourselves down to the size of a bacterium and enter, say, the human large intestine, we would see a community of competing but *interdependent* organisms, most of which are bacteria, but one of which is us. What bacteria get from participating in this community is food and habitat. What humans get is a fully functional digestive system. How do we know that bacteria are helping maintain this system? Consider that rats whose bacteria have been wiped out through laboratory techniques require 30 percent more calories to maintain their body weight than do normal rats. Without bacteria, the structure of these rats' intestines is altered in a way that's unhealthy: They have low numbers of the cells that move nutrients from the digestive tract to the bloodstream. Researchers have made mice "germ free," then reintroduced bacteria into them and watched as mouse genes were turned on that help metabolize sugars and fats. Bacteria even metabolize sugars that we cannot digest, and they produce some vitamins as well. The essential message here is that, within the digestive tract, mammals and bacteria have had such a long working relationship that each has become dependent on the other.

21.5 Bacteria and Human Disease

Many of our resident bacteria are not beneficial to us but instead are *commensal* with us—they benefit from the relationship, while we are unaffected by it. And, of course, there are bacteria that are **pathogenic,** which is to say disease-causing. These are not bacteria that routinely inhabit any part of our body in large numbers. Instead, they are opportunists that invade specific tissues. Among the diseases they cause are tuberculosis, syphilis, gonorrhea, cholera, tetanus, leprosy, typhoid fever, and diphtheria, not to mention all manner of food poisonings and blood-borne infections. In the fourteenth century, the bacterially caused bubonic plague wiped out a *third* of Europe's population in just 4 years. Closer to home, you may recall a substance referred to as *anthrax* that was maliciously mailed to various offices after the September 11, 2001, attacks. Anthrax actually is a bacterium (*Bacillus anthracis*) that, in nature, occasionally infects farm animals.

How do pathogenic bacteria cause illness? A few invade human cells and reproduce there. More often, however, bacterial damage comes from substances bacteria either secrete or leave behind when they die. These compounds are *toxins,* which is to say substances that harmfully alter living tissue or interfere with biological processes. In the case of respiratory anthrax, *Bacillus anthracis* secretes a trio of toxins that

cause blood vessels in the lungs and brain to "hemorrhage" or leak. The botulism bacterium, *Clostridium botulinum,* secretes a toxin that blocks the signals that go from nerves to muscles. The end result can be paralysis of the muscles that control the diaphragm, in which case victims lose the ability to breathe. Of course, all pathogenic bacteria must have a way to get into the body in the first place. The bacterium that causes bubonic plague, *Yersinia pestis,* enters on the bite of a flea, while the tetanus bacterium, *Clostridium tetani,* may hitch a ride in on a rusty nail. Meanwhile, the tuberculosis bacterium, *Mycobacterium tuberculosis,* can simply be inhaled.

Killing Pathogenic Bacteria: Antibiotics

Prior to the 1930s, doctors were nearly powerless to stop any of these bacterial invaders. Some progress was made in the late 1930s with the development of the synthetic chemicals called sulfa drugs. But modern medicine was born in the 1940s with the development of **antibiotics,** meaning chemical compounds produced by one microorganism that are toxic to another microorganism. The first antibiotic, penicillin, was a substance produced by a fungus. Like all antibiotics, it had two critical qualities: It could kill microorganisms within human beings while leaving the humans themselves unharmed. (For an account of penicillin's development, see "The Discovery of Penicillin" on page 398.)

How can antibiotics be toxic to bacteria but not to people? They exploit the differences between bacterial cells and human cells. Remember earlier when we noted that almost all bacteria have cell walls, while human cells don't? Penicillin and several other antibiotics work by blocking cell-wall construction, which bacteria have to undertake when they divide. Penicillin confiscates a construction tool; it binds with a bacterial enzyme that helps stitch the cell wall together. A bacterium without a cell wall is doomed: It ruptures, floods, and dies. But the *human* cells around it—lacking cell walls—are left unharmed.

It is hard to overstate how much of human health hinges today on antibiotic processes such as these. If you know anyone who was alive in the 1930s, they may well have had friends or relatives who died of tuberculosis or one of the staphylococcal infections better known as blood poisoning. But do you know of anyone who, during your lifetime, has died of such an illness? Probably not. Antibiotics have made all the difference.

The Threat of Antibiotic Resistance

This power of antibiotics ought to spark alarm in us about something that is happening today, which is that antibiotics are steadily *losing* their ability to kill bacteria. How could this happen? An estimated 30 percent of antibiotic prescriptions written today are thought to be needless, in the sense that the person taking the antibiotic doesn't even have a bacterial infection but rather is suffering from a viral or other illness. (So, why do people get such prescriptions? They ask their doctors for them, and the doctors go along.) Even when people do have bacterial infections, they often take their antibiotics only until they start feeling better, rather than following through with the full course of recommended treatment, which can last weeks or even months.

Those of you who have read through the chapters on evolution may be able to see what this leads to. Normal bacteria may be wiped out by a needlessly short course of antibiotics. But a few bacteria will survive these inadequate treatments because they have sets of genes that allow them to do so. In the *absence* of antibiotics, these survivors might not have had anything special going for them. (They aren't *generally* superior bacteria; they just resist antibiotics better.) But with antibiotics, these survivors have been left without bacterial competitors for food and habitat. As a result, they flourish, giving rise to antibiotic-resistant *lines* of bacteria. Moreover, they will do this rapidly since one generation of bacteria can give rise to another in as little as 20 minutes.

Other factors also enter into this picture. It may surprise you to learn that nearly half the antibiotics used in the United States don't go into people at all; they are put into animal feeds because they serve as growth stimulants. In a similar vein, farmers spray huge tracts of fruit trees with antibiotics to ward off bacterial infections. Then among consumer products there are antibacterial hand-cleaners, which, according to a panel convened by the U.S. Food and Drug Administration, are no more effective than plain soap in reducing the spread of infections.

Methicillin-Resistant Staph

The upshot of this overuse of antibiotics is that bacterial infectious diseases are making a comeback. The problem is most pressing in hospitals, where physicians are seeing one formerly useful drug after another fail to cure infections. But antibiotic-resistant infections aren't limited to hospitals anymore. Indeed, they're now turning up in some settings that usually are brimming with health: high school and college locker rooms.

Students who participate in contact sports have always been subject to skin infections caused by the bacterium *Staphylococcus aureus*. In the past, these infections could easily be cured by a family of antibiotics that includes methicillin. What's now appeared, however, is the bacterium known as methicillin-resistant *Staphylococcus aureus*, or MRSA. Once seen almost entirely in the very old, the very young, or those with weakened immune systems, "methicillin-resistant staph" is now showing up in the general populace. Athletes are particularly prone to MRSA infections because one route to acquiring them is to make contact with an infected individual through a break in the skin—something that could easily happen during sporting events. To be sure, MRSA has mostly caused mild, though persistent, infections among the athletes it has affected. Nevertheless, the fact that an otherwise healthy group of young people is now having to deal with a general threat of bacterial infection ought to give society pause about what it is doing with antibiotics. If we can't stay ahead of bacterial evolution by developing new antibiotics—while cutting back on the needless use of existing ones—we may find ourselves returning to the days of our grandparents, when a simple cut could be life-threatening.

21.6 Archaea: From Marginal Player to Center Stage

At one time, almost all biology textbooks referred to the archaea as archae*bacteria,* and most mentioned these microbes as a kind of marginal life-form, existing in only a few extreme habitats, such as hot-water pools. Today, the archaea are recognized as constituting their own domain in life—standing alongside Domains Bacteria and Eukarya—and they're known to exist in large numbers in many environments. So, why were the archaea lumped together with bacteria for so long, and what kind of environments do they actually live in? Let's take these questions in order.

The Separate Status of Domain Archaea

Even under the microscope, archaea really are similar to bacteria in some ways. All of them are single-celled, and all of them are prokaryotes that reproduce through simple cell splitting. Since we saw these same qualities in bacteria, why do the archaea constitute their own domain of life?

To answer this question, let's think about what is *fundamentally* different in organisms as opposed to what is *superficially* different in them. Remember the cell wall we talked about that forms the outer boundary of most bacterial cells? As it turns out, archaea have cell walls too, but their cell walls do not contain the peptidoglycan found in bacterial cells—nor the cellulose found in plant cells, nor the chitin found in fungal cells. The materials that make up archaeal cell walls are unique to the archaea. To understand the importance of this, imagine that you are a construction worker who is inspecting the outer walls of some houses. You do a little scraping and discover that one house has a wall that is made from a material you've never seen before. You'd rightly regard this as a fundamental difference between this house and any others. So it is with the archaea. In essence, these microbes have a deep, chemical structure that is unique to them. If we look at their plasma membrane—the cellular lining that lies just inside the cell wall—we find that it is so chemically unique that it takes a special set of enzymes just to build it.

Structural differences such as these have to be based on genetic differences, and this is indeed the case with the archaea. In 1996, when scientists sequenced the first genome of an archaeon, they were stunned to find that 56 percent of its genes were completely unknown to science—they were unlike anything seen in either bacteria or in eukaryotes. As for the remaining 44 percent of the genome, some genes worked like those of eukaryotes, while others worked like those of bacteria.

Findings such as these produced the picture you can see in **Figure 21.9**; they convinced scientists that life evolved along three principal evolutionary lines, one of which is the archaea.

Archaea and Their Habitats

So, what about the second confusion we talked about—the misunderstanding about where archaea live? A large number of archaea species do in fact live in "extreme" environments, as we'll see. But archaea also live in large numbers in a variety of common habitats. Scientists divide the ocean into a series of vertical zones, one of which—starting at 200 meters down—is informally dubbed the "twilight zone" because it lies just beneath the level at which sunlight penetrates strongly. An eye-opening survey done in the 1990s found that archaea account for 40 percent of the microbial life in this zone over vast stretches of the ocean. This alone makes the archaea "one of the most abundant organisms on the planet," in the words of researchers Stephen Giovannoni and Ulrich Stingl. More recently, archaea have been found to outnumber bacteria in the sediment that *underlies* the ocean in regions as diverse as coastal Japan and Peru. Beyond this, archaea have recently been found to exist in abundance in common soil; there actually are more archaea than bacteria taking part in one phase of the "nitrogen-fixing" process we talked about earlier.

Extremophiles

All this said, many species of archaea do live in environments that are harsh or forbidding. We can thus think of some archaea as being **extremophiles:** organisms that grow optimally in one or more conditions that would kill most other organisms. Archaea are not the only extremophiles; many bacteria, some fungi, and even some organisms such as lichens thrive under tough conditions as well. Some of these organisms can withstand high pressure, while others can resist radiation; some flourish in cold temperatures, while others can get by with very little water. Here are three important categories of extremophiles, each of which has many species of archaea within it:

- **Thermophiles.** These are microbes that make their homes in extremely hot environments, such as the hot-water vents on the ocean floor or hot-water pools such as exist in Yellowstone National Park.

- **Halophiles.** These are microbes that live in environments so *salty* that few other types of organisms can survive in them. Utah's Great Salt Lake and the Dead Sea that separates Israel and Jordan are examples of *hypersaline* environments, meaning environments with salt concentrations greater than those found in seawater.

- **Anaerobes.** These are microbes that either can live without oxygen or that actually are poisoned by it and thus can only live in oxygen-free environments. You might think it would be impossible to get away from oxygen on Earth, but oxygenless environments are surprisingly widespread. They exist in ocean sediments, swamps, rice fields, and the digestive tracts of many animals, including ourselves. (The microbial menagerie within the human gut is mostly made up of anaerobic bacteria, but it includes archaea as well.) One group of anaerobic microbes—all of them archaea—produce the gas methane in the course of their metabolism and thus are *methanogens.* Their production of this gas can be substantial; the amount diffusing from rice fields alone has been estimated at a minimum of 20 million tons per year. The problem with this? Methane is a potent greenhouse gas—it contributes to global warming.

Domain Bacteria   **Domain Archaea**   **Domain Eukarya** (Protists, Plants, Animals, Fungi)

Universal ancestor

Figure 21.9 Archaea and the Universal Tree of Life
Archaea form one of three main branches on the universal tree of life. Note that they appear to be more closely related to eukaryotes (Domain Eukarya) than to bacteria (Domain Bacteria). The archaea and eukaryotes shared a common ancestor that was not shared by bacteria.

SO FAR . . .

1. The relationship between human beings and bacteria that are resident in the human digestive tract can be characterized as one of _____, which is to say a relationship in which both parties benefit.

2. Antibiotics are chemical compounds produced by one microorganism that are _____ to another.

3. Name three ways that bacteria and archaea are similar life-forms.

21.7 Protists: Pioneers in Diversifying Life

We've so far looked at two of life's domains, Bacteria and Archaea. As noted, the third domain, Eukarya, is so diverse we will look at only one of its four kingdoms in this chapter, the mostly microscopic organisms known as protists.

What's a protist? No one can provide a satisfactory definition. Domain Eukarya has within it three well-defined kingdoms—plants, animals, and fungi—but the protists within Eukarya are defined in terms of what they are *not* relative to these other life-forms: **Protists** are eukaryotic organisms that do not have all the defining characteristics of a plant, an animal, or a

fungus. Why do we have such an unsatisfactory definition for this one group of organisms? The root of the problem is that the term *protist* is a label of convenience rather than a label that reflects evolutionary reality. **Figure 21.10** shows the difference between naming and reality. You can see the three domains of life in the figure, the rightmost of which is Eukarya. Note that, early on in eukaryotic evolution, there was a branch that, toward its top, diverged into red algae on the one hand and plants on the other. Now note that there is a separate branch—once again starting out early in eukaryote evolution—that, toward the top, split into animals on the one hand and a group called the choanoflagellates on the other. Now, nobody calls animals and plants by a single name. But note that the choanoflagellates that are the "sister" group to animals and the red algae that are the sister group to plants *are* called by a single name—they're both "protists." Red algae are as distantly related to choanoflagellates as plants are to animals, yet both the red algae and choanoflagellates go under the catch-all title of protist. It is as if we had multiple family lines—the Garcias, the Lees, the Beesons—and then decided to call all of them the Johnsons.

This naming convention is partly a holdover from the past: Only recently have we understood how early the branching occurred among various evolutionary lines of eukaryotes. But this convention also is with us because it's convenient to have a single name for any living thing that's (a) a eukaryote and (b) not a plant, animal, or fungus. We'll use this convention in this chapter, but keep in mind that the term *protist* actually refers to many different evolutionary lines of organisms.

Figure 21.10
Many Evolutionary Lines, One Name: The Protists

The problem with the term *protist* is that this single name is applied to several different evolutionary lines of organisms. Within Domain Eukarya, on the right, protists make up one kingdom (Kingdom Protista), which has evolutionary lines that exist within the blue cone. Plants, animals, and fungi make up Eukarya's other kingdoms (shown outside the cone). Note that, among the protists, choanoflagellates and red algae evolved along separate lines and are no more closely related to each other than animals are to plants. Yet, plants and animals are regarded as members of separate kingdoms, while red algae and choanoflagellates are both regarded as members of one kingdom, Protista.

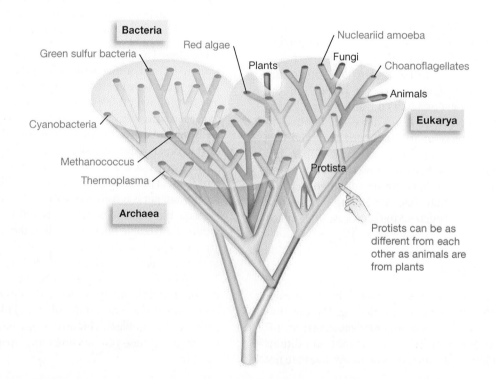

Protists can be as different from each other as animals are from plants

Given how distantly related many protists are to each other, it's not surprising that, as a group, they don't have much in common. Beyond being eukaryotic, about the only characteristic that all of them share is that they live in environments that are moist, if not fully aquatic—you can find them on damp forest floors as well as in oceans and lakes. Many are single-celled, and most are microscopic, but some are very large, as you'll see. Perhaps the way to think of protists is as organisms that occupy a kind of middle ground of complexity in the living world; they are more complex than bacteria or archaea, but tend to be less complex than plants, animals, or fungi (all of which evolved from protists). About 100,000 species are known to exist.

Although only a small proportion are parasites that affect humans, the rogue's gallery of protists is a formidable one. A microscopic protist, *Plasmodium falciparum,* causes one of the world's most widespread diseases, malaria, by passing between human and mosquito hosts. Campers in the United States are aware of the intestinal parasite *Giardia,* which contaminates water. Other protists cause sleeping sickness and amoebic dysentery. Pathogenic protists also affect humans in less direct ways. The cause of the great Irish Potato Famine of the 1840s was a fungus-like protist, *Phytophthora infestans,* that devastated the Irish potato fields. A close relative of this pest, *Phytophthora ramorum,* is now wiping out stands of California oak trees and bay laurels.

21.8 Protists and Sexual Reproduction

When we look at the living world as a whole, the protists in it are fascinating because they are the organisms that made the break with prokaryotic life—with life as nothing but single-celled bacteria and archaea. After life first appeared on Earth, it consisted solely of bacteria and archaea for almost 2 billion years. The first lifeforms to appear other than bacteria and archaea were the protists. And in these organisms, we can see how the living world branched out; we can see how living things made transitions to life as we know it today.

One such transition has to do with reproduction. You may recall that bacteria and archaea reproduce through a simple splitting of one cell into two. And as it turns out, most protists reproduce through this means as well (though they employ a different process than do bacteria or archaea). Many protists, however, can reproduce by mixing genetic material from *two* individuals; they give rise to offspring through *sexual* reproduction, in other words. This change was terrifically important to evolution because it meant that offspring would be different from their parents. Bacterial daughter cells are clones of their parent cell—

they are genetically identical to it. But the offspring of sexually reproducing organisms have a mixture of genes from both parents, meaning these offspring will not be identical to either parent. Once variation started appearing simply as a consequence of reproduction, evolution was off to the races in terms of creating new life-forms because so much variation was being produced.

This does not mean, however, that life went in one step from reproduction by simple cell splitting to reproduction as we now know it today in, say, human beings. Remember, the protists show us transitions. Let's look at what sexual reproduction is like in an ancient, early-evolving protist.

The protist in question is a type of single-celled water-dweller called *Chlamydomonas.* Most of the time, *Chlamydomonas* reproduces through cell splitting. In times of little nutrition, however, *Chlamydomonas* switches over to sexual reproduction. This begins with two normal *Chlamydomonas* cells, which means two cells that are haploid—that contain only a single set of chromosomes. You may recall that bacteria and archaea are always haploid. It makes sense, then, that the usual state for *Chlamydomonas* is haploid since, on life's family tree, it lies so close to the bacteria and archaea. Yet, *Chlamydomonas* has made a switch, as you can tell by looking at **Figure 21.11**. Note that at one point, two haploid *Chlamydomonas* cells fuse to create a zygote—the same thing that takes place with human sperm and egg cells. The result is a cell with *two* sets of chromosomes, one set coming from each parent. This cell then undertakes the meiosis reviewed in Chapter 10. You may recall that meiosis always entails a swapping of pieces between the chromosomes that came from parent A and those that came from parent B. Further, these chromosomes then assort randomly, such that any "daughter" cell will get a different mix of chromosomes from each parent. In *Chlamydomonas,*

Figure 21.11
Sexual Reproduction in a Protist
The simple algae *Chlamydomonas* normally is a haploid organism, meaning one that possesses a single set of chromosomes. In reproduction, however, *Chlamydomonas* cells of opposite mating types (+ and −) can fuse to create a zygote or fertilized egg that is diploid—that has a paired set of chromosomes. Meiosis then ensues in the zygote, and the result is four haploid *Chlamydomonas* cells, each of which differs genetically from the others thanks to the mixing of chromosomes that took place in meiosis.

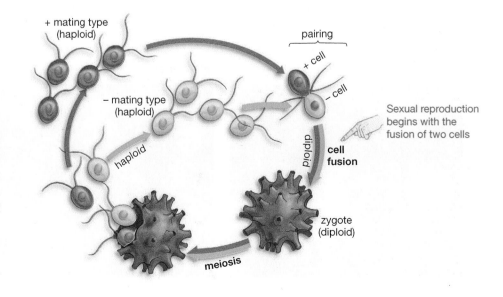

+ mating type (haploid)

− mating type (haploid)

haploid

pairing

+ cell

− cell

diploid

cell fusion

Sexual reproduction begins with the fusion of two cells

zygote (diploid)

meiosis

four new offspring cells are produced from the fusion of the original two cells. The critical thing is that, because of the shuffling done in meiosis, each of these cells has a unique mixture of chromosomes from each parent. The difference between bacteria and *Chlamydomonas* is the difference between clones and diverse offspring.

One more detail about this process is important. You may wonder about the little plus (+) and minus (−) signs next to the *Chlamydomonas* cells in Figure 21.11. This is an early protist version of what it means to be male and female. There are so-called + and − "mating types" of *Chlamydomonas,* and only these opposites can come together in sexual reproduction. (A + cell cannot fuse with another + cell.) The whip-like flagella that extend from + and − mating types differ in their microstructure. As a result, only opposite types of flagella can adhere to one another—something that is necessary to get the fusion process going. What we think of as male–female differences are later-arriving variations on this theme.

With this as background, let's now look at a few representatives of the protists. We'll review them not within their evolutionary groupings, but within categories that have to do with how they obtain their nutrition. We'll look at some protists that perform photosynthesis and some that do not.

21.9 Photosynthesizing Protists

The protists that perform photosynthesis are perhaps the only large group of protists known to the average person. The catchall name for them is **algae.** If you look at **Figure 21.12**, you can see the three varieties we'll be reviewing. Figure 21.12a shows a microscopic golden alga called *Synura scenedesmus* that can be found in freshwater ponds in the United States. In this species, we can see a transition between the single-celled life carried out by bacteria and the multicelled

life carried out by more complex organisms. All varieties of golden algae come in species that exhibit **colonial multicellularity:** a form of life in which individual cells form stable associations with one another but do not take on specialized roles. Each of the three objects you see in the picture of *Synura* is a cluster of *Synura* cells—a colony of them. Each member of the colony keeps its two whip-like flagella pointed to the outside of the group, the flagella beat back and forth, and the colony literally rolls through the water. None of these cells, however, performs a function different from any other cell, which is why this *Synura* is referred to as colonial and not truly multicellular.

If you look at Figure 21.12b, you can see a form of *green* algae, called *Volvox,* that represents an evolutionary step beyond *Synura.* The beautiful, translucent circles that outline *Volvox* are a gelatinous material that initially encloses a single layer of anywhere from 500 to 60,000 *Volvox* cells, all of them spaced around the periphery of the sphere. Almost all of these cells have flagella that they move back and forth in unison, so that *Volvox* moves slowly through the water in a given direction, spinning along an axis as it goes (something like a torpedo). For our purposes, the key thing about *Volvox* is that not all of the cells in this colony will reproduce. Only a select group of cells without flagella, generally at the rear pole of the axis, will divide to produce new colonies. These colonies in turn give rise to new spheres that exist inside the original parent sphere. Eventually, the gelatinous material around the parent sphere ruptures, and the daughter spheres emerge, each of them then continuing the process.

The important point is that *Volvox* has cells that specialize. As such, *Volvox* has arguably achieved **true multicellularity:** a form of life in which individual cells exist in stable groups, with different cells in a group specializing in different functions. In human beings, of course, we can see a great specialization in, for example, nerve and muscle cells. *Volvox* shows us specialization in a rudimentary form.

Figure 21.12
Transitions Visible in Algae

(a) Three colonies of the golden algae *Synura,* each of which is composed of a cluster of individual cells. *Synura* is a colonial protist in that none of the cells in a colony takes on any specialized function.

(b) Colonies of the green algae *Volvox* with daughter colonies growing inside. *Volvox* colonies can be regarded as truly multicellular organisms in that they have specialized reproductive cells. The largest *Volvox* colonies can be seen with the naked eye.

(c) A frond of the brown algae known as sea kelp. These unusually large protists have assemblages of cells that conduct food throughout the organism.

(a) Golden algae

(b) Green algae

(c) Brown algae

Finally, if you look at Figure 21.12c, you can see some representative brown algae—the giants of the protist world. One variety of brown algae, the sea kelp, has individuals that may be 60 meters long and that often grow in enormous kelp forests. For our purposes, brown algae are notable because their leaf-like "blades" and stem-like "stalks" represent another leap up in complexity: They contain organized groups of cells that conduct food throughout the organism.

One other thing is important about the algae. Note that the golden algae and *Volvox* share three characteristics: They are microscopic, aquatic, and carry out photosynthesis. If we were to go through all the algae, we would find these same qualities in countless species. Creatures in this category, including some bacteria, are known as **phytoplankton:** small photosynthesizing organisms that float near the surface of water. Such organisms are extremely important to life on Earth for two reasons. First, they produce most of the Earth's atmospheric oxygen. Second, they sit right at the base of most aquatic food chains. All large life-forms on Earth ultimately depend on photosynthesizers for their food. On land, lions may eat zebras, but zebras eat grass. In the oceans, whales may eat the shrimp-like creatures called krill, but krill eat phytoplankton.

21.10 Heterotrophic Protists

Lots of species of protists do not get their nutrients from photosynthesis, as algae do, but instead get them from consuming other organisms or bits of organic matter that they find. This makes them heterotrophs (or "other-eaters").

Heterotrophs with Locomotor Extensions

Some of these protists have slender extensions, called cilia and flagella, that allow them to move toward their prey or away from danger. **Figure 21.13** shows two varieties of these highly mobile heterotrophic protists.

Figure 21.13a shows a *Paramecium*, which is known as a ciliate because of all the hair-like cilia that cover its exterior. These cilia beat in unison, allowing paramecia to move forward or back in an exacting fashion—toward or away from objects in its environment. A *Paramecium* may be single-celled, but it is complex. It takes food in through a mouth-like passageway called a gullet, digests it in a special organelle called a food vacuole, and then empties the resulting waste into the outside world through a special pore on its exterior. Some species even have tiny dart-like structures that they can shoot out when threatened. Most animals require different *groups* of cells to do all these things, but a *Paramecium* does them within a single cell. Given this, it may be that paramecia represent the most complex single cells in all of nature.

Figure 21.13b shows a famous human parasite that enters human beings through contaminated water, the "camper's parasite," *Giardia lamblia,* which can live in the intestines of animals. It gets around not by cilia like the *Paramecia,* however, but by pairs of whip-like flagella, as we saw in the algae protists.

Heterotrophs with Limited Mobility

Figure 21.14a, on the next page, shows a so-called amoeboid protist, meaning a protist that gets around by means of a pseudopod or "false foot." The amoeba sends out a slender extension of itself (the foot), and then the rest of its body flows into this extension. It takes in bits of food by encircling them with extensions and then fusing these extensions together. What once had been outside the amoeba is now inside, being digested. Many amoeboid protists are parasites, and one of them, *Entamoeba histolytica,* is a serious

(a) A *Paramecium*

(b) The *Giardia* parasite

Figure 21.13
Movement through Cellular Extensions

(a) The many hair-like cilia extending from this paramecium allow it both to move through the water and to bring food to its mouth-like gullet, visible in the center.

(b) The parasite *Giardia lamblia* within the human small intestine. Seen here as the pear-shaped green and white objects, *Giardia* use sucking disks to attach themselves to fingerlike extensions of the intestine's inner lining.

Figure 21.14
Life as a Blob

(a) This member of the species *Amoeba proteus* has encircled a much smaller protist by extending two pseudopodia around it. Soon thereafter it ingested its prey, which it then began to digest with enzymes.

(b) This member of the plasmodial slime mold species *Physarum polycephalum* was photographed while moving slowly across a fallen log in southern Canada.

(a) Amoeba

(b) Plasmodial slime mold

human parasite that causes an estimated 100,000 deaths per year, mostly in the tropics, by entering the human digestive system through contaminated water. When a parasite invades the human intestinal wall, the resulting condition is known as *dysentery*. When that parasite is an amoeba, the result is amoebic dysentery.

Figure 21.14b shows a protist known as a plasmodial slime mold. This organism assumes several forms during its life cycle. In the form you see in the picture, its name is appropriate because it is essentially moving slime. If you looked at this organism under a microscope, you would see lots of cell nuclei but none of the *boundaries* (the plasma membranes) that normally separate one cell from another. The result is a free-flowing but slowly moving mass of cytoplasm—the interior of a single cell spread out over a large area, with only one plasma membrane at its periphery. This material moves by the same "cytoplasmic streaming" you saw in the amoeboids. As it rolls over rocks or forest floor, it consumes underlying bacteria, fungi, and bits of organic material. Should an object stand in its path, it simply flows around it, or even through it, if the object is porous enough.

All this makes the plasmodial slime molds sound like very primitive protists, but these single-celled creatures arguably possess an early-evolving form of a trait we normally associate only with animals: intelligence. In 2008, Japanese researchers reported that the slime mold *Physarum polycephalum,* which you can see in Figure 21.14b, has the capacity to remember what it has experienced and to act on the basis of its experience. In nature, *P. polycephalum* moves at differing rates depending on the humidity of the air around it—faster in humid air, slower in drier air. In the laboratory, the Japanese researchers provided three pulses of dry air around *P. polycephalum,* with each pulse spaced an hour apart. They then watched as the mold slowed down at the time when a fourth pulse was due, even though none was provided. Indeed, the mold would sometimes repeat its slow-downs a second and third time, right at the hourly intervals, in the absence of the pulses of dry air.

By now, you may be getting the impression that protists could be star contestants in a show called "Can You Top This for Strangeness?" If you look at **Figure 21.15,** you can see another contestant, a

Figure 21.15
Changing Forms

(a) A *Dictyostelium* in its slug stage, composed of individual cells that have come together to produce an organism capable of moving across the forest floor. Although the slug is composed of tens of thousands of cells, it is no bigger than a grain of sand.

(b) Cells in the slug eventually arrange themselves into this tower-like reproductive structure. Reproductive cells called spores will be dispersed from the top of the structure to the forest floor. There they will begin life as individual *Dictyostelium* cells.

(a) *Dictyostelium* slug

(b) *Dictyostelium* reproductive structure

much-studied organism, *Dictyostelium discoideum,* that is a so-called social amoeba. This may sound like a contradiction in terms, but consider the varying forms that this protist takes. At one point in its life cycle it exists as a collection of individual amoeba cells that crawl along the forest floor feeding on bacteria. Each "Dicty" is on its own at this stage, but if the bacterial food runs low, these individual cells begin "aggregating," or coming together in an organized group. Eventually, they develop into a barely visible "slug" of up to 100,000 cells that has front and back ends and that migrates to a more fertile area of the forest. Then, at a certain point, these cells change form again. They arrange themselves into a tower-like reproductive structure that has, at its top, spores that will be dispersed and develop into new individual cells that once again crawl along the forest floor. The whole aggregation process will not take place unless starvation is imminent, however; without the danger of starvation as a motivator, the individual cells stay separate.

Now, once you get past the shock of realizing that such a thing could happen—that individual cells could just collect themselves and create a larger, moving organism—you can begin to see what interesting questions it raises. What's the signaling mechanism that brings 100,000 separate cells together? How do they begin to cooperate to form these various structures? (To put this another way, how does multicellularity begin to work?) And, perhaps most intriguingly, why should some cells sacrifice themselves by serving on the *stalk* of the reproductive structure—from which location they will die, without reproducing themselves—while others get to be at the top and disperse to a new life in better hunting grounds? If evolution is all about passing on genes, why should some cells give up the chance to pass on theirs? Scientists study Dicty in hopes of learning more about all these questions.

On to Fungi

The bacteria, archaea, and protists reviewed in this chapter represent only a portion of the living world. Coming up is a life-form that is as close as the toadstool on our front lawn or the athlete's foot between our toes. What we'll be looking at next is fungi.

SO FAR ...

1. In contrast to bacteria and archaea, all protist cells have a _____, which makes protists eukaryotes. While some protists are large, most are _____; all of them live in environments that are at least moist if not fully _____.

2. The organisms known as phytoplankton are important to life in general for two reasons: They produce most of the world's atmospheric _____ and they lie at the base of most aquatic _____.

3. The catchall term for protists that perform photosynthesis is _____.

THE PROCESS OF SCIENCE

The Discovery of Penicillin

In wartime England, late in 1940, as the German bombings raged, a 43-year-old policeman lay dying in the Radcliffe Infirmary in Oxford. Albert Alexander was, however, not a victim of the German air raids. His enemy was smaller and more subtle. A few months earlier, he had scratched his cheek on a rosebush thorn. This minor wound had then become infected, and from that point he steadily went downhill as bacteria worked away inside him. By December his face was a mess of festering wounds, one of which cost him an eye.

Incomprehensible as it may seem, in 1940 a scratch from a rosebush thorn could do this to a person. The notable thing about Albert Alexander was not that he became deathly ill from such a trivial injury, but that he came close to beating his tiny enemies. He happened to live near an Oxford University laboratory where a handful of researchers were hurriedly trying to extract, from a common fungus, a product that the world eventually came to know as penicillin. When Albert Alexander became the first human being to receive a therapeutic dose of penicillin in February 1941, the results were startling. His fever dropped, his infection began to clear; even his appetite returned. But there was to be no happy ending for him, for the researchers had only a 5-day supply of the drug. Trying everything they could think of, they even extracted precious micrograms of penicillin from Alexander's own urine to put back into him. But it was not enough; he died days later.

Nevertheless, Alexander's case had shown that penicillin could work in human beings, and clear-cut successes with the drug were not long in coming. A 15-year-old boy with an infected hip underwent a remarkable turnaround when injected with it; children had their eyesight saved when blindness would have been the expected outcome.

These early trials made clear that, if ever there was a "miracle drug," penicillin was it. Prior to its advent, doctors could only watch and hope for the best as their patients were wracked by infections that ranged from pneumonia to meningitis to diphtheria to blood poisoning. With the advent of penicillin, at last doctors could do something.

How did it happen that a small band of researchers in wartime England ended up realizing the wondrous potential of this substance? The story begins not in the 1940s, but in 1928, when another scientist

The team had to brew up liters of fungal fluid to get mere millionths of a gram of active penicillin.

in England, Alexander Fleming, discovered the existence of penicillin through a combination of perceptiveness and luck. Returning to his hospital laboratory from a summer vacation, he noticed a spot of mold (a type of fungus) in one of the Petri dishes in which he was growing or "culturing" bacteria. Such bacterial cultures can easily become contaminated; this dish probably became tainted by means of fungal spores wafting in from another lab in the building. Something about this particular contamination caught Fleming's eye, however: The bacteria in the vicinity of the mold had clearly burst—they were dead. Realizing that chance had brought to him a substance that had the power to kill bacteria, Fleming grew more of the fungal mold, prepared a broth from it, tested its power against several kinds of deadly bacteria, and even went so far as to inject it into healthy mice to see if it had adverse effects (which it didn't). This last finding was crucial. There are lots of substances that can kill bacteria; the trick is to find one that can kill bacteria while leaving human beings unharmed.

Having advanced his work with penicillin to this point, however, Fleming then abandoned it. He had clearly recognized its therapeutic potential right from the start, but his subsequent research seemed to convince him that penicillin was just one bacteria killer among many that had no future in medicine. He found that it was unstable; that it appeared very difficult to purify from the stew of fungus chemicals it existed in; and that it quickly lost its power to kill bacteria once they had been exposed to it. After 1931, Fleming didn't publish anything on penicillin or encourage his students to work with it. He seemed to regard it as a substance that was useful mostly for killing off unwanted bacteria in Petri dishes. A great deal of credit goes to him for being perceptive enough to recognize what had been laid in front of him. But had research on penicillin ended with him, there never would have been a drug called penicillin. By 1935, as Trevor Williams has written, "There was not one person in the world who believed in penicillin as a practical aid to medicine."

But this was soon to change, thanks to the work of two immigrants to Britain. One was Howard Florey, an Australian trained as a medical doctor who was then head of a school of pathology at Oxford University. The other was Ernst Chain, a refugee from Hitler's Germany who had been hired by Florey to develop a biochemistry unit in the school. The critical decision the two made in 1938 was to investigate substances in the same class as penicillin—antibiotics, which is to say substances made by one microorganism that are toxic to another. Critically, one of the compounds Florey and Chain decided to investigate was penicillin; they knew of its existence from reading the earlier papers of Fleming and others.

From the beginning, the team's research on penicillin proceeded on two tracks. One was simply seeing if the substance worked. The other was finding out what the substance *was* and trying to get enough of it to work with. Remember that penicillin is the product of a living organism—originally the fungus *Penicillium notatum*—and as such it existed within a mixture of thousands of other compounds the fungus produces. The trick was to isolate and characterize the germ-killing substance within the fungal soup. This biochemical work was the job of Chain. While this was going on, the team had to brew up liters of fungal fluid to get mere millionths of a gram of active penicillin.

Finally armed with enough of the drug to put it to the test, the group carried out the critical experiment. On the morning of May 25, 1940, they injected eight mice with deadly doses of streptococcal bacteria, and an hour later they injected four of the mice with penicillin. Then, a round-the-clock watch began. Normally, the bacterial dose given would have killed all the mice within 24 hours, and indeed by 3:30 a.m. the next day the four unprotected mice were dead. But the four mice given the penicillin were all fine! A long road lay ahead with human subjects such as Albert Alexander, but penicillin had done in mice what had so long been sought: It killed bacterial invaders while leaving their "host" unharmed.

This effort was being carried out against the backdrop of the outbreak of World War II. By the time the mouse experiments were started, much of Europe had fallen to Hitler, and it was feared that England might be next. (The wartime importance of a drug such as penicillin was clear to the Oxford team, which had contingency plans to destroy all its lab equipment and notes in the case of a successful German invasion. Only the precious *P. notatum* spores would be retained, by means of the researchers rubbing them into their clothing.) In this chaotic environment, the scientists were forced to go outside England to get the help they needed to ramp up the production of penicillin to an industrial scale. Howard Florey thus went to America to enlist aid there. Oxford researchers eventually found themselves working with chemical engineers from the U.S. Department of Agriculture in the unlikely location of Peoria, Illinois. Where once the English scientists had fermented penicillin in milk bottles, eventually they and their American colleagues were brewing it up in 25,000-gallon tanks.

Getting to this point meant coming up not only with better fermenting methods but also with better starting ingredients. To this end, military pilots collected soil samples from around the world in an effort to find a *Penicillium* species that would yield more of the precious drug.

As luck would have it, a species that did the trick was found on the project's doorstep. In 1943, lab worker Mary Hunt bought a moldy cantaloupe at a Peoria market. The melon contained a fungus, *Penicillium chrysogenum,* that doubled the amount of penicillin produced; its daughter spores are the ones used to this day to produce penicillin.

Despite some detours, this crash program was a smashing success. The drug that once was restricted to mice, then to a few human subjects, was put into commercial production early in 1944. By the time of the Allied invasion of Europe, in June 1944, enough was being produced that every soldier who needed it could have it. Not much later, all restrictions on it were lifted; penicillin was available by prescription from the corner drugstore.

In 1945, Alexander Fleming, Howard Florey, and Ernst Chain were awarded the Nobel Prize in Physiology or Medicine for their work in discovering this wonder drug. Bestowing the prize just after the war ended, the Nobel committee noted:

In a time when annihilation and destruction through the inventions of man have been greater than ever before in history, the introduction of penicillin is a brilliant demonstration that human genius is just as well able to save life and combat disease.

Penicillin's Discoverers

The three scientists who were awarded the Nobel Prize for their work on the development of penicillin. From left to right, Alexander Fleming, Howard Florey, and Ernst Chain.

CHAPTER

21 REVIEW

Go to the Study Area at www.masteringbiology.com for practice quizzes, myeBook, BioFlix™ 3-D animations, MP3 Tutor Sessions, videos, current events, and more.

Mastering BIOLOGY™

Summary

21.1 Life's Categories and the Importance of Microbes

- All living things on Earth can be classified as falling into one of three domains: Bacteria, Archaea, or Eukarya. All the members of Domains Bacteria and Archaea are single-celled and microscopic. Domain Eukarya is further divided into four kingdoms: plants, animals, fungi, and protists. (p. 380)

- Microbes are indispensable to life. They produce more than half of Earth's atmospheric oxygen; the bacteria and archaea among them are responsible for putting atmospheric nitrogen into a form plants can use; and bacteria and fungi are the most important decomposers of the natural world. (p. 380)

- Microbes live in all environments in which larger life-forms exist. They are present in numbers so immense that their combined biomass exceeds the biomass of all of Earth's larger life-forms. (p. 381)

21.2 Viruses: Making a Living by Hijacking Cells

- Viruses are noncellular replicating entities that must invade living cells to carry out their replication. Most scientists do not classify them as living things. (p. 382)

- The HIV virus has two structures common to all viruses: genetic material and a protein coat, called a capsid, surrounding this material. HIV also has an fatty membrane, called an envelope, which surrounds the capsid. HIV does its damage by invading immune system cells called helper T-cells, which are then destroyed. (p. 382)

- Most viruses: (1) get their genetic material inside a "host" cell; (2) turn out viral parts; (3) construct new virus particles from these parts; and (4) move the new particles out of the cell, at which point the particles go on to infect more cells. (p. 382)

- Viruses cause a host of human illnesses. Health officials worldwide must constantly be on alert for the emergence of new members of a particularly dangerous class of viruses, the influenza A viruses, one of which was the H1N1 virus that infected people around the world in 2009. (p. 384)

21.3 Bacteria: Masters of Every Environment

- Bacteria are microscopic, single-celled organisms that are prokaryotes. Bacteria have only a single organelle (the ribosome) and reproduce asexually through binary fission. Millions of species of bacteria exist. Some bacteria make their own food through photosynthesis, and others consume organic material in their environment. (p. 385)

21.4 Intimate Strangers: Humans and Bacteria

- Bacteria live on and in human beings in great numbers. In the digestive tract, the relationship between humans and many bacteria is one of mutualism: Bacteria get food and habitat; human beings get an efficiently functioning digestive system. (p. 388)

21.5 Bacteria and Human Disease

- Only a small proportion of bacteria are pathogenic, but these bacteria are responsible for some of humanity's worst diseases. A few pathogenic bacteria cause harm by invading human cells, but bacteria generally do their damage by either releasing toxins or by leaving them behind when they die. (p. 389)

- The primary human medical defense against pathogenic bacteria is antibiotics, which work by exploiting the differences between bacterial and human cells, such that they kill bacteria while leaving human cells unharmed. (p. 389)

- The power of antibiotics is being threatened by the emergence of antibiotic-resistant strains of bacteria. These bacteria are evolving in greater numbers because of an overuse of antibiotics in medicine, agriculture, and consumer products. (p. 389)

21.6 Archaea: From Marginal Player to Center Stage

- Archaea were once thought to be a form of bacteria but are now known to constitute their own domain of life. Archaea are superficially similar to bacteria in that they are single-celled prokaryotes that reproduce through simple cell splitting. However, archaea are unique in the living world at the level of their genes and the chemical structure of their cells. (p. 390)

- Archaea exist in large numbers in some common environments. They make up 40 percent of the microbial life in large portions of the world's oceans, and they are seen in large numbers in soil, where they join bacteria in carrying out one phase of the nitrogen-fixing process. (p. 391)

- Many species of archaea are extremophiles; three large classes of extremophiles are thermophiles, halophiles, and anaerobes. (p. 391)

21.7 Protists: Pioneers in Diversifying Life

- A protist is a eukaryotic organism that does not have all the defining features of a plant, an animal, or a fungus. This unsatisfactory definition stems from the fact that the term *protist* doesn't refer to a single evolutionary grouping but instead is used as a label for several different evolutionary lines of organisms. (p. 392)

- Protists are mostly microscopic, and all of them live in environments that are at least moist, if not aquatic. About 100,000 species are known to exist. (p. 393)

21.8 Protists and Sexual Reproduction

- Protists were the first life-form to evolve other than bacteria or archaea; they were the organisms that made transitions to many of the capabilities and forms seen in larger organisms today. Among these transitions was the change to sexual reproduction, which protists were the first to practice. (p. 393)

21.9 Photosynthesizing Protists

- Protists that get their nutrition by performing photosynthesis are known as algae. Some algal species provide examples of colonial multicellularity. Others provide examples of true multicellularity. (p. 394)

- Microscopic algae are important phytoplankton—small photosynthesizing organisms that float near the surface of water—which are important to life because they produce most of Earth's atmospheric oxygen and because they form the base of so many aquatic food chains. All phytoplankton are either algae or bacteria. (p. 395)

21.10 Heterotrophic Protists

- Heterotrophic protists get their nutrients from consuming either other organisms or bits of organic matter. Some have evolved tiny cilia and flagella, with which they move toward prey or away from danger. (p. 395)

- The protists called amoeba move through use of pseudopodia. Likewise, the protists called plasmodial slime molds and social amoeba move by means of this "cytoplasmic streaming." (p. 395)

- The plasmodial slime mold *Physarum polycephalum* arguably displays a primitive form of intelligence, while the social amoeba called *Dictyostelium discoideum* exists as a collection of individual cells that can come together during times of little food to form a single slug-like organism. (p. 396)

Key Terms

algae   394

antibiotics   389

binary fission   387

capsid   382

colonial multicellularity   394

eukaryote   387

extremophile   391

mutualism   388

pathogenic   389

phytoplankton   395

prokaryote   387

protist   392

true multicellularity   394

virus   382

Understanding the Basics

Multiple-Choice Questions

(Answers are in the back of the book.)

1. Microbes:
   a. produce most of the world's atmospheric oxygen.
   b. make nitrogen available to plants.
   c. recycle dead organic matter.
   d. account for most of the world's biomass.
   e. All of the above.

2. Viruses:
   a. are the smallest living things.
   b. have only one organelle.
   c. are beneficial to most organisms.
   d. replicate only by invading living cells.
   e. have circular chromosomes.

3. All viruses possess _____, which they _____.
   a. toxins; kill cells with
   b. cell walls; protect themselves with
   c. DNA or RNA; copy inside themselves
   d. many cells; insert inside a host cell
   e. DNA or RNA; transfer into a host cell

4. Bacteria:
   a. are single-celled eukaryotes.
   b. live outside cells.
   c. reproduce sexually or asexually.
   d. are multicelled prokaryotes.
   e. are single-celled prokaryotes.

5. Within the human body, bacteria exist in greatest numbers in the _____, with most of these bacteria having a _____ relationship with their human host.
   a. lungs; commensal
   b. feet; antagonistic
   c. digestive tract; mutualistic
   d. digestive tract; pathogenic
   e. kidneys; mutualistic

6. Archaea (select all that apply):
   a. are single-celled prokaryotes.
   b. are restricted to marine environments.
   c. are superficially similar to bacteria.
   d. are restricted to extreme environments.
   e. constitute one of the three domains of life.

7. Protists were the first life-forms to (select all that apply):
   a. appear on Earth.
   b. reproduce through binary fission.
   c. reproduce sexually.
   d. evolve following bacteria and archaea.
   e. exhibit true multicellularity.

8. Phytoplankton are important because they (select all that apply):
   a. produce antibiotics.
   b. produce oxygen.
   c. sit at the base of terrestrial food chains.
   d. sit at the base of aquatic food chains.
   e. fight viruses.

Brief Review

(Answers are in the back of the book.)

1. How do plants get the nitrogen they need?

2. Why do most biologists classify viruses as non-living?

3. Antibiotics used in humans must have at least two qualities. What are they?

4. How can we say that archaea are superficially like bacteria and yet fundamentally different from them?

5. Name three features of more complex organisms that first appeared in protists.

6. What is an amoeba? What class of diseases is associated with them?

Applying Your Knowledge

1. What does it mean to be a "successful" organism? Bacteria are certainly the most numerous organisms on Earth, they live in nearly all environments, and they are the least susceptible to being eliminated through environmental catastrophe. Are they Earth's most successful organisms?

2. What does it mean to be an "organism"? The cellular slime mold *Dictyostelium discoideum* exists initially as a collection of separate cells moving over the forest floor. In times of starvation, these cells come together to form a single "slug" that moves to more fertile territory. Eventually, it will change into a new structure that will throw off separate cells again. Is "Dicty" an organism or a group of temporarily cooperating cells?

3. What would life on Earth be like if there were no decomposers?

22

Fungi:
The Diversity of Life 2

Fungi have a powerful ability to break down and consume most of the materials that nature produces— something that has both good and bad consequences for human beings.

Mushrooms of the fungus *Amanita muscaria* sit side by side with several species of plants in a Russian forest.

Common houseflies can suffer a hostile takeover by a fungus called *Entomophthora muscae*. It's not unusual for one organism to live off another, but in the case of *E. muscae,* the story has a bizarre twist. This fungus gets inside flies either by drilling through their tough outer skeleton or by squeezing between some cracks in it. The strange thing is that,

on entry, the first thing *E. muscae* does is send out extensions of itself to the fly's brain—specifically to parts of the brain that control crawling behavior. Eventually, the fly begins to crawl upward. This usually means upward on a plant stem or leaf, but it may mean upward on the wall of a house, toward the ceiling. Like any fungus, *E. muscae* lives by digesting organic material, and in this case the organic material is the fly's body. By the time the fly begins making its upward trek, it is nearly dead from the internal damage *E. muscae* has done.

If you look at **Figure 22.1**, you can see the end result of all this: a fly that has crawled up on a conifer needle and, in one of its last acts, has put its mouthparts on the needle, to which they are now glued by the fungus. The white growths you see around the fly's abdomen

are fungal spores. Soon they will be showered over everything *beneath* the fly—including, perhaps, some more flies, which then can be parasitized as well. Fungi have various ways of getting their spores up off the ground for dispersal. The structure we call a mushroom is essentially a spore-dispersal tower. But *E. muscae* has taken another tack. It gets its prey to lift it to higher ground, and sticks its prey in place; then it uses the prey as a launching pad for a shower of fungal spores. *E. muscae* shows us once again that, while nature is certainly diverse, it is not always pretty.

22.1 The Fungi: Life as a Web of Slender Threads

Entomophthora muscae is a member of one of the "kingdoms" of the living world, the fungi. There are lots of fungi that make their living as parasites, as *E. muscae* does, but then again there are fungi that live in a beneficial association with plants and fungi that do us the favor of decomposing fallen trees (**Figure 22.2** on the next page.). At first glance, fungi and plants may seem to be alike. After all, they're fixed in one spot and tend to grow in the ground. But as you'll see, the main connection between plants and fungi is that many of them have struck up underground partnerships. When it comes to evolution, the surprising thing is that fungi and *animals* are more closely related than fungi and plants. A single, common protist ancestor gave rise to animals on the one hand and fungi on the other, with plants only distantly related to the members of either kingdom (**Figure 22.3** on the next page.).

But if a fungus is not a plant, what is it? As the fly example shows, fungi do not make their own food as plants do. Instead, fungi are heterotrophs—they consume existing organic material in order to live. They make a living by sending out webs of slender, tube-like

Figure 22.1
Doing a Parasite's Bidding
Pictured is a root maggot fly (genus *Delia*) that has been killed by an *Entomophthora* fungus; the white spores of the fungus can be seen bursting out from the fly's abdomen.

(a)

(b)

(c)

Figure 22.2
Fungal Diversity

(a) What happens to dead branches on a forest floor? They are decomposed, mostly by fungi. The mushrooms sprouting from this branch are outgrowths of a network of fungal fibers that are growing within the branch. These fibers digest and absorb nutrients from the branch, a process that eventually breaks the branch down into its chemical component parts, which are then recycled back into the soil.

(b) Fungi are also human pests. Pictured is a human nail with fungal spores on it that are the cause of athlete's foot.

(c) Fungi distribute their spores in various ways. Pictured are spores being expelled from some puffballs in Costa Rica. What brings about the expulsion? Drops of rain falling on the puffballs.

threads to a food source. This food source could be a fly, as in *E. muscae*'s case, but it could just as easily be bits of organic matter below ground or a fallen log in a forest.

Whatever the case, fungi cannot immediately take in or "ingest" their food in the way that animals do. Fungal cells have cell walls, which means that only relatively small molecules can pass into the fungal filaments. As such, fungi digest their food *externally*, through digestive enzymes they release. When the food has been broken down sufficiently by these enzymes, the resulting molecules are taken up into the filaments. Almost all fungi obtain nutrition in this manner. Whether we are talking about a microscopic bread mold or extensive webs of fungi that spread underneath the forest floor, this is a defining characteristic of fungi. This characteristic and others can be stated in a more formal way:

- Fungi largely consist of slender, tube-like filaments called **hyphae.**

- Fungi get their nutrition by dissolving their food externally and then absorbing it into their hyphae.

- Collectively, the hyphae make up a branching web, called a **mycelium.** If you look at **Figure 22.4**, you can see the nature of this structure. You may have thought of a mushroom as the main part of a fungus, but in reality it is merely a reproductive structure, called a *fruiting body,* that sprouts up from the larger mycelium below. A fruiting body amounts to a large, folded-up collection of hyphae.

- Most fungi are **sessile,** or fixed in one spot, but their hyphae grow. The fungal mycelium does not move, but its individual hyphae grow toward a food source. This growth comes, however, only at the tips of the hyphae, not throughout their length.

- Fungi are almost always multicellular. The primary exception to this is the yeasts, which are unicellular and thus do not form mycelia.

photosynthetic protists   nonphotosynthetic protists

plants   animals   fungi

ancestral protist

Figure 22.3
Fungal Evolution

Fungi may superficially resemble plants, but they actually are more closely related to animals than they are to plants. The evolutionary line that led to plants diverged from the line that led to fungi and animals about a billion years ago, whereas the fungi and animal lines did not diverge until sometime between 35 and 200 million years later. The evolutionary divergence between plants on the one hand and fungi and animals on the other can be thought of as a divergence between organisms that make their own food through photosynthesis (as plants do) and organisms that consume existing organic material (as fungi and animals do).

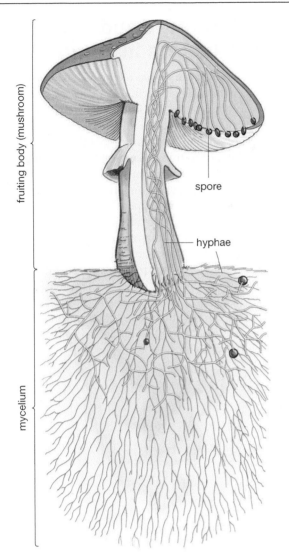

Figure 22.4
Structure of a Fungus
Fungi are composed of tiny slender tubes called hyphae. The hyphae form an elaborate network called a mycelium. The same hyphae also form a reproductive structure called a fruiting body, which in this case is the familiar mushroom.

This last point leads to a more general concept about the living world. You may recall from the last chapter that all bacteria and archaea are single-celled and that protists are usually single-celled. But protists are the limit of single-celled life. With fungi, plants, and animals, life becomes almost completely multicellular. There is no such thing as a single-celled plant or animal, and the one large group of single-celled fungi, the yeasts, seem to have evolved into this state from an earlier multicelled form. This is not to say that all life becomes *big* once we get past the protists. As you'll see, there are plenty of microscopic fungi (and even some microscopic animals). But from here on out, all the life-forms we'll be looking at are made up of more than one cell.

22.2 Roles of Fungi in Society and Nature

Like bacteria, fungi are mostly hidden from us—and mostly known to us by the trouble they cause. This trouble is considerable, as fungi are responsible for mildew, dry rot, vaginal yeast infections, bread molds, general food spoilage, toenail and fingernail infections, and a variety of related skin afflictions, among them athlete's foot, "jock itch," and ringworm. The agricultural blights of corn smut and wheat rust are fungal infections. Indeed, fungi probably are the single worst destroyers of crop plants. One survey in Ohio indicated that only 50 plant diseases there were caused by bacteria and 100 by viruses but 1,000 by fungi. If you look at **Figure 22.5**, you can see an example of what happened to American elm trees in cities across the United States beginning in the 1930s because of a fungus called *Ophiostoma ulmi*—the cause of Dutch elm disease. In recent years, there has been great concern about the fungi commonly called molds and the effects they have on both houses and the people who live in them.

Even given all this fungal pestilence, however, we could say of the fungi what we said of bacteria: While we could do without some of them, we could not live without others. Mold in houses may be a huge problem, but there is another mold that is the source of penicillin. Fungal infections may be a problem, but organ transplants are made possible today by the immune-system-suppressing drug cyclosporin, which is derived from a fungus. If you know someone who has high cholesterol, he or she may control it with the drugs lovastatin or pravastatin, both of which are derived from a fungus. In the realm of food production, brewer's yeast makes bread rise and beer ferment, and blue cheese is blue because of the veins of mold within it. Most soft drinks contain citric acid that is produced from a fungus, and we simply eat fungi outright in the form of mushrooms. Out in nature, fungi join bacteria as the major decomposers of the living world, breaking down organic material such as the wood in fallen logs and turning it into inorganic compounds that are recycled into the soil. In fact, the final breakdown of woody material is almost entirely the work of fungi. And, as noted, fungi are involved in a critical association with plants, about which you'll learn more later.

Figure 22.5
The Effects of Dutch Elm Disease

(a) Elm-lined street, Detroit, 1971

(b) Street after Dutch elm epidemic, 1984

Some 70,000 species of fungi have been identified so far, but this is just a fraction of the number that actually exist. Because fungi tend to grow in inaccessible places, most of them are unknown to us. By one estimate, the total number of fungal species may be about 1.5 million.

SO FAR . . .

1. The essential structure of most fungi is a set of slender filaments called _____ that collectively make up a structure called a _____.

2. Which of the following is not a characteristic of fungi: (a) usually fixed in one spot; (b) make their own food; (c) tend to be multicellular?

3. Fungi are indispensable to the natural world because of their role in _____.

22.3 Structure and Reproduction in Fungi

Let's now look at one type of fungus as a means of learning something about fungi in general. In **Figure 22.6**, you can see a so-called club fungus that we know as the common mushroom. If you look at the figure's lower-right portion, you can see that the mushroom's hyphae amount to thin lines of cells—something that is true of all hyphae. In many cases, individual cells in the hyphae are separated from one another by dividers called septa. But as it happens, septa are somewhat porous dividers; they have tiny openings that allow for a fairly free flow of cellular material between one cell and the next. This allows for rapid movement of cellular resources right to the tip of the hyphae—the site of hyphal growth. The result is that hyphae can grow very quickly, whether they are growing toward a food source or organizing themselves into a mushroom cap. Did it ever seem to you that a mushroom sprouted in your yard overnight? It probably did.

Figure 22.6
The Life Cycle of a Fungus

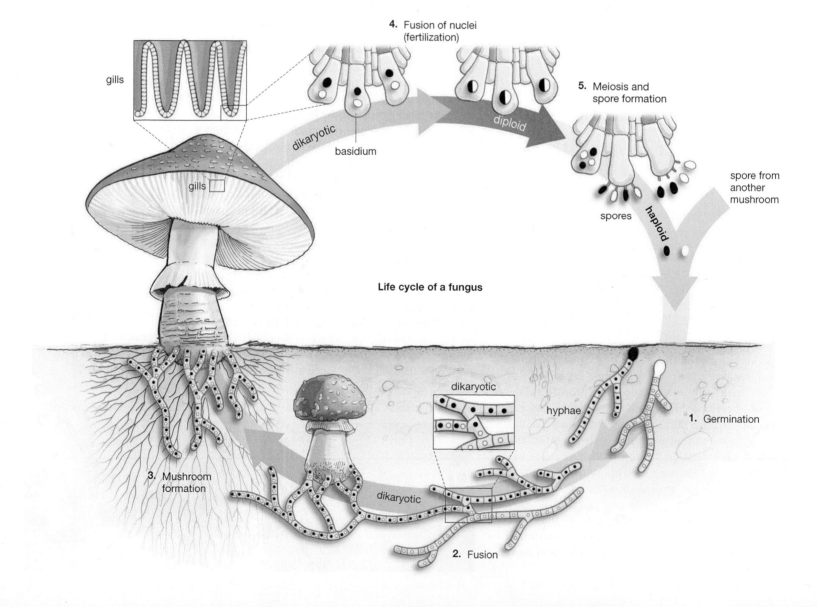

Life cycle of a fungus

In the upper left of the figure, you can see how the mushroom cap is structured. The underside of each cap is made up of a profusion of accordion-like folds called gills. Each gill is simply a collection of hyphae. And right at the tip of some of these hyphae is a reproductive structure called a basidium. Reproductive cells called spores are produced within the basidium and then ejected from it. Caught by the wind, these spores are then carried away to new ground on which they can "germinate," or sprout new hyphae. Fungal spores are, however, something like lottery tickets: A multitude are made, but only a few will be winners. Such a tiny fraction of spores end up germinating that huge numbers must be released in order for all nearby environments to receive some. Tens of millions will be ejected each hour from the underside of a fairly small mushroom cap.

The mushroom cap is one example of a large fungal structure, but most fungi don't have this kind of size. Think of a flat circle of blue-gray mold on some spoiled bread. It has its own mycelium, with reproductive structures topped by spores, but magnification is necessary to make out any of this detail, as you can see in **Figure 22.7**. To a great extent, fungi can be regarded as microbes.

The Life Cycle of a Fungus

The mushroom caps and spores we've been looking at are important players in the life cycle of club fungi, which is to say the set of steps by which one generation of these fungi gives rise to the next. If we look at this life cycle from its beginning—in Figure 22.6, over

Figure 22.7
Bread Mold up Close
The dark spots on moldy bread are composed of a mycelium that forms stalks tipped by spores, visible in this micrograph as tiny black balls. The spores will be dispersed to produce new mycelia elsewhere—perhaps on more bread. These are spores of the mold *Rhizopus nigricans,* growing on the surface of some bread.

at step 1— you can see that it starts with spores that have been released from fruiting bodies. These spores germinate, generate hyphae, and in step 2, two of these hyphae fuse: Two hyphal cells come together and become one cell, from which a single hypha grows. Note, however, that the cells in this new hypha have *two* nuclei each (symbolized by the little black and white dots within them). This is an unusual condition for a cell; in the normal case, one cell has one nucleus. This condition has come about because, while two cells fused in step 2, their nuclei remained separate. Thus begins a phase of life that is unique to two types of fungi: the **dikaryotic phase,** in which cells in a fungal mycelium have two nuclei.

And what is the nature of the genetic material in these nuclei? Each nucleus exists in what is known as a haploid state—there is but a *single* set of chromosomes in each one. This contrasts with the diploid state in almost all human cells. Our nuclei have *paired* sets of chromosomes within them (one set inherited from our father, the other from our mother). The haploid state of these nuclei may seem like a technical detail, but it's important for what's coming up. Once a mushroom mycelium enters the dikaryotic phase it can stay there for a long time. The phase can go on for years, in fact, and ends only when the most visible manifestation of the mycelium, the mushroom cap, sprouts above ground, as seen in step 3.

Sex in Fungi

The dikaryotic state initially exists in all the cells in the mushroom—even the cells that make up the spore-releasing basidia that line the gills. But in some of these cells, right at the tips of the basidia, this will change. The two nuclei in these cells will fuse into one nucleus, as seen in step 4. This change means these cells have become diploid; they now have a single nucleus that contains *two* sets of chromosomes.

Now, think about where each of these sets of chromosomes came from. One of them came originally from the black spore over at step 1, while the other came from the white spore. They existed separately in a single cell for a while, but now they have fused. With this, we have had a fusion of genetic material from two separate organisms—sex has taken place. It's not the merger of egg and sperm we're used to in human reproduction, but it's sex nevertheless.

Next, as you can see in step 5, each of the cells in which this fusion has taken place undergoes the meiosis that was reviewed in Chapter 10. This means a mixing of chromosomes from the two parents and two rounds of cell division. The result is four haploid spores attached like little bags to the tip of a basidium; these will be among the millions of spores released from the mushroom cap. Each of these spores will be of one "mating type" or another—symbolized by the black and white colors in the figure. Just as only opposite sexes can come together to create offspring in humans, so only opposite mating types can come together (in hyphae fusion) to create offspring in fungi when they reproduce sexually.

The Nature of Spores

This gets us to the nature of a **spore,** which can be defined as a reproductive cell that can develop into a new organism without fusing with another reproductive cell. Note the difference between the spores of the mushroom and the *gametes* of a human being—eggs or sperm. A human being cannot develop from an egg or a sperm; a fusion of both cells is required. Meanwhile, the spores that our mushroom developed from did not undergo fusion. A fungal spore was produced in meiosis, and once it came into being, it was dispersed and developed into a whole new mycelium by itself.

Reproduction in Other Types of Fungi

The life cycle we've just looked at actually amounts to only one means of fungal reproduction among many that exist. Under some conditions, fungi that are capable of sexual reproduction will instead utilize *asexual* reproduction. The little black balls you can see on top of the bread mold in Figure 22.7 are spores that were produced through mitosis, or simple cell division, as carried out by one organism. There was no fusion of the cells and nuclei from two organisms to produce these spores—there was no sex, in other words. Spores such as the ones on the bread mold develop through cell division, after which they disperse to form new mycelia; then these mycelia develop new spores through cell division and the process continues. Note that the constant within fungal reproduction is spores—they are employed no matter what. But spores can be produced either sexually or asexually. And the sexual processes that fungi employ can vary considerably. In short, fungi exhibit great diversity in the means by which they reproduce themselves.

22.4 Categories of Fungi

We're used to dividing the animal world up into various categories, such as insects, mammals, and reptiles. So, what are the major categories of fungi? It turns out there are four principal groups or "phyla" of fungi, and that three of these phyla are defined by their reproductive structures. As you've seen, toadstool-shaped mushroom fungi have a reproductive structure called a basidium; accordingly, these mushrooms are in the fungal group known as the basidiomycetes. Likewise, there is a group called the ascomycetes and one called the zygomycetes—both named for the reproductive structures they have. Finally, there is a group called the chytrids whose members give us an idea of how close the evolutionary relationship is between fungi and animals. Let's look briefly now at each of these four fungal phyla.

- **Basidiomycetes.** Toadstool-shaped mushrooms are the best-known members of Phylum Basdiomycota, but this group also includes two banes of the agricultural world—the rusts and the smuts—along with the familiar "shelf" fungi that often are seen sprouting from trees (**Figure 22.8**). You may recall that the spore-releasing basidium on a mushroom is shaped something like a club. It is this shape that gives the basidiomycetes the common name of the club fungi. Most of the living world benefits from the work of basidiomycetes as they serve as a major group of decomposers. This is small comfort to farmers worldwide, however, who must live with the incredible agricultural damage caused by the basidiomycete smuts and rusts. Wheat, corn, barley, oats, soybeans, coffee—all these crops and more are infected by these fungi, which can sweep through crops in epidemic waves. In 1993, leaf rust destroyed over 40 million bushels of wheat in Kansas and Nebraska alone.

- **Ascomycetes.** Morel mushrooms are members of Phylum Ascomycota, as are the highly prized

Figure 22.8
Basidiomycete Fungi

(a) The basidiomycetes include the well-named shelf fungi, such as this *Ganoderma* fungus, seen growing from the trunk of a beech tree in England.

(b) The agricultural scourges called smuts are also basidiomycetes. Here fungal outgrowths called smut galls can be seen sprouting from an ear of corn that has been infected by basidiomycete fungus *Ustilago zeae.*

(a) Shelf fungus on beech tree trunk

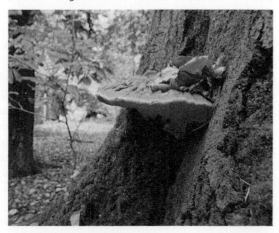

(b) Smut outgrowths on corn ear

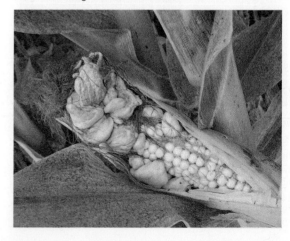

(a) Common morel mushroom (*Morchella esculenta*)

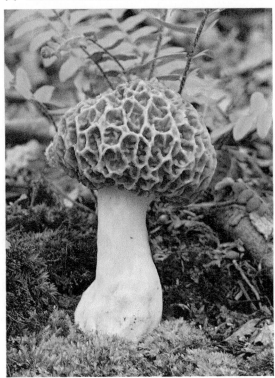

(b) Orange peel fungus (*Aleuria aurantia*)

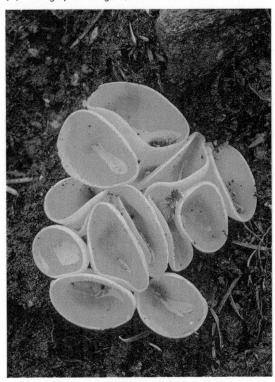

Figure 22.9
Ascomycete Fungi

(a) The ascomycetes include the edible morel mushrooms, all of which are in the genus *Morchella*. The mushroom seen here is a member of the "yellow morel" species *Morchella esculenta*.

(b) Another group of ascomycetes are "cup" fungi, such as this orange peel fungus (*Aleuria aurantia*), growing in Scotland.

truffles that are used in cooking. On the other hand, the cause of Dutch elm disease is the ascomycete *Ophiostoma ulmi,* and if you see some brown rot on a peach or other stone fruit, it is likely to be the ascomycete *Monilinia fructicola*. All members of this phylum reproduce by using tiny spore-releasing structures whose sac-like shape gives the ascomycetes their common name: the sac fungi. In ascomycete mushrooms, these sacs can be contained in a large fruiting body that is shaped like a cup (**Figure 22.9**). The Ascomycetes are a sister evolutionary group to the Basidiomycetes in that fungi in both of these late-evolving fungal phyla go through the dikaryotic phase in their life cycle, whereas no other fungi do.

• **Zygomycetes.** When you see a patch of blue-gray mold on bread, you're probably looking at a fungus that's part of Phylum Zygomycota. This is so much the case that a common name for the zygomycetes is the bread molds. There are only about 1,050 known species of zygomycetes, which is a small number compared to the more than 22,000 known basidiomycetes or the 32,000 ascomycetes. Nevertheless, the zygomycetes are diverse. Many of them form underground associations with plant roots, but one group of them makes a living by parasitizing insects. (Remember the *Entomophthora* species from the start of the chapter that parasitized the fly? It was a zygomycete.) What all zygomycetes have in common is the use of a spore-releasing structure called a sporangium that is shaped something like a lollypop; you can get a close-up view of this structure in **Figure 22.10**.

(a) Bread mold (*Mucor mucedo*) growing on bread

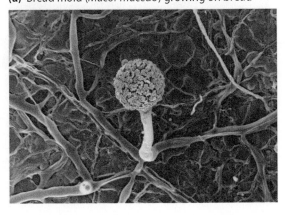

(b) Close-up of spore-laden bread mold sporangium

Figure 22.10
Zygomycete Fungi

(a) When they reproduce asexually, zygomycetes employ variations on the lollipop-like reproductive structure, called a sporangium, you can see in the photo on the left. In this zygomycete (*Mucor mucedo*), seen here from above, growing on a piece of bread, the nutrient-absorbing filaments of the mycelium can be seen forming a network below the sporangium.

(b) A closer view of a spore-laden zygomycete sporangium.

Figure 22.11
The Chytrid Fungi

(a) In this highly magnified micrograph, a Chytrid fungus can be seen releasing a cloud of spores even as it feeds on a pollen grain, visible as the pale brown circle at the photo's center.

(b) Like many of its fellow amphibians, this great barred frog has been infected by the Chytrid fungus *Batrachochytrium dendrobatidis*. Such infections have caused steep, continent-wide declines in some frog species and have brought about the actual extinction of other species. *B. dendrobatidis* invades the skin of frogs, altering it in ways that can be lethal.

(a) Chytrid fungus growing on a pollen grain

(b) Frog infected with a chytrid fungus

● **Chytrids.** The fungi of Phylum Chytridiomycota are very different from any of the others we've looked at. For one thing, most of them live in water. But beyond this, all of them are *mobile* at one point in their life cycle. Indeed, these fungi move through the water using the kind of tail-like flagellum that we saw last chapter in various species of protists. (To picture a flagellum, just think of the "tail" of a human sperm.) And some chytrids don't develop a mycelium but instead are like the yeasts in that they are single-celled.

Given all this, you might wonder why the chytrids are classified as fungi at all. The answer is that they duplicate their DNA in a manner used by all fungi; their cell walls are partly composed of a material found in most fungal cell walls (chitin); and contemporary sequencing of their DNA shows that their closest relatives are fungi rather than any other life-form. The fascinating thing is that the chytrids probably give us an idea of what fungi were like *originally*—back when fungi first evolved from protists. The sessile fungi we've been looking at seem to have evolved from a group of mobile fungi that resembled today's chytrids. Moreover, the chytrids show us how close the association is between fungi and animals. Think of it: DNA sequencing tells us how close fungi and animals are to each other; the chytrids show us what the early, mobile fungi were like; and a good deal of evidence indicates that early animals had the flagellated form of the chytrids. Given all this, the message is that primitive animals probably were not all that different from primitive fungi. Like most of the fungi we've looked at, the chytrids take a toll on other life-forms. One species of chytrid, *Batrachochytrium dendrobatidis*, has been decimating populations of frogs worldwide in recent years (**Figure 22.11**).

Yeasts: *Saccharomyces cerevisiae*

Several times so far, we've taken note of the single-celled fungi called yeasts. Where do they fit within the four-phylum structure of the fungi? The answer is

that, with the exception of the chytrids, each of the fungal phyla has yeast species within it—there are basidiomycete yeast, ascomycete yeast, and zygomycete yeast, in other words. Thus, "yeast" is not a taxonomic category; it merely describes a form that fungi can take. Most yeasts are ascomycetes, but the basidiomycetes are well represented in this category as well. We can define a **yeast** as any single-celled fungus that tends to reproduce by budding. This, of course, raises the question: What's budding? **Figure 22.12** shows it in action. As you can see, budding is not a splitting of one cell down the middle; it is a means of fungal reproduction in which daughter cells are produced as outgrowths of parental cells.

The particular yeast that's shown in the picture deserves special mention since it has been tremendously useful to people for as long as human civilizations

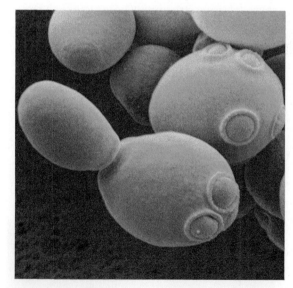

Figure 22.12
Our Partner in Food and Drink

The fungal yeast *Saccharomyces cerevisiae* has been used by human beings for thousands of years in baking and brewing. The *S. cerevisiae* cell at the forefront of the picture is giving rise to a daughter cell through the process of budding. The circular areas on this cell and the one behind it are bud scars—areas from which previous daughter cells have broken away.

ESSAY

A Psychedelic Drug from an Ancient Source

In 1943, chemist Albert Hoffman of Switzerland's Sandoz pharmaceutical company found himself working with a substance that had a long history, most of it tragic. The substance came from a fungus in the genus *Claviceps*, which infects several grain crops, among them rye. The visible manifestation of a *Claviceps* infection is little sickle-shaped growths of black hyphae that pop out among the rye grains (**Figure 1**). Centuries ago, the French perceived these growths to look like an ergot—a little spur that some birds have on their legs—and the name stuck.

In nature, when wild grasses get ergot infections, the effect is not all that notable.

Figure 1
Damaging Intruder
Black ergots of the *Claviceps purpurea* fungus sprout from among the grains of a wheat plant.

The fungus takes some plant nutrition away, the ergot growths fall to the ground in autumn, and spores from it infect the next generation of grass in the spring. The problem for humans comes when the fungus infects *food* crops such as rye and the ergot are ground up along with the rye grains. The result is that ergot becomes a flour ingredient. This is serious because ergot contains a powerful alkaloid; its active ingredient is a member of the family of alkaline substances that also includes cocaine, nicotine, and morphine, along with such poisons as hemlock. In numerous instances, recorded in Europe since the Middle Ages, ergot made its way into the bread that people ate, and the results were disastrous. France in particular had repeated instances of "ergotism," with two of these episodes alone resulting in 50,000 deaths. What did ergot do? Here is a description by Oswald Tippo and William Louis Stern. Ergot's effects included:

> Abortions in pregnant females; burning sensation in extremities; feelings of being consumed by fire; constriction of blood vessels leading to the blockage of circulation and resulting in the appearance of blue discolored areas on the body; onset of gangrene; shriveling and falling off of hands, arms, and legs; experiencing of hallucinations such as wild beasts in pursuit of the victim.

Horrible as these effects were, medical people hearing of them recognized that ergot had the ability to do good as well as harm. Unwanted abortions are a terrible

thing, but labor sometimes needs to be *induced* when a fetus is overdue; likewise, the constriction of blood vessels has its uses when properly controlled. Alkaloids often have such double-edged capabilities. Cocaine was first isolated from the coca plant in 1860, but in the 1880s it became a miracle drug for eye surgery when it served as the first local anesthetic. Morphine, which is derived from poppy plants, is used in medicine as a painkiller. Thus, it's not surprising that drugs were also isolated from ergot over time. In the 1930s, for example, a drug called ergonovine—still in use today—was developed that helps stop bleeding after childbirth.

Thus it was that Albert Hoffman found himself working with ergot in his Basel lab in 1943. He was looking for other useful alkaloids that the fungus might yield. Years before, he had isolated from ergot a chemical core—a compound called lysergic acid—and added to it a manufactured compound called diethylamine, but the results seemed uninteresting to him. This time, however, he apparently absorbed a tiny quantity of the substance through his skin. The outcome, as he later wrote, was that:

> I was seized by a peculiar sensation of vertigo and restlessness. Objects appeared to undergo optical changes and I was unable to concentrate on my work. . . . With my eyes closed, fantastic pictures of extraordinary plasticity and intensive color seemed to surge toward me.

Although he had not intended to, Albert Hoffman had discovered one of the world's most powerful psychoactive drugs: lysergic acid diethylamide, which the world would come to know by its initials, LSD.

have existed. *Saccharomyces cerevisiae* is the most important yeast by far in making bread rise and in making wine and beer ferment. The alcohol in wine is simply a product of *S. cerevisiae*—it feeds on the sugars in grape juice and produces alcohol in the course of its metabolism. In a similar vein, the rise that we see in yeasted breads usually comes from the carbon dioxide given off by *S. cerevisiae* as it feeds on other bread ingredients. As if all this weren't enough, *S. cerevisiae* is a mainstay of scientific research: An entire field of genetics has been built around the study of it.

22.5 Fungal Associations: Lichens and Mycorrhizae

Fungi obtain their nutrition in three basic ways. Any fungus that gets its nutrition from a living organism is a **parasite**—an organism that feeds off another organism but does not kill it immediately and may not kill it ever. Many fungi are parasites: Think of a basidiomycete rust feeding on a wheat crop, a chytrid fungus living in the skin of a frog, or an ascomycete fungus living between your toes (thus giving you athlete's foot). Against this, if a fungus extracts its nutrition from *dead* organic matter, it is a **saprophyte.** Thus, all the basdiomycetes that make a living by breaking down fallen logs are said to be saprophytic, and this same thing is true of any zygomycete that can be found covering an old piece of bread. Some fungi, however, obtain their nutrition not by being parasitic or saprophytic but by being *cooperative* with other organisms. Indeed, one of the cooperative associations that fungi have entered into is so close that it has resulted in two organisms that function as one.

Lichens

Everyone has seen the thin, sometimes colorful coverings called lichens that seemingly can grow anywhere—on rocks as well as on trees, in Antarctica as well as in a lush forest (**Figure 22.13**). As it turns out, lichens are not a single organism. A **lichen** is a composite organism composed of a fungus and either algae or photosynthesizing bacteria. If you look at **Figure 22.14**, you can see that this association can be structured as a kind of sandwich, with an upper layer of densely packed fungal hyphae on top, then a zone of less-dense hyphae that includes a layer of algal or bacterial cells, then another layer of densely packed hyphae on the bottom that sprout extensions down into the material the lichen is

Figure 22.13
Life on the Rocks
Lichens growing on sandstone rocks near the Montana–Wyoming border.

growing on (such as a rock). The example shown is an association between a fungus and an alga, which is the case in about 90 percent of lichens. In these cases, the fungal hyphae either wrap tightly around the algal cells or actually extend into them.

A lichen is mostly a fungus, then, but it is a fungus that could not grow without its algal partner. Why? Because the alga makes its own food through photosynthesis and then proceeds to supply the fungus with

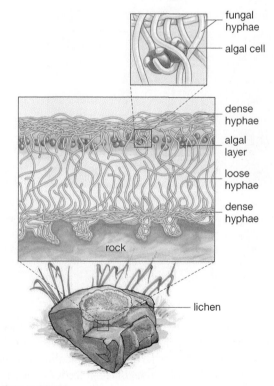

fungal hyphae
algal cell
dense hyphae
algal layer
loose hyphae
dense hyphae
rock
lichen

Figure 22.14
The Structure of a Lichen

most of the nutrients it needs. A debate existed for years about whether the fungus was in turn doing something for the alga, but this has now been settled. The relationship between a fungus and an alga is one of **mutualism**—both parties are benefiting from it. The alga may be supplying food *to* the fungus, but it is getting several things *from* the fungus in return: water, carbon dioxide, minerals, and protection from the elements. This last factor explains why lichens are often so colorful. Their fungi produce brightly colored pigments that can screen out harsh sunlight—something that's important in the exposed environments lichens can be found in.

In nature, the general significance of lichens comes from their role as pioneers in barren habitats where life is just getting established. Because the algae in lichens make their own food, and because the fungi in them can dig into rock itself, lichens can make a living in these tough habitats, whereas most other organisms cannot. Beyond this, lichen fungi produce acids that can help break down rock and build up soil—activities that create habitat for *other* organisms.

Lichens have an ability not only to establish themselves in tough environments but also to persist in them for a long time. If left undisturbed, they can survive for thousands of years in colder climates. The lives of lichens, however, could be characterized not only as long but as slow. At most, they spread out at a rate of about 20 millimeters per year, which is about three-fourths of an inch. Indeed, they have been observed to grow as little as 0.2 millimeters per year, at which pace they would grow by about three-fourths of an inch per century. What accounts for this sluggish rate of expansion? In times of little water, lichen algae stop performing photosynthesis. This puts the entire organism into a state of dormancy—a kind of suspended animation—that persists until water becomes available again.

Mycorrhizae

By some estimates, 90 percent of seed plants live in a cooperative relationship with fungi. The linkage here is one of plant roots and fungal hyphae, with both the plants and the fungi benefiting. What the fungus gets from the association is food, in the form of carbohydrates that come from the photosynthesizing plant; what the plant gets is minerals and water, absorbed by the fungal hyphae. So important is this relationship to plants that some species of trees, such as pine and oak, cannot grow without fungal partners. Other plants will have stunted growth without a fungal partner.

Fungal hyphae generally grow into the plant roots, but in some instances they wrap around the root

Figure 22.15
Underground Partners
Mycorrhizae are associations between plant roots and fungal hyphae that benefit both the plant and the fungus. Here the association can be seen in a highly magnified image of a root and its surrounding hyphae.

without penetrating it. In either case, the root–hyphae associations of plants and fungi are known as **mycorrhizae** (**Figure 22.15**). The mycorrhizal relationship is one of the oldest and most important in nature. It appears that at least 460 million years ago, when the very first plants made the transition to life on land, they did so with fungal partners.

On to a Look at Animals

In this chapter and the one that preceded it, you've looked at bacteria and archaea and at two of the kingdoms within the eukaryotic domain—protists and fungi. Coming up next is a kingdom that is arguably the most familiar of all because we human beings are part of it. Yet it is a kingdom so diverse that it holds a good many surprises as well. It's the kingdom of animals.

SO FAR . . .

1. A lichen is a composite organism, always composed of a _____ and either _____ or _____.

2. In a lichen, the _____ is providing the _____ or _____ with water, carbon dioxide, minerals, and protection from the elements.

3. The cooperative associations called mycorrhizae provide the _____ with sugars, while providing the _____ with water and minerals.

22 REVIEW

Go to the Study Area at www.masteringbiology.com for practice quizzes, myeBook, BioFlix™ 3-D animations, MP3 Tutor Sessions, videos, current events, and more.

Mastering
BIOLOGY™

Summary

22.1 The Fungi: Life as a Web of Slender Threads

- Fungi are heterotrophs: They consume existing organic material to live. Fungi consist largely of webs of slender tubes, called hyphae, that grow toward food sources. Fungi cannot immediately ingest the food the hyphae reach since only small molecules can pass through the cell walls of fungal cells. Fungi thus digest their food externally, through release of digestive enzymes, and then bring the resulting small molecules into the hyphae. (p. 403)

- Collectively, hyphae make up a structure called a mycelium, which forms the bulk of most fungi. Many fungi have a reproductive structure called a fruiting body that produces and releases reproductive cells called spores. All fruiting bodies are organized collections of hyphae. (p. 404)

- Most fungi are sessile, but their hyphae grow toward food sources. Such growth comes only at the tips of the hyphae, not throughout their length. (p. 404)

- Most fungi are multicellular. The primary exception to this, the single-celled yeasts, are thought to have evolved into the single-celled state from an earlier multi-celled condition. (p. 404)

22.2 Roles of Fungi in Society and Nature

- Fungi can be destructive, but they are also sources of medicines and are used extensively in food processing. In nature, fungi join bacteria as major decomposers of the living world. (p. 405)

22.3 Structure and Reproduction in Fungi

- Individual cells that form hyphae often are separated by septa, which are porous enough to allow for a free flow of cellular material between one hyphal cell and the next. Because hyphae can bring resources quickly to the point of growth at the hyphal tips, fungi can grow quickly. (p. 406)

- A mushroom cap, one kind of fruiting body, is made up of accordion-like gills that produce and release spores. Only a tiny fraction of fungal spores will successfully germinate, so fruiting bodies release huge quantities to ensure new fungal growth. (p. 407)

- Two groups of fungi have a dikaryotic phase of life in which the fusion of cells from different parental hyphae produces a single hypha whose cells each have two haploid nuclei—one nucleus coming from one parental hypha, the other from the second parental hypha. (p. 407)

- When the below-ground mycelium in a mushroom sprouts into the above-ground mushroom cap, all the cells in the cap initially are dikaryotic, including those in the reproductive structure called the basidium. The nuclei in certain cells of the basidia then undergo fusion, meaning sex has taken place. The resulting diploid cells then undergo meiosis, thus producing four haploid spores attached to the tip of the basidium. These spores are released and blown by the wind to new locations, where they may germinate. (p. 407)

- A spore is a reproductive cell that can develop into a new organism without fusing with another reproductive cell. (p. 408)

- Most fungi can reproduce by asexual as well as sexual means. In asexual reproduction, fungal spores are produced through mitosis (or simple cell division), which is carried out by one organism. In sexual reproduction, fungal spores are produced through a fusion of nuclei from two separate fungi. (p. 408)

22.4 Categories of Fungi

- There are four phyla of fungi: basidiomycetes, ascomycetes, zygomycetes, and chytrids. The first three are defined by their reproductive structures. (p. 408)

- The basidiomycetes, also known as the club fungi, include "toadstool" mushrooms, "shelf" fungi that can be seen sprouting from trees, and the agricultural pathogens called smuts and rusts. The ascomycetes, also known as the sac fungi, include truffles, morel mushrooms, and fungi that attack stone fruits. The zygomycetes, also known as the bread molds, include many fungi that form associations with plant roots but also include one group of fungi that live by parasitizing insects. The chytrids are a primitive group of mostly aquatic fungi, all of which are mobile at one point in their life cycle. The chytrids give us an idea of what the earliest fungi were like, as the sessile fungi that are so common today seem to have evolved from chytrid-like ancestors. Early fungi were probably similar to early animals. (p. 408)

- A yeast is any single-celled fungus that tends to reproduce by budding, a process in which fungal daughter cells are produced as outgrowths of parental cells. All fungal phyla except the chytrids have yeast species exist within them. The majority of yeasts are ascomycetes, but many are basidiomycetes. (p. 410)

22.5 Fungal Associations: Lichens and Mycorrhizae

- Some fungi obtain their nutrition from living organisms and are thus parasites; some extract nutrition from dead organic matter and are thus saprophytes; and still others obtain nutrition through cooperative associations with other life-forms. One of these associations results in the formation of lichens: composite organisms made up usually of fungi and algae but sometimes of fungi and bacteria. The relationship between fungi and their algal partners in lichens is one of mutualism, in that both parties benefit from the interaction. (p. 412)

- Up to 90 percent of seed plants live in a mutualistic association with fungi that links plant roots with fungal hyphae. In this association, called mycorrhizae, plants supply fungi with food produced in photosynthesis, while the fungi supply plants with minerals and water, gathered by the web of fungal hyphae. (p. 413)

Key Terms

dikaryotic phase	407
hyphae	404
lichen	412
mutualism	413
mycelium	404
mycorrhizae	413
parasite	412
saprophyte	412
sessile	404
spore	408
yeast	410

Understanding the Basics

Multiple-Choice Questions

(Answers are in the back of the book.)

1. Fungi (select all that apply):
   a. are more closely related to plants than animals.
   b. make their own food.
   c. use existing organic material as their food.
   d. digest their food externally.
   e. are usually multicellular.

2. Most fungi are composed almost entirely of:
   a. ball-shaped objects called hypha.
   b. leaves and stems.
   c. reproductive cells called spores.
   d. slender filaments called hyphae.
   e. slender filaments called septa.

3. Fungi cause (select all that apply):
   a. tetanus.
   b. athlete's foot.
   c. common colds.
   d. dry rot.
   e. wheat rust.

4. Fungi are important to humans as (select all that apply):
   a. a source of citric acid.
   b. photosynthesizing organisms.
   c. the source of some antibiotics.
   d. decomposers of dead organic material.
   e. producers of oxygen.

5. Fungi reproduce through cells called spores that (select all that apply):
   a. have a single set of chromosomes.
   b. often are released from structures called fruiting bodies.
   c. usually are released in huge numbers.
   d. must fuse with another spore to bring about germination.
   e. germinate without fusing with another cell.

6. Fungi that obtain their nutrition from living organisms are referred to as _____, while fungi that obtain their nutrition from dead organic material are referred to as _____.
   a. carnivores; herbivores
   b. saprophytes; parasites
   c. omnivores; herbivores
   d. parasites; saprophytes
   e. saprophytes; herbivores

7. The association between fungi and algae (or bacteria) in forming lichens is one of _____ in that _____.
   a. parasitism; only one party benefits from the relationship
   b. competition; neither party benefits from the relationship
   c. competition; both parties are vying for the same resources
   d. mutualism; both parties are benefiting from the relationship
   e. saprophytism; one party is feeding on the dead remains of the other

8. The mycorrhizae formed by the association between fungal _____ and plant _____ are found in _____ seed plants.
   a. hyphae; roots; only a few
   b. spores; leaves; only a few
   c. hyphae; roots; the vast majority of
   d. fruiting bodies; roots; the vast majority of
   e. hyphae; stems; only a few

Brief Review

(Answers are in the back of the book.)

1. Explain the phrase "animals ingest then digest, while fungi digest then ingest."

2. Fungi could be said to take a "lottery" approach to reproduction. In what respect?

3. How does a spore differ from a gamete?

4. Match the fungal phylum on the left with the description on the right

   a. Basidiomycota — Bread molds, spore-releasing sporangium

   b. Ascomycota — Mobile, water-dwelling, early-evolving

   c. Zygomycota — Club-fungi, rusts and smuts, toadstools

   d. Chytridiomycota — Sac fungi, morel mushrooms, truffles

5. Name two defining features of yeast fungi.

Applying Your Knowledge

1. Vaginal yeast infections are caused by the fungus *Candida albicans,* which is one of a community of microorganisms that are always present in the vagina in low concentrations. One of the factors that can bring about a yeast infection is the initiation of the use of certain antibiotics. Why would the use of antibiotics foster an unhealthy multiplication of *C. albicans* in the vagina?

2. The *Entomophthora muscae* fungal parasite that invades flies has no consciousness, yet it manages to undertake actions that affect the behavior of the flies it attacks. (It sends hyphae into the flies' brains, and as a result, the flies crawl upward.) Almost all parasitism is disturbing to human sensibilities, but this brand is particularly unsettling. Why should this be so?

23

Animals:
The Diversity of Life 3

The diversity of animals is one of the wonders of the natural world.

The blue darner dragonfly (*Aeshna cyanea*). The darner's name seems to have come from a folk belief that they use their slender bodies to sew up, or "darn," the lips of misbehaving children.

We human beings are, in a sense, intimate strangers with the bacteria and fungi that were reviewed in the last two chapters. We are intimate with these organisms in that we carry out our lives right along beside them: We walk through clouds of them, wash off layers of them, and have trillions of bacteria living inside us. That said, except for the

occasional outbreak of athlete's foot or case of upset stomach, these organisms never cross our minds. So small are bacteria and most fungi that, while they may be everywhere, for us they are effectively nowhere. It's a different story with the animals that are the subject of this chapter. Our cats and dogs and neighborhood birds are part of our conscious lives. We pay attention to a new spider web on our porch or to the lizard on our hiking path. We wonder about the circling hawk overhead.

Animals come from the long evolutionary line of *other* feeders: the heterotrophs, who cannot manufacture their own food but must get their nutrition from outside themselves. Many bacteria fit into this category, as do lots of protists and all fungi. But animals, in their quest for food, added something that is unique to them: a nervous system; a system for transmitting complex messages rapidly over long pathways in the body. Once this happened, the living world was off to the races in terms of adding novel abilities. Think of sight, hearing, smell, flight, walking, singing, and reading. Then there are such things as the echolocation of bats and the waggle dance of honey bees. For the average person, to be alive means to sense, to investigate, to respond, to move. In all these areas, animals reign supreme in the living world.

This chapter is about the broad diversity that exists in the animal kingdom (**Figure 23.1** on the next page). Given that animals are part of our daily lives, some of what follows will be familiar, but there are likely to be many surprises as well.

23.1 What Is an Animal?

In coming to an understanding of animals, we first have to understand what separates animals from other varieties of living things. And to do this, the question that needs to be answered is: What charac-

teristics do *all* animals have that other organisms *don't* have? It turns out there is a single, rather technical feature that is sufficient to set animals apart from all other living things.

- Animals pass through something called a blastula stage in their embryonic development. A *blastula* is a hollow, fluid-filled ball of cells that forms soon after an egg is fertilized by sperm. All animals go through a blastula stage, but no other living things do.

Four other characteristics are found in all animals, but they're found in other kinds of organisms as well. All animals:

- Are multicelled; there are no single-celled animals.
- Are heterotrophs; they must get their nutrition from outside themselves.
- Are mobile or "motile" for at least part of their lives. (There are, however, animals that are as "sessile" or immobile as any plant during most of their lives.)
- Are composed of cells that do not have cell walls. (The outer lining of animal cells is the plasma membrane. By contrast, all plants and most other creatures have a relatively thick additional lining—the cell wall—outside their plasma membrane.)

Then there are characteristics of animals that don't fit our preconceived notions. While it's true that animals generally are large relative to bacteria or protists, some animals are microscopic. We often think of animals as creatures with backbones (or "vertebral columns"), but there are far more **invertebrates,** or animals without vertebral columns, than animals with them. Indeed, 99 percent of all animal species are invertebrates. We think of animals primarily as land-living or terrestrial creatures, but there is far more animal diversity in the ocean than on land. This makes sense because animals existed in the sea for at least 100 million years before any of them came onto land.

SO FAR . . .

1. A feature common only to animals is that all animals pass through a _____ stage in their _____ development.

2. Four other features that all animals share are that they are _____ for at least part of their lives, _____, _____, and their cells do not have _____.

3. Vertebrates make up a _____ portion of the animal kingdom.

23.2 Lessons from the Animal Family Tree

One way to get a handle on the range of animal life is to look at the large-scale categories of animals and see how the creatures in these categories differ from one another. The animal kingdom's broadest categories are known as phyla, with each phylum informally defined as a group of organisms that shares a basic body structure. Depending on who is counting, there are between 36 and 41 animal phyla. So, in what ways are the members of these various phyla related to one another? To put this another way, what does the animal family tree look like?

(a) Jellyfish

(b) Feather star

(c) Octopus

(d) Nudibranch

(e) Water flea

(f) Bonobo

Figure 23.1
Animal Diversity
(a) Like all jellyfish, these West Coast sea nettles (*Chrysaora fuscescens*) use stinging extensions to immobilize prey.
(b) This feather star (*Oxycomanthus bennetti*), a relative of sea stars, feeds by catching drifting bits of food.
(c) Octopuses such as this one are marine molluscs, in the same phylum as snails and clams.
(d) Nudibranchs such as this one are also marine molluscs.
(e) Water fleas, from the genus *Daphnia,* are tiny aquatic crustaceans. Note the animal's prominent digestive tract.
(f) Bonobos (*Pan paniscus*) are close relatives of chimpanzees.

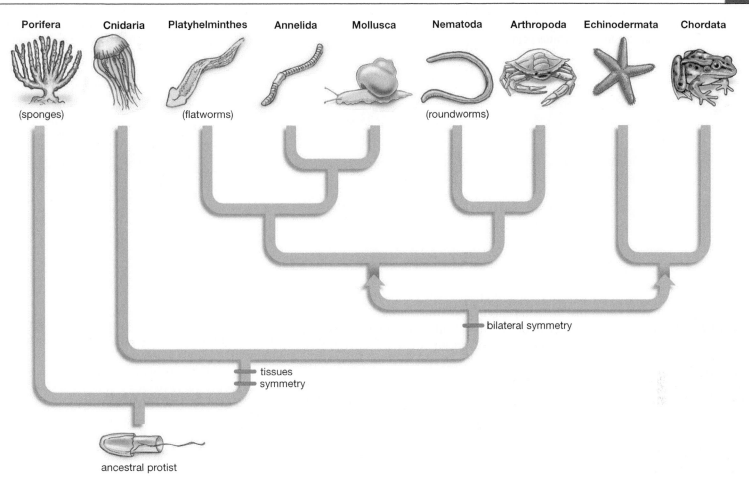

Figure 23.2
A Family Tree for Animals
The animal kingdom is divided into groups called phyla. The members of each phylum have in common physical features that are evidence of shared ancestry. Nine of the estimated 36 to 41 animal phyla are shown here. All these phyla are regarded as having evolved from an ancestral species of protist, shown at lower left in the family tree.

If you look at **Figure 23.2**, you can see one version of it. One way to conceptualize this tree is that, over time, animals became more complex through a series of *additions* to the characteristics found in more primitive animals. The twist is that only some varieties of animals evolved to get these additions, while others retained the primitive, ancestral condition. To get a handle on this large-scale evolution, a good place to start is with some little red lines you can see at the bottom of the tree. We're concerned first with one animal trait labeled there as tissues and another labeled as symmetry. Later on we'll look at the significance of the trait of organs.

Tissues

A **tissue** is a group of cells that perform a common function. In your own body, you have cells that perform the common function of contracting. These are muscle cells, and a group of them constitutes a muscle tissue. Likewise, you have nervous tissue and connec-

tive tissue, and other varieties. Looking down at the trunk of the tree in Figure 23.2, you can see that all animals have a common ancestor—probably a single-celled protist that swam through use of a tail-like flagellum. Now notice that the tree splits above this common ancestor and yields, over to the left, the phylum Porifera, which is made up of sponges. Porifera are truly the outliers of the animal world in that, almost alone among animals, they lack true tissues (and symmetry, which we'll get to in a second). If you look again at the split above the common ancestor, this time going to the right, you can see that the animals on this branch did develop tissues. Note also that this right branch leads to all the other animal phyla. Thus, all the animals that stem from this branch will have tissues. If we looked, for example, at the Cnidarian phylum (which includes jellyfish), we'd see that its members have nervous and muscle tissue. But sponges? They are more like a collection of cells that have come together to form an organism. In a given sponge, each cell acquires its own oxygen and eliminates

(a) Radial symmetry:
Symmetry around a central point

(b) Asymmetry:
No planes of symmetry

(c) Bilateral symmetry:
Symmetry across the sagittal plane

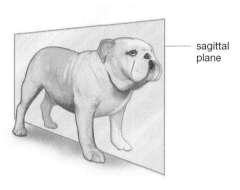

sagittal plane

Figure 23.3
Symmetry Is an Equivalence in Body Sections

If an imaginary plane drawn through an animal can divide that animal into sections that are mirror images of one another, then that animal has symmetry.

a. Radial symmetry. The imaginary planes drawn through the jellyfish show that it has radial symmetry: a symmetry in which body sections are distributed evenly around a central point.

b. Asymmetry. The sponge has no symmetry—no plane drawn through the sponge body would yield sections that are mirror images of one another.

c. Bilateral symmetry. The dog has a kind of symmetry common to most animals: bilateral symmetry, in which the sides of an animal are mirror images of one another.

its own wastes, and there are no groups of sponge cells that function together as true tissues. Tissues are a marker of organization, and in the animal kingdom, only sponges lack this organization.

Symmetry

So what about this second quality noted with a red line, symmetry? If you look at **Figure 23.3a**, you can see that the jellyfish that's pictured can be thought of as being divided by imaginary planes, thus yielding body sections. These sections are mirror images of one another; they have **symmetry,** meaning an equivalence of size, shape, and relative position of parts across a dividing line or around a central point. The jellyfish actually has a particular kind of symmetry. It has **radial symmetry,** meaning a symmetry in which body parts are distributed evenly around a central point. In simpler terms, the symmetry of jellyfish is the symmetry of pie sections.

To appreciate symmetry, consider what a lack of it is like by looking again at our outlier, the sponge, in **Figure 23.3b**. Where is its symmetry? There isn't any, because there is no section of the sponge that is a mirror image of any other.

Symmetry can, however, come in several forms. Look at the dog in **Figure 23.3c**, divided by what is known as a sagittal plane. The dog obviously has symmetry, but it is a different kind of symmetry from that of the jellyfish. As it turns out, the dog has a kind of symmetry that unifies most of the animal kingdom. Animals usually are *different* front-to-back and top-to-bottom, but *symmetrical* side-to-side. Put another way, your head is different than your feet, and your chest is different than your back, but your left *side* is very similar to your right. This is what it means to have **bilateral symmetry:** a bodily symmetry in which opposite sides of a sagittal plane are mirror images of one another. In looking at the animal family tree, you can see that bilateral symmetry was an evolutionary innovation that affected all modern-day animals except for the sponges and the cnidarians.

The Body Cavity

The animal family tree has one other lesson for us regarding unity and diversity among animals. Your stomach expands when you've just had a big meal, but then contracts when you're busy for a few hours. Your heart expands and contracts perhaps 70 times a minute. You bend over to tie your shoes and, unbeknownst to you, many of your internal organs slide out of the way. What allows you to do all this? The answer is an internal space you have: a centrally placed, fluid-filled body cavity called a **coelom.** We humans are not alone in having such a cavity. There are only three animal phyla in Figure 23.2 that *don't* have one: the sponges, the cnidarians, and the members of phylum Platyhelminthes (the flatworms).

What's the value of such a cavity? Well first, it allows for an expandable stomach, which is to say a stomach whose dimensions can vary in accordance with how much food we've ingested, which means it doesn't take up a constant, large amount of space. Along similar lines, it allows reproductive organs to expand to accommodate eggs or offspring. Then there's the fact that if a heart couldn't expand and contract, it couldn't work at all. Finally, a central cavity protects organs from bodily blows and provides a large part of the body with flexibility.

In most instances the coelom surrounds another physical structure, the *digestive tract*—meaning the tube, functioning in digestion, that runs from the mouth to the anus. We can therefore think of the coelom as one tube that encircles another; the coelom is generally tube-shaped, and it surrounds the tube that is the digestive tract. **Figure 23.4** shows you what it means to have no coelom, as in flatworms, and a *true coelom,* as in earthworms. (Not shown is another variation on this theme, a pseudocoel, which roundworms have.) You may wonder why there are no red lines on Figure 23.2 showing where the coelom evolved. So valuable is this internal space that it seems to have evolved independently several times among animals.

Having reviewed a few broad-scale characteristics of the animal kingdom, we'll now look briefly at each of the nine phyla featured in the animal family tree set forth in Figure 23.2. Once we've finished with this review, we'll look at some of the ways animals handle such basic functions as movement, reproduction, and circulation.

SO FAR . . .

1. The sponges in phylum Porifera are outliers in the animal kingdom in that, almost alone among animals, their bodies are not composed of _____ and their body structure lacks the quality of _____.

2. All animal phyla except sponges and cnidarians exhibit _____ symmetry in their body plans, meaning a symmetry in which _____ of their body are mirror images of one another.

3. A coelom is an internal _____ possessed by almost all animals except sponges, jellyfish, and flatworms.

No coelom. Phylum Platyhelminthes, composed of flatworms, is one of the phyla that has no coelom. Note that from its gut to its exterior, the flatworm is composed of uninterrupted tissue.

Coelom. The earthworm is one of many animals that has a coelom — a fluid-filled central cavity that usually surrounds the gut.

Figure 23.4
An Important Space

Most animal bodies have an enclosed cavity or coelom—an internal space that surrounds their digestive tract or other internal structures.

23.3 Across the Animal Kingdom: Nine Phyla

Phylum Porifera: The Sponges

The lives of the most primitive members of the animal kingdom hinge entirely on carrying out a single activity: moving water into, through, and then out of themselves. Because adult sponges are fixed in one spot (generally on the seafloor), everything they need in the way of food and oxygen must come to them in water currents while everything they need to get rid of must be washed away from them in these same currents. If you look at **Figure 23.5**, you can see the body plan that allows sponges to carry out this continual transfer of water. The simple variety of sponge pictured there has a layer of outer cells that is pockmarked with thousands of microscopic pores. Millions of so-called collar cells wave tiny, whip-like flagella that keep water moving into these pores. As the water passes through the sponge cells, the food in it is filtered out and the oxygen captured, after which the resulting waste water is expelled through a large opening at the top of the sponge called an *osculum*. Almost all the 5,000 species of sponges identified to date are marine (meaning ocean-dwelling), but a few freshwater varieties exist as well.

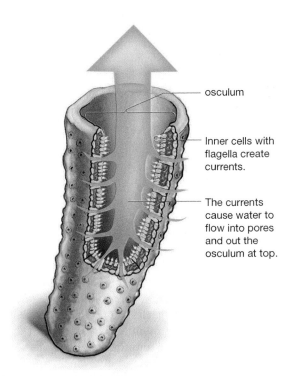

Figure 23.5
A Body Plan for a Simple Lifestyle

Sponges filter water through themselves in order to live. Cells on their interior surface have hairlike extensions, called flagella, whose rapid back-and-forth movement draws water in through pores in the sponge's side walls. After filtering this water for nutrients, the sponge then expels it through a large opening at the top of its body, called an osculum.

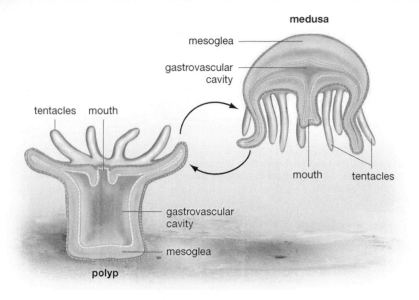

Figure 23.6
Two Stages of Life for Many Cnidarians

Many cnidarians go through both a polyp stage, in which they are attached to a solid surface beneath them, and a medusa stage, in which they swim freely through the water. Note that in the polyp stage, the cnidarian's mouth and tentacles face upward, while in the medusa stage, they face downward. The gastrovascular cavity of the cnidarian functions in both digestion and circulation. The mesoglea noted in the figure is a secreted, gelatinous material that makes up the bulk of the medusa stage in jellyfish cnidarians.

Phylum Cnidaria: Jellyfish and Others

If the signature activity of sponges is filtering water to get food, the signature activity of cnidarians is stinging prey to get it. In the main, cnidarians (knee-DAR-ee-uns) harpoon their prey with extensions that are not only barbed but that may release poisons. Jellyfish are the symbols of this ancient phylum, though sea anemones and the tiny animals that make up coral reefs are also included in it. Almost all the 9,000 identified cnidarian species are marine, though a few live in freshwater.

Most cnidarians have two life stages: a medusa stage that is free-swimming (think of a jellyfish) and a polyp stage that is attached to a surface (think of a sea anemone). The basic body plan in both of these stages is that of a sack, although it is often a sack that is turned upside down. If you look at **Figure 23.6**, you can see how this plays out in connection with an idealized jellyfish. In its familiar adult or medusa stage, its mouth is on the *underside* of its body, while in its immature polyp stage its mouth is on top. Medusa and polyp stages are present in many cnidarians, although corals, sea anemones, and animals called hydra only exist in the polyp stage. In all medusa and in many polyps, however, the basic body plan is the same: a single opening to the outside, serving as both mouth and anus, that is surrounded by tentacles that both sting prey and bring the prey to the mouth.

The mouth is the opening to the jellyfish's gastrovascular cavity, which functions in both digestion and circulation. Surrounding this cavity is the mesoglea, a secreted gelatinous material whose consistency gives jellyfish their name. Cnidarians such as jellyfish can move and exhibit predatory behavior because, unlike sponges, they possess groups of cells that

are organized into the muscle and nervous tissues we talked about earlier.

Phylum Platyhelminthes: Flatworms

The flatworms of phylum Platyhelminthes fit our everyday notions of what animals look like in that they have the bilateral symmetry of most animals, along with a front or "anterior" body portion that is a primitive version of a head (**Figure 23.7**). As we'll see later, flatworms occupy an interesting position in the animal kingdom in that they are the most primitive animals to possess not just the tissues that cnidarians have but organs as well, meaning highly organized structures formed of several kinds of tissues. (Your stomach is an organ that includes nerve and muscle tissues, for example.) Despite this complexity, flatworms lack a good many features that exist in almost all the phyla further up the complexity ladder. They have no coelom or enclosed internal cavity. Thus, except for the tube of their digestive tract, they have very little internal space in them, which limits their flexibility. Further, they have no system of blood circulation. Therefore, every cell in a flatworm must get its oxygen directly from the environment around it, through diffusion from water or air outside the body. This is why flatworms are flat—they have to maximize the number of cells that are near an exterior surface, as opposed to being buried deep inside. (How flat are they? About the width of a sheet of paper.)

Those flatworms that are on land tend to be found under stones or rotting wood; many live at the bottom of the ocean, and a few live in freshwater. Some 25,000 species of flatworm have been identified. Humans are unlikely to notice flatworms because, of the minority

Figure 23.7
Flatworm

Flatworms have the bilateral symmetry seen in most animals, along with a head-like concentration of sensory tissue at their anterior ends. Most flatworms are free-living marine animals like this one, but there are also many parasitic flatworms that live for at least part of their lives inside a host.

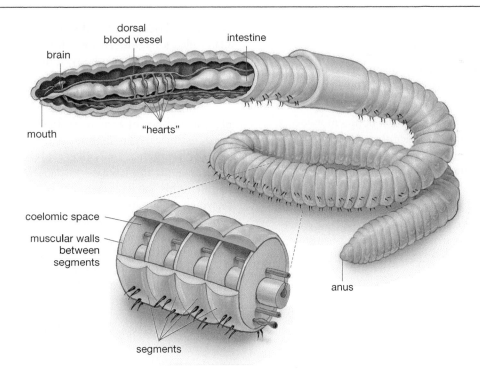

Figure 23.8
The Body Plan of an Earthworm

The segmentation of body parts—a widespread feature in the animal kingdom—is clearly seen in earthworms, whose segments are repeated hundreds of times. The earthworm also expands our notion of what a "heart" amounts to. It has a dorsal blood vessel that contracts, as do human hearts, giving the main impetus to the circulation of red blood that moves through the worm's system. But it also has five pulsating vessels on each side of its intestine that serve as accessory hearts. The coelomic spaces visible in the lower drawing are filled with fluid that serves as a hydrostatic skeleton for the worms.

that live around us, most are very small. When they do come into our consciousness, it is often in the unpleasant role of **parasites,** defined as organisms that feed off prey but do not kill it immediately and may not kill it ever. Most notorious among the flatworm parasites are the animals known as flukes, which are the cause of schistosomiasis, a disease that affects more than 200 million people in tropical areas around the world.

Phylum Annelida: Segmented Worms

The common earthworms that can be seen in such abundance on American lawns after heavy rains are the best-known members of phylum Annelida, the phylum of segmented worms. Annelids provide the clearest example of a feature that exists in numerous animals, including ourselves: **body segmentation,** which can be defined as a repetition of body parts in an animal. In the case of the human body, think of the vertebrae that make up our backbone; 24 of them run in a line from our neck to the base of our back, each of them having a similar structure and a similar function (flexible support and protection). In the case of the earthworm, each of their highly visible "rings" is a marker of a separate segment of their body, as you can see in **Figure 23.8.** Segmentation is valuable to animals in general because it provides a combination of strength and flexibility. (Think of our own backbones, which are highly flexible and yet allow us to push with great force, lift heavy objects, and so forth.)

Earthworms employ this flexible power to burrow in the dirt for hours at a time, ingesting soil for the nutrients it contains and eating leaves or other decaying vegetation.

Earthworms actually represent only the most familiar species in phylum Annelida, which contains about 17,000 named species. Most annelids are ocean dwelling, and some of these colorful creatures, the polychaetes, do not fit in with our idea of drab worms (**Figure 23.9**). The smallest class of annelids is composed entirely of leeches, most of which live up to their reputation of being bloodsucking parasites. Although most leeches live in freshwater, some live in the ocean, and others dwell in damp-land habitats.

Figure 23.9
Annelid Diversity

Not all annelid worms are drab and not all live underground. Polychaetes are ocean-dwelling annelids. Pictured is a Hawaiian Christmas tree worm in the genus *Spirobranchus*. These polychaetes stay in one spot, burrowed into tubes they themselves have constructed, generally within a coral. The bushy "Christmas trees" that extend from the worm's head are structures called radioles that it uses to filter feed from the water.

SO FAR . . .

1. Sponges obtain nutrition and oxygen, and get rid of wastes, by _____ through themselves.

2. Cnidarians tend to exhibit both a mobile _____ stage in which their mouths are on _____ of their bodies, and a sessile _____ stage, in which their mouths are _____.

3. Every cell in a flatworm of phylum Platyhelminthes must get its oxygen directly from the environment around it because flatworms lack a _____ system.

Phylum Mollusca: Snails, Oysters, Squid, and More

Everyone has seen a snail, many of us have eaten clams or mussels, and squid and octopus are probably known to us from television or books. But molluscs are even more varied than these examples would suggest. Some molluscs are slugs and others wormlike; some have highly developed brains and others no brains at all; some are filter feeders and others fierce ocean predators. Depending on the expert consulted, there are between 50,000 and 100,000 described species of molluscs that live in freshwater, saltwater, and on land. Each of these species is a member of one of eight mollusc classes, the most familiar of which are the *gastropods* (snails, slugs), the *bivalves* (oysters, clams, mussels), and the *cephalopods* (octopus, squid, nautilus).

What features unite this huge, diverse group as a single phylum? Outside the realm of technical anatomical details, there really is only one feature common to all molluscs. If you look at **Figure 23.10**, you can see an aquatic snail that displays this feature along with oth-ers. Note a layer near the dorsal (top) surface of the snail called a *mantle*. This is a fold of skin-like tissue that surrounds the upper body of the mollusc and that usually secretes material that forms a shell (although there are lots of molluscs without shells).

In addition to this universal feature, the snail displays a number of structures that are common to most molluscs. The mantle generally drapes over part of the mollusc body like a tablecloth, meaning there is a mantle cavity—a space underneath the mantle. This cavity generally is the site of gills, by which all aquatic molluscs obtain oxygen and by which the filter-feeding bivalves (clams, mussels, oysters) obtain not only oxygen but food. In land-dwelling molluscs, such as garden snails, much of the cavity is a primitive lung that evolved from the gill. Note, in the blowup of the snail's mouth, there is a tooth-covered membrane called the *radula*. Present in most molluscs except the bivalves, this organ can be extended outside the mouth, where it serves as a kind of rasping file. Molluscs use it for scraping a surface or for cutting small prey, then they retract it back into the mouth, thus moving food into their digestive tracts.

Phylum Nematoda: Roundworms

Nematodes, commonly referred to as roundworms, exist in such enormous numbers that it is impossible to imagine life without them. They fit into numerous ecological roles, such as that of "detritivore," meaning an organism that feeds on dead or cast-off organic material. Nevertheless, many farmers in the United States would *like* to imagine life without them because several species of these animals are a major cause of damage to such crops as soybeans and corn. Farmers and research scientists have been united for decades in an entrenched battle against them. In addition, some are human parasites. The disease trichinosis, usually brought on by eating undercooked pork, is caused by a roundworm; likewise, there is hookworm, which affects hundreds of millions of people in warmer climates throughout the world (**Figure 23.11**).

Figure 23.10
Body Plan of a Mollusc
Aquatic snails such as this one have features that are common to many molluscs. All molluscs possess a skin-like tissue called a mantle, which secretes material that can form a shell, whether it is an external shell (as in the snail) or an internal shell (as in a squid). Snails also possess a tooth-covered rasping structure for feeding, called a radula. The unitary "foot" of the snail which works through wave-like contractions is another common mollusc feature.

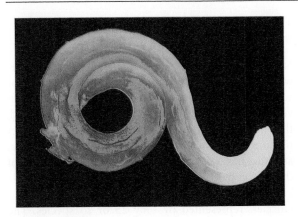

Figure 23.11
Roundworms

The tiny worms called nematodes are a normal part of many ecosystems, including soil ecosystems. However, a small number of roundworm species are harmful to humans, either directly as parasites or indirectly as crop pests. Pictured is a color-enhanced micrograph of the nematode *Toxocara canis,* a parasite that infects dogs. Humans can become infected with *T. canis* eggs if they have contact with an infected dog or contaminated soil.

An acre of prime farmland might contain several hundred billion roundworms, but you don't have to go to farmland to find these animals. They exist in desert sands, polar ice, ocean bottoms, lakes—name a place where life is going on, and nematode worms are likely to be among the living. Indeed, scientists have only the vaguest idea of how many *species* there are; about 15,000 have been catalogued, but 100,000 seems to be the minimum number that actually exist.

Most roundworm species are very small—the crop pests, which feed on roots, generally are microscopic—but some parasitic roundworms are several meters long. The roundworms that have been studied most intensely are those that cause disease and crop damage, and these have a characteristic appearance: transparent, smooth, C-shaped, and cylindrical with tapered ends (hence the term *roundworm*). Across the breadth of roundworm species, however, there is a great diversity in form.

Phylum Arthropoda: Insects, Lobsters, Spiders, and More

Phylum Arthropoda is so large that there are more species in one arthropod group, the insects, than there are in all other animal phyla combined. One way to get a handle on this enormous phylum is to think of it in terms of three subphyla: Uniramia, which includes not only insects but millipedes and centipedes; Crustacea, which includes shrimp, lobsters, crabs, and barnacles; and Chelicerata (chel-is-er-AH-ta), which includes spiders, ticks, mites, and horseshoe crabs.

What characteristics could be shared by a group of animals as varied as these? First, all arthropod animals have a feature we'll be looking at later called an **exoskeleton,** which can be defined as an external material covering the body, providing support and protection. You can see an example of an exoskeleton in the grasshopper pictured in **Figure 23.12**. Second, all arthropods engage in a process of *shedding* their exoskeleton several times during their life—a process known as molting that we'll look at later. Third, all arthropods have what are known as paired, jointed appendages, which are just what they sound like: appendages, such as legs, that come in pairs and that have joints. (The word *arthropod* actually means "jointed leg.") The jointed appendages that arthropods possess come in many forms. Apart from legs, there are claws for predation and defense and wings for flying. These appendages are flexible and often come with sensory attachments, such as sensory "hairs," that keep the arthropod in touch with its environment. The arthropod combination of jointed appendages and an exoskeleton makes for an animal that is often nimble and well defended—one of the reasons arthropods are so numerous.

Phylum Echinodermata: Sea Stars and More

If you look back at the animal family tree in Figure 23.2, you can see that the echinoderms form a "sister" evolutionary lineage to our own phylum, Chordata, which means echinoderms are more closely related to us than they are to, say, arthropods or molluscs. You might expect that, as our close relatives, echinoderms would have the kind of sophisticated features we associate with vertebrate animals—brains, well-developed sense organs, high mobility—but none of

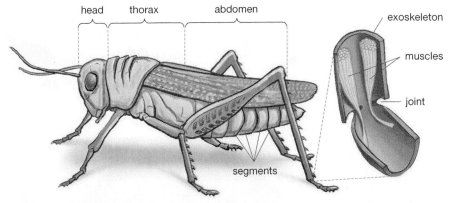

Figure 23.12
Arthropod Features

Arthropods have paired, jointed appendages, as with the legs of this grasshopper. The insects among the arthropods have bodies made up of three large-scale sections: head, thorax, and abdomen. Like the annelid worms, arthropods are segmented. This segmentation is clearly visible in the abdomen region of the grasshopper but is less pronounced in the head and thorax because there the segments have fused. The entire arthropod body is covered in a rigid exoskeleton that is jointed to allow movement.

Figure 23.13
Sea Star Echinoderms

Sea stars such as this one are fierce predators. Here a sea star is managing to open the shell of a bivalve known as a rock cockle. Note the tubed feet with which the sea star grasps the material beneath it.

this is true of the best-known echinoderm, the sea star (**Figure 23.13**). It has no brain, its only sensory organs are the primitive eyespots found on the tips of its arms, and it's capable only of very slow movement. Even the bilateral symmetry that you've seen in every animal since the jellyfish is absent in the adult sea star: It has radial symmetry, like the jellyfish.

This is not to say, however, that the sea star and its echinoderm relatives are completely primitive. Sea stars have a remarkable system for moving that involves forcing water into a series of suction-tipped tube feet that extend from the underside of their arms. Moreover, sea stars evolved into radial symmetry *from* bilateral symmetry. How do we know? Sea star larvae have bilateral symmetry, a quality that is lost when the larvae develop into adults. Taken together, features such as these make sea stars something of a mystery to scientists, as these animals seem to exhibit characteristics from all over the animal map. Joining them in the echinoderm phylum are sea urchins, with their spine-covered spherical bodies, and the less familiar but well-named sea cucumbers (**Figure 23.14**). There are about 7,000 identified species of echinoderms, all of them ocean dwelling and nearly all of them inhabiting the ocean floor, although "floor" in this case may just mean the bottom of a tide pool. Their shared habitat and slow pace of movement make sense when we realize that the entire phylum evolved from a group of sessile filter feeders.

Figure 23.14
A Different Kind of Echinoderm

Despite their resemblance to a vegetable, sea cucumbers are animals that, like their sea star relatives, possess a series of tubed feet with which they crawl across the ocean floor.

Phylum Chordata: Mostly Animals with Backbones

Say the word *animal* and most people think of a vertebrate animal—be it tiger, elephant, deer, lizard, or some other large and probably toothy creature. Yet vertebrates don't even constitute a phylum; instead, they make up only a subphylum, Vertebrata. The larger phylum into which vertebrates fit, called Chordata, actually has two additional subphyla in it. One of these (Cephalochordata) is made up of only a single kind of animal, a small, eel-like creature called a lancelet, represented by only 25 or so species. The other subphylum (Urochordata) has about 3,000 ocean-going species in it but is represented by only three classes of animals. The largest of these classes is made up of the tunicates, whose practice of expelling water earns them their alternative name of sea squirt.

What distinguishes vertebrates from these other chordates? Only the vertebrates have just what you'd expect: a **vertebral column**. Better known as a backbone, this is a flexible column of bones that extends from the anterior to the posterior ends of an animal's dorsal side. Conversely, what unites all the chordates? Four features, which you can see pictured in a lancelet in **Figure 23.15**. At some point in their lives, all chordates have:

- A *notochord:* a stiff, rod-shaped support structure composed of cells and fluid and surrounded by a lining of fibrous tissue, running from the chordate's head to its tail
- A *dorsal nerve cord:* a rod-shaped structure consisting of nerve cells, running from the chordate's head to its tail
- A series of *pharyngeal slits:* openings to the pharyngeal cavity
- A *post-anal tail:* a tail located posterior to the anus

At this point, as a chordate, you may be wondering where your *own* post-anal tail or pharyngeal slits went, so a little explanation of these features is in order. Although the word *notochord* sounds like "nerve cord," the notochord is a flexible but tough *support* structure, not a nervous system feature. A lancelet retains its notochord throughout life, but most vertebrates lose theirs in embryonic life. (Its outer portion develops into the backbone.) A nerve cord may not seem like a feature unique to chordates, but it is the qualifier *dorsal* that makes the difference. Nerve cords exist in annelids and arthropods but these are ventral cords, meaning they are on the underside of these animals.

The pharyngeal slits you see in the lancelet in Figure 23.15 take on more meaning when you understand that, in both humans and lancelets, the pharynx is a passageway just behind the mouth that can be thought of as the first chamber of the digestive tract. Pharyngeal *slits,* then, are perforations of the pharynx,

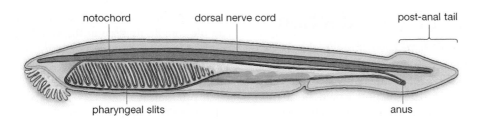

notochord   dorsal nerve cord   post-anal tail

pharyngeal slits   anus

Figure 23.15
Four Universal
Chordate Features
All chordates possess four structures at some point in their lives: pharyngeal slits, a support structure called a notochord, a dorsal nerve cord, and a post-anal tail. In the lancelet, all these features are present in the adult. In humans, only the dorsal nerve cord is clearly evident in adults.

and these serve different functions in different chordates. In the filter-feeding lancelets, they serve to trap food. Meanwhile, in embryonic fish, the slits *develop into* gills, which fish use to obtain oxygen. And in people? If you look at a month-old human embryo, you can see a series of pharyngeal clefts that for a time have openings in them. These pharyngeal slits, however, develop not into gills, but into various other structures, including the space inside the middle ear.

Finally, what about that tail? If you look at **Figure 23.16**, you can see an 8-week-old human embryo with a very clearly developed tail. By the time the embryo is 10 weeks old, however, the tail has almost disappeared. All chordates have a tail at some point. In our oceangoing ancestors, it was used to help move them through the water, as is the case with modern fish. In human adults, though, all that remains of our embryonic tails is a small bone, called the coccyx, located at the base of our vertebral column.

About 50,000 vertebrate chordate species have been identified so far—a small number of species compared to the 1 million species of insects, but a fairly large number as animal phyla go. There are more species of vertebrates than there are of sponges, cnidarians, or flatworms, for example, and vertebrate species numbers may match those of molluscs. In other ways, too, the vertebrates have been a big success. All the largest and swiftest animals are vertebrates, whether in water or in air or on land. And the sheer variety of sensory capabilities that vertebrates have—from echolocation to reading—is unrivaled anywhere in the living world.

Having reviewed some broad-scale features of the various animal phyla, let's now look at some of the ways that varying groups of animals take care of business. How do they reproduce, how do they get oxygen, how do they circulate their bodily fluids, and how do they move?

SO FAR . . .

1. The three most familiar classes of molluscs are the gastropods, one example of which is _____; the bivalves, one example of which is _____; and the cephalopods, one example of which is _____.

2. All arthropods share the features of an _____ or external material that provides support and protection, and _____, _____ appendages.

3. Which of the following traits are not shared by all chordates at some point in their lives: notochord, dorsal nerve cord, exoskeleton, pharyngeal slits, sessile living, post-anal tail?

(a) Human embryo tail at 8 weeks

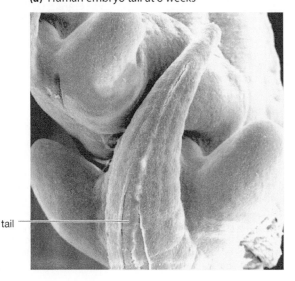

tail

(b) Human embryo tail at 10 weeks

Figure 23.16
The Human Tail
(a) Eight weeks after conception, the human embryo has a very clearly developed tail.
(b) Two weeks later, the tail has almost disappeared. In adult humans, the only vestige of our embryonic tail is a small bone at the base of the vertebral column, the coccyx.

23.4 Animal Reproduction

Those of you who have been through this book's chapters on microbes and fungi know that living things reproduce in a lot of different ways. You might expect that animal reproduction would be a little more familiar, but the range of reproductive "strategies" or practices that animals employ is extremely varied, as you'll see.

Asexual Reproduction

Perhaps the most basic distinction in reproduction has to do with whether it is sexual or asexual—do reproductive cells from two different individuals come together and fuse their genetic material (sexual reproduction), or is there reproduction without this fusion (asexual reproduction)? We're used to thinking of animal reproduction as being sexual because the animals we're most familiar with—the vertebrates—almost always reproduce sexually. But when we look over the animal kingdom as a whole, we find that the more primitive animal phyla are

apt to reproduce *both* sexually and asexually. As we move up the complexity scale in the kingdom, sexual reproduction becomes more and more the norm, but asexual reproduction occasionally exists even in very complex animals, as you'll see.

If you look at **Figure 23.17**, you can see an example of a primitive animal that reproduces both sexually and asexually. The creature is *Obelia*, a tiny jellyfish-like cnidarian, and its sexual reproduction is straightforward: Female medusa-stage *Obelia* produce eggs, the males produce sperm, both kinds of reproductive cells are ejected into the water, sperm fertilize eggs, and a new generation of *Obelia* begins development. But note that the larva that represents this new generation develops into a "polyp" stage *Obelia* that implants on a surface (perhaps on some algae or a rock). Once this happens, the polyp reproduces by **budding:** a form of asexual reproduction in which an offspring is produced as an outgrowth of a parent organism. The polyp that results from this budding could be thought of as a colony that in turn develops polyps of two kinds: those that are specialized for feeding and

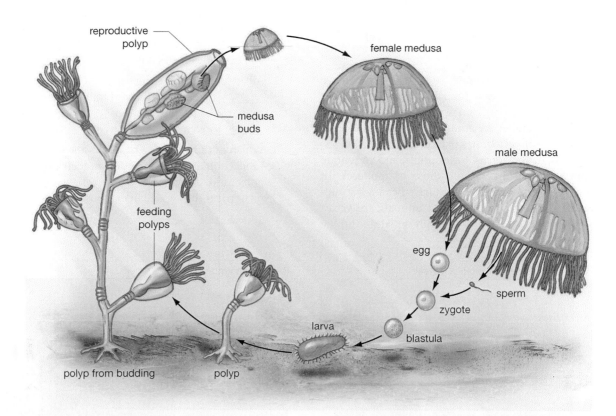

Figure 23.17
Sexual and Asexual Reproducer

This cnidarian, known as *Obelia*, reproduces through both sexual and asexual means. Sexual reproduction can be observed at the right of the figure, where male and female medusae release sperm and eggs, respectively, that fuse to form the new generation of *Obelia*. The polyp that results from this fusion, however, can reproduce by asexual means. Cells bud off from the first polyp (center) and grow into another polyp, shown at left, which may be the first of many that will develop this way. Polyps within these larger colonies specialize. Some are involved in feeding, while others function in reproduction. The reproductive polyps have medusae developing inside them (the medusa buds), which are released to the surrounding water, starting the life cycle over again. The different stages of the life cycle are drawn at different scales.

Figure 23.18
Obelia Up Close

A micrograph of the tiny cnidarian *Obelia* in its colonial polyp stage. The red, central stalk attaches to two kinds of polyps: those without tentacles, which are reproductive; and those with tentacles, which function in feeding. The reproductive polyps contain medusa buds that are being released into the water as mature medusae.

those that are specialized for the production of medusa-stage *Obelia*—the very thing our life cycle started with. These medusa *Obelia* then go on to engage in sexual reproduction, and the whole cycle repeats (**Figure 23.18**).

Forms of asexual reproduction other than budding are possible as well. Within the flatworm phylum (Platyhelminthes), certain worms can reproduce by what is known as *fission,* which simply means they break themselves roughly in half. The posterior (tail) portion of the worm grasps the material beneath it, while the anterior (head) portion moves forward. The separated halves then grow whatever tissues they need to make themselves complete worms.

Next, there is a form of asexual reproduction that is found among bees and ants, and that even exists in a small number of reptile species. Among common honeybees (*Apis mellifera*), a queen bee might lay 2,000 eggs per day. Nearly all of these eggs are fertilized by sperm the queen has received during one of her "nuptial" flights, and each one of these eggs will develop into one of the worker bees of the colony— every one of them a female. A queen can, however, choose to let some of her eggs go unfertilized; no

sperm from a male ever fuses with these eggs, yet bees develop within them and hatch from them. Since egg and sperm do not come together in this process, this is not sexual reproduction. Instead, each of these bees has been derived through **parthenogenesis:** a form of asexual reproduction in which an unfertilized egg develops into an adult organism.

Among the honeybees, all the bees derived through parthenogenesis are males—these are the few "drones" of a bee colony. But in other animals, parthenogenesis can produce females. Indeed, if you look at **Figure 23.19** you can see a lizard whose species produces nothing *but* females by employing parthenogenesis. All the members of this species are female, and all reproduction in the species comes through parthenogenesis. Thus, each new lizard develops solely from one of her mother's eggs, meaning that each is a clone of her mother.

Variations in Sexual Reproduction

Having looked at some of the ways animals reproduce asexually, you might think that all sexual reproduction in animals would follow the pattern we saw with *Obelia:* Sperm and eggs are produced by male and female members of a species; these reproductive cells come together and result in offspring. But the animal kingdom is more varied than this. If you look at **Figure 23.20** on the next page, you can see one variation in the form of the flatworm *Dugesia,* which is part of the phylum Platyhelminthes. Note that *Dugesia* has both testes *and* ovaries, along with both a penis and a genital pore (which is analogous to a vagina). *Dugesia* is a **hermaphrodite,** meaning an animal that possesses both male and female sex organs. When two *Dugesia* copulate, each projects its penis and inserts it in the genital pore of the other. (Can a given flatworm fertilize itself? It occasionally happens in the class of parasitic flatworms known as tapeworms.)

Figure 23.19
All-Female Species

Pictured is a whiptail lizard, *Aspidoscelis uniparens,* that reproduces solely through parthenogenesis. Because the eggs these lizards produce are not fertilized by males, they contain only one set of chromosomes, the mother's. As a consequence, each hatchling is genetically identical to her mother—each is a clone of her mother.

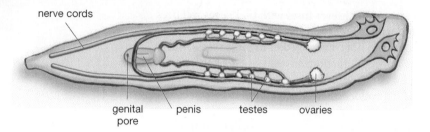

nerve cords

genital pore   penis   testes   ovaries

Figure 23.20
Hermaphrodite
The flatworm *Dugesia* is a hermaphrodite, as it possesses both the sex organs of a male (penis and testes) and those of a female (ovaries and genital pore).

Several variations exist on the theme of hermaphrodism. If we look at the oysters that are part of phylum Mollusca, we find that, while they have separate sexes, a given individual can *change* its sex between mating seasons. A frequent course of events is for an oyster to mature as a male and then change to a female later on. This kind of male-to-female transition is surprisingly common in the animal kingdom; some fish, eels, snails, and shrimp go through it as well. Female-to-male transitions are less common, but they do occur.

SO FAR . . .

1. Sexual reproduction in animals entails a fusion of _____ and _____ from different individuals.

2. Budding, fission, and parthenogenesis are all forms of _____ practiced by animals. In parthenogenesis, an _____ develops into an adult organism.

3. An animal that possesses both male and female sex organs is known as a _____.

23.5 Egg Fertilization and Protection

If we look strictly at sexual reproduction in animals, a central question across the animal kingdom is one we've touched on already: How do eggs get fertilized, and how are they taken care of until such time as off-spring result from them? If we think again about the jellyfish-like creature *Obelia* noted earlier, you may recall that it has a very simple strategy on both counts: Eggs are deposited by the female directly into the ocean, after which sperm from the male likewise are deposited; then water currents bring the two kinds of reproductive cells into contact, after which neither parent provides any kind of care to the fertilized eggs. *Obelia* thus provides an example of what is generally regarded as the most primitive and ancestral condition in the animal kingdom. Both males and females simply "broadcast" their eggs and sperm into the environment at the same time. Neither male

nor female attempts to protect these gametes (eggs and sperm), the gametes themselves are fragile, and the union of gametes is a matter of water currents and chance.

If we followed the twin issues of gamete union and fertilized egg protection across the animal kingdom, what we would see, with movement up the species complexity scale, is a general trend toward fewer eggs, more directed means of bringing these eggs together with sperm, and greater protection for the fertilized eggs that result.

With respect to bringing gametes together, a fundamental question is whether fertilization takes place outside the female (external fertilization, as in *Obelia*) or takes place inside the female (internal fertilization, as in the human female). As it turns out, external fertilization is rarely seen in animals except in aquatic environments, for the simple reason that unfertilized eggs desiccate—they perish by drying out—when they are not either in a body of water or in a female's reproductive tract.

You might expect that all instances of internal fertilization would involve something that is familiar to us from the world of mammals: **copulation,** which is to say the release of sperm within a female by a male reproductive organ. But the animal kingdom is more varied than this. The males of many species produce what are known as spermatophores (sperm packets), which in some cases must be introduced into the female reproductive tract by the females themselves. The male of a European amphibian called the great crested newt (*Triturus cristatus*) will do a courtship dance in front of a female, waving his tail, and then deposit a spermatophore on the ground in front of her and block her path in hopes that she will scoop the packet into the opening of her reproductive tract.

Protection for Eggs: The Vertebrates

With respect to the other issue we're concerned with, the protection of fertilized eggs, different strategies are followed across the animal kingdom. But we're going to focus here on just a few reproductive snapshots from one small part of the kingdom, the vertebrates in phylum Chordata.

In **Figure 23.21,** you can see the life cycle of a familiar amphibian vertebrate, the frog, whose reproduction usually involves the kind of contact between the male and female that you can see in the figure: the male clasps the female in an embrace called amplexus, which can go on for hours or even days. This stimulates the female in such a way that she lays her eggs into the water, after which the male deposits his sperm on top of them. These eggs are fragile, however, and predators tend to be plentiful in the environments in which frogs live. A common response of frogs to this situation is to invest time and effort in

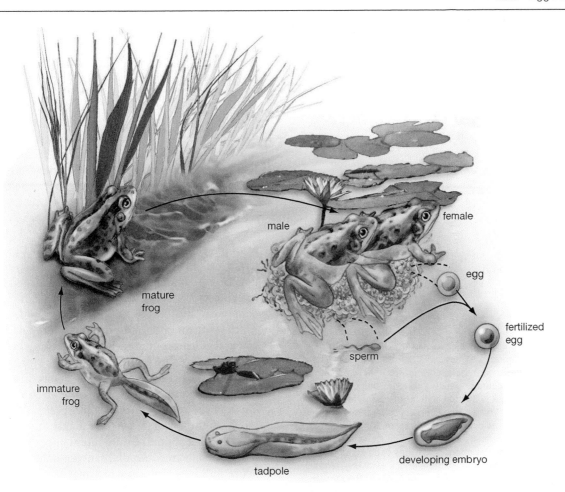

Figure 23.21
Fragile Eggs, Aquatic Environment

Amphibians such as frogs utilize external fertilization, generally releasing both eggs and sperm into water. The eggs must remain in an environment that is at least moist, lest the embryos in them perish from drying out. The tadpoles that hatch out of the eggs in this species are likewise aquatic until such time as they lose their tails, develop lungs, and begin living on land.

keeping the eggs protected. A clear, if unusual, example of this is seen in the Central American frog *Physalaemus pustulosus,* whose females will, while locked in amplexus with the male, secrete a mucus that both frogs then proceed to beat into a froth with their legs. What results is a foam nest, resting on top of the water, that the eggs and sperm are deposited into (**Figure 23.22**). Four days later, little tadpoles drop out of the underside of the nest and start swimming away.

Egg protection efforts of this sort are common across much of the animal kingdom. What interests us is to follow the evolutionary progression in such protection that starts with amphibians. Note that the frogs we looked at laid their eggs in the water. They did so because their eggs were vulnerable not just to predators but to the drying out we talked about earlier. So critical is this issue of desiccation issue to frogs that even those species that are completely terrestrial must lay their eggs in environments that are at least moist if offspring are to result.

Those of you who went through Chapter 19 know, however, that amphibians gave rise to another vertebrate line that was able to completely break the tie between water and reproduction and thus move inland in great numbers. How did these later-evolving creatures preserve their eggs out of water? They

Figure 23.22
Stirring Up Protection

Two tungara frogs (*Physalaemus pustulosus*) stir up foam that will serve as a protective hiding place for eggs that will be deposited by the female and fertilized by the male. These frogs were photographed in the Panamanian rainforest.

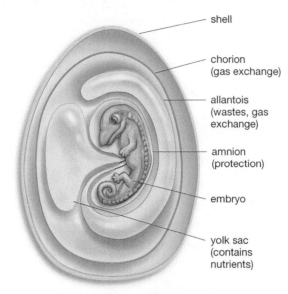

shell

chorion
(gas exchange)

allantois
(wastes, gas
exchange)

amnion
(protection)

embryo

yolk sac
(contains
nutrients)

Figure 23.23
An Egg for Many Environments

The amniotic egg was an evolutionary development that allowed vertebrates to move inland from the water. The egg's features meant that, in dry environments, the embryo would not desiccate or perish through a loss of fluids. The egg's tough shell is the first line of defense; it limits evaporation of fluids. The amnion is one of several membranes that provide some cushioning protection for the embryo. The allantois serves as a repository site for the embryo's waste products. The chorion provides cushioning protection and works with the allantois in gas exchange, meaning the movement of oxygen to the embryo and the movement of carbon dioxide away from it. The yolk sac provides the nutrients the embryo will need as it develops.

employed a different kind of egg. If you look at **Figure 23.23**, you can see the **amniotic egg:** an egg produced primarily by reptiles and birds whose shell and system of membranes provide protection and life support to a developing embryo. Protection? The shell maintains a watery environment *inside* the egg, while several of the egg's membranes provide cushioning. Life support? Other membranes in the egg allow for oxygen to flow to the embryo, for carbon

dioxide to flow from it, and for waste products to be stored away.

Protection of the Young

Modern reptiles generally lay their eggs and then abandon them before the young ever hatch out of them. If we ask why reptiles do this, one answer might be: because they can. The amniotic egg provides such a protective environment that parental guarding of the eggs isn't necessary. There are, however, some fascinating exceptions to this rule. If you look at **Figure 23.24**, you can see a reptile family tree that starts, at the base, with an ancestral reptile. Note that, early on, mammals evolved from this reptile line (over on the left). What really interests us, however, are the three evolutionary lines at upper right: dinosaurs, birds, and crocodilians (meaning both crocodiles and alligators). Now, among contemporary creatures who employ an amniotic egg, which of them also *guard* not only the eggs but the young that hatch out of them? The answer is birds and crocodiles. Birds are well known for their protective behavior toward their eggs and hatchlings, but female crocodiles also turn out to be fierce protectors of their eggs and young. (In some crocodile species, the mother stays with the young for over a year after they hatch.)

Now, what about the third line at upper right in the reptile family tree, the dinosaurs? Recent fossil evidence indicates that dinosaurs may have stayed with their newly hatched young too. The phrase "attentive parents" may not readily come to mind in connection with dinosaurs, but this may have been the case. In 2004, fossils of a plant-eating dinosaur were found in China surrounded by 34 juvenile dinosaurs—a configuration that is hard to explain unless the adult had a close association with the juveniles (**Figure 23.25**). Taking a step back from this, the interesting thing is that protective behavior toward the young may have developed in an evolutionary line that began with the common ancestor of ancient crocodilians and dinosaurs and that then continued in the birds that descended from dinosaurs.

Figure 23.24
The Evolution of Offspring Protection

Most reptiles do not stay with their eggs through the time that hatchlings emerge from them. This is not the case, however, with crocodilians or with birds (who evolved from dinosaurs). They guard both their eggs and, for a considerable time, the young that hatch out of them. Some recent evidence indicates that dinosaurs may have done this as well. Note that mammals evolved from a different lineage of reptiles.

mammals   turtles   snakes   lizards   crocodilians   dinosaurs   birds

ancestral reptile

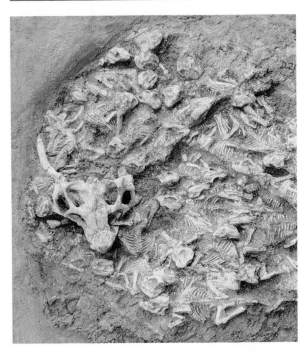

Figure 23.25
Parent and Offspring?
Researchers in China found the fossilized remains of a parrot-like dinosaur, *Psittacosaurus,* surrounded by 34 juveniles. The 125-million-year-old fossils provide evidence that dinosaurs provided care to their young after they were hatched.

Protection in Mammals

So, thus far we've seen protective behavior on the part of amphibians, a more protective egg that evolved in reptiles, and this egg combined with protective behavior among a select group of reptiles. What else could vertebrate evolution produce in the way of protection for offspring? A dandy of an innovation, as it turned out. When we look at *mammals,* we find that their embryos are protected and nurtured by the mother's entire body. An egg that is fertilized in a mammalian female's reproductive tract then *stays* in it, implanting in the female's uterus and developing there. Most mammals are thus **viviparous:** Reproduction occurs by means of fertilized eggs developing inside the mother's body. In contrast, most reptiles and all birds are **oviparous:** Reproduction occurs by means of the young developing in fertilized eggs that are laid outside the mother's body.

In most mammals, implantation of the embryo triggers the formation of a network of blood vessels and membranes, called the placenta, through which nutrients and oxygen flow to the embryo and through which wastes and carbon dioxide flow from it. Most mammals are thus said to be placental, but there are some well-known exceptions to this rule. A small group of early evolving mammals lay eggs, just as reptiles do. These are the monotremes, represented by the duck-billed platypus (**Figure 23.26a**). And there are mammals in which the young develop only to a limited extent inside the mother's body. These are the marsupials, which include kangaroos (**Figure 23.26b**). But the vast majority of mammals today are placental (**Figure 23.26c**).

Mammalian care doesn't stop with the birth of the young, of course. Indeed, mammals are the supreme caregivers of the living world. If we look, for example, at elephants, we find that an elephant calf might be nurtured by its mother and a larger kinship group for the first 10 years of its life. To see an even more stellar example of parental care, however, we need look no further than a species that is very familiar to us, the primate known as *Homo sapiens.* We human beings lavish more care on our offspring than any other creature in nature.

Figure 23.26
Three Types of Mammals
Mammals differ in their reproductive strategies.

(a) This duck-billed platypus is a monotreme—a mammal that lays eggs.

(b) Kangaroos are marsupials—they give birth to physically immature young, which then develop further within the mother's pouch. Pictured are a mother and her fairly mature "joey" in eastern Australia.

(c) The young of placental mammals, such as this brown bear (*Ursus arctos*), develop to a relatively advanced state inside the mother, with nutrients supplied not by an egg but by a network of blood vessels and membranes—the placenta.

(b) Marsupial

(a) Monotreme

(c) Placental mammal

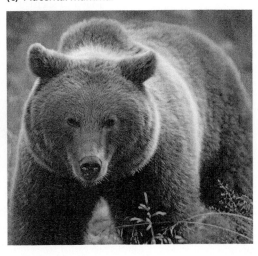

SO FAR . . .

1. With respect to egg fertilization and protection, the primitive, ancestral state in the animal kingdom is believed to be one in which eggs and sperm are _____ into water and brought together by water currents, after which parents provide _____ care to fertilized eggs.

2. The more complex the animal in the animal kingdom, the _____ the number of eggs that are likely to be produced and the _____ amount of care parents are likely to provide to fertilized eggs.

3. The amniotic egg, which evolved in _____, was important because it allowed eggs to be laid _____.

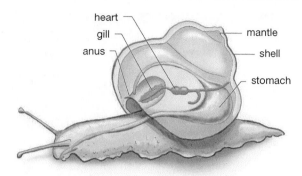

Figure 23.28
Organ Complexity

Gastropods such as this snail have a sophisticated set of organs. For example, the snail has gills to transfer oxygen into its body, a heart to pump its blood, and a stomach to hold and digest its food.

23.6 Organs and Circulation

Figure 23.27 shows you a creature we talked about earlier in connection with reproductive anatomy, the flatworm *Dugesia*. You can see that, in addition to having the testes and ovaries mentioned earlier, *Dugesia* has two primitive eyes and two collections of nerve cells (called cerebral ganglia), which might be thought of as a primitive brain, along with a highly branched intestine that delivers nutrients to all parts of its body. Meanwhile, the pharynx you can see is a muscular feeding structure that *Dugesia* can use to penetrate the bodies of prey animals.

What all this adds up to is that *Dugesia* has **organs:** highly specialized structures that generally are formed of several kinds of tissues. (You may recall that tissues are formed of collections of similar cells.) We're so used to the idea of animals having organs—such as a heart or a liver—that *Dugesia*'s possession of organs may not seem all that impressive. But as we saw earlier, *Dugesia*'s phylum, Platyhelminthes, actually is where

organs *start* in the animal kingdom. Sponges don't even have tissues, and jellyfish have nothing as organized as testes or ovaries. From Platyhelminthes all the way up the ladder of complexity, however, organs are the rule.

You may recall, however, that while a flatworm such as *Dugesia* is organizationally sophisticated compared to some animals, it is organizationally *simple* compared to others. Like all its fellow flatworms, *Dugesia* has no circulatory system, which means that every one of its cells must get its oxygen directly from the environment around it. In addition, it lacks a complete digestive tract, in that it has no anus, which means that waste must be expelled through its mouth.

All this stands in contrast to what you can see in **Figure 23.28**, which is a simplified representation of the aquatic snail we looked at earlier in connection with phylum Mollusca. Notice that the snail has organs that are familiar to us—a heart and stomach—along with gills, which serve to move oxygen into its circulation. Among the items that have helped free the snail from the constraints of shape and size seen in *Dugesia* are its coelom, or internal body cavity, which allows an expandable stomach and a beating heart, and its circulatory system, which allows nutrients to get to tissues that exist far away from its surface.

Figure 23.27
Organs in an Early Form

In addition to its sexual organs, the flatworm *Dugesia* has other organs—primitive eyes, for example, branched intestines, a pharynx that functions in feeding, and clusters of nerve cells (the cerebral ganglia) that function like a brain.

Open and Closed Circulation

The snail's circulatory system turns out to offer us another comparative lesson, this time not relative to a flatworm but relative to ourselves. We have what is known as a **closed circulation system**—a system of circulation in which blood *stays within* the blood vessels. There is some leakage of the liquid portion of our blood, but the basic arrangement is that, while oxygen and nutrients diffuse out of our blood vessels, most of the blood itself stays confined. In contrast, the snail and most other molluscs have an **open circulation system**—a circulation system in which blood flows out of blood vessels altogether, into spaces or sinuses where it bathes the surrounding tissues. Veins then collect the blood (or hemolymph) in these sinuses for a return trip to the gills and the heart. The most complex molluscs, the cephalopods (squid, octopus, etc.), have a closed circulation system like ours; but this isn't surprising, since only a closed system has the efficiency to support an animal as large as a squid. The animal kingdom as a whole is mixed with respect to open and closed systems. All vertebrates have closed systems, for example, while all arthropods have open systems.

23.7 Skeletons and Molting

How do we raise our arm? Two things are required: a muscle to exert force and an object to exert this force against—a bone, which is part of a support network called a skeleton. If we look at the human body, we take for granted that our skeleton lies interior to our muscles. But this isn't always the case in the animal kingdom. You may recall that when we looked at arthropods (insects, crustaceans, etc.), we saw that they have an exoskeleton, meaning an external material covering of the body that provides support and protection. Arthropod muscles pull against a skeleton, but this skeleton lies external to the arthropods' muscles.

Having a skeleton on the outside of the body, however, means that the arthropod body can only grow so much before it expands right into the skeleton. When this happens, arthropods are able to continue their growth only after engaging in **molting:** a periodic shedding of an old skeleton followed by the growth of a new one. If you look at **Figure 23.29**, you can see a picture of a crab that has just slipped out of its old skeleton. Molting activity of this sort is not limited to the arthropods. The roundworms of phylum Nematoda also have an exoskeleton, and it turns out that they shed it four times during their lives. Since roundworms and arthropods make up such a large proportion of the animal kingdom, the way to think of molting is as a widespread phenomenon among animals.

Figure 23.29
Old and New

Arthropods have an outer skeleton, or exoskeleton, of a fixed size. They are able to grow by periodically shedding, or molting, this stiff skeleton. The crab in the photograph has just finished molting; its old exoskeleton lies nearby.

The exoskeletons that are part of molting stand in contrast not only to our own *endo*skeleton but to a third variation on animal skeletons, exemplified in the earthworms of phylum Annelida. Now, an earthworm has muscles and everyone knows it can move; yet it has no bones for its muscles to pull against. So *how* does it move? Each of the earthworm's many segments contains a so-called coelomic space (which you can see in Figure 23.8 on page 423). Each space is filled with fluid, and it is this fluid that serves as the earthworm's skeleton. Here's how it works. Imagine squeezing a water-filled balloon. The volume of the water doesn't change, but the *shape* of the balloon does, in response to the pressure of the water. In the same way, the earthworm can squeeze one set of muscles and *lengthen* a set of its segments. Thus, the earthworm employs what is known as a **hydrostatic skeleton,** a skeleton in which the force of muscular contraction is applied through a fluid. Hydrostatic skeletons are common in the animal kingdom. Apart from annelids like the earthworm, they exist in cnidarians (jellyfish, etc.), flatworms, and roundworms.

Table 23.1, on the next page, presents a summary of all the phyla reviewed in this chapter.

On to Plants

The animals we've looked at this chapter set the standard for mobility in the living world, but if you look outside your window, the vast majority of living things you'll see aren't mobile at all, but instead are fixed in one spot from the time they come into being to the time they die. Nevertheless, these organisms are vigorously alive. They are constantly building themselves up with what they take from the Earth and the air; they push their roots into the ground and their stems toward the sky; they produce flowers, fruits, fragrances, wood, and oxygen by the ton. These are the plants, the subject of Chapter 24.

Table 23.1

Animal Phyla

Phylum	Members include	Live in	Characteristics
Porifera	Sponges	Ocean water (marine), with a few living in freshwater	Sessile (fixed in one spot) as adults, no symmetry. System of pores through which water flows serves to capture nutrients. Bodies do not have organs or true tissues. Sexual and asexual reproduction
Cnidaria	Jellyfish, hydrozoans, sea anemones, coral animals	Almost all marine; a few in freshwater	Radial symmetry, medusa (swimming) and polyp (largely sessile) stages of life. Use stinging tentacles to capture prey. Have tissues. Can reproduce sexually or by budding.
Platyhelminthes	Flatworms (including flukes, tapeworms)	Marine, freshwater, or moist terrestrial environments	Bilateral symmetry, hermaphroditic, possess organs, no central cavity. Many are parasites. Can reproduce through fission.
Annelida	Segmented worms	Most are marine, some freshwater and moist terrestrial	Distinct body segmentation in varieties such as earthworms. Leeches are annelids.
Mollusca	Gastropods (snails, slugs), bivalves (oysters, clams, mussels), cephalopods (octopus, squid, nautilus)	Marine, freshwater, moist terrestrial	Mantle that can secrete material that becomes shell; mantle cavity housing gill or lungs.
Nematoda	Roundworms	Almost all environments	Small size in most, but some are several meters long. Many are crop pests, other animal parasites.
Arthropoda	Vast group that includes insects, spiders, mites, crabs, shrimp, and centipedes	Many aquatic and terrestrial environments	External skeleton; paired, jointed appendages; molting; open circulation system.
Echinodermata	Sea stars, sea urchins, sea cucumbers	Always marine, most on ocean floor	Generally have radial symmetry as adults; tube feet in some species, slow ocean floor movement in most.
Chordata	Vertebrates, lancelets, sea squirts	Great variety of aquatic and terrestrial environments	At some point, all possess notochord, dorsal nerve chord, pharyngeal slits, post-anal tail. Vertebrates have vertebral column.

SO FAR . . .

1. In closed circulation systems, blood _____ blood vessels, while in open circulation systems, it _____ to bathe surrounding tissues.

2. Insects and crustaceans have a skeleton different from ours. Theirs

is an _____: a skeleton that forms an _____ on an animal body.

3. Animals with an exoskeleton are able to continue to grow by employing the practice of _____, which can be defined as _____.

Go to the Study Area at www.masteringbiology.com for practice quizzes, myeBook, BioFlix™ 3-D animations, MP3 Tutor Sessions, videos, current events, and more.

Summary

23.1 What Is an Animal?

- Only animals pass through a blastula stage in embryonic development. A blastula is a hollow, fluid-filled ball of cells that forms once an egg is fertilized by sperm. (p. 417)

- In addition, all animals are multicelled, are motile at some point in life, are heterotrophs, and are composed of cells that do not have cell walls. (p. 417)

23.2 Lessons from the Animal Family Tree

- Except for the sponges in Porifera, the members of all the phyla reviewed have bodies composed of tissues. (p. 419)

- Except for Porifera and Cnidaria, all phyla reviewed exhibit bilateral symmetry. Cnidaria exhibits radial symmetry while Porifera exhibits no symmetry. (p. 420)

- The members of all phyla reviewed other than Porifera, Cnidaria, and Platyhelminthes possess a central body cavity known as a coelom. (p. 420)

23.3 Across the Animal Kingdom: Nine Phyla

- Phylum Porifera's sponges live by drawing water into themselves through a series of tiny pores on their exterior and then filtering the food from this water while extracting oxygen from it. (p. 421)

- Phylum Cnidaria (jellyfish, sea anemones, hydras, and reef-building coral animals) use stinging tentacles to capture prey. Many cnidarians have both an adult, medusa stage of life, which swims in the water, and an immature, polyp stage of life, which generally remains fixed to a solid surface. (p. 422)

- The flatworms of phylum Platyhelminthes are mostly small creatures, dwelling either in aquatic or moist terrestrial environments. Flatworms have bilateral symmetry and organs, but have no coelom or system of blood circulation. (p. 422)

- The worms of phylum Annelida provide a clear example of body segmentation. Most annelids are marine, and some dwell in freshwater, though common earthworms are terrestrial. (p. 423)

- Three important classes of phylum Mollusca are the gastropods (snails, slugs); the bivalves (oysters, clams, mussels); and the cephalopods (octopus, squid, nautilus). All molluscs possess a fold of skin-like tissue called a mantle that usually secretes material that forms a shell. (p. 424)

- The mostly microscopic roundworms of phylum Nematoda exist in enormous numbers in all kinds of habitats on Earth. A number of roundworms are agricultural pests and some are human parasites. (p. 424)

- Phylum Arthropoda has three subphyla in it: Uniramia (millipedes, centipedes, insects); Chelicerata (spiders, ticks, mites, horseshoe crabs); and Crustacea (shrimp, lobsters, crabs, barnacles). All arthropods have an exoskeleton and paired, jointed appendages and all molt. (p. 425)

- All members of phylum Echinodermata (sea stars, sea urchins, sea cucumbers) are marine and inhabit the ocean floor. (p. 425)

- Phylum Chordata has three subphyla in it: Vertebrata, which includes all the vertebrates; Cephalochordata, made up of creatures called lancelets; and Urochordata, made up of three classes of animals, including the tunicates or sea squirts. Only the vertebrates have a vertebral column. All chordates possess, at some point in their lives, a notochord; a nerve cord on their dorsal side; a post-anal tail; and a series of pharyngeal slits. (p. 426)

23.4 Animal Reproduction

- Sexual reproduction in animals always entails the fusion of eggs and sperm from two individuals, while asexual reproduction does not. Members of the less complex animal phyla commonly reproduce both sexually and asexually. Sexual reproduction is the norm with more complex animals, but asexual reproduction is sometimes seen in them. (p. 428)

- Forms of asexual reproduction include budding, fission, and parthenogenesis. (p. 428)

- Sexual reproduction can be practiced by hermaphrodites. Some animals change sex over the course of their lifetimes. (p. 429)

23.5 Egg Fertilization and Protection

- In animals, eggs and sperm are brought together and eggs are protected following fertilization in a number of ways. The most primitive, ancestral method is that of parents broadcasting both eggs and sperm into an aquatic environment and thereafter providing no care for the eggs that become fertilized. With movement up the scale of animal complexity, species tend to produce fewer eggs, to exhibit more directed means of bringing these eggs together with sperm, and to provide greater protection to the fertilized eggs that result. (p. 430)

- Fertilization can be external or internal. Only some species that employ internal fertilization also employ copulation. Other species rely on females to insert sperm packets (spermatophores) into their own reproductive tracts. (p. 430)

- Vertebrate evolution resulted in a range of strategies for protecting fertilized eggs and the offspring that develop from them. Reptile evolution resulted in the amniotic egg, whose shell and system of mem-

branes allows it to be laid in dry environments, whereas mammalian evolution produced the placental system, in which fertilized eggs develop inside a mother's body. (p. 430)

23.6 Organs and Circulation

- Organs are complex bodily structures composed of several types of tissues. Organs are found in all the animal phyla reviewed except Porifera and Cnidaria. (p. 434)

- Vertebrates have closed circulation systems. Arthropods and small molluscs have open circulation systems. (p. 435)

23.7 Skeletons and Molting

- Three kinds of skeletons are found in animals: endoskeletons, exoskeletons, and hydrostatic skeletons. (p. 435)

- To continue their growth, animals with exoskeletons must periodically molt. (p. 435)

Key Terms

amniotic egg   432

bilateral symmetry   420

body segmentation   423

budding   428

closed circulation system   435

coelom   420

copulation   430

exoskeleton   425

hermaphrodite   429

hydrostatic skeleton   435

invertebrate   417

molting   435

organ   434

open circulation system   435

oviparous   433

parasite   423

parthenogenesis   429

radial symmetry   420

symmetry   420

tissue   419

vertebral column   426

viviparous   433

Understanding the Basics

Multiple-Choice Questions
(Answers are in the back of the book.)

1. Animals (select all that apply):
   a. go through a blastula stage in development.
   b. have cells with cell walls.
   c. can be single-celled.
   d. are heterotrophs.
   e. are mostly vertebrates.

2. Bilateral symmetry is a condition in which:
   a. no one animal species can overpower another.
   b. the top and bottom halves of an animal are symmetrical.
   c. two animal species evolve along parallel lines.
   d. one side of an animal is symmetrical to the other.
   e. one side of an animal is as strong as the other.

3. A coelom is:
   a. an enclosed body cavity, not found in sponges, cnidarians, or flatworms.
   b. an enclosed body cavity, found only in vertebrates.
   c. a digestive organ, found in all animals except sponges.
   d. an example of a type of tissue.
   e. an offspring that arises from asexual reproduction.

4. In earthworms, we can see a clear example of the widespread animal feature known as:
   a. filter feeding.
   b. body segmentation.
   c. viviparous reproduction.
   d. a post-anal tail.
   e. a radula.

5. If an animal has an exoskeleton, paired jointed appendages, and goes through the process of molting, it is:
   a. a segmented worm.
   b. a roundworm.
   c. a chordate.
   d. a cnidarian.
   e. an arthropod.

6. Forms of asexual reproduction found in the animal kingdom include (select all that apply):
   a. binary fission.
   b. fission.
   c. budding.
   d. copulation.
   e. parthenogenesis.

7. Larger animals, such as vertebrates and large molluscs (squid, octopus) have _____ circulation systems, while arthropods and smaller molluscs (snails) have _____ circulation systems.
   a. closed; open
   b. closed; no
   c. open; closed
   d. open; no
   e. open; open

8. In a hydrostatic skeleton, the force of muscular contraction is applied through:
   a. a skeleton external to the muscles.
   b. a skeleton that will be shed through molting.
   c. a skeleton internal to the muscles.
   d. a fluid.
   e. a circulation system.

Brief Review

(Answers are in the back of the book.)

1. Do all animals have a single ancestor, or do the different animal phyla have different ancestors? Can you think of any evidence to support your answer?

2. Why is it fair to characterize sponges as "primitive" animals?

3. A coelom amounts to internal space in an animal. Why is such a feature valuable?

4. Match the phylum on the left with the description on the right.

Cnidaria	Sea stars, sea urchins
Nematoda	Fish, amphibians, reptiles
Mollusca	Earthworms, leeches
Annelida	Jellyfish, sea anemones
Arthropoda	Insects, lobsters, spiders
Echinodermata	Roundworms
Chordata	Snails, squid

5. In animals such as arthropods, what growth issue is solved through the mechanism of molting?

Applying Your Knowledge

1. One of the distinguishing features of animals is that their cells do not have the thick outer lining known as a cell wall. Plant cells have a cell wall, as do fungi cells. Why would a feature such as this be advantageous to plants but disadvantageous to animals?

2. Plants can have elaborate defense systems, and they can respond in sophisticated ways to their environment—for example, in preserving resources, they can go into a dormant state in winter. Given this, can plants have intelligence? Or is it only animals that have this trait, to one degree or another?

3. The female Atlantic oyster (*Crassostrea virginica*) can produce up to 100 million eggs per year, which she broadcasts into the water and provides no care for thereafter. By contrast, a human female will release 13 eggs per year on average (through ovulation), but in most cases will provide years of care to that small fraction of eggs that become fertilized and develop into babies. Why, with movement up the complexity scale in the animal kingdom, does a trend exist toward fewer eggs but greater parental care for each offspring?

24

Plants:
The Diversity of Life 4

Plants may be silent and fixed in one spot, but they are extremely active and they respond to the world around them in some surprising ways.

Earth's plants come in an amazing variety of forms, including wildflowers and the familiar saguaro cactus (*Carnegiea gigantea*), seen here in Arizona's Sonoran Desert.

The optometrist has almost completed the examination but would like a better look at the interior of the patient's eyes. Would she agree to have her pupils dilated with the application of a couple of drops to each eye? The patient tilts her head back, and in her pose, it's possible to imagine her as a lady of the Italian Renaissance, lifting her eyes upward and applying

to them a few drops of a substance she believes will make her a *bella donna*—a beautiful lady. And what does this substance do? It dilates her eyes just slightly, making her pupils large and entrancing.

Spin back further in time to the eleventh century in Scotland where, as legend has it, the Scottish leader Earl Macbeth poisons an invading army of Danish soldiers by lacing their drinks with juice from a plant known as sleepy nightshade. Only later will the English-speaking world call this plant by the name used today: *Atropa belladonna* (**Figure 24.1**).

Skip forward to 1831, when scientists isolate from the belladonna plant one of its active ingredients, a compound called atropine. This is the substance that actually dilated the eyes of the Italian ladies and that, at one time, dilated eyes in optometry clinics. Then, come forward to the summer of 2004, when the federal government announces that it will soon be supplying states with an assortment of antidotes to chemical weapons. As a response to the threat posed by terrorists, the government says, it will distribute sets of "chem-packs" that include the drug atropine.

This makes sense because U.S. armed forces units have been outfitted for years with "auto-injectors" that can pump a dose of atropine into the thigh of any soldier who has been gassed. Now step back from the government officials making their announcement and observe, just a few miles away, some paramedics hard at work. They're making use of atropine, too, although not in connection with a terrorist assault. In ambulances and emergency rooms, atropine is used to revive heart attack victims. An injection of it can bring a pulse back to a person whose heart is failing.

24.1 The Roles and Characteristics of Plants

Like a talented employee, belladonna keeps getting called back to work by human beings. If you were keeping track, we humans have derived, from just this one plant, a poison, an antidote to poison, a cosmetic, an aid to visual diagnosis, and a heart medicine. But that's the way with plants. The number of things they do for human beings is enormous. The best-known thing they do, of course, is provide us with food. But even in this role, their significance is not fully appreciated. In the world today, up to 90 percent of the calories human beings consume come directly from plants. Indeed, as some botanists have noted, there are about a dozen plants that stand between humanity and starvation. (The most important of these plants is rice, with wheat coming in second.) Plants are able to serve this function because they make their own food through photosynthesis. The bounty they produce through this process has made Earth a planet of surplus—a planet of grains and leaves and roots that are available for the taking. Along these same lines, plants also produce much of the oxygen that most living things require. Then there are the products that human beings have

Figure 24.1
A Plant That Has Served Many Purposes
The flowering plant *Atropa belladonna*.

learned to derive from plants, among them lumber, medicines, fabrics, fragrances, and dyes (**Figure 24.2**).

Apart from these uses, plants are a kind of anchoring environmental force. Their roots prevent soil erosion, while their leaves absorb such pollutants as sulfur dioxide and ozone. One of the main greenhouse gases warming Earth is carbon dioxide, and plants absorb carbon dioxide when they perform photosynthesis. Thus, there is not only a *production* side to atmospheric carbon dioxide—in significant part the pollution human beings produce—there is also a *consumption* side to it in the amount plants absorb. One proposed way to fight greenhouse warming, therefore, is to plant trees. Over the course of a summer, a single mature maple tree will absorb about 1,000 pounds of carbon dioxide from the atmosphere.

Plants can take on these varied roles because of a unique set of physical traits they possess. But what are these traits? Put another way, how are plants structured and how do they function? The goal of this chapter is to give you an introduction to these subjects. We'll start by looking at the characteristics that all plants possess and then move on to a consideration of the major types of plants found in the living world. Then we'll finish up by looking at the ways nature's most dominant plants, the angiosperms, interact with the world around them.

The Characteristics of Plants

We all have an intuitive sense of what plants are, although not all plants match our intuitions. A few are parasites (on other plants) and some, like the Venus flytrap, consume animals. Allowing for such exceptions, all plants share the following characteristics:

- Plants are photosynthesizing organisms that are fixed in place, multicelled, and mostly land-dwelling. We know that plants are fixed in one spot (sessile), and that they make their own food through photosynthesis. That they are multicelled follows from the fact that they develop from embryos, which are multicelled by definition. During the course of their evolution from algae, plants made a transition from water to land, and land is where most of them are found today—although some have made the transition back to water, as with water lilies.

- Plant cells have cell walls. Both plant and animal cells are enclosed by a plasma membrane, but plant cells have something just outside the membrane: a **cell wall,** defined as a relatively thick layer of material that forms the periphery of all plant and fungal cells and many types of bacterial, archael, and protist cells (**Figure 24.3**). The plant cell wall is composed in large part of a tough, complex compound called cellulose. In woody plants, cellulose is joined by a strengthening compound called lignin. Why are trees able to grow so tall? Because of the cellulose and lignin found in their cell walls.

- Plant (and algae) cells have organelles called **chloroplasts** that are the sites of photosynthesis. If there is one feature that has fundamentally shaped plant evolution, it is the chloroplast.

Figure 24.2
Uses Galore

Plants are used by human beings in innumerable ways.

(a) Food, here in the form of grapes.

(b) Wood, being harvested from a forest in British Columbia.

(c) A foxglove plant, which yields the heart medicine digitalis.

(a)

(b)

(c)

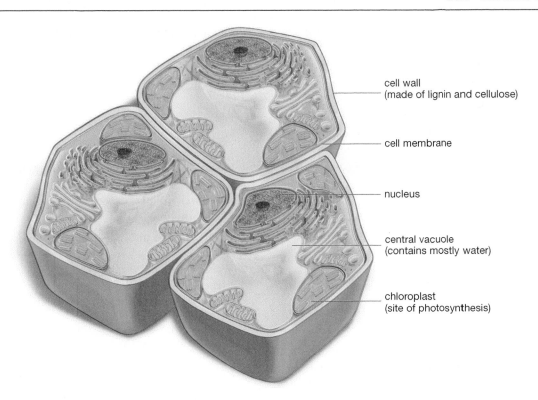

Figure 24.3
Characteristics of Plants

All cells have an outer membrane, but plant cells have a wall external to this membrane. The compounds cellulose and lignin, which help make up the cell wall, impart strength to it. Plant cells have a higher proportion of water in them than do animal cells, with much of this water located in an organelle called a central vacuole. The sites of photosynthesis in plants are the organelles called chloroplasts.

cell wall
(made of lignin and cellulose)

cell membrane

nucleus

central vacuole
(contains mostly water)

chloroplast
(site of photosynthesis)

Why are plants able to be fixed in one spot? Because they make their own food in chloroplasts and thus don't need to move toward food, as animals do.

- Successive generations of plants go through what is known as an alternation of generations.

One way to conceptualize this characteristic is to compare plant reproduction with human reproduction. The eggs and sperm that human beings produce are so-called gametes that are *haploid* cells, meaning they have but a single set of chromosomes in them. When these haploid cells fuse in the moment of conception, what's produced is a *diploid* fertilized egg, meaning an egg with two sets of chromosomes—one set from the father and one from the mother. This egg gives rise to more diploid cells through cell division, and the result is a whole new human being (**Figure 24.4a**).

A typical plant in its diploid phase will, like human beings, produce a specialized set of haploid reproductive cells. Instead of these cells being egg or sperm, however, what's produced is a spore: a reproductive cell that can develop into a new organism without fusing with another reproductive cell. Like the spores we saw in fungi, plant spores have the ability to grow into a new generation of plant all on their own. In some plants, this spore lands on the ground, starts dividing, and after a time a mature plant exists. When *this* plant reproduces, however, it does not do so through more spores. It produces gametes—eggs and sperm. These go on to fuse, and the result is a diploid plant just like the one we started with.

The upshot of all this, as you can see in **Figure 24.4b**, is that plants move back and forth between

(a) Human reproduction

meiosis

multicellular
diploid
adults

egg

sperm
1n

2n

fertilization

mitosis and
development

zygote

(b) Plant alternation of generations

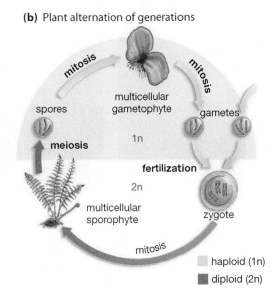

mitosis

mitosis

spores

multicellular
gametophyte

gametes

1n

meiosis

fertilization

2n

multicellular
sporophyte

zygote

mitosis

☐ haploid (1n)
■ diploid (2n)

Figure 24.4
The Alternation of Generations in Plants, Compared to the Human Life Cycle

(a) Humans. Almost all cells in human beings are diploid, or 2n, meaning they have paired sets of chromosomes in them. The exception to this is human gametes (eggs and sperm), produced through meiosis, which are haploid, or 1n, meaning they have a single set of chromosomes. In the moment of conception, a haploid sperm fuses with a haploid egg to produce a diploid zygote that grows into a complete human being through cell division or mitosis.

(b) Plants. In plants, conversely, diploid (2n) plants—the multicellular sporophyte fern in the figure—go through meiosis and produce individual haploid (1n) spores that, without fusing with any other cells, develop into a separate generation of the plant. This is the multicellular gametophyte shown. This gametophyte-generation plant then produces its own gametes, which are eggs and sperm. Sperm from one plant fertilizes an egg from another, and the result is a diploid zygote that develops into the mature sporophyte generation.

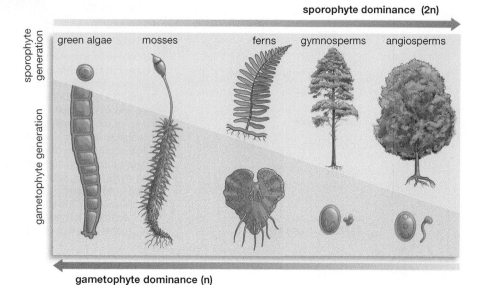

sporophyte dominance (2n)

green algae   mosses   ferns   gymnosperms   angiosperms

gametophyte dominance (n)

through an **alternation of generations:** a life cycle practiced by plants in which successive plant generations alternate between the diploid sporophyte condition and the haploid gametophyte condition.

SO FAR . . .

1. Which of the following traits is *not* characteristic of plants? (a) fixed-in-place, (b) no cell wall, (c) photosynthesizing, (d) mostly land-dwelling.

2. All plants go through an alternation of generations in which one generation produces the reproductive cells called _____, while the alternate generation produces the reproductive cells that fuse in reproduction, _____ and _____.

Figure 24.5
Generational
Dominance

In more primitive plants, the gametophyte generation is larger and more dominant. In mosses, for example, the gametophyte generation houses the sporophyte generation. By contrast, in the most recently evolved plants, the angiosperms, the gametophyte generation has been reduced to a microscopic entity that is almost wholly dependent on the sporophyte generation. Although not plants, green algae are included for comparative purposes.

two different kinds of generations, one of them spore-producing, the other gamete-producing. In this cycle, the generation of plant that produces spores is known as the **sporophyte generation,** while the generation of plant that produces the gametes is the **gametophyte generation.** If you look at **Figure 24.5,** you can see how physically different these generations can be. In a massive organism such as a redwood tree, the tree that is familiar to us is the sporophyte generation. But what do its spores develop into? On the male side, barely visible pollen grains. On the female side, small collections of cells, hidden deep within a redwood "pinecone." The fact that these gametophyte individuals are tiny, however, doesn't mean that they are unnecessary. The eggs and sperm they produce are required to bring about a whole new redwood tree. In sum, all plants go

24.2 Types of Plants

The physical characteristics we've been looking at are common to all plants, but within the plant kingdom there are four fundamentally different types of plants, each of which has its own unique set of physical features. These are the bryophytes, which include mosses; the seedless vascular plants, which include ferns; the gymnosperms, which include coniferous ("cone-bearing") trees; and the angiosperms, a vast division of flowering plants—by far the most dominant on Earth today—whose diversity is broad enough to include not only orchids and pear trees but corn and cactus as well (**Figure 24.6**). We'll look at all

mosses ferns conifers flowering plants

flowers

seeds

vascular tissue

multicellularity

green algae (ancestors)

(a) Moss

(b) Ferns

(c) Conifers

(d) Flowering plants

Figure 24.6
Four Main Varieties of Plants

The most primitive type of plant (a) the bryophytes (moss in the figure) lack a fluid-transporting vascular system. (b) Ferns, representing the seedless vascular plants, have a vascular system but do not have seeds. (c) Gymnosperms (pine trees in the picture) do utilize seeds. (d) Flowering plants (blossoming trees in the picture) produce seeds and are responsible for several other plant innovations, among them fruit.

four types of plants briefly here. Chapter 25 will provide a detailed description of the anatomy and physiology of flowering plants.

Bryophytes: Lying Low in Moist Environments

If you look in low-lying, wet terrain, you are likely to see a carpet-like covering of moss. In countries such as Ireland, whole fields of peat moss grow and are harvested to be used as fuel for heating and cooking. Mosses are the most familiar example of a primitive type of plant called a **bryophyte,** which can be defined as a type of plant lacking a true vascular system (**Figure 24.7**). What's a vascular system? A network of tubes within an organism that serves to transport fluids. We can get a sense of what the bryophytes are like by looking at the mosses.

Like all bryophytes, mosses are close living relatives of the earliest plants that made the transition from living in water to living on land. As such, mosses can be conceptualized as plants that have made only a partial break with the aquatic living of the evolutionary ancestors of all plants, the green algae. In living on land, mosses have to deal with something the algae don't, which is the effect of gravity. Lacking a vascular system, they cannot transport water and other substances very *far* against the force of gravity; instead, they must lie low, hugging the surface to which they are attached while spreading out horizontally to maximize their exposure to sunlight. Nevertheless, mosses are hearty competitors in some tough environments, such as the arctic tundra and the cracks in sidewalks.

In keeping with their aquatic origins, mosses have sperm that usually get to eggs by swimming through water, although not much water is necessary. (A thin film left over from the morning dew will suffice.) For decades, scientists believed that this was the only means by which moss sperm got to eggs, but in 2006 they reported that the bodies of animals also carry out this transport function. Mites and tiny insects called springtails move moss sperm from one kind of moss "tuft" to another. This was a revelation because, up until this point, scientists thought that only one kind of plant used animals as sperm couriers—the flowering plants we'll be looking at shortly.

(a) Mosses

(b) Liverworts

(c) Hornworts

Figure 24.7
Three Kinds of Bryophytes

These plants have no vascular tissue and thus tend to be small. The sperm of bryophytes usually travels through water to get to eggs, although mites and tiny insects can serve this function. Bryophytes are found most often in moist environments.

Given the close ties that mosses have to water, it's not surprising that they can usually be found in moist environments. Like all bryophytes, mosses have no roots at all but instead use single-celled extensions called rhizoids to anchor themselves to their underlying material, which may be soil or rock or wood. You might expect that rhizoids would serve to absorb water, as roots do, but this is true only to a very limited extent. Bryophytes take in water almost entirely through their above-ground exterior surface.

Seedless Vascular Plants: Ferns and Their Relatives

As noted, all plants except the bryophytes have a vascular system, or network of fluid-conducting tubes that transport both food and water. When we begin to look at vascular plants, we find that the most primitive variety of them is a group called the **seedless vascular plants:** plants that have a vascular system but that do not produce seeds as part of reproduction.

Easily the most familiar representatives of the seedless vascular plants are ferns, with their often beautifully shaped leaves, called fronds (**Figure 24.8**). These plants have moved a step further in the direction of separation from an aquatic environment. Their vascular system allows them to grow up as well as out, and it allows for roots that extend into the ground, where they serve their absorptive function. Despite this evolutionary innovation, the sperm of the seedless vascular plants is like that of most of the bryophytes: It needs to move through water to fertilize eggs.

The First Seed Plants: The Gymnosperms

There are two kinds of seed plants, the gymnosperms and the angiosperms, but putting things this way makes it sound as though these plants are on a kind of equal footing with the bryophytes and seedless vascular plants. In reality, the gymnosperms replaced seedless vascular plants as the most dominant plants on Earth, although this event took place a long time ago—about the time the dinosaurs came to dominance. Then the gymnosperms lost this status to the angiosperms, which began flourishing about 80 million years ago. Today, there are only about 1,000 gymnosperm species

Figure 24.8
Three Kinds of Seedless Vascular Plants

Because these plants have vascular tissue, they are able to grow taller than most bryophytes. Like bryophytes, however, they do not produce seeds and are tied to moist environments.

(a) Ferns

(b) Horsetails

(c) Club mosses

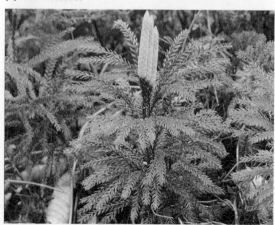

compared to 300,000 angiosperm species. Nevertheless, the gymnosperm presence is considerable, especially in the northern latitudes, where they exist as vast bands of coniferous trees, including pine, fir, and spruce. Conifers such as these provide most of the world's lumber (**Figure 24.9**).

(a) Spruce tree

(b) *Ginkgo biloba*

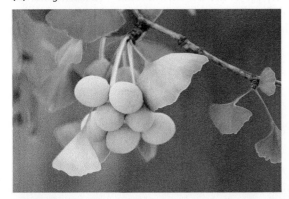

Figure 24.9
Gymnosperms

(a) This spruce tree is a member of the grouping of gymnosperms known as conifers, which account for about three-fourths of all gymnosperm species. The conifers also include redwood, pine, juniper, and cypress trees.

(b) There are other types of gymnosperms as well. Pictured are the leaves and seeds of the maidenhair tree *Ginkgo biloba,* which are used today in herbal preparations.

Reproduction through Pollen and Seeds

Why were the gymnosperms able to out-compete so many of the seedless vascular plants back in the dinosaur days? Part of the answer lies in sperm transport. In gymnosperms, sperm are contained in tiny spheres called pollen grains. Critically, these grains are transported to the female eggs through the *air*, rather than being limited to swimming to them or being carried on the bodies of tiny, crawling animals. Given this innovation, the gymnosperms could propagate over great distances, which gave them a competitive advantage over the seedless plants.

Another advantage the gymnosperms had were their seeds, which can be thought of as tiny packages of food and protection. If you look at **Figure 24.10**, you can see one example of a gymnosperm seed, this one from a pine tree. **Figure 24.11**, on the next page, then shows you how this seed fits into the life cycle of the pine. As you can see, pollen grains are carried by the wind to the female reproductive structure, which resides in the familiar pinecone. Then the sperm within the pollen grain comes together with an egg in the reproductive structure, and the result is a fertilized egg that begins to develop as an embryo. This is no different in principle from human egg and sperm coming together to create a human embryo. In the pine tree, however, the embryo is developing inside a seed, a structure that is unique to plants. Seeds have a tough coat, inside of which is not only the embryo but also a food supply for it—a kind of sack lunch of stored carbohydrates, proteins, and fats. In sum, a **seed** is a plant structure that includes a plant embryo, its food supply, and a tough, protective casing. When seeds reach the ground, they contain all the starting materials necessary to bring about germination of a new generation of plant.

Gymnosperm seeds turn out to differ from the seeds produced by angiosperms. Angiosperm seeds come wrapped in a layer of tissue—called fruit—that gymnosperm seeds do not have. The details of this anatomical feature are presented in Chapter 25. For now, just

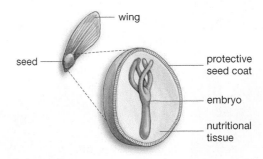

Figure 24.10
A Gymnosperm Seed

Seeds are tiny packages of food and protection. They come in many shapes and sizes, but they all contain an embryo, some food, and a protective seed coat.

Figure 24.11
The Life Cycle of a Gymnosperm
Pine trees have two kinds of cones. Pollen is produced within the smaller male cones, while eggs are produced within the larger female cones. When the wind carries pollen onto the female cone, the sperm within the pollen fertilizes one of the eggs within the cone. An embryo then begins to develop inside a seed, which falls to the ground. Once conditions are suitable, the seed germinates, and a whole new pine tree begins to grow.

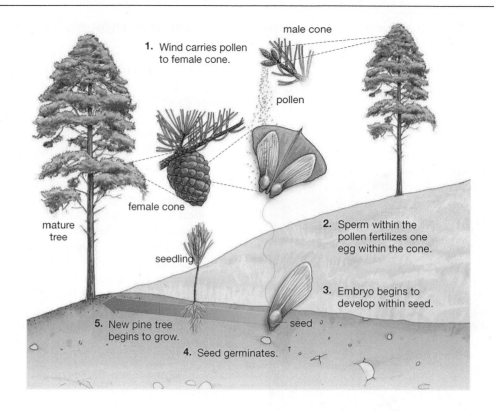

1. Wind carries pollen to female cone.

male cone

pollen

mature tree

female cone

seedling

2. Sperm within the pollen fertilizes one egg within the cone.

3. Embryo begins to develop within seed.

seed

5. New pine tree begins to grow.

4. Seed germinates.

be mindful that a **gymnosperm** can be defined as a seed plant whose seeds are not surrounded by fruit. The very name *gymnosperm* comes from the Greek words *gymnos,* meaning "naked," and *sperma,* meaning "seed."

Angiosperms: Nature's Most Dominant Plants

As noted, there are about 300,000 known species of the flowering plants, or angiosperms. The term *flowering plants* may bring to mind roses or tulips, and indeed, these flowers are angiosperms. But the angiosperm grouping includes all manner of other plants as well—almost all trees except for the conifers, all our important food crops, cactus, shrubs, common grass; the list is very long (**Figure 24.12**). As noted, **angiosperms** are defined by an aspect of their anatomy: Their seeds are surrounded by the tissue called fruit. The details of angiosperm anatomy and physiology are covered in Chapter 25. For the balance of this chapter, we'll focus on the ways these important plants interact with the world around them. First we'll look at their interactions with animals, after which we'll look at the ways they respond to signals they get from their environment. (To learn something about the nutrients that angiosperms need to stay healthy, see "What Is Plant Food?" on page 449.)

Figure 24.12
Angiosperm Variety
The incredible diversity of angiosperms can be seen in the differences among these three types of angiosperm plants.

(a) Calla lilies on the California coast

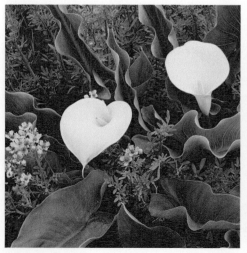

(b) Cholla cactus in California

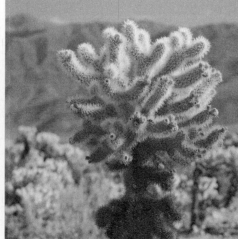

(c) Corn in a field

ESSAY

What Is Plant Food?

Plants are able to make their own food through photosynthesis if they have access to just four things: water, sunlight, carbon dioxide, and a few nutrients. Water, sunlight, and probably even carbon dioxide are no mystery to you by now, but what exactly are these nutrients?

A nutrient is simply a chemical element that is used by living things to sustain life. Recall from Chapter 2 that elements are the most basic building blocks of the chemical world. Silver is an element, as is uranium, but these are not nutrients because living things do not need them to live. In the broadest sense, carbon, oxygen, and hydrogen are nutrients. And it turns out that almost 96 percent of the weight of the average plant is accounted for by these three elements, which come to plants primarily from water and air.

Plants need at least another 13 elements to live, however, and not all of these are supplied by water and air. When we think of common "plant food," we are generally referring to those nutrients that plants can *use up* in their soil and that thus must be replenished to ensure continued growth and reproduction. Of these, the most important three are nitrogen, phosphorus, and potassium, whose chemical symbols are N, P, and K. When you look at a package of an average plant fertilizer, you will see three numbers in sequence on it (for example, 10-20-10). What these refer to is the percentage of the fertilizer's weight accounted for by these nutrients (**Figure 1**).

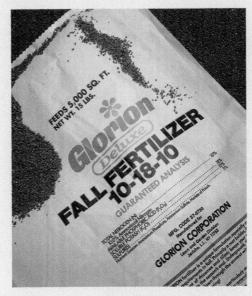

Figure 1
Needed Nutrients

Plants make their own food from sunlight, water, carbon dioxide, and a few nutrients, some of which come from the soil. The most important of these nutrients are nitrogen (N), phosphorus (P), and potassium (K). Because garden plants and houseplants are isolated from natural ecosystems, they must often get these nutrients in the form of fertilizer.

The growth of plants usually is enhanced by a fertilizer that has equal ratios of the three elements, but if increased *blooming* is your goal, an increased phosphorus ratio generally is recommended, as with the 10-20-10 example.

It is not just houseplants or lawns that benefit from fertilizer, but farm crops as well. Indeed, the planting of a crop on a parcel of land generally requires a large investment in fertilizer because a crop such as wheat removes a great deal of N, P, and K from the soil in a single season. Historically, fertilizers used on farms were *organic*, meaning they came from decayed living things, such as the fish that Native Americans taught the Pilgrims to use when planting corn. Nowadays, however, commercial fertilizers generally are *inorganic*, meaning they are mixtures of pure elements within binding materials, produced by chemical processes.

Nature is, of course, perfectly capable of producing a green bounty in such places as forests and marshes without the aid of any human-made fertilizer. Decaying plant and animal matter puts nutrients back into the soil, and bacteria are able to fix nitrogen, meaning to absorb it from the air and transform it into a form that plants can take up. Looked at one way, however, houseplants and farm crops are *isolated* plants whose participation in this web of life is very limited, and thus they require a helping hand from humans in order to remain robust.

SO FAR . . .

1. A seed is a plant structure that includes a plant _____, its _____ supply, and a tough _____.

2. Of the following plants, which produce(s) seeds? (a) moss, (b) fern, (c) spruce tree, (d) orchid.

3. In their role as the male gametophyte generation of seed plants, pollen grains contain plant ____.

24.3 Angiosperm–Animal Interactions

For an angiosperm such as a new honeysuckle plant to come into existence, a two-part process must take place. First, sperm—developing once again inside a pollen grain—must get to an egg and fertilize it, which produces the embryo encased in a seed coat. Next, this seed must land on a patch of soil somewhere and begin to germinate or sprout.

Now, in the angiosperms, how is it that sperm gets to the egg in the first place? Remember that with gymnosperms, pollen grains are carried by the wind. By

Figure 24.13
Animals Help Pollen Get from Here to There

Flowering plants take advantage of the mobility of animals to transport pollen from one plant to another. Relationships between flowers and pollinators can be species specific, which helps to ensure that the pollen will be delivered to the right address.

(a) Pollen-covered honeybee on a dandelion

(b) Ruby-throated hummingbird pollinating a flower

(c) Lesser long-nosed bat pollinating a cactus

contrast, the angiosperms have induced *animals* to carry pollen from one plant to another—to pollinate them. Not all angiosperms are pollinated in this way; some are pollinated by wind, and a few aquatic species rely on water currents. But most are pollinated with the help of animals, be they bees, birds, or even bats (**Figure 24.13**).

Angiosperms use various attractants to encourage animal pollination. The most important of these is food in the form of nectar (which is essentially sugar-water). But angiosperms don't stop there. So critical is pollination to them that evolution produced within them a set of physical characteristics that effectively serve as advertising for pollinators. How about a fragrance that, say, bees are sensitive to? How about colors that they're attracted to? Insect-pollinated flowers generally have both sweet fragrances and specialized coloration patterns—nature's equivalent of homing signals and landing lights. These serve to get an animal to a flower in the first place and then into the right position for feeding and pollination (**Figure 24.14**).

Why do angiosperms spend so much energy attracting animal pollinators while gymnosperms let the wind do the work? Windborne pollination in gymnosperms can be thought of as a kind of scattershot approach: If the wind happens to blow a pollen grain onto the female reproductive structure, then pollination occurs. Think how much more directed things are with animal pollination. It is essentially door-to-door service. Animal pollination is one of the reasons that angiosperms are by far the most dominant plants on Earth.

Seed Endosperm: More Animal Food from Angiosperms

Once pollination has occurred, the resulting seed, with the embryo inside, has to reach the ground and then germinate in it. All seeds contain food reserves

Figure 24.14
Food Lies This Way

Animals may be attracted to a particular flower by its fragrance, color, or pattern of visual elements. Insects are guided into the nutrients in the center of the flower by color patterns called nectar guides, visible to an insect—because it perceives ultraviolet light—but not to us.

(a) This is what we see (normal sunlight).

(b) This is what the bee sees (ultraviolet light).

(c) This is what the bee "thinks."

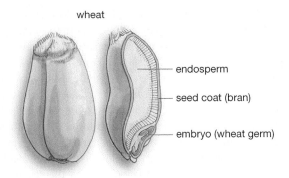

Figure 24.15
Food for the Seedling, Food for Humans
Endosperm is a food reserve in angiosperm seeds. In nature, its function is to feed a growing plant embryo in the period before the embryo germinates into a grown plant and starts making its own food through photosynthesis. It is this same endosperm that nourishes humans throughout the world in the form of wheat, corn, rice, and even coconut.

for the growing embryo, but angiosperm seeds develop a special kind of nutritive tissue, called **endosperm,** that often surrounds the embryo (**Figure 24.15**). As it turns out, this endosperm supplies much of the food for *human beings* throughout the world. Rice and wheat grains are seeds consisting in large part of endosperm whose role in nature is to sustain the plant embryo. It's worth noting that whole-grain wheat is wheat that still has its embryo (usually called "wheat germ") and its seed coat (usually called "bran"). By contrast, white bread, regular pasta, and so forth are made from wheat whose wheat germ and bran have been removed through processing. The problem with such processing? Wheat germ is a source of healthy oils and vitamin E, while bran is a terrific source of "fiber" or plant material that doesn't get digested within us and thus provides a host of health benefits. (You can read more about this in Chapter 31.)

Fruit: An Inducement for Seed Dispersal

Some flowering plants also add an inducement for the *dispersal* of their seeds: the tissue called fruit. This is not fruit in the technical sense, but fruit as that term is commonly understood—the flesh of an apricot or cherry, for example. As such, it represents one more piece of bounty that plants provide to animals. To understand how fruit benefits plants as well, imagine a bear that consumes a wild berry, which consists not only of the fruit flesh but of the seeds inside this flesh. The fruit is digested by the bear as food, but the *seeds* are tough; they are passed through its system intact to be deposited, with bear feces as fertilizer, at a location that may be very remote from the place where the bear ate the berry. The result is seed dispersal at what may be a promising new location for a berry plant (**Figure 24.16**).

If we take a step back from processes such as this, it's easy to see that many animals and angiosperms have an interdependent relationship with one another. Angiosperms supply food *to* animals, but they also derive benefits *from* animals in the forms of pollination and seed dispersal. We don't often think of animals and plants as partners in the living world, but that's the case to a high degree with animals and angiosperms.

24.4 Responding to External Signals

Plants may lack a nervous system, but this doesn't mean they can't respond to their environment. They must do so, actually, because their life depends on it. They sense the march of the seasons by measuring available light and the surrounding temperature; they use internal clocks to synchronize their development

(a) Wild berries induce seed dispersal

(b) Burrs help seeds travel

Figure 24.16
Seed Carriers
Angiosperms have taken advantage of the mobility of animals not only to transfer pollen but also to disperse seeds.

(a) Some seeds are wrapped in tasty fruit that is consumed by animals, such as bears.

(b) Other seeds come wrapped in burrs and spines that stick to the fur of animals and are carried away.

and physical functioning; they respond to touch, heat, cold, and pH, among other things. Let's look now at some of the ways the angiosperm plants respond to the world around them. We'll begin with the way they respond to a very familiar force.

Responding to Gravity: Gravitropism

When a seed first starts to sprout, or "germinate," its roots and shoots must go in very specific directions: The root must go down, toward the water and minerals the plant needs, and the shoot must go up, toward the sunlight it requires. Imagine a seed that has simply fallen on the ground; it would not do for either root or shoot to grow *horizontally;* each must grow vertically. If you look at **Figure 24.17**, you can see dramatic evidence of a plant's ability to sense which way is up. The bean plant in Figure 24.17 was placed on its side, and in less than a day its shoot began curving upward, as you can see. What this exemplifies is **gravitropism,** meaning a bending of a plant's shoot or root in response to gravity. But how do shoots or roots "know" which way is up or down, and how do they orchestrate a course correction when they need one? Logically, there must be at least two elements at work here: first, a gravitational *sensing* mechanism and then a means of *responding* to gravitational cues, such that corrective bending points shoot or root the right way.

The consensus among botanists today is that the sensing mechanism in gravitropism is the "sedimentation" that various plant cell organelles perform in response to gravity. Recall that organelles are small but highly organized structures inside cells. (Mitochondria and chloroplasts are organelles, for example.) Like the bubble in a carpenter's level, some plant-cell organelles can be seen changing position in response to gravity. The most important of these organelles is a group of starch-storing structures called *amyloplasts* (although some plants seem to employ alternate organelles). When these organelles move in response to gravity, it sets in motion the responding mechanism in gravitropism. The organelles "land" on other structures inside the cell (such as the cytoskeleton), and the resulting impact triggers a redistribution of a **hormone:** a substance that, when released in one part of an organism, goes on to prompt physiological activity in another part of that organism. In this case, the hormone is known as IAA, and its redistribution to a different portion of the plant has the effect of bringing about *growth* in that portion of the plant—one *side* of the plant stem or root will grow more than the other side. With this growth, a stem that is oriented horizontally will start bending up toward the sky, while a root that is oriented horizontally will start bending down toward the ground.

Responding to Light: Phototropism

Many plants will bend toward a source of light, with the value of this perhaps being obvious: Plants produce their own food, and that production depends on light. Thus, a plant needs to respond when its sunlight becomes blocked by another plant or some other physical object in its surroundings. As it turns out, it is once again the hormone IAA—this time produced in the shoot tips of growing plants—that controls this **phototropism,** defined as a curvature of shoots in response to light. When light strikes one side of the shoot, it causes IAA to migrate to the other side, where the IAA acts to promote the *elongation* of cells on this far side. The effect is to make the shoot curve toward the light (**Figure 24.18**).

Responding to Contact: Thigmotropism

We've all seen plants that manage to climb upward by encircling the stem of another plant. Whole stems can undertake such encircling, but it is often a thin, modified leaflet called a tendril that does so (**Figure 24.19**). But how is a tendril able to wrap around another object? Once again, through differential growth—more rapid growth on one side of a tendril than on the other. Contact with the object is perceived by outer, or epidermal, cells in the tendril. This sets into motion the differential growth, which probably is controlled by the hormones IAA and ethylene. This process is called **thigmotropism,** meaning growth of a plant in

Figure 24.17
Plants Respond to Gravity
A potted bean plant demonstrates the effects of gravitropism.

Figure 24.18
Plants Respond to Light

(a) When sunlight is overhead, the IAA molecules produced by the apical meristem are distributed evenly in the shoot.

(b) Once the sunlight shines on the shoot at an angle, the IAA molecules move to the far side and induce the elongation of cells on that side.

(c) Cell elongation results in the bending of the shoot toward the light.

response to touch. Plants with this capability can piggyback on plants or other objects to get more access to sunlight.

Responding to the Passage of the Seasons

Trees that exhibit a coordinated, seasonal loss of leaves are called **deciduous** trees. But why should these broad-leafed trees lose their leaves—their

Figure 24.19
Moving Up by Curling Around
This dodder plant is able to curl around its host plant because of thigmotropism—a plant's ability to grow in response to touch.

primary sites of photosynthesis—while the evergreen pines and firs keep the modified leaves known as needles?

First, there is relatively little water available in winter in cold climates (most of it being frozen in the ground), and trees are just like all vascular plants in that most of the water they absorb through their roots ends up being released into the air through their leaves. Indeed, it's been estimated that 99 percent of the water the average plant takes in through its roots eventually will move out through its leaves (as water vapor) in the process known as transpiration. For our purposes, the important point is that flat-leafed deciduous trees transpire more than evergreens do. In addition, because of the way wind flows over flat leaves, they lose more heat than do the pine needles of evergreens, meaning deciduous leaves could freeze in winter if they were retained—a condition that would damage them and hence result in a tree that was vulnerable to infection by fungi and bacteria.

For deciduous trees, then, any benefits that would come with performing photosynthesis in winter would not be worth the water loss and leaf damage that would result. These trees thus employ a strategy that is a matter of straight economics: Lose the leaves in fall, grow new ones the following spring, and in the meantime perform no photosynthesis at all but exist instead completely on food reserves. This state, in which growth is suspended and metabolic activity is low, is called **dormancy.** Evergreens can exhibit dormancy, too, in low temperatures, but deciduous trees are locked into it until the coming of spring.

Limitation of Loss in the Deciduous Strategy

The dormancy that deciduous trees enter into makes even more sense when we consider one means by which these trees prepare for it: Before losing their

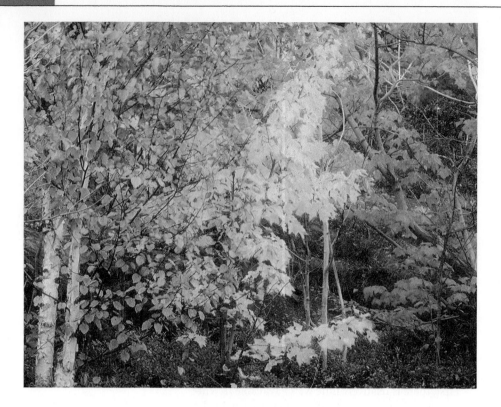

Figure 24.20
Seasonal Marker
Brightly colored maple and birch leaves in Ontario, Canada in fall. Plants have a number of mechanisms that allow them to respond to the passage of the seasons.

leaves, they reclaim the proteins and nutrients that exist in them. Proteins are broken down by enzymes and shipped, along with the nutrients, to storage cells in a tree's trunk and roots. By the time a leaf is ready to detach from the tree, it is little more than an empty shell of cell walls.

Before this happens, however, the well-known change in leaf coloration takes place. It may surprise you to learn there is less adding of new colors in this process than an unmasking of colors that existed in the leaves all along. With the approach of fall, green chlorophyll, which is the main pigment in photosynthesis, begins to break down in the leaf. With it gone, the yellow and orange colors provided by pigments called carotenoids become visible (**Figure 24.20**). New colors are added as well; blue and red come with the synthesis of pigments called anthocyanins. (These pigments are largely responsible for the stunning red color of many maples in the fall.) The combination of carotenoids and anthocyanins gives us the final result, which is multi-hued leaves.

Photoperiodism

But how does a deciduous tree sense when it's time to begin preparing for cold weather? In general, it is an interaction between two factors. First, there is cold itself, which brings about changes in metabolism. In addition, there is a phenomenon known as **photoperiodism,** which is the ability of a plant to respond to changes it is experiencing in the daily duration of darkness, relative to light. This is another example of the plant's ability to respond to its envi-

ronment, but it should not be confused with the phototropism, or *bending* toward the light, that was discussed earlier. In photoperiodism, plants are making seasonal adaptations based on the length of the nights they are experiencing.

Most plants in Earth's temperate regions and many in the subtropics exhibit photoperiodism, which can affect such processes as the timing of flowering as well as the onset of dormancy. The value of such a sensing mechanism becomes apparent when we think about the kind of trouble plants could get into if they relied solely on temperature signals to provide them with seasonal cues. It's entirely possible to have, say, an unusual cold snap in September—one that, on its own, would be a signal to start losing leaves. A tree that acted on such a false signal would, however, miss out on weeks of growth and food production. In contrast, seasonal dark/light cues are much more reliable—there is no such thing as an unusual *light* condition for a given month. Given this, it makes sense that photoperiodism has an important place in providing plants with a sense of the seasons as they pass.

To get a feel for how photoperiodism works, consider ragweed, a plant that is the bane of many hayfever sufferers. After sprouting in the spring and reaching a certain level of maturity, a ragweed flowers only when it is in darkness for 10 hours *or more* per day. When would this threshold be crossed? When nights begin to get longer. Ragweed thus joins a group of plants, called long-night plants, whose flowering comes only with an *increased* amount of darkness. As you can imagine, most of these plants are like ragweed in that they flower only in late summer or early fall. Their counterparts are the so-called short-night plants, which flower only when the nights get short enough—that is to say, when nighttime hours are *decreasing* as a proportion of the day. Predictably, these plants tend to flower in spring to midsummer.

The mechanism by which photoperiodism works is now fairly well understood in one short-night plant, a member of the mustard family called *Arabidopsis*. Flowering in *Arabidopsis* is controlled by a protein, known as CO, that can switch on genes by binding to DNA. When enough CO accumulates in *Arabidopsis*, the genes that set flowering in motion are switched on. So, what can bring about CO levels that are high enough to get the flowering started? Shorter nights. Substances called *photoreceptors,* which are sensitive to light, act mostly to allow CO to accumulate during the day, but then predominantly act to destroy it at night. As the nights grow shorter, the balance is shifted toward CO accumulation. When this accumulation reaches a certain threshold, the relevant genes are switched on and flowering begins.

On to a More Detailed Picture of Angiosperms

This chapter has served to introduce you to the basic features of plants—their general traits, their varieties, and the means by which the flowering plants among them interact with animals and respond to environmental signals. We've hardly scratched the surface, however, regarding two important aspects of flowering plant life: the nature of their component parts and the ways these parts interact to produce a functioning organism. Put another way, we've yet to look at the anatomy and physiology of angiosperms. That's just what we'll do in the chapter that's coming up.

SO FAR . . .

1. The pollen of gymnosperms generally is transported by _____, while the pollen of angiosperms generally is transported by _____.

2. Plants respond to gravity, touch, and the direction of sunlight through the _____ growth of roots or stems.

3. Plants in temperate climates make seasonal adjustments based on the relative length of the _____ they are experiencing.

CHAPTER 24 REVIEW

Go to the Study Area at www.masteringbiology.com for practice quizzes, myeBook, BioFlix™ 3-D animations, MP3 Tutor Sessions, videos, current events, and more.

Mastering BIOLOGY

Summary

24.1 The Roles and Characteristics of Plants

- The photosynthesis that plants perform indirectly feeds many life-forms. The oxygen plants produce as a by-product of photosynthesis is vital to many organisms, and many plant products are important to human beings. (p. 441)

- With a few exceptions, all plants are multicelled, fixed in one spot, and carry out photosynthesis. All plant cells have a cell wall and most contain the organelles called chloroplasts, which are the sites of photosynthesis. (p. 442)

- Plants reproduce through an alternation of generations: a life cycle in which one plant generation reproduces through use of the reproductive cells called spores (the sporophyte generation) while the next reproduces through use of the reproductive cells known as gametes (the gametophyte generation). The sporophyte and gametophyte generations

of different plant types can differ greatly in size and structure. (p. 443)

24.2 Types of Plants

- The four principal categories of plants are bryophytes (exemplified by mosses), seedless vascular plants (ferns), gymnosperms (coniferous trees), and angiosperms (a wide array of plants). (p. 444)

- Bryophytes are close relatives of the earliest plants that made the transition from living in water to living on land. They lack a fluid transport, or vascular system and tend to be low-lying. Bryophytes tend to inhabit damp environments and their sperm get to eggs primarily by swimming through water. (p. 445)

- Seedless vascular plants have a vascular system but do not produce seeds in reproduction. Their sperm must move through water to fertilize eggs. (p. 446)

- Gymnosperms are seed-bearing plants whose seeds are not encased in tissue called fruit. There are only about 1,000 gymnosperm species, but their presence is

considerable, particularly in northern latitudes, where gymnosperm trees, such as pine and spruce, often dominate landscapes. In carrying out their reproduction, gymnosperms produce seeds: reproductive structures that include a plant embryo, its food supply, and a tough, protective casing. (p. 446)

- The most dominant group of plants, angiosperms, produce seeds that are encased in fruit. Angiosperm species include plants with flowers and most trees, except for conifers; all important food crops; cactus; shrubs; and common grasses. (p. 448)

24.3 Angiosperm–Animal Interactions

- Angiosperm pollen grains generally are transferred from one plant to another by animals. Flowers produce nectar, colorations, and fragrances that induce animals to carry out pollination. (p. 449)

- Angiosperm seeds contain endosperm, which functions as food for the growing embryo. Endosperm supplies much of the food that human beings eat. (p. 450)

- Angiosperm seeds are unique in the plant world in being wrapped in a layer of tissue called fruit. Edible fruit functions in seed dispersal because animals will eat and digest the fruit but then later excrete the tough seeds inside it, often in a different location. (p. 451)

24.4 Responding to External Signals

- Gravitropism is the ability plants have to sense their orientation and to direct their roots toward the ground and shoots toward the sky. (p. 452)

- Plant shoots can gain additional access to light by bending toward a source of it. This process is called phototropism, meaning a curvature of shoots in response to light. (p. 452)

- Thigmotropism is the growth of a plant shoot in response to touch. Through it, plant shoots can climb upward on other objects by encircling them, thus gaining additional access to light. (p. 452)

- Gravitropism, phototropism, and thigmotropism are made possible by differential growth on one side of a root or stem. (p. 452)

- In temperate climates, deciduous trees exhibit a coordinated, seasonal loss of leaves and enter into a state of dormancy. Dormancy evolved in deciduous trees because any photosynthesis they could perform in winter would not offset the water loss and leaf damage that would result from the retention of leaves. (p. 453)

- Photoperiodism is the process through which plants respond to seasonal changes in the daily duration of darkness relative to light. Some plants that exhibit photoperiodism are long-night plants, meaning those whose flowering comes only with an increased amount of darkness. Others are short-night plants, meaning those whose flowering comes only with a decreased amount of darkness. (p. 454)

Key Terms

alternation of generations   444

angiosperm   448

bryophyte   445

cell wall   442

chloroplast   442

deciduous   453

dormancy   453

endosperm   451

gametophyte generation   444

gymnosperm   448

gravitropism   452

hormone   452

photoperiodism   454

phototropism   452

seed   447

seedless vascular plant   446

sporophyte generation   444

thigmotropism   452

Understanding the Basics

Multiple-Choice Questions
(Answers are in the back of the book.)

1. Plants (select all that apply):
   a. obtain nutrition by consuming existing organic material.
   b. obtain nutrition by performing photosynthesis.
   c. produce much of Earth's oxygen.
   d. absorb atmospheric carbon dioxide.
   e. are a cause of soil erosion.

2. Defining characteristics of plants include (select all that apply):
   a. multicelled
   b. hyphae
   c. cell walls
   d. reproduction through fruiting bodies
   e. land-dwelling

3. In the alternation of generations seen in plants (select all that apply):
   a. one generation produces flowers, the next does not.
   b. one generation produces spores, the next produces eggs and sperm.

c. succeeding generations tend to be about the same size.
   d. succeeding generations tend to differ in size.
   e. all generations produce spores.

4. Match the plant type on the left with the plant category on the right.
   a. moss   angiosperm
   b. cactus   gymnosperm
   c. pine tree   angiosperm
   d. rose   bryophyte
   e. fern   seedless vascular plant

5. Only angiosperms (select all that apply):
   a. perform photosynthesis.
   b. produce seeds.
   c. encase seeds in fruit.
   d. have seeds containing endosperm.
   e. have eggs encased in pollen grains.

6. Pollen grains contain:
   a. hormones.
   b. food for the new plant generation.
   c. eggs that will be fertilized by sperm.
   d. sperm.
   e. chloroplasts.

7. Phototropism and gravitropism lead to the bending of shoots or roots toward or away from a stimulus (light or gravity, respectively). Such bending is brought about by:
   a. increased growth over the general surface of the root or shoot.
   b. differential growth on opposite sides of the root or shoot.
   c. muscular contractions, leading to a curvature in the root or shoot.
   d. loss of water into the atmosphere.
   e. all of the above.

8. Photoperiodism allows some plants to respond to _____ by timing such things as _____ in accordance with the amount of _____ they are exposed to.
   a. predators; dormancy; moisture
   b. competition; growth; moisture
   c. the seasons; growth; toxins
   d. other plants; flowering; IAA
   e. the seasons; flowering; darkness

Brief Review

(Answers are in the back of the book.)

1. Distinguish between the sporophyte and gametophyte generations of plants.

2. How does a seed differ from a gamete?

3. Describe two means by which angiosperm reproduction is aided by animals.

4. Distinguish among gravitropism, phototropism, and thigmotropism.

5. What factor in a plant's external environment controls photoperiodism?

Applying Your Knowledge

1. As readers of the evolution section of this book know, a lack of genetic diversity can be harmful to a population of living things (see Chapter 17, page 308, for more). Can you think of an aspect of plant functioning that (a) has grown more sophisticated over evolutionary time and that (b) helps ensure genetic diversity among plants?

2. All plant cells have a relatively thick and often strong cell wall, but no animal cells have such a feature. Why does it make sense that plant and animal cells should differ in this way?

3. How are the bryophytes of the plant kingdom like the amphibians of the animal kingdom?

The Angiosperms:
Form and Function in Flowering Plants

Plants are fixed in one spot and have almost no moving parts, yet they manage to reproduce, transport fluids inside themselves, and keep growing for as long as they live.

The flowering plant sometimes called the chinche-rinchee (*Ornithogalum thyrsoides*) is native to South Africa. Its flowers grow on a stem that can be up to three feet long.

Insects that eat plants are not much of a surprise, but plants that eat insects? About 500 species of flowering plants are carnivorous, with at least one variety, the tropical pitcher plant *Nepenthes,* able to capture animals up to the size of a small bird. But the most famous plant predator of them all undoubtedly is the Venus flytrap (*Dionaea muscipula*), which is

native to the wetlands of North and South Carolina. So, how does this plant, which has no muscles and is fixed in one spot, end up consuming insects?

Each trap is a single leaf folded in two, with the interlocking "fingers" of the two halves able to snap together in less than half a second, imprisoning any small wanderer (**Figure 25.1**). But what keeps the leaf halves from wasting their energy by snapping together in pursuit of wind-borne blades of grass or other objects? The chemical reaction that puts the trap in motion is set off by a series of trigger hairs on the inside of each of the leaf's two sections. The trick is that *two* trigger hairs must be tripped for the halves of the leaf to snap shut. Insects wandering around inside the leaf are likely to trip two hairs, but blades of grass are not. And how does the plant slam its "jaws" shut without muscles? When the trigger hairs are tripped, they set off a chemical reaction that engorges cells at the base of the leaf with water. This rapid movement causes the leaf halves to come together. Enzymes are then released that begin to digest the struggling insect.

It may surprise you to learn that Venus flytraps make their own food through photosynthesis, just like any other plant. So, why do they need these side orders of insects? For nutritional supplements. Like many other carnivorous plants, Venus flytraps grow naturally in mineral-poor soil, and the insects they catch are a good source of nitrogen and phosphate.

The world of plants is filled with species as unique in their own way as the Venus flytrap. Queen Victoria water lilies (*Victoria regia*) have circular leaves that can be nearly 6 feet in diameter and that can serve as a floating platform for a person if pressed into service (**Figure 25.2** on the next page). The seeds of orchids are so tiny that they resemble dust more than seeds, while the seeds of the double coconut come wrapped in a fruit that might be 2 feet across.

Given such diversity, it may surprise you to learn that the orchid and the coconut are united with the water lily and the Venus flytrap in being members of a single group of plants—the flowering plants that are the subject of this chapter. Readers of Chapter 24 may recall that there are four principal types of plants in the living world: the bryophytes, represented by mosses; the seedless vascular plants, represented by ferns; the gymnosperms, represented by coniferous (evergreen) trees; and the flowering plants, which also are known as angiosperms. Chapter 24 introduced all

Figure 25.1
One with Prey, One without
The venus flytrap leaf in the foreground has slammed its two halves together, trapping an insect inside. Meanwhile the leaf in the background will stay open until such time as an insect enters.

Figure 25.2
Floating Platforms

A woman plays a violin while standing atop a Victoria water lily at the Missouri Botanical Garden in St. Louis at the turn of the twentieth century. The lilies are native to South America. Some South American Indians call the lilies *Yrupe,* which can be translated as "big water tray."

Figure 25.3
Angiosperm Variety

(a) A trumpet vine (*Clytostoma callistegiodes*) spreading on a bush.

(b) Saguaro cacti in Arizona's Saguaro National Park.

(c) The cereal grain rye (*Secale*) growing in a field.

One problem in recognizing how dominant these plants are has to do with their name: The term *flowering plant* is likely to bring to mind nothing more than plants that have recognizable flowers on them— say, roses or tulips. These plants are indeed angiosperms, but food crops such as rice and wheat are angiosperms, too, as are all cacti, almost all the leafy trees, innumerable bushes, ice plant, cotton plants— the real challenge is to name familiar plants that *aren't* angiosperms (**Figure 25.3**). In this chapter, you'll get an overview of how angiosperms are structured and how they function. A formal definition of them will be provided once you've learned a little about them.

25.1 The Structure of Angiosperms

Let's begin our tour of the angiosperms by looking at their component parts.

The Basic Division: Roots and Shoots

We'll first look at the larger-scale structures of the angiosperms, starting with a simple, two-part division that rhymes: roots and shoots. Plants live in two worlds, air and soil, with their root system below ground and their shoot system above it (**Figure 25.4**).

The function of the root system is straightforward: Grow toward water and minerals, absorb these substances from the soil, and then begin transporting

four varieties of plants, but in this chapter we'll focus strictly on flowering plants. Why pay so much attention to just one type of plant? Because of the overwhelming dominance of these plants. There are about 16,000 species of bryophytes, 13,000 species of seedless vascular plants, and 1,000 species of gymnosperms in the world today, but there are an estimated 300,000 species of flowering plants.

(a)

(b)

(c)

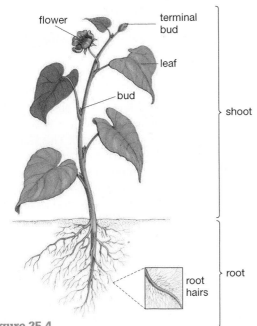

Figure 25.4
A Life-Form in Two Parts

Flowering plants live in two worlds, with their shoots in the air and their roots in the soil. Although flowering plants differ enormously in size and shape, they generally possess all the external features shown.

(a) Taproot system   **(b)** Fibrous root system

Figure 25.5
Two Root Strategies

(a) Dandelions such as this one employ a taproot system—a large central root and a number of smaller lateral roots.

(b) The chrysanthemum plant employs a fibrous root system—a collection of roots that are all about the same size.

them up through the rest of the plant. Most roots also serve as anchoring devices for plants, and some act as storage sites for food reserves.

The function of the shoot system is more complex. Photosynthesis takes place in this system, primarily in leaves, which means leaves must be positioned to absorb sunlight. Plants are in competition with one another for sunlight, which is a primary reason so many plants are tall. Once food is produced in photosynthesis, it must be distributed throughout the plant, starting with the shoots. But it is not just plant food production that is centered in the shoot system; it is plant reproduction as well. Within flowers and their derivatives, we find all the components of reproduction—seeds, pollen, and so forth. Now let's look in more detail at the components of the root and shoot systems.

Roots: Absorbing the Vital Water

If you look at **Figure 25.5**, you can see pictures of the two basic types of plant root systems, one a **taproot system** consisting of a large central root and a number of smaller lateral roots, and the second a **fibrous root system** consisting of many roots that are all about the same size. **Figure 25.6** then shows you another feature common to root systems: **root hairs,** thread-like extensions of roots that greatly increase their absorptive surface area. Each root hair actually is an elongation of a single outer cell of the root. Between roots and root

hairs, the root structure of a given plant can be extensive. One famous analysis, conducted in the 1930s on a rye plant, concluded that its taproot and lateral roots alone, if laid end to end, would have stretched out for some 386 miles; meanwhile, this same plant had almost 6,600 miles of root hairs! This from a plant whose *shoot* stood 3 inches off the ground.

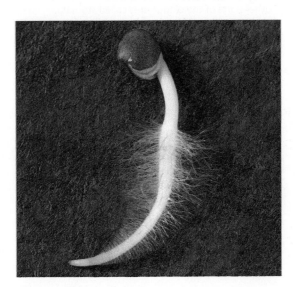

Figure 25.6
Root Hairs

Root hairs enormously increase the surface area of a root. The greater the surface area, the more fluid absorption can occur. Shown here are root hairs on the seedling of a radish.

Why do plants lavish such resources on their roots? Essentially because they have such a great need to take up water, and roots are the structures that allow them to do this. To perform photosynthesis, plants must have a constant supply of carbon dioxide, which enters the plants through microscopic pores, called *stomata,* that exist mostly on the undersides of their leaves. Open stomata, however, don't just let carbon dioxide in; they let the plant's water *out,* as water vapor. To accommodate this loss while still keeping vital tissues moist, plants continually pass water through themselves, from roots, up through the stem, and into the leaves (at which point it exits as water vapor). This process of water movement out of the plant is known as **transpiration;** through it, more than 90 percent of the water that enters a plant through its roots evaporates into the atmosphere. And the scale of this operation can be immense: The roots of a single tall maple tree can absorb nearly 60 gallons of water per *hour* on a hot summer day. Given this, it's easy to see why plants spend so much energy on development of their roots: their basic metabolism makes it a necessity. And the nutrient storage function of roots that was mentioned earlier? We human beings benefit from it along with plants—both sweet potatoes and carrots are roots.

Shoots: Leaves, Stems, and Flowers

Now let's turn to the shoot system, looking first at the leaves within it.

Leaves: Sites of Food Production

The primary business of leaves is to absorb the sunlight that drives photosynthesis, which is why most leaves are thin and flat (**Figure 25.7a**). This leaf shape maximizes the surface area that can be devoted to absorbing sunlight while minimizing the number of cells in leaves that are irrelevant to photosynthesis. Beyond this, through their tiny stomata, leaves serve as the plant's primary entry and exit points for gases. As noted, the most important gas that's entering is carbon dioxide, which is one of the starting ingredients for photosynthesis. What's exiting is the by-product of photosynthesis, oxygen, along with the water vapor.

The broad, flat leaves that are so common in nature have in essence a two-part structure—a **blade** (which we usually think of as the leaf itself) and a **petiole,** more commonly referred to as the leaf stalk. If you look at the idealized cross section of this leaf in **Figure 25.7b**, you can see that the blade can be likened to a kind of cellular sandwich, with layers of cuticle, or waxy outer covering, on the outside, and a layer of epidermal cells just inside them. In the leaf's interior, there are vascular

Figure 25.7
Site of
Photosynthesis

(a) Leaves tend to be broad and flat to increase the surface area exposed to sunlight.

(b) Photosynthesis occurs primarily within the mesophyll cells in the interior of the leaf. The vascular bundles carry water to the leaves and carry the product of photosynthesis, sugar, to other parts of the plant. Pores called stomata, mostly on the underside of leaves, allow for the passage of gases in and out of the leaf.

(c) Guard cells of the stomata control the opening and closing of the stomata. When sunlight shines on the leaf during the day, the guard cells engorge with water that makes them bow apart, thus opening the stomata. When sunlight is reduced, water flows out of the guard cells, causing the stomata to close.

compound
leaves

simple
leaves

leaves modified
as spines

highly reduced leaves
(needles)

leaves modified
as tendrils

Figure 25.8
Leaves Come in Many Sizes, Shapes, and Colors
Simple leaves have just one blade. In compound leaves, the blade is divided into little leaflets. Some leaves are so modified that the average person can hardly recognize them as leaves—for example, the spines of a cactus.

bundles, which bear some relation to animal veins in that they are part of a fluid transport system. Then there are several layers of mesophyll cells. It is these cells that are the sites of most photosynthesis.

Now note, on the underside of the blade, the openings called **stomata.** These are the pores, mentioned earlier, that let water vapor out and carbon dioxide in—but for most plants only during the day. When the sun goes down, photosynthesis can no longer be performed, and it is not cost-effective for a plant to lose water without gaining carbon dioxide. As such, in most plants the stomata close up until photosynthesis begins again the following day. If you look at **Figure 25.7c,** you can see how this opening and closing of stomata is achieved: Two "guard cells," juxtaposed like the sides of a coin purse, are arranged around the stomata. When sunlight strikes the leaf, these cells engorge with water, which makes them bow apart. Then, in the absence of light, water flows out and the door closes again. A given square centimeter of a plant leaf may contain from 1,000 to 100,000 stomata.

Figure 25.8 gives you some idea of the varied forms of leaves. In addition to the so-called simple leaf we've been looking at, there are compound leaves in which individual blades are divided into a series of "leaflets." Pine needles and cactus spines are likewise actually leaves. The cactus, in particular, has reduced the amount of leaf surface it has as a means of conserving water. So, how does it perform enough photosynthesis to get along? It carries out most of its photosynthesis in its stem.

Stems: Structure and Storage

We all generally understand what the stem of a plant is, although it is less generally appreciated that the trunk of a tree is simply one kind of plant stem. The main functions of stems are to give structure to the plant as a whole and to act as storage sites for food reserves. In addition, water, minerals, hormones, and food are constantly shuttling through (and to) the stem, with water on its way up from the roots and food on its way down from the leaves to the rest of the plant.

Figure 25.9
**The Stem and
Its Parts**

Stems provide support to the rest of the plant, act as nutrient storage sites, and conduct fluids. Vascular plants have a "plumbing" system that transports food, water, minerals, and hormones. The vascular bundles in the figure are groups of tubes, running in parallel, that serve this transport function.

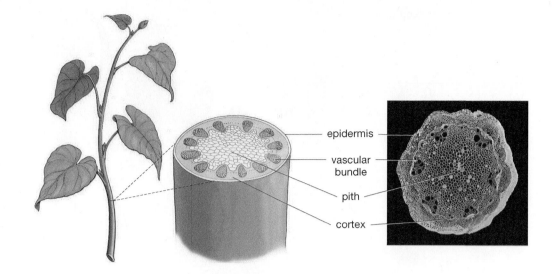

If you look at **Figure 25.9**, you can see a cross section of one type of plant stem, showing the vascular bundles or veins you saw in leaves and the outer, or epidermal, tissue just as the leaves had. You can also see so-called ground tissue of two types: an outer cortex and an inner pith, both of which can play a part in food storage and wound repair and provide structural strength to the plant. We'll look at all these types of tissues later.

Flowers: Many Parts in Service of Reproduction

Flowers are the reproductive structures of plants. A single flower generally has both male and female reproductive structures on it, which might make you think that a given plant would fertilize *itself*. This is indeed the case with some plants, such as Gregor Mendel's pea plants, reviewed in Chapter 11. However, because the evolutionary benefit of sexual reproduction comes with mixing genetic material from *different* individual organisms, natural selection has worked against self-fertilization by endowing many flowering plants with ways to reduce the incidence of it. For example, the male pollen of a given plant might be genetically incompatible with that plant's female reproductive structures. Some of the illustrations you'll be seeing show a plant fertilizing itself, but this is done only for visual simplicity.

If you look at **Figure 25.10**, you can see the components of a typical flower. Taking things from the bottom, there is a modified stem, called a pedicel, which widens into a base called a receptacle, from which the flowers emerge. Flowers themselves can be thought of as consisting of four parts: sepals, petals, stamens, and a carpel. The **sepals** are the leaf-like structures that protect the flower before it opens. (Drying out is a problem, as are hungry animals.) The function of the

Figure 25.10
Parts of the Flower

Flowers are composed of four main parts: sepals, petals, stamens, and a carpel. The sepals protect the young bud until it is ready to bloom. The petals attract pollinators. The stamens are the reproductive structures that produce pollen grains (which contain sperm cells). The carpel is the female reproductive structure; it includes an egg-containing ovary.

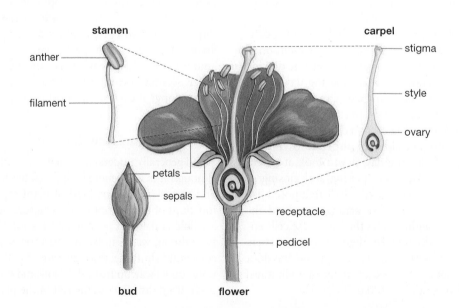

colorful **petals** is to announce "food here" to pollinating animals.

The heart of the flower's reproductive structures consists of the stamens and the carpel. If you look at Figure 25.10, you can see that the **stamens** consist of a long, slender **filament** topped by an **anther.** These anthers contain cells that ultimately will yield sperm-bearing pollen grains. Thus, the anthers are the place in the flower where *male* reproductive cells are produced. Pollen grains ultimately will be released from the anther and then carried—perhaps by a pollinating bee or bird—to the carpel of another plant. As Figure 25.10 shows, a **carpel** is a composite structure composed of three main parts: the **stigma,** which is the tip end of the carpel, on which pollen grains are deposited; the **style,** a slender tube that raises the stigma to such a prominent height that it can easily catch the pollen; and the **ovary,** the area in which fertilization of the female egg and then early development of the plant embryo take place. Thus, the ovary is the structure in the flower that houses the *female* reproductive cells, and it is the structure in which the male and female reproductive cells come together.

SO FAR ...

1. The primary function of roots is to absorb _____ and _____.

2. The primary function of leaves is to serve as sites of _____.

3. Flowers are the _____ structures of plants.

25.2 Monocots and Dicots

The roots, stems, and flowers we've been looking at represent the so-called gross anatomy of angiosperms, which is to say the large-scale physical makeup of these plants. To understand how angiosperms actually function, however, it's necessary to look at their anatomy on a smaller scale. What's the *detailed* makeup of roots, stems, and flowers, and how does this makeup produce a functioning plant? Before we begin looking into this question, it will be helpful to make a distinction between two broad classes of flowering plants. These are the monocotyledons and dicotyledons, which are almost always referred to as monocots and dicots. A **cotyledon** is an embryonic leaf, present in the seed of a plant, as you can see in **Figure 25.11. Monocotyledons** are plants that have one embryonic leaf; **dicotyledons** are plants that have two.

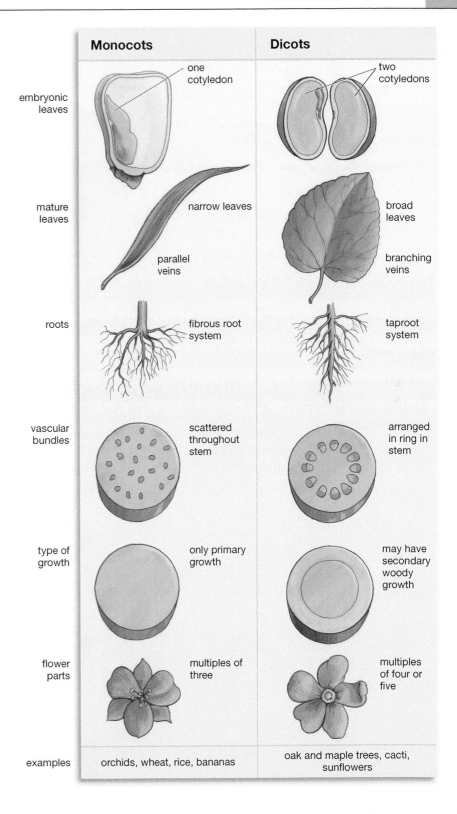

This distinction in the embryos is only one of the differences between monocots and dicots. Their roots are different, their leaves are different, and their transport tubes, or vascular bundles, are arranged differently. More than 75 percent of all flowering plants are the broad-leafed dicots. But given the 300,000 known species of flowering plants, this still leaves nearly 75,000 species of narrow-leafed monocots, which

Figure 25.11
Monocots and Dicots Compared

Plants with one embryonic leaf (the monocots) are structured differently from plants with two embryonic leaves (the dicots), as shown in the figure.

(a) Monocot plant

(b) Dicot plant

Figure 25.12
Categorizing Plants by Physical Features

(a) The plant *Dracaena fragrans,* commonly known as a corn plant, is a narrow-leafed monocot.

(b) Geraniums such as this one are broad-leafed dicots.

common function of contracting. These are muscle cells, and a group of them constitutes a muscle tissue. So, what kinds of tissues are there in angiosperms? The short answer is dermal, ground, vascular, and meristematic. Dermal tissue can be thought of as the plant's outer covering, vascular tissue as its transport or "plumbing" tissue, meristematic tissue as its growth tissue, and ground tissue as almost everything else in the plant.

If you look at **Figure 25.13**, you can see the location of all four kinds of primary tissue in a dicot. Looking at the stem in cross section, you can see that ground tissue is well named because visually it forms a kind of background against which you can see the tubes of the vascular tissue. Dermal tissue then is at the periphery of the plant, forming a "skin" layer around the ground tissue. The placement of the meristematic tissue is discussed shortly. Before we get to it, let's look in a little more detail at dermal, ground, and vascular tissue.

Dermal Tissue Is the Plant's Interface with the Outside World

Plants can't move from one location to another, they can't bite, and, as already noted, they must carefully control their water supply. All this makes their dermal tissue, or *epidermis,* very important. In the non-woody plants or "herbaceous" plants, this outer coat is generally only one layer of cells thick, but it serves to

include most of the important food crops (corn, wheat, rice). **Figure 25.12** shows you an example of both a monocot and a dicot.

25.3 Plant Tissue Types

We'll begin our small-scale anatomical review of angiosperms by looking at so-called tissue types in them. Readers of Chapter 23 may recall that a **tissue** is a group of cells that carries out a common function. In our own bodies, we have cells that perform the

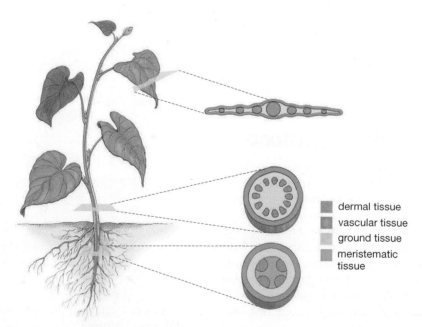

dermal tissue
vascular tissue
ground tissue
meristematic tissue

Figure 25.13
Four Types of Tissue in Primary Plant Growth
Dermal tissue (dark green) is found on the outside of the plant and is the interface between the plant and its environment. Ground tissue (pale green) is found throughout the plant and gives the plant its shape, stores food, and is active in photosynthesis. Vascular tissue (purple) transports water, nutrients, and sugar throughout the plant. Meristematic tissue (blue) occurs at the tips of shoots and roots and at leaf bases and gives rise to the entire plant, through the production of cells that develop into the other three tissue types.

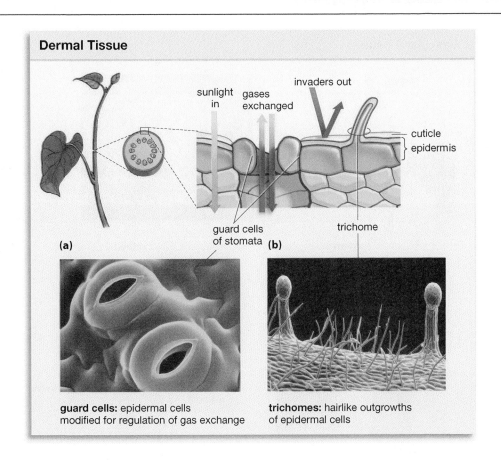

Dermal Tissue

sunlight in

gases exchanged

invaders out

cuticle
epidermis

guard cells of stomata

trichome

(a)

(b)

guard cells: epidermal cells modified for regulation of gas exchange

trichomes: hairlike outgrowths of epidermal cells

Figure 25.14
Where Plant Meets Environment

Dermal tissue serves as the interface between a plant and the environment around it. The waxy cuticle and the single layer of cells in the epidermis work together to protect the plant and to control interactions with the outside world.

(a) Specialized epidermal cells called guard cells regulate the opening of the plant pores called stomata, thus controlling gas exchange between the plant and its environment.

(b) Some epidermal cells have hair-like projections, called trichomes, that serve various functions. Two kinds of trichomes are visible in this rose plant. The larger of the two varieties, with the bulbous tips, help secrete chemicals that guard against plant-eating predators.

protect the plant and control its interaction with the outside world (**Figure 25.14**). A plant's first line of defense against outside predators is a waxy coating called the *cuticle,* which covers the epidermis of the plant's shoot. The cuticle is a kind of waterproofing, serving to keep water in, and an invader-proofing, helping to keep infecting bacteria and fungi out.

Plants need to exchange gases with their environments, however. They take in carbon dioxide and emit oxygen and water vapor through the microscopic stomata noted earlier. Stomata also represent a kind of weak point for plants, however, because they provide a passageway for microbial invaders and a conduit for excessive loss of moisture.

Dermal tissue also forms several kinds of extensions, called trichomes, that protrude from the plant's surface. We actually looked at one variety of these extensions earlier: the root hairs, meaning the thread-like outgrowths of individual epidermal root cells. Other types of trichomes serve not to absorb substances but to secrete them. In some plants, trichomes secrete toxic chemicals that ward off plant-eating animals.

Ground Tissue Forms the Bulk of the Primary Plant

Most of the primary plant is ground tissue, which can play a role in photosynthesis, nutrient storage, and plant structure.

Vascular Tissue Forms the Plant's Transport System

As noted earlier, the plant's vascular system has two main functions. First, it must transport water and minerals; second, it must transport the food made in photosynthesis. In line with this, there are two main components to the plant vascular system. First, there is **xylem,** the tissue through which water and dissolved minerals flow. Second, there is **phloem,** the tissue that conducts the food produced in photosynthesis, along with some hormones and other compounds (**Figure 25.15** on the next page). The movement of water through xylem is directional—from root up through stem and then out through leaves as water vapor. Meanwhile, the food made in photosynthesis must travel through phloem to every part of the plant, although in temperate climates the net flow is downward in summer (from food-producing leaves) but upward in early spring (from root and stem storage sites).

Xylem and phloem are arranged in the *vascular bundles* noted earlier, which is to say collections of xylem and phloem tubes that run together in parallel in the stem—xylem tubes toward the inside of the stem, phloem tubes toward the outside. Such bundles are arranged in different ways within a stem depending on whether the plant is a monocot or a dicot; the circular arrangement seen in Figure 25.15 is the one found in dicots.

Figure 25.15
Materials Movers

Vascular tissue transports fluids throughout the plant. Xylem is composed of cells called tracheids and vessel elements that transport water and dissolved minerals. Phloem is composed of sieve elements (and their companion cells), which transport the food produced during photosynthesis. These cell types are stacked on one another to form long tubes.

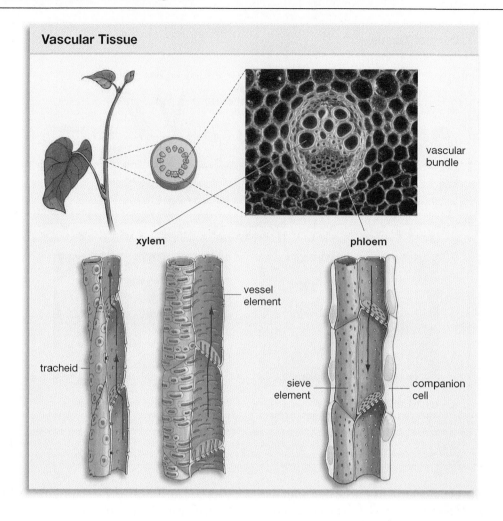

Vascular Tissue

vascular bundle

xylem

phloem

vessel element

tracheid

sieve element

companion cell

SO FAR . . .

1. Most plants fall into the category of the broad-leafed _____, but many of our most important food crops are narrow-leafed _____.

2. Dermal tissue is tissue located at the _____ of a plant, while vascular tissue forms a plant's _____ system.

3. Xylem is the tissue through which _____ and _____ flow, while phloem is the tissue that conducts the _____.

25.4 Primary Growth in Angiosperms

So, you've seen three types of plant tissues—dermal, ground, and vascular. The question now is: How do these get produced? The answer is that the fourth type of tissue mentioned earlier, meristematic tissue, gives rise to all of them. Put another way, meristematic tis-

sue is responsible for all the *growth* that occurs in plants. (We're concerning ourselves here only with a plant's "primary" or vertical growth, but even the so-called secondary or lateral growth that woody plants exhibit comes about through meristematic tissue.)

In coming to understand how this one type of tissue can produce all the others in a plant, it's important to realize that plants do not grow the way people do—throughout their entire length—but instead grow only at the *tips* of their roots and shoots. If you look at **Figure 25.16**, you can see what this means. A boy of, say, eight decides to drive a long nail into the trunk of a secluded tree. Ten years later, he happens to walk by the same tree and, on seeing it, a couple of things occur to him. First, he has grown, but the nail is in the same place; he would have to bend down now to pull it out. Second, to judge by the nail's height, the tree's trunk may not have moved up, but its *top* certainly has; it's much taller than he remembered it. Finally, if the boy continued to visit the tree every 10 years or so, he would get one more lesson about its growth: That there's no point at which it comes to a complete halt. While the boy probably stopped growing at age 18, the tree might keep on growing for decades. Why? Because plant growth is indeterminate—it can go on throughout the life of most plants.

When Billy was eight ...   When Billy was eighteen ...

Figure 25.16
The Basic
Characteristics of
Plant Growth
If a young boy drives a long nail into a tree and returns 10 years later, two things will be apparent: The nail is at the same height it used to be, but the tree is much taller than it used to be. What does this say about tree growth? Trees do not elongate throughout their whole length, but only at their tips in their primary or vertical growth.

When we put the concept of indeterminate growth together with that of growth at the tips, it follows that there must be cells at the root and shoot tips of plants that remain perpetually young—or more accurately, perpetually embryonic. That is, these cells are able to keep giving rise to both more of themselves and to cells that then differentiate into all the tissue types we just went over. And this is just what takes place; everything in a plant develops ultimately from these cells, which are meristematic cells that form a series of **apical meristems:** groups of plant cells, located at the tips of roots and shoots, that give rise to all the tissues in a plant.

If you look at **Figure 25.17**, you can see the apical meristem locations in a typical plant. Note that in this plant with a taproot, each lateral root tip has its own apical meristematic tissue that is capable of giving rise to yet more roots. In the shoot, plants tend to confine their growth to the shoot apices that lie at the tip of each stem. Why? The better to compete for precious sunlight. It is the shoot apical meristem you can see in the figure that gives rise to all the cells that allow the plant's shoot growth.

Note, however, that there is a second location for meristematic tissue in the shoot—the area nestled between leaf and stem. It's here that we find lateral buds. Any **bud** is an undeveloped shoot, composed mostly of meristematic tissue. A lateral bud is meristematic tissue that may give rise to a branch or a flower (which obviously ends up growing laterally from the stem). Lateral buds are, however, just like any other shoot tissue in that they are the products of the shoot apical meristem. You could think of them as collections of meristematic tissue that are left behind, in a sense, by the apical meristem tissue as it continues its growth. (If you look again at the topmost picture in Figure 25.17, you can see two small collections of darker-colored cells on each side of the apical meristem dome.

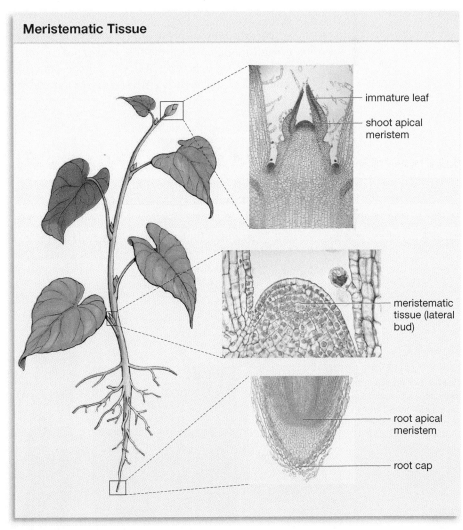

Meristematic Tissue

immature leaf

shoot apical meristem

meristematic tissue (lateral bud)

root apical meristem

root cap

Figure 25.17
Giving Rise to the Whole Plant

Growth in plants originates from meristematic tissue. The shoot and root elongate at the apical meristems, while new branches originate at the lateral buds (which are derived from apical meristem). The root cap noted in the bottom micrograph is tissue that protects the meristematic cells above it while secreting a lubricant that helps the root move into the ground.

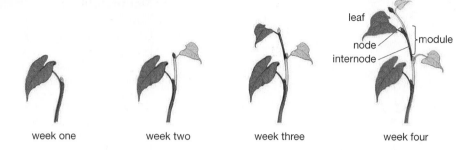

leaf

node
internode

module

week one   week two   week three   week four

Figure 25.18
Vertical Growth
Occurs in Modules

Each growth module (indicated here by alternating dark green and light green segments) consists of an internode, a node, and one or more leaves. This plant progresses from one module in week 1 to four modules in week 4.

These are collections of meristem tissue that have been left behind by the shoot apical meristem.) Lateral buds can serve as a kind of insurance policy for the plant in that they can switch roles. Should the plant's apical meristem become damaged, one of the lateral buds steps in to assume the role of the shoot apex, thus allowing the plant to maintain its vertical growth. As long as the original apical meristem is intact, however, it generally will produce hormones that *suppress* the growth of the lateral buds near it, leaving them dormant.

We can think of plant vertical growth in terms of growth modules. Each module consists of an internode (the stem between leaves), a node (the area where a leaf attaches to stem), and one or more leaves (**Figure 25.18**).

SO FAR . . .

1. Unlike the case with animals, plant growth comes only at _____ of roots and shoots and can go on _____.

2. Everything in the plant ultimately develops from _____ tissue, through collections of this tissue known as _____.

25.5 Fluid Movement: The Vascular System

You have had some opportunity already to look at the plant's vascular or "plumbing" system as it relates to plant tissues, but now it's time to take a closer look at how the vascular system actually works, starting with the water-conducting xylem and then continuing to the food-conducting phloem.

How the Xylem Conducts Water

Two types of cells make up the water-conducting portions of plant xylem. These are **tracheids** and **vessel elements.** Both types of cells are peculiar in that they take on their primary function of conducting water only after they die. This happens when they've matured, after which their contents are then cleared out. What's left is a strand of empty, thick-walled cells stacked one on top of another—tubes, in other words (**Figure 25.19**). The walls of these xylem cells remain intact, however, with the upshot that xylem represents not only a transport system but a *load-bearing* system, which is why something as massive as a tree can grow so tall. Indeed, this load-bearing function remains in a given group of xylem cells long after they have ceased to act as a conduit for the water and dissolved nutrients that are sometimes called xylem sap. (To get an idea of one of the uses human beings have for this sap, see "The Syrup for Your Pancakes Comes from Xylem" on page 475.)

Solar Energy and Water Movement

In the tallest trees, water coming from the roots goes through a vertical journey of up to 300 feet before it gets to the topmost leaves of the tree. What kind of force can move water such a long way? As it turns out, plants themselves spend no energy at all on this transport. Instead, it is transpiration—the movement of

Figure 25.19
Water Carriers

The fluid-conducting cells of the xylem are tracheids and vessel elements. Both kinds of cells stack to form tubes.

xylem

tracheid

vessel element

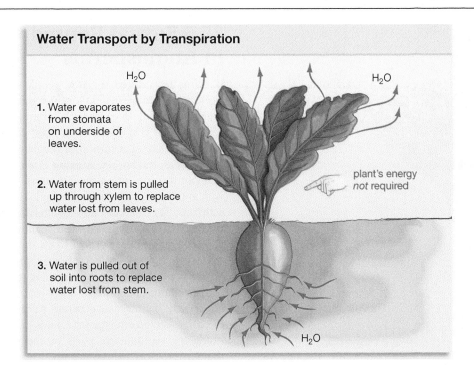

Water Transport by Transpiration

1. Water evaporates from stomata on underside of leaves.

2. Water from stem is pulled up through xylem to replace water lost from leaves.

plant's energy *not* required

3. Water is pulled out of soil into roots to replace water lost from stem.

H_2O

Figure 25.20
Suction Moves Water through Xylem
When water evaporates from leaves, a low pressure is created that pulls more water up to fill the void. Water is so cohesive that it moves up in a continuous column. The sun's energy, rather than the plant's energy, fuels this process.

BioFlix™

Water Transport in Plants

water vapor from plant leaves into the atmosphere—that is the primary force that moves water through xylem. As the water vapor evaporates into the air, it creates a region of low pressure, and this pulls a continuous column of water upward (**Figure 25.20**). Ultimately, the energy source for this movement is the sun; its warm rays power the evaporation of water at the leaf surface.

Food Transport through Phloem

Now let's turn from water transport to food transport. What is the nature of the food that flows through phloem? It's mostly sucrose—better known as table sugar—that is dissolved in water. Hormones, amino acids, and other compounds move through phloem as well, but sucrose and water are the main ingredients of this material, which is known as phloem sap.

The phloem cells that this sap moves through are called **sieve elements.** Unlike xylem cells, sieve elements are alive at maturity, though in a curiously altered state. Each one has lost its cell nucleus, which you may remember is the DNA-containing information center of a cell. Sieve elements continue to function as living cells, however, because each one has associated with it one or more *companion cells* that retain their DNA and that seem to take care of all the housekeeping needs of their sister sieve elements (**Figure 25.21**). The association between the two kinds of phloem cells is so intimate that when sieve elements die out, as they often do at the end of a growing season, their companion cells die as well. The reason sieve elements lose their nuclei seems to be to make room for the rapid flow of nutrients through them. The reason they are called *sieve* elements is that the ends of adjoining cells

are studded with small holes, much like a sieve. Stacked on top of each other, these cells form the plant's food-conducting pipes, the *sieve tubes.*

The force that moves food into and through these tubes is different from the one that moves water through xylem. With food, a plant does not get a free ride on transport via transpiration. Instead, it must expend its own energy to take the first step in nutrient transport, which is *loading* sucrose into sieve element cells. Once this happens, a principal player in moving sucrose through the phloem is a force that readers of Chapter 5 are familiar with: osmosis. When sucrose is loaded into the phloem, it sets up an osmotic flow that moves *water* into the phloem—something that is no different in principle than sending water into a

Figure 25.21
Food Carriers
The micrograph at right shows a cross section through a sieve element cell (looking at it from above) and an adjacent companion cell. A plant's phloem sap moves from one sieve element to another through the perforations visible in the cell.

phloem

sieve element

companion cell

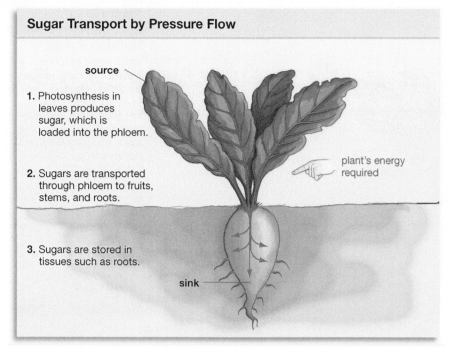

Sugar Transport by Pressure Flow

source

1. Photosynthesis in leaves produces sugar, which is loaded into the phloem.

2. Sugars are transported through phloem to fruits, stems, and roots.

plant's energy required

3. Sugars are stored in tissues such as roots.

sink

Figure 25.22
How Food Moves through the Plant
Sucrose is produced in the leaves (source) by photosynthesis, after which the plant expends its own energy to load the sucrose into the phloem. A movement of water into the phloem follows, which produces a fluid pressure that transports the sucrose through the plant, both for use and for storage (sink).

garden hose from an outside source. In both cases, such water is under pressure and it is this pressure that moves the sucrose from one location in the plant to another. The loading site of this system is called a *source* and the unloading site is called a *sink,* but these sites could also be called the "producer" and the "consumer" or perhaps "producer" and "bank" (**Figure 25.22**). Sources tend to be sugar-producing leaves, while sink sites tend to be storage tissue such as roots, along with growing fruits and stems. With this, let's move from a review of transport in angiosperms to a consideration reproduction in them.

SO FAR . . .

1. The water-conducting portions of xylem are made up of two kinds of cells, _____ and _____.

2. The transpiration that moves water through xylem is ultimately powered by _____.

3. To move dissolved sucrose through phloem, a plant must first _____ sucrose into _____ cells. This produces an osmosis that results in a fluid _____ that transports the sucrose.

25.6 Sexual Reproduction in Angiosperms

If plants reproduced the way people do, then maple trees, as an example, would produce gametes—eggs and sperm—that would come together and result in a new generation of maple trees. But plants don't reproduce this way. What a generation of maple trees produces is not gametes but spores. A **spore** is a reproductive cell that can develop into a new organism without fusing with another reproductive cell. Maple tree spores do exactly this: They develop into an alternate generation of the maple tree plant. To say the least, however, this alternate generation does not *look* like a maple tree. On the male side, the mature alternate generation amounts to pollen grains, each one of which is microscopic and consists of three cells and an outer coat, at most. On the female side, the alternate generation is a small collection of cells, called an embryo sac, that is hidden away deep inside the reproductive parts of the maple tree. Although these individuals are tiny, they have a critical role to play: *They* will produce the eggs and sperm that, once fused, will result in more maple trees.

As may be apparent from this account, plants exhibit a back-and-forth between generations. In their reproduction, they go through an *alternation of generations,* which was reviewed in Chapter 24 (see page 443). Because the generation that is familiar to us—the maple tree—produces spores, it is known as the sporophyte generation. Because the generation that is less familiar to us produces gametes, it is called the gametophyte generation. Given how small the gametophyte generation is in angiosperms, most people have trouble seeing it *as* a generation. From a human perspective, pollen grains and embryo sacs look like small component parts of the sporophyte generation. Nevertheless, gametophytes are a separate generation of plant, with their own critical role to play in angiosperm reproduction.

With this in mind, look again, in **Figure 25.23**, at the reproductive parts of an angiosperm—at the flowers that we went over earlier. What you're seeing in the illustration is mostly the *sporophyte* generation of this angiosperm. There is, for example, the stamen mentioned earlier, which consists of a long, slender filament that is topped by an anther. Every anther has chambers within it, however, containing cells that will develop into sperm-containing **pollen grains,** which are the mature *gametophyte* generation of the angiosperm on the male side. Meanwhile, you can also see the carpel, a composite structure composed of three parts: the stigma, style, and ovary. Each of these is a part of the sporophyte generation of plant, but the ovary houses cells that eventually will develop into the egg-containing **embryo sac** you can see in the figure—the mature gametophyte generation of the angiosperm on the *female* side.

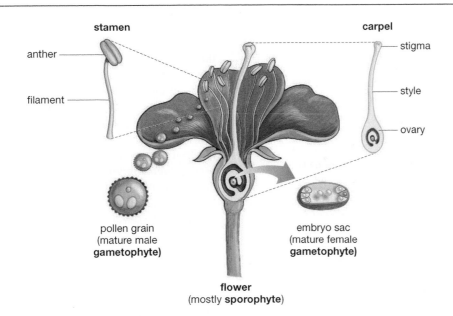

Figure 25.23
The Sporophyte and Gametophyte Generations

All plants reproduce through an alternation of generations. In angiosperms, this means an alternation between a larger sporophyte generation and a smaller gametophyte generation. The gametophyte generation either develops entirely within the sporophyte plant (the female embryo sac on the right) or largely within it (the male pollen grains on the left).

Now, with these component parts of the two generations in mind, how does reproduction work in angiosperms? If you look at **Figure 25.24**, you can see the process in overview. Note that we're starting with a mature sporophyte plant whose anthers produce the cells, called microspores, that develop into sperm-containing pollen grains. Meanwhile, the ovary of a second sporophyte contains a cell, called a megaspore, that will develop into the egg-containing embryo sac.

Next, a pollen grain from our first plant moves to the stigma of our second, lands on it, thus pollinating it, and a sperm cell from the pollen grain moves down to the egg in the embryo sac and fuses with it, thus fertilizing it. The result is a sporophyte zygote, or early-stage embryo. When this embryo has become surrounded with both nutritive and protective tissue, the result is the reproductive structure known as a seed. When this seed lands on the ground, the embryo

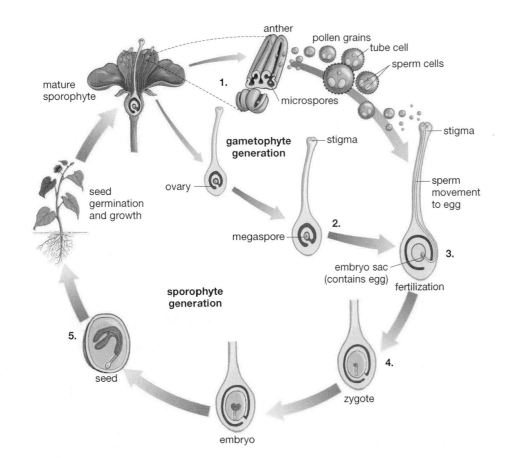

Figure 25.24
Overview of Angiosperm Reproduction

1. The mature sporophyte flower produces many male microspores within the anther and a female megaspore within the ovary. The male microspores then develop into pollen grains that contain the male gamete, sperm. 2. Meanwhile, the female megaspore produces the female gamete, the egg. 3. A pollen grain with its sperm inside, moves to the stigma of a plant and a sperm from the grain moves down through the carpel, reaches the egg, and fertilizes it. 4. This results in a zygote that develops into an embryo protected inside a seed. 5. This seed leaves the parent plant and sprouts or "germinates" in the earth, growing eventually into the type of sporophyte plant that began the cycle.

pollination   **pollen tube growth**   **double fertilization**

Figure 25.25
Double Fertilization in Angiosperms

When the male pollen grain (shown greatly enlarged) lands on the stigma, the tube cell within it sprouts a pollen tube, through which the two pollen grain sperm pass in moving to the embryo sac. One sperm cell fertilizes the egg in the sac, forming a zygote—the new sporophyte plant. The other sperm cell fuses with the two nuclei of the central cell in the sac, forming the endosperm that will later nourish the embryonic plant.

it contains will grow into the same kind of sporophyte plant we started with.

A key event in this process obviously comes when the sperm from the first plant fertilizes the egg from the second. But if you look closely at the pollen grains in Figure 25.24, you can see that each one actually contains *two* sperm cells (which are encased inside the larger tube cell that takes up most of the volume of the pollen grain). So, if one egg plus one sperm makes one zygote, why are there two sperm cells inside a pollen grain? And how does a sperm cell get from the stigma at the *top* of the carpel (where the pollen grain lands) to the embryo sac at the *bottom* of the carpel (where the egg lies)?

If you look at **Figure 25.25**, you can see the answer. When the pollen grain lands on the stigma, the tube cell within it then begins to germinate on the stigma—it sprouts a *pollen tube* that grows down through the style. Once this has taken place, one of the sperm in the grain travels through the tube, gets to the female egg, and fertilizes it. And what happens to the other sperm cell? It too travels down the pollen

tube, but it is destined to fuse not with the egg in the embryo sac, but with the two nuclei in the middle of the sac that are part of its large *central cell*. This too is a fertilization, but the product of it is not an embryo, but food for it. What this fertilization produces is endosperm: tissue rich in nutrients that can be used by the embryo that will now develop from the zygote. Thus, the pollination of this plant has resulted in two fertilizations—what has taken place is the phenomenon of **double fertilization,** meaning the fusion of gametes and of nutritive cells that occurs at the same time in angiosperm plants.

Double fertilization is an innovation that belongs almost solely to the angiosperm plants, but it has ended up being a boon to all kinds of *animals*, including people. It is endosperm that supplies much of the food we human beings consume. The rice and wheat grains we're familiar with consist in large part of endosperm meant to sustain the plant embryo (**Figure 25.26**).

SO FAR . . .

1. The plants with which we're familiar, such as maple trees, do not produce gametes (eggs and sperm), but instead produce _____, making them the _____ generation of plants. This generation alternates with the _____ generation, which on the male side consists of _____ and on the female side consists of small collections of cells, each one of which is known as a(n) _____.

2. For a new generation of sporophyte plant to be produced, _____ from one plant must land on the _____ of a plant, a necessary step in allowing the fusion of _____ with _____ that will bring about reproduction.

3. One of the fertilizations in double fertilization produces a _____, which is the original cell in the new generation of _____ plant. The other fertilization produces _____ in the form of the tissue called _____.

corn
(monocot)

seed coat

endosperm

cotyledon

embryo

Figure 25.26
Endosperm Is Food for the Embryo

In monocots such as corn, endosperm persists in the mature seed, providing nutrition for the embryo inside. The cotyledon in the figure is the corn plant's embryonic leaf.

25.7 The Developing Plant

As noted, egg fertilization produces a zygote that develops into an embryo. Our new generation of sporophyte plant will develop from this embryo, but before this can happen, two kinds of tissue must develop *around* the embryo—tissues that will serve protective and reproductive functions. If you look at Figure 25.25 again, you can see that the embryo sac is nearly

ESSAY

The Syrup for Your Pancakes Comes from Xylem

In late February or early March, when winter is winding down in New England and eastern Canada, farmers who own sugar maple trees are kept busy in a game of drilling and watching. What they are drilling is a series of 2- to 3-inch holes, about three of them per maple tree. What they are watching is the weather, because they need a series of freezing nights followed by warmer days to get what they want. Such nights prompt the maple trees to convert nutrients they have stored into sugar; the warmer days then bring about a flow of this sugar, upward in sap through the tree's xylem. This material can then be "tapped" through spigots inserted into the drilled holes. The clear white sap that drips out—as much as 40 gallons from a single tree—is the starting material for pure maple syrup. Vermont is the chief maple-syrup-producing state in the United States, with an output of 920,000 gallons in 2009. Canada, however, produces about 80 percent of the world's maple syrup.

The "maple syrup" that most Americans buy in stores actually has very little maple syrup in it (perhaps 2–3 percent, the bulk being made up of corn syrup and syrup from regular sugar). This is understandable because pure maple syrup is expensive; the best varieties cost anywhere between $30 and $45 per gallon. One reason for this expense is that harvesting the syrup is a labor-intensive business; each tap must be put in by hand, just as it was hundreds of years ago (see **Figure 1**). Beyond this, it takes about 40 gallons of sap to make a single gallon of maple syrup. The sap must be boiled down until its sugar concentration reaches 66.5 percent.

Too many taps can kill a tree, but experienced syrup harvesters know how to tap the same tree year after year—potentially for hundreds of years—without harming it. The 40 gallons of sap a tree can yield sounds like a lot, but it may account for only 10 percent of a tree's total supply of sugar.

In the text, you've read much about the plant's food supply flowing through *phloem*, not xylem. But in sugar maples and some other deciduous trees, the food produced in summer's photosynthesis is stored as starch in xylem cells, to be broken down into sugar and released to the growing upper portions of the tree in early spring.

Figure 1
Source of Maple Syrup
Maple trees in Vermont being tapped for their xylem sap, which will become the key ingredient in maple syrup.

surrounded by tissue from the sporophyte plant called an ovule. Once fertilization occurs, tissue from this ovule will develop into a **seed coat** that will protect the embryonic plant until it germinates in the ground. What once was an ovule with a sporophyte embryo inside is now a **seed:** a reproductive structure of a plant that includes an outer seed coat, an embryo, and nutritional tissue for the embryo (the endosperm).

The Development of Fruit

As the seed coat is developing, another layer of tissue is taking shape outside of it. As you can see in Figure 25.25, the ovule we just talked about is surrounded by the *ovary* of the sporophyte plant. The wall of this ovary now develops into something that has a familiar name: fruit. Strictly speaking, **fruit** is the mature ovary of any flowering plant. Given this, *all* flowering plants develop fruit, but it's clear that most of the 300,000 species of flowering plants are not fruits as we commonly understand that term. It follows that the botanical definition of fruit differs from the common definition; under the botanical definition, fruits can take on lots of forms. The pod of a pea plant is a fruit, for example, as is the outer covering of a kernel of corn (although here fruit has fused with the corn seed coat, leaving scarcely anything separate that can be recognized as fruit). On the other hand, fruits can

Figure 25.27
Fruits Come in Many Forms

A fruit, the mature ovary of a flowering plant, surrounds a seed or seeds. Thus, **(a)** the flesh of an apricot fits this definition of fruit, but so does **(b)** the pod of a pea, which has several seeds inside. The structure we commonly think of as **(c)** the strawberry fruit actually is the strawberry plant receptacle, with each receptacle having many fruits on its surface. What are commonly thought of as strawberry "seeds" are tiny strawberry plant carpels, each complete with its own fruit and seed.

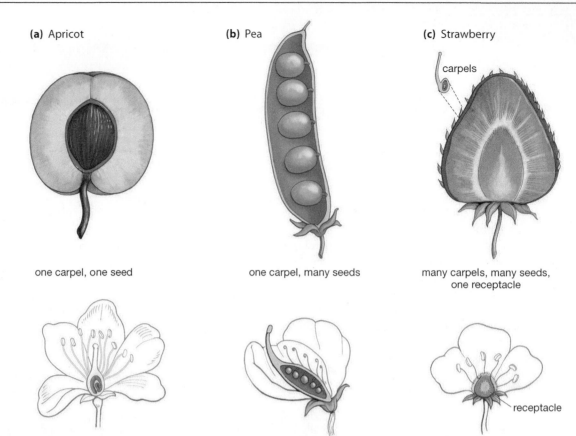

(a) Apricot

one carpel, one seed

(b) Pea

one carpel, many seeds

(c) Strawberry

carpels

many carpels, many seeds, one receptacle

receptacle

take exactly the form we're used to, as with the flesh of an apricot or cherry. To add another twist, where is the fruit in a strawberry? The answer, shown in **Figure 25.27**, may surprise you.

Fruit develops in all angiosperms, and it develops *only* in angiosperms. Thus, angiosperms can be defined by this anatomical feature. An **angiosperm** is a plant whose seeds develop inside the tissue called fruit. What is common to many fruits is that they serve a protective function for the underlying seed, and many act as *attractants* for seed dispersal. As noted in Chapter 24 (page 451), the wild berry that a bear eats consists not only of the fruit flesh but of the seeds it surrounds. The fruit is digested by the bear as food, but the seeds pass through the bear's digestive tract. In this way, the seeds get dispersed to what may be a promising new location for a berry plant.

The fruit-encased seed that contains the embryo eventually separates from the sporophyte parent plant and makes its way into a suitable patch of earth, there to sprout both roots and shoots. Once the plant has germinated and matured a little, you could take a cross section of its stem and find concentric circles of the tissue types mentioned near the start of this chapter: dermal, vascular, and ground. Meanwhile, meristematic tissue could be found at the tips of the root and shoot, allowing the plant to grow further. With this, we have come full cycle: Another generation of plant is maturing.

On to the Human Body

In the last two chapters, you've looked at a group of living things that are silent, fixed in one spot, and have almost no moving parts. Now it's time to shift gears; we're going to turn to a group of living things that might be characterized as noisy, highly mobile, and in possession of many moving parts, one of which is so active it contracts and expands ceaselessly within them from the fourth week of their embryonic life to the day they die. These members of the living world are called human beings; the story of how their bodies function is the subject of the next eight chapters.

SO FAR . . .

1. In all angiosperms, a growing embryo is first surrounded by a _____, which will serve to _____ the embryo until it germinates in the ground.

2. Fruit can be defined as the mature _____ of an angiosperm. Fruit in this sense lies outside the _____ that surrounds the angiosperm embryo.

Go to the Study Area at www.masteringbiology.com for practice quizzes, myeBook, BioFlix™ 3-D animations, MP3 Tutor Sessions, videos, current events, and more.

Mastering
BIOLOGY

Summary

25.1 The Structure of Angiosperms

- Plants consist of a set of above-ground shoots and below-ground roots. Roots absorb water and nutrients, anchor the plant, and often act as nutrient storage sites. Shoots include the plant's leaves, stems, and flowers. (p. 460)

- Leaves serve as the primary sites of photosynthesis in most plants. Leaves have a profusion of stomata that open and close in response to light, thus controlling the flow of carbon dioxide into the plant and the flow of oxygen and water vapor out of the plant. (p. 462)

- Stems give structure to plants and are storage sites for nutrients. (p. 463)

- Flowers are the reproductive structures of plants, with most flowers containing both male and female parts. The male reproductive structure, the stamen, consists of a slender filament topped by an anther, the chambers of which contain the cells that will develop into sperm-containing pollen grains. The female reproductive structure, the carpel, is composed of a stigma, on which pollen grains are deposited; a style, which raises the stigma high enough to catch pollen; and an ovary, in which fertilization of the egg and early development of the embryo take place. (p. 464)

25.2 Monocots and Dicots

- Angiosperms are classified according to how many cotyledons, or embryonic leaves, they have: Narrow-leafed monocotyledons have one and the more numerous broad-leafed dicotyledons have two. Monocots and dicots differ in structure in many ways. (p. 465)

25.3 Plant Tissue Types

- There are four tissue types in the plant body: Dermal tissue can be thought of as the plant's outer covering, vascular tissue as its "plumbing," meristematic tissue as its growth tissue, and ground tissue as almost everything else. (p. 466)

25.4 Primary Growth in Angiosperms

- Plants grow only at the tips of their roots and shoots and plant growth can go on for the life of most plants. (p. 468)

- The entire plant develops from meristematic cells located in regions called apical meristems. Meristematic cells remain perpetually embryonic, able to give rise to more of themselves as well as to cells that differentiate into all the plant's tissue types. (p. 469)

- In a plant with a taproot, each lateral root tip has its own apical meristematic tissue. In the shoot, meristematic tissue lies at the tip of each stem and forms lateral buds in the area between each leaf and stem. (p. 469)

25.5 Fluid Movement: The Vascular System

- The two types of cells that make up the water-conducting portions of xylem tissue are tracheids and vessel elements, both of which are dead in their mature state. (p. 470)

- Water movement through xylem is driven by transpiration. As water evaporates into the air, it pulls a continuous column of water upward through the plant. The energy for this process comes from the sun, whose rays power water evaporation at the leaf surface. (p. 470)

- The sugar sucrose is the main material that flows through phloem. The fluid-conducting cells of the phloem, sieve elements, lack cell nuclei in maturity. Each sieve element cell has associated with it one or more companion cells, which retain their nuclei and support their related sieve element. (p. 471)

- Plants expend their own energy to load the sucrose they produce into the phloem's sieve element cells. This produces an osmotic flow of water into the cells that results in a fluid pressure that serves to transport the sucrose from "sources," such as food-producing leaves, to "sinks," such as nutrient-storing roots. (p. 471)

BioFlix™

Water Transport in Plants

25.6 Sexual Reproduction in Angiosperms

- Plants reproduce through an alternation of generations. A sporophyte generation (a familiar tree or flower) produces spores that develop into their own generation of plant, the gametophyte generation. This gametophyte generation produces the eggs and sperm necessary to give rise to a new sporophyte generation. In angiosperms, the mature male gametophyte is the sperm-containing pollen grain, while the mature female gametophyte is the egg-containing embryo sac, which is housed in the ovary of the sporophyte plant. (p. 472)

- In the fertilization of a gametophyte egg by sperm, a sperm-bearing pollen grain from one plant moves to the stigma of a second and lands on it, thus pollinating it, and a sperm cell from the pollen grain then moves down to the egg in the embryo sac and fuses with it, thus fertilizing it. This produces a sporophyte zygote, or early-stage embryo. When this embryo has become surrounded with both nutritive and protective tissue, the result is the reproductive structure known as a seed.

When this seed is planted in the ground, the embryo it contains will grow into a new generation of sporophyte plant. (p. 473)

- Each pollen grain contains two sperm cells and a tube cell. When a pollen grain lands on a stigma, the tube cell within it sprouts a pollen tube that grows down to the embryo sac. Both sperm cells from the pollen grain move through the pollen tube to the embryo sac, but only one fuses with the egg there. The second sperm cell fuses with the two nuclei of the central cell in the embryo sac, thus initiating the development of tissue called endosperm, which will provide nutrition to the embryo during its early stages of growth. This second fertilization completes the process of double fertilization. (p. 474)

25.7 The Developing Plant

- With fertilization, ovule tissue that surrounded the embryo sac begins to develop into the protective seed coat that will surround the growing sporophyte embryo. The ovary that surrounded the ovule then starts to develop into a layer of tissue that will surround the seed—fruit, defined as the mature ovary of any flowering plant. An angiosperm can be defined as a plant whose seeds develop inside the tissue called fruit. (p. 474)

Key Terms

angiosperm 476
anther 465
apical meristem 469
blade 462
bud 469
carpel 465
cotyledon 465
dicotyledon (dicot) 465
double fertilization 474
embryo sac 472
fibrous root system 461
filament 465
fruit 475
monocotyledon (monocot) 465
ovary 465
petal 465
petiole 462

phloem 467
pollen grain 472
root hair 461
seed 475
seed coat 475
sepal 464
sieve element 471
spore 472
stamen 465
stigma 465
stomata 463
style 465
taproot system 461
tissue 466
tracheid 470
transpiration 462
vessel element 470
xylem 467

Understanding the Basics

Multiple-Choice Questions
(Answers are in the back of the book.)

1. Plants take in _____ and _____ through their roots, but take in _____ primarily through tiny pores on their leaves.
   a. minerals; carbon dioxide; water
   b. oxygen; carbon dioxide; water
   c. water; carbon dioxide; minerals
   d. oxygen; minerals; carbon dioxide
   e. minerals; water; carbon dioxide

2. Which of the following are not functions of roots? (Select all that apply.)
   a. nutrient storage
   b. loss of water through transpiration
   c. loss of oxygen in photosynthesis
   d. grow to water supplies
   e. absorption of water

3. Dermal tissue _____, while vascular tissue _____.
   a. protects the plant; conducts fluids
   b. provides strength; facilitates growth
   c. facilitates reproduction; protects the plant
   d. facilitates growth; provides strength
   e. protects the plant; facilitates reproduction

4. Which of the following statements about the ascent of water in tall trees is true? (Select all that apply.)
   a. Plants must expend their own metabolic energy to power the ascent of water into treetops.
   b. The evaporation of water from leaf surfaces pulls water from the roots to the canopy of a tall tree.
   c. The ascent of water in the xylem is fastest when the stomata are closed.
   d. The ultimate source of energy for the ascent of water is the sun.
   e. All of the above are true.

5. Pressure develops inside phloem sieve tubes because:
   a. osmotic uptake of water occurs when sugars are loaded into the sieve elements.
   b. sieve elements lack a nucleus.
   c. sieve elements are dead at maturity.
   d. sucrose is a bulky molecule that exerts a pressure against the sieve tube walls.
   e. All of the above are true.

6. Which of the following statements about plant spores is true? (Select all that apply.)
   a. They are another name for gametes.
   b. The multicellular gametophyte generation develops from them.
   c. They produce the eggs and sperm that fuse to produce a new sporophyte generation.
   d. They are part of the sporophyte generation.
   e. They are much smaller than gametes.

7. Which of these is a gametophyte plant? (Select all that apply.)
   a. petal
   b. stigma
   c. embryo sac
   d. sepal
   e. pollen grain

8. Endosperm is formed when:
   a. two sperm from the pollen grain fuse with each other.
   b. two nuclei from the embryo sac fuse with each other.
   c. a sperm nucleus from the pollen fuses with the egg nucleus in the embryo sac.
   d. a pollen grain lands on a stigma.
   e. a sperm nucleus from the pollen grain fuses with two central cell nuclei in the embryo sac.

9. The difference between a seed coat and fruit is that (select all that apply):
   a. fruit is always edible; seed coats are not.
   b. seed coats are always hard; fruits are always soft.
   c. seed coats develop from ovules while fruit tissue develop from ovaries.
   d. dicots produce seed coats while monocots produce fruit.
   e. fruit is tissue that develops outside the seed coat.

Brief Review

(Answers are in the back of the book.)

1. The stomata that exist mostly on leaves allow important gas exchanges to take place in plants. What gases are exchanged through the stomata and in which direction? What other substance do plants lose as a result of gas exchange and how do they deal with this loss?

2. What functions do roots perform? What are the main types of roots produced by flowering plants?

3. List the main parts of a flower and describe the functions performed by each part.

4. What is meristematic tissue? Describe its organization.

5. Compare the structure and function of the water-conducting (xylem) and food-conducting (phloem) cells in a plant.

6. Describe the process of double fertilization in plants.

Applying Your Knowledge

1. The "race for sunlight" in plants led to the evolution of the tallest living things in existence, trees. But sunlight is not the only thing that stands to make a tree successful or not in reproducing. Think about how plants function and then answer this question: What are the costs of being taller, as opposed to shorter?

2. It's sometimes said that plants are much more efficient organisms than animals, in that they consume fewer resources and produce fewer waste products. Evaluate this statement in light of what you have learned about the functioning of angiosperms.

3. Gardeners often speak of outdoor plants having become "established," meaning the plants have reached a point at which they need less human care. What threshold does a plant have to cross to become established?

Body Support and Movement:

The Integumentary, Skeletal, and Muscular Systems

Just as several individuals may make up an office, and several offices a department, so our bodies are organized into a number of working units that go on to make up a functioning human being. Three of the larger units involve skin, bone, and muscle.

How is the human body structured and how does it work? The disciplines of human anatomy and physiology are dedicated to finding out.

There is an old country saying that goes, "You don't miss your water until your well runs dry." Doesn't this seem applicable to the way we think of our bodies? We go along taking for granted our ability to eat or talk or run—until the day comes when we can't do one of these things. If you've ever, say, broken a leg and ended up with a cast and crutches, you

know that just walking around with ease can look like the most wonderful thing in the world. Broken bones heal, of course, and that reassures us—until we run up against a condition that won't heal. While still in his 20s, the actor Michael J. Fox woke up one morning and noticed, as he later remembered, that "the pinky in my left hand was twitching. It was a curiosity as much as anything because I couldn't stop it, no matter how I tried to." About a year later, after many doctor's visits, Fox got definitive word that he had Parkinson's disease, which is incurable. By then, it was not just his little finger that was twitching; it was both hands. Imagine if being able to hold your hands steady seemed as beautiful as the moon and just as far away.

We take our bodies for granted partly because they work so well most of the time, but partly because what goes on inside them is hidden from us and so complicated that our physical functioning just seems mysterious. The next eight chapters of this book are aimed at clearing up some of this mystery. At their conclusion, you will have a basic understanding of how your heart beats, for example, of how your immune system fights off invaders, and of how your eyes and brain provide you with a picture of the world.

If you think about just the first of these things—the workings of the heart—you can get a sense of what's in store. The human heart beats about 100,000 times *each day*, pumping about 8,800 quarts of blood through the body in the process. Moreover, it keeps this rhythmic contraction up without a second's rest from the third week of our embryonic life to the day we die. As if this weren't enough, it is carrying out this feat mostly with its original equipment. Only about 40 percent of the heart's muscle cells will divide over a person's lifetime; as a result, most of the cells that are working for us at age 8 are the cells that are working for us at age 80.

An engineer who could invent such a machine would be considered a genius. But the truly remarkable thing is that there are lots of organs and systems in the body that are just as impressive as the heart. Once you've learned how these things work, it's hard to take your body for granted in the same way because you've come to understand what an incredible machine the human body is.

26.1 How the Body Regulates Itself

When we study the makeup or functioning of any complex organism, we have entered the realms of two overlapping disciplines in biology: anatomy and physiology. All organisms have an anatomy and a physiology. But in these chapters, our primary concern is with the human organism. Within this framework, human anatomy is the study of the body's structure and the relationships between the body's constituent parts. Human physiology is the study of how these parts work. Thus, anatomy tells us where the heart is, for example, how it is structured, and how it is situated in relation to other organs. Physiology describes to us *how* the heart works.

Before we get to specifics regarding either of these subjects, it will be helpful to go over a couple of general concepts about the body's structure and functioning. One of these concepts concerns the question: Who's in charge here? We are in charge of our conscious actions, of course; human beings get to decide what they are going to do from one moment to the next. But what about the huge number of unconscious actions that the body undertakes each second—getting oxygen to cells, getting rid of waste, being prompted to breathe while asleep? You might think the brain would be in charge of all this, and indeed messages from the brain do prompt a lot of physical activity. But there are plenty of physical processes that don't involve brain signals, and the brain *gets* lots of messages that say, in effect, "Get this process going now." Human society is hierarchical to a great degree; we're used to bosses and employees who work in a straight line of authority. But the body doesn't work this way. Instead, it functions through a process of *circular* causation in which A prompts B and B prompts C, but in which C may then prompt A. It is a system of self-regulation in which all parts work together to influence each other.

In understanding self-regulation, it's useful to think about what kind of internal environment the body needs to function properly. The answer is a *stable* environment. The human body must guard against being too hot or too cold; too dehydrated or too hydrated; too stimulated or too relaxed. If it is to exist at all, it must avoid extremes. To put this another way, it must seek **homeostasis,** meaning the maintenance of a relatively stable internal environment. And it turns out that a single process is almost solely responsible for bringing about homeostasis. Let's look at this process by way of an analogy.

Most people are aware of how a home heating system works. Falling temperature causes a thermostat to turn on a furnace. To look at this another way, there is a stimulus (cold air) that brings about a response (furnace operation). The *product* of this response is hot air. When enough hot air circulates to raise the temperature, the thermostat senses this and shuts the furnace down.

Now, let's think of your body, which has, as an example, a certain amount of oxygen circulating through it. All of this oxygen comes in through the lungs and is loaded into red blood cells, which then move through the bloodstream and drop off the oxygen where it's needed. The body requires a great deal

of oxygen in order to function and cells in our kidneys are capable of sensing whether circulating oxygen levels are adequate or not. When oxygen levels fall too low (stimulus), these kidney cells release a hormone, called EPO, which moves through the bloodstream and prompts stem cells in the marrow of our bones to begin producing more red blood cells (response). Thus, the product of *this* stimulus-response chain is more red blood cells and hence a greater amount of oxygen in circulation. When circulating oxygen once again reaches adequate levels, the cells in our kidneys likewise sense this and reduce their production of EPO (**Figure 26.1**).

With both the thermostat and the kidney's sensor cells, we can see that their responses to a stimulus bring about a decrease in their own activity. In other words, their responses feed back on their activity in a negative way—they reduce it. This is **negative feedback,** which can be defined as a process in which the elements that bring about a response have their activity reduced by that response. The EPO example is only one of countless negative-feedback loops that exist in the body. In it, we can see not only how the body maintains homeostasis but how the body is self-regulating. Think of it: There was no central boss giving commands in the regulation of oxygen levels. Instead two elements (oxygen levels and sensor cells in the kidneys) influenced each other to bring about stability. This is the way the body generally works.

Large-Scale Features of the Body

Many of the large-scale features of a human being—four limbs, one trunk, and so forth—are obvious, but a couple of features are hiding in plain sight, we might say. The first of these is an internal body cavity. All animals more complex than a flatworm have such a cavity. Humans and other mammals actually have two primary body cavities. The first of these is a dorsal (back) cavity that is further divided into cranial and spinal cavities, into which our brain and spinal cord fit (**Figure 26.2**). The second is a ventral (front) cavity that includes a thoracic or "chest" portion containing the lungs and heart as well as a lower abdominopelvic cavity containing such organs as the stomach, liver, and intestines. A muscular sheet called the diaphragm separates the thoracic and abdominopelvic cavities. Cavities provide flexibility and protection. With the space provided by a cavity, an organ like the stomach can expand as we eat and is protected from external blows to some extent.

Humans also have an internal skeleton that supports the body. We take for granted a skeleton that exists inside our skin, but it actually stands in contrast to what most animals have, which is either an *external* skeleton (as with crabs and grasshoppers) or no solid skeleton at all (as with jellyfish).

Figure 26.1
Oxygen Levels: An Example of Negative Feedback

Oxygen levels in the body are regulated in part by cells in the kidneys that are capable of sensing when oxygen levels in the bloodstream have fallen too low. In response, these cells secrete a hormone, called EPO, that causes stem cells in the bone marrow to produce more red blood cells. Production of these oxygen-carrying cells brings about adequate circulating oxygen levels, which the cells in the kidneys can likewise sense. In response, they reduce their production of EPO.

START
blood O₂ is low

END
return to normal blood O₂

Kidneys sense low O₂ levels, secrete EPO

EPO

red blood cells (carry O₂)

Bone marrow senses EPO, increases production of red blood cells

(a) Side view of body cavities   **(b)** Front view of body cavities

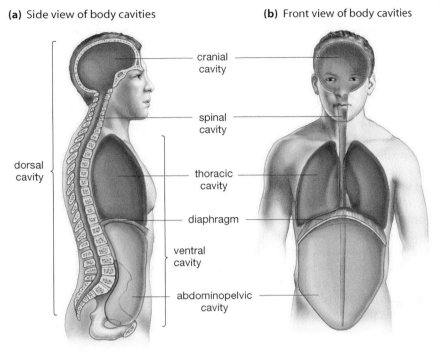

cranial cavity

spinal cavity

dorsal cavity

thoracic cavity

diaphragm

ventral cavity

abdominopelvic cavity

**Figure 26.2
Body Cavities**

(a) A side or "lateral" view of the two main cavities in the human body—the dorsal (back) and ventral (front) cavities—and the smaller cavities within them.

(b) A front or "ventral" view of the body's cavities.

cell
(muscle)

tissue
(muscle)

organ
(heart)

organ system
(cardiovascular)

**Figure 26.3
Levels of
Organization in the
Human Body**

A group of cells that performs a common function is a tissue; here, muscle cells have formed heart muscle tissue (whose common function is heart muscle contraction). Two or more tissues combine to form an organ such as the heart. (The heart contains both muscle and connective tissue, for example.) The heart is one component of the cardiovascular system; other parts of the system are blood and blood vessels. All the organ systems combine to create an organism, in this case a human being.

SO FAR . . .

1. The study of where the component parts of the body are located and how they are structured is called _____, while the study of how the component parts of the body work is called _____.

2. Negative feedback occurs when the elements that bring about a response have their activity _____ by that response.

3. Negative feedback is important because it preserves homeostasis in the body, meaning a _____ internal state.

26.2 Levels of Physical Organization

Features of the human body, such as a skeleton, fit into a larger organizational framework that is common to all living things. In our everyday world, several individuals may make up an office, several offices a department, and several departments a working company. In a similar fashion, each living thing is built up from a series of individual units that go on to make up a working organism. Here's how these units

are organized if we consider just the animals among life's creatures (one of which is us). Recall from Chapter 4 that the basic unit of all life is the cell. Cells and cellular products that work together to perform a common function are known as **tissues.** There is, for example, muscle tissue—a group of cells that perform the common function of contracting. Tissues in turn are arranged into various types of **organs,** meaning complexes of several kinds of tissues that perform a special bodily function. The stomach is an organ that has both muscle and nerve tissue within it. Organs then go on to form **organ systems,** which are groups of interrelated organs and tissues that serve a particular function. Contractions of the heart push blood into a network of blood vessels. The heart, blood, and blood vessels form the *cardiovascular system*, which is one of 11 systems in the human body. **Figure 26.3** shows the various levels of structural organization within the human body, using the cardiovascular system as an example.

26.3 The Four Basic Tissue Types

Looking at the smallest level of organization we're interested in, the tissue, we can then ask: What kinds of tissues are there in humans and other animals? It turns out there are only four fundamental tissue types: epithelial, connective, muscle, and nervous. All other tissue varieties are subsets of these fundamental types. Let's look briefly at the characteristics of these four varieties.

Epithelial Tissue

The key word regarding epithelial tissue is *surfaces* because **epithelial tissue** is tissue that *covers* surfaces exposed to an external environment. The outside of our body is exposed to the external environment, and as such, the outer layer of our skin is composed of epithelial tissue. But there are other surfaces as well. Think of a pipe; it has not only an external surface but also an internal surface that comes into contact with something that is external to it—the fluid that runs through it. Similarly, your body has arteries and veins that have the fluid called blood running through them, and the tissues that line the internal blood vessel surfaces are epithelial tissues. Likewise, the lining of your stomach and the lining of your lungs are surfaces that come into contact with something from outside you; again, this contact is made by epithelial tissues. Given their location, epithelial tissues often serve as a barrier, as in the case of our skin; but many epithelial tissues are "transport" tissues that materials are moved *across*. (The food that enters your bloodstream does so by being transported across the epithelial tissue that lines your small intestines.) Epithelial tissues can be several layers of cells thick or as thin as a single layer, depending on their function (**Figure 26.4**).

Epithelial tissues often produce substances that aid in various bodily processes. The skin has epithelial tissue that produces the water-resistant protein keratin, for example, while the stomach has epithelial tissue that produces digestive juices. This substance-producing function can be carried out by isolated epithelial cells, but it is sometimes undertaken by concentrations of cells. Such concentrations are known as **glands:** organs or groups of cells that are specialized to secrete one or more substances. Later, we'll look at two basic kinds of glands.

Connective Tissue

Connective tissue, defined as tissue that stabilizes and supports other tissue, is very different from epithelial tissue. Whereas epithelial tissue is always in contact with an external environment, connective tissue never is. Whereas epithelial tissue is almost completely composed of cells, connective tissue usually is composed of cells that are separated from each other by an extracellular material—a material that is secreted by the connective tissue cells themselves. Indeed, the prime function of many connective tissues is to produce this kind of material.

We can see these qualities in the connective tissues known as bone and cartilage. These tissues clearly are connecting something (bodily structures), and their support and stabilization role is obvious. In addition, they lie within an extracellular material, which is properly referred to as a *ground substance*. The ground substance of bone, which the bone cells themselves secrete, is a mix of closely packed protein fibers and calcified material. The hard bones we're familiar with are largely made up of these substances.

But ground substances need not be hard. Adipose or fat tissue is connective tissue, and its ground substance is soft. Indeed, a ground substance can even be fluid, as is the case with blood and a bodily fluid called lymph. How can a ground tissue be a fluid? Well, to take blood as an example, the ground substance that surrounds blood cells is mostly water, with electrolytes, proteins, and other materials in the mix.

Muscle Tissue

Muscle tissue is tissue that is specialized in its ability to contract or shorten. There are three kinds of muscle tissue—skeletal, smooth, and cardiac—which differ in their structure and in the way they are prompted to contract. **Skeletal muscle** is the ordinary muscle that is attached to bone and is contained in, for example, our biceps. It is under our conscious control and has a striped or "striated" appearance when looked at under a microscope owing to the parallel orientation of some long, fibrous units that make it up. **Cardiac muscle** exists only in the heart and likewise is striated, but it contracts under the influence of its own pacemaker cells. **Smooth muscle,** which gets its name from its lack of a striated appearance, is muscle responsible for contractions of the uterus, the digestive tract, blood vessels, and the passageways of the lungs. As you might guess from this list of tasks, smooth muscle is not under voluntary control.

Nervous Tissue

Nervous tissue is tissue that is specialized for the rapid conduction of messages, which take the form of electrical impulses. There are two basic types of nervous tissue cells: neurons, which actually carry the nervous system messages, and glial cells, which perform support functions for the neurons.

26.4 Organs Are Made of Several Kinds of Tissues

Having looked at the four types of tissue the body has, let's now see how they combine to form an organ—the human stomach, which is a typical organ in that it is made up of all the kinds of tissue we've been

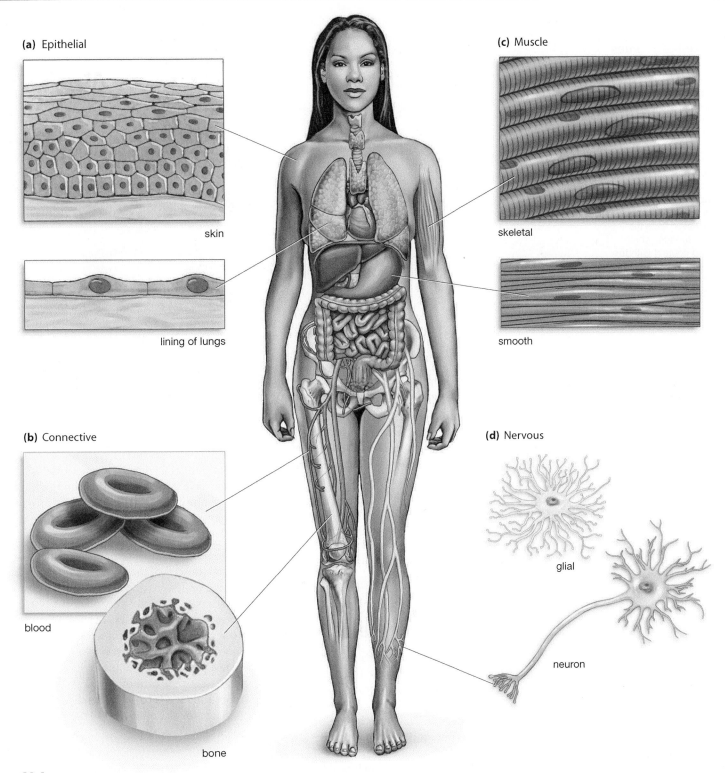

(a) Epithelial

skin

lining of lungs

(b) Connective

blood

bone

(c) Muscle

skeletal

smooth

(d) Nervous

glial

neuron

Figure 26.4
Four Types of Tissue

There are four basic tissue types in the human body: epithelial, muscle, nervous, and connective. Pictured are examples of each of the four types in some representative locations.

(a) Epithelial tissue, which always covers a surface exposed to an external environment, can take the form of many layers of cells (as with the skin) or a single layer of cells (as with the lining of lungs).

(b) Connective tissue, which supports and stabilizes other tissue, can take such diverse forms as bone and blood.

(c) Muscle tissue, which is specialized for contraction, comes in a striped or "striated" form (in both skeletal and cardiac muscle) and in a smooth form that lines the digestive tract, blood vessels, and other structures.

(d) Nervous tissue is specialized for the transmission of electrical signals. The two types of nervous tissue cells are neurons, which conduct nervous system signals, and glial cells, which support the neurons.

Figure 26.5
Organs Are
Composed of Tissues
The stomach is a typical organ in that it is composed of various tissue types. Nervous tissue controls the release of digestive juices into the stomach and also controls the contractions of a second type of tissue found in the stomach, its muscle tissue. Connective tissue helps support and stabilize the other tissues around it. Epithelial tissue lines the stomach's surface, which comes into contact with the food we eat. The individual epithelial cells pictured secrete digestive acids and enzymes.

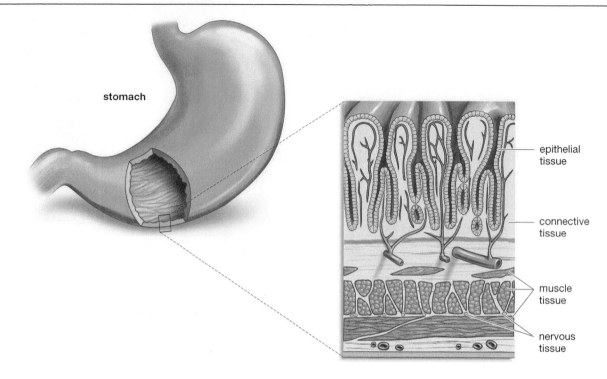

discussing. If you look at **Figure 26.5**, you can see that the stomach has several layers of smooth muscle, which bring about contractions that help digest food and move it into the small intestines. Likewise, there is nervous tissue, which controls the release of digestive juices and the contractions of the stomach's muscles. Supportive connective tissue exists as well. And, of course, since the inner lining of the stomach is a surface coming into contact with an external environment, there is epithelial tissue. True to what you saw earlier, some of this epithelial tissue is secretory—that is, it secretes substances that help with digestion.

26.5 Organs and Tissues Make Up Organ Systems

You've now seen how cells make up tissues and how tissues make up organs. Let's now take the final step and see how tissues and organs together make up organ systems. What follows is a brief look at each of the body's 11 organ systems. Once you have finished reviewing them, the balance of this chapter will be devoted to a more detailed look at the first three of these systems. In Chapters 27 through 33, you'll be taking a look at the other eight.

Organ Systems 1: Body Support and Movement—The Integumentary, Skeletal, and Muscular Systems

- The **integumentary system** (**Figure 26.6a**) is sometimes thought of simply as skin, but a number of structures are associated with skin, including hair and nails and the glands we noted

earlier. In addition to serving as an outer, protective wrapping, skin also helps keep body temperature stable.

- The **skeletal system** (**Figure 26.6b**) is composed not only of bones but of cartilages and ligaments. This is a complex framework, as human beings have 206 bones in their body, along with a large number of cartilages. Bones provide support and protection, and they can store fat and minerals.

- The **muscular system** (**Figure 26.6c**) includes all the skeletal muscles of the body—about 600 of them. These muscles provide for movement, posture, and support. They are also vital players in homeostasis in that our bodies are largely warmed by the heat given off from muscle contraction. The smooth and cardiac muscle tissues noted earlier are not part of the muscular system. Cardiac muscle is part of the cardiovascular system, and smooth muscle is part of several systems—in the stomach, for example, it is part of the digestive system.

Organ Systems 2: Coordination, Regulation, and Defense—The Nervous, Endocrine, and Immune Systems

- The nervous tissue reviewed earlier goes on to make up the **nervous system** (**Figure 26.6d**), a rapid communication system in the body that includes the brain, spinal cord, all the nerves outside the brain and spinal cord, and sense organs such as the eye and ear.

- The endocrine system (**Figure 26.6e**) bears comparison with the nervous system in that both systems are in the business of sending signals throughout the body. The **endocrine system,** however, is a communication system that works through chemical messengers called **hormones:** substances secreted by one set of cells that travel through the bloodstream and affect the activities of other cells. Many human hormones are produced in specialized glands. Remember the earlier remark that there are two basic varieties of glands in the body? One of these varieties is named for the endocrine system. **Endocrine glands** are glands that release their materials directly into surrounding extracellular fluid or into the bloodstream. This is what the thyroid gland does, for example. In contrast, **exocrine glands** are glands that secrete their materials through tubes or "ducts." We'll see examples of these glands later.

- The **immune system** is a collection of cells and proteins whose central function is to rid the body of invading microbes. In **Figure 26.6f**, you can see a key component of the immune system, the body's **lymphatic network,** which serves a dual function. First, it acts as a kind of drainage system, collecting fluid that lies outside cells and routing it back to the bloodstream. Second, it acts as an *inspection* system. Lymphatic organs contain heavy concentrations of the body's defenders—its immune system cells—and these cells monitor lymphatic fluid as it passes by for signs of invading microbes. Lymphoid organs include the well-known lymph nodes located under the arms and elsewhere, along with the thymus gland, tonsils, and spleen. Immune system cells and proteins don't reside solely within the lymphatic network, however, but exist throughout the body.

Organ Systems 3: Transport and Exchange with the Environment—The Cardiovascular, Respiratory, Digestive, and Urinary Systems

- The **cardiovascular system** (**Figure 26.6g** on the next page) consists of the heart, blood, and blood vessels and an inner, "marrow" portion of bones where red blood cells are formed. The cardiovascular system is the body's mass transit system. It carries nutrients, dissolved gases, and hormones *to* tissues throughout the body, and it carries waste products *from* tissues to the sites where they are removed: the kidneys and the lungs.

(a) The integumentary system

hair
skin
nails

(b) The skeletal system

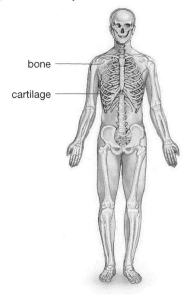

bone
cartilage

(c) The muscular system

skeletal
muscles

(d) The nervous system

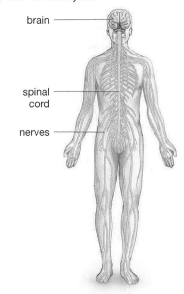

brain
spinal
cord
nerves

(e) The endocrine system

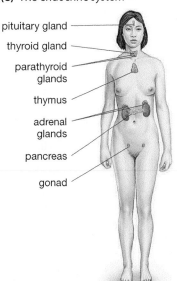

pituitary gland
thyroid gland
parathyroid
glands
thymus
adrenal
glands
pancreas
gonad

(f) The immune system
(lymphatic network)

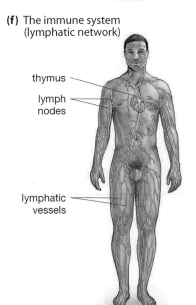

thymus
lymph
nodes
lymphatic
vessels

Figure 26.6a–f
The Organ Systems of the Human Body

(g) The cardiovascular system

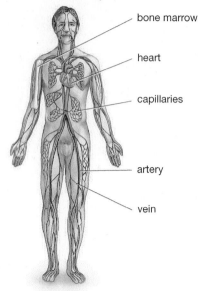

- bone marrow
- heart
- capillaries
- artery
- vein

(h) The respiratory system

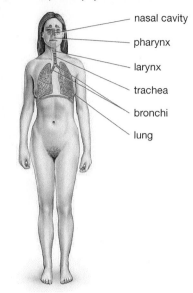

- nasal cavity
- pharynx
- larynx
- trachea
- bronchi
- lung

(i) The digestive system

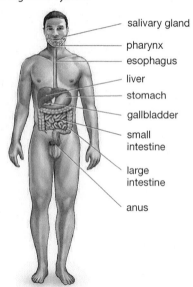

- salivary gland
- pharynx
- esophagus
- liver
- stomach
- gallbladder
- small intestine
- large intestine
- anus

(j) The urinary system

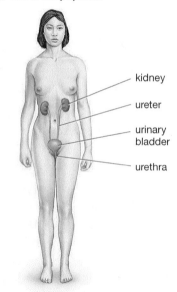

- kidney
- ureter
- urinary bladder
- urethra

(k) The male reproductive system

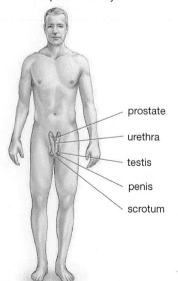

- prostate
- urethra
- testis
- penis
- scrotum

(l) The female reproductive system

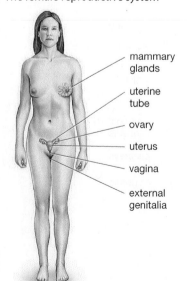

- mammary glands
- uterine tube
- ovary
- uterus
- vagina
- external genitalia

- The **respiratory system** (**Figure 26.6h**) includes the lungs and the passageways that carry air to and from the lungs. Through this system, oxygen comes into the body, and carbon dioxide is expelled from it.

- The central feature of the **digestive system** (**Figure 26.6i**) is the digestive tract, a long tube that begins at the mouth and ends at the anus. Along its course, there are the digestive organs of the system—the stomach, small intestines, and large intestines—and accessory glands, such as the pancreas and liver.

- The **urinary system** (**Figure 26.6j**) has two major functions, one of them well known, the other not so much appreciated. The well-known function is the elimination of waste products from the blood through the production of urine. The underappreciated function is conservation. The system is very good at retaining what is useful to the body—water, proteins, and so forth—even as it eliminates what is useless. The primary organs that carry this selection process out are the kidneys, but the system also includes various other parts, such as the bladder.

- Males and females have different **reproductive systems** (**Figures 26.6k** and **Figures 26.6l**). The two are linked, of course, in that together they produce offspring. Both systems are discussed in detail in Chapter 33.

With this brief review of the organ systems completed, you're ready to look in more detail at the first three organ systems noted earlier—the integumentary, skeletal, and muscular systems. They are batched together in this chapter because each has to do with body support and movement. We'll start with the integumentary system.

SO FAR . . .

1. Going from least inclusive to most inclusive, how would the following levels of organization be ordered in a human being: organ system, cell, tissue, organ?

2. What are the four basic tissue types in a human being?

3. _____ tissue is specialized in its ability to contract, while _____ tissue is specialized in its ability to conduct electrical impulses.

Figure 26.6g–l

26.6 The Integumentary System

The primary component of the integumentary system is the organ known as skin. It may seem strange to think of skin as an organ since it is not a compact, neatly defined structure like the heart or the liver. But remember the definition of an organ: a complex of several kinds of tissues that performs a special bodily function. Clearly, that's what skin is. Joining skin to make up the integumentary system are the related structures of hair, nails, and a variety of exocrine glands.

The primary function of skin is easy to see: It covers the body and seals it off from the outside world. Skin also protects underlying tissues and organs, however, and helps regulate our temperature. In addition, it stores fat and makes vitamin D. Meanwhile, exocrine glands that are accessories to the skin excrete materials such as sweat, water, oils, and milk, and specialized nerve endings in the skin detect such sensations as pressure, pain, and temperature.

The Structure of Skin

Skin is an organ that is organized in two parts: a thin outer covering, the epidermis, and a thicker underlying layer, the dermis, which is composed mostly of connective tissue. Beneath the dermis—and not part of the skin proper—is another layer, called the hypodermis, made up of connective tissue that attaches the skin to deeper structures such as muscles or bones. You can see a cross section of human skin in **Figure 26.7.**

The Outermost Layer of Skin, the Epidermis

The outer layer of our skin, the epithelial tissue called the **epidermis,** seems to face an impossible task. On the one hand, it has to serve as a permanent, protective barrier, keeping out everything from water to invading microorganisms; on the other, it has to continually renew itself, given that it is cut, scraped, and simply worn away each day. How does it manage to do both things? The answer lies in the many *layers* of cells the epidermis is organized into. If we could take a microelevator down to the innermost layer of the epidermis, we would see a group of rounded cells rapidly dividing and, in the process, pushing the cells on top of them *up*, toward the surface of the skin. As we move toward the surface, we notice that the epidermal cells are flattening out. Furthermore, they're getting less active; at a certain point, they cease dividing altogether. What is happening is that they are now so far from the underlying blood vessels (down in the dermis) that they are losing their blood supply. They are still carrying out a task, however, which is the production of **keratin**—a flexible, water-resistant protein, abundant in the outer layers of skin, that also makes up hair and fingernails. By the time epidermal cells reach the surface, they are scarcely cells at all anymore. They are dead and don't even have the remnants of internal organelles within them. Instead, they have become a series of tightly interlocked keratin sacs. In another 2 weeks, they will be scraped or washed away, replaced by the next cells that have pushed up from the inner epidermis.

**Figure 26.7
Our Outer Wrap: What Is Skin Made Of?**

(a) A micrograph of human skin, showing its epidermal and dermal layers and the subcutaneous hypodermis tissue beneath them. Note the sloughing off of dead cells at the surface of the epidermis. The holes visible in the dermis are spaces through which its blood vessels run.

(b) A cross section of the skin's epidermis and dermis layers and the hypodermis layer beneath them.

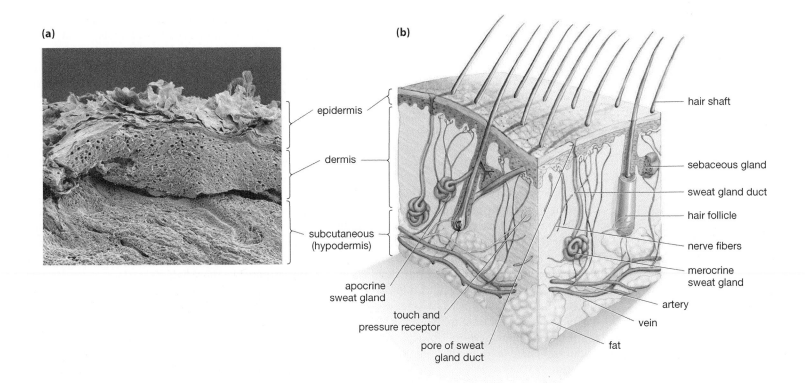

(a)

epidermis

dermis

subcutaneous (hypodermis)

(b)

hair shaft

sebaceous gland

sweat gland duct

hair follicle

nerve fibers

merocrine sweat gland

artery

vein

fat

apocrine sweat gland

touch and pressure receptor

pore of sweat gland duct

Beneath the Epidermis: The Dermis and Hypodermis

Whereas the epidermis is epithelial tissue, the inner layer of skin, the **dermis,** is mostly connective tissue. But if you look again at Figure 26.7, you can see that nerves and muscles exist in the dermis as well, along with sweat glands, hair follicles, and more. This is just another example of how all the various kinds of tissues tend to exist side by side in a typical organ.

Many of the structures in the dermis are serving the epidermis. For example, the nervous system touch and pressure receptors shown in Figure 26.7 allow us to know when something makes contact with our skin, and the blood vessels pictured provide a blood supply to the dividing lower cells of the epidermis. But the dermal blood supply takes on another role as well. It plays a big part in controlling our temperature. If you get too cold, the dermal blood vessels will constrict, thus moving blood away from your surface and retaining the heat that's in the blood. If you get too hot, the dermal blood vessels expand, thereby moving blood toward your surface so that the heat that's in blood can radiate to the outside world (making your skin feel "flushed"). One more thing to note about the dermis is that its cells are relatively fixed, unlike those of the outer epidermis. Ever wonder why a tattoo must be made with a needle sunk into the skin? The tattoo's pigment must be deposited into the fixed cells in the dermis rather than the ever-changing cells of the epidermis.

As noted earlier, the "hypodermis," the layer beneath the dermis, is not actually part of the skin. But it deserves special mention here because of one of the aspects of it you can see in Figure 26.7—its abundant adipose or fat tissue. This tissue makes up the body's *subcutaneous fat*, which can be thought of as a layer of fat located just beneath the skin that varies in thickness throughout the body. The body also has what is known as *visceral fat*, however, which is fat that lies deep within the abdomen (inside the abdominopelvic cavity we talked about). This "belly fat" doesn't exist as a single layer but instead surrounds organs such as the liver. When it exists in excess amounts, it is a more serious health risk than is an excess of subcutaneous fat. You can read more about this in "Why Fat Matters and Why Exercise May Matter More," on page 492.

The term *hypodermis* may ring a bell because it sounds like the more familiar term hypoder*mic*, as in needles. The deeper tissue of the hypodermis doesn't have much of a blood supply and thus is a good place to inject medicines that need a relatively slow, steady entry into circulation. Here's one final thing about the skin. If you want to make it age fast, one sure way to do it is to spend a lot of time in the sun or in one of today's popular tanning salons. You can read more about this in "There Is No Such Thing as a Fabulous Tan" on page 495.

Accessory Structures of the Integumentary System

As noted, skin has a number of accessory structures associated with it, including hair, glands, and nails.

Hair

Five million or so hairs exist on the human body, although only about 100,000 of them are on the human head. Hair clearly serves a major cosmetic role in modern society, but why does it exist on human beings in the first place? You might think that heat retention for our ancestors would have been its main function, but maybe not. Rub your hand with just the lightest stroke over the hair on your head and you can get a sense of how exquisitely sensitive hair is to our sense of *touch*. Like a cat's whiskers, hair may have served primarily to fine-tune our sense of contact with the world around us.

How can hair have this quality since it is not alive but merely a shaft of the protein keratin, which is a product of underlying cells? If you look at Figure 26.7, you can see that each hair grows out of a tube-like structure called a *hair follicle* that begins fairly deep in the dermis. Each follicle is a tissue complex that has not only its own blood vessels and muscles but its own nerve endings as well. Thus, when you touch a hair, you stimulate a hair follicle's nerve endings.

True to what we noted at the start of the chapter, the body's hair is perhaps more missed when it is gone than appreciated when it is here. Many men start losing the hair on their heads in their early 20s, a trend that accelerates as they get older. Women can lose hair, too, although their loss tends to come later in life and usually involves a general thinning of the hair rather than receding hairlines or bald spots. What causes hair loss? Follicles go through growth and resting phases, with a given hair on our heads growing for anywhere from 2 to 6 years until a short resting phase is reached. At that point, the hair drops out, and its follicle's growth phase starts again. Hair loss generally is a condition in which an ever-growing proportion of follicles start to shrink, resulting in a briefer growing phase and hair that comes out either short and fine (like a baby's) or doesn't come out at all. Genes clearly play a part in this process, although contrary to popular belief, it is not just genes from the mother's side of the family that are involved. Hormones called *androgens* are involved as well; men have higher circulating levels of such androgens as testosterone and thus experience more hair loss.

Both men and women are, of course, subject to a *graying* of their hair with increasing age. What causes hair to lose its color? About midway down through the dermal portion of the hair follicle you can see in Figure 26.7b there are cells called melanocyte stem cells. When we are young, these cells produce a steady stream of cells that first migrate to near the bottom of the hair follicle and then differentiate into cells called mature melanocytes. These are the cells that produce the pigments that give hair its color. We thus have a kind of pigment-producing assembly line in our hair follicles, but it's one that aging tends to disrupt in two ways. One is that our melanocyte stem cells can die off altogether; the other is that our mature melanocytes can start maturing too quickly—they differentiate *before* they have migrated to the deepest part of the follicle, which is the only location in which they can function properly.

Glands

You may remember that when we went over the endocrine system, you saw that glands come in two varieties: those that secrete their substances directly into the bloodstream or surrounding tissue (endocrine glands) and those that secrete their substances through the tubes called ducts (exocrine glands). Skin contains two types of exocrine glands. The first of these are known as **sebaceous glands:** glands that produce an oily substance called sebum that is secreted into hair follicles and that then moves through them onto the skin (see Figure 26.7b). Once on the skin, sebum lubricates the hair and inhibits bacterial growth in the surrounding area.

The problem with this process is that, under hormonal influence, sebaceous glands can be *too* active—they can produce too much sebum, particularly in teenagers. When this excess sebum mixes with skin cells that are being shed from the sebaceous follicle, the result can be a blocked follicle that swells with sebum—a whitehead. Once this blockage occurs, bacteria normally found on the skin begin to multiply within the follicle, producing irritating substances that can cause general inflammation and pimples. Taken together, these various skin afflictions are known as *acne.* No matter what you may have heard, acne is not caused by eating fatty foods, stress, or a lack of face scrubbing. As with baldness, the hormones called androgens are the culprits. They prompt the increased sebaceous activity; since males at puberty have more androgens in them than females, it is males who suffer more from acne.

The second type of exocrine gland in the skin is the **sweat gland,** simply defined as a gland that produces the fluid sweat. This can mean a couple of different things, however, because sweat glands come in two varieties. One type is a *merocrine* gland that produces the clear, saltwater-like fluid we normally think of as sweat. We have, at a minimum, 2 million merocrine sweat glands on our bodies. They exist on almost all skin surfaces, but we have an especially dense concentration of them on our feet, forehead, and palms (hence "sweaty palms"). The primary function of the merocrine sweat glands is to bring sweat to the surface of the skin so that it can cool us by evaporating. These

glands have their own ducts and follicles, which begin deep in the dermis.

The other sweat glands in the body, called *apocrine* glands, are very different from the merocrine glands. First, they only exist in a few places—notably the groin, the anal area, and the armpits. As such, they have little effect on body cooling. Second, they secrete their products into hair follicles, not up through their own ducts. Most important, apocrine gland secretions contain not only regular sweat but a fatty, milky fluid whose function in humans is unknown. The *effect* of this fluid is very well known, however. Bacteria feed on it, and the resulting bacterial by-products are the cause of body odor. Apocrine glands only begin functioning at puberty, which is why children seldom have body odor.

Nails

Our final accessory structure of the integumentary system is the nails found on our fingers and toes. Like hair, nails are made of a variety of the protein keratin. They are clearly useful for protection and for prying, scratching, and picking up objects. Nails allow us to look, in a sense, at the blood vessels underlying the dermis because it's the reddish color of these vessels that gives nails their pink hue.

SO FAR ...

1. The primary component of the integumentary system is an organ called _____, which is composed of two primary layers, an outer layer called the _____ and an inner layer called the _____.

2. Fat exists in the human body in two primary locations. First there is subcutaneous fat, which can be thought of as a layer of fat located _____; second there is visceral fat, which is fat that surrounds _____ deep within the _____.

3. Each hair that we have grows out of a tissue complex called a _____.

26.7 The Skeletal System

We now shift gears, going from a consideration of our outer covering to a consideration of the framework that underlies it—our skeletal system. This system has only three structural elements to it: bone, ligaments, and cartilage. Most of us are quite familiar with **bone,** which can be defined as a connective tissue that provides support and storage capacity and that is the site of blood cell production. Ligaments are fairly inaccessible to us;

ESSAY

Why Fat Matters and Why Exercise May Matter More

At one time, scientists thought of the body's billions of fat cells as little more than fuel depots—as storage sites for the calories we ingest but don't burn up (**Figure 1**). This model began to fall apart in 1994, however, with the discovery of a hormone called leptin that plays a role in regulating hunger and that is *produced* by fat cells. Two years later, scientists made an even more puzzling discovery when they found that fat cells also produce a signaling molecule, called tumor necrosis factor (TNF), that helps activate the body's

It's perfectly possible for a person who is overweight and active to be healthier than a person who is slim but sedentary.

immune system during periods of viral or bacterial infection. Leptin made sense as a fat-cell hormone, since the message it conveys to the brain—"you're full now"—is one that is consistent with the role fat cells have of storing nutrients. But what did fat cells have to do with the immune system?

In the years that followed the TNF discovery, this mystery deepened, when it was discovered that *several* immune signaling molecules are secreted by fat cells and that several specialized varieties of immune system cells take up residence within collections of fat cells. Continuing research revealed, however, that it isn't all fat cells that are involved in these immune system activities, but instead only a select group, located in one part of the body.

As the main text notes, human beings have concentrations of fat cells in two separate areas. On the one hand, we have subcutaneous fat, which is the layer of fat that exists just beneath the skin throughout the body. On the other, we have visceral fat, which is fat that surrounds our internal organs deep within the abdomen. Over the years, research has confirmed that it's this

"belly fat" that draws in immune system cells, that puts significant amounts of TNF into circulation, and so forth. Indeed, the picture that has emerged is that excess visceral fat sets off a low-level immune system response—the inflammation response. When prompted by microbial attack, this response has the virtue of ramping up the body's microbe-fighting capabilities within a limited time frame: Attack-driven

Figure 1
Where Excess Calories Go

Fat cells, such as the one shown here, often contain several lipid droplets whose size dwarfs the cell's other components. In this case, the three large central droplets do just this. The cell's nucleus is the purple object near the top.

Figure 26.8
Elements of the Skeletal System

Bones are the basic element of the skeletal system. Ligaments link one bone to another, and cartilage often serves as padding between bones. Tendons, while not part of the skeletal system, always link bone to muscle.

Three components of the skeletal system:

bone

ligaments

cartilage

Tendons are connective tissues that join bone to muscle

but if you look at **Figure 26.8**, you can see some typical ligaments carrying out a typical task—linking bones together. You can also see the third element of the skeletal system, cartilage. Note that cartilage is located *in between* bones in the foot, and this turns out to be one of its common functions. **Cartilage** is a connective tissue that serves as padding in most joints. It is more familiar to us, however, in other parts of the body. It forms our larynx (voice box), the C-shaped "rings" on our trachea (windpipe), and our nose tip and outer ears, and it links our ribs to our breastbone. In all its capacities, cartilage is a very flexible, resilient tissue, which is not surprising given that it is mostly made up of water.

It's a good idea to look at Figure 26.8 to get a sense not only of the difference between bone, ligaments, and cartilage but also of the difference between all of these skeletal elements and another type of tissue that is pictured, tendons. Although not part of the skeletal system, tendons are always associated with inflammation begins with the microbial invasion and ends when all the microbes have been vanquished. By contrast, an excess of visceral fat engenders *chronic* inflammation, meaning an inflammation that exists day in, day out, for as long as a person carries the fat.

What's the harm in this? Well, consider the signaling protein TNF noted earlier. One of its effects is to make the body's muscle, liver, and fat cells resistant to the effects of another signaling protein, insulin. In a person who is, say, under attack by a virus, this effect may be helpful: The body's immune system cells need extra energy during times of attack and to the extent that insulin resistance is keeping blood sugar from moving into muscle cells, it is making this sugar available to immune system cells. In a state of chronic inflammation, conversely, this effect is anything but helpful. When cells enter into a state of *long-term* resistance to the effects of insulin, the body has started down the path to type 2 diabetes. Blood sugar is persistently kept from entering muscle, liver, and fat cells, with the result that these cells start breaking down their own proteins and lipids just to stay alive.

Since fat-driven inflammation is a systemic, or body-wide, physical condition, it's not surprising that its effects extend beyond those of spurring on diabetes. Consider, for example, a condition called congestive heart failure, in which the heart loses its ability to pump sufficient blood throughout the body. In 2009, researchers released the results of a study of more than 80,000 Swedish men and women whose health status they had tracked for seven years. The scientists found that an excess of visceral fat was a risk factor for heart failure even in persons whose *overall* weight was healthy (as measured by body-mass index, or BMI). Meanwhile, in 2008, researchers in California reported that men and women they studied who were overweight and had large bellies at ages 40–45 were more than three times as likely to be diagnosed with Alzheimer's or other dementias at age 70–75 than were subjects who originally had normal weight and belly size. Critically, subjects who had a large belly size, but who were of *normal* weight in their 40s were still almost twice as likely to have dementia 30 years later than were persons of both normal weight and belly size.

The central message of these research findings is that, while fat matters, the location of that fat seems to matter even more. The good news about this is that something can be done about it. Visceral fat often is the last to be added during weight gain, which means it is likely to be the first to be lost during any program of weight reduction. Beyond this, moderate "endurance" exercise, such as walking or swimming, has been shown to reduce levels of chronic inflammation in the body, irrespective of any weight loss this activity may bring about. Indeed, so strong are the effects of exercise that it's perfectly possible for a person who is overweight and active to be healthier than a person who is slim but sedentary. Evidence of this was provided in 2008 by researchers who looked at a representative sample of 5,400 American adults and ranked their "metabolic fitness" on the basis of such factors as blood pressure and insulin sensitivity. Weight in general, and larger waist size in particular, did tend to make individuals less metabolically fit, but the researchers also found that 51 percent of overweight subjects were metabolically healthy, while 23 percent of normal-weight subjects had two or more indications of poor metabolic health. What factors tended to push slimmer people into the less healthy category? One was the simple fact of getting older, but the other was a lack of regular physical activity.

the bones of the system. Looking at all four elements in the figure, here's one way to think of them. Bones are the basic framework; cartilage often serves as padding between bones; **ligaments** are tissues that join bone to bone; and **tendons** are tissues that join bone to muscle.

Function and Structure of Bones

It's tempting to think of bones as nothing more than support beams, but this conception is wide of the mark in two ways. First, support beams are not alive, but bone is very much a living, dynamic tissue, as you'll see. Second, bones do more than just support us. Once we are past infancy, all of our blood cells (both red and white) are produced in the interior of our bones. Some bones store fat, in the form of yellow marrow, as a kind of energy reserve, and bones serve as the storage sites for important minerals such as calcium and phosphate.

Beyond this, the only reason we can move at all is that our muscles are attached to bones. When we contract our bicep, for example, our forearm is raised by means of the bicep pulling on the bones of the forearm.

The Structure of Bone

Each bone in our body actually is considered a separate organ because each bone is composed of several kinds of tissue. There is the calcified or "osseous" tissue we think of as bone, to be sure, but each bone also has its own blood vessels and nerves. (Cartilage, meanwhile, has neither its own blood vessels nor nerves, which is why torn cartilage takes so long to heal—nutrients must diffuse to it from surrounding fluids, rather than being delivered to it by blood vessels.) Bones are a great example of connective tissue in that the *cells* in bones may account for as little as 2 percent of bone mass. What is the other 98 percent of bone made of? It is overwhelmingly a ground substance, secreted by bone cells, that is composed of hard, calcium-containing crystals and tough, yet flexible collagen fibers. This combination means that bones are hard without being brittle—they can support our weight and yet can bend or twist a little without breaking.

Large-Scale Features of Bone

The typical features of a long bone such as the humerus (in the arm) are shown in **Figure 26.9**. A long bone has a central shaft, or diaphysis, and expanded ends, or epiphyses (singular, epiphysis). There are two types of bone. **Compact bone,** which is relatively solid, forms the outer portion of the bone (all the way around it, as you can see in Figure 26.9b). **Spongy bone** then fills the epiphyses and is well named. It is porous enough that it contains another type of tissue, **red marrow,** which is the tissue in which all the blood cells of the adult body are produced. (These cells include not only the oxygen-carrying red blood cells but the white blood cells that are the central cells of the immune system.) Meanwhile, **yellow marrow,** a tissue largely made up of energy-storing fat cells, is found in the *marrow cavity* of the type of long bones seen in Figure 26.9.

Small-Scale Features of Bone

Dropping down to the microscopic level and looking at bone *cells,* we find that three different types are involved in the growth and maintenance of bone. **Osteoblasts** are immature bone cells that are responsible for the production of new bone. They secrete the material that becomes the bone ground substance. Once osteoblasts are surrounded by this material, they reduce their production of it, and this marks their transition to osteocytes, the second type of bone cell. **Osteocytes** are mature bone cells; they *maintain* the structure and density of normal bone by continually recycling the calcium compounds around themselves. The third type of bone cell, the osteoclasts, could be thought of as the demolition crew of bone tissue. **Osteoclasts** are cells that move along the outside of bones, releasing enzymes that eat away at bone tissue, thus liberating minerals stored in the bone. This may sound harmful, but it actually is essential for bone growth and for the regulation of blood levels of calcium. The upshot of all this is that, at any given moment, osteoblasts are adding to bone, osteocytes are maintaining it, and osteoclasts are removing it.

Within compact bone, the basic functional unit is the osteon seen in Figure 26.9c (which is also known as the Haversian system). The essence of bone growth is that, within each osteon, osteoblasts produce layer after layer of concentric cylinders of bone—much like layers of insulation wrapped around a pipe. These layers surround what could be thought of as the hole in the pipe, which is a central canal (also known as a

Figure 26.9
Large- and Small-Scale Features of a Typical Bone

Note that in **(c)**, the building units of compact bone, the osteons, run parallel to the long axis of the bone. Spongy bone does not contain osteons, but instead is composed of an open network of calcified rods or plates.

ESSAY

There Is No Such Thing as a Fabulous Tan

The constant message from health professionals these days is to avoid exposure to the sun, but this is a message society has not really taken to heart. Consider that there are an estimated 50,000 businesses in the United States devoted to *giving* people tans through exposure to ultraviolet light—the very thing the sun delivers. On an average day, more than a million Americans will visit tanning salons, with more than 70 percent of these people being women (Figure 1). The ongoing attraction that tanning salons hold may in part be attributable to a message the tanning industry tries hard to convey, which is that tanning beds provide a form of "safe tanning." Unfortunately, the scientific evidence says this is not the case.

For starters, the radiation provided by tanning beds is not likely to be less intense, nor of a fundamentally different nature,

Figure 1
Skin Aging in Progress
A young woman soaks up ultraviolet radiation in a tanning bed.

than the radiation that comes from the sun. The ultraviolet sunlight that reaches Earth during summer months in North America is at least 96 percent UVA radiation, with the balance being the shorter-wave UVB radiation. Meanwhile, the radiation delivered by most tanning beds is

The vitamin D produced by UV exposure is chemically identical to the vitamin D that can be obtained by taking a common vitamin pill.

about 95 percent UVA. It's not clear how much this distinction matters, however, because both UVA and UVB radiation are mutagenic—both cause mutations to the DNA in skin cells—though UVB radiation is more powerful in this respect. Summarizing a great deal of research on this subject, dermatologist Thanh-Nga T. Tran and his colleagues noted in a 2008 review that the chemical pathway that produces a tan in the body is the same pathway that leads to skin cancer. Given this, "safe tanning" through UV exposure "may be a physical impossibility," the researchers wrote. A 2006 analysis of studies that looked at tanning bed exposure and the most serious form of cancer, melanoma, underscored the validity of this message. It found a 15 percent greater risk of contracting melanoma among people who had ever used tanning beds, compared to people who had never used them, and a 75 percent greater risk among people who first used the beds before age 35.

The tanning industry has attempted to counter scientific findings such as these with claims that sun-bed tanning offers health *benefits*—notably a boost in vitamin D levels in the body through UV exposure. Left unsaid is the fact that the vitamin D produced by UV exposure is chemically identical to the vitamin D that can be obtained by taking a common vitamin pill.

The customers who flock to tanning beds may be unaware of the details of this health picture, but they understand in a general way that UV exposure is not healthy. So why do they continue to subject themselves to it? Lots of factors undoubtedly are at play in their decision—they simply think a tan looks good, they minimize the risk they are undertaking, they fall prey to false messages about the benefits of tanning. In the last few years, however, scientists have discovered another factor that might be at work. It turns out that UV-induced DNA damage results not only in the production of the substance melanin (which is what gives you a tan) but in the production of something called beta-endorphin, an opiate compound that brings on sensations of pleasure when released in the brain.

In 2004, Wake Forest University dermatologist Steven Feldman and his colleagues decided to see whether beta-endorphin release made a difference in whether people used tanning beds or not. The researchers had a set of 14 volunteers undertake sessions in one of two "tanning" beds, one of which actually had its UV rays blocked by a filter (a fact known only to the researchers). All the volunteers were regular users of tanning beds, and for six weeks all of them were given access to one research bed on Mondays and the other bed on Wednesdays. They were then given the option of getting additional tanning exposure in *either* bed on Fridays. The result? Volunteers who elected to get the additional Friday exposure selected the UV tanning bed 95 percent of the time. Moreover, volunteers who used the beds on any day reported feeling more relaxed and less tense after having been in the UV bed than in the bed with the UV filter. It may be that people continue to tan not only because of the way it makes them look but because of the way it makes them feel.

Haversian canal). These canals parallel the long axis of the bone and have blood vessels and nerves running through them—a kind of support system for the bone.

Unlike compact bone, spongy bone has no osteons. It consists of an open network of interconnecting calcified rods or plates. The red marrow fills the spaces within this network.

Practical Consequences of Bone Dynamics

Now, let's think about the practical consequences of this structure. Remember the earlier observation that bone is a living tissue? With its three kinds of cells constantly adding, maintaining, and breaking down the tissue, you can see the truth of this. Indeed, the bone "remodeling" that these cells undertake is so extensive that our entire skeleton is replaced through it every 10 years.

But bone is more dynamic than even this would indicate in that bones are responsive to our activities. As physiologist Frederic Martini has noted, when you undertake an exercise like jogging, which stresses your bones, the calcium-containing crystals of the affected bones create small electrical fields that apparently attract osteoblasts. On arrival, these osteoblasts begin producing bone. The result? If you take up jogging, you get denser leg bones. But there's a flip side to this: People who are using crutches to take the weight off a broken leg bone may temporarily lose up to a third of the mass in this bone because it is now scarcely being stressed at all.

Interestingly, although we develop almost all our height by late adolescence, we are still gaining in bone density up until about the age of 30. Then, beginning in middle age, the body may start removing more bone than it adds. This phenomenon particularly afflicts women, in the form of a condition known as *osteoporosis,* meaning a thinning of bone tissue that can result in bone breakage and deformation (**Figure 26.10**). Why should osteoporosis affect more women than men? Hormonal changes that come with

menopause can increase the activity of the bone-depleting osteoclasts relative to the activity of the bone-building osteoblasts. One way to guard against osteoporosis is to reach the age of 30 with as much bone density as possible—the equivalent of putting money in the bank as a hedge against a later withdrawal. And there are a couple of proven ways to get more bone density before 30: Take up programs of "weight-bearing" exercise such as jogging or walking and modestly increase calcium intake.

The Human Skeleton

Taking a step back from the microscopic world, you can see in **Figure 26.11** that there are a lot of bones in the skeletal system—206 of them in all. (Only the major bones are visible in the figure.) There are two main divisions to the skeletal system: the **axial skeleton,** whose 80 bones include the skull, the vertebral column, and the rib cage that attaches to it; and the **appendicular skeleton,** whose 126 bones include those of our paired appendages—the arms and the legs, along with the pelvic and pectoral "girdles" to which they are attached. Also note the blue-colored tissue joining ribs to our breastbone and lying in between each of the vertebrae. These are but a few of the cartilages in the body.

Joints

Joints, or articulations, exist wherever two bones meet. What qualities are required of a joint? Well, some only need strength. We think of our skull as being a single bone, but in fact, it's composed of several bones that interlock with each other in joints that are immovable. For other joints, flexibility is the key requirement. The ball-and-socket joint at our shoulder permits a range of motion so extensive that movement of our upper arms is limited more by our shoulder muscles than by our bones.

Highly movable joints are typically found at the ends of long bones, such as those in the legs as well as the shoulder. You can see a view of such a joint—the human knee joint—in **Figure 26.12** on page 498. A joint such as this must serve two competing functions. On the one hand, it must keep the massive femur (thigh bone) and large tibia (shin bone) in a stable arrangement. On the other, it serves as a hinge that allows the tibia to swing as free as a screen door off the femur. How does it do both things? Well, the two bones are partly held in place by four main ligaments, two of which are visible in the figure. Recall that ligaments link bone to bone, but there are also tendons, which attach bone to muscle; the knee joint has these in place as well.

With respect to the motion that such a joint allows, a critical element is that one bone does not actually

Figure 26.10
Bones Weakened by Osteoporosis

The damaging effects of osteoporosis can be seen in this micrograph of a spinal vertebra that has been "thinned" by the condition. Note the many small, circular holes or indentations in the bone; these are areas where bone tissue has been removed at a greater rate than it has been added. The result is a bone that is more susceptible to fractures. The micrograph is of the spongy bone portion of the vertebra; the larger circular holes are thus part of the bone's normal structure.

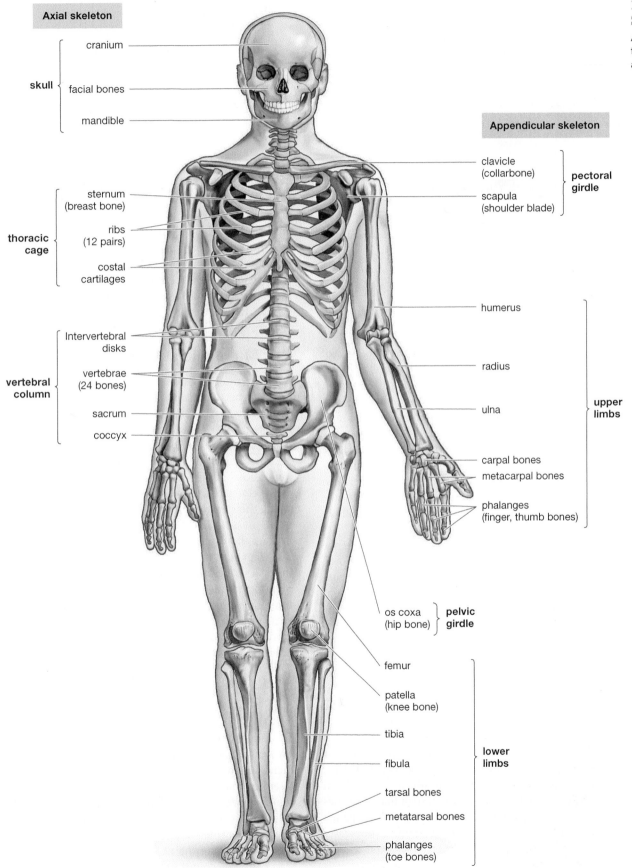

Axial skeleton

skull
- cranium
- facial bones
- mandible

thoracic cage
- sternum (breast bone)
- ribs (12 pairs)
- costal cartilages

vertebral column
- Intervertebral disks
- vertebrae (24 bones)
- sacrum
- coccyx

Appendicular skeleton

pectoral girdle
- clavicle (collarbone)
- scapula (shoulder blade)

upper limbs
- humerus
- radius
- ulna
- carpal bones
- metacarpal bones
- phalanges (finger, thumb bones)

pelvic girdle
- os coxa (hip bone)

lower limbs
- femur
- patella (knee bone)
- tibia
- fibula
- tarsal bones
- metatarsal bones
- phalanges (toe bones)

Figure 26.11
Solid Framework
A view of the human skeleton, which has two divisions, axial and appendicular.

anterior
cruciate
ligament

articular
cartilage

ligament

patella

fat pad

joint cavity

articular
capsule

ligament

menisci

Figure 26.12
A Highly Moveable
Joint

A simplified view of the
human knee joint, which links
the femur (thigh bone) to the
tibia (shin bone). Note that
the two bones never touch
each other because they are
covered with cartilage. The
menisci that you can see are
additional cartilage tissue
that serves an important
shock-absorbing function
while also helping to stabilize
the joint. The anterior cruciate ligament is the "ACL" we
hear about so much in sports
injuries. It is one of four main
ligaments that keep the
femur and tibia in a stable
arrangement.

SO FAR...

1. The three elements of the skeletal system
   are _____, _____, and _____.
2. Name two functions of bone other than
   support.

touch another. Instead, an extensive network of
padding and lubricating tissues in between the bones
performs the same function as the "gel" found in
running shoes. Note that the top of the tibia and bottom of the femur are surrounded by cartilage, and
that more cartilage—in the form of the meniscus tissue—lies on each side of the joint. The yellow tissue
shown is fat padding that fills in spaces that are created when the bones move, and the space in between
the bones (the joint cavity) is filled with a thick, vis-
cous fluid that not only lubricates joints but aids in
their metabolism.

Joints can get injured, of course, and as we age
they can wear down altogether. If you follow sports,
the name of one of the ligaments shown in Figure
26.12 may ring a bell. The anterior cruciate ligament
(ACL), which runs from the back of the femur to the
front of the tibia, is a frequent site of injury for
athletes who participate in sports that involve rapid
"cutting" movements, such as volleyball, soccer, and
basketball. An athlete will come to a quick stop, hear
a pop, and be down with a torn or ruptured ACL that
usually will have to be replaced by grafting tissue
onto it from another part of the body. For older people, the usual problem is not a sudden injury, but
rather a slow, steady degeneration of hip, knuckle, or
knee joints in the disease known as osteoarthritis.
Such "wear-and-tear" arthritis results in a breakdown
of the cartilage in between bones, such that joints become swollen, with bone sometimes grinding against
bone. Although osteoarthritis generally appears later
in life, young people can take steps to avoid it. Risk
factors for the condition include being overweight
and injuring the joints through the traumatic colli-
sions that can take place in sports like football and
soccer.

26.8 The Muscular System

Bones may provide a scaffolding for the body, but how
is it that this scaffolding is capable of movement? The
answer is muscles, specifically the skeletal muscles that
were introduced earlier, which are numerous and large
enough that they account for about 40 percent of our
body weight. Like bones, skeletal muscles are organs in
that they contain a variety of tissues. At each end of a
muscle, fibers of the outer muscle layer come together
to form the tendons that attach muscle to bone.

The Makeup of Muscle

As you can see in **Figure 26.13**, each muscle has within
it a number of oval-shaped bundles called fascicles.
Inside each fascicle there is a collection of muscle cells,
but the term *cell* here may be misleading because any
one of these cells can be as long as the muscle itself—a
gigantic length relative to the strictly microscopic
dimensions of most cells. Because skeletal muscle cells
are so elongated, they are referred to as **muscle fibers.**
Along their length, muscle fibers are divided into a set
of about 10,000 repeating units, called **sarcomeres,**
that are the fundamental units of muscle contraction.
But what is it that's contracting in a muscle? A look
inside a single muscle fiber reveals that it is composed
of more strands—perhaps a thousand long, thin structures called *myofibrils* that run the length of the cell.
Each myofibril, in turn, has a large collection of two
kinds of strands inside it that alternate with one another; these are thin filaments made of the protein
actin and thick filaments made of the protein *myosin*.
It is these filaments that contract, as you'll now see.

How Muscles Work

To understand contraction, note first that the thick
myosin filaments lie in the *center* of a given sarcomere. Meanwhile, the thin actin filaments are attached
to either *end* of the sarcomere and extend toward the
center, where they overlap with the thick filaments
(**Figure 26.14**). In contraction, the thin filaments slide
toward the center, causing the unit to shorten, which
is to say, causing the muscle to contract. To understand this, place just the tips of the fingers of your
right hand in between the tips the fingers of your left
hand. Now slide your right hand as far as it will go to
the left. Note that neither set of *fingers* shortened in

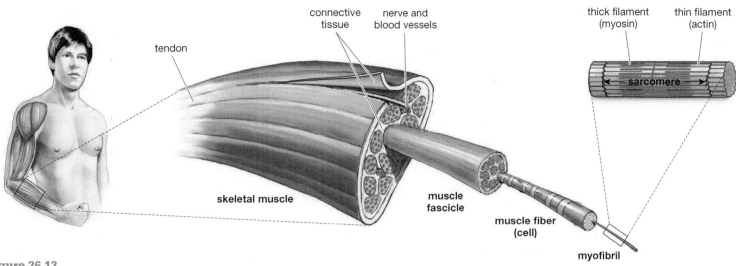

Figure 26.13
Structure of Skeletal Muscle

Skeletal muscles have oval-shaped bundles within them, called fascicles, that are composed of a number of muscle cells, each one of which is so elongated it is referred to as a fiber. Each fiber is composed of many thin myofibrils, and each myofibril has within it a collection of alternating thick and thin protein strands called filaments. The thin filaments are made of the protein actin, the thick filaments of the protein myosin. Each myofibril is divided lengthwise into a series of repeating functional units called sarcomeres.

Figure 26.14
How a Skeletal Muscle Contracts

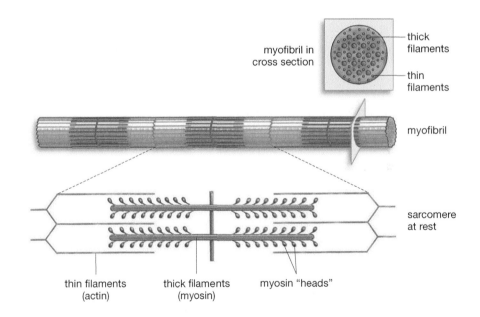

(a) Muscle at rest

The myofibril contains several sarcomeres, one of which is shown at rest. The thin filaments within the sarcomere, made of actin, overlap with adjacent thick filaments, made of myosin. The thick filaments have club-shaped outgrowths, called heads. The myofibril is also shown in cross section, at a location where thick and thin filaments overlap.

(b) Muscle contraction

Muscle contraction is a matter of the thin actin filaments sliding together within a sarcomere. This comes about when the myosin heads attach to the actin filaments and pull them toward the center of the sarcomere. The myosin heads pivot at their base and are capable of alternately binding with, or detaching from, the thin filaments.

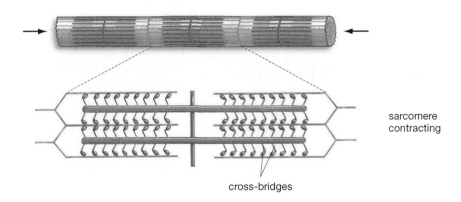

length, but that the total distance made up by both sets of fingers did shorten—exactly what happens within a sarcomere.

But what enables the thin filaments to slide? The thick myosin filaments have numerous club-shaped "heads" extending from them. These myosin heads are capable of alternately binding with or detaching from the adjacent thin filaments, creating so-called cross-bridges. The myosin heads pivot at their base, as if they were on a hinge. Here's the order of their activity: Attach to the actin filament, pull it toward the center of the sarcomere, detach from the actin, reattach to it, and pull again. In actual muscle contraction, this process happens many times in the blink of an eye; at any one point in a contraction, some myosin heads will be pulling an actin filament while others are detaching from it and still others binding to it.

This whole process gets going only when a signal arrives from a nerve telling a muscle to contract—often when a person has decided to move. This is why we speak of skeletal muscles as being under voluntary control, although it's easy to find exceptions to this rule. (The diaphragm that allows you to breathe is a skeletal muscle, but normally there is little that's voluntary in using it.) When a nerve signal arrives, the actual message doesn't go directly from nerve to muscle. Instead, a kind of ferryboat operation takes place in which the nerve end secretes a chemical, called a *neurotransmitter,* that travels across a tiny gap that lies between nerve and muscle. Once the neurotransmitter arrives at the muscle, it binds with it, setting in motion an internal chemical reaction that results in calcium ions (Ca^{2+}) being released inside a sarcomere.

This release of these ions has the effect of allowing the myosin heads to bind to the actin filaments, which of course has to happen before the myosin heads can *pull* the actin filaments.

On to the Nervous System

Having looked at the basic characteristics of the body and at three of its organ systems, we're now ready to move on to another system, one that functions in communication. Routine as this may sound, the system in question actually is responsible, more than any other, for providing us with the qualities that make us human. Hearing, seeing, tasting, feeling, planning, talking, remembering? For all this and more, we're indebted to our nervous system, the subject of Chapter 27.

SO FAR . . .

1. Muscle cells are referred to as muscle _____ because of their unusual _____.

2. Muscle contraction works through the process of a _____ of two kinds of muscle filaments past each other within a muscle unit known as a _____.

3. In this process, relatively thick _____ filaments pull relatively thin _____ filaments toward the center of the _____.

Go to the Study Area at www.masteringbiology.com for practice quizzes, myeBook, BioFlix™ 3-D animations, MP3 Tutor Sessions, videos, current events, and more.

CHAPTER 26 REVIEW

Summary

26.1 How the Body Regulates Itself

- Anatomy is the study of the structure of the body and the relationships between the body's parts. Physiology is the study of how these parts work. (p. 481)

- The body regulates itself through a system of circular control in which A prompts B and B prompts C, but in which C may then prompt A. Through use of such circular systems, the body maintains the stable state called homeostasis, largely through the mechanism of negative feedback. (p. 481)

- Humans have two primary body cavities: a dorsal cavity that is subdivided into cranial and spinal cavities; and a ventral cavity that is subdivided into a thoracic cavity, which contains the lungs and the heart, and an abdominopelvic cavity, which contains such organs as the stomach and liver. (p. 482)

26.2 Levels of Physical Organization

- Animal bodies function through a series of working units, whose order, from smaller to larger, runs: cells, tissues, organs, and organ systems. (p. 483)

26.3 **The Four Basic Tissue Types**

- The fundamental tissue types in humans are epithelial, connective, muscle, and nervous. (p. 483)

- Epithelial tissue such as skin covers body surfaces exposed to an external environment and can form glands. (p. 484)

- Connective tissue such as bone supports and protects other tissues. Connective tissue cells are embedded in a "ground" material that they themselves generally secrete. (p. 484)

- Muscle tissue is specialized in its ability to contract. The primary types of muscle tissue are skeletal, cardiac, and smooth. Skeletal muscle is always attached to bone and is under voluntary control. Cardiac muscle exists only in the heart and contracts under the control of its own pacemaker cells. Smooth muscle is not under voluntary control and is responsible for contractions in, for example, blood vessels and the digestive tract. (p. 484)

- Nervous tissue is specialized for the rapid conduction of electrical impulses. It is made up of neurons, which transmit the impulses, and glial cells, which are support cells for neurons. (p. 484)

26.4 **Organs Are Made of Several Kinds of Tissues**

- The stomach provides a case in point for how various tissue types come together to form a working organ. A typical cross section of the stomach is made up of muscle, nervous, connective, and epithelial tissues. (p. 484)

26.5 **Organs and Tissues Make Up Organ Systems**

- There are 11 organ systems in the body. The first three—integumentary, skeletal, and muscular—function in body support and movement. The integumentary system is made up of skin and associated structures. The skeletal system is made up of bones, ligaments, and cartilages. The muscular system includes all the skeletal muscles but not smooth or cardiac muscles. (p. 486)

- The nervous, endocrine, and immune systems function in communication, regulation, and defense of the body. The nervous system is a rapid communication system that includes the brain, spinal cord, nerves, and sense organs. The endocrine system is a communication system that works through hormones. The immune system is a network of cells and proteins whose central function is to eliminate microbial invaders. It works in part through the lymphatic network, whose vessels collect extracellular fluid and deliver it to the blood vessels. Immune cells within lymph glands inspect lymph as it passes by to identify invading microbes. (p. 486)

- The cardiovascular, respiratory, digestive, and urinary systems function in transport and in exchange with the environment. The cardiovascular system consists of the heart, blood, blood vessels, and that portion of the bone marrow in which red blood cells are formed. The respiratory system includes the lungs and the passageways that carry air to them. The central feature of the digestive system is the digestive tract, a tube that begins at the mouth and ends at the anus. Along its course, there are digestive organs of the system: the stomach, small intestines, and large intestines and such accessory glands as the liver and pancreas. The urinary system functions to eliminate waste products from the blood, through the formation of urine, and to retain useful substances. It is made up of the kidneys and various other structures, such as the bladder. (p. 487)

26.6 **The Integumentary System**

- The primary component of the integumentary system is the organ called skin. In addition to covering the body, skin protects underlying tissues and organs, controls the evaporation of body fluids, regulates heat loss, stores fat, and makes vitamin D. Exocrine glands associated with skin excrete such materials as water, oils, and milk. (p. 489)

- Skin has a thin outer epithelial covering, the epidermis, and a thicker underlying dermis. Beneath the dermis—and not part of the skin—is the hypodermis. Epidermal skin cells are constantly worn away and replaced by new epidermal cells being pushed up from the inner epidermis. The dermis is filled with accessory structures and contains blood vessels and nerves that support the surface of the skin. The blood supply of the dermis is important in controlling body temperature. (p. 489)

- The hypodermis is the location for the body's layer of subcutaneous fat. Separate from this tissue is the body's visceral fat, which surrounds organs deep in the abdomen. An excess of visceral fat is more harmful to health than is an excess of subcutaneous fat. (p. 490)

- Hairs originate in tiny organs called hair follicles and may have been important for our evolutionary ancestors in both heat retention and touch sensitivity. (p. 490)

- The skin contains two types of exocrine glands: sebaceous glands, which produce a material called sebum that lubricates hair and limits bacterial growth; and sweat glands, which produce sweat that cools the body by evaporating. Overactive sebaceous glands are the cause of acne. (p. 491)

- Nails are made of the protein keratin. (p. 491)

26.7 **The Skeletal System**

- The human skeletal system is composed of bone, ligaments, and cartilage. Bone is a connective tissue that provides support and storage capacity and that is the site of blood cell production. Cartilage serves as padding in most joints, forms our larynx and trachea, and links ribs to the breastbone. Ligaments are tissues that link bone to bone. Tendons link bone to muscle but are not part of the skeletal system. (p. 491)

- Each bone of the skeleton is an organ that contains connective tissue, blood vessels, and nervous tissue. (p. 493)

- The typical long bone features a central shaft, called a diaphysis, and expanded ends, called epiphyses. There are two types of bone within this structure: compact bone and spongy bone. In long bones, spongy bone is filled with red marrow, which is the site of the production of all the blood cells in the adult body. Long bones have a central marrow cavity that is filled with yellow marrow, which is composed largely of energy-storing fat cells. (p. 494)

- Three different types of cells are involved in bone growth and maintenance: osteoblasts, which produce new bone; osteocytes, which maintain normal bone; and osteoclasts, which release enzymes that break bone down. (p. 494)

- The basic functional unit of compact bone is the osteon. Osteoblasts produce concentric layers of bone around a central canal of the osteon, which parallels the long axis of the bone and has blood vessels and nerves running through it. (p. 494)

- The human skeleton has 206 bones, in two main divisions: an axial skeleton, whose 80 bones include the skull, the vertebral column, and the rib cage; and an appendicular skeleton, whose 126 bones include those of the arms and legs and the pelvic and pectoral girdles to which they are attached. (p. 496)

- Joints exist wherever two bones meet. Some joints provide a strong linkage between bones, while others provide great flexibility. Normally, the bony surfaces of highly movable joints do not meet directly, but are instead covered with cartilages and pads that absorb shock and provide lubrication. (p. 496)

26.8 The Muscular System

- Because of their tremendous elongation, muscle cells are called muscle fibers. Along their length, they are divided into sarcomeres, which are the basic units of muscle contraction. Each muscle fiber is composed of myofibrils, which are in turn composed of alternating strands of thin filaments made of the protein actin and thicker filaments made of the protein myosin. (p. 498)

- Actin filaments attached to the end of each sarcomere overlap with the myosin filaments that lie in the center of each sarcomere. The myosin filaments bring about contraction by attaching to the actin filaments, pulling them toward the center of the sarcomeres, detaching, and then pulling again. As the actin filaments slide toward the center of the sarcomere, the sarcomere shortens. (p. 498)

- Skeletal muscles contract only when prompted by a signal from a nerve, which initiates a chemical cascade inside muscle tissue that allows the myosin filaments to bind to the actin filaments. (p. 500)

BioFlix™

Muscle Contraction

Key Terms

appendicular skeleton   496
axial skeleton   496
bone   491
cardiac muscle   484
cardiovascular system   487
cartilage   492
compact bone   494
connective tissue   484
dermis   490
digestive system   488
endocrine gland   487
endocrine system   487
epidermis   489
epithelial tissue   484
exocrine gland   487
gland   484
homeostasis   482
hormone   487
immune system   487
integumentary system   486
keratin   489
ligaments   493
lymphatic network   487
muscle fiber   498
muscle tissue   484
muscular system   486
negative feedback   482
nervous system   486
nervous tissue   484
organ   483
organ system   483
osteoblast   494
osteoclast   494
osteocyte   494
red marrow   494
reproductive system   488
respiratory system   488
sarcomere   498
sebaceous glands   491
skeletal muscle   484
skeletal system   486
skin   489
smooth muscle   484
spongy bone   494
sweat gland   491
tendons   493

tissue   483
urinary system   488
yellow marrow   494

Understanding the Basics

Multiple-Choice Questions

(Answers are in the back of the book.)

1. To survive, the human body needs to maintain _____ and does so primarily through the means of self-regulation known as _____.
   a. high energy output; positive feedback
   b. adequate fat layers; exocrine secretion
   c. bone density; muscle contraction
   d. homeostasis; negative feedback
   e. nerve signal transmission; hormonal secretion

2. The four basic types of tissue in the human body are:
   a. epithelial, connective, muscle, nervous.
   b. epithelial, blood, muscle, nervous.
   c. skin, bone, muscle, nervous.
   d. skin, connective, heart, nervous.
   e. epithelial, bone, connective, muscle.

3. Muscle fibers that are striated and voluntary are found in:
   a. cardiac muscle.
   b. skeletal muscle.
   c. smooth muscle.
   d. rough muscle.
   e. all four types of muscle.

4. Hormones and the glands or cells that secrete them make up the:
   a. cardiovascular system.
   b. respiratory system.
   c. lymphatic system.
   d. urinary system.
   e. endocrine system.

5. Surface epidermal cells of the skin:
   a. rapidly divide and are filled mostly with keratin.
   b. never divide and remain in place through adult life.
   c. rapidly divide and are in place only a short time.
   d. are dead and filled with keratin.
   e. rapidly divide and are filled with fat.

6. Cells called _____ build bone tissue, _____ maintain it, and _____ break it down.
   a. osteoblasts; osteoclasts; osteocytes
   b. osteoclasts; osteons; osteoblasts
   c. osteoblasts; osteocytes; osteoclasts
   d. osteons; osteocytes; osteoclasts
   e. osteocytes; osteoblasts; osteoclasts

7. The essence of muscle contraction is that thick and thin muscle proteins:
   a. slide past each other.
   b. link irreversibly with each other.
   c. are short enough to respond quickly.
   d. stay completely separate.
   e. pull in opposite directions.

8. No skeletal muscle can contract without first:
   a. receiving a hormone signal.
   b. checking on the status of nearby skeletal muscles.
   c. lining up its actin and myosin filaments.
   d. receiving a nervous system signal.
   e. linking to a bone.

Brief Review

(**Answers are in the back of the book.**)

1. What is negative about negative feedback?

2. What role does the lymphatic network play in immune function?

3. Why is our skin water-resistant?

4. What are the two principal locations for fat tissue in the body?

5. List three functions of the skeletal system.

6. A sample of bone shows an interconnecting network of calcified rods and plates filled in with red marrow. Is this sample from the shaft (diaphysis) or the end (epiphysis) of a long bone?

Applying Your Knowledge

1. Cells called melanocytes that lie deep in the epidermis produce a pigment, called melanin, that gives skin its color. Exposure to ultraviolet light—from the sun or a tanning bed—causes melanocytes to produce more melanin, which they pass along to the skin cells above them, yielding a suntan. But why would sun exposure prompt this increased melanin production? What is the function of a tan, in other words?

2. The text notes that bone density can increase in response to exercise. Imagine two fairly inactive people who decide to start exercising. One becomes a runner while the other becomes a swimmer. Who experiences the greater increase in bone density: the swimmer (in the arm bones) or the runner (in the leg bones)?

3. Acids secreted by the stomach give the materials within it a pH level that can lie between that of lemon juice and battery acid. Yet our small intestines, which the stomach feeds into, have chemical buffers flowing into them that raise the pH level of the material coming from the stomach. Why should the stomach need such an extreme pH level while the small intestines do not?

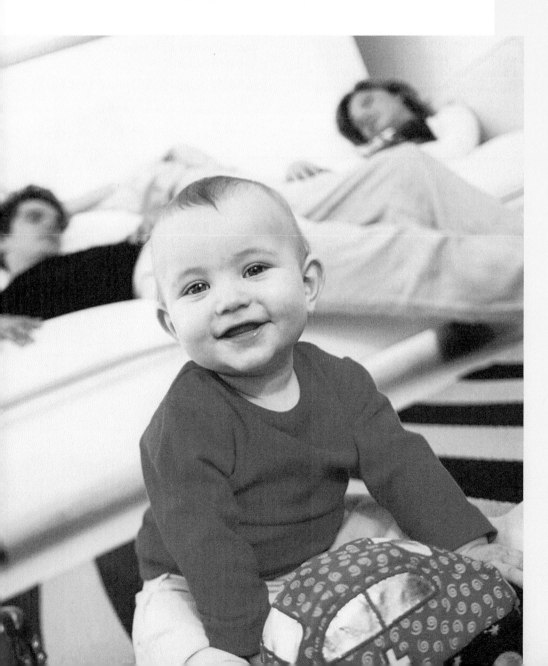

CHAPTER

33

How the Baby Came to Be:
Human Reproduction

To produce a child, human males and females must first produce sperm and eggs, which come together in an act of fusion known as conception. The fertilized egg that results will, over the next 38 weeks, develop into a fully formed baby.

Baby makes three at the end of a long and complicated process.

M emorable events mark every human life, but for parents, one event that is sure to be indelibly etched into memory is the birth of a child. The mother's labor, the final "pushing" that brings the baby forth, the first real look at the infant, and the infant's first look at the world: these are moments that, once experienced, are never forgotten.

The birth of a child is a beginning, of course, and yet it is also a culmination. Human beings must grow to a certain level of biological maturity before being capable of reproduction. After this, finding a partner may be difficult and getting pregnant more difficult yet. Eventually, however, two very special "seeds"— *this* egg and *this* sperm, out of all the millions a man and a woman produce in a lifetime—fuse to create this child.

In this chapter, you'll trace the biology of human reproduction, which might be defined as all the biological steps that must fall into place before a child can be born. The process of development you studied in Chapter 32 represents part of what you'll be looking at, but other elements are involved as well.

33.1 Overview of Human Reproduction and Development

Taking the story of reproduction from the beginning means picking up a narrative that was begun in Chapter 10, when you went over the formation of the reproductive cells called *gametes*—eggs in females, sperm in males. (**Figure 33.1**). In this chapter, the focus widens, taking into account the physical setting in which egg and sperm are formed and the steps that bring these cells together. Finally, you will look at the human development that takes place once egg and sperm have merged. (For information on some of the methods humans use to *prevent* conception, see "Methods of Contraception" on page 642.)

The first part of reproduction, the formation and delivery of egg and sperm, is a straightforward story in outline. The eggs a woman possesses exist in her in a precursor form, called oocytes, that lie within two walnut-shaped structures called ovaries. These exist just right and left of center within the female pelvic area (**Figure 33.2** on the next page). Each oocyte sits in the ovaries within a nurturing complex of cells and fluids called a **follicle.** On average, once every 28 days one follicle-oocyte complex is brought to a state of maturity such that the oocyte and some accessory cells that surround it rupture from their ovary and begin a slow journey to the uterus. This trip takes place inside the structure called the **uterine tube** (or Fallopian tube). The release of the oocyte is called **ovulation.** If, during this trip, the oocyte encounters a male sperm, the two may fuse, in which case conception has occurred.

Sperm in men are produced, in unfinished form, in sets of tubules in the two male testes. They then are transported to a structure called the epididymis (one for each testis) for further development. Then, with

Figure 33.1
Oocyte and Sperm
Numerous sperm surround a single oocyte.

Figure 33.2 Reproductive Anatomy of the Human Female

(a) Eggs develop in the ovaries within nurturing complexes called follicles. Once every 28 days, on average, an egg is expelled from one ovary or the other and journeys through the uterine tube to the uterus. If the egg encounters sperm on the way, pregnancy will result when egg and sperm fuse. The fertilized egg then continues traveling through the uterine tube and implants in the lining of the uterus, the endometrium.

(b) A lateral view of female reproductive anatomy. The labia majora are two folds of skin that enclose two other folds of skin, the labia minora, which in turn enclose a small bud of nerve-dense sensory tissue, the clitoris. The labia minora, vagina, and clitoris all engorge with blood during sex, and stimulation of the clitoris can lead to orgasm.

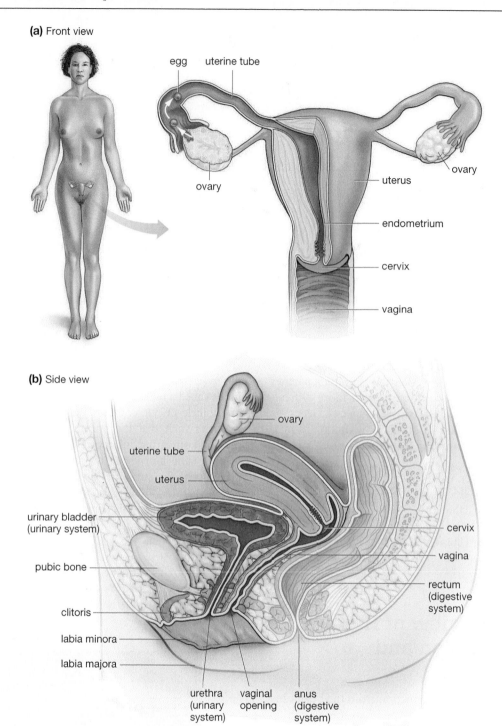

(a) Front view

egg · uterine tube · ovary · uterus · endometrium · cervix · vagina · ovary

(b) Side view

ovary · uterine tube · uterus · urinary bladder (urinary system) · pubic bone · clitoris · labia minora · labia majora · cervix · vagina · rectum (digestive system) · urethra (urinary system) · vaginal opening · anus (digestive system)

sexual excitation, sperm are transported in a loop: up and over the urinary bladder through two ducts, each called a vas deferens (**Figure 33.3**). The contents of these ducts then empty into a single duct, called the urethra, from which they are ejaculated into the female vagina. Along the way, materials secreted by several glands join the sperm in a process that can be likened to tributaries feeding into a common stream. The resulting mixture of sperm and glandular materials is called **semen.**

Whereas the female releases an average of one oocyte per month, the male releases an average of 200 million sperm per ejaculation. Of the millions of sperm that begin the journey, a few dozen may encounter the female oocyte as it continues its journey from ovary to uterus. The first sperm to breach the coating that surrounds the oocyte fuses with it, while the rest are shut out through a kind of gate-slamming mechanism. When this one sperm has joined with an oocyte, conception has occurred. The now-fertilized egg still floats

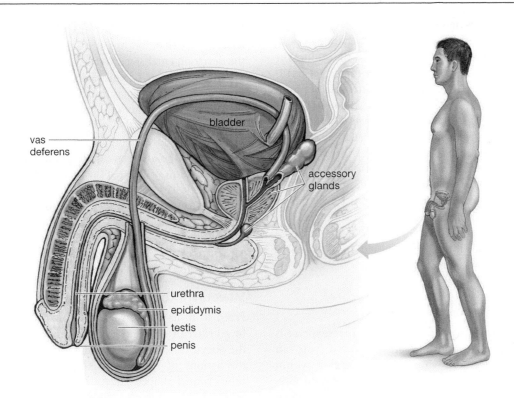

Figure 33.3
Reproductive
Anatomy of the
Human Male
Sperm are produced in the testes and transported to the epididymis, where they mature and are stored. With orgasm, the sperm are transported through the vas deferens and then the urethra, from which they are ejaculated. Along the way, they are joined by materials secreted by several accessory glands.

freely in the uterine tube, where it begins to develop in the ways described in Chapter 32: One cell becomes two, two become four, and so on. Four days after fertilization, the developing embryo enters the uterus; three days more and it implants itself in the tissue of the uterine wall known as the endometrium and continues to develop.

Both the male and female reproductive systems are greatly influenced by the actions of hormones—chemical signaling molecules that move through the bloodstream. Indeed, the reproductive organs are primary sites of production for some of the most important of these hormones: testosterone in men and estrogen and progesterone in women.

With this outline of human reproduction as background, let's move on now to take a closer look at both the female and male reproductive systems, first as they function separately and then as they function together to produce a baby.

33.2 The Female Reproductive System

The Female Reproductive Cycle

Although hormones operate in both sexes, in females they bring about a reproductive *cycle* that repeats itself about once every 28 days (although it can range from 21 to 42 days). In males, conversely, there is no cycle, but instead a steady production of sperm and a destruction or removal of the sperm that are

not ejaculated. Why a cycle for females and not for males? The answer lies partly in the two roles the female reproductive system must fulfill. It must form an egg *and* create an environment in the uterus in which a fertilized egg can develop. An important part of this uterine environment is essentially built up and then dismantled once every 28 days—except in those rare instances in which an oocyte is fertilized. The end result of the dismantling of the uterine environment is **menstruation:** a cyclical release of blood and the inner portion of a specialized uterine tissue, the **endometrium,** from the female reproductive tract. The endometrium is tissue that lines the interior of the uterus; it is tissue that *would have* housed an embryo had one been implanted there (see Figure 33.1a).

Why Does Menstruation Exist?

From this, it's reasonable to ask: Why do women have this monthly cycle of buildup and destruction rather than just a permanent environment for an embryo? After all, menstruation has some obvious costs attached to it; apart from discomfort, there is a loss of blood and other tissue. (On average, women lose about 40 milliliters—or about 1.4 fluid ounces—of blood in a menstrual cycle and about that much other tissue as well.) So, in the face of these costs, why has menstruation been preserved throughout human evolution? Scientists have no firm answers here, but they do have a couple of favored hypotheses. One is that, costly as menstruation may be, in terms of expended energy it is not *as* costly as the alternative of maintaining a permanent embryonic environment in the uterus. The other has to do with a change in form that the endometrium undergoes each month. As the time approaches in which an oocyte might get fertilized and then implanted, the endometrium goes from being a tissue whose primary activity is growing (in its "proliferative" phase) to one whose primary activity is secreting a nutrient-rich mucus (in its "secretory" phase). The assumption is that a fertilized egg can implant itself only in a secretory-phase endometrium, but that a secretory-phase endometrium cannot perpetuate itself—it must develop from a proliferative-phase endometrium, after which it cannot stay in secretory phase for long. Given this, it makes sense that the endometrium washes a part of itself out every 28 days or so and starts its growth anew.

How Does an Egg Develop?

As noted earlier, eggs develop from precursor cells called **oocytes.** If you look at Figure 33.4, you can track the process by which oocytes develop within each ovary. Any oocyte that moves very far through the process of development ends up being surrounded by a sphere of accessory cells, called *follicle cells*, that eventually provide the oocyte with nutrients. The complex of an oocyte and its accessory cells and fluids is called an **ovarian follicle;** it is the basic unit of oocyte development.

Follicle Development and Ovulation

Every oocyte that matures into an egg must go through the developmental steps you see in Figure 33.4. This is a monthly process of selection, running from a large starting set of follicles, through fewer *primary follicles* that develop from them, to a greatly reduced number of *secondary follicles* that continue development, and finally to a single *tertiary follicle* that nurtures an oocyte through its time in the ovary. Responding to hormonal influence midway through the menstrual cycle, the tertiary follicle ruptures, thus expelling the oocyte and some surrounding accessory cells not only from the follicle but from the ovary as well (**Figure 33.5**). With this event, ovulation has occurred. It takes place in this way in one ovary each month, with one ovary or the other selected through an unknown process.

Movement through the Uterine Tube

Freed from its ovarian housing but still surrounded by an exterior coat and a collection of accessory cells, the oocyte is now swept into the uterine tube through the actions of the finger-like *fimbriae* lying at the tube's funnel-shaped end (see **Figure 33.6**). Propelled by liquid currents and the uterine tube's whip-like cilia, the oocyte—technically not yet an egg—makes a journey of about 10 centimeters (or 4 inches) through the uterine tube over the next 4 days. While within the tube, the oocyte may encounter sperm and become fertilized prior to entering the uterus.

ovary

Figure 33.4

Steps Leading to an Egg

Eggs develop within ovaries by going through the set of developmental stages seen in the figure. First, the precursor of an egg, a primary oocyte, becomes part of a nurturing complex of cells and fluids called an ovarian follicle. Then, on the periphery of the ovary, one follicle will mature, once every 28 days, by becoming first a primary, then a secondary, and finally a tertiary follicle. The oocyte contained in the tertiary follicle is expelled from the ovary at the end of the process, at which point it begins a journey through the uterine tube. With the oocyte's expulsion, the ruptured tertiary follicle is transformed into the corpus luteum, which for a time produces hormones that facilitate pregnancy. If no pregnancy results from the ovulation, the corpus luteum begins degenerating within about 12 days.

1. primary oocyte
2. primary follicles
3. secondary follicle
4. ovulation through rupture of tertiary follicle
5. corpus luteum (yellow body)
6. degeneration of corpus luteum

Meanwhile, the ruptured tertiary follicle now takes on a new role: It develops into a body called the **corpus luteum** ("yellow body"), a structure that secretes hormones that first prepare the female reproductive tract for pregnancy and that then maintain the tract during the early phases of pregnancy. If pregnancy does not occur, the corpus luteum begins degenerating after about 12 days. With the corpus luteum, you can see again the part that hormones play in the monthly female reproductive cycle. For details on this hormonal regulation, see "Hormones and the Female Reproductive Cycle," on page 636.

Changes through the Female Life Span

In between the creation of oocytes and the journey of one oocyte down the uterine tube lies a multistep process that could be characterized by the phrase "Many are called, but few are chosen." A 6-month-old female fetus has in its ovaries about 7 million oocytes that have become part of follicle complexes. At birth, however, this number has been reduced to about 800,000, primarily because of the process of *atresia,* or the natural degeneration of follicles. By puberty, the number has declined to about 400,000. A small

number of these follicles are "recruited" monthly for further development, but as you've seen, only *one* of these will go on to develop into the oocyte that is expelled from the ovary each month. The only exception to this rule comes in the 1 percent or so of ovarian cycles that result in multiple ovulations, in which case fraternal twins, triplets, and other multiple births are possible. In sum, the oocyte that begins the journey down the uterine tube each month has been selected from more than 7 million initially created and is one of

Figure 33.5
Ovulation in Progress
A human oocyte and its surrounding accessory cells emerge from a tertiary follicle. This photo—by far the clearest ever taken of human ovulation—was captured in 2008 through a piece of good luck: A Belgian surgeon was performing a routine hysterectomy on a 45-year-old patient when she began ovulating in mid-procedure. (The gray structure on the right is a surgical instrument.) Images the surgeon captured of the entire process gave reproductive experts reason to doubt a long-held belief about ovulation: that it takes place very rapidly, through a sudden expulsion of an oocyte from its surrounding follicle. This ovulation took a full 15 minutes to complete.

(a)
1. ovulation
uterine tube
fimbriae
ovary
2. fertilization
3. development
uterus
4. implantation in uterine wall

(b)

Figure 33.6
Journey to Pregnancy

(a) Surrounded by accessory cells, an oocyte is expelled from the ovary into the uterine tube, where it encounters sperm and is fertilized by one of them. Now a fertilized egg (or zygote), it begins the process of development and completes its journey with implantation in the endometrium of the uterine wall.

(b) A micrograph of an unfertilized oocyte moving through folds of tissue in a uterine tube.

Hormones and the Female Reproductive Cycle

In females, reproduction is carried out through a *cycle*, which is to say a series of events that repeat themselves regularly—on average, once every 28 days. But how can the female reproductive system "keep time" like this? What is the clock that governs the cycle?

A real clock is actually a good analogy for what happens. If you look at an old-fashioned mechanical watch, what you'll see is a central spring that exerts a force through a series of gears. Given these parts, it takes 12 hours for the physical mechanism of the "small hand" on the watch to make its way through a complete cycle—to end up where it began. In women, the substances called hormones set in motion a group of physical processes that take about 28 days to complete. The last of these processes leaves the body right where it began, at the start of another cycle.

We actually should speak of female reproductive *cycles*, because several are going on in reproduction, all of them inter-linked. There is the ovarian cycle, which has to do with the development and release of oocytes. Then there is the menstrual or "uterine" cycle, which concerns the regular buildup and then breakdown of tissue in the inner lining of the uterus. Finally, there are several hormonal cycles, which help govern both menstruation and egg production.

If you look at **Figure 1**, you can see a time line for all these cycles as tracked over a period of 28 days, which you can see marked off at the bottom. To give you a feel for the processes at work, let's follow just the menstrual cycle, whose "first day," over on the far left, is defined as the first day of menstruation. What the graph tracks is the state of the tissue (the endometrium) lining the inside of the uterus. As you can see, beginning on day 1, this tissue goes through a breakdown that lasts about 6 days, after which it begins a steady buildup that continues all the way to about day 21—at

which point it starts to break down again. Now look at what is going on in the ovarian cycle (the second one down from the top). This part of the graph is following the single "successful" oocyte (of many that begin development) through its progression into the oocyte that bursts from the ovary on day 14.

The real lesson, however, is to think about the menstrual and ovarian cycles as they relate to *each other:* The endometrium is built up in the uterus as a means of creating an environment in which an egg could implant itself should one be fertilized. If such an egg begins its journey on

How can the female reproductive system "keep time"? What is the clock that governs the cycle?

day 14 and then takes another 7 days or so to implant itself in the uterus, you can see what stage the *endometrium* will be in at this point: near its maximum thickness (and at a highly productive stage of synthesizing a blood vessel system). Such an environment is just what an implanted embryo would need.

And what of the figures over on the right side of the ovarian cycle? They represent the corpus luteum, the "remains" of the follicle that the successful oocyte broke out of. The corpus luteum is much more than a spent vessel at this point, however. Hormones it secretes will promote the growth of the endometrium. Without a pregnancy occurring, the corpus luteum carries out such secretion only for about a week. After that, it begins to degenerate, and *this* means the degeneration of the endometrium, which washes out, along with some of the blood that supplied it, in the process called menstruation.

Which hormones are secreted by the corpus luteum? Look now at the ovarian hormone cycle, and you'll see a line for "progestins"—a family of hormones whose most important member is progesterone.

As you can see, the level of progestins takes a sharp turn upward just as the corpus luteum is formed—no surprise because it is the corpus luteum that is secreting them.

There is a circularity to all this hormonal control, with the hormones involved influencing each other in different ways as the cycle goes on. Let's arbitrarily take as a starting point, however, first the development of a follicle and then the release of an egg from it.

One important hormone in the cycle is produced in neither the ovaries nor the uterus but in the brain. A brain structure called the hypothalamus releases vanishingly small amounts of a hormone called **gonadotropin-releasing hormone,** whose function is spelled out in its name: It brings about the release of *other* hormones active in reproduction, the gonadotropins.

Two gonadotropins are spurred into production in this way, **follicle-stimulating hormone (FSH)** and **luteinizing hormone (LH),** both of which are produced in a gland located beneath the hypothalamus, the anterior pituitary gland. You can see both FSH and LH levels charted in the gonadotropic hormone cycle at the top of Figure 1.

After being secreted by the anterior pituitary, both FSH and LH have their primary early-cycle effects at the site of the ovarian follicles. FSH promotes the development *of* the follicles, while LH stimulates the synthesis of a hormone *by* the follicles, estrogen (which actually is a family of hormones). The more the follicles develop, the more estrogen they secrete. The result, as you can see in Figure 1, is that while estrogen levels are essentially maintained through the first week or so of the cycle, after that they begin to rise.

Estrogen is a hormone that is doing two things in the female reproductive cycle: It is promoting the growth of the endometrium in the uterus, and it is controlling the release of both FSH and

LH. Early on, the relatively low levels of estrogen act to *decrease* FSH—not enough to stop development of the follicles but enough to slightly reduce FSH levels over the first 10 days or so of the cycle, as you can see in Figure 1. In the second week of the cycle, however, estrogen output is greatly increased thanks to the development of the tertiary follicle, whose oocyte will burst forth from the ovary. At this level, estrogen acts to *increase* not only FSH production but LH production as well. The result, as seen in Figure 1, is the "spike" of LH production that begins just before day 14 of the cycle. This hormonal surge is what causes the oocyte to break out from both follicle and ovary.

Now the former tertiary follicle has a new identity, the corpus luteum. In this role, it produces progesterone, which as noted acts on the uterine lining to develop it for embryo implantation. Then, in tandem with estrogen, progesterone has another effect. It acts on the hypothalamus and pituitary to *lower* FSH and LH levels. But it turns out that the corpus luteum needs LH to remain healthy. In the absence of pregnancy, falling LH levels spell the end for the corpus luteum. This in turn causes a decline in progesterone levels, which brings about the degeneration of the endometrium, essentially by depriving it of a blood supply. Now, in the absence of a corpus luteum or developed follicles, the levels of estrogen and progesterone are *low*. Such low levels *stimulate* FSH and LH production in the anterior pituitary, and this is where we started: The cycle begins again as LH and FSH stimulate the growth of another set of follicles.

So, what keeps this cycle from continuing when pregnancy does occur? The implantation of an embryo in the endometrium causes release from the embryo of a hormone (called human chorionic gonadotropin), which acts like LH in that it keeps the corpus luteum robust and generating progesterone and estrogen, which in turn maintains the endometrium.

With this knowledge, you're in a position to understand what birth control pills do. In general, they are compounds that contain both synthetic estrogen and a synthetic progestin. Women usually take them beginning five days after the start of menstruation for three weeks (and during the fourth week take a chemically functionless "spacer" or nothing). Think about what is required at the beginning of a cycle to prompt the development of follicles: *low*

levels of estrogen. (Recall that this low level stimulates the hypothalamus and pituitary to secrete FSH.) The pill provides a *higher* level of estrogen than exists naturally, thus suppressing the release of FSH and the development of follicles. Second, the progestin in the pill suppresses LH release by the pituitary, which prevents the *ovulation* of any follicle that might manage to develop because the LH surge is required for ovulation.

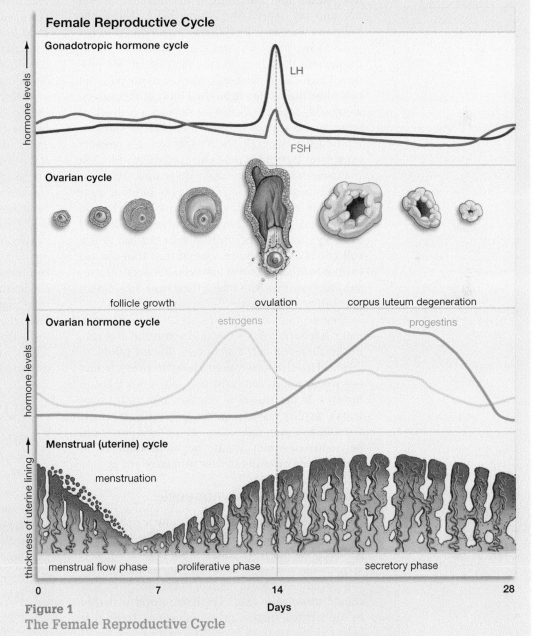

Figure 1
The Female Reproductive Cycle

only 500 or so that will make this trip in a woman's lifetime (about 13 a year for 35 or 40 years).

Follicle Loss and Female Fertility

Given that a woman begins puberty with about 400,000 follicles, you might think that her supply would never run out. This is not the case, however, because the process of atresia continues at a steady pace from puberty through a woman's mid-30s and then accelerates beginning in a woman's late 30s. By the time a woman reaches her early 50s, perhaps 1,100 follicles remain; this scarcity is thought to be the most important factor in bringing about **menopause,** or the cessation of the monthly ovarian cycle.

Taking a step back from this story, you can see that its underlying assumption is that, while a woman will lose follicles over the course of her lifetime, she will not gain any. Indeed, the assumption is that all the follicles a woman will ever have are produced in her prior to her birth. It's clear that men remain fertile throughout their lives because their sperm are produced each day by stem cells, which is to say cells that never lose their ability to produce more of themselves, along with sperm cells. But for decades a bedrock of reproductive science has been that women have no reproductive stem cells. In 2004, however, a research team from Harvard stunned the medical world when it announced that female mice do possess stem cells that are capable of giving rise to eggs and that these stem cells remain active throughout life. Then in 2009, scientists from China announced that they had not only identified such cells in mice but had grown collections of them in the lab and then transplanted them into other mice that had been sterilized. The result? After mating with males, these once-sterile mice gave birth to healthy sets of offspring.

Despite the seeming strength of these findings, many scientists remain skeptical about the existence of female reproductive stem cells. Recent results in this field have, however, given a boost to efforts to find out whether such cells exist not only in mice but in humans. If the answer is yes, then our ideas about female fertility may change fundamentally. If female reproductive stem cells exist—and if their power can be harnessed—then fertility might be returned to older women or be boosted for women of any age.

The Mystery of Menopause

Irrespective of whether female reproductive stem cells exist, the massive loss of follicles over the female life span is real, and it presents science with a mystery: Why should women steadily lose follicles and, as a result, become infertile in midlife? Put another way, why should menopause exist? The living world is shaped by differential success in reproduction. Traits that help a given organism to produce relatively *more* offspring normally are retained over evolutionary time.

Yet the trait of menopause developed in the course of evolution, and it seemingly leads to fewer offspring for women. Through it, contemporary women are taken out of reproduction altogether for the last 20 or 30 years of their lives, during which time they suffer from such menopause-related maladies as osteoporosis. Given these factors, why does menopause exist?

As was the case with menstruation, we have no firm answers, but we do have several candidate hypotheses. One is that menopause is simply a product of women living longer today than their evolutionary ancestors did. Proponents of this view point out that a number of female mammals undergo what amounts to menopause but then live only long enough to raise one additional generation of offspring after this loss of reproductive capacity sets in. Human females may once have followed this pattern and lived to, say, 60 years old—just long enough to give birth to a final child in their late 40s and then raise that child to a self-sustaining age of 10 or so. Today, however, women don't live until 60; they live until 75 or 85 and thus have decades of life following menopause.

A very different hypothesis holds that menopause is "adaptive," as biologists say—it arose through evolution because it actively helps females perpetuate their genes. The starting point for this "grandmother hypothesis" is the observation that what counts in evolution is not just whether you have children; it is whether you have children who themselves go on to have healthy children. Now, how is a given woman most likely to achieve this? Under this hypothesis, she best achieves it not by continuing to give birth throughout life but by leaving direct reproduction behind at a certain point and becoming a grandmother who provides both for her children and her grandchildren. We now have evidence, from eighteenth- and nineteenth-century groups in Finland and Canada, that things actually can work this way—that an increased duration of "postmenopausal" life in women can positively affect the reproductive success of their children.

SO FAR . . .

1. While they are in development, the reproductive cells a woman produces are known as _____ and are produced in the organs called _____.

2. Every 28 days, on average, one of these reproductive cells is released in the process called _____ and then begins a journey down one of the woman's _____.

3. Menstruation, the release of blood and a portion of the uterine tissue called the _____, occurs when there has been no _____ during the reproductive cycle.

33.3 The Male Reproductive System

Switching now to males, if you look at **Figure 33.7,** you can see another view of the male reproductive system. Here you see the large-scale structures of the system. There is the **testis,** in which sperm begin development; the **epididymis,** the tubule in which sperm mature and are stored; and the **vas deferens,** the tube through which sperm move in the process of ejaculation. (All three of these structures exist in pairs, although the second member of each pair is not visible in the figure.) Then there is the single **urethra,** the tube each vas deferens empties into and through which sperm leave the male body. There are also several accessory glands whose contributions are added to sperm as it proceeds: the seminal vesicles, the prostate gland, and the bulbourethral glands. (The seminal vesicles and bulbourethral glands also exist in pairs.)

Structure of the Testes

The testes are surrounded by a muscle whose contractions help to regulate the temperature of the sperm inside. Sperm development requires temperatures somewhat cooler than those found in the rest of the body, which is why the testes are *external* to the body's torso. Sperm cannot develop in temperatures that are too cold, however. Thus, when a male steps into, say, a cold swimming pool, the muscle surrounding the testes will contract, drawing the testes up closer to the torso—and warming the sperm.

Figure 33.7a shows that the testes are divided into a small series of lobes, and that within each lobe there are a number of highly convoluted tubes, the **seminiferous tubules:** structures that are the sites of initial sperm development in men. If you now look at a single seminiferous tubule in cross section, in Figure 33.7b, you'll see how this development proceeds: from the outside of each tubule—where sperm precursors are in their *least*-developed state—toward the interior

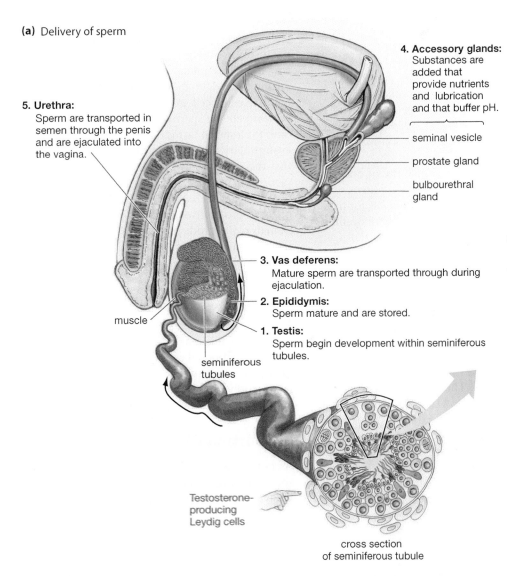

(a) Delivery of sperm

5. Urethra:
Sperm are transported in semen through the penis and are ejaculated into the vagina.

4. Accessory glands:
Substances are added that provide nutrients and lubrication and that buffer pH.

seminal vesicle

prostate gland

bulbourethral gland

3. Vas deferens:
Mature sperm are transported through during ejaculation.

2. Epididymis:
Sperm mature and are stored.

1. Testis:
Sperm begin development within seminiferous tubules.

muscle

seminiferous tubules

Testosterone-producing Leydig cells

cross section of seminiferous tubule

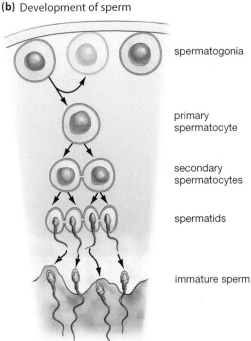

(b) Development of sperm

spermatogonia

primary spermatocyte

secondary spermatocytes

spermatids

immature sperm

Figure 33.7 Delivery and Development of Sperm
(a) How sperm are delivered.
(b) How sperm mature.

cavity of each tubule, where sperm are in a more developed, though still immature, state. Eventually, they are released into the interior cavity and are transported up it, moving then to the epididymis for further processing and storage. As you can see, there is an assembly-line quality to sperm production, starting with initial development at the periphery of the tubules, continuing in the interior of the tubules, and ending with storage in the epididymis. Older sperm that are not ejaculated are destroyed (by other cells) or eliminated in the urine. Inside the testes, surrounding the seminiferous tubules, there exist numerous *Leydig cells,* which are the cells that produce testosterone.

Male and Female Gamete Production Compared

The production of sperm bears an interesting comparison with the development of eggs. The cells from which sperm develop are called **spermatocytes.** In going back to the precursors of *these* cells, however, we see a significant difference between males and females. The cells that give rise to spermatocytes are the stem cells called **spermatogonia;** they exist at the periphery of the seminiferous tubules, and through normal cell division, they actually lead to two kinds of cells. One is the primary spermatocyte, which goes on to develop into a sperm; the other, however, is another spermatogonium. Thus, spermatogonia are "sperm factories," if you will, that give rise not only to sperm but to more sperm factories as well. This is the reason males *keep* producing sperm throughout their lives while, as we've noted, females may have a fixed quantity of oocytes. Although male sex hormone production lessens with age and sperm decline in quality, it is possible for male reproductive capability to remain intact until death. If you look at Figure 33.7b, you can see how the male sperm progression works in the testes: from spermatogonium, through spermatocyte to spermatid, and finally to immature sperm.

Further Development of Sperm

As you can see in Figure 33.7a, the seminiferous tubules eventually feed into the epididymis, a single convoluted tubule (one for each testis) that is about 7 meters, or 23 feet, long. This structure serves as the site of storage and final sperm development and as a kind of materials recycling site for damaged sperm. By the time sperm arrive at the bottom portion of the epididymis, they are fairly mature but not yet fully mature. They won't become mobile until fluid from a type of supporting gland noted earlier—the seminal vesicles—mixes with them on ejaculation, thus supplying them with nutrients.

Time Sequence and Sperm Competition

How long does this whole process of sperm development take? About 2.5 months from the start of development to storage in the epididymis. About 200 million sperm are produced in this assembly line each day, which you may recall is about the number that are ejaculated in an average orgasm.

As noted, the watchword for oocyte selection could be "Many are called but few are chosen." How much more extreme is the selection that goes on with sperm! The number expelled with *each ejaculation* vastly exceeds the number of oocytes a woman ever has stored in her ovaries. However, only a single sperm per ejaculation will be able to fertilize an egg—assuming an egg is present in the uterine tube at the right time.

Why is there such an enormous difference between the number of sperm produced and the number that will fertilize eggs? The essential answer here seems pretty clear: Just as males often are in competition with other males to mate with females, so the sperm of males is in competition with the sperm of other males to *fertilize* female eggs. This general phenomenon of *sperm competition* goes on throughout the animal kingdom—in insects, birds, and reptiles as well as in mammals. Its root cause is that there are very few animal species in which females or males are truly monogamous. As a result, mating by itself does not guarantee offspring. If a female who is fertile over a period of several days mates with a number of males during these days, then each male's chance of fatherhood is enhanced to the degree that his sperm can outcompete the sperm of the other males. This is the basis for a sperm "arms race" that has taken place over evolutionary time. Looking at various species, we find that their sperm has gotten longer, or more "motile" (active), or has been produced in greater numbers—qualities that each evolved in various species because of the reproductive edge they provided. This is why human males produce so many sperm. You might say that sperm production in them has followed the lottery principle: The more tickets you have, the more likely you are to win.

From Vas Deferens to Ejaculation

Maturing sperm are stored in both the epididymis and the vas deferens. With sufficient sexual stimulation, ejaculation takes place through the contractions of muscles that surround the penis at its base. This contraction pushes the sperm through the urethra and out the urethral opening at the tip of the penis.

Supporting Glands

As noted, several other kinds of materials join with sperm before ejaculation to form the substance known as semen. Indeed, given the number of sperm ejaculated, it may be surprising to learn that sperm don't account for much of the volume of semen; some 95 percent of the ejaculated material comes from the accessory glands already mentioned: two seminal vesicles, the prostate gland, and two bulbourethral glands. It's helpful to think of sperm as getting "outfitted" for their travels by these glands just as they are exiting from the body. In addition to the nutrients the seminal vesicles supply, accessory glands provide alkaline and lubricating substances (which neutralize the acidic environment of the vagina and facilitate transportation).

One of these supporting glands may sound familiar. The **prostate gland** is a structure that surrounds the male urethra near the bladder and contributes a substantial amount of material to semen. Later in life, a significant percentage of men develop either enlarged prostate glands or, worse, the growth of cancerous cells in the prostate, which is to say, prostate cancer. Given that the prostate encircles the urethra— and that the urethra transmits not only semen but urine as well—you can see why a warning sign of these conditions is reduced urine flow. But with both urine and semen traveling through the urethra, how does the body make sure that one substance doesn't mix with the other? Traffic control is provided by the prostate gland. During ejaculation, a circular muscle in it contracts, thus sealing off the contents of the bladder.

SO FAR . . .

1. Sperm begin development in the _____ and continue development and are stored in the convoluted tubules called the _____.

2. The material that is ejaculated from the penis, _____, is composed of both _____ and fluids secreted by three supporting _____.

3. Males are able to remain fertile throughout their lives because the cells called spermatogonia are reproductive _____ that give rise to more of themselves and to the _____ that develop into sperm.

33.4 The Union of Sperm and Egg

To this point, we've reviewed the process by which male sperm and female egg are first created and then *positioned* so that they can come together. Now let's look at the final steps that lead to the fusion of these two cells.

When the oocyte is expelled from the ovaries, there still is no solitary oocyte in transit, but rather an oocyte surrounded by an extracellular coat that in turn is surrounded by a group of accessory cells (**Figure 33.8b**). When we look at sperm, we find that each one has a "head" that contains not only the nucleus and its vital complement of chromosomes but an outer compartment, called an **acrosome,** which contains enzymes (**Figure 33.8a**). These enzymes, which are released externally, have the ability to dissolve the bonds between the accessory cells that

(a) Structure of a sperm cell

(b) How sperm fertilizes egg

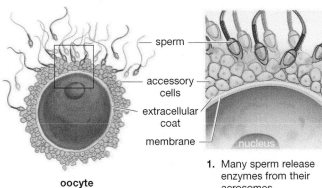

Figure 33.8
Anatomy of a Sperm and Steps in Fertilization

(a) The "head" of each sperm includes not only its complement of chromosomes but also an acrosome, which contains enzymes that, when released externally, break down the bonds between accessory cells that surround the oocyte. Behind the sperm head are the mitochondria that supply the energy for the motion of the tail that propels the sperm.

(b) The process by which a sperm fertilizes an oocyte.

1. Many sperm release enzymes from their acrosomes.

2. The enzymes dissolve bonds between accessory cells, enabling one sperm to pass through.

3. The one sperm uses its own enzymes to clear a path through the extracellular coat.

4. The sperm and oocyte membranes fuse, allowing the sperm to move inside the oocyte.

ESSAY

Methods of Contraception

Selected methods of contraception are presented here, ranked according to how effective each has been shown to be in preventing unwanted pregnancy during an initial year of use. "Typical use" refers to use as practiced by most individuals or couples. "Perfect use" refers to use in which a method is used correctly either during every instance of sexual intercourse (in the case of a method such as condoms) or over the course of consecutive months (in the case of a method such as birth control pills).

Table 33.1

Methods of Contraception

Form	Effectiveness (typical/perfect use)	Description	Works by
Birth control implant (Implanon)	**99.9**/99.9 percent	Matchstick-sized plastic rod inserted under skin of upper arm, lasts up to 3 years following implantation.	Released hormones prevent ovulation, inhibit sperm movement.
Vasectomy (male sterilization)	**99.8**/99.9 percent	Surgical procedure for producing permanent infertility, though procedure can sometimes be reversed.	Cutting of vas deferens blocks movement of sperm during ejaculation. Does not affect hormonal production, capacity for erection, or ability to ejaculate.
Tubal ligation (one method of female sterilization)	**99.5**/99.5 percent (rarely, tubes may reconnect themselves)	Surgical procedure for producing permanent infertility, though procedure can sometimes be reversed.	Cutting and tying of uterine tubes cuts off movement of unfertilized eggs through them. Does not affect feminine characteristics, hormonal production, or sexual performance.
Intrauterine device (IUD), ParaGard (copper-releasing) and Mirena (progestin-releasing)	**99.2**/99.4 percent (ParaGard) **99.8**/99.8 percent (Mirena)	T-shaped plastic device, inserted into uterus by health professional. ParaGard effective up to 10 years; Mirena effective up to 5 years.	Both block sperm movement; may also prevent implantation of embryo in uterus. ParaGard secretes small amounts of copper; Mirena secretes small amount of progestin, which suppresses ovulation.
Birth control shot (Depo-provera)	**97**/99.7 percent	Shot administered by health professional provides contraception for 12 weeks.	Progestin hormone prevents ovulation, inhibits sperm movement.

Table 33.1

(Continued)

Form	Effectiveness (typical/perfect use)	Description	Works by
Birth control patch (Ortho Evra)	92/99.7 percent	Beige patch placed on skin; new patch once per week, three weeks out of four.	Released hormones prevent ovulation, inhibit sperm movement.
Birth control pill	92/99.7 percent	Estrogen-progestin combination pills (most common) or progestin-only pills.	Released hormones prevent ovulation, inhibit sperm movement.
Birth control vaginal ring (NuvaRing)	92/99.7 percent	Flexible ring inserted into vagina by user; left in place for 3 weeks and then removed for 1 week, after which new ring is inserted.	Released hormones prevent ovulation, inhibit sperm movement.
Emergency contraception (Plan B product)	Reduces chances of pregnancy by up to **89** percent if started within 72 hours of unprotected sex.	Two pills taken after instances of unprotected sex; available over the counter to women 18 and older; rules for availability to younger women in flux.	Progestin hormone prevents ovulation; may inhibit sperm movement and implantation of embryo in uterus.
Condom	85/98 percent	Sheath that covers erect penis; only contraceptive method that offers some STD protection to both partners.	Catches sperm before it can move into vagina and uterine tubes.
Diaphragm	84/94 percent When used with spermicide	Circular rubber barrier inserted by women into vagina before sex. Should be used in tandem with spermicide.	Diaphragm covers cervix, preventing sperm from reaching uterine tubes; spermicide decreases mobility of sperm.
Withdrawal	73/96 percent	Removal of penis from vagina prior to ejaculation.	Prevents ejaculated sperm from reaching uterine tubes; spermicide decreases mobility of sperm.
Spermicide	71/82 percent	Available in foams, creams, gels, vaginal suppositories, and vaginal films that are inserted into the vagina.	Physically block cervix; decrease mobility of sperm.

surround the oocyte. It takes dozens of sperm to release enough enzymes such that *one* sperm can move
between the accessory cells and arrive at the external
coat that is the last barrier between sperm and
oocyte.

When this sperm makes contact with the coat, it
binds with receptors on it, an event that triggers the
release of this sperm's own complement of digestive
enzymes. These enzymes clear a path through the coat
that the sperm moves through. With this, the sperm
reaches the oocyte, at which point the outer membranes
of sperm and oocyte fuse—the two membranes become one, much as two soap bubbles might become
one when they come into contact. With this, the contents of the sperm cell move inside the oocyte, which
means that the two cells have effectively become one.
Once this happens, the nuclei of oocyte and sperm
combine, the oocyte at last becomes an egg, and fertilization is complete.

How Latecomers Are Kept Out

But what of the other dozens of sperm surrounding
the oocyte? None of them can be allowed entry because an embryo could not survive getting two sets of
male chromosomes but only one set of female chromosomes. To guard against this possibility, a kind of
gate-slamming process is put into motion. The fusion
of the first sperm with the oocyte causes the oocyte
to release thousands of tiny granules into the space
just outside itself. These granules release substances
that harden the membrane immediately outside the
oocyte while inactivating the sperm receptors on it.
The result is that, with rare exceptions, only one
sperm gets in. (The sexual activity that is so important to human reproduction also carries with it the
risk of sexually transmitted disease, which you can
read about in the essay on page 648.)

33.5 Human Development Prior to Birth

Having seen how sperm and egg form and get together, you have reached a point in human reproduction that should be familiar: *development*, meaning
the process by which a fertilized egg is transformed,
step-by-step, into a functioning organism. As you'll
see, processes you looked at in Chapter 32 in connection with frogs and flies have counterparts in human
development. What may be surprising is how *early*
in human development many of the critical events of
development occur. Here is a list of some of the key
developmental processes discussed in Chapter 32:

- Formation of the blastula, or hollow body of
  cells (called a *blastocyst* in humans and other
  mammals)

- Gastrulation, in which the three primary layers of
  cells are formed
- Formation of the neural tube (which gives rise to
  the brain and nervous system)
- Organogenesis, in which the organs of the body
  start to take shape

Now, keeping in mind that a human pregnancy
lasts an average of 38 weeks, consider the time line for
these major developmental events. Blastocyst formation begins 4 or 5 days after conception; gastrulation
begins 16 days after conception; neural tube formation
begins in the third week after conception; and organogenesis begins in the fourth week. By the end of 12
weeks, immature versions of all the major organ systems have formed. To place some of these events in the
context of what the mother experiences, organogenesis is occurring about the time the first menstrual period is missed, and formation of the immature organ
systems is being completed at about the same 12-week
point at which morning sickness generally ends.

The embryo's development over time can be con-
trasted with its *growth* over time. By the end of the third
week—after blastocyst formation and gastrulation—
a human embryo is perhaps 2 millimeters (or less than
a tenth of an inch) in diameter. Skip to the twelfth week
after conception, when major portions of organogenesis are concluding, and the fetus may still be only about
9 centimeters, or a little over 3.5 inches, in length.

The message here is that development is concentrated early in pregnancy, while the simple growth of
what *has* developed comes later. So pronounced are
the changes during development that biologists use
different terms for the growing organism over time.
The original cell—the fertilized egg—is a **zygote.**
In humans, about 30 hours after the zygote is formed, it
undergoes its first cell division; at this point, the developing organism is referred to as an **embryo,** a name
that will be applied to it through the eighth week of
development. From the ninth week of development to
birth, the organism is referred to as a **fetus.** The typical 9-month pregnancy is divided into periods of
roughly 3 months each, called **trimesters.** The first
trimester ends at about the time organogenesis does.

Early Development

You saw earlier that the zygote/embryo moves from
ovary to uterus during the first 4 days after fertilization. It arrives in the uterus on about day 4 as the
morula, or tightly packed ball of cells noted in
Chapter 32 (see Figure 32.1, page 620). Over the next
2 days, the morula becomes the blastocyst, which
implants itself in the endometrial lining. Actually,
this "implantation" is more like an invasion. The
blastocyst carves out a cavity for itself by releasing
enzymes that effectively digest endometrial cells
(**Figure 33.9**). Implantation normally occurs in the

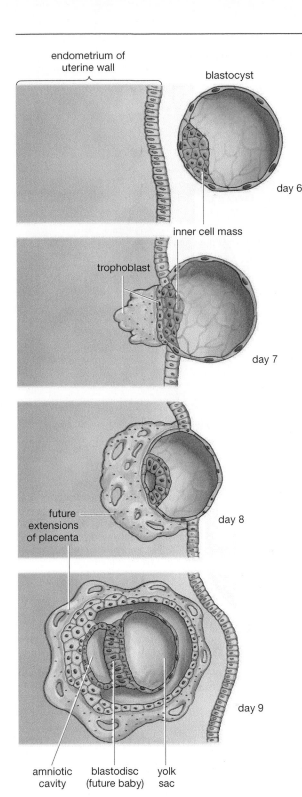

endometrium of
uterine wall

blastocyst

day 6

inner cell mass

trophoblast

day 7

future
extensions
of placenta

day 8

amniotic
cavity

blastodisc
(future baby)

yolk
sac

day 9

Figure 33.9
Implantation of the Embryo in the Uterus
Six days after conception, the embryo, now in the
blastocyst stage of development, arrives at the uterine
wall. It is composed of both an inner cell mass, which
develops into the baby, and a group of cells called a
trophoblast, which carves out a cavity for the embryo
in the uterine wall and then begins establishing physical
links with the maternal tissue. The outgrowth of this
linkage is the placenta.

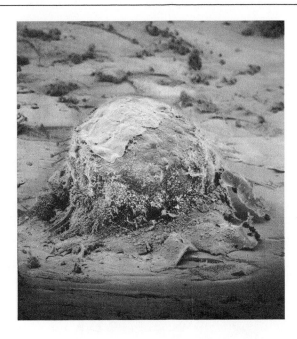

Figure 33.10
Implantation Accomplished
Twelve days after conception, the embryo is firmly implanted in the uterine wall.

dorsal wall of the uterus (**Figure 33.10**). Occasionally, however, a blastocyst attaches itself inside the uterine tube, or sometimes to the **cervix,** which is the lower part of the uterus that opens onto the vagina. This is an **ectopic pregnancy:** a pregnancy in which the embryo has implanted in a location other than the uterine wall. An embryo will almost never survive such an implantation.

Two Parts to the Blastocyst

Figure 33.9 shows you the arrangement of cells in the blastocyst. On one side, you can see a group of cells called the **inner cell mass:** the portion of the blastocyst that develops into the baby. The periphery of the blastocyst, however, is formed by cells called the **trophoblast.** These are the cells that etch their way into the uterine wall; with implantation, they begin extending farther into the endometrium, establishing indirect links with the maternal blood supply. In time, these cells grow into the fetal portion of a well-known structure in pregnancy, the **placenta:** a network of maternal and embryonic blood vessels and membranes that allows nutrients and oxygen to diffuse *to* the embryo (from the mother), while allowing carbon dioxide and other wastes to diffuse *from* the embryo (into the maternal bloodstream). See **Figure 33.11** on the next page for a look at how the placenta functions within a uterine environment as it exists at about nine weeks.

The tissue that links the fetus with the placenta is the **umbilical cord,** which houses fetal blood vessels that move blood between the fetus and the placenta. So pressing is the embryo's need for nutrients and waste removal that its circulatory system, which includes the umbilical cord, becomes functional before any other organ system.

(a) Nutrient and gas exchange in the placenta

(b) The placenta in context

maternal vein maternal artery maternal blood pools fetal vein fetal arteries

placenta

9-week fetus

yolk sac

umbilical cord

uterus

endometrium of uterine wall

cervix

mother ← | → fetus

Figure 33.11
Nutrient and Gas Exchange in the Placenta

(a) Oxygen- and nutrient-rich blood comes from the mother through the maternal arteries and moves, through smaller arterial vessels, into the maternal blood pools in the placenta. Oxygen-poor blood from the embryo, transported through the umbilical cord's fetal arteries, does not flow into the maternal blood pools but instead stays within the fetal blood vessels, which project into the maternal blood pools. Oxygen and nutrients in the maternal blood pools move into the fetal blood vessels, however, through the process of diffusion. The resulting oxygen- and nutrient-rich blood is carried back to the embryo through the umbilical cord's fetal vein. Meanwhile, carbon dioxide from the embryo moves the other way—into the maternal blood pools—to be carried away through maternal veins.

(b) Larger structure of the placenta and uterine environment at about 9 weeks.

The Origins of Twins

Having learned a little about fetal development, you're now in a position to understand something about how twins come about. Identical twins can develop at any time in the very early stages in pregnancy—from the time the zygote undergoes its first division through the seventh day after fertilization. In all cases, identical twins result from two *parts* of the embryo developing into separate human beings. This may be a matter of the two cells produced by the zygote's first division each developing as separate embryos, or it may entail the inner cell mass of the blastocyst separating into two masses, with each then giving rise to a different person.

In contrast, **fraternal twins** (or triplets, and so on) are twins who are produced first through multiple ovulations in the mother, followed by multiple fertilizations from separate sperm of the father, and then multiple implantations of the resulting embryos in the uterus. This means that fraternal twins are like any other pair of siblings except that they happen to develop at the *same time*. Meanwhile, **identical twins** are twins who develop from a single zygote. Strictly speaking, they are a single organism at one point in their development and as such have the same genetic makeup.

Development through the Trimesters

If you look at the series of pictures and diagrams that make up **Figure 33.12**, you can see how an embryo and then fetus develop at selected points in the 38 weeks of pregnancy. Here's an overview of what happens over time during the three trimesters of a pregnancy.

First Trimester

As noted, blastocyst formation, gastrulation, and neural tube development all take place within the first month of conception; but much more happens during this period as well. By the twenty-fifth day, a primitive heart has formed in the human embryo and has

(a) Embryo Development:

Vertical lines show embryo's actual size; measurements are head-to-rump lengths

0.1 inch

0.2

0.3

0.5

0.7

1.2

3 weeks	4 weeks	5 weeks	6 weeks	7 weeks	8 weeks
Gastrulation and neural tube formation.	Heart beats. Arm buds, tail, and gill grooves form. Somites form.	Eye development begins. Leg buds form. Brain enlarges.	Fingers and external ears form. Tail and gills disappearing.	Toes form. Bones begin to harden. Eyelids form.	Arms bend at elbows. Genitals begin to develop.

(b) Fetus Development:

3.5 inches

7.5 inches

10.5 inches

13.5 inches

3 months	5 months	7 months	9 months
Well-defined neck appears. Genital formation complete. Sucking reflex appears.	All major organs have been formed. Head and body hair appear. Movements felt by mother.	Lungs and lung circulation develop. Eyelids open. Fat deposited under skin. May be viable if born.	Fetus usually viable if born. Body hair lost, head hair well developed. Most senses are well developed.

(c)

Figure 33.12
Development through the Trimesters

(a) Development of the human embryo (3 weeks to 8 weeks).

(b) Development of the human fetus (3 months to 9 months).

(c) Photos of a human embryo at 6 weeks (left), 11 weeks (middle), and 5 months (right).

6 weeks

11 weeks

5 months

ESSAY

Sexually Transmitted Disease

Given the necessity of sex for the continuation of human life, it may seem surprising that so much risk can be associated with it, but such is the case. The root of the problem is that microorganisms that literally couldn't stand the light of day—that is, that couldn't exist for long in an exterior environment—are quite well adapted to life inside human tissue. More important, these microbes can be transmitted from one human being to another during the act of sex.

The risk of sexually transmitted diseases (STDs) varies in accordance with lots of things: the disease itself, the type of sexual activity a person engages in, and the precautions that are taken to avoid trouble. But one rule that holds true for all STDs and all behaviors is that as the number of partners goes up, so does risk. Here are the most common STDs, their incidence in the United States, and the methods of treatment for them.

Table 33.2

Sexually Transmitted Disease

Disease	Caused by	Possible consequences	New cases in the United States each year	Treatment
Chlamydia	*Chlamydia trachomatis* bacterium	Spread to uterine tubes in women, causing pelvic inflammatory disease (PID), which can lead to sterility.	2.8 million	Curable with timely use of antibiotics.
Gonorrhea	*Neisseria gonorrhoeae* bacterium	Arthritis, pelvic inflammatory disease.	716,000	Curable with timely use of antibiotics though antibiotic-resistant strains now exist.
Syphilis	*Treponema pallidum* bacterium	Heart, nervous system, bone damage if allowed to progress.	11,500	Curable with timely use of antibiotics though antibiotic-resistant strains now exist.
Genital herpes	Herpes simplex virus	Recurrent skin lesions, eye damage, pregnancy complications.	1 million	Occurrence and severity of outbreaks can be lessened with treatment, but no cure exists.
Genital warts	Human papilloma virus	Cervical infection in women, association with increased risk of cervical cancer and penile cancer.	6.2 million HPV infections	Topical treatments exist for warts, but will not eliminate infection; Gardasil vaccine approved in 2006 for females aged 11–26.
AIDS	Human immuno-deficiency virus (HIV)	Death, dementia, injury from a variety of opportunistic infections.	56,000 new infections; 1 million persons living with HIV	No cure; treatments to reduce symptoms exist.

begun pumping blood; the somites or repeating segments you read about in Chapter 32 have begun to take shape for muscular and skeletal formation.

Second Trimester

The fetus lengthens considerably during this period, but most of its weight gain takes place in the third trimester. Midway through a pregnancy, a fetus has achieved about half of its birth length (which is about 50 centimeters, or 20 inches, on average), but only about 15 percent of its birth weight (which averages 3.3 kilograms, or 7.3 pounds).

The heartbeat of a fetus can be heard through a stethoscope during the second trimester, and the mother can feel the baby begin kicking by the end of the fourth month. Kicking is only one of several

Figure 33.13
Tough Going Early On
A pediatric nurse attends to a premature baby. The incubators such infants are kept in provide them with optimal temperature, humidity, and oxygen levels.

movements the fetus is capable of at this point; others include facial movements and the sucking reflex.

Third Trimester

Along with the terrific growth that takes place during the third trimester, fetuses are running through a series of activities that can be thought of as practice for life outside the uterus (or womb). The fetus is surrounded by a protective and nutritive fluid in the uterus, the **amniotic fluid,** which fills its lungs. It therefore doesn't breathe, but it periodically exercises its breathing muscles by using them to move amniotic fluid in and out of the lungs.

Premature Babies and Lung Function

The end of the second trimester and the start of the third also mark the critical period for a baby being able to survive outside the uterus. Clinically, any baby born before 37 weeks of gestation is defined as premature, but many babies born between 35 and 37 weeks after conception require little special care. The more premature a baby is, however, the greater its risk of having difficulties with physical and cognitive development, at least for the first few years of life. In very premature babies, survival itself is called into question (**Figure 33.13**).

A critical factor in determining whether a premature baby can live outside the uterus is lung function. As it turns out, the respiratory system is the last one to develop in a fetus. Working against the survival of very early "preemies" is the fact that, when they exhale, the alveoli or air sacs in their lungs tend to collapse and then stick together, after which they can be reopened only with great effort. Why doesn't this happen with the lungs of a full-term 38-week fetus? Because, beginning late in pregnancy, fetuses begin synthesizing a lung surfactant—a soap-like fatty substance that keeps lung sacs from collapsing. Babies born before the twenty-sixth week of pregnancy must undergo intensive lung therapy to survive because they have not produced much lung surfactant up to this point. Usually, their therapy includes the administration of a manufactured surfactant.

33.6 The Birth of the Baby

As the fetus grows, the uterus becomes an increasingly cramped place, and fetal movements become more restricted. In late pregnancy, the fetal head normally will lodge near the base of the mother's spine (**Figure 33.14** on the next page). In this "upside-down" position, the fetus is ready to make its entrance into the world. What triggers this journey? The immediate cause is **labor:** the regular contractions of uterine muscles that sweep over the fetus from its legs to its head. The pressure this generates opens or "dilates" the cervix (ultimately to approximately 10 centimeters, or about 4 inches). This creates an opening large enough for the baby to pass through. These things must occur in stages, however. The first phase of the uterine contractions is given over to cervical dilation; then comes the expulsion of the baby, and finally expulsion of the placenta (also called the *afterbirth*, for obvious reasons).

(a) Fetus's position prior to birth

placenta
uterus
umbilical cord
bladder
pubic bone
cervix
vagina
rectum

(b) Movement through birth canal

(c) Structure of "afterbirth"

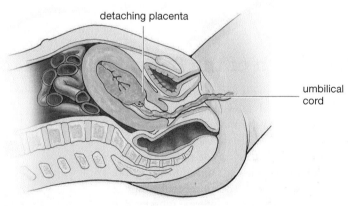

detaching placenta
umbilical cord

Figure 33.14
Birth of the Baby
With uterine contractions, the cervix dilates, allowing room for the baby to pass through the birth canal and to the outside world. The placenta and its associated fluids and tissues are expelled shortly afterward as the "afterbirth."

But what sets this train of events into motion in the first place? Put another way, what is the trigger that initiates labor? Despite a great deal of research on this question, we don't know. One hypothesis is that, as the fetus grows larger, it reaches the point at which even the highly efficient placental system can no longer supply it with enough nutrients. As a result, it secretes hormones that break down nutrients for increased energy, and this secretion triggers a hormonal cascade that brings on labor.

What happens if 38 weeks have passed and labor still doesn't begin? After a period of watching and waiting, a physician may recommend inducing labor through use of a synthetic form of the hormone oxytocin. From Chapter 28, recall that when labor begins naturally, it is accelerated by oxytocin that is released from the mother's pituitary gland. (This oxytocin brings about muscle contractions that push the fetus down further into the uterus, and this pushing brings about the production of more oxytocin.) When a baby is overdue, synthetic oxytocin can help get labor started.

On to Ecology

In this chapter and the seven that preceded it, you followed the workings of the cells and tissues that allow animals to function in their marvelously diverse ways. But animals—and for that matter all the other varieties of living things—are not self-contained units. Rather, they are constantly *interacting* with each other and with the nonliving world around them. In the next three chapters, you'll be looking at life at the level of this integrated web. What you will be studying is ecology.

SO FAR. . .

1. The number of sperm that can fuse with an oocyte is limited to _____. This is vital in order to make sure that a fertilized egg has a balanced number of _____ from the father and the mother.

2. With the implantation of the fertilized egg in the wall of the _____, cells in the egg grow into the fetal portion of a network of blood vessels and membranes that support the fetus. This is the _____.

3. Labor can be defined as regular _____ of uterine _____ that help bring about the birth of the baby.

Go to the Study Area at www.masteringbiology.com for practice quizzes, myeBook, BioFlix™ 3-D animations, MP3 Tutor Sessions, videos, current events, and more.

Mastering
BIOLOGY

CHAPTER 33 REVIEW

Summary

33.1 Overview of Human Reproduction and Development

- Human male and female reproductive systems produce their respective gametes (sperm and eggs) and then deliver them to a place where they can fuse, in the moment of fertilization. (p. 631)

- The precursors to eggs, called oocytes, exist in the ovaries, which lie just left and right of center in the female pelvic area. Oocytes mature within nurturing complexes of cells and fluids called follicles. On average, once every 28 days, one follicle-oocyte complex is brought to a state of maturity. The oocyte and some of its accessory cells then rupture from the follicle and ovary and begin a journey through the uterine tube to the uterus. Conception can occur if the oocyte encounters a sperm on the way to the uterus. (p. 631)

- Sperm are produced in the male testes and then develop further in a structure called the epididymis. With sexual stimulation, they move through two types of ducts, the vas deferens and the urethra, after which they are ejaculated from the penis into the female vagina. Materials secreted by three separate sets of glands will join with the sperm before ejaculation. The resulting mixture of sperm and glandular materials is called semen. The first of the sperm to reach the oocyte moving through the uterine tube may fertilize it. (p. 631)

33.2 The Female Reproductive System

- A portion of the female reproductive system is built up and then dismantled in a reproductive cycle that takes approximately 28 days. The result of the dismantling is menstruation, a release of blood and the specialized tissue it infuses, the endometrium, which lines the uterus and which is tissue that an embryo implants itself in if pregnancy occurs. (p. 633)

- The basic unit of oocyte development is the ovarian follicle, a complex that includes the oocyte that develops into an egg and its surrounding accessory cells and fluids. (p. 634)

- On average, a single follicle each month will develop into a tertiary follicle that ruptures, expelling the oocyte and its accessory cells from the ovary. This complex of cells then begins a journey through the uterine tube to the uterus. The ruptured tertiary follicle develops into the corpus luteum, which secretes hormones that prepare the reproductive tract for pregnancy and that maintain it during the early phases of pregnancy. (p. 634)

- The number of follicles a woman possesses decreases throughout her lifetime. The scarcity of follicles a woman has in middle age is the primary factor that brings about menopause. Recent research has called into question the long-standing assumption that women lack reproductive stem cells. (p. 635)

33.3 The Male Reproductive System

- Sperm begin development in the testes and continue development and are stored in the adjacent epididymis. Sperm move from the epididymis through the vas deferens and then the urethra in ejaculation. Accessory glands contribute material to the sperm before ejaculation. (p. 639)

- Within the testes, sperm development takes place in the seminiferous tubules. Developing sperm are transported from the interior of a tubule to the epididymis for further development and storage. (p. 639)

- Sperm development in the testes begins with spermatogonia, which develop into spermatocytes and then into immature sperm. In cell division, spermatogonia give rise not only to spermatocytes but to more spermatogonia. This self-generation of sperm precursors is the reason men keep producing sperm throughout their lifetimes. (p. 640)

- A human male produces about 200 million sperm each day—about the number of sperm ejaculated with each orgasm. Males produce such a huge number of sperm because of the sperm competition that has taken place over evolutionary time. (p. 640)

- Materials secreted by the seminal vesicles, the prostate gland, and the bulbourethral glands make up 95 percent of semen that is ejaculated; sperm makes up the other 5 percent. (p. 640)

33.4 The Union of Sperm and Egg

- An unfertilized oocyte moving through the uterine tube is surrounded by an external coat that, in turn, is surrounded by a group of accessory cells. Each sperm has an outer compartment, called an acrosome, that can release enzymes capable of dissolving the bonds between the oocyte's accessory cells. Enzymes released by dozens of sperm allow a single sperm to move between the accessory cells and reach the oocyte's external coat. This single sperm binds with receptors on the coat and releases its own complement of enzymes, which clear a path through the coat that the sperm moves through to fuse with the egg. (p. 641)

- Fusion of the sperm and oocyte brings about release of substances from the oocyte that block the entry of any other sperm. (p. 644)

33.5 Human Development Prior to Birth

- Human development proceeds through formation of the blastocyst, gastrulation, formation of the neural tube, and organogenesis. Many of the most important stages in development are completed by the end of 12 weeks of pregnancy. The developing organism is called a zygote at conception, an embryo from the zygote's first division through the eighth week of pregnancy, and a fetus from the ninth week of pregnancy to birth. (p. 644)

- The blastocyst implants itself in the endometrial lining of the uterus during the first week of pregnancy. It consists initially of an inner cell mass, which develops into the baby, and a peripheral group of cells called a trophoblast, which grows into the placenta. (p. 644)

33.6 The Birth of the Baby

- The immediate cause of birth is labor. The pressure that results from uterine contractions dilates the cervix, creating an opening large enough for the baby to fit through. It is not clear what the triggering mechanism is for the initiation of labor. When labor does not begin naturally following a full-term 38-week pregnancy, it can be chemically induced. (p. 649)

Key Terms

acrosome 641

amniotic fluid 649

cervix 645

corpus luteum 635

ectopic pregnancy 645

embryo 644

endometrium 633

epididymis 639

estrogen 636

fetus 644

follicle 631

follicle-stimulating hormone (FSH) 636

fraternal twin 646

gonadotropin-releasing hormone 636

identical twin 646

inner cell mass 645

labor 649

luteinizing hormone (LH) 636

menopause 638

menstruation 633

oocyte 634

ovarian follicle 634

ovulation 631

placenta 645

prostate gland 641

semen 632

seminiferous tubule 639

spermatocyte 640

spermatogonia 640

testis 639

trimester 644

trophoblast 645

umbilical cord 645

urethra 639

uterine tube 631

vas deferens 639

zygote 644

Understanding the Basics

Multiple-Choice Questions

(Answers are in the back of the book.)

1. The precursors of the eggs produced by females are (select all that apply):
   a. released from ovaries.
   b. released at the rate of about six per month.
   c. called oocytes.
   d. surrounded by fluids and accessory cells.
   e. put into blood circulation.

2. The structure in which sperm are stored and complete their maturation is the:
   a. epididymis.
   b. oviduct.
   c. penis.
   d. prostate gland.
   e. vas deferens.

3. The tertiary follicle (select all that apply):
   a. contains a maturing spermatocyte.
   b. contains a maturing oocyte.
   c. is transformed into the corpus luteum.
   d. is washed away with the endometrial lining.
   e. expels an oocyte in ovulation.

4. Associate each term on the left with a description on the right.
   a. acrosome — produces fluid found in semen
   b. spermatogonium — enzyme-containing compartment in sperm
   c. spermatocyte — sperm stem cell
   d. prostate gland — duct through which sperm are ejaculated
   e. urethra — maturing sperm cell

5. The natural degeneration of follicles during a woman's lifetime is referred to as:
   a. menopause.
   b. ovulation.
   c. puberty.
   d. atresia.
   e. apoptosis.

6. The portion of the blastocyst called the trophoblast eventually helps form the:
   a. head of the baby.
   b. legs of the baby.
   c. entire baby.
   d. nervous system of the baby.
   e. placenta.

7. Birth of identical twins results from unusual events during:
   a. egg production.
   b. sperm production.
   c. early cell divisions after fertilization.
   d. ovulation.
   e. second trimester.

8. Arrange the following events in their proper sequence:
   a. uterine muscle contractions
   b. birth of baby
   c. assumption of fetal head-down position
   d. expulsion of placenta
   e. dilation of cervix

Brief Review

(Answers are in the back of the book.)

1. Describe the hormonal changes that regulate the female reproductive cycle.

2. How do the testes act to protect developing sperm?

3. Menstruation is costly to females in some ways. Why do scientists believe it occurs?

4. Compare and contrast the tertiary follicle and the corpus luteum.

5. Describe the mechanism that ensures that only one sperm will be able to fuse with a given oocyte.

6. Outline the events in human development that occur up through the time the embryo implants in the uterine wall.

7. Define the term *premature* with respect to human development.

8. How do birth control pills work?

Applying Your Knowledge

1. When a couple is having trouble conceiving a child, the first thing fertility specialists generally will look at is the fertility of the prospective father. What do you think a specialist would be looking for?

2. Most mammals are "placental," which is to say their embryos get nourishment within the mother through the placental system of blood vessels reviewed in the text. By contrast, amphibian and reptilian embryos are nourished by substances contained in eggs the mother lays. Can you think of any advantages mammals derive from the placental means of development? Can you think of any disadvantages?

3. Forty years after birth control pills for women came into widespread use, there is still no birth control pill for men. One reason for this is the basic difference between female production of an oocyte each month and the male production of sperm. Why should it be easier to suppress fertility in women than in men?

34

An Interactive Living World 1:
Populations in Ecology

Ecology is the study of how living things interact—with each other and with their physical environment. One way of studying these interactions is to focus on populations, meaning all the members of a single species living in one area.

A school of bluecheek butterfly fish (*Chaetodon semilarvatus*) photographed in the Red Sea.

South Mountain Reservation is an oasis of about 2,000 acres of parkland nestled among four suburban New Jersey towns that lie directly west of New York City. Though normally a place for hiking, walking dogs, and enjoying nature, South Mountain briefly became the site of a very different kind of activity in the winters of 2008 and 2009. Volunteer sharpshooters recruited by county government baited the parkland with food, climbed up into park trees, and then waited for white-tailed deer to come collect the food, at which point they shot the deer. In all, almost 300 deer were killed over 18 days of shooting in 2008 and 2009; meat from the animals was distributed to the poor and homeless.

This exercise in animal control was not undertaken lightly or in haste; indeed, a discussion about what to do with South Mountain's deer ran on for years prior to the shootings of 2008. One of the notable aspects of this discussion was that a prominent supporter of killing the deer was the New Jersey Audubon Society, a group normally known for its passionate defense of nature. So why would the Society end up supporting an organized killing of one of nature's creatures? Because this particular creature was threatening to make South Mountain "biologically destitute," in the words of the Society. When deer become numerous enough in a given area, the Society has noted, environmental trouble follows in a fairly predictable way. Some of the first casualties are the flowering plants and herbs that help make up the "understory" of a forest, meaning the plant life that spreads out at low levels beneath large trees. A grown white-tailed deer can consume up to 10 pounds of vegetation per day, and these animals are partial to flowering plants and herbs. Then comes the destruction of the shoots of young shrubs and trees. Large, mature trees aren't being affected, because the deer are powerless to kill them, but a forest that is losing its shoots is losing its future. This decimation of plant life then has an effect on animal life. For some birds, it's difficult to have nests at all in locations that have been heavily browsed by deer, but birds that succeed in hatching out young in these areas may still have their efforts go for nothing, the Society noted in 2005. Early in life, fledglings tend to seek out shrubby forested areas for feeding—areas that only exist far from home when deer are present in high numbers. The problem is that young birds flying long distances are easy marks for predators. As a result, the Society said, "Young birds in a heavily browsed forest are doomed."

Of course, suburban New Jersey is not the only place in the country having a problem with white-tailed deer; just ask any of the estimated 1.5 million Americans involved in car crashes with these animals each year. Why are these accidents happening with such frequency now? The answer is straightforward: The deer population in America has exploded. From a low of about half a million in the early 1900s, deer numbers rose to about 16 million in 1987 and then doubled by 2006, going to an estimated 32 million. How does such an increase come about? Here's the recipe: First, get rid of key deer predators, such as wolves, bears, and bobcats, by

In the Danger Zone

The deer population in the United States has soared in recent decades, creating numerous instances of conflict between deer and human beings.

driving them to extinction in most areas. Then build houses farther and farther out into the suburbs, on land adjacent to fields and forests. Now the deer have plenty of land to graze on (suburban lawns) that doesn't even have *human* predators on it. Then couple a growing sensibility about animal rights to a decline in hunting across the country. (Hunters are a potent force in this issue; in Wisconsin alone, they killed 452,000 deer in 2008.) The result? Deer right in your backyard, on your streets, ruining your forest preserve. You might think that the silver lining to this is that the *deer* are at least coming out of it fat and content, but this is not the case at all. An overabundance of deer in a given area produces deer that are emaciated, sick, and beset by parasites; when deer have picked an environment clean, the deer themselves will suffer along with other forms of life.

For our purposes, the story of deer in the United States drives home the message that living things do not live in isolation from one another. What happens with one species affects another. What happens with wolves affects deer, then deer affect plants, and plants affect birds. In short, all these things are part of an *interrelated* web of life. Moreover, this is a web of life that exists in a larger context yet: the *non*living world, which is to say the Earth's climate and atmospheric gases, its sea currents and volcanoes, and the energy it gets from the sun. Life doesn't exist apart from these things. Instead, it is very much conditioned by them—although, as you'll see, some of these things are in turn conditioned by life.

34.1 The Study of Ecology

In your walk through biology so far, you have made it through the molecular world (DNA, for example) and through the world of whole organisms, such as fungi and plants. Now it is time to take the last steps up; in this chapter and the two that follow, you will consider biology's largest realm of all, **ecology,** defined as the study of the interactions that living things have with each other and with their environment.

In common speech, the word *ecology* has become synonymous with the conservation of natural resources or with the "environmental movement" in all its political dimensions. Under this view, you might assume that the job of an ecologist is to help preserve the natural world. In fact, however, the job of an ecologist is to *describe* the natural world in its largest scale—to say what is, rather than what should be. Are ecologists environmentalists? Most are, but this shouldn't be surprising. We would no more expect ecologists to be indifferent to the environment than we would expect art historians to be indifferent to paintings. Moreover, there is a branch of biology,

Figure 34.1
An Ecologist on the Job
Ecologists spend a good deal of time going out into nature to study the conditions that exist in various ecosystems—however inaccessible those ecosystems may be. Here, a researcher is ascending into the canopy of a rainforest in Indonesia.

conservation biology, that is directly concerned with preserving natural resources.

But the business of ecology per se is to tell us about the large-scale interactions that go on in the natural world. This work has an important use in that it provides the information base that society can use to make decisions about the environment. Does species diversity make for healthier natural communities? How many gray whales are there in the world? How important are prairie dogs to the prairie? To answer these questions, ecologists end up working in some places you might expect—in tents near the Arctic Circle or at treetop level in tropical rain forests (**Figure 34.1**). They also work in some locations you might not expect, however, such as in offices, hunched over computers, seeing how mathematical models of global warming work out.

Path of Study

In this chapter and the next two, you'll follow a bottom-to-top approach by moving from smaller ecological units to larger ones. What are the scales of life that concern ecology? The smallest is that of the physical functioning, or physiology, of given organisms. At this level, ecologists are examining individual living things, but at all other scales they are looking at groups of organisms or species. For the ecologist, life is conceptualized as being organized into

- Populations
- Communities
- Ecosystems
- The Biosphere

From Individuals to a Population

The smallest level of group organization is a **population,** defined in Chapter 17 as all the members of a single species that live together in a specified geographic region. The North American bullfrog (*Rana catesbeiana*) is a species that can be found from southern Canada to central Florida, but all the *R. catesbeiana* in a given pond constitute a single population of this species. Of course, it's possible to define our population to be all the bullfrogs in *two* ponds, or two states, or in two countries—whatever geographic region is most useful for the question an ecologist is asking.

From Populations to a Community

Going up the scale, if you take the populations of *all* species living in a single region, you have a **community.** Often, the term *community* is used more restrictively to mean populations in a given area that potentially interact with one another.

From a Community to an Ecosystem

If you add to the community all the *non*living elements that interact with it—rainfall, chemical nutrients, soil—you have an ecosystem. More formally, an **ecosystem** is a community of organisms and the physical environment with which they interact. Ecosystems can be of various sizes; you'll be looking at a range that goes from fairly small (a single field, for example) up through the enormous ecosystems called biomes that may take up half a continent.

From Ecosystems to the Biosphere

The largest scale of life is the **biosphere,** which can be thought of as the interactive collection of all the Earth's ecosystems. Given what you've reviewed about ecosystems, this means all life on Earth and all the nonliving elements that interact with life. Sometimes, however, the term *biosphere* is used purely in a territorial sense—to mean that portion of the Earth that supports life. If you look at **Figure 34.2,** you can see a graphic representation of ecology's scales of life. We'll now begin to look at ecology through these levels of biological organization, starting small, with the population.

34.2 Populations: Size and Dynamics

So, what is it ecologists want to know about a population? Well, they need to know how to count it, how and why it is distributed over its geographical area, and how and why its size changes over time—what its *population dynamics* are, to use the term employed by ecologists.

Estimating the Size of a Population

The reason ecologists want to count the members of a given population is straightforward: Without such a count, there is no way to answer a question such as how much territory a group of cheetahs must have to flourish or how fast a population of finches recovers from a drought. (How would you know about the latter unless you could compare the population after the drought with the population before it?)

Figure 34.2
The Scales of Life that Concern Ecology
A population is made up of all the organisms of a single species that live together in a defined region—in the example shown, a population of sea lions living together off the California coast. A community is a more inclusive grouping: all the members of all species that live together in a defined region. In the example, this means not only the sea lions but giant kelp, fish, and a multitude of other species. An ecosystem includes living community members and the nonliving factors that interact with them (such as the tides and wind currents that affect the California coast). The biosphere is then the interactive collection of all the Earth's ecosystems.

organism
(sea lion)

population
(colony)

community
(giant kelp forest)

ecosystem
(Southern California coast)

biosphere
(Earth)

With large, immobile species such as trees, taking a census can sometimes be easy; just mark off an area and count. Things become more difficult when the area under consideration is so large that not all individuals in it can be counted, but rather must be estimated based on a population counted in a smaller, representative area. Estimating becomes more difficult yet when the individuals are numerous and mobile, as with birds. Ecologists employ various means to estimate such populations; they survey bird populations as they migrate, for example.

In some cases, the stakes for coming up with accurate counts of given populations are very high, and in these instances ecologists can spend considerable time simply devising counting techniques that hold promise of yielding meaningful numbers. To take one example, no more than 3,500 tigers are thought to remain on Earth, of which about 2,000 exist on the Indian subcontinent. For years, counts of these elusive animals (*Panthera tigris*) were developed by making plaster casts of their paw or "pug" marks, the idea being that each animal left a unique pug impression that could be identified through the casts. Experts long ago concluded, however, that human beings cannot reliably distinguish one pug mark image from another, which meant that game reserve superintendents in India had only a rough idea of how many tigers they were managing. In the face of this lack of information, ecologists took on the task of devising more accurate counting techniques and managed to come up with three of them. One is computer-driven pug mark interpretation, complete with its own software (Pugmark 1.0); a second is digital camera-trapping identification, in which pairs of remotely placed infrared cameras produce footage of the stripe patterns on tigers (which can distinguish one animal from another); and a third is genetic identification, in which DNA "fingerprints" of tigers are produced through their feces. Over the years, numerous techniques such as these have been devised to get counts of species that are elusive, endangered, or both.

Figure 34.3
Arithmetic and Exponential Growth

When the same number of objects is produced in a given interval of time—in this case, cars from a factory each day—arithmetic growth is at work. By contrast, the populations of most organisms, such as the water flea *Daphnia*, can exhibit exponential growth, at least for a time, meaning the population grows in proportion to its own size.

Growth and Decline of Populations over Time

How is it that populations *change* size? As you begin to think about this question, it's worth going over a more general concept, which is the way a population of anything might increase in number. If you look at, say, the number of cars coming off the end of a production line, there might be 1,000 on Monday, then 1,000 on Tuesday, and so forth. The important thing to note is that the number of cars produced on Tuesday is not related to the number produced on Monday. The increase in the number of cars is thus an **arithmetical increase:** Over each interval of time (a day in this case), an unvarying number of new units (cars) is added to the population.

Now contrast this with what happens to living things. In most cases, each new unit (each living thing) is capable of playing a part in giving rise to more units, which certainly is not the case with cars. Population increases for living things are thus *proportional to* the number of organisms that already exist. Thus, the increase in a population of organisms comes about through a different sort of increase, an **exponential increase,** which occurs when, over an interval of time, the number of new units added to a population is proportional to the number of units that exist. **Figure 34.3** gives an example of the difference between the two kinds of growth over a period of weeks, using cars for arithmetic growth and the tiny water flea *Daphnia* for exponential growth. Let's assume we start out at the end of day 1 with the 1,000 cars produced that day and with 1,000 water fleas existing in an optimal laboratory environment. As you can see, *Daphnia* is a relatively slow starter, but its population quickly overwhelms that of the car population—not surprising, because the *Daphnia* population doubles every 3 days.

Population Growth in the Real World

As noted, the *Daphnia* were growing in an "optimal" laboratory environment—plenty of food, habitat kept clean, no predators. Thanks to human intervention, this was a kind of paradise for water fleas, in other words. But could any population ever grow like this in the real world? In all cases, the answer is "not forever," and in most cases the answer is "not for long," but some population growths can be dramatic while they last.

In 1859, Thomas Austin released 24 wild European rabbits (*Oryctolagus cuniculus*) onto his estate in southern Australia, near Melbourne, to provide more game for sport hunting. His was not the first attempt to introduce rabbits to Australia, but it was by far the most successful—or perhaps the most fateful. Having no natural predators in Australia, this alien species spread north and west like wildfire; within 16 years, it had expanded its range through the entire latitude of

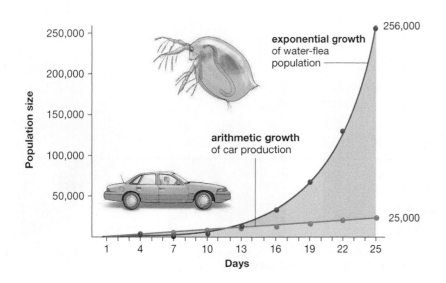

the continent, a distance of almost 1,100 miles. And this invasion was not a matter of a rabbit here and a rabbit there; the European rabbits became a scourge that, even today, has only been brought under partial control through the use of two rabbit-killing viruses. Here is Eric Rolls' description in *They All Ran Wild* of the rabbit problem east of Peterborough in South Australia in 1887:

> For over a hundred miles most trees and plants had been killed. Outalpa head-station was a thousand square miles of rabbits . . . . Rabbits crawled like possums in branches several feet off the ground. They had burrowed under the beautiful granite homestead; they had taken possession of the cellar; they were in the turkeys' coop; they ran in and out of the men's huts apparently without fear; they took no notice of the dogs nor the dogs of them.

There are lots of instances of such seemingly un-controlled growth. Charles Darwin devoted some thought to the issue as a theoretical matter. He wrote that "There is no exception to the rule that every organic being naturally increases at so high a rate, that, if not destroyed, the Earth would soon be covered by the progeny of a single pair." To put a little finer point on this, a single pair of carrion flies (which are a little larger than a housefly) could in theory give rise to enough flies in a single year to cover the state of New Jersey to a depth of 3 feet.

The Shape of Growth Curves

If you look at **Figure 34.4a**, you can see what growth of this type, **exponential growth,** looks like when plotted on a graph. This is called the *J-shaped growth curve* because it can be so extreme that when plotted it looks like the letter J. It may look familiar because it is the growth form you just saw with *Daphnia*. As with *Daphnia*, there is relatively slow growth at first, then faster growth, then faster yet. This is growth, in other words, in which the *rate* of increase keeps accelerating. In the real world, the curve eventually drops off, often sharply, for reasons we'll go over soon.

Now, look at **Figure 34.4b** to see a second model of growth for natural populations, the *S-shaped growth curve*, which tracks **logistic growth.** This starts like exponential growth, but eventually the rate of growth slows and finally ceases altogether, stabilizing at a certain level, denoted here as *K* (which you'll learn the significance of shortly).

What has intervened to account for the difference between the dizzying increase of the J-shaped curve and the moderate increase of the S-shaped curve? All the forces of the environment that act to limit population growth, which in ecology are known as **environmental resistance.** Organisms will run out of food or have their sunlight blocked; greater numbers of predators will discover the population; the wastes

Figure 34.4
Three Models of Growth for Natural Populations

(a) Exponential growth

(b) Logistic growth

Population size →

K

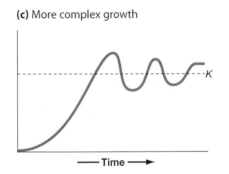

(c) More complex growth

K

← Time →

produced by the organisms will begin to be toxic to the population.

There are populations whose dynamics over time look something like either the J- or S-shaped curve, but in the real world, population size is likely to vary in more complex patterns. In **Figure 34.4c**, you can see one example of such a pattern.

Calculating Exponential Growth in a Population

You've seen that ecologists have ways to count natural populations, but is it possible for them to *predict* the size of populations given certain pieces of starting information? The answer is yes, as you'll now see. Let's look first at a simplified means of calculating exponential growth, meaning the J-shaped curve. For now, assume the population is isolated—that is, that no individuals are moving in or out of it.

What first needs to be done is to pick a time period to evaluate population change. This period may be 40 minutes (for bacterial populations) or 50 years (for elephants), but some unit of time needs to be chosen for the analysis. The next step is to learn the difference between the birth rate and the death rate in the population over the time period you've picked. This, of course, raises the question: What's a birth rate? It is

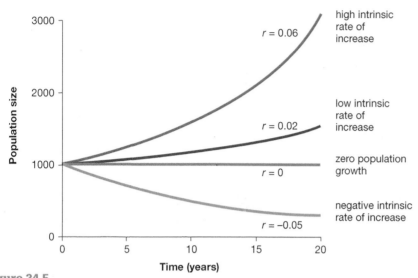

Figure 34.5

A Population's Potential for Growth: The Intrinsic Rate of Increase (r)

If the birth rate exceeds the death rate, then the population size will increase over time (r = 0.02 and 0.06 in the example). If the birth rate equals the death rate, then the population size will stay constant (r = 0). Finally, if the birth rate is lower than the death rate, the population size will decrease over time (r = −0.05). Note what dramatic effects a small change in r can have over time, in this case on a population whose starting size is 1,000 individuals.

the number of individuals born in a given time period, expressed as a proportion of the whole population. Thus, if a population of 1,000 had 100 births in a year, its birth rate would be 0.10, or 10 percent, per year. Figuring the death rate is similar; if a population of 1,000 had 80 deaths per year, its death rate would be 0.08, or 8 percent, per year.

The *difference* between these birth and death rates, of course, is 2 percent. This number is the population's growth rate in an optimal setting, denoted as r—standing for the *intrinsic rate of increase*—and it is very important. With it in hand, you can predict what the population's size will be in the future. Growing at 2 percent per year, the population of 1,000 will increase to 1,020 in the first year and to about 1,480 in 20 years.

Growth rate (r) is critical because a small change in it can mean a big change in population over time. Take a population of another species, once again with 1,000 individuals in total, but this time with an r of 6 percent rather than 2 percent. In the first year, this population would grow by 60 individuals, giving it 1,060 members as opposed to the first population's 1,020. Go 20 years out, however, and this population has about 3,200 individuals in it—it's now more than twice the size of the first population even though both were the same at the start. Meanwhile, if a population's r is less than zero—that is, if the number of deaths exceeds the number of births—the population is shrinking. If r is zero on the nose, meaning that births exactly match deaths in a given period, the population is at **zero population growth** (**Figure 34.5**).

As noted, the r figure goes by another name, which is a population's **intrinsic rate of increase:** the rate at which a population would grow if there were no external limits on its growth. You could think of it as a population's potential for growth. Importantly, populations of each species have characteristic rates of increase. It won't surprise you to learn that this rate is higher for *Daphnia* populations than it is for whale populations; you can see some examples of an important factor in rate of increase, the time it takes to produce a new generation, in **Figure 34.6**.

Logistical Growth of Populations

You've now observed exponential, or J-shaped, growth, but you've seen that such growth never occurs for long in nature, since environmental resistance will always begin to assert itself. In some instances, there will be a flattening out of the population increase and in time perhaps a complex pattern with the curve moving above and below the line denoted earlier as K. But what is K? What is this point around which the population hovers? It is the maximum population density of a given species that a defined geographical area can sustain over time. The term for this measure is an area's **carrying capacity (K).**

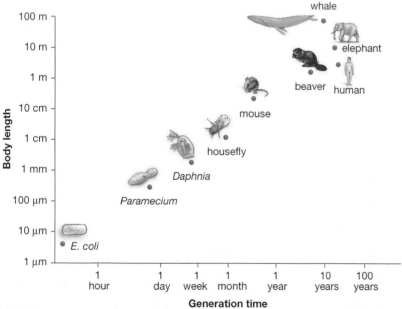

Figure 34.6

How Long between Generations?

An important factor in the population dynamics of any species is its generation time, meaning the time that elapses between the birth of one generation and the birth of the next. Shown on the graph are the minimum generation times for a few selected species, along with a measurement of the length of each organism at the time it reproduces. The larger a species is, the longer its generation time tends to be.

(Redrawn from J. T. Bonner, *Size and Cycle: An Essay on the Structure of Biology*, Princeton University Press, 1965.)

An Example of Carrying Capacity

There is an island in the San Francisco Bay called Angel Island, just a short boat ride from the Golden Gate side of the Bay, that had a small population of deer introduced to it by humans early in the twentieth century. The problem was that the island lacked any natural predators for the deer, with the result that the deer population proliferated way beyond what the island's vegetation could support. Had this taken place in a purely natural environment, the deer population would have shrunk in accordance with the amount of available vegetation. But there were human hikers on Angel Island, and seeing emaciated deer, they did what you might expect: They fed the deer with what they brought along in their backpacks. Surviving through this artificial means, however, *more* deer came to live on the island and stripped it of its vegetation, thus reducing its carrying capacity.

The main lesson here is that there are limits to how many members of a given species an expanse of territory can support. Note also, however, that carrying capacity is not fixed; in the case of Angel Island, it was lowered as the deer, artificially fed by human beings, stripped the island of vegetation. In other instances, carrying capacity might be raised for given periods (perhaps through abundant rainfall). The environments that many species live in tend to be stable over time, however, meaning that their carrying capacities will tend to be stable as well.

The K line can generally be established for a given population by estimating its numbers over an extended period of time. For many species, their population may exceed or "overshoot" K at times, but this excess will be offset by periods during which the population is under K. Once K is known, it is valuable in predicting the change in a population's size because it often serves as a factor that can be used in mathematical equations to calculate the limits to population growth. The higher a population is relative to K, the more severely its growth will be limited.

SO FAR ...

1. A _____ is all the members of a species that live together in a defined geographical region. A _____ is all the populations of all species living in a single region. An _____ is a community of organisms and the physical environment with which they interact.

2. Environmental resistance can be defined as all the forces of the environment that act to _____.

3. Carrying capacity can be defined as the maximum _____ of a given species that a defined geographical region can _____.

34.3 *r*-Selected and *K*-Selected Species

It's well known that for human beings, about 9 months will elapse between conception and birth, but it's less well known that for an elephant this same process takes almost 2 years. For any given human or elephant female, then, births are relatively few and far between. And once the offspring come, the amount of attention lavished on them is great indeed. It's not unusual for an elephant calf to be nurtured by its mother and a larger kinship group for at least the first 10 years of its life. In the first year of this period, a mother might not ever let her calf wander farther than 20 meters away from her. Meanwhile, humans may lavish 18 years of care and concern on a child before the domestic bonds are finally broken. In contrast, if we look at the common housefly, we find that it can produce a new generation once a month and that the parental generation provides no care whatsoever to the offspring.

Houseflies and elephants lie at opposite ends of a continuum of reproductive strategies, meaning characteristics that have the effect of increasing the number of fertile offspring an organism bears. So, how does the strategy of elephants differ from the strategy of houseflies? This may be apparent from what you've observed already. For elephants, the strategy is to bring forth few offspring but lavish attention on them. For houseflies, it is to bring forth a multitude of offspring but give no attention to any of them. These strategies are in turn related to other characteristics of these species, as you'll now see.

K-Selected, or Equilibrium, Species

Elephants will not seek out a totally new environment; they experience their environment as a relatively stable entity; and they compete among themselves and with other species for resources within it. Given this stability, species like elephants are known as an *equilibrium species*. In line with this, the elephant population stays relatively stable compared to a fly population; its numbers will fluctuate in a relatively narrow range above and below the environment's carrying capacity. This is another way of saying that the population regularly bumps up against carrying capacity (K), which is the density of population that a unit of living space can support. Two things follow from this. First, elephants are said to be a **K-selected species:** one whose population sizes tend to be limited by carrying capacity. The second point, which follows from this definition, is that the pressures on the elephant population are **density dependent:** As the density of the population goes up, the factors that limit the

Figure 34.7
K-Selected and
r-Selected Species

The elephants on the left are a *K*-selected species. Here, a mother stays close to her calf, providing the kind of careful attention typical of *K*-selected species. The pond flies on the right are an *r*-selected species, bearing many young but giving no attention to them after birth.

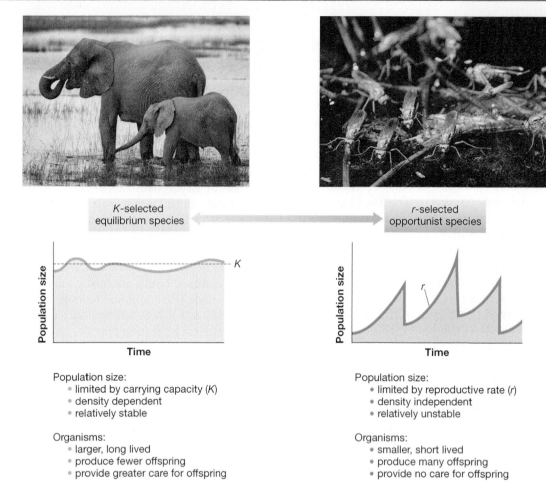

K-selected
equilibrium species

r-selected
opportunist species

Population size:
- limited by carrying capacity (*K*)
- density dependent
- relatively stable

Population size:
- limited by reproductive rate (*r*)
- density independent
- relatively unstable

Organisms:
- larger, long lived
- produce fewer offspring
- provide greater care for offspring

Organisms:
- smaller, short lived
- produce many offspring
- provide no care for offspring

BioFlix™
Population Ecology

population—food supply, living space—assert themselves ever more strongly (**Figure 34.7**).

r-Selected, or Opportunist, Species

In contrast to elephants, houseflies are known as an *opportunist species*—a species whose population size tends to fluctuate greatly in reaction to variations in its environment. Should favorable weather suddenly arrive or a food supply suddenly appear, the fly population in the area will skyrocket. When the food is gone or if the temperature suddenly changes, this same population will plunge in number. In short, environment tends to be highly variable for fly populations, and the flies have a high population growth rate that allows them to take advantage of environmental opportunities. For these animals, the strategy is to produce a multitude of offspring very fast. Flies are therefore said to be an **r-selected species,** meaning one whose population sizes tend to be limited by reproductive rate.

This definition implies that fly population numbers have nothing to do with fly population *density*, at least for a time. The pressures on the population are thus said to be **density independent.** The forces at work in these populations tend to be *physical* forces—

frost, temperature, rain—as opposed to the *biological* forces that operate in density-dependent control (competition for food, disease). Given this, the *r*-selected strategy of many offspring/little attention is understandable. When you exist at the whim of environmental forces, "life is a lottery and it makes sense simply to buy many tickets," as ecologists R. M. May and D. I. Rubinstein have phrased it.

The *r*- and *K*-selected groupings are categories invented by human beings, and as usual, nature refuses to fit neatly into such boxes. It is true that small, short-lived species tend to lie at the *r*-end of the continuum and that large, long-lived species lie at the *K*-end, but sea turtles are long-lived, and they give no care at all to their newborns. Meanwhile, flies can be limited in a density-dependent way for at least part of their population cycle—by predators and by competition among themselves. All sorts of variations exist on this theme. We've looked at animals as examples of *r*- and *K*-selection, but the concept applies to plants as well. A plant such as ragweed is at the *r*-selected extreme in the plant world, while oak trees and cacti are at the *K*-selected extreme. The ragweed grows rapidly and has a short life span, while the oak grows slowly and lives a very long time.

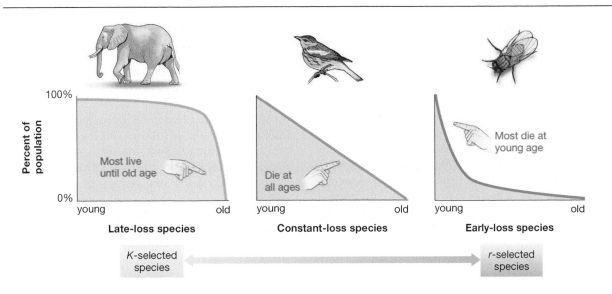

Figure 34.8
When Is Death Likely to Come?

An organism's chance of living a long life is related to the reproductive strategy of its species, as reflected in these survivorship curves. Elephants and humans (late-loss species) produce few young, but most survive until old age. At the other extreme, flies (early-loss species) produce many young, but most die young. In between are constant-loss species; they produce a moderate number of young, which die at a fairly constant rate during a typical life span.

Survivorship Curves

K- and *r*-strategies are related to the concept of "survivorship curves," which as you can see in **Figure 34.8** are thought of in terms of three ideal types: late loss, constant loss, and early loss (sometimes referred to as types I, II, and III). Humans and most of our fellow *K*-selected mammals fall into type I because we tend to survive into old age (our lives are lost late). Insects and many amphibians are type III because their death rates are very high early in life but level out thereafter. Other types of living things, such as birds, fall into type II because they die off at a constant rate through their life span.

34.4 Thinking about Human Populations

We'll look at the final elements in population dynamics in connection with human populations. Some of the concepts involved could be applied to any population of living things. But here, the focus is on human beings, so that you can consider population principles along with the real-world issue of human population growth, which figures so prominently in environmental issues.

Survivorship Curves and Life Tables

The survivorship curves you just looked at are constructed by developing what are known as **life tables** for the species in question. To create these, scientists divide the species' life span into suitable units of time—days for fruit flies, years for human beings—and see how likely it is that an average species member will be alive after a given number of days or years. The

technique for doing this was not invented by biologists who wanted to know about the survival of flies, but by a nineteenth-century British actuary—a person trained to calculate probabilities—who knew the information would be useful for life insurance companies. How likely is it that a person will be alive at 10, or 20, or 80 years of age? If you look at **Table 34.1**, you can see the answer for an average group of 100,000 persons born in the United States in the year 2004.

Table 34.1

A Life Table for the United States

At age	Number still living	Average remaining lifetime, in years
10	99,129	68.5
20	98,709	58.8
30	97,776	49.3
40	96,517	39.9
50	93,735	30.9
60	88,038	22.5
70	76,191	15.1
80	53,925	9.1
90	22,219	5.0
100	2,510	2.6

Taking a hypothetical group of 100,000 persons born in the United States in 2004, the table shows the number likely to still be living at the ages indicated and the average remaining lifetime for persons at each age. The numbers are averaged for men and women, a choice that masks significant differences between the sexes in older age cohorts. Of 100,000 women born in 2004, for example, about 61,000 are likely to be alive at age 80, whereas for men the figure is about 46,000.

Source: National Center for Health Statistics

Population Pyramids

You've seen that population growth in the natural world can be exponential (for a time) because a population of living things grows in proportion to its own size. However, all members of a population do not count equally in calculating this growth. If scientists want to peer into the future of a given population, what they want to know is: What proportion of the population is *past* the age of reproduction as opposed to the proportion that is, or will be, of reproductive age? If you look at **Figure 34.9**, you can see the answer to this question, expressed as a population pyramid for two countries in the year 2009. Each bar on the graph represents a 5-year age grouping, or "cohort" of the population (those who are 0–4 years old, 5–9, and so on), with the length of each bar representing the size of the cohort. The reproductive age range for humans generally is considered to be between 15 and 45. If you look at the graph for Kenya, you can see that it has many more individuals of reproductive and pre-reproductive age than of post-reproductive age. What does the future hold for Kenya? In all probability, a large growth in the population. In contrast, the age-structure diagram for the United States shows that a much greater proportion of its population is at or beyond reproductive age.

The World's Human Population: Finally Stabilizing

You probably noticed that there is a third graph in Figure 34.9 that displays Kenya's expected population pyramid for the year 2050. It's easy to see that this projected age distribution for Kenya looks something like the current age distribution for the United States. As a result, Kenya can look forward to slower population growth in the years after 2050. This Kenyan projection actually is just one example of a momentous shift that is going on with human population around the world today. Only in the last few years has it become clear that, following centuries of explosive growth, the human population finally appears to be stabilizing.

To put this change into a larger context, look at **Figure 34.10**, which shows you how human population has grown during "historical time," which is to say the last 12,000 years. For centuries, human numbers grew relatively little but then began an upward climb about 1700. Improved sanitation, better medical care, and increases in the food supply came together to produce the rate of growth you see. The Earth's human population didn't pass the 1-billion mark until 1804; it then took 123 years to double to 2 billion (in 1927), then 48 years to double to 4 billion

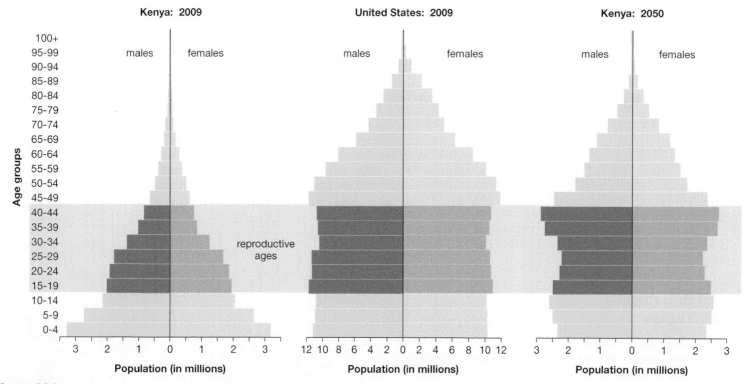

Figure 34.9

Age Structure in Populations: Kenya and the United States

Each bar on the graphs represents a 5-year age grouping of the population. Note the greater proportion of the 2009 Kenya population that is of "pre-reproductive" age—an indication of greater population increases in the future than is the case with the United States. The graph on the right shows the change expected to come about in Kenya's age structure by the middle of the century.

(Data from the U.S. Census Bureau.)

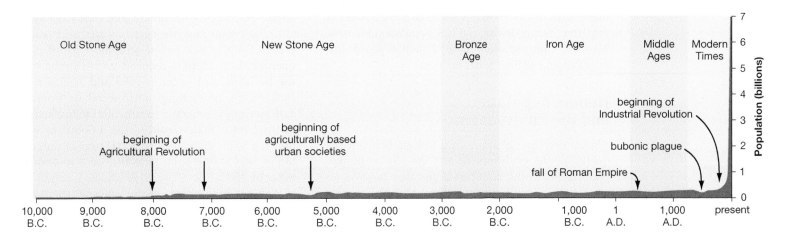

Figure 34.10
Human Population Levels through the Centuries

(in 1974), and is now projected to reach 7 billion in 2012. The curve you see that resulted from this growth may look familiar because it is a more extreme version of the J-shaped curve, although greatly elongated on its left side. Were we to see this kind of growth curve in any species other than our own, we would predict that this kind of increase could not go on for long; that environmental resistance would assert itself, and that the population might even crash in one catastrophic sense or another.

But something has changed. In 1992, demographers with the United Nations were predicting that, by 2050, the Earth would have 12 billion people on it. But in reports issued beginning in 2003, the UN predicted that the human population will be about 9.1 billion by 2050. Further, while the human population will still be growing then, its rate of increase will have dropped considerably. In the period 1990–1995, the world was adding an estimated 82 million people per year; by 2050, that figure should be down to 31 million people per year. In the longer term, it appears the human population may stabilize or even drop to some extent.

What has brought this change about? The key measurement used by demographers to predict human population change is the **total fertility rate,** which can be informally defined as the average number of children born to each woman in a population. In more developed countries, the "replacement" fertility rate is 2.1. If fertility is above 2.1, the population will grow; if it's below 2.1, the population will shrink. (Why 2.1 instead of 2.0? Some children will not live to have children of their own.)

With this in mind, look at **Figure 34.11**. Pictured are fertility levels for a selected group of countries in two periods: 1960–1965 and 2000–2005. The dramatic declines you can see are not being repeated in all countries. Indeed, in some countries fertility is dropping very little. But when all the world's countries are averaged together, we find that global fertility has been cut nearly in half over the past 50 years. Whereas it stood at 5 in the period 1950–1955, it now

stands at 2.56 (and is expected to drop to 2.02 by 2045–2050).

This global average, however, masks some tremendous differences between more-developed and less-developed countries. Think of it this way. In 2005, the world's population was increasing by 154 people per *minute*. And of these 154 additional people, 151 were born in less-developed countries. The South Asian country of Bangladesh, which is about the size of Iowa, is expected to have a population increase of more than 100 million people between 2005 and 2050. Meanwhile, in the countries of Europe, the fertility rate is now so low—at 1.6 on average—that the population is expected to decline by about 36 million people by 2050, even when immigration is factored in.

Where does the United States stand in this spectrum? In the coming decades, it is expected to have more population growth than any other large, developed country. The U.S. population is expected to go from 307 million people today to 439 million people in 2050—a 43 percent increase. What makes the United States different from the other developed countries? Partly the American fertility rate, which at 2.1 is much

Figure 34.11
Big Changes in Fertility

Pictured are female fertility rates in six countries during two periods: first during the 1960s and then for the period 2000–2005. Changes such as these have brought about a remarkable decline in the worldwide total fertility rate.

(Source: Population Reference Bureau.)

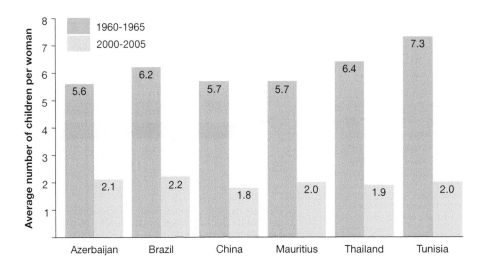

higher than that of most developed countries. Another important factor driving the U.S. population increase, however, is immigration. About 1 million people immigrate to the United States each year.

Human Population and the Environment

Almost everyone is aware of a linkage between the quality of the environment and the size of human populations. Some scientists argue that there is no greater single environmental threat than the continued growth of the human population. The basis for this conclusion is that population affects so many environmental issues: the use of limited natural resources, the amount of waste that is pumped into the environment daily, the reduction of species habitat, the decimation of species through hunting and fishing. Look at almost any environmental problem, and you are likely to find human population growth playing a part in it.

Given that the human population is still growing—but that stabilization of it is on the horizon—it's possible to see the twenty-first century as a crucial moment in time for the environment. The biologist Edward O. Wilson has characterized our century as an environmental *bottleneck*: as a period in which the Earth's ecosystems will be under the greatest assault they are ever likely to face. On the other side of the bottleneck, with human population probably stabilized, the pressures on the environment should ease. The question is: How many species and habitats can make it *through* the bottleneck? How many primate species can be preserved? How many acres of rainforest can be kept intact? How many acres of American wetlands can remain as they are?

Some experts argue that it is not population per se but rather the use of resources *per person* that is of most pressing concern. Consider that the United States used less water in 2000 than it did in 1980 even though the U.S. population grew by 24 percent during the period. What brought this reduction about? A host of government and industrial efforts aimed at promoting *efficiency* in water use. As water expert Peter Gleick has noted, the City of Albuquerque, New Mexico, reduced its per capita water use by 30 percent between 1989 and 2001 through such means as washing machine rebate programs and landscape retrofits; meanwhile, manufacturers in the United States reduced the amount of water they use to produce steel from 200 tons of water per ton of steel at one point to as little as 3 to 4 tons of water by 2003.

Another perspective on the power of per capita consumption is provided by the use of resources in more-developed, as opposed to less-developed, countries. If you look at **Figure 34.12**, you can get a sense of the differences that exist. The carbon tracked in the figure is put into the atmosphere in the form of carbon dioxide (CO_2), a gas that is a by-product of the burning of fossil fuels, such as coal or gas. The CO_2 that is produced by human activities is now regarded as the most significant cause of global warming—the rise in Earth's surface temperature that has occurred over the past century.

The Figure 34.12 graph shows the amount of carbon emitted per capita by human activity in the United States and in China in two different years, 1997 and 2006. A quick glance at the figure shows how little carbon China emitted per person in either year compared to the United States. In 2006, carbon emissions in the United States totaled more than 5 metric tons per person, while in China they came to about 1.27 tons per person. Also note, however, that China's per capita emissions grew by 76 percent between 1997 and 2006, while U.S. emissions declined slightly. To see the effects of this change, look at the graph on the right. As it shows, the carbon emissions for China as a *country* went from 59 percent of those in the United States in 1997 to 106 percent of those in the United States in 2006. What's going on in China? Very little population growth, at least in proportional terms. What is going on is development, which drives the per capita use of resources. China is industrializing at a

Figure 34.12
Per Capita and Total Carbon Emissions

The increase in China's per capita CO_2 emissions between 1997 and 2006 brought about a big change in China's total carbon emissions relative to those of the United States.

(Data from Tom Boden, Gregg Marland, and Robert J. Andres, "National CO_2 Emissions from Fossil-Fuel Burning, Cement Manufacture, and Gas Flaring: 1751–2006," Carbon Dioxide Information Analysis Center, Oak Ridge National Laboratory, Oak Ridge, Tennessee, 2009.)

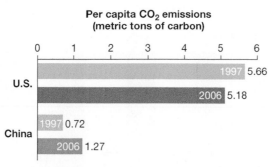

U.S. per capita CO_2 emissions far exceed those in China, but China's per capita emissions grew by 76 percent between 1997 and 2006 . . .

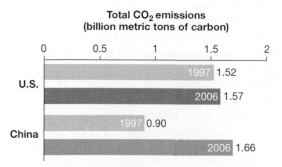

. . . When coupled with China's large population, this per capita growth meant that China's total CO_2 emissions went from 59 percent of those in U.S. in 1997 to 106 percent of those in U.S. in 2006.

rapid rate, and it is fueling its industrialization largely with coal. The CO_2 output that is resulting from this industrialization provides a clear, if depressing, lesson: When a large human population increases its per capita use of resources, the result can be big trouble for the environment.

On to Communities

The populations we've looked at this chapter have been abstractions, in a sense, in that we've thought of each of them as existing in a kind of isolation. To be sure, populations do have their own internal dynamics. In an elephant population, for example, only a few young will be born, great care will be lavished on those who are born, and so forth. Yet every elephant population is constantly interacting with populations of other species. Consider that, in the wild, an African elephant can consume up to 200 kilograms, or 440 pounds, of grasses, leaves, and roots each day. Moreover, it's not uncommon for elephants to pull down small trees as a means of getting at some of this material. So African elephant populations can have a significant negative impact on African tree populations. On the other hand, the only way the seeds of some African trees get dispersed is through elephants—*literally* through elephants, in that the seeds pass through the elephant digestive system, after which they're deposited, in elephant dung, at new sites for germination and growth. African elephants and trees thus interact in some complex ways.

When we start thinking about such interactions, we are thinking about life at the level of a community, meaning all the populations of all species that live in a defined geographical area. So, in what ways can community members interact? Beyond this, how do communities get established and then become stabilized? And are some species more important than others in preserving a community's structure? These are some of the questions we'll take up in Chapter 35.

SO FAR . . .

1. *K*-selected or equilibrium species tend to have _____ offspring to whom they provide _____ care. Conversely, *r*-selected or opportunist species tend to have _____ offspring to whom they provide _____ care.

2. A country whose population pyramid is widest at the bottom can expect to have _____ population growth in the near future than a country whose population pyramid is of uniform width throughout.

3. A country's human population changes can be predicted by looking at its total fertility rate, informally defined as the _____. The "replacement" level for fertility in more-developed countries is _____.

Go to the Study Area at www.masteringbiology.com for practice quizzes, myeBook, BioFlix™ 3-D animations, MP3 Tutor Sessions, videos, current events, and more.

Mastering
BIOLOGY

Summary

34.1 The Study of Ecology

- Ecology is the study of the interactions living things have with each other and with their environment. (p. 656)

- The five scales of life that concern ecology are physiology, populations, communities, ecosystems, and the biosphere. (p. 656)

34.2 Populations: Size and Dynamics

- To understand any population, ecologists count the number of individuals in it; various techniques are used to estimate the size of populations whose members can't be counted directly. (p. 657)

- An arithmetical increase occurs when, over a given interval of time, an unvarying number of new units is added to a population. An exponential increase occurs when the number of new units added to a population is proportional to the number of units that exists. (p. 658)

- The rapid growth that sometimes characterizes populations of living things is referred to as exponential growth or the J-shaped growth curve. Populations that initially grow, but whose growth later levels out, have experienced logistic growth, or the S-shaped growth curve. (p. 659)

- The size of populations is limited by environmental resistance, defined as all the forces that limit population growth. (p. 659)

- Exponential growth can be calculated by subtracting a population's death rate from its birth rate, which yields the population's rate of growth. Denoted as r, this rate is also known as the population's intrinsic rate of increase. (p. 659)

- Carrying capacity, denoted as K, is the maximum population density of a given species that can be sustained within a defined geographical area over an extended period of time. (p. 660)

34.3 r-Selected and K-Selected Species

- Different species have different characteristics that affect the number of fertile offspring they bear. K-selected species tend to be physically large, experience their environment as relatively stable, and lavish attention on relatively few offspring. The pressures on K-selected species tend to be density dependent, meaning that as a population's density goes up, factors that limit its growth assert themselves more strongly. (p. 661)

- r-selected species tend to be physically small, experience their environment as relatively unstable, and give little or no attention to the numerous offspring they produce. The pressures on r-selected species tend to be density independent. (p. 662)

- Survivorship curves describe how soon species members tend to die within the species' life span. Three idealized types of survivorship curves are late loss, constant loss, and early loss. (p. 663)

BioFlix™
Population Ecology

34.4 Thinking about Human Populations

- Survivorship curves are created from life tables, which set forth the probabilities of a member of a species being alive after given intervals of time. (p. 663)

- When calculating the growth of human populations, it is important to learn what proportion of the population is at or under reproductive age. (p. 664)

- The world's human population is now growing at a much slower rate than in the past because of a global decrease in the total fertility rate. The global reduction in fertility masks enormous, ongoing differ-

ences between fertility in more-developed and less-developed countries. (p. 664)

- Some scientists believe that there is no greater threat to the environment than the continued growth of the human population. Others argue that a more important concern is the use of natural resources per person. (p. 666)

Key Terms

arithmetical increase   658
biosphere   657
carrying capacity (K)   660
community   657
density dependent   661
density independent   662
ecology   656
ecosystem   657
environmental resistance   659
exponential growth   659
exponential increase   658
intrinsic rate of increase (r)   660
K-selected species   661
life table   663
logistic growth   659
population   657
r-selected species   662
total fertility rate   665
zero population growth   660

Understanding the Basics

Multiple-Choice Questions

(Answers are in the back of the book.)

1. A(n) _____ consists of all members of a single species that live in a defined geographic region, while a(n) _____ consists of the populations

of all species that live in a defined region.
a. ecosystem; community
b. ecosystem; biosphere
c. community; ecosystem
d. population; community
e. biome; ecosystem

2. A community and all the nonliving elements that interact with it (sunlight, nutrients, soil, etc.) is called
a. a population group.
b. a biosphere.
c. an ecosystem.
d. a biome.
e. a social system.

3. The largest scale of life, which can be thought of as the interaction of all of Earth's ecosystems, is called
a. the biome.
b. the ecosphere.
c. the biosphere.
d. the environment zone.
e. the ionosphere.

4. When population growth increases in proportion to the number of members of a population, _____ growth is said to have occurred.
a. density-dependent
b. density-independent
c. *K*-selected
d. arithmetical
e. exponential

5. *K*-selected species tend to (select all that apply):
a. experience their environments as unstable.
b. have stable populations.
c. have their populations limited by carrying capacity.
d. provide little care to their offspring.
e. be most affected by biological forces.

6. *r*-selected species tend to (select all that apply):
a. have their populations limited by reproductive rate.
b. experience their environments as unstable.
c. provide abundant care to their offspring.
d. have populations that are strongly affected by physical forces.
e. face density-dependent pressures on their populations.

7. The human total fertility rate (select all that apply):
a. is the average number of children born to each family in a population.
b. has been dropping worldwide in recent decades.
c. must be at about 3 for a population to be at replacement level.
d. is generally much lower in less-developed countries.
e. is higher in the United States than in most developed countries.

Brief Review

(**Answers are in the back of the book.**)

1. Name the four levels of group organization of living things in order of increasing complexity.

2. Compare and contrast *r*-selected and *K*-selected species and give an example of each. Are humans *r*-selected or *K*-selected?

3. Explain what is meant by environmental resistance and its relationship to population growth.

4. What kinds of forces tend to limit the growth of *K*-selected species?

5. Which factor has been most important in bringing about the apparent long-term stabilization of Earth's human population? Is this stabilization expected to occur soon?

Applying Your Knowledge

1. Does the concept of carrying capacity apply to human beings? Does the planet as a whole have a human carrying capacity, or do human beings have an infinite capacity to improve life through such means as obtaining greater crop yields and becoming more energy efficient?

2. Is human disease a form of environmental resistance?

3. Some scientists argue that no single factor poses a greater threat to the environment than the continued growth of the human population, while others believe the use of resources per person is a more critical factor. What arguments can you think of for or against either proposition?

An Interactive Living World 2:
Communities in Ecology

A community is all the populations of all the species living in one area. Members of different species within a community interact with each other in a variety of ways, some of them competitive, others supportive. Communities establish themselves through a long-term process called succession.

A watering hole is a natural congregation spot for members of a community in Botswana's Okavango Delta.

M ost people are aware that tropical rainforests are places of great biological diversity, but some years ago Smithsonian biologist Terry Erwin was able to attach a startling number to this diversity. While doing research in Panama, Erwin examined a single tree and found an estimated 1,700 species of beetle living in it. Not 1,700 beetles,

mind you—1,700 *species* of beetle. Of course, these beetles were only one part of a larger group of insects that were living in the tree, and the insects in turn were only one variety of animal living in it. Joining these animals were the fungi that did their best to extend their filaments into the tree's bark each day and the bacteria that lived by the billions in or on all the other organisms that inhabited the tree.

We saw last chapter that a **community** can be defined as all the populations of all the species that inhabit a defined area. This means all the plants, animals, fungi, bacteria, protists—every living thing, in other words. If we think of our tree in Panama as being a defined area, we can get a sense of the mind-boggling diversity that can exist within a single community. And yet, by examining communities from the tropics to the poles, ecologists have found that there is a standard set of questions that can be asked about any community. How diverse is it? Which species in it are dependent on which others? Which species in it are the predators and which are the prey?

If we look for a common thread among these questions, it's not hard to find: The study of communities is first and foremost the study of *relationships* among species. When ecologists ask about predators and prey in a community, it's not the species themselves they're chiefly concerned with; it's the relationships between these varieties of species that interests them. Accordingly, relationships are what we'll primarily be looking at this chapter. How do species relate to each other when living in a common area? Put another way, what makes a community tick? Let's find out.

35.1 Structure in Communities

Large Numbers of a Few Species: Ecological Dominants

If we think about the differences between a tropical rainforest, a prairie, and a desert, it's easy to see that there's a tremendous variability in the mix of species found in different communities. A common feature of many types of communities, however, is that they are dominated by only a few species. Forests tend to be populated by certain kinds of trees, stretches of prairie by certain kinds of grasses, deserts by certain kinds of shrubs or cacti. The small number of species that are abundant in a given community are called **ecological dominants** (**Figure 35.1** on the next page). These generally are plants, but they can be other life-forms, as is the case with the tiny animals known as corals that are the ecological dominants in coral reefs.

Importance beyond Numbers: Keystone Species

Ecologists have long recognized that there are also species that may not be numerous in a given area but that play a role in a community that cannot be assumed by any other community member. Each of these is a **keystone species:** a species whose absence from a community would bring about significant change in that community. The concept of the keystone species was introduced in the 1960s by marine ecologist Robert Paine, who went with his students to a shallow-water zone of the Pacific Ocean in Washington State and for 6 years regularly removed all sea stars in

Figure 35.1
Ecological Dominants

(a) A Colorado forest floor dominated by aspen trees

(b) A Kansas prairie field dominated by tallgrass

the genus *Pisaster* from a small area. Such a sea star may sound harmless enough, but *Pisaster* was, in fact, the **top predator** in the area: It preyed on other species, but no species preyed on it (**Figure 35.2**). The impact of the *Pisaster* removal was big. Before the change, there had been 15 species of marine animals in the area; after it, there were 8. One species of mussel, freed from its former predator's control, took over much of the attachment space in the area, crowding out other animals, such as barnacles.

Figure 35.2
Keystone Species

When the predatory sea star *Pisaster ochraceus* was removed from a small area of rocky shore along the Pacific coast of the United States, the species composition of the community changed drastically—more so than if one of the other species had been removed. Pictured are several *Pisaster* sea stars on the Pacific Northwest coast.

Over time, the keystone species concept has undergone some modification. Where once scientists thought of keystones as always sitting at the top of food chains, they now recognize that organisms in other positions can take on a keystone role—beavers building dams, for example, or even lichens that are critical in getting communities going in the desert. Beyond this, it turns out that there are communities without keystones; remove any one species from such a community, and its role will be taken over by another species.

Variety in Communities: What Is Biodiversity?

Apart from ecological dominants and keystones, a third element important to any community is the range of species found within it. This touches on the more general concept of biodiversity, which in the broadest sense simply means variety among living things. In everyday speech, **biodiversity** is thought of as being the same thing as species diversity—to the average person, biodiversity means a diversity *of species* in a given area. This definition of biodiversity is too limited, however. While species diversity is indeed an important type of biodiversity, it is only one of three principal types that exist. To understand the importance of a second type, consider an imaginary experiment that has been put forward by the ecologist Paul Ehrlich.

Suppose that you could get a few members of every species on Earth, but that you restricted each species to a single population housed somewhere (in a single zoo or an aquarium or botanical garden). Species diversity would not drop at all in such a scenario—you'd still have some of each kind of creature, after all—but the Earth quickly would become barren because what's needed is a rich distribution of species in populations across the planet. This geographical distribution of species populations is the second type of biodiversity.

The third type exists *within* populations of different species. It is genetic diversity, meaning a diversity of alleles or variants of genes in a population. Without such diversity, populations are vulnerable to disease; their members may die young or suffer from a variety of inherited mental and physical afflictions (see "The Price of Inbreeding" in Chapter 17, page 308). In summary, there are three principal types of biodiversity among living things: species diversity, geographic diversity, and genetic diversity (**Figure 35.3**).

The Effects of Species Diversity

In the last 10 years, two intensively researched questions in ecology have concerned species diversity. The first of these questions is: Do diverse communities tend to be more productive communities? In ecology, productivity is a measure of how much energy plants and other photosynthesizers are able to "capture" from the sun's rays and then turn into living material or "biomass." A really productive community is one that is rich with biomass—rich in leaves, seeds, and roots and the animals that feed on them. So, does a diverse community tend to be more productive than one that is not diverse? The answer seems to be yes. The reason for this may be that, in diverse communities, each community member is able to exploit a different portion of the resources available. Some plants will bloom early in a season, while others bloom late; some plants will do well with only a little water, while other plants will flourish with more. In this respect, communities may be something like Jack Sprat and his wife from the old nursery rhyme. Recall that Jack could eat no fat and that his wife could eat no lean, but that between them they licked the platter clean.

A second question about species diversity is whether it leads to greater stability in communities—to a greater ability to recover from a drought, for example, or to a greater ability to resist invasion by new species. Here again, the answer seems to be yes: more diverse communities tend to be more stable communities.

High biodiversity   **Low biodiversity**

(a) Species diversity

many different species   few species

(b) Geographic diversity

broad distribution of species   narrow distribution of species

(c) Genetic diversity

high genetic diversity within population   low genetic diversity within population

**Figure 35.3
Three Types of Biodiversity**

35.2 Types of Interaction among Community Members

Having considered some structural issues regarding communities, let's now turn to the subject of how members of a community might interact with each other. Here are four primary modes of community interaction:

- Competition
- Predation and parasitism
- Mutualism
- Commensalism

Before continuing with the exploration of these modes, let's go over a couple of concepts that will apply to them all.

Habitat and Niche

A **habitat** is the physical surroundings in which a species can normally be found. Although two populations of a species may be widely separated, they can generally be found dwelling in similar types of natural surroundings. Thus, while the bass-like fish known as groupers can be found in warm-water oceans around the world, they tend to spend their adult lives in a particular type of physical surroundings within the oceans—the coral reef. Habitats such as coral reefs are sometimes described as a species' "address," but a more accurate metaphor might be a species' preferred type of neighborhood.

The word **niche** has been defined in several ways, but it is useful to conceptualize it in terms of a simple metaphor: A niche can be thought of as an organism's occupation. How and where does the organism make a living? What does it do to obtain resources? How does it deal with competition for these resources? The horseshoe crab has found a niche walking on the bottom of shallow coastal waters, feeding on food items that range from algae to small invertebrates. Note that this is about more than what the horseshoe crab eats. It includes specific surroundings (shallow ocean waters), specific behaviors (ocean-floor crawling), and perhaps seasonal or daily feeding times, among other things. If you were to specify all the things that define a horseshoe crab's niche, the odds are that no other organism would exactly fit into it.

With these definitions of habitat and niche in mind, let's look at the ways organisms interact in communities, starting with a familiar type of interaction: competition.

SO FAR ...

1. A keystone species can be defined as any species whose _____ a community would bring about significant change in it.

2. There are three principal types of biodiversity: _____, _____, and _____.

3. A habitat is the _____ in which a species can _____, while a niche can be thought of as an organism's _____.

35.3 Interaction through Competition

Even though niches tend to be specific to given organisms, some species—particularly closely related species—have niches that *overlap* to some degree in a community. A large proportion of both species' diet may be made up of a given organism, or both species may occupy similar kinds of spaces on rocks, branches, or pond surfaces. What arises in such instances is **interspecific competition,** meaning competition between two or more species.

What may come to mind with interspecific competition is a never-ending series of physical battles between two species, but things seldom work like this. For one thing, competition tends to be indirect. It often is a competition for *resources*, in which the winner generally triumphs not by fighting, but by being

more efficient at doing something, such as acquiring food. Lots of animals, including birds and many large mammals, are territorial—meaning they will attempt to keep other creatures out of a territory they have laid claim to—but this usually is a matter of them trying to repel members of their own species.

When the niches of two species greatly overlap, it's unlikely that you'd see long-standing competition among them, for the simple reason that one species or the other is likely to win such a competition in fairly short order. Because the competition is for nothing less than vital resources, the result is that the losing species will be driven to local extinction.

It was a laboratory experiment, performed by the Russian biologist G. F. Gause in the 1930s, that pointed the way on this latter principle. Gause grew two species of *Paramecium* protists, *P. caudatum* and *P. aurelia*, in culture and found that in time, *P. aurelia* was always the sole survivor. True to what was just noted, *P. aurelia* wasn't eating or wounding *P. caudatum*; instead, it grew faster and thus used more of the surrounding resources. Nevertheless, the outcome was always the death of all the *P. caudatum*. This led Gause to formulate what came to be called the **competitive exclusion principle:** When two species compete for the same limited, vital resource, one will always outcompete the other and thus bring about the latter's local extinction (**Figure 35.4**).

Ecologists wouldn't expect to witness the competitive exclusion principle operating much in nature, however. This is because, as noted, the *Paramecium* scenario is likely to be played out quickly. Nevertheless, competitive exclusion has been observed in nature, often when humans have a hand in things. For example, humans introduced a Southeast Asian vine, the kudzu, to the American South on a large scale in the 1930s. Growing at up to 30 centimeters, or 1 foot, per day, kudzu has now taken over millions of acres in the South, locally eliminating many plants in its path in a process of competitive exclusion (**Figure 35.5**).

Resource Partitioning

Competitive exclusion notwithstanding, there are instances in nature in which two related species will use the same kinds of resources from the same habitat over a long period of time. So why isn't one of them eliminated? The answer is contained in another experiment conducted by Gause. He took the successful species from the earlier experiment, *P. aurelia*, and placed it in a test tube with a different paramecium, *P. bursaria*. This time, neither species was eliminated (see Figure 35.4b). Instead, the two species divided up the habitat, *P. aurelia* feeding in the upper part of the test tube, and *P. bursaria* flourishing in the lower part. (*P. bursaria* had an advantage in the lower, oxygen-depleted water because it has symbiotic algae that grow with it, producing oxygen.) In a nutshell, this result describes a situation that often

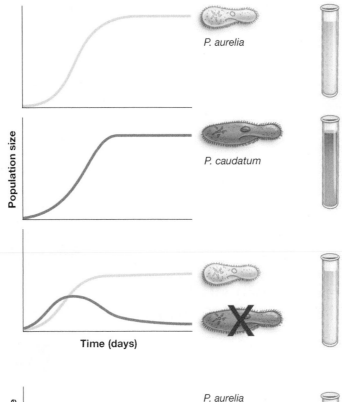

(a) Competitive exclusion

When two species compete for the same limited, vital resource, one will always drive the other to local extinction—as the paramecium *P. aurelia* did to the paramecium *P. caudatum*. This is the competitive exclusion principle at work.

P. aurelia

P. caudatum

Time (days)

(b) Resource partitioning

Conversely, when Gause put *P. aurelia* together with another paramecium, *P. bursaria*, the two species divided up the habitat, and both survived. This is a demonstration of resource partitioning.

P. aurelia

P. bursaria

Time (days)

Figure 35.4
Competition for Resources among Species

Laboratory experiments by G. F. Gause showed that competition for resources between two species can have two possible outcomes.

exists in nature: **coexistence** (meaning a sharing of habitat) through a practice called **resource partitioning,** which can be defined as a dividing up of scarce resources among species that have similar requirements. If you look at **Figure 35.6** on the next page, you can see how this works among some species that are a little more familiar—several varieties of warbler. The main message here is that species often flourish by specializing; they derive resources by feeding from different locations (or during different times) within the same habitat.

SO FAR ...

1. The competitive exclusion principle states that when two populations compete for the same _____, one will always outcompete the other and thus bring about the latter's _____.

2. Habitat often is shared within a community by means of _____, defined as a dividing up of scarce resources among species that have similar requirements.

Figure 35.5
Kudzu Vines Run Wild

The kudzu plant was introduced in the American South in the 1930s and has since spread at a rapid rate, locally eliminating many plants in its path. This is competitive exclusion in action. Here, kudzu has overgrown an abandoned house in Mississippi.

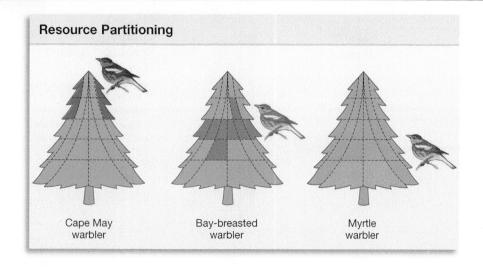

Resource Partitioning

Cape May warbler

Bay-breasted warbler

Myrtle warbler

Figure 35.6
Resource Partitioning
Ecologist Robert MacArthur spent long stretches of time over several years in the 1950s observing the feeding patterns of several species of warblers. All of them ate caterpillars, but from substantially different, though overlapping, parts of the tree.

35.4 Interaction through Predation and Parasitism

It is one thing for two species to compete for resources; it is another for one species to *be* a resource for another—to be eaten or used by another species. Thus do ecologists distinguish one mode of interaction in communities, competition, from a second mode, predation.

Predation can be defined as one organism feeding on parts or all of a second organism. Note that the prey here can be plants, protists, animals—whatever is preyed on. Predation is generally thought of in terms of animals killing other animals, but note that the definition given includes such things as animals consuming whole plants or their seeds. **Parasitism** is a variety of predation in which the predator feeds on prey but does not kill it immediately—and may not kill it ever. Parasites that come to mind tend to be animals, but there are an estimated 3,000 species of parasitic plants, one of which can be seen in **Figure 35.7**.

Predation and parasitism are the features of nature that many nature lovers can't stand, perhaps because these practices seem cruel or unfair from a human point of view. These modes of interaction have arguably been valuable, however, in that they have stimulated the "arms race" that has resulted in evolutionary adaptations such as vision and flight. (One organism's predatory adaptation spurs the development of another organism's defensive adaptation and vice versa.) Whatever we may think of it, predation is simply a fact of nature, and it is impossible to imagine life without it. But it's also true that to admire the beauty of nature is in significant part to admire the handiwork of predation since it has done so much to shape the living world. You can read about a very familiar predator, the house cat, in "Purring Predators: House Cats and Their Prey" on page 677.

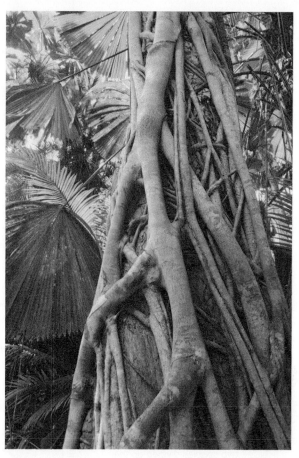

Figure 35.7
A Parasitizing Plant
The strangler fig tree (*Ficus aurea*) is well-named in that it wraps its roots and trunk around a host tree, taking nutrients from it, depriving it of sunlight, and eventually killing it. In the United States, strangler figs are native to South Florida. This tree was growing on a host in Queensland, Australia.

Predator–Prey Dynamics

It may be obvious that although predators attack prey, predators are also *dependent* on prey as a food source. An ongoing question in ecological research is how tight this linkage is. To what extent do predator and prey population sizes tend to move up and down together? It's clear that the population dynamics of some predator and prey species are very tightly linked.

The small lemmings (*Dicrostonyx groenlandicus*) of northeast Greenland are fed on by only four predators: the stoat, the arctic fox, the snowy owl, and another bird called the long-tailed skua. Of these, the stoat is a "specialist" predator in that it feeds almost entirely on lemmings. If you look at **Figure 35.8**, you can see that both the lemming and stoat populations predictably go through 4-year up-and-down population cycles. Moreover, note that the movement up or down in stoat population *lags* the change in lemming

ESSAY

Purring Predators: House Cats and Their Prey

House cats are famous for bringing home animals they've killed or captured, of course; intrigued by the carnage brought into their own homes in the 1980s, Peter Churcher and John Lawton decided to make a scientific study of the predatory behavior of the domestic cat. To do so, they enlisted the help of 172 households in the small English village of Bedfordshire, where Churcher lived. The two researchers asked the locals to "bag the remains of any animal the cat caught" and turn the evidence over to them once a week. This process went on for a year with a high degree of cooperation from the cat owners.

Some of the results were not surprising. Young cats hunt more than older cats; small mammals, such as mice, are the favored prey; and cat hunting is not based purely on hunger—all the cats were fed by their owners and yet hunting was widespread.

What was remarkable, however, was the *scale* of the killing. Concentrating on the village's house sparrow population, Churcher and Lawton found that cats were responsible for between one-third and one-half of all sparrow deaths in the village, a figure they believed no other single predator could match. When they looked at all animals killed and projected the village figures onto the whole of Great Britain, the researchers calculated that cats were responsible for about 70 million deaths a year.

Given that birds account for somewhere between 30 and 50 percent of these kills, this means that cats kill at least 20 million birds a year in Britain. The "at least" here may be an important qualifier. An American biologist, the researchers noted, found that cats bring home only about half of the food they catch.

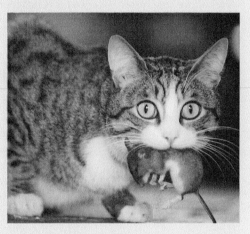

Predator on the Loose
A domestic cat carrying its prey.

population, generally by a few months. What happens is that a higher lemming population means more food for the stoats, which then increase in population. This increase, of course, then means more predation of the lemmings, but the fall you can see in lemming population is not brought about solely by the increase in stoat numbers. When the lemmings' density reaches high levels, the arctic fox, snowy owl, and long-tailed skua begin to prey on them. It is this predation, in combination with the increased stoat predation, that then drives the lemming numbers down. Once the lemmings exist in low densities again, the stoat be-comes the only predator, lemming numbers go up, and the cycle repeats.

The Finnish and German researchers who reported these findings determined that declines in lemming numbers could be explained *entirely* by predation; neither the food nor the space available to the lemmings, for example, played any part in reductions of their population. (And, what about the famous mass suicides of the lemmings? Don't they help keep lemming numbers down? The answer is no, because there are no lemming mass suicides; the whole idea is a myth.)

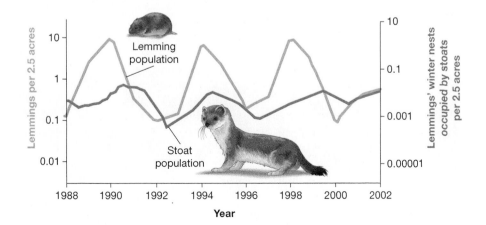

Figure 35.8
Predator and Prey Populations

The population dynamics of a prey species (the lemming) and one of its predators (the stoat) in northeast Greenland over a period of 14 years.

(Reprinted with permission from "Cyclic Dynamics in a Simple Vertebrate Predator-Prey Community," by O. Glig et al., *Science*, 302:867, 2003.)

The crystal-clear connection between predation and the size of the lemming population naturally raises the question of how *common* such a linkage is in nature. What we can say for certain is that, in most species, population dynamics involve more than just predator–prey relationships. Environmental resistance can take many forms, of which increased predation is only one. You might say that the connection between lemmings and their predators serves as an example of how strong predator–prey linkage *can* be, but it is not representative of how strong such linkage is likely to be.

Parasites: Making a Living from the Living

Let's look now at the special variety of predation mentioned earlier, parasitism. Some familiar parasites, such as leeches and ticks, have a straightforward strategy: Get on, hold on, and consume material from the prey, known as the **host.**

But the relationship between parasites and hosts can be much more sophisticated than this. Take, for example, the barely visible roundworm *Strongyloides stercoralis,* which lives throughout the tropics and has, as one of its hosts, human beings in the southeastern United States. The worm comes into the human body from the soil in a thread-like larval form, then makes its way into the veins, which it travels through to get to the lungs. From there, it moves up the trachea and then down into the digestive system, ending up in the small intestine. There it lays eggs that develop into larvae that this time move out, with feces, back into the Earth to start the whole life cycle over again.

Strongyloides is not just using humans as an incubator, however; it can worm its way, you might say,

directly from the small intestines into the bloodstream, bringing about a continuous cycle of infection whose symptoms range from severe diarrhea to lung problems. (Lest all of this seem too disturbing, take heart—there is a medicine that can clear this pest from human bodies.) So, note the complexity here: *Strongyloides* not only feeds on a host but uses the host in its reproduction cycle, something that actually is fairly common among parasitic worms and protozoans. Were you to start examining the range of host–parasite dynamics, you would find lots of interactions as elaborate—and chilling—as this. As you can see in "Why Do Rabid Animals Go Crazy?" on 684, parasites sometimes alter the behavior of their hosts.

The Effect of Predator–Prey Interactions on Evolution

Earlier, we noted the "arms race" spurred on by predator–prey interactions: One organism's predatory adaptation spurs the development of another organism's defensive adaptation and vice versa. So, what forms do these evolutionary adaptations take? To see an example on the predator side, look at the warm-water "frogfish" in **Figure 35.9**. These fish have evolved a spine on their dorsal fins that is tipped with a piece of flesh that looks for all the world like a small worm floating free in the ocean. When a would-be predator tries to snatch up this "worm," however, it finds *itself* the prey. On the prey side, look at **Figure 35.10** to see the amazing kinds of camouflage that animals use to keep themselves hidden from the eyes of predators. Another example of prey adaptation may be as close as your own skin. Why are human beings the only primates whose bodies are not covered with a coat of hair? One hypothesis holds that, while hair

Figure 35.9
Fooling Predators about Prey

The predatory frogfish uses a modified spine resembling a worm to lure its prey. Here, a striped frogfish (*Antennarius striatus*) clearly shows its lure while lying in wait in the coastal waters off the Indonesian island of Sulawesi.

(a) Buff-tip moths

(b) Casque-headed chameleon

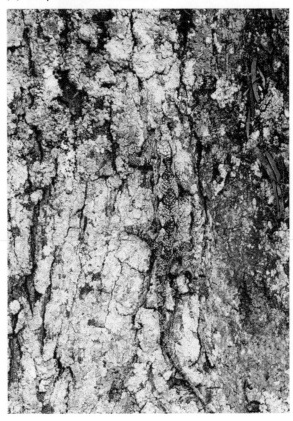

Figure 35.10
Avoiding Predation through Camouflage

(a) A couple of odd-looking pieces of twig on a branch? No, these are moths—two buff-tip moths (*Phalera bucephala*), native to Europe, whose color and shape make them almost invisible when they are at rest on a forest floor.

(b) The casque-headed chameleon likewise can be very well camouflaged. This one was resting against a tree in Kenya.

warmed our evolutionary ancestors, it also provided a home for many parasites that preyed on them— lice, fleas, and ticks. The adaptation of losing our hair allowed us to lose these parasites to a great extent.

Needless to say, predator–prey evolution goes on within all the kingdoms of life. Plants have developed not only spines, thorns, and other protective structures but also a vast array of chemical compounds—more than 15,000 have been characterized so far—that protect them from predators.

Mimicry Is a Theme in Predator–Prey Evolution

One special form of evolutionary adaptation brought on by predator–prey interaction is **mimicry,** a phenomenon through which one species has evolved to assume the appearance of another. One type of mimicry involves three participants: a model, a mimic, and a dupe. If you look at **Figure 35.11**, you can see a model on the left, the yellow jacket wasp, which obviously can provide a painful lesson to any animal that tries to eat it. On the right you can see the mimic, the clearwing moth, which is harmless but looks a great deal like a wasp. For the dupe, you could select any predator species that sees a clearwing moth and passes it by, believing it to be a dangerous yellow jacket. This is called **Batesian mimicry:** the evolution of one species to resemble a species that has a superior protective capability.

In a second type of mimicry, **Müllerian mimicry,** several species that *have* protection against predators come to resemble each other (**Figure 35.12** on the next page). This creates a visual warning that becomes known to an array of predators. Given this, a would-be predator learns, by interacting with an individual from one species, to keep away from all individuals in any look-alike species. The result is that fewer individuals in these species will be disturbed or killed.

Figure 35.11
Harmless, but Looking Dangerous

In an example of Batesian mimicry, the clearwing moth (on the right) has no sting but has evolved to look like an insect that does, the yellow jacket wasp (on the left). The yellow jacket is the model, and the moth is the mimic.

Figure 35.12
Müllerian Mimicry

The South American butterflies *Heliconius cydno* (top) and *Heliconius sapho* are different in some ways, but they share the characteristic of tasting bad to predators. Over time, they evolved to look like each other, with their appearance serving as a warning to would-be predators. Natural selection favors this Müllerian mimicry because predators can learn about the butterflies' unpalatable taste from both species. The result is that fewer members of either species are likely to be killed or bothered by predators.

35.5 Interaction through Mutualism and Commensalism

The competitive, predatory, and parasitic modes of interaction we've been reviewing have an each-organism-against-all quality to them, but other kinds of relationships also exist within communities. Consider **mutualism,** meaning an interaction between individuals of two species that is beneficial to both individuals. There's a good example of this in Chapter 22 (page 413), with the linkage between plant roots and the slender, below-ground extensions of fungi called hyphae. What the fungi get from growing into the plant roots is food that comes from the photosynthesizing plant; what the plants get is minerals and water, absorbed by the network of hyphae. By some estimates, 90 percent of seed plants have this relationship with fungi. Perhaps the most famous example of mutualism, however, is between the rhinoceros and oxpecker birds. Sitting on the back of the rhino, the oxpecker removes parasites and pests (ticks and flies), thus getting food and a safe place to perch, while the rhino gets relief from its tiny adversaries (**Figure 35.13**).

Our final variety of community interaction is **commensalism,** meaning an interaction between individuals in two species in which one benefits while the other is neither harmed nor helped. Birds can make their nests in trees, and benefit from this, but generally don't affect the trees in any way. Along similar lines, one particular type of bird, the cattle egret (*Bubulcus ibis*), commonly derives a benefit from doing its hunting in fields populated by grazing animals such as cattle and elephants (**Figure 35.14**). The hoof movements of the grazing animals turn over the soil in such fields, thus exposing ground-dwelling insects to the egrets, but the grazing animals are neither harmed nor helped by their interaction with the birds.

Coevolution: Species Driving Each Other's Evolution

Earlier, you read about the effect that predator–prey interactions have had on the evolutionary arms race among species. Yet it's clear that organisms have

Figure 35.13
Mutually Beneficial

(a) Rhinoceros and oxpecker birds

Several oxpecker birds sit atop a black rhinoceros, ridding the rhino of ticks and other pests, while the rhino provides a safe habitat for the birds. This is a demonstration of mutualism—an interaction between two species that is beneficial to both.

(b) Randall's shrimp and flag-tail shrimp-gobi

The randall's shrimp (*Alpheus randalli*), on the left, and the flag-tail shrimp-gobi (*Amblyeleotris yanoi*) also exhibit mutualism. Here the gobi stands guard next to the nearly-blind shrimp, which burrows a hole into the sand into which both animals retreat when the gobi senses danger.

affected each other's evolution through mutualism as well. Indeed, species that are tightly linked in any way over a long period of time are likely to shape one another's evolution. Perceiving this, scientists Paul Ehrlich and Peter Raven developed the concept of **coevolution,** meaning the interdependent evolution of two or more species.

Some of the clearest examples of coevolution involve flowering plants and the animals that pollinate them. Recall from Chapter 22 that many flowers have both fragrances that attract insects and ultraviolet color patterns (invisible to us) that guide the insects to the proper spot for pollination. These features are nature's own homing signals and landing lights, respectively communicating the messages "Food lies this way" and "Land here" (**Figure 35.15**). Now, one of the organisms linked with flowering plants in this way is the honeybee. And it turns out that the color vision of honeybees is most sensitive to the colors that exist in the very flowering plants they pollinate. What seems likely is that honeybee eyesight evolved in response to plant coloration, and that plant coloration evolved to be maximally attractive to the pollinating insects. These groups of organisms coevolved, in other words.

Having considered how community members interact with one another, let's now go on to consider how communities change over time. **Table 35.1** summarizes all the kinds of interactions you've gone over in this chapter.

Figure 35.14
Following in the Footsteps
A group of cattle egrets follow a bull elephant across a field in Botswana, Africa, capturing insects that are exposed in the soil the elephant turns over as it walks.

(a) What we see   **(b)** What a bee sees

Figure 35.15
Coevolution of Plants and Their Pollinators
This flower has an ultraviolet color pattern that is not normally visible to humans, but that attracts bees. It is likely that these color patterns evolved in the flowers because they aided in attracting the bees. Meanwhile, the bees developed vision that was sensitive to the colors exhibited by these same plants.

SO FAR . . .

1. In the interaction known as _____, one species feeds on all or parts of a second organism; in the interaction known as _____, a predator feeds on prey but does not kill it immediately and may not ever kill it.

2. In predator–prey interactions, _____ mimicry has occurred when one species has evolved to resemble another species that has superior protective ability. When several species that have protective ability have evolved to resemble each other _____ mimicry has occurred.

3. Mutualism is an interaction between individuals of two species that is _____. Commensalism is an interaction between individuals of two species in which one is _____ while the other is _____.

Table 35.1

Community Interactions

In this type of interaction . . .	One organism . . .	While the other . . .
Competition	Is harmed	Is harmed
Predation and parasitism	Gains	Is harmed
Mutualism	Gains	Gains
Commensalism	Gains	Is unaffected

35.6 Succession in Communities

When Washington State's Mount St. Helens volcano erupted in May 1980, it first collapsed inward, thus sending most of the mountain's north face sliding downhill in the largest avalanche in recorded history. Then came the actual eruption, which sent a huge volume of rock and ash hurtling not straight up but out at an angle, toward the north. Some stands of forest in the path of this blast were instantly incinerated down to bare rock; another 35,000 hectares (86,000 acres) of trees were snapped in two like so many twigs. Then came the mudslides caused by the vast expanse of snow and ice melted in the explosion; then came the fall of hundreds of millions of tons of ash, some of it landing as far away as Wyoming. After viewing the devastated area around the blast, President Jimmy Carter said that it "makes the surface of the moon look like a golf course."

But today? No one would claim that the Mount St. Helens area has returned to anything like its former state, but look at the pictures in **Figure 35.16** to get an idea of the transition that has occurred at one location around Mount St. Helens.

The exact form of this rejuvenation may surprise us, but don't we intuitively expect something like this? Just from our everyday experience of watching, say, an abandoned urban lot becoming progressively weed filled, don't we expect this would generally be the case? As it turns out, our intuition is right because almost any parcel of land or water that has been either abandoned by humans or devastated by physical forces will be "reclaimed" by nature, at least to some degree.

The question is, how does this reclamation proceed? Areas that are rebounding don't just get one type of vegetation and then retain it. Instead, the vegetation changes through time—one type of growth *succeeds* another—with a general movement toward more and larger greenery as time goes by. Ecologists call this phenomenon **succession,** meaning a series of replacements of community members at a given location until a relatively stable final state is reached. Within this framework, there are two kinds of succession. The first of these, generally caused by some sort of major ecological disturbance, is **primary succession,** meaning succession in which the starting state is one of little or no life and a soil that lacks nutrients. This is the type of succession that began in parts of the Mount St. Helens environment in 1980. Then there is **secondary succession,** which is succession in which the final state of a habitat has been disturbed by some force, but life remains and the soil has nutrients. The classic example of this is land that has first been cleared for farming but later abandoned by the farmer.

Figure 35.16
Rebound from Disaster
Mount St. Helens, with its crater in the distance, as it appeared in June 1980, one month after the blast, and as it appeared in 1998. This is an example of ecological succession in action.

The relatively stable community that develops at the end of any process of succession is called a **climax community.** There will be some shifts over time in a climax community, just as there are in any other. A prolonged drought will cause some change in the mix of the community's animal and plant life, for example. But, with some exceptions, what does not happen is a shift to a *fundamentally* different mix of life-forms, barring a major change in climate. Grassland stays grassland, and forest stays forest.

Succession can be fairly predictable within small geographical areas. Two abandoned farm plots that lie close together will have very similar kinds of succession—so much so that local farmers or naturalists can sometimes tell to within a few years how long it's been since a field was abandoned. As you may be able to tell, succession generally is thought of in terms of the various *plant* communities that succeed one another, although modern ecology is attempting to bring animals into the picture as well.

An Example of Primary Succession: Alaska's Glacier Bay

One of the best examples of primary succession comes from Alaska's 65-mile-long Glacier Bay, whose lower-lying areas were covered by a glacier until about 240 years ago, when the glacier began retreating. Such withdrawal initially leaves behind a rocky terrain that is completely devoid of organic matter—no fallen leaves or branches, no decomposing animals. Indeed, what's left is not soil but a pulverized rock (called till) that has a high pH and no available nitrogen—not a promising environment for life to establish itself. But establish itself it does. In the case of Glacier Bay, its succession particulars—what species succeeded what—are not important for our purposes. What is important is the general process that occurred. Here's what happened in the eastern arm of Glacier Bay after the glacier retreated (**Figure 35.17**).

In the 20 years immediately following the retreat, the first "pioneer" species to come were lichens and photosynthesizing bacteria, which essentially have the ability to flourish on rock. In addition, there were some primitive plants called horsetails and liverworts.

Over the next 10 years, a gradual transition took place in which an Arctic dwarf shrub, called *Dryas*, took over from the pioneers, growing in a mat that was broken up only by occasional trees. *Dryas* and other early-stage plants have a capability that is critical not only to their own growth in these environments but to the growth of plants that come after them. These plants harbor bacteria in their roots that can *fix nitrogen*—that can take nitrogen from the air and convert it into a form that plants can use. This is how the larger plant community could get started on the till in Glacier Bay, which *lacked* nitrogen.

The *Dryas* community was succeeded by a plant called the alder bush that excluded almost everything else—it was a highly successful dominant, in other words, and its success in the environment meant the end of the *Dryas*. Fifty years after the glacier's retreat, alders were growing in stands that were 10 meters, or about 33 feet, tall. With their growth, the terrain got a great deal of nitrogen and, through acidic alder leaves that fell to the ground, a rapid lowering of pH.

The alder sowed the seeds of its own elimination, however. With the lowered soil pH, an extensive population of Sitka spruce trees could develop; when they did, they "shaded out" the smaller alders by blocking

Figure 35.17
One Example of Primary Succession: Glacier Bay, Alaska

ponds and bogs eventually?

exposed till

pioneer species: lichens, bacteria, horsetails, and liverworts

Dryas shrub

alder bush

spruce

spruce-hemlock

ESSAY

Why Do Rabid Animals Go Crazy?

There is a tiny worm, called *Plagiorhynchus cylindraceus,* that lives its adult life as a parasite in the intestines of starlings and other songbirds. While in a starling, this worm produces eggs that pass out of the bird in its feces. After this, both eggs and feces may be eaten by pillbugs, which are the familiar little arthropods that "roll up into a ball." The worm eggs, however, are not digested by the pillbugs. As a result, a worm *hatches* inside a pillbug, which makes the bug the second "host" for this parasite. And here is where things get interesting, as researcher Janice Moore has shown.

The pillbug is dark, but once infected by a worm, it starts spending more time on light-colored surfaces. What's more, it stops sheltering itself under overhanging objects such as leaves. And the females among the bugs start moving around more and resting less. The effect of all this is that worm-infected pillbugs are more visible to their predators and thus are more likely to be eaten by them. And who are these predators? Some of them are starlings.

Now, when a starling eats a pillbug, the pillbug dies, but the worm inside the bug remains unharmed. Indeed, this is the way the worm gets back inside a starling host

(where it will develop into an adult, lay eggs, and so forth). And that's just the point: It appears that the worm brings about the self-destructive behavior of the pillbug. Through some unknown mechanism, this parasite prompts the pillbug to become an accomplice in its own death. When the pillbug is infected, its behaviors are such that it might as well have a sign on it saying, "Please eat me." The starling is happy to oblige, but the real winner is the *P. cylindraceus* worm, which gets to move from one of its hosts to another.

It would be nice to report that such behavioral takeovers by parasites are rare, but in fact they are common. "Horsehair" worms need to mate in the water, but they spend most of their lives inside arthropods such as ants, whose abdomens they feed on. Just before an ant dies from this,

---

their sunlight. About 100 years after the glacier's retreat, a spruce forest existed—one that, within 30 more years, started becoming a combined spruce-hemlock forest.

For most of Glacier Bay, the spruce-hemlock forest appears to be the end of the line—the climax community. It's worth noting, however, that on the outer coast of the area there has been one more successional stage. Water-absorbing mosses started to grow and, with them, the forest floor became watery, the tree roots couldn't absorb the oxygen they needed, and the trees died. What eventually was left was land that was filled with ponds and watery bogs. Ecologists have speculated that all of Glacier Bay may be headed in this direction, although this transition could take thousands of years.

Common Elements in Primary Succession

In the Glacier Bay succession, you can see developments that apply to many primary successions, namely:

- An arrival of photosynthesizing pioneer species—in this case, the bacteria and lichens—that can establish themselves in the most barren environments.
- A steady increase in biomass compared to the starting state. This increase eventually stops in all successions. In parts of Glacier Bay, it actually was reversed with the appearance of the late-stage mosses.

- A general movement toward longer-lived species. *Dryas* can live for 50 years, but alders can live for 100 years and spruce trees for 700.
- A general trend toward an increase in species diversity, although not without some reversals (the alder bushes, for example).
- The facilitation of the growth of some later species (the Sitka spruce here) through the actions of earlier species (the shedding of leaves by the alders). More formally, **facilitation** is a process within ecological succession in which the qualities or actions of some early-arriving species enable the success of later-arriving species.
- The competitive driving out of some species (the alder bush) by the actions of later species (the blocking of sunlight by the spruce trees).

Lessons in Succession from Mount St. Helens

Ecologists have been studying succession for about 100 years now, but it remains a field filled with basic questions. Spirited debate has gone on for years about which factors hold true in all instances of succession and which models of development best describe succession. (Is facilitation more important than competition?)

It turns out, however, that in just the past 30 years, Washington's Mount St. Helens has provided a treasure trove of insight into how primary succession however, it aids the worm in one final way—it makes a journey to water. Indeed, a worm-infected ant seemingly has an uncontrollable urge to get wet as it will return repeatedly to water if blocked. Once it wades into a pool or puddle, however, things proceed quickly. In a matter of minutes, the worm inside it will emerge, ready to mate with another worm.

Now, think about all this in connection with one of the things children are taught to fear from an early age: a rabid animal. Rabies is caused by a virus that spreads through animal saliva. In the "furious" form of the disease, the virus is passed on by means of one animal biting another, thus injecting its saliva into the second animal. Not surprisingly, one of the things the virus does is affect salivary tissue in an infected animal's head and neck.

This ensures that there is plenty of saliva to be transmitted. The virus also inhibits swallowing in an infected animal, which ensures more saliva. Finally, the virus affects the animal's central nervous system in such a way that it brings about the famous *behavioral* change in infected animals—frenzied, unprovoked attacks on other animals. Thus, rabid raccoons or dogs are not simply "going crazy" because of their disease. Their behavior has a function. To be sure, it's a *perverse* function from a human perspective, but then again, aren't the behaviors of infected pillbugs or ants disturbing in a similar sort of way? The general message here is straightforward but hard to take: Living things can be forced to act in ways that benefit the very organisms that have infected them.

Accomplice to Its Own Death
The common pillbug *Armadillidium vulgare,* whose behavior can be manipulated by the parasitical worm *P. cylindraceus.*

works. If there is a silver lining behind the Mount St. Helens explosion, it is that it has given ecologists an unparalleled opportunity to understand succession. This is so because the Mount St. Helens succession began on a crystal-clear starting date (May 18, 1980) and proceeded from such well-defined starting states—obliteration of some habitats and major or minor damage to others.

So, what have we learned from Mount St. Helens? Perhaps the most important lesson is this: What is left from the past is crucial to the future. When trees were knocked over in the blast, their roots were yanked above ground. In this moment of destruction, however, these roots literally carried the seeds of rejuvenation with them. Soil, small plants, and seeds were pulled up with the roots, and they stayed on them—above the deadening layer of ash below. Dead wood, left strewn about after the blast, provided habitat and food for wood-boring insects. These insects in turn attracted birds, which were able to build nests in "snags," meaning trees that were dead but standing. Gophers survived the blast in large numbers because they live below ground, where they feed on roots. They actually flourished in the years following the explosion, and their activity not only turned over the soil—mixing fertile soil below with ash on top—but also provided a kind of subway system for other animals, which were migrating among patches of viable habitat (**Figure 35.18**). So important were the gophers, snags, and surviving seeds to renewal at Mount St. Helens that a collective term for them has now

entered the ecological lexicon. They are examples of **biological legacies:** living things, or products of living things, that survive a major ecological disturbance.

Succession at Mount St. Helens has yielded some other surprises as well. "Classical" primary succession, as outlined in the Glacier Bay example, assumes that life will come to a devastated area from the outside. Seeds and spores will be carried in on the wind, and succession will proceed, in a general way, from the periphery of the barren area to its interior. Although this happened to some degree at Mount St. Helens, in the main recovery was internal: Thousands

**Figure 35.18
Important Survivor at Mount St. Helens**

The pocket gopher (*Thomomys talpoides*) played a role in the restoration of the Mount St. Helens environment. The gopher's underground habitat allowed it to survive the blast, after which it continued to feed on roots, turning over soil in the process. This gopher is in Wyoming.

of small patches of plant habitat rejuvenated without being seeded from the outside. When organisms did come in from the outside, many were the "pioneer" species predicted by classical succession theory. However, ecologists also found solitary tree seedlings—supposedly latecomers in succession—growing right out of some of the most devastated terrain in the blast area, with no pioneer species setting the stage for them. And some of the external help that did arrive took an unexpected form. In the years immediately following the blast, insects and spiders were blown in on the wind in significant quantity. Once these creatures landed, most of them died, but they themselves went on to serve as food for indigenous ants and other species.

Given all this, another lesson from Mount St. Helens seems to be that succession is more varied and habitat-specific than our theories had predicted. Put another way, we still have a lot to learn about succession.

On to Ecosystems and Biomes

In the past two chapters, you have looked at populations and communities. In populations, you saw the building blocks of communities. In communities, you looked through a lens of the interactions of different species. But it's obvious that community members interact with *nonliving* forces and factors, such as weather and soil composition. When living things and nonliving factors are considered together, the resulting whole is called an *ecosystem*—the subject of the first part of Chapter 36. Very large-scale ecosystems are called *biomes*; a review of them forms the concluding portion of Chapter 36 and will bring to a close this book's coverage of ecology.

SO FAR . . .

1. Succession can be defined as a series of _____ of community members at a given location until a relatively _____ is reached.

2. In primary succession, over time, biomass tends to (pick the correct term from the two) decrease/increase; species tend to be shorter-lived/longer-lived; and species diversity tends to decrease/increase.

3. Succession at Mount St. Helens revealed the importance of biological legacies, meaning living things or products of living things that _____.

35
REVIEW

Go to the Study Area at www.masteringbiology.com for practice quizzes, myeBook, BioFlix™ 3-D animations, MP3 Tutor Sessions, videos, current events, and more.

Mastering
BIOLOGY

Summary

35.1 Structure in Communities

- An ecological community is all the populations of all species that inhabit a given area. Many communities are dominated by only a few species; abundant species in a given area are ecological dominants. A keystone species is one whose absence from a community would bring about significant change in it. (p. 671)

- Biodiversity takes three forms: a diversity of species in a given area, a geographic distribution of species populations, and genetic diversity within species populations. (p. 672)

- Species diversity tends to enhance community productivity and community stability. (p. 673)

35.2 Types of Interaction among Community Members

- There are four primary types of interaction among community members: competition, predation (and a special variety of it, parasitism), mutualism, and commensalism. (p. 673)

- Habitat is the physical surroundings in which a species normally can be found. Niche can be defined as the means by which a species obtains the resources it needs. (p. 673)

35.3 Interaction through Competition

- The competitive exclusion principle states that when two species compete for the same limited, vital resource, one always outcompetes the other and thus brings about the latter's local extinction. (p. 674)

- Coexistence through resource partitioning refers to instances in which two similar species use the same kinds of resources from the same habitat over an extended period of time but divide the resources up such that neither species undergoes local extinction. (p. 674)

35.4 Interaction through Predation and Parasitism

- Predation is defined as one free-standing organism feeding on parts or all of a second organism. Parasitism is a variety of predation in which the predator feeds on prey (known as the host) but does not kill it immediately and may not kill it ever. (p. 676)

- Predator and prey population sizes can move up and down together in a fairly tight linkage, but predator–prey interaction generally is only one of several factors that control the population levels of either kind of community member. (p. 676)

- Predator–prey interactions have spurred the evolution of physical modifications in both predator and prey species. One example of such modification is mimicry, in which one species has evolved to assume the appearance of another. Batesian mimicry occurs when one species evolves to resemble a species that has superior protective capability. Müllerian mimicry occurs when several species that have protection against predators evolve to resemble each other. (p. 679)

35.5 Interaction through Mutualism and Commensalism

- Mutualism is an interaction between individuals of two species that is beneficial to both individuals. Commensalism is an interaction in which an individual from one species benefits while an individual from another species is neither harmed nor helped. (p. 680)

- Coevolution is the interdependent evolution of two or more species. (p. 680)

35.6 Succession in Communities

- Parcels of land that have been abandoned by humans or devastated by physical forces will almost always be reclaimed by nature via succession, a series of replacements of community members at a given location until a relatively stable final state is reached. (p. 682)

- Primary succession proceeds from an original state of little or no life and soil that lacks nutrients. Secondary succession occurs when a final state of habitat is first disturbed by some outside force, but life remains and the soil has nutrients. The final community in any process of succession is known as the climax community. (p. 682)

- Primary succession usually includes the arrival of "pioneer" photosynthesizers, facilitation of the growth of some later species through the actions of earlier species, and the competitive driving out of some earlier species by the actions of later species. As succession proceeds, species diversity tends to increase within communities, and smaller, shorter-lived species tend to be replaced by larger, longer-lived species. (p. 684)

- The rejuvenation of the Mount St. Helens area that has occurred since 1980 has provided ecologists with a wealth of information regarding both primary and secondary succession. (p. 684)

Key Terms

Understanding the Basics

Multiple-Choice Questions

(Answers are in the back of the book.)

1. The Everglades in south Florida contain vast expanses of the sawgrass plant *Cladium jamaicense*. Therefore, in the south Florida Everglades, sawgrass is:
   a. a host.
   b. a model.
   c. a ecological pioneer.
   d. an ecological dominant.
   e. a mimic.

2. If a species preys on others within a community but is not itself preyed upon, and if its absence would bring about significant change within the community, that species is (select all that apply):
   a. an ecological dominant.
   b. a parasite.
   c. a top predator.
   d. a host.
   e. a keystone species.

3. A parasite will often feed on its _____, while using it as part of its _____.
   a. host; reproduction cycle
   b. dupe; camouflage
   c. model; resource partitioning
   d. dupe; reproduction cycle
   e. model; coevolution

4. Plants such as soybeans house bacteria in their roots that receive food from them, while the bacteria provide the soybeans with a usable form of nitrogen. This is an example of:
   a. parasitism.
   b. mutualism.
   c. fertilization.
   d. mimicry.
   e. commensalism.

5. The process by which one species evolves to resemble another species is called:
   a. mimicry.
   b. mutualism.
   c. behaviorism.
   d. parasitism.
   e. natural deception.

6. In communities undergoing primary succession, there are general trends toward (select all that apply):
   a. shorter-lived species.
   b. longer-lived species.
   c. smaller species.
   d. greater species diversity.
   e. less species diversity.

7. In primary succession, pioneer species will predominately be _____ because they ____.
   a. migratory animals; can go elsewhere for their food
   b. cold-weather species; can withstand harsh conditions
   c. insects; can live in so many environments
   d. photosynthesizing organisms; can make their own food
   e. trees; can run roots deep into the soil for water

Brief Review

(Answers are in the back of the book.)

1. In architecture, a keystone is a stone at the top of an arch that holds the entire arch in place. In what way can certain species be thought of as keystones for their communities?

2. Name the four primary modes of interaction in a community.

3. A wasp from the group known as the ichneumons sometimes will paralyze a caterpillar by injecting a toxin into it, after which the wasp deposits its eggs into or onto the caterpillar's body. When the eggs hatch, the resulting wasp larvae live by consuming the caterpillar, which remains alive while paralyzed. What mode of interaction are the wasp and the caterpillar practicing? What is the role of the caterpillar in this interaction?

4. Lichens are composite organisms, usually made up of upper and lower layers of fungi, with a layer of algae in between. Fungi benefit from their association with the photosynthesizing algae in that they receive food from them. At one time, however, scientists questioned whether the algae were in turn benefiting from their relationship with fungi. It now appears, however, that algae do benefit from their association with fungi in that they receive water, carbon dioxide, and protection from the elements from them. For the sake of argument, assume that the fungi are not providing any benefit to the algae; which mode of interaction would the two types of organisms be practicing? In light of the benefits the fungi are providing to the algae, which mode of interaction are they actually practicing?

5. The red-spotted newt *Notophthalmus viridescens* secretes toxins from its skin that make predators avoid it. The red salamander *Pseudotriton ruber* has no such secretions but resembles the red-spotted newt and gains protection from this resemblance. What is this an example of? Which is the model, the mimic, and the dupe?

6. A volcano erupted in Hawaii, and lava covered land that had been farmed for centuries. Eventually, new lichens, and

then plants, grew on the lava. Is this an example of primary or secondary succession?

Applying Your Knowledge

1. In the movie *The Godfather,* Michael Corleone and Enzo the baker stand on the steps outside the hospital where Michael's father is recovering from gunshot wounds and pretend to be holding guns inside their coats as a means of keeping assassins from entering the hospital and killing Michael's father. Allowing for some differences between the natural world and human society, what form of mimicry were Michael Corleone and Enzo the baker practicing?

2. The world's first farmers were not human beings but the leaf-cutter ants of the genus *Atta.* These ants do not eat the leaves they carry off. Instead, they bring them down into their nests, where they process the leaves into a pulp and then spread the pulp onto a fungus that grows only in their nests. The fungus then feeds on the food that has been brought to it and grows, after which the ants harvest the knob-like stalks of the fungus and consume them. What is the mode of interaction between the ants and the fungus in this community?

3. The clearwing moth pictured on page 679 has no protective capability, but has evolved to look like a species—the yellow jacket wasp—that does have such capability. As such, what mode of interaction are the clearwing and the yellow jacket practicing? What mode of interaction is being practiced between two species that have protective capability and that have evolved to look alike?

36

An Interactive Living World 3:
Ecosystems and Biomes

The living world is affected by the larger physical world around it— and vice versa. The interconnected web of living things is being damaged in many ways by human activity.

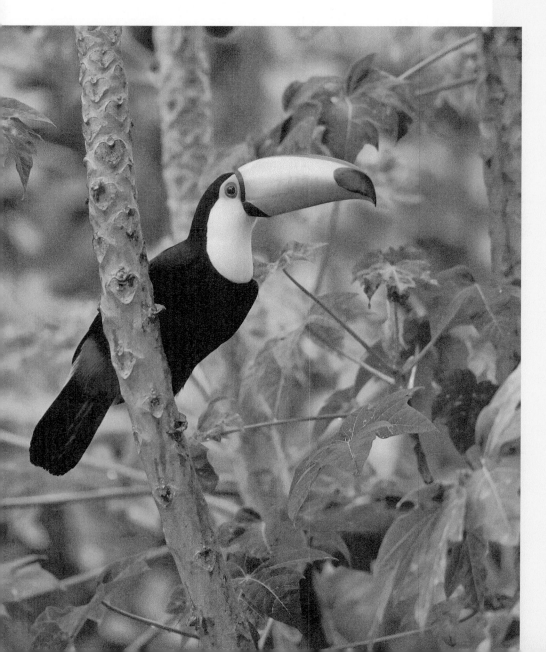

A toco toucan (*Ramphastos toco*) rests in a tree in the world's largest freshwater wetland, the Panatal of Brazil, Bolivia, and Paraguay.

The word *system* is much in use today. We hear about a given country's political system or its economic system. The term was first used in this context by academics who needed a way to refer to complex entities composed of many interacting parts. This way of looking at things is, however, as applicable to ecology as it is to economics or politics. In Chapter 35,

when you went over ecological communities, you actually were studying something in isolation: the interactions of all the living things in a given area. It goes without saying, however, that these living things also interact with many *non*living entities. To get a complete picture of how the living world functions, then, it's necessary to understand how living things interact not only with each other but with these nonliving elements.

36.1 The Ecosystem

What do nonliving elements add to life? All communities need an original source of energy, generally meaning the sun; they all need a supply of water and a supply of nutrients, such as nitrogen and phosphorus; and all organisms need to exchange gases with their environment (think of your own breathing). The sun's energy is making a one-way trip through the community, ultimately being transformed into heat, but water and nutrients are being *cycled*—from the Earth into organisms and then back again into the Earth. Looking at this, we can begin to perceive the reality of ecological *systems*: of functional units that tightly link both living or **biotic** factors and nonliving or **abiotic** factors to form a whole.

Given this, an important unit in ecology is the **ecosystem**, which can be defined as a community of organisms and the physical environment with which they interact. This chapter begins with a look at small-scale ecosystems and concludes with a look at the very large-scale ecosystems called biomes. In today's world, it's impossible to note the ways in which ecosystems function without also noting the ways in which human activity is damaging them.

36.2 Nutrient and Water Cycling in Ecosystems

In Chapters 34 and 35, you learned a good deal about two of the biotic factors of the ecosystem, namely, individual populations of living things and the communities that are made up of these populations. This chapter focuses on some of the abiotic factors in an ecosystem. In overview, these abiotic factors fall into two categories. First are the *resources* that exist in the ecosystem, such as water and nutrients; second are the *conditions* in which an ecosystem exists, such as average temperature. Resources are considered first in this chapter and conditions later.

The Cycling of Ecosystem Resources

Those of you who went through Chapter 2, on chemistry, know what a chemical **element** is: a substance that is "pure" in that it cannot be broken down into any set of component substances by chemical means. The 92 stable elements include such familiar substances as gold and helium, but only 30 or so of these elements are vital to life and are thus called **nutrients.** Some nutrients, such as iron or iodine, are needed only in small or "trace" quantities by living things, but others are needed in large quantities, among them carbon, oxygen, nitrogen, and phosphorus. Living things also have a great need for water, which is not an element but a molecule composed of two elements, hydrogen and oxygen. Water and nutrients move back and forth between the biotic and abiotic realms, with the term for this movement being a mouthful: **biogeochemical cycling.** Let's look now at the cycling of two elements, carbon and nitrogen, and then at the cycling of water.

Carbon as One Example of Ecosystem Cycling

A certain amount of cosmic debris makes its way to Earth's surface in the form of meteorites, but this material is pretty sparse. What else comes to Earth from space? The sun's rays, to be sure, as well as light from distant stars, and some other forms of radiation. But when we're talking about chemical elements, the Earth really is a spaceship: It carries a fixed amount of resources with it. Nothing much comes to Earth *from* the outside, and relatively little leaves Earth *for* the outside. For an ecologist, this self-containment simplifies things: What we possess in terms of elements is all we'll ever possess. Thus, the question becomes not so much what we have, but where we have it.

In recent years, there has been considerable concern about the buildup of the heat-trapping gas carbon dioxide (CO_2) in the Earth's atmosphere as this increase is now known to be the primary cause of global warming. Well, if Earth has this fixed quantity of elements—in this case, the carbon and oxygen that make up CO_2—how could there be a buildup of carbon dioxide in the atmosphere? The answer is that carbon has been *transferred* from one place on Earth to another. It has moved from the "fossil fuels" of coal and oil, where it was stored, into the atmosphere.

Storage and transfer: These two concepts are fundamental to biogeochemical cycling. When we look a little deeper into carbon cycling, we find other players involved in carbon's storage and transfer. Plants need CO_2 to perform photosynthesis, and they take in great quantities of it for that purpose, producing their own food as

a result. While the plants are alive, they use some of the carbon they take in to grow—it becomes part of their leaves and stems and roots. And as long as these structures exist, they will store carbon within them, just as coal and oil do. (Thus, one of the proposed solutions to global warming is to grow a huge number of trees, each of which could be thought of as a kind of piggy bank for carbon.) Eventually, the plants die, of course, after which their decomposition by bacteria and fungi releases carbon into the soil and atmosphere, again as CO_2. With this, you can begin to see the whole of the carbon cycle in the natural world (**Figure 36.1**).

Some plants will, of course, be eaten by *animals*, who need carbon-based molecules for tissues and energy, just as plants do. The difference is that animals get these molecules *from plants*—in the form of seeds and leaves and roots—rather than from the air. These animals will likewise lock up carbon for a time, only to return it to the soil with their death and decomposition. Note, however, the critical difference between animals and plants: Carbon comes into the living world only through plants (and their fellow photosynthesizers algae and some bacteria). An animal might take in some carbon dioxide in breathing, but nothing life-sustaining happens as a result. Conversely, a plant that takes in carbon dioxide can *incorporate* it into a life-sustaining molecule, in this case a sugar that is the initial product of photosynthesis. With this sugar as a food source, plants grow, and this bounty ultimately feeds everything else. Look at this simplified cycle:

Figure 36.1
The Carbon Cycle

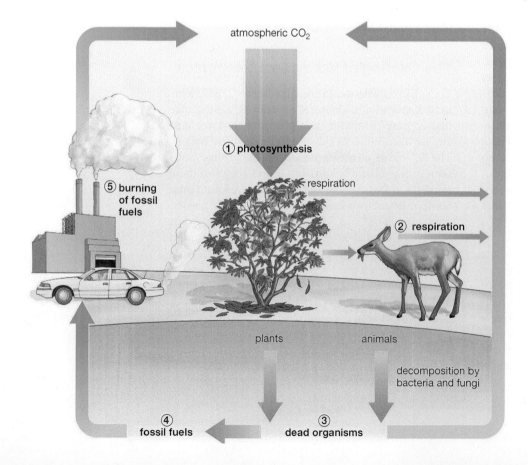

atmospheric CO_2

① photosynthesis

⑤ burning of fossil fuels

respiration

② respiration

plants   animals

decomposition by bacteria and fungi

④ fossil fuels   ③ dead organisms

The carbon cycle

1. Plants and other photosynthesizing organisms take in atmospheric carbon dioxide (CO_2) and convert or "fix" it into molecules that become part of the plant.

2. The physical functioning or respiration of organisms converts the carbon in their tissues back into CO_2.

3. Plants and animals die and are decomposed by fungi and bacteria. Some CO_2 results, which moves back into the atmosphere.

4. Some of the carbon in the remains of dead organisms becomes locked up in carbon-based compounds such as coal or oil.

5. The burning of these fossil fuels puts this carbon into the atmosphere in the form of CO_2.

atmospheric CO_2 → plants → animals →
decomposers → atmospheric CO_2

What does it track, the path of carbon or the path of food? The answer is both. This is one of the reasons that biologists refer to life on Earth as "carbon based."

How Much Atmospheric CO_2?

In following the carbon trail, it's probably apparent that, just as money is a medium of exchange in our economy, CO_2 is the living world's medium of exchange for carbon; photosynthesizers take *in* carbon as CO_2 and decomposers yield *up* carbon as CO_2. (All organisms also release CO_2 as a by-product of carrying out life's basic processes, as with your own exhalations in breathing.) Given how much **biomass,** or material produced by living things, there is in the world, you might think there would have to be a great deal of CO_2 in the atmosphere. But as a proportion of atmospheric gases, CO_2 is a bit player, making up about 0.035 percent of the atmosphere. But what an important player it is! It's critical in feeding us all, and relatively small changes in its atmospheric concentration are now leading to significant changes in global temperature (something we'll look into in detail later).

The Nitrogen Cycle

Like carbon, nitrogen is an element; and like carbon, nitrogen cycles between the biotic and abiotic domains. Nitrogen makes up only a small proportion of the tissues of living things, but it is a critical proportion because it is required for DNA, RNA, and all proteins. All living things need this element, then. The question is, how do they get it?

The source for all the nitrogen that enters the living world is atmospheric nitrogen, which exists in great abundance. You've seen that carbon dioxide makes up less than 1 percent of the atmosphere, and it turns out that oxygen makes up about 21 percent. But nitrogen makes up 78 percent of the atmosphere. So rich is the atmosphere in this element that a typical garden plot has tons hovering above it. The problem? All this nitrogen is in the form of pairs of nitrogen atoms (N_2) that have a great tendency to stay together, rather than combining with anything else. Thus, in a case of so near and yet so far, plants have no direct access to atmospheric nitrogen. So, how do they obtain it? In the natural world, the answer essentially is, through the actions of bacteria. It is bacteria that are carrying out the process of **nitrogen fixation,** meaning the conversion of atmospheric nitrogen into a form that can be taken up and used by living things.

Bacterial Fixation of Nitrogen

You can see nitrogen fixation and the rest of the nitrogen cycle diagrammed in **Figure 36.2**. The essence of the cycle is that several types of nitrogen-fixing bacteria take in atmospheric nitrogen (N_2) and convert it into

Figure 36.2
The Nitrogen Cycle

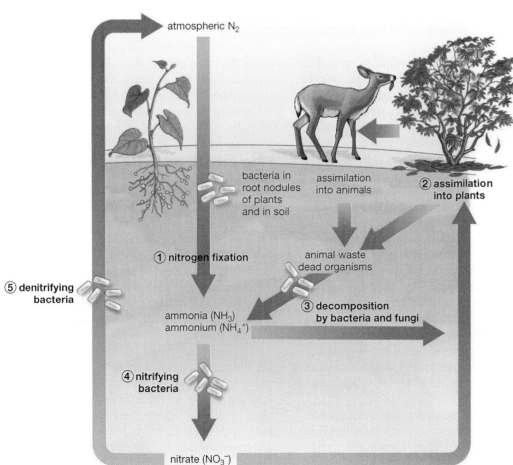

The nitrogen cycle

1. Nitrogen-fixing bacteria convert N_2 into ammonia (NH_3), which converts in water into the ammonium ion (NH_4^+). The latter is a compound that plants can assimilate into tissues. In the diagram, bacteria living symbiotically in plant root nodules have produced NH_4^+, which their plant partners have taken up and used. Meanwhile, free-standing bacteria living in the soil have likewise produced NH_4^+.

2. Other plants take up NH_4^+ that has been produced by soil-dwelling bacteria and assimilate it. Animals eat plants and assimilate the nitrogen from the plants.

3. Animal waste and the tissues of dead animals are decomposed by fungi and by other bacteria, which turn organic nitrogen back into NH_4^+.

4. Other "nitrifying" bacteria convert NH_4^+ into nitrate (NO_3^-), which likewise can be assimilated by plants.

5. Some nitrate, however, is converted by "denitrifying" bacteria back into atmospheric nitrogen, completing the cycle.

atmospheric N_2

bacteria in root nodules of plants and in soil

assimilation into animals

② **assimilation into plants**

① **nitrogen fixation**

⑤ **denitrifying bacteria**

animal waste dead organisms

③ **decomposition by bacteria and fungi**

ammonia (NH_3)
ammonium (NH_4^+)

④ **nitrifying bacteria**

nitrate (NO_3^-)

ammonia (NH_3). This ammonia then is converted (either in water or by other microbes) into two types of nitrogen-containing compounds that plants can *assimilate*—can take up and use. And, as you've seen, what comes into the plant world will come into the animal world when animals eat plants. The two usable nitrogen compounds produced in the cycle are the ammonium ion (NH_4^+) and nitrate (NO_3^-). Some of the nitrate that results from this process is used by yet another kind of bacteria, denitrifying bacteria, which can convert nitrate back into atmospheric nitrogen, completing the cycle.

Nitrogen as a Limiting Factor in Food Production

If you were to look at the nitrogen story 100 years ago, there would be little more to it than what you've just gone over. In other words, through most of human history, nitrogen was fixed solely by bacteria (with a small assist from lightning, which can produce a usable form of nitrogen that falls to the Earth in rain). Human beings had a problem with this single route to nitrogen, however, because nitrogen is critical for all plant growth, including *agricultural* plant growth. Indeed, for centuries a lack of nitrogen was a primary limiting factor in getting more food from a given amount of land. Long before anyone knew what nitrogen was, farmers were trying to get more of it to crops in two ways. One was by applying organic fertilizer, such as rotting organic material, to their fields. (Remember how the Pilgrims were taught by Native Americans to bury dead fish around their corn plants?) The second was by planting crops that carried their own nitrogen-fixing bacteria within them. This is the case with certain legumes, such as soybeans, which carry symbiotic bacteria in their root nodules. So great was the need for nitrogen that nitrogen-fixing plants were sometimes grown as "green manures"—as crops that were plowed right back into the ground to serve as fertilizers.

Early in the twentieth century, however, a momentous change came about in the use of nitrogen when the German chemist Fritz Haber developed an *industrial* process for turning atmospheric nitrogen into ammonia. In essence, human beings became nitrogen fixers, and by the 1960s, they had taken up this activity on a grand scale. In 2005, 121 million metric tons of biologically active nitrogen were manufactured, and human beings planted crops that resulted in the production of perhaps another 40 million metric tons. Put together, these human-produced quantities of nitrogen were greater than the amount of terrestrial nitrogen that all of nature produced on its own.

What are the consequences of this revolution in nitrogen production? One is that much more food can be grown on Earth's arable land. Indeed, the world's

human population could not be fed without the nitrogen fixation that human beings carry out. This massive human intervention in the nitrogen cycle has a downside as well, however. Remember that human-manufactured nitrogen ends up being used in a very *concentrated* way—it is poured onto farmland. A good deal of this nitrogen does not end up in the crops it was intended for, however, but instead departs as runoff. The amount of runoff generated by each farm adds up, and the end result can be large amounts of nitrogen flowing into creeks, ponds, and rivers. On a regional basis, such nitrogen flows can be enormous. The Mississippi River carries an estimated 1.5 million metric tons of nitrogen into the Gulf of Mexico each year.

You might think that since nitrogen is a nutrient, this would be a good thing for the Gulf waters, but the opposite is true. The nitrogen brings on a seasonal "bloom" of algae, the decaying algae feed a huge bacterial population, and the bacteria use up most of the available oxygen at the water's lower depths. The result is a giant "dead zone" that drives away mobile fish and that kills immobile, bottom-dwelling sea creatures (**Figure 36.3**). This problem of *nutrient pollution* is not limited to the Gulf of Mexico, however; it is played out in coastal waters around the world. An analysis delivered in 2008 identified more than 400 coastal regions that are oxygen-depleted or "hypoxic," either seasonally (during summer) or in episodes that may occur once every few years.

The Cycling of Water

Now, let's turn from nutrient to water cycling. Those who went through the material on water in Chapter 2 know how important water is to life. The human body is about 66 percent water by weight, and any living thing that does not have a supply of water is doomed in the long run. As with nitrogen or carbon, all water is either being cycled or is locked up. Carbon may be stored in coal or trees, but water can be stored in ice located on land—in glaciers or in polar ice, for example.

The oceans hold more than 95 percent of Earth's water, but thankfully for us, when the oceans' saltwater evaporates, it falls back to Earth as freshwater. We can also be grateful that not all ocean water falls back to Earth on the oceans; instead, about 10 percent falls on land (**Figure 36.4**). This water represents about 40 percent of the precipitation that land areas get; the other 60 percent comes from a form of cycling reviewed in Chapter 25, *transpiration*, meaning the process by which water is taken up by the roots of land plants, then moved up through their stems and out through their leaves as water vapor. After evaporating into the atmosphere, water returns to Earth as rain, fog, snow—all the forms of precipitation possible. The driving force behind the hydrologic cycle is heat from the sun, which powers both evaporation and transpiration.

(a) Runoff from the Atchafalaya and Mississippi Rivers...

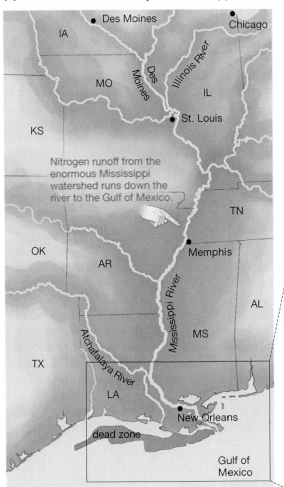

Figure 36.3
The Gulf of Mexico "Dead Zone"

(a) In 2008, the seasonal "dead zone" in the Gulf of Mexico stretched from the mouth of the Mississippi River to eastern Texas. The waters in the zone are hypoxic, or oxygen depleted, particularly at their lower depths. The primary cause is the tremendous amount of nitrogen carried into the Gulf from both the Mississippi and the Atchafalaya rivers. This nitrogen originates as fertilizer that is applied to farmland all the way up the Mississippi River basin.

(b) Why is this hypoxic zone so extensive? One factor at work is prevailing winds, which carry the discharge of the Mississippi and Atchafalaya Rivers westward, toward Texas. This satellite image of the region was taken in 2007.
(Image courtesy of the Louisiana State University Earth Scan Laboratory.)

(b) ...is given a wide distribution westward in the Gulf of Mexico.

Figure 36.4
The Hydrologic Cycle

Figure 36.5
Earth's Water

Although there is a tremendous amount of water on our planet, only a small fraction of it is available to us as freshwater.

With more than 95 percent of Earth's water in the oceans, perhaps as little as 2.5 percent of the Earth's water is freshwater at any given time. Of this freshwater, more than 75 percent is locked up in glaciers and other forms of ice (**Figure 36.5**). Thus, any snapshot we would take of Earth would show that as little as 0.5 percent of its water is available as liquid freshwater, but even here we have to qualify things. About 25 percent of this freshwater is **groundwater,** meaning water that moves down through the soil until it reaches porous rock that is saturated with water. In line with this, about

20 percent of the water used in the United States comes from groundwater, and at least a quarter of the world's population depends on groundwater to satisfy basic needs. Groundwater is stored in porous rock called an **aquifer,** an example of which is pictured in **Figure 36.6**. Major aquifers can be enormous, as you can see from the map of the High Plains Aquifer in **Figure 36.7**. Even an aquifer of this size, however, can lose more water through pumping than it gains through replenishment from rain. In 2007, the High Plains Aquifer stored about 2.9 billion acre-feet of water—the equivalent of 2.9 billion acres of water a foot deep. This is a lot of water to be sure, but it is some 270 million acre-feet less than the aquifer contained in 1950.

Global Human Use of Water

Given the sheer number of people on Earth and the importance of water to each of them, it will not surprise you to learn that human beings are laying claim to a great deal of Earth's freshwater; civilization now uses more than half the world's accessible supply. But from what you've seen so far, think of what this means. There is no less *water* than there ever was. Like nitrogen or carbon, all the water we have is either being recycled or is stored. What's changed is that the human population is using an ever-greater proportion of the water that's available. Since 1960, for example, the amount of water countries have impounded behind dams has quadrupled. Even so, the relentless

Figure 36.6
Aquifers Store Groundwater

When water seeps into the ground, it moves freely through layers of sand and porous rock but moves either extremely slowly or not at all through layers of impermeable rock. Water thus becomes trapped in different underground layers, from which humans can withdraw it. Unconfined aquifers receive water directly from a large surface area and therefore tend to be more vulnerable to pollution by chemicals such as fertilizers and pesticides. Confined aquifers are located between layers of impermeable rock. They are replenished more slowly but tend to contain purer water.

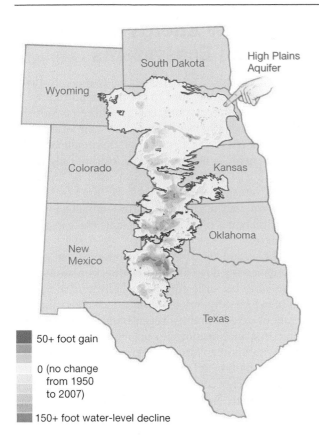

Figure 36.7
Enormous Store of Underground Water

The High Plains Aquifer, perhaps the largest aquifer in the world, underlies 174,000 square miles of land stretching across eight states. Billions of gallons of water are withdrawn from it each day, mostly for agriculture. As the figure shows, large portions of the aquifer have experienced little or no change in depth from 1950 to 2007. In some areas, however, water depth has declined greatly; in one part of Texas, it has been reduced by 234 feet.

(Modified from U.S. Geological Survey Figure 1, "Changes in Water Levels and Storage in the High Plains Aquifer, Predevelopment to 2007," Fact Sheet 2009–3005, February 2009.)

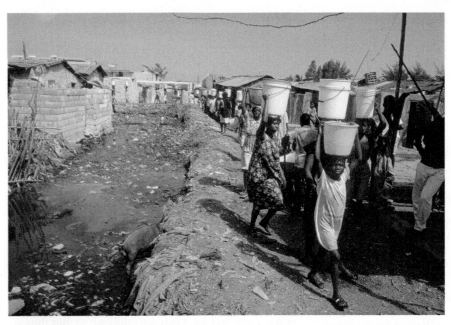

Figure 36.8
Freshwater Is a Limited Resource

Women carry drinking water through a polluted slum in Port-au-Prince, Haiti.

growth of the human population has meant that water remains a scarce commodity for human beings in locations throughout the world. Indeed, sanitary water is so scarce that an estimated 1 billion people worldwide lack access to it (**Figure 36.8**). A large part of the problem is that there is a mismatch between the location of freshwater and the location of human populations. Sixty percent of the world's population lives in Asia, while only 36 percent of Earth's precipitation falls there. Meanwhile, 6 percent of the world's people live in South America, but 26 percent of the world's precipitation falls there. (The Amazon River alone discharges 200,000 cubic meters of freshwater per *second* into the Atlantic Ocean, an amount so large that it constitutes 20 percent of the entire planet's freshwater runoff.)

Another part of the human water problem, water expert Peter Glieck has noted, is that humans make

such poor use of the water they capture. Mexico City's leaky water system *loses* enough water to meet the needs of a city the size of Rome. If the toilet in your house is more than 16 years old, chances are it uses 3.5 gallons of water with each flush, and may use as much as 5.5 gallons. Meanwhile, if it was manufactured since 1995, following imposition of new federal standards for low-flow toilets, it probably uses a mere 1.6 gallons.

When we think of societal use of water, however, household use actually is relatively small. About 70 percent of the water we humans withdraw from rivers, lakes, and groundwater goes to agricultural irrigation. People need food, of course, but the *way* irrigation is carried out in much of the world is extremely wasteful: Water moves from, say, a river to crops by means of an open channel. En route, much of this water either evaporates or is taken up by land that isn't being irrigated. An efficient alternative is "micro-irrigation," in which water gets piped to crops.

Human beings are, of course, capable of diverting water from species that have no say in this division of resources. More than 20 percent of all freshwater fish species are estimated to be threatened or endangered precisely because their water has been dammed or diverted for human use. California's natural populations of coho salmon have been reduced by some 94 percent since the 1940s, in significant part through diversions of the freshwater streams that the salmon swim up in order to spawn. If you look at **Figure 36.9** on the next page, you can get a quick idea of humanity's impact on water and on the two elements we just reviewed, carbon and nitrogen.

(a) Atmospheric CO_2 concentration

76% naturally occurring | 24% human-caused

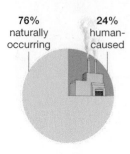

(b) Terrestrial nitrogen fixation

42% naturally occurring | 58% human-caused

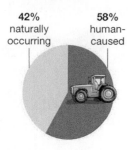

(c) Accessible surface water

46% available | 54% used

Figure 36.9
Human Impact on Resources

(a) Nearly a quarter of the current atmospheric carbon dioxide concentration is produced by human activity, primarily through the burning of fossil fuels.

(b) Over half of terrestrial nitrogen fixation comes about because of human activity, including the manufacture of fertilizer for agriculture.

(c) Over half of the Earth's accessible surface water is now diverted for use by humans, mostly for agriculture. Percentages are approximate.

Human Beings Are Not Separate from the Earth on Which They Live

One final thing about nutrient and water cycling: The average person, who has no knowledge of these cycling processes, may regard human beings as a kind of independent line that stretches back in time. Under this view, water and food may pass through us, but they are as separate from us as gasoline is from a car engine.

From your reading of this section, however, it may now be apparent to you that this is not true. Some of the carbon in the bread you ate this morning could have been contained in a tree that decomposed in China 100 years ago. After moving into the atmosphere as CO_2 and staying there for decades, this carbon was taken up by a wheat plant in America whose seeds were ground up, yielding flour that ended in the bread on your shelf. This carbon may be burned by your body to supply the energy it needs, it's true, but it may also become part of your bones or your nerves. Then, when you die, the material you are made of will go *back* to the Earth to be recycled in the ways you've been reading about, perhaps to be part of a tree or a person in a future generation. We are intertwined with the Earth in some basic, physical ways.

SO FAR . . .

1. An ecosystem includes a _____ of organisms and the _____ with which they interact.

2. The carbon that helps make up the living world moves into it by means of organisms that perform _____. Carbon then returns to the soil and atmosphere through means of the _____ of organic material by the organisms called _____ and _____.

3. Almost all the nitrogen that enters the living world by natural means does so through the actions of _____. Nitrogen is then returned to the atmosphere by the actions of _____.

36.3 How Energy Flows through Ecosystems

Having looked at the abiotic elements of nutrients and water, let's now turn to another important component of any ecosystem, energy. Those of you who read through Chapter 6 know that one of energy's inflexible laws—the first law of thermodynamics—is that energy is never gained or lost but only transformed. The sun's energy is not used up by green plants; rather, some of it that is captured by them is *converted* into a chemical form—initially into the chemical bonds of a sugar that plants make in photosynthesis.

The second law of thermodynamics is that energy spontaneously flows in only one direction: from more ordered to less ordered. The carbohydrate molecules in bread are very ordered things—so many atoms of carbon, oxygen, and hydrogen bonded together in a precise spatial relationship to one another. Contrast this with another form of energy, heat, which is the *random* motion of molecules—clearly a disordered form of energy compared to the chemical bonds in a carbohydrate. Indeed, heat is the last stop on the energy line because it is the least-ordered form of energy. And because all energy spontaneously moves toward less order, heat is the ultimate *fate* of all energy. Energy relentlessly ratchets down toward the form of heat because, like a casino that must get a "cut" of each bet laid down, heat gets a cut of each energy transaction. The chemical bonds in gasoline can be broken through combustion and thus be used to power a car engine, but not all the energy released from the combustion drives the engine. Some dissipates as heat, and this happens *every* time energy is used, whether we're talking about a piston firing or a cell dividing.

All of this provides a framework to conceptualize an important part of ecosystems, which is how energy flows through them. Think of the sun, with the energetic rays that leave it as a starting point; now, think of the ultimate destiny of all this energy, which is heat, randomly dispersed in the universe. Looked at one way, life on Earth *intervenes* in this flow. Life is an enormous energy collection and storage enterprise, gathering some of the sun's energy and locking it up for a time in the form of chemical bonds. These bonds can then be broken—think of digesting a muffin—which *releases* this stored energy so that an organism can grow and reproduce. Life does not stop the march of the sun's energy into heat, but it does intervene in it by transforming it into chemical bonds that have order and stability.

Once we see life in these terms, we can begin to think of the *flow* of energy through it. That's what you'll be looking at in the sections that follow.

Producers, Consumers, and Trophic Levels

One way to look at food and energy is in terms of production and consumption. Plants and other photosynthesizers (algae and some bacteria) are an ecosystem's **producers,** while the organisms that eat plants are one kind of **consumer:** an organism that eats other organisms, rather than producing its own food. But as you know, there are consumers *of* consumers—grass is eaten by zebras, but zebras are eaten by lions. Thus do we get to the concept of feeding levels or, as ecologists put it, trophic levels. More formally, a **trophic level** is a position in an ecosystem's food chain or web, with each level defined by a transfer of energy between one kind of organism and another. Producers are one level, and then there are several levels of consumers. Here's a list of trophic levels through four stages:

First trophic level:	**Producers—** (photosynthesizers)
Second trophic level:	**Primary consumers—** plant predators (herbivores)
Third trophic level:	**Secondary consumers—** herbivore predators (carnivores)
Fourth trophic level:	**Tertiary consumers—** organisms that feed on secondary consumers (carnivores)

It is the sun's energy that is locked up at the first trophic level, in leaves and stems, and it is this energy that is being passed along through all the other trophic levels. Note that the levels are not just categories that could be put in any order. We must have primary consumers to have secondary consumers; sharks cannot exist on algae (**Figure 36.10**). You may remember that an animal that eats only plants or algae is a **herbivore;** then there are **carnivores,** which eat only meat, and **omnivores,** which eat both plants and meat. Of course, many organisms cannot be assigned to just a single trophic level. Most human beings, for example, are primary, secondary, and tertiary consumers.

You have thus far thought in terms of food chains, which is to say trophic *lines* in which a single organism follows another. In reality, of course, nature is much more complex than this; what really exists are feeding patterns called *food webs,* one example of which you can see in **Figure 36.11** on the next page.

A Special Class of Consumers: Detritivores

To this scheme of trophic levels, ecologists add a special class of consumers, the **detritivores.** These are con-

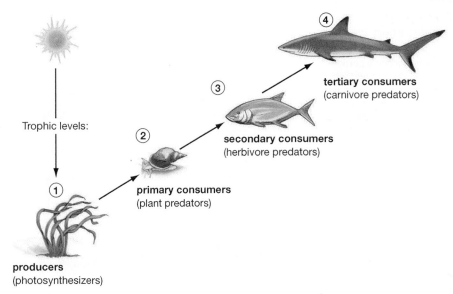

Figure 36.10
Trophic Levels

Plants, algae, and some bacteria are called producers because they use the sun's energy to produce their own food through photosynthesis. Organisms at all other trophic levels ultimately derive their energy from these photosynthesizers.

sumers that feed on detritus, which in normal usage simply means a collection of debris. In ecology, however, detritus is the remains of dead organisms or cast-off material from living organisms (a fallen branch from a living tree, for example). A worm or a dung beetle feeding on such material would fit this description of a detritivore.

Of particular interest, however, is a special kind of detritivore: a **decomposer,** which is an organism that, in feeding on dead or cast-off organic material, breaks it down into its inorganic components, which then can be recycled through the ecosystem. *Inorganic* here can be thought of as building blocks. (More technically, it means a compound that does not contain carbon bound covalently to hydrogen.) The most important decomposers are fungi and bacteria. A number of detritivores usually are responsible for breaking up organic material, first into pieces and then into the inorganic components that are recycled into the Earth and the atmosphere (**Figure 36.12** on the next page).

Stepping back from this, it's worth noting what complete use the living world makes of its own materials. Think of it this way: What does nature produce that it does not eventually decompose and recycle? The answer is, nothing at all. Every twig and beetle and bone that comes into existence eventually will be broken down into its component materials, which then will be used again. This is all to the good, actually, because if there were any natural garbage, spaceship Earth would sooner or later be filled up with this useless material. This very thought ought to give us some pause about the compounds human beings currently are putting into the environment

Figure 36.11
A River Food Web
The diagram indicates who eats whom along a portion of the Eel River in northern California. The arrows have been color coded by trophic level. Note that there are up to five trophic levels in the web.

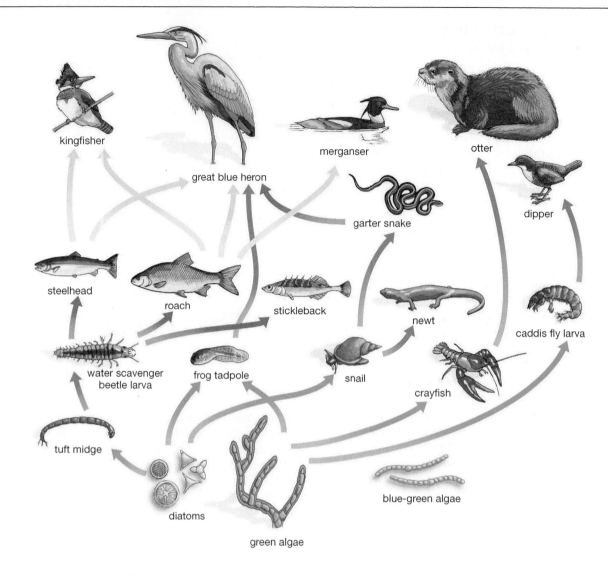

Figure 36.12
How Organic Material Is Broken Down
Different kinds of detritivores consume the organic material in a branch that has fallen from a tree. Most of these animals are consuming pieces of the log, but the detritivore called a decomposer (a fungus in the figure) is breaking organic materials into their inorganic components, thus returning nutrients to the soil.

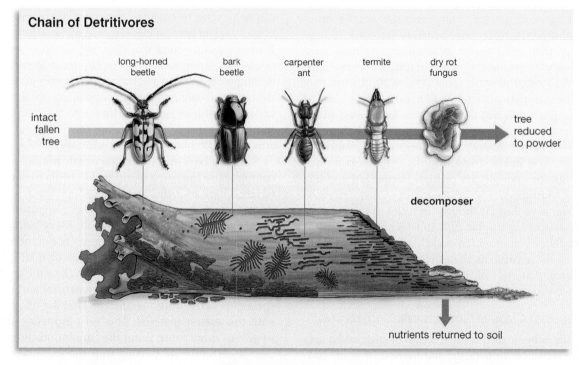

Chain of Detritivores

long-horned beetle   bark beetle   carpenter ant   termite   dry rot fungus

intact fallen tree   tree reduced to powder

decomposer

nutrients returned to soil

that are not **biodegradable,** meaning capable of being decomposed by living organisms. Of particular concern here are plastics, many of which will remain intact for hundreds of years following their production.

Accounting for Energy Flow through the Trophic Levels

All natural substances may be recycled in ecosystems, but this is not true of energy, which is just passing through, on its way to becoming heat. Two interesting questions arise from this: How *much* of the sun's energy does the living world collect in the first place, and then how much of the collected energy makes it through to each successive trophic level?

This may seem like a routine set of questions, but the first ecologists who thought in these terms brought about a revolution in ecology. Working in the 1940s at Minnesota's Cedar Bog Lake, ecologist Raymond Lindeman was the first to conceptualize ecosystems as units in which energy is first captured by given organisms and then transferred to others. This conceptualization is today known as the **energy-flow model** of ecosystems. Part of the impetus for Lindeman's research was to answer a very down-to-earth question, succinctly expressed by ecologist Paul Colinvaux: Why are big, fierce animals rare? (If you doubt that they are, think of this. It's utterly routine to see plants, insects, or small birds, but it's often the experience of a lifetime to see a bear or a shark.) The energy-flow model explained the small numbers of big, fierce animals, as you'll see, but it then went on to shed light on all kinds of ecological relationships. Why? Because energy is a kind of currency in the natural world; all organisms use it, and it is transferred among them. Moreover, it can be measured, usually in units called **kilocalories** (the amount of heat it takes to raise 1 kilogram of water 1 degree Celsius). If we know that a field mouse must use 68 percent of the kilocalories it consumes just to stay alive—to move, to keep a constant body temperature—but that a weasel must use 93 percent of its kilocalories for this purpose, that gives us a meaningful basis for comparison between these two animals. Beyond this, weasels *eat* field mice, and with the energy-flow model we have some basis for tracking this important commodity as it moves through an ecosystem.

The Capture of Energy by Plants

So, what has energy-flow research told us? To take things from the beginning, how much of the sun's energy do plants capture? As you can see in **Figure 36.13,** very little; only about 2 percent of the sun's energy that falls around plants is taken in for photosynthesis. This raises an important point, which is noting the

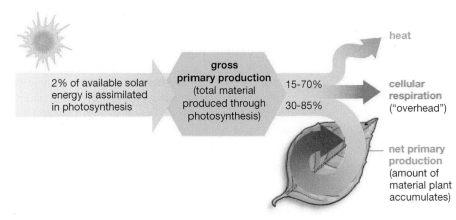

Figure 36.13
Absorption and Use of Solar Energy by Plants
Only 2 percent of the solar energy reaching the Earth's surface is taken in by plants for photosynthesis. Of this energy, only a fraction ends up being contained in plant material, such as leaves. It is this material (the plant's net primary production) that is available to the next trophic level in a food chain. The remaining energy is either dissipated as heat or used by photosynthesizers to power their own physical processes.

difference between the energy that *comes to* an organism and what the organism *does with* that energy.

The amount of material that a plant produces as a result of photosynthesis is known as its **gross primary production.** Those of you who have been through Chapter 8 know that the initial product of photosynthesis is a sugar that serves as a starting "building block" for all the material in the plant. Every time a molecule of this sugar is produced in photosynthesis, the plant has added to its gross primary production. But plants don't get to retain all the material they produce in this way. Why? Because plants incur energy *costs* in just staying alive. It takes energy to perform photosynthesis, to move sap from one end of the plant to the other, and so forth. Such costs are subsumed under the heading of "cellular respiration," but you could also think of them as the plant's overhead; they are the price of doing business. Apart from this, we know that, in every energy transaction, some of the energy is lost as heat. After subtracting these various costs, the plant is left with its **net primary production:** the amount of material a plant accumulates as a result of photosynthesis. This is the material that serves to build the plant up—its stems, leaves, and roots.

One question that arises from this framework is: What fraction of the energy a plant receives from the sun ends up as net primary production? How efficient are plants, in other words, at turning solar energy into stems, leaves, and roots? Of the solar energy that plants receive, somewhere between 30 and 85 percent is transferred into net primary production. In other words, at the low end of this range, only 30 percent of the solar energy a plant assimilates is transferred into material that is even potentially available to the next trophic level up.

Up a Level, to Primary Consumers

Now, what happens when you go up to that trophic level—to those primary consumers? Well, in the first place, they can't *get to* a lot of the tissue that's been produced, since it's in roots that are buried or in leaves that are too high to reach. A good deal of the material is inedible in any event, except by detritivores. Critically, most of the energy these scavengers take in is making an exit from the trophic chain; it won't be available to primary consumers, which means it won't be available to secondary or tertiary consumers either. Adding all this up, you can begin to see that, of the energy locked up by plants, very little is assimilated by organisms at the next step up. And this pattern of energy reduction is then repeated in the successive trophic levels. Indeed, the reductions tend to get more severe because animals have higher energy costs than plants have. (The warm-blooded animals we're most familiar with spend a great deal of energy keeping a constant body temperature—producing heat, which obviously is energy lost to the food chain.)

All of this leads to what you see in **Figure 36.14**: a reduction in available energy at each trophic level. The amount that is passed on between levels varies by community, but there is a rule of thumb in ecology that for each jump up in trophic level, the amount of available energy drops by 90 percent. Take all the energy converted into tissue by, say, second-level herbivores (rabbits, mice), and of this, only 10 percent ends up being converted into tissue by third-level carnivores (foxes, weasels). There is a great variability in conversion rates, however, and 10 percent probably is more like a maximum passed on.

The Effects of Energy Loss through Trophic Levels

So, what are the consequences of these reductions in energy at the various trophic levels? To a large extent, they are responsible for the makeup of the living world. Walk through a forest and what do you see? Innumerable small plants and trees, a fair number of small animals—birds, insects, squirrels—and, on very rare occasions, a predator such as a bobcat or a fox. The energy reduction that comes with each tropic level largely dictates these proportions. If you had a field that could feed 100 field mice, how many weasels could the field support if those weasels were existing solely on the mice? Remembering that, at most, only 10 percent of a trophic level's energy is likely to be passed along to the next level, you might guess that 10 weasels could make a living in the field, but even this number would be too high. For 10 predators to make a living from 100 mice, these predators would have to be no *bigger* than the mice, which is certainly not true of weasels. Extending this further, not even a single hawk could survive on the available weasels in the field. Why are big, fierce animals rare? Because of the loss of available energy at each step in the trophic chain. Because weasels are not about to start eating the same things as mice, weasels are locked into a trophic level with a more limited energy supply. When there's only so much energy, there can be only so many weasels.

Even so, do trophic energy reductions *entirely* explain the proportions of different life-forms in a given area? Probably not. More than 50 years ago, a trio of ecologists led by Nelson Hairston proposed that the overwhelming domination of plants within ecosystems comes about not solely because of trophic energy reductions but also because of a form of top-down predator control: the degree to which second-level herbivores are consumed by third-level carnivores. In 2006, Duke University's John Terborgh and his colleagues provided strong evidence that this kind of control does in fact help determine the makeup of ecosystems. The researchers looked at 4,300 square kilometers in Venezuela that had been flooded by government action in 1986, thus creating not only a human-made lake but a series of islands within it, all of which were large enough to support a collection of herbivores (leaf-cutter ants, rodents) but only some of which were large enough to support both herbivores *and* carnivores that preyed upon them (armadillos, large snakes). The result? Islands that lacked carnivores were stripped of vegetation by their now super-abundant herbivores, while islands that retained carnivores were able to retain their pre-flood greenery. The take-home message from this is that, while the makeup of ecosystems is powerfully conditioned by the bottom-to-top reductions of available energy, control is also exerted in the other direction—from predators down to producers. (The issue of energy loss by trophic level has relevance to a human issue, which is eating meat that comes from grain-fed cattle, as you can see in "A Cut for the Middleman: Livestock and Food," on page 706.)

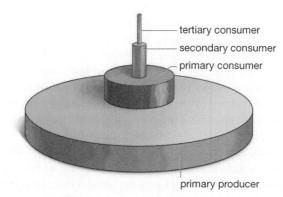

tertiary consumer

secondary consumer

primary consumer

primary producer

Figure 36.14
Energy Pyramid

Only a small fraction (10 percent or less) of energy at each trophic level is available to the next higher trophic level.

Primary Productivity Varies across the Earth by Region

Primary productivity concerns *biomass*, or material produced by first-level photosynthesizers, as measured by weight. It will come as no surprise that some areas of the Earth are more productive than others in this sense. If you look at **Figure 36.15**, you can get an idea of the differences around the globe. The reasons for these differences are explored in this chapter's section on the large ecosystems called biomes. For now, suffice it to say that much of what you see in Figure 36.15 is intuitive. Productivity is very low in such desert areas as North Africa and very high in such tropical rainforest areas as equatorial Africa. Yet why should one part of the Earth be a rainforest and another part a desert? The answer has to do with Earth's large-scale physical environment.

SO FAR . . .

1. All the organisms at the first trophic level perform _____ and thus are referred to as _____. Any organism that feeds solely on first-trophic-level organisms would have to be a (choose one) carnivore/herbivore/omnivore.

2. All material produced by living things is capable of being broken down into its inorganic components by the class of living things called _____. This material is thus said to be _____.

3. There are fewer predator than prey animals due to drastic reductions of _____ at each _____.

36.4 Earth's Physical Environment

Earth itself exists within an environment, called the **atmosphere,** which is the layer of gases surrounding the planet. One of the main things to realize about Earth's atmosphere is how it differs from outer space. There's something *to* Earth's atmosphere (a mix of gases), while outer space really is *space;* there's almost nothing in it.

The atmosphere is divided into several layers, but here you need be concerned with only two of them, which you can see illustrated in **Figure 36.16** on the next page. The lowest layer of the atmosphere, called the **troposphere,** starts at sea level and extends upward about 12 kilometers (or 7.4 miles), and it contains the bulk of the gases in the atmosphere. Nitrogen and oxygen make up 99 percent of the troposphere, but as you've seen, carbon dioxide exists there in small amounts, as do some other gases, such as argon and methane. After a transitional zone, the next layer above the troposphere is the **stratosphere.** Of greatest concern in it is a gas that reaches its greatest density at about 20 to 35 kilometers (13 to 21 miles) above sea level.

The oxygen we breathe comes in the form of two oxygen molecules bonded together (O_2). When ultraviolet sunlight strikes O_2 in the stratosphere, however, it can convert it into a form of three oxygen molecules bonded together (O_3). This is the gas known as **ozone.** Created initially as a *product* of life—since all atmospheric oxygen came from photosynthesis—this ozone layer ultimately came to *protect* life by blocking some 99 percent of the ultraviolet (UV) radiation the sun showers on the Earth. It was this blockage that allowed large life-forms to come on to land some 460 million years ago, and it is this blockage that protects life now. The UV radiation that pours from the sun can wreak havoc on living tissue, bringing about cancer and immune-system problems in people, and damaging vegetation as well.

Figure 36.15

Primary Productivity by Geographic Region

Primary productivity around the globe. This composite satellite image shows how the concentration of plant life varies on both land and sea. On land, the areas of lowest productivity are tan colored, as with the enormous swath of land that begins with the eastern Sahara Desert in North Africa. More productive land areas are yellow, more productive yet are light green, and the most productive of all are dark green. On the oceans, the gradient runs from dark blue (the least productive), through lighter blue, green, yellow, and orange-red (the most productive). The ocean measurements are of concentrations of phytoplankton—the tiny, photosynthesizing organisms that drift on the water and form the base of the marine food web. Note the high productivity of the oceans in both the far northern and southern latitudes. Antarctica itself is gray because the imaging technique did not work well for it.

Figure 36.16
Earth's Atmosphere

The two lowest layers of the atmosphere are shown, with Mount Everest (the tallest mountain) included for vertical scale. The troposphere contains most of the atmosphere's gases—mostly nitrogen and oxygen, with some carbon dioxide, methane, and other gases. The stratosphere contains the ozone layer, which blocks 99 percent of the sun's harmful ultraviolet radiation.

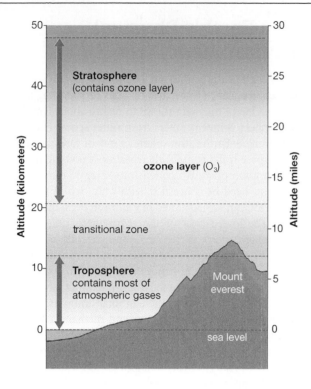

The Worrisome Issue of Ozone Depletion

Given the importance of the ozone layer, it is sobering to contemplate how fragile it is. Some human-made chemical compounds have the effect of destroying stratospheric ozone, and such destruction went on unchecked for years until atmospheric chemists Sherwood Rowland and Mario Molina revealed, in 1974, that compounds called chlorofluorocarbons posed a direct threat to the ozone layer. Chlorofluorocarbons, or **CFCs**—found at one time in spray cans, refrigerators, and plastic foams—are undoubtedly the most famous of the ozone-depleting compounds, but they are by no means the only chemicals that have this effect. Other harmful compounds include methyl bromide, which is used as a pesticide and herbicide, notably on tomato and strawberry crops; and bromine, which is found in a group of fire-extinguishing chemicals. The damage that these compounds have done to stratospheric ozone has brought about the spectacle of annual reports on how big the "ozone hole" is over the South Pole, along with a concern about a general thinning of the ozone layer.

Despite the ominous nature of this news, the long-term outlook on ozone depletion actually is good. In an agreement signed in Montreal in 1987, many of the world's nations pledged to phase out production of ozone-depleting chemicals, and this agreement is working. Production of CFCs was banned in the United States even before the Montreal agreement was signed and has dropped dramatically throughout the world in recent years. This reduction has brought about a reduction in the levels of ozone-depleting compounds

in Earth's atmosphere. As a consequence, the thickness of Earth's ozone layer stabilized beginning in the mid-1990s, according to a United Nations assessment published in 2006. If current trends continue, the Earth's ozone layer outside the polar regions should return to its pre-1980 levels about the middle of this century. The annual Antarctic ozone hole will be a feature of life for decades, but even the Antarctic ozone layer should return to its pre-1980 thickness by 2060 to 2075, according to the U.N.

36.5 Global Warming

Scientists are not nearly so hopeful about a second environmental issue that concerns Earth's atmosphere—the issue of global warming. Identified as a concern as far back as the 1950s, global warming has emerged as perhaps the most pressing environmental problem of our time, a status that's not surprising given that its reach really is global and that its effects stand to be profound: Residents of low-lying areas from Florida to Bangladesh must worry about its ability to raise sea levels; residents of coastal areas from Texas to the Philippines must worry about its ability to increase the intensity of tropical storms; and farmers from Nebraska to Argentina must worry about its ability to change rainfall patterns.

The seriousness of these issues has prompted an intense worldwide research effort that has managed to answer some questions about global warming while leaving other questions open. Uncertainty is a given in almost any analysis of global warming, however, because the most crucial questions about it concern not the effects it's having now, but rather the effects it stands to have in the future.

Warming and Its Causes

Our most authoritative judgments on global warming come from a United Nations group called the Intergovernmental Panel on Climate Change, or IPCC, which has issued four reports since 1990, each of them the work of hundreds of scientists who have reviewed the findings of thousands of their fellow researchers. In its latest report, released in 2007, the panel was able to provide some detail on one of the most basic questions about global warming: How much of it is taking place? In the 100 years that elapsed between 1906 and 2005, the panel said, the Earth's surface temperature increased by about 0.74 degrees Celsius, or about 1.3 degrees Fahrenheit. Moreover, it noted, the warming trend over the 50 years before 2005 was nearly twice that for the previous 100 years, and 11 of the 12 years between 1995 and 2006 were the warmest that have been recorded since such measurements started being taken in the middle of the nineteenth century. A more recent

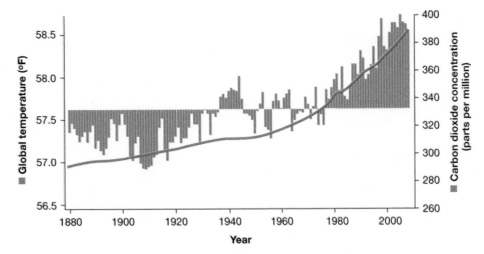

Figure 36.17

With a Rise in CO₂ Levels, a Rise in Temperature

How did global temperatures for each of the years between 1880 and 2000 vary against the average temperature for the entire twentieth century? As the figure shows, yearly temperatures before the late 1930s were uniformly below the century's average, while yearly temperatures after 1980 were uniformly above it. The red line tracks the period's rise in atmospheric CO₂ concentrations, which correlates strongly with the global temperature increases.

(Adapted from "Global Temperature and Carbon Dioxide," *Global Climate Change Impacts in the United States,* Thomas R. Karl, Jerry M. Melillo, and Thomas C. Peterson (eds.), Cambridge University Press 2009, p. 17.)

analysis performed by NASA found that the 10 years between 2000 and 2009 were the warmest in the historical record.

So, what's causing this increase? We humans are transferring large amounts of heat-trapping gases into Earth's atmosphere through several means. First and foremost, we are burning fossil fuels, such as oil and coal, which results in a massive transfer of carbon dioxide (CO₂) into the atmosphere. Next, the cattle we raise and the rice we grow put large amounts of the heat-trapping gas methane into the atmosphere. Third, the deforestation we are carrying out—particularly in the tropics—either puts CO₂ directly into the atmosphere, when trees are burned, or results in less CO₂ being taken *out* of the atmosphere, since trees that are killed no longer take up CO₂ to perform photosynthesis.

So, how significantly have these activities altered Earth's atmosphere? To look just at CO₂, it turns out that a greater concentration of it exists in the atmosphere now than at any time in the last 650,000 years. In 2008, Earth's atmospheric CO₂ concentration was 385 *parts per million*—for every million molecules of dry air, there were 385 molecules of CO₂. In contrast, the highest CO₂ concentration ever recorded over the previous 650,000 years was 300 parts per million. (Scientists can look this far back in time by analyzing the CO₂ in ancient ice cores.) If you look at **Figure 36.17**, you can see how CO₂ concentrations have changed from 1880 forward, and how this change correlates with the rise in global temperatures. **Figure 36.18** then shows you how unlikely it is that anything other than human activity could be responsible for the rise in Earth's temperature.

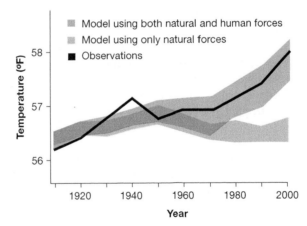

Figure 36.18

A Warming Caused by Human Activity

Scientists who worked on the 2007 IPCC report produced climate models—the blue and red lines in the figure—showing how Earth's temperature would have been expected to change over the course of the twentieth century under two different scenarios: with human inputs (such as CO₂ emissions) and without them. They then overlaid Earth's actual temperature change on these models and found there is a very good fit between what has actually occurred on Earth and what was predicted for it when the human inputs were factored in. Findings such as these have convinced scientists that human activity is responsible for most of the warming Earth has experienced over the last half-century. Were it not for human activity, in fact, Earth probably would have experienced a slight cooling over this period, as the blue line in the figure shows.

(Adapted from "Global Temperature and Carbon Dioxide," *Global Climate Change Impacts in the United States,* Thomas R. Karl, Jerry M. Melillo, and Thomas C. Peterson (eds.), Cambridge University Press 2009, p. 20.)

ESSAY

A Cut for the Middleman: Livestock and Food

It may be difficult to think of cows in a field as occupants of one of the trophic levels you've been looking at, but that's just what they are, with some provocative consequences for human beings and food. People can't survive on grass the way cows and sheep can, and it follows that these

It takes 9 pounds of feed to produce 1 pound of beef ready for human consumption.

animals are turning food that is useless to human beings into products that are use*ful* to human beings—meat, wool, and milk. In this sense, then, these animals are a boon to the efficiency of worldwide agriculture in that they allow us to get more human food and other products from the same amount of land.

There is another side to this story, however, having to do with the *loss* of food that occurs as we move up through the trophic levels. Recall that, as a rough rule of thumb, 90 percent of the energy that is locked up in one trophic level is lost to the organisms in the next trophic level. If cattle and other domesticated animals were

doing nothing but foraging—if they were being fed solely on the grass available in pastures—this would not be a matter of concern because the grass is not useful to humans as a food source anyway. But in developed countries such as the United States, much of the diet of domesticated animals comes from *grain* that is grown on farms. A large portion of this animal feed could go directly to human beings, but it instead passes through the trophic level of animals, with a predictable result: It takes 9 pounds of feed to produce 1 pound of beef ready for human consumption. What does this mean in practice? A harvest of 2,000 pounds of grain will feed five people for a year. Take roughly this same harvest, feed it to livestock, and then feed the livestock products to people, and you will feed only *one* person for a year.

This calculation takes on added importance when considering the scale of the grain-fed operation. In the feedlot, while

being fattened for slaughter, an average steer consumes up to 2,700 pounds of grain. It may be apparent that such consumption adds up quickly; some 70 percent of the grain produced in the United States is fed to livestock, a figure that becomes understandable in light of the fact that there are about 70 million cattle in the United States and Canada alone.

Fattening at the Feedlot
About 40,000 head of cattle are fed for meat production at this commercial feedlot in Imperial Valley, California.

Figure 36.19
The Greenhouse Effect

The high-energy rays of the sun can easily penetrate the layer of gases in the troposphere. However, the lower-energy radiation (heat) that reflects from Earth's surface cannot penetrate the layer of gases as easily. Carbon dioxide and methane thus take on the role of glass panes in a greenhouse: They let solar energy in, but they retain a good deal of heat.

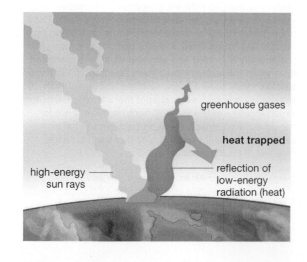

greenhouse gases

heat trapped

high-energy sun rays

reflection of low-energy radiation (heat)

What Is the Greenhouse Effect?

But why should the atmospheric concentration of gases such as CO_2 have anything to do with a warmer planet? Sunlight that is not filtered out by ozone comes to Earth in the form of very energetic, short waves that can easily pass through the atmosphere (**Figure 36.19**). Once this energy reaches the land and ocean, most of it is quickly transformed into heat that does all the things you've just read about: warms the planet, drives the water cycle, and so forth. This heat ultimately is radiated back toward space. But heat is not short-wave radiation; it is *long*-wave radiation, and it can be trapped by certain compounds, among them carbon dioxide and methane.

Global Warming's Consequences

All of this leads to the most critical question about global warming: What will its consequences be? The answer to this question hinges in large part on what the world's industrialized nations do in coming years with respect to their emissions of greenhouse gases. If they put higher levels of these gases into the atmosphere, then the world can expect higher global temperatures, higher sea levels, and so forth. To allow policy makers and the public to understand the linkage between given levels of emissions and the effects they would have, the 2007 IPCC report provided a set of "scenarios" that envisioned humanity either reducing its future emissions by a substantial amount (lower emissions scenarios) or reducing them very little (higher emissions scenarios). In the United States, a federal panel called the U.S. Global Change Research Program then used these alternate scenarios to try to predict what global warming stands to mean in the United States over the course of this century. If you look at **Figure 36.20**, you can see three of the panel's predictions, culled from a list of scores it produced. Looking at the bigger picture,

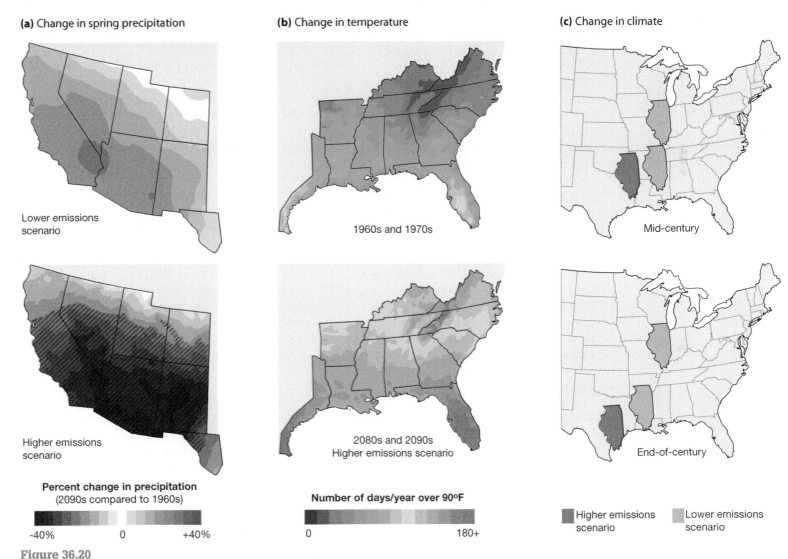

(a) Change in spring precipitation

Lower emissions scenario

Higher emissions scenario

Percent change in precipitation
(2090s compared to 1960s)

−40%   0   +40%

(b) Change in temperature

1960s and 1970s

2080s and 2090s
Higher emissions scenario

Number of days/year over 90°F

0   180+

(c) Change in climate

Mid-century

End-of-century

Higher emissions scenario   Lower emissions scenario

Figure 36.20
Drier West, Warming East, Warming Midwest
Three likely effects of global warming in the United States during the twenty-first century, as predicted by the U.S. Global Change Research Program.

(a) Under either lower or higher emissions scenarios, the Southwest of the late twenty-first century will be a drier place in spring—much drier under the higher emissions scenario.

(b) Under a higher emissions scenario, the United States from the Atlantic seashore to East Texas is likely to experience a great increase in the number of days each year in which the temperature climbs above 90. By the end of the century, North Florida will have more than 165 such days annually, whereas in the 1960s and 1970s, it had about 60.

(c) Under both lower emissions scenarios (orange icons) and higher ones (red icons), the Illinois climate of the mid- and late twenty-first century will resemble the Alabama and Texas climates of today.
(Adapted from "Global Temperature and Carbon Dioxide," *Global Climate Change Impacts in the United States,* Thomas R. Karl, Jerry M. Melillo, and Thomas C. Peterson (eds.), Cambridge University Press 2009, pp. 112, 117, 130.)

global warming is certain to produce some large-scale alterations in Earth's physical environment. Among these are:

- **Changes in sea levels.** In 2007, the IPCC predicted that, by century's end, global sea levels could be expected to rise by somewhere between 7 inches and 1.9 feet, depending on levels of greenhouse gas emissions, but it noted that it could not factor one important variable into its calculations: how much the massive ice sheets of Greenland and Antarctica stand to melt over the course of this century because of global warming. Since 2007, scientists have been able to take this melting into account and as a result have come to a revised consensus about how much sea-level rise we can expect: roughly a meter, or about 3.2 feet. What would this mean in practice? The U.S. Environmental Protection Agency has estimated that a 2-foot rise in sea levels would eliminate some 10,000 square miles of land in the United States, including undeveloped wetlands, with south Florida and Louisiana being most vulnerable to these effects. Apart from such outright losses of land, rising sea levels will also intensify the effects of flooding and will increase the salinity of freshwater sources, such as groundwater tables.

- **Changes in precipitation.** Under higher emissions scenarios, rainfall and snowfall actually stand to increase in winter months in the northern United States and Canada but to decrease across the southern United States. In summer, meanwhile, rainfall will decline all across the country, except in relatively small portions of the East Coast and the Southwest, where there is expected to be no change.

- **Changes in habitat.** Each 1.8° Fahrenheit of temperature change on Earth moves ecological habitat by about 100 miles, so that a North American species that today is adapted to life near, say, Des Moines, Iowa, would in the future find its ideal habitat shifted to a latitude near Minneapolis, Minnesota, if global temperatures rise by 4.0°F. Of course, only some animal and plant species will be capable of making such "poleward" migration, or of changing their behavior in accordance with warming—by, for example, flowering earlier in the year—so that the mix of species in different habitats stands to be altered in coming decades. Temperatures are not increasing at uniform rates throughout the world, however; Earth's arctic regions are warming at two to three times the global rate, and many arctic species have nowhere colder to go than their current habitat.

A Narrow Window to Take Action

Predictions such as these often are looked at by the general public as outcomes that are merely hypothetical or that can be avoided by future action. But scientific evidence is increasingly indicating that society has a very narrow time frame in which to take significant action on global warming. To get a sense of what's in play, consider that, in the years since the last IPCC report was issued, scientists have been focused intently on ways to hold warming to no more than 3.6°F above the temperature levels that existed in the pre-industrial era. This is so because there is growing scientific consensus that any increases beyond 3.6°F stand a good chance of producing what is called "dangerous climate change," meaning catastrophic or irreversible climate alteration, such as regional dry-season rainfall levels comparable to those seen in the U.S. "dust bowl" in the 1930s.

Given this possibility, scientists have calculated what the world would have to do to hold warming to the 3.6°F level, and the challenge appears to be daunting. When all greenhouse gases are considered, long-term atmospheric CO_2 concentrations would need to be stabilized at the equivalent of 400 parts per million—a mere 15 parts per million above the levels that existed in 2008.

This would still seem to leave societies some room to maneuver, but in recent years worldwide carbon emissions have not merely been rising; they've been rising at levels higher than those the IPCC anticipated in 2007 even under its worst-case scenarios. The problem this confronts society with has been framed by scientists in the following way: To stand a 75 percent chance of avoiding warming in excess of 3.6°F, no more than 275 billion metric tons of carbon could be added to the atmosphere during the 50 years between 2000 and 2050. But nearly a third of this amount of carbon was added to the atmosphere during the first *nine years* of this period—from 2000 to 2009. If the world is to stand a good chance of avoiding catastrophic warming, then, it essentially has two options: Cut greenhouse gas emissions significantly beginning very soon, or cut them dramatically, through what would doubtless be a wrenching, traumatic process in the more distant future.

A Challenge to Societies

But can emissions be reduced significantly in the near future? Certainly there is no shortage of ideas about how to accomplish this; economists, scientists, and politicians have put forward a long list of proposals. And there is broad agreement about the kinds of steps societies must take to achieve this reduction: They have to use less energy, reduce the degree to which they use fossil fuels as energy sources, find a way to safely store or "sequester" some of the carbon dioxide that continues to be produced, and slow the destruction of

Earth's tropical rainforests. All these ideas, however, involve economic trade-offs. Since the mid-nineteenth century, human societies have been powered mostly by fossil fuels because these have been the cheapest fuels available. To change now means turning to alternatives that are more costly in an economic sense but less costly in an environmental sense. In coming years, we'll see if human societies are up to the task of paying an economic price for getting a healthier planet.

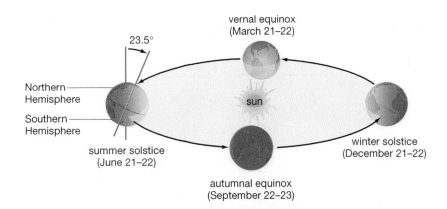

SO FAR . . .

1. Ozone is a gas composed entirely of the element _____ that reaches its greatest density in the layer of the atmosphere known as the _____ and that has the effect of keeping _____ from reaching Earth's surface.

2. Most of the energetic short-wave radiation from the sun is transformed into _____, which can be trapped by greenhouse gases such as _____ and _____.

3. Global warming is certain to produce a _____ in global sea levels and a(n) _____ in precipitation in the United States.

36.6 Earth's Climate

Why Are Some Areas Wet and Some Dry, Some Hot and Some Cold?

Did you ever look at a globe representing the Earth and wonder why it is tilted? Earth exists in space, after all, so what could it be tilted against? When we say that a rod stuck in the ground is tilted, we mean that it is not perpendicular to the ground. Here, of course, we're thinking of the ground as a flat surface—a plane. Earth, too, can be viewed as existing on a plane, in this case the plane of its orbit around the sun. (We generally think of this orbit as looking like a large hula hoop with the sun as a yellow ball in the middle.) Now think of the spherical Earth on this plane as having a rod sticking through it in the form of its north–south axis—the imaginary line that runs from the North Pole straight through to the South Pole. The critical thing is that this rod does not stick straight up and down with respect to the plane of the Earth's orbit; it is tilted, at an angle of 23.5 degrees. This tilt dictates a good deal about Earth's climate, and Earth's climate dictates a great deal about life on Earth. Once again, in other words, the sun determines the basic conditions for life.

You can see the effects of Earth's tilt in **Figure 36.21**: In June, our Northern Hemisphere tilts toward the sun, while in January it tilts away from it. Thus, the sun's rays strike us more directly in June, and the days are warmer (and longer) than days in January. The angle at which the sun's rays strike a given portion of the Earth is very important. Relative to, say, Brazil, sunlight strikes the Arctic at an indirect or "oblique" angle. Thus, the far north gets less of the solar energy that powers photosynthesis.

The Circulation of the Atmosphere and Its Relation to Rain

The variation in temperature caused by these sunlight differences is the most important factor in the circulation of Earth's atmosphere. Near the equator, Earth simply gets more warmth, and, critically, warm air rises. Warm air also can retain more *moisture* than cold air. You've seen an example of this whenever you've looked at the beads of "sweat" that form on the outside of a cold glass in summer. Moisture-laden warm air comes into contact with the cooler air immediately around the glass; thus cooled, the air cannot hold as much moisture and releases it onto the glass.

This same thing happens with the warm air that rises on both sides of the equator. Because of the heat of the tropics, air is rising in quantity from the tropical oceans; because this air is warm, it is carrying with it a great deal of moisture. The air cools as it rises, however, and then drops much of its moisture on the tropics, which is why they're so wet.

Following this a step further, this volume of air is now cooler, drier, and moving toward the poles in both directions from the equator (**Figure 36.22** on the next page). At about 30° N and 30° S of the equator, it descends, warming as it drops and actually absorbing moisture *from* the land. The land will be dry at these latitudes because this is where the dry, hot air descends.

The air that has descended now flows in two directions from the 30° point. In the Northern Hemisphere, this means north toward the North Pole

**Figure 36.21
Earth's Tilt and the Seasons**

The Northern Hemisphere gets more sunlight in June and less in January, while the reverse is true for the Southern Hemisphere. This is the reason for seasonal climate variations over large portions of the globe.

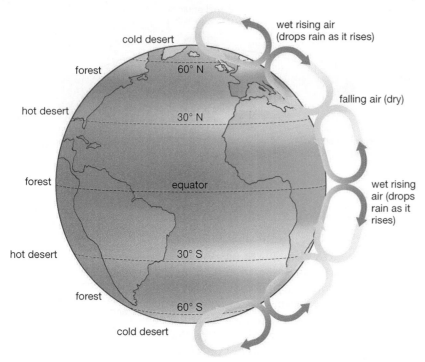

Figure 36.22
Earth's Atmospheric Circulation Cells

Because the Earth receives its most direct sunlight at the equator, this region is warm—and warm air holds moisture and rises. This air moves north and south from the equator, cooling as it rises, and then loses its moisture as rain, with the result that the land and ocean immediately north and south of the equator get lots of rain. As the now-dry air moves farther north and south, it cools and sinks again at about 30° in both hemispheres. Thus, the land at these latitudes tends to be dry. Two other bands of circulation cells exist at higher latitudes, operating under the same principles.

lation cells" of moving air, each existing all the way around the planet at its latitude, and each acting like a conveyor belt that is dropping rain on the Earth where it rises but drying the Earth where it descends.

The Impact of Earth's Circulation Cells

The full meaning of this becomes obvious only when you look at a map such as the one in **Figure 36.23** (or better yet, a globe). Draw your finger across the equatorial latitude on the map and look at how much green there is—Southeast Asia, equatorial Africa, the Amazon. This is no surprise because we expect the equator to be wet and green. Now, however, do the same thing at the dry 30° N latitude. Look at how much desert there is at this latitude all around the globe—it's where we find the Sahara, the Arabian, and the Sonoran deserts, among others. And there's more desert territory at 30° S, with the Australian desert and Africa's Namib. From this, you can see that the climatic fate of Earth's various regions is largely written in our globe's large-scale wind patterns.

Mountain Chains Affect Precipitation Patterns

Latitude doesn't tell the whole story about precipitation on Earth, however. Mountain ranges force air upward, and this air also cools as it rises, dropping its moisture on the windward side of the range. Then the air descends on the opposite (leeward) side of the range, only this time it is dry air and is thus picking up moisture from the ground rather than depositing it (**Figure 36.24**). A dramatic example of this "rain-shadow" effect can be seen on the Pacific Coast of the United States in southern Oregon, where the western side of the Cascade Mountains is lush with greenery all year round, while the basin below the eastern slopes is a desert.

and south toward the equator. Traveling at a fairly low altitude, this air eventually picks up moisture, rises, and deposits its moisture, this time at about 60° N and near the equator, with the same events happening at the same locations in the Southern Hemisphere.

What you get from this rising and falling is what you see in Figure 36.22: a set of interrelated "circu-

Figure 36.23
Earth's Atmospheric
Circulation Cells and
Precipitation

The wettest regions of the Earth lie along the equator, while the driest regions lie along the latitudes 30° N and 30° S. Compare these regions to the circulation cells shown in Figure 36.22. The variations of rainfall patterns within cells are explained by factors such as the presence of mountain ranges.

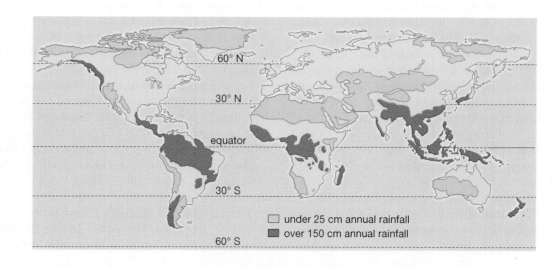

☐ under 25 cm annual rainfall
■ over 150 cm annual rainfall

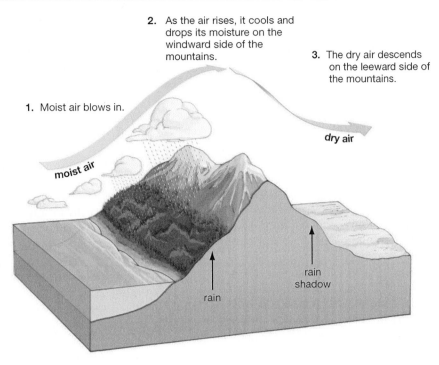

2. As the air rises, it cools and drops its moisture on the windward side of the mountains.

3. The dry air descends on the leeward side of the mountains.

1. Moist air blows in.

dry air

moist air

rain

rain shadow

Figure 36.24
Rain Shadows
Mountain ranges force moving air to rise. This cools the air, causing it to lose its moisture on the windward side of the range. This creates a rain shadow, meaning a lack of precipitation, on the leeward side of the range.

Beyond this, we know that it's possible to be in a warm latitude, such as that of Ecuador in South America, and still be very cold—if you go to the top of the Ecuadorian Andes. As altitude increases, temperature drops, in other words. The changes in climate that occur as you move from flatland to mountain peak are similar to the changes that occur as you move from the equator to one of the poles.

The Importance of Climate to Life

The factors you have just reviewed are among the most important in shaping the large-scale **climates**, or average weather conditions, we find on Earth. It's obvious that climate has a great deal of influence on life since we never see polar bears in Panama or monkeys in Montana, but this influence is even greater than you might think. Looking over the globe, you see different forms of dominant vegetation in different areas—grassland in America's Great Plains, rainforest in northern Brazil. So strongly does climate affect this pattern that Earth's vegetation regions essentially are defined by Earth's climate regions. Far in Canada's north, there is a fairly distinct boundary at which Canada's vast coniferous forest gives way to the mat-like vegetation called tundra. North of this line there is tundra; south of it are the forests. What is this line? In summer, it is the far southern reach of a mass of cold air called the arctic frontal zone (**Figure 36.25**).

Vegetative formations generally overlap one another to a greater extent than is seen with Canada's tundra and coniferous forest, so that the closer we get to a vegetation boundary, the less distinct it looks. Nevertheless, there are discrete regions of vegetation on Earth whose boundaries are largely determined by climate—particularly by temperature and rainfall. Vegetative exceptions within these regions tend to be mountains, whose climates can vary greatly from base to peak.

Figure 36.25
Line of Transition
In Alaska's Denali National Park, a region of forested taiga vegetation gives way to a region of grassy tundra vegetation in a fairly abrupt way.

36.7 Earth's Biomes

When these large land vegetation formations are looked at as ecosystems—complete with animals, fungi, nutrient cycling, and all the rest—they go by the name **biomes:** large terrestrial regions of the Earth that have similar climates and hence similar vegetative formations. Grasslands, whether found in Russia or in the American Midwest, are ecologically very similar to one another and thus constitute one type of biome. The tropical rainforests found in Africa, South America, and Asia constitute another. The world can be divided into any number of different biome types—this is a human classification system overlaid on nature—but six are recognized as the minimum: tundra, taiga, temperate deciduous forest, temperate grassland, desert, and tropical rainforest. Polar ice and mountains often are recognized as separate biomes as well, as is another grassland variation, the savanna, found most famously in equatorial Africa. There is also chaparral, a shrub-dominated vegetation formation found in "Mediterranean" climates such as those on California's coast. See **Figure 36.26** for an overview of locations of these biome types throughout the globe.

The fact that two biomes are of the same type does not mean that they are identical. Two areas that are broadly the same in climate can end up with some significant differences in life-forms. Let's look briefly now at each of Earth's major biome types and then at its aquatic ecosystems.

Figure 36.26
Distribution of Biomes across the Earth

Cold and Lying Low: Tundra

Along with polar ice, **tundra** is the biome of the far north, stretching in a vast, mostly frozen, ring around the northern rim of the world. So inaccessible is tundra that the average person may never have heard of it, yet it occupies about a fourth of Earth's land surface. The word *tundra* comes from a Finnish word that means "treeless plain," and the description is apt. Its flat terrain stretches out for mile after mile with little change in the vegetational pattern of low shrubs, mosses, lichens, grasses, and the grass-like sedges (**Figure 36.27**).

Tundra is a paradoxical biome in that it gets an average of about 25 centimeters (or 10 inches) of rain per year, which almost puts it in the desert category. Yet it is marshy in summer, with numerous shallow lakes dotting its surface. How can both things be true? Once the summer rain falls, it essentially has no place to go. No more than a meter below the surface, the ground is permanently frozen down to a depth of as much as 500 meters, or a quarter mile (although this is changing because of global warming). This is the **permafrost,** or permanent ice, which acts as a boundary beyond which neither water nor roots can go. Because water cannot drain far into the soil, it sits on top of the tundra in summer, which makes for the bogs and small lakes. The low-lying tundra vegetation makes the most of a short growing season—lasting as little as 50 days—by producing a year's worth of food through photosynthesis in only a few weeks.

The tundra has a good deal of animal life, particularly in the summer when migrating animals move north to feed on the vegetation. Large mammals such as caribou and musk oxen live there. Arctic hares and foxes are year-round residents, as are arctic lemmings—herbivores that are key to much of the tundra's animal food web.

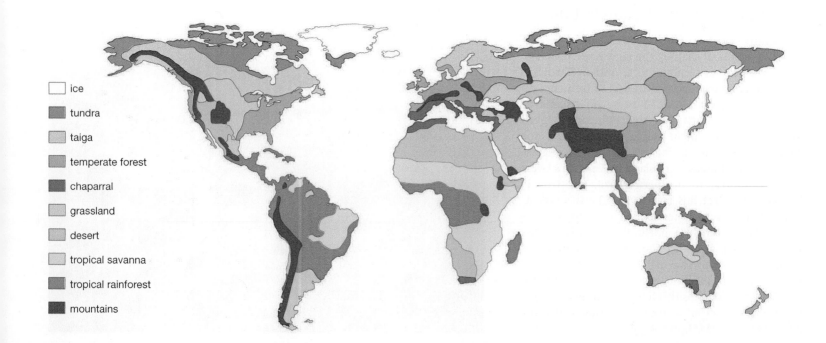

- ice
- tundra
- taiga
- temperate forest
- chaparral
- grassland
- desert
- tropical savanna
- tropical rainforest
- mountains

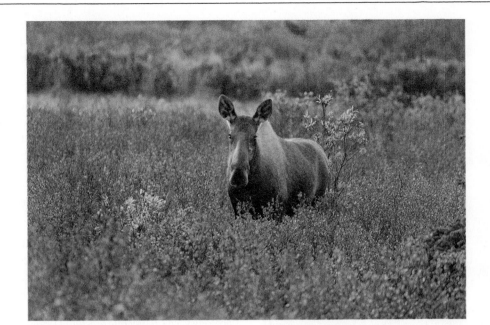

Figure 36.27
Tundra
An Alaska-Yukon moose (*Alces alces*) in the Alaskan tundra in fall.

Northern Forests: Taiga

The **taiga,** or boreal (northern) forest, includes the enormous expanse of coniferous trees mentioned earlier that juts up against the tundra. Conditions are still fairly dry and cold, and the growing season is short in this northern biome, but in all three respects the taiga is less severe than the tundra. Note in Figure 36.26 that, as with tundra, taiga is found almost solely in the Northern Hemisphere. This is so because there is little land in the Southern Hemisphere at the extreme latitudes of these biomes.

The taiga is a model of species uniformity, as only a few types of trees—spruce, fir, and pine—are the ecological dominants, but they are present in great numbers. The taiga's vegetation supports lots of animals, including large mammals such as moose, bear, and caribou (**Figure 36.28**). When thinking of the fur trade, you might have in mind some freezing, coniferous territory in the far north. The taiga turns out to be it. Sables, minks, beavers, arctic hares, wolverines—this harsh biome has an abundance of these furred creatures.

Hot in Summer, Cold in Winter: Temperate Deciduous Forest

Temperate deciduous forest is a biome familiar throughout much of the United States, as it exists roughly from the Great Lakes nearly to the Gulf of Mexico and from the western Great Lakes to the Atlantic Ocean. The pine forests that cover large parts of the southeastern United States generally are considered to be part of the temperate deciduous biome because the pines are a successional stage *leading to* deciduous forest. Meanwhile, the warm Gulf Coast is not temperate deciduous forest per se but a variant on

Figure 36.28
Taiga
Alaskan caribou in winter in the northern-forest biome known as taiga.

it called temperate evergreen forest. Much of Europe and eastern China fit within the temperate deciduous classification, although large parts of Europe have few forests left, and the same is true of China.

Temperate deciduous forests are the forests of maple, beech, oak, and hickory (**Figure 36.29** on the next page). The *deciduous* in the name refers to trees that exhibit a pattern of loss of leaves in the fall and regrowth of them in the spring. Trees do not dominate these forests to the extent they do the taiga, however. Making use of the good soil, a robust "understory" of woody and herbaceous plants will spring up on the floor of the deciduous forest. Some of this activity occurs early in the growing season,

Figure 36.29
Temperate Deciduous Forest

Plenty of water and seasonally warm temperatures lead to abundant plant and animal life in the biome known as temperate deciduous forest. This landscape is part of Pennsylvania's Allegheny National Forest.

before the trees have "leafed out" and blocked the sunlight. Temperate forests grow where there is plenty of water—between 75 and 200 centimeters (or 30 to 78 inches) per year, with the lower amount being three times what the tundra gets. It's worth noting that while the tundra has no reptiles or amphibians and the taiga has only a few, the temperate deciduous forest has an environment that is wet and warm enough to support a variety of both animal forms.

When Europeans first came to North America in significant numbers, in the seventeenth century, there

Figure 36.30
Temperate Grassland

The Samuel H. Ordway Prairie in South Dakota provides some idea of what America's prairies looked like prior to the arrival of Europeans, as most of the land in it was never plowed under for crops.

probably were more than a billion acres of forest in what would become the United States. By 1907, about 250 million acres of this forest had been cleared, primarily for agricultural use. The temperate deciduous forest cover in the eastern United States reached its lowest level by about 1860, after which it began to rebound because of the westward movement of farming into the Midwest. Between 1997 and 2002, forested land in the United States as a whole actually increased by about 10 million acres.

Dry but Very Fertile: Temperate Grassland

There is an irregular line in western Indiana that forms the boundary between deciduous forest and prairie. What is "prairie" in the United States is known as "steppes" in Russia, "pampas" in Argentina, and "veldt" in South Africa. These are all names for the biome that ecologists call *temperate grassland* (**Figure 36.30**).

Looked at one way, grasslands are what often literally lie between forests and deserts. Whereas the precipitation range for deciduous forests is from 75 to 200 centimeters per year (30 to 78 inches), for grassland the range is from 25 to 100 centimeters per year (10 to 39 inches). The North American grassland has its own internal division based on the amount of rainfall. It ranges from tallgrass prairie in Illinois to a drier mixed-grass prairie that begins at about the middle of Kansas and Nebraska—this is where the Great Plains begin—to a short-grass prairie that lies in the rain shadow of the Rocky Mountains. (This same tallgrass/short-grass gradient exists in the steppes of Asia, only there the gradient runs from north to south.) Other American grassland areas can be found in California's Central Valley and eastern Washington and Oregon.

A type of tropical grassland, the **tropical savanna,** exists in Australia, Africa, and South America. Tropical savanna is characterized by seasonal drought, small changes in the generally warm temperatures throughout the year, and stands of naturally occurring trees that punctuate the grassland. This is the homeland of many of the great mammals we associate with Africa, such as lions and zebras.

When Europeans first beheld the American grasslands, they could scarcely believe what they saw: a territory that had essentially no trees but instead a sea of grasses that could grow up to 10 feet tall in the wetter tallgrass prairie. Prairie soil turned out to be some of the most fertile on Earth, however, and that fact eventually spelled the end of natural prairie in the United States and most of the rest of the world. Almost all the tallgrass and mixed-grass prairie in the United States eventually was plowed under for cultivation, while the short-grass prairie is now used for crops and cattle grazing. Prior to the coming of Europeans, 22 million acres of Illinois were prairie; today, that figure stands at slightly more than 2,000 acres. From the former prairie, however, the United States feeds itself and some of the world outside its borders. Illinois, Kansas, and Nebraska are still grasslands, but the grasses that grow there now are not the native big bluestem or needlegrass; they are corn and wheat.

Chaparral: Rainy Winters, Dry Summers

Chaparral is not grassland but instead is a biome dominated by evergreen shrub vegetation that is dotted with pine and scrub oak trees. Chaparral is found in areas that have a so-called Mediterranean climate. There are five of these areas in the world, all very similar in appearance. One of them is the Mediterranean basin itself; then there is southwestern Australia, central Chile, a small part of western South Africa, and parts of coastal California. What these areas have in common is that they are on the west coast of a landmass. Thus, they lie in the path of ocean winds that bring wet, mild winters and very dry summers.

The Challenge of Water: Deserts

Deserts can be defined as biomes in which rainfall is less than 25 centimeters, or 10 inches, per year, and water evaporation rates are high relative to rainfall (**Figure 36.31**). Note that deserts are not defined by temperature. There can be temperate deserts (the Mojave in Southern California), cold deserts (the Gobi in China), and hot-weather deserts (the Sahara in Africa). Around the globe, some 20 major deserts collectively cover about 30 percent of Earth's land surface. What we think of as desert can transition imperceptibly into dry grassland.

Precipitation is not only low in the desert, it is sporadic; that is, most of the moisture a desert gets will come in just a few days during the year. Given this, desert life has relentlessly been shaped by one overriding requirement: Collect water and then conserve it. The flowering plant grouping called bromeliads have a species, *Tillandsia straminea,* that is blown around on the deserts of coastal Peru much like a dead tumbleweed, only this is a living plant, nearly rootless, that gets all its moisture from *fog* that it is able to absorb.

Desert animals are no less remarkable in this respect. The kangaroo rat (genus *Dipodomys*) can be found in many parts of the American Southwest. It comes out of its underground burrow only at night when temperatures fall, it has no sweat glands, and it generally does not drink standing water (there being almost none available). Instead, the kangaroo rat gets by on the water produced by metabolizing the seeds it eats.

Lush Life, Now Threatened: Tropical Rainforests

Many people have an idea that the Earth's **tropical rainforests** are important, but they're not quite sure why. There are two main reasons. First, along with coral reefs and algal beds, they are the most productive biome type in the world, meaning they produce more biomass per square meter of territory than any other. Second, no other ecosystem can touch them in terms of species diversity. As noted earlier, for mile after mile in the taiga, trees might be limited to one or two species. In the tropical forests of the Amazon, meanwhile, more than 300 species of trees have been identified in a single hectare of land, which is about 2.5 acres. In Chapter 35, you read about a researcher who found an estimated 1,700 species of beetle in one tree in the Panamanian rainforest. In a sense, this isn't surprising because half of all the identified plant and animal species on Earth reside in tropical rainforests. This despite the fact that, compared to the other biomes you've looked at, they don't occupy a lot of territory: about 7 percent of the Earth's surface.

The problem, as most people know, is that the rainforests are disappearing—significant portions of them are being either burned down or cut down. The period of great temperate forest loss came before the twentieth century, but we are living in the period of great tropical forest loss. How significant is the reduction? The United Nations estimates that, in Brazil alone, rainforest losses from 2000 to 2006 totaled about 50,000 square miles—an area about the size of Alabama. The Brazilian forest makes up the lion's share of what is by far the world's largest tropical rainforest, the nearly two-million-square-mile Amazon Basin Forest, which runs from Venezuela south to Bolivia and at one point nearly from the Atlantic to the Pacific. Significant rainforests also can be found in Central America, equatorial Africa, and regions of Southeast Asia near the equator.

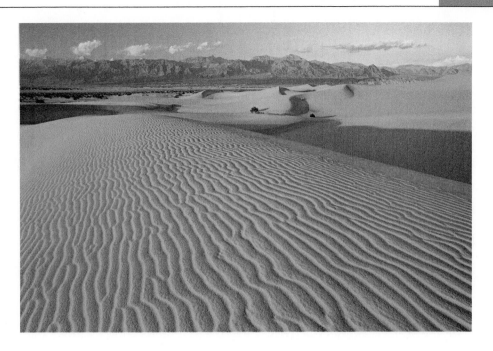

Figure 36.31
Desert

When water gets sparse, life does, too. Shown are the Mesquite Flat Sand Dunes in California's Death Valley National Park.

Figure 36.32
Tropical Rainforest
Abundant rain and warm weather mean abundant growth and a great diversity in life-forms in the biome known as the tropical rainforest. Shown is a lowland rainforest on the Segama River in Borneo.

Rainforests are lands of rain and stable, warm temperatures (**Figure 36.32**). The norm for rainfall is between 200 and 450 centimeters, or about 78 to 175 inches, a year, but some areas get up to 1,000 centimeters annually, which is 390 inches. You've seen that much of the richness of the temperate grasslands can be found in their soil. In the tropical rainforest, however, almost all the richness is on display above ground (much of it 20 to 40 meters above ground in the extensive forest "canopy"). The rainforest has such a large and efficient group of detritivores that organic material dropping to the forest floor is decomposed by them and absorbed almost immediately by plant roots rather than by the surrounding soil. This means the soil never gets built up; it is nutrient poor and often acidic. How can this be squared with this biome's fantastic productivity? The nutrients are simply bypassing the soil, going from plant to detritivore and back to plant.

Figure 36.33
Ocean Zones

36.8 Life in the Water: Aquatic Ecosystems

We turn now from life on land to life in the water. Because we humans are land creatures, it might be good to get our bearings by thinking about how one kind of aquatic environment, the ocean, can be divided up in terms of the life in it.

Marine Ecosystems

The ocean's **coastal zone** extends from the point on the shore where the ocean's waves reach at high tide to a point out at sea where an ocean-floor formation called the continental shelf drops off (**Figure 36.33**). Beyond this point, there is the *open sea*. Within the coastal zone, there is an area bordered on one side by the ocean's low-tide mark and on the other by its high-tide mark. This is the **intertidal zone.**

If you look next at the ocean strictly in its vertical dimension, all of the water from the ocean's surface to its floor is called the *pelagic zone*, while the ocean floor itself is called the *benthic zone*. Within the pelagic zone, from sea level down to a depth of at least 100 meters (about 330 feet), the sun's rays can penetrate strongly enough to drive photosynthesis. This zone of photosynthesis is known as the *photic zone*.

More Productive Near the Coasts, Less Productive on the Open Sea

Each of these zones marks off an area that is meaningful in relation to life. Start first at the intertidal zone. This is a world *in between*, we might say, because the creatures in it live part of the time submerged in the ocean and part of the time exposed to the air. It turns out that the intertidal zone is extremely productive for a reason that you might think would make it unproductive: The ocean waves, which bring in nutrients,

Good News about the Environment

A sense of gloom about the environment may arise from between the lines of these pages as the list of current or potential environmental problems piles up: global warming, nitrogen buildup, overuse of water resources, tropical rainforest destruction. These are real problems, but their existence should not blind us to the fact that there has been a great deal of good news about the environment in the past 40 years, much of it showing how effective government can be when prodded into action by its citizens.

If there was a time for unrestrained gloom about the environment in the United States, it probably would have been in the late 1960s, when the country had plenty of endangered species but no Endangered Species Act; when levels of smog in Los Angeles were almost twice what they are now; when there was plenty of household trash to be recycled, but almost no recycling going on; when only a third of the bodies of water in the country were safe for fishing and swimming, whereas today two-thirds are.

As a symbol of change, consider Cleveland, Ohio, whose Cuyahoga River was so polluted in 1969 that it *caught fire*, while southwestern Lake Erie, into which the Cuyahoga flows, was essentially a dead zone for fish during the late summer. The lake came to this low state in part because of the nearly 80 metric tons of phosphorus—then regularly added to washing detergents—that were dumped into it each day. That figure has now been reduced by perhaps 85 percent, and Lake Erie is biologically very active and a major freshwater fishery. Meanwhile, the Cuyahoga River, once virtually dead to all forms of life, now has 20 species of fish swimming in it near Cleveland and eagles and blue herons now nest along its banks farther upstream. How did this change come about? After the 1969 fire, the region worked tirelessly to clean up its waterway, spending $3.5 billion on the effort.

Similar stories could be told about other regions across the United States. Simply put, there has been a profound change with respect to the environment over the past 40 years. From pollution controls to species protection to personal recycling, environmentalism has entered not only our law books but, more impor-

Environmentalism has entered not only our law books but, more important, our consciousness.

tant, our consciousness. When populations of Atlantic swordfish were observed to be declining in the late 1990s, a campaign titled "Give Swordfish a Break" was organized that quickly enlisted 27 top New York chefs. What could chefs do about

environment—in this case, the sensitivity of a group of American chefs. And sensitivity to the environment has grown not just in America but in most developed countries. The cleanup of Lake Erie required the cooperation of the United States and Canada; the heartening trend in preservation of the Earth's ozone layer is the product of an international agreement.

None of this is to say that mechanisms are in place such that we need not worry about the environment. Far from it: Largely because of the growth in human population and the greater per capita use of natural resources, the environment is threatened on thousands of fronts and will remain so as far out as we can see into the future. But the record of the past 40 years is not just one of environmental loss; it is

Back to Healthy Numbers
Populations of Atlantic swordfish (*Xiaphas gladius*) were severely depleted by the late 1990s. A campaign spearheaded by environmentalists spurred governmental action that brought the swordfish numbers back to healthy levels by 2002—just three years after an international conservation program was put in place.

swordfish populations? They pledged to take swordfish off their restaurants' menus. It was government action that brought the Atlantic swordfish population back to healthy levels, but initial public awareness of the swordfish campaign came about because of *personal* sensitivity to the

one of great environmental accomplishment as well. Perhaps the period's most important lesson is that there is nothing inevitable about environmental degradation. Concerned, hardworking people have made a great deal of difference in this issue.

(a) A man and two children investigate tide pools

(b) Penguins swimming underwater

(c) Fish swimming near coral reef

carry away wastes and expose more of the surface area of photosynthesizers to sunlight.

Ocean life continues to be abundant out past the intertidal zone and in general remains so all the way to the end of the coastal zone. In short, ocean life is most productive in its shallower depths (**Figure 36.34**). Once past the continental shelf and into the open ocean, productivity can drop off to levels that are less than those of a desert. Why should this be so? Remember that sunlight strong enough to power photosynthesis penetrates ocean waters only to a depth of 100 meters or so. Meanwhile, the average depth of the ocean is about 3,000 meters, or 1.8 miles. Thus there is a vast depth of open ocean that simply isn't very productive. Indeed, life at greater ocean depths essentially depends on organic particles, referred to as "marine snow," that rain down from above. One measure of the coastal zone's importance is that it is the location of all the world's great fisheries, some of which are now beginning to show signs of returning to health after years of being degraded—something you can read more about in "Hopeful Signs for the World's Fish" on page 720.

More Productive Near the Poles, Less Productive Away from Them

Apart from the shallow-to-deep transition, the ocean also has one other gradient with respect to the amount of life it harbors. In the pelagic zone, there is relatively more ocean life toward the poles, with this concentration decreasing with movement toward the equator—the exact opposite of what we find with land life. The oceans that surround Antarctica are filled with life. **Phytoplankton,** meaning floating, microscopic photosynthesizers such as algae and cyanobacteria, are the base producers for it all. These are consumed by the tiny floating animals known as **zooplankton.** Shrimp-like crustaceans called krill feed mostly on the phytoplankton and serve as the principal source of food for the whales and seals we associate with this area.

Cities of Productivity: Coral Reefs

Despite the richness of the colder oceans, the tropical oceans do boast marine communities that are as productive as any in the ocean—indeed, as any on

Figure 36.34
Diversity in Ocean Life

(a) A man and two children investigate tide pools, a part of the ocean's intertidal zone. The deeper water beyond them can be seen both above and below the surface.

(b) The seas off Antarctica are teeming with aquatic life. Here, emperor penguins (*Aptenodytes forsteri*) dive in Antarctic waters.

(c) Coral reefs are sites of high productivity and diversity. Here, a group of raccoon butterfly fish (*Chaetodon fasciatus*) stand out against the background of a coral reef in the Red Sea.

Earth. These are the coral reefs, which lie in shallow waters at the edge of continents or islands at tropical latitudes. **Coral reefs** are warm-water ocean structures composed of the remains of coral animals. Each animal, known as a polyp, is a tiny relative of the more familiar sea anemones. Coral polyps secrete calcium carbonate, better known as limestone, a practice they share with a type of symbiotic red algae that live inside them. The limestone forms an external skeleton for the corals, and when each coral dies, its limestone skeleton remains. Thus, coral reefs are composed largely of the stacked-up remains of countless generations of coral polyps along with the remains of their symbiotic algae. But the thin outer veneer of each reef is composed of *living* algae and the latest generation of pinhead-sized corals.

You can get an idea of how many generations of coral are piled up by considering that most reefs are between 5,000 and 8,000 years old—and some are millions of years old. What the reef as a whole creates is *habitat*: nooks and crannies and tunnels and surfaces that are home to an amazing array of living things. So rich is this habitat that it covers only 2 percent of the ocean's floor but is home to perhaps 25 percent of the ocean's species. One coral reef, Australia's Great Barrier Reef, also is one of the largest structures created by any living thing, including humans. It measures some 2,000 kilometers, or 1,200 miles, in length.

Sadly, coral reefs are now imperiled cities of biological productivity. By one estimate, 27 percent of the world's coral reefs have now been lost as functioning ecosystems, although with coral reefs, loss of activity is not always permanent. The greatest single source of this destruction was the El Niño-caused ocean warming of 1997–1998, which brought about a phenomenon known as *coral bleaching,* meaning a discoloration of the reefs due to the death of symbiotic algae that live within the coral animals. Temporary weather events aside, the longer-term threat to coral reefs is human activity. Oil is dumped into the ocean, sewage and runoff from cities harms the reefs, divers may trample them.

The biggest threat that coral reefs face, however, may be another product of the worldwide change we looked at earlier, global warming. Some of the excess atmospheric carbon that drives global warming has been absorbed by the oceans in recent decades, and this carbon is making the oceans more acidic. The problem is that ocean acidification may interfere with the ability of corals and their algal partners to pull dissolved calcium out of ocean water—something these organisms must do to produce their skeletons. We know that coral calcium absorption declined in Australia's Great Barrier Reef by about 14 percent from 1990 to 2005 and that a decline greater than this occurred among some corals in Bermuda over the last few decades. The question now before scientists is

whether these declines have come about because of ocean acidification.

Freshwater Systems

Whereas the oceans cover almost three-quarters of Earth's surface, freshwater ecosystems—inland lakes, rivers, and other running water—together cover only about 2.1 percent of Earth's surface. Like the ocean, lakes can be divided into biological zones. The most productive zone in a lake is the shallow-water area along its edge, the *littoral zone,* whose outer boundary is defined as the point at which the water is so deep that rooted plants can no longer grow. Then there is the *photic zone,* which starts at the surface of the lake and extends down to the point at which sunlight no longer penetrates strongly enough to drive photosynthesis. Finally, there is the area beneath the photic zone, the *profundal zone,* in which photosynthesis can't be performed (**Figure 36.35**).

Nutrients in Lakes

Lakes can be naturally *eutrophic,* meaning nutrient rich, or *oligotrophic,* meaning nutrient poor. A lake that has few nutrients will have relatively few photosynthesizers, and this in turn means few animals. Oligotrophic lakes generally are clear (and deep), while eutrophic lakes often have an abundant algal cover.

Nutrient enrichment can happen naturally over time, or it can take place because of human intervention. The latter variety is known as *artificial eutrophication,* a process that sometimes is undertaken intentionally just to increase the yield of fish from a lake or pond. There is such a thing as having too *many* human-added nutrients in a body of water, however. We touched on this earlier in connection with the Gulf of Mexico's "dead zone," which results from the tons of nitrogen that flow into it. But

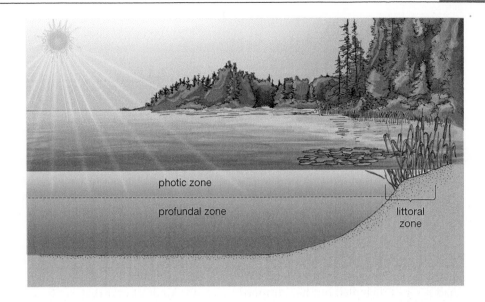

Figure 36.35
Zones in a Lake

The littoral zone starts at water's edge and extends out to the point at which rooted plants can no longer grow. The photic zone starts at the lake's surface and extends down to the point at which sunlight no longer drives photosynthesis. The profundal zone is the area beneath the photic zone in which photosynthesis cannot be performed.

photic zone

profundal zone

littoral zone

Hopeful Signs for the World's Fish

At one time, marine wildlife experts thought that the bounty of fish in the world's oceans was so immense it could never be exhausted. But that idea began to be challenged in the late 1980s, and by the mid-1990s it was effectively dead as it became clear that the numbers of certain kinds of fish had not just dwindled but had dropped to alarmingly low levels. The enormous populations of Atlantic cod once found off the Canadian coast were gone by the early 1990s, for example, and in 2003 researchers reported that the global ocean has lost 90 percent of the fish in its big predatory species—bluefin tuna, blue marlin, Antarctic cod, and sharks among them.

In 2009, however, one of the most comprehensive assessments ever conducted of the world's fisheries yielded a more hopeful message. While 63 percent of the world's ocean fish stocks have been depleted to levels that require them to be rebuilt, fish populations in well-managed fishing areas are recovering and they are doing so through methods that can be applied to fisheries in general: Reducing allowable catches, putting restrictions on the kinds of gear that can be used in fishing, closing off certain areas to fishing altogether, and giving fishermen shares of ownership in regional fish harvests. Such management techniques have stabilized fish populations in five of the world's Large Marine Ecosystems, or LMEs—coastal fishing areas so enormous that one of them includes the entire northeast continental shelf of the United States. Three other LMEs are still being over-fished, however, while two others have never been depleted. Historically, the problem in most fisheries is that rebuilding efforts in them "only begin after there is drastic and undeniable evidence of overexploitation" in the words of the assessment, which was authored by a team of scientists led by ecologist Boris Worm of Dalhousie University in Canada and fisheries scientist Ray Hilborn of the University of Washington, Seattle.

The overexploitation examined in the assessment essentially has come about because, in recent decades, the world's fishing fleets have gotten more efficient at scouring the Earth for large populations of fish. By using ever-more-sophisticated technology, the fleets have managed to find fish no matter what kind of terrain they are located in. Ultimately, however, such fishing practices cannot be sustained because, beyond a certain point of exploitation, fish populations cannot renew themselves. The good news is that proper management techniques can seemingly allow fish populations to remain robust indefinitely.

Figure 36.36
Too Many Nutrients

A pond with an overabundance of nutrients has experienced an overgrowth of algae—an algal bloom—that may be detrimental to other life-forms in the pond.

smaller bodies of water can undergo eutrophication as well. An overabundance of such nutrients as phosphorus or nitrogen brings on an overabundance of algae—a so-called **algal bloom**—and this eventually means an overabundance of dead algae falling to the bottom of the lake (**Figure 36.36**). When this happens, decomposing bacteria flourish, and they are using oxygen—so much of it that the fish in a lake can suffocate. How do these harmful levels of phosphorus or nitrogen get into freshwater aquatic ecosystems? Fertilizers from lawns or agriculture and construction that disturbs bedrock, sewage, and detergents are some of the sources (although in many states phosphate-containing detergents have been banned for decades). This is one form of human environmental impact that can be reversible in a straightforward way: Reduce the nutrients that are flowing into the ecosystem.

Estuaries and Wetlands: Two Very Productive Bodies of Water

There is one important type of aquatic water system that always straddles the line between a freshwater

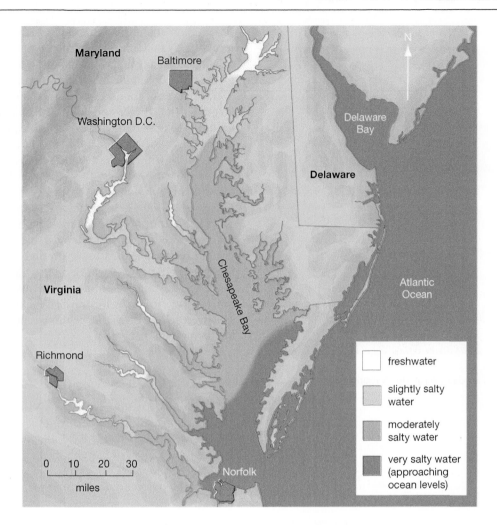

Figure 36.37
Where Saltwater and Freshwater Meet
The Chesapeake Bay is one of the largest and most productive estuaries in the world. In it, the freshwater of 19 principal rivers meets the saltwater of the ocean, forming zones of different degrees of saltiness. Each zone supports specific communities of organisms.

(Redrawn from A. J. Lippson and R. L. Lippson, *Life in the Chesapeake Bay*, Johns Hopkins University Press, Baltimore, 1984.)

Map legend:
- freshwater
- slightly salty water
- moderately salty water
- very salty water (approaching ocean levels)

and saltwater habitat. This is the **estuary,** an area where a stream or river flows into the ocean. Estuaries rank with tropical forests and coral reefs in being the most productive ecosystems on Earth. The cause of this productivity is the constant movement of water—the same force at work in the ocean's intertidal zone. Ocean tides and river flow are constantly stirring up estuary silt that is rich in nutrients. Plants and algae thus get an abundance of these substances, grow in abundance, and pass their bounty up the food chain. In **Figure 36.37**, you can see an image of an important estuary in the United States, the Chesapeake Bay.

Another important type of aquatic ecosystem is **wetlands,** which are just what they sound like—lands that are wet for at least part of the year. "Wet" here covers a variety of conditions, from soil that is merely temporarily waterlogged—a prairie "pothole" in Minnesota, for example—to a cover of permanent water that may be several feet in depth (the bayous of Louisiana). Wetlands go by such specific names as swamps, bogs, marshes, and tidal marshes; the overwhelming majority of them are freshwater inland wetlands rather than the ocean-abutting coastal wetlands, which can be freshwater or saltwater (**Figure 36.38** on the next page). Wetlands are sites of great biological productivity, and they serve as vital habitat for migratory birds. It's been estimated that the amount of wetlands in the United States has been reduced by 55 percent since the arrival of Europeans— 120 million of the 215 million acres that were originally wetlands have been drained or paved over. Currently, the state of Florida and the federal government are working on one of the most far-reaching and expensive habitat restoration efforts in history as they try to bring the largest expanse of wetlands in the nation, the Florida Everglades, to a healthier condition over the next 20 years.

Life's Largest Scale: The Biosphere

In this chapter, you've been reviewing life on a very large scale, which is to say the aquatic ecosystems and biomes of the Earth. But there is one larger scale of life yet, which is the collection of all the world's ecosystems, the **biosphere,** which is also thought of as that portion of the Earth that supports life. Much could be said about the biosphere, but here's just one

(a) Prairie pothole ponds in North Dakota's Lostwood National Wildlife Refuge

(b) An overhead view of the sawgrass prairie in Florida's Everglades National Park

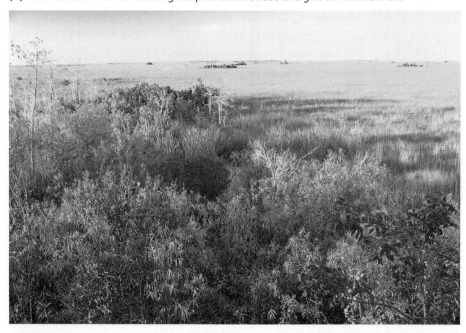

Figure 36.38
Inland Wetland and Coastal Wetland

observation about life on this global scale. The Earth is about 24,000 miles in circumference, with life existing along any line you could draw all around the globe. If we look at life in its *vertical* dimension, however, it has been found to exist only about 1.8 miles below Earth's surface and about 5.2 miles above sea level (in the upper Himalayas). This means that all of life on Earth exists in a band that is at most about 7 miles thick, with the vast bulk existing in an even narrower span. Actually, this is all the life that we know of in the *universe,* so that if we could imagine ourselves traveling by cosmic elevator, we could potentially come up from the molten center of Earth, pass through the bacteria lodged between underground rocks, and then move through a tissue-thin layer of a green living world, after which we might never see anything like it again, no matter how far out into the universe we traveled. Taking this perspective, the really remarkable thing is not how much life there is, but how little.

SO FAR . . .

1. With increasing distance from the shoreline toward open sea, the abundance of marine life _____. With increasing distance from the ocean's surface toward the ocean floor, the abundance of marine life _____.

2. The tiny organisms collectively called _____ lie at the base of most marine food webs, thanks to their ability to _____.

3. An estuary is an area where a stream or river _____.

Go to the Study Area at www.masteringbiology.com for practice quizzes, myeBook, BioFlix™ 3-D animations, MP3 Tutor Sessions, videos, current events, and more.

Mastering
BIOLOGY

Summary

36.1 The Ecosystem

- An ecosystem is a community of organisms and the physical environment with which they interact. (p. 691)

36.2 Nutrient and Water Cycling in Ecosystems

- Chemical elements that are vital to life are known as nutrients. Along with water, nutrients move back and forth between abiotic (nonliving) and biotic (living) domains on Earth in a process called biogeochemical cycling. Nutrients can be stored in living things, transferred between them, or transferred between them and the abiotic domain. (p. 691)

- Plants, algae, and some bacteria take in atmospheric carbon dioxide to perform photosynthesis. Animals obtain their carbon by consuming these photosynthesizing organisms. Carbon then moves back into the atmosphere in the form of carbon dioxide, which is produced naturally through the respiration of living things and through their decomposition following death. Carbon dioxide, which is vital to life and greatly affects global temperature, makes up a small but critical proportion of the Earth's atmosphere. (p. 692)

- Prior to the twentieth century, nitrogen entered the biotic domain mostly through the action of certain bacteria that have the ability to convert atmospheric nitrogen into forms that can be taken up and used by plants. Other bacteria can convert this organic nitrogen back into atmospheric nitrogen, thus completing the nitrogen cycle. Early in the twentieth century, an industrial process was invented for producing a biologically useful form of nitrogen that can be applied to crops. Nitrogen runoff from agriculture is a form of nutrient pollution that can harm aquatic ecosystems. (p. 693)

- All of Earth's water either is being cycled or is being stored—in such forms as glaciers or polar ice. As little as 0.5 percent of Earth's water is available as fresh, liquid water, with about 25 percent of this being groundwater, which generally is stored in aquifers. (p. 694)

- Fresh, sanitary water is a scarce commodity even for human beings, despite the fact that civilization now uses more than half the world's accessible water. This scarcity of water can be traced in significant part to the inefficient ways in which humans use it. Human diversion of water from natural environments is having harmful effects on other species. (p. 696)

BioFlix™

The Carbon Cycle

36.3 How Energy Flows through Ecosystems

- Plants and other photosynthesizers are an ecosystem's producers, while the organisms that do not perform photosynthesis are its consumers. Every ecosystem has a number of feeding or trophic levels, with producers forming the first trophic level and consumers forming several additional levels. (p. 699)

- A detritivore is a class of consumer that feeds on the remains of dead organisms or cast-off material from living organisms. A decomposer is a special kind of detritivore that breaks down dead or cast-off organic material into its inorganic components, which can then be recycled. (p. 699)

- The energy-flow model of ecosystems measures energy as it is used by and transferred among members of an ecosystem. (p. 701)

- In general, for each jump up in trophic level, the amount of available energy drops by 90 percent. This reduction in energy by trophic level largely explains the superabundance of plants, the smaller abundance of herbivores, and the smaller-

yet abundance of carnivores. The makeup of given ecosystems can also be affected by the consumption of second-level herbivores by third-level carnivores. (p. 702)

36.4 Earth's Physical Environment

- The atmosphere is the layer of gases surrounding the Earth. Nitrogen and oxygen make up 99 percent of the lowest layer of the atmosphere, the troposphere, which also contains small amounts of carbon dioxide and gases such as argon and methane. (p. 703)

- Ozone, which exists primarily in the stratosphere, screens out 99 percent of the sun's potentially harmful ultraviolet radiation. Human-made compounds such as chlorofluorocarbons (CFCs) can destroy ozone. International action taken on this issue in the 1980s is bringing the ozone layer back to health. (p. 703)

36.5 Global Warming

- Global warming refers to the increasing temperature of the Earth's atmosphere. Between 1906 and 2005, Earth's surface temperature increased by about 1.3°F, and the planet may warm by more than this amount in coming decades, as a result of human activities such as deforestation and the emission of carbon dioxide (CO_2) and methane. (p. 704)

- All of the long-term consequences of global warming cannot be predicted because such consequences will vary with the amount of greenhouse gases emitted in coming years. Among the certain consequences are a rise in sea levels, a change in rainfall patterns, and an alteration in the mix of species in different geographical regions. (p. 707)

- Recent scientific calculations indicate that societies may have a short time frame in which to take action if the phenomenon of dangerous climate change is to be avoided. (p. 708)

36.6 Earth's Climate

- Earth is tilted at an angle of 23.5° relative to the plane of its orbit around the sun, which dictates much about climate on Earth, which in turn dictates much about life. (p. 709)

- Sunlight strikes the equatorial region more directly than the polar regions. The differential warming that results produces a set of enormous interrelated circulation cells of moving air, each of which drops rain on the Earth where the moving air rises but dries Earth where it descends. (p. 709)

- A climate is an average weather condition in a given area. Large vegetative formations essentially are defined by climate regions. (p. 711)

36.7 Earth's Biomes

- Biomes are large terrestrial regions that have similar climates and hence similar vegetative formations. Six types of biomes are recognized at a minimum: tundra, taiga, temperate deciduous forest, temperate grassland, desert, and tropical rainforest. Polar ice, mountains, savannas, and chaparral often are recognized as separate biomes. (p. 712)

- Tundra, the biome of far northern latitudes, is frozen much of the year but has a seasonal vegetation formation of low shrubs, mosses, lichens, grasses, and the grass-like sedges. (p. 712)

- Taiga is found at northern latitudes and exhibits a great deal of species uniformity, with only a few types of trees serving as ecological dominants. (p. 713)

- Temperate deciduous forests, which grow in regions of greater warmth and rainfall than is the case with tundra or taiga, are composed of an abundance of trees, complemented by a robust understory of woody and herbaceous plants. (p. 713)

- Temperate grassland (also known as prairie and steppes) is characterized by less rainfall than that of temperate forest and by grasses as the dominant vegetation. Such regions can be fertile agricultural land. (p. 714)

- Chaparral is a biome dominated by evergreen shrub vegetation. Such regions have mild, rainy winters and very dry summers. (p. 715)

- Deserts are characterized by both low rainfall and water evaporation rates that are high relative to rainfall. Deserts may be hot, cold, or temperate, but all desert life is shaped by the need to collect and conserve water. (p. 715)

- Tropical rainforest is characterized by warm, stable temperatures, abundant moisture, great biological productivity, and great species diversity. Rainforest productivity is concentrated above the forest floor, often in the canopy high above ground. Tropical rainforests are being significantly reduced in size today through cutting and burning. (p. 715)

36.8 Life in the Water: Aquatic Ecosystems

- Marine ecosystems are most biologically productive near the coasts. Coastal areas benefit from wave actions that bring in nutrients, carry away wastes, and expose more of the surface area of photosynthesizers to sunlight. (p. 716)

- There is relatively more ocean life toward the poles, with this concentration decreasing with movement toward the equator. The food webs in the oceans surrounding Antarctica are based on photosynthesizing phytoplankton. (p. 718)

- Coral reefs provide a habitat that results in a rich species diversity. The health of many of the world's coral reefs is being imperiled by human activity. (p. 718)

- Freshwater ecosystems cover only about 2.1 percent of Earth's surface. Freshwater lakes are most productive near their shores and near their surface. Lakes can be naturally eutrophic, meaning nutrient rich, or oligotrophic, meaning nutrient poor. (p. 719)

- Estuaries are areas where streams or rivers flow into the ocean. They are characterized by high biological productivity because of the constant movement of water, which stirs up nutrients. (p. 720)

- Wetlands are lands that are wet for at least part of the year. Wetland soil may merely be waterlogged for part of the year or under a permanent, relatively deep cover of water. Wetlands are very productive and are important habitats for migratory birds. (p. 721)

Key Terms

Understanding the Basics

Multiple-Choice Questions
(Answers are in the back of the book.)

1. Carbon (select all that apply):
   a. is an element
   b. is a nutrient.

c. moves into the living world through animals.

d. moves into the atmosphere through the work of decomposers.

e. makes up about 21 percent of Earth's atmosphere.

2. Nitrogen (select all that apply):
   a. is not a nutrient.
   b. is transferred into the living world in nature through the actions of plants.
   c. is transferred into the living world in nature through the actions of bacteria.
   d. has been manufactured by humans since the early twentieth century.
   e. exists in such low concentrations in some coastal waters that "dead zones" are the result.

3. Associate each term on the left with one on the right.

   a. herbivore — photosynthesizing organism
   b. net primary production — material produced through photosynthesis
   c. gross primary production — position in an ecosystem's food chain
   d. trophic level — organism that eats plants
   e. producer — material accumulated through photosynthesis

4. There is a simple food chain in an eastern Oregon desert grassland: Mice are consumed by several species of snakes, which are consumed by hawks. The hawk is a _____ and occupies the _____ trophic level in this ecosystem.
   a. tertiary consumer; fourth
   b. secondary consumer; fourth
   c. tertiary consumer; third
   d. secondary consumer; third
   e. primary consumer; third

5. A dung beetle (can you guess what it eats?) is an example of a:
   a. detritivore.
   b. omnivore.
   c. carnivore.
   d. herbivore.
   e. producer.

6. Concentrations of heat-trapping "greenhouse" gases such as carbon dioxide are measured in:
   a. kilograms.
   b. tons.
   c. parts per billion.
   d. parts per million.
   e. millions of molecules.

7. The greenhouse effect is caused by:
   a. incoming long-wave radiation that is trapped as short-wave radiation by the atmosphere.
   b. short-wavelength light that is re-radiated as long-wave radiation and is trapped by certain gases.
   c. heat that is stored as short-wave radiation by rough surfaces of the Earth and then re-radiated as long-wavelength light.
   d. cold air masses that mix with the warm gases and produce warm atmospheric gases.
   e. reactions in the stratosphere between these greenhouses gases and ozone, producing long-wave heat.

8. You walk in on the middle of a nature program on television and see aerial shots of huge expanses of one or two types of coniferous trees. The type of biome you are looking at probably is:
   a. chaparral.
   b. taiga.
   c. tundra.
   d. savanna.
   e. temperate forest.

9. Donna is measuring rainfall over a large elevation gradient in the Cascade Mountains of Oregon. As she walks up the west side, she notices that rainfall increases and that when she reaches the top and walks down the east side, it is much drier. This is because:
   a. dry air from the equator flows east at this latitude, dropping moisture on the west side.
   b. wet air from the tropical equator flows east at this latitude, dropping moisture on the west, and then becomes dry by the time it reaches the eastern side.
   c. air is flowing from the west and drops moisture as it rises and cools, then absorbs moisture from the land as it descends and warms.
   d. warm air from 30° latitudes picks up moisture as it travels to 60° north, then drops this moisture as it cools.
   e. the rain-shadow effect means that cool, moist air drops rainfall as it warms with a rise in elevation.

10. A lake affected by high levels of artificial eutrophication will have:
    a. high nutrient levels, large phytoplankton populations, and low oxygen levels at depth.
    b. high levels of nutrients, low phytoplankton levels, and high oxygen levels in surface waters.
    c. low nutrient levels, large phytoplankton populations, and low oxygen levels at depth.
    d. low nutrient levels, low phytoplankton populations, and high oxygen levels at depth.
    e. low nutrient levels, large zooplankton populations, and low phytoplankton levels.

Brief Review

(Answers are in the back of the book.)

1. In a large reserve in Idaho, Forest Service wildlife scientists measured wolf populations as well as elk populations and found that the wolf population was much lower than that of the elk population. If wolves feed on elk, why aren't the population sizes similar?

2. Explain why most deserts across the globe occur at about 30° N and 30° S of the equator.

3. What relationship does climate have to the large-scale vegetation patterns that are seen on Earth?

4. A great many dead fish are found floating on the surface of an algae-covered pond. What might be the cause of such a fish kill?

5. Name several ways in which the tundra and taiga biomes differ.

Applying Your Knowledge

1. The filmmakers in the movie *King Kong* land on the imaginary Skull Island, which is the home not only of the giant ape Kong but of a host of meat-eating dinosaurs as well. Setting aside the impossibility of an ape as big as Kong, from an ecological perspective, why could a real Skull Island never have existed, even when dinosaurs roamed the Earth?

2. Bacteria and fungi are vitally important to the living world. If all bacteria and fungi were somehow instantly eliminated, almost no life-forms would survive for long. This is so because of the role bacteria and fungi play in ecological processes. Can you name two of these processes?

3. Tundra and desert are in some ways more fragile biomes than are grasslands or forests. Why should this be so?

Appendix 1

Metric–English System Conversions

Length

1 inch (in.) = 2.54 centimeters (cm)

1 centimeter (cm) = 0.3937 inch (in.)

1 foot (ft) = 0.3048 meter (m)

1 meter (m) = 3.2808 feet (ft) = 1.0936 yards (yd)

1 mile (mi) = 1.6904 kilometers

1 kilometer (km) = 0.6214 mile (mi)

Volume

1 cubic inch (in.^{3}) = 16.39 cubic centimeters (cm^3 or cc)

1 cubic centimeter (cm^3 or cc) = 0.06 cubic inch (in.^{3})

1 cubic foot (ft^3) = 0.028 cubic meter (m^3)

1 cubic meter (m^3) = 35.30 cubic feet (ft^3) = 1.3079 cubic yards (yd^3)

1 fluid ounce (oz) = 29.6 milliliters (mL) = 0.03 liter (L)

1 milliliter (mL) = 0.03 fluid ounce (oz) = 1/4 teaspoon (approximate)

1 pint (pt) = 473 milliliters (mL) = 0.47 liter (L)

1 quart (qt) = 946 milliliters (mL) = 0.9463 liter (L)

1 gallon (gal) = 3.79 liters (L)

1 liter (L) = 1.0567 quarts (qt) = 0.26 gallon (gal)

Area

1 square inch (in.^{2}) = 6.45 square centimeters (cm^2)

1 square centimeter (cm^2) = 0.155 square inch (in.^{2})

1 square foot (ft^2) = 0.0929 square meter (m^2)

1 square meter (m^2) = 10.7639 square feet (ft^2) = 1.1960 square yards (yd^2)

1 square mile (mi^2) = 2.5900 square kilometers (km^2)

1 acre (a) = 0.4047 hectare (ha)

1 hectare (ha) = 2.4710 acres (a) = 10,000 square meters (m^2)

Mass

1 ounce (oz) = 28.3496 grams (g)

1 gram (g) = 0.03527 ounce (oz)

1 pound (lb) = 0.4536 kilogram (kg)

1 kilogram = 2.2046 pounds (lb)

1 ton (tn), U.S. = 0.91 metric ton (t or tonne)

1 metric ton = 1.10 tons (tn), U.S.

Metric Prefixes

Prefix	Abbreviation	Meaning
giga-	G	$10^9 = 1,000,000,000$
mega-	M	$10^6 = 1,000,000$
kilo-	k	$10^3 = 1,000$
hecto-	h	$10^2 = 100$
deka-	da	$10^1 = 10$
		$10^0 = 1$
deci-	d	$10^{-1} = 0.1$
centi-	c	$10^{-2} = 0.01$
milli-	m	$10^{-3} = 0.001$
micro-	μ	$10^{-6} = 0.000001$

Appendix 2

PERIODIC TABLE OF THE ELEMENTS

Answers

CHAPTER 1

So Far . . .

page 8

1. guess; principles; nature
2. hypothesis
3. constant; variable

page 9

1. revision; evidence
2. negation
3. natural; supernatural

page 15

1. molecule, cell, organ, organism, community, ecosystem
2. modification; species
3. life

Multiple-Choice

1. c 2. d 3. d 4. a, d, e 5. c 6. e

Brief Review

1. Science is a body of knowledge regarding nature and a formal process for acquiring that knowledge. It is thus a collection of unified insights and a way of learning about the physical world. Unlike religion, science does not acknowledge any immutable truths or unquestioned authority figures. Instead, all scientific principles are open to modification based on the discovery of new evidence.

2. An experiment is said to be controlled when the experimenter controls both the factors in it that will change and those that will be held constant. Suppose a scientist wanted to test the effect of the insecticide DDT on the reproductive development of lab rats. In this case, the experiment might consist of feeding DDT-laced food to one group of rats, while another similar group—called the control group—would receive the same food without DDT. It is important that the two groups of rats be as closely matched as possible in all other factors. For instance, both groups must consist of the same strain of lab mice; both must be the same gender or mix of genders; they must be given the same amount of food and water and housed in identical environments. Suppose differences were observed in, for example, the size of the offspring born to one group of rats as opposed to the other. If the starting conditions were not controlled in the experiment, then there

would be no way to tell whether the DDT or some other factor (such as different housing) was responsible for these differences.

3. Pasteur investigated the notion, widely held during his time, that living things can arise spontaneously from basic chemicals. He hypothesized that instances in which life appeared to arise in a seemingly lifeless medium could be explained as the result of contamination of the medium by unseen airborne microscopic organisms. He sterilized meat broth in a flask with a long, S-shaped neck by heating both the broth and the flask. Although the mouth of the long tube remained open, any incoming dust particles laden with microscopic organisms would be trapped in the bent neck and could not gain access to the meat broth. Under these conditions, the broth remained free of any visible signs of life. In other tests, the S-shaped neck was broken off or the flask tilted so that broth made contact with the neck of the flask; in these instances, the broth came "alive" with teeming bacteria and fungi. Pasteur inferred from these experiments that the appearance of lifeforms depended on whether the broth was contaminated by airborne microscopic organisms. When the airborne organisms had no access to the broth, however, it remained sterile. There was no evidence, in other words, of life coming about through spontaneous generation.

4. All living things, as we know them on this planet, acquire, store, and use energy; they respond to stimuli in their environment; they maintain a relatively constant internal environment (homeostasis); they reproduce, using DNA to transmit hereditary information; they exhibit a high level of organization; and they show evidence of having evolved from other organisms.

5. Atoms, molecules, organelles, cells, tissues, organs, organ systems, organisms, populations, communities, ecosystems, the biosphere.

CHAPTER 2

So Far . . .

page 22

1. proton; neutron; electron
2. element; protons
3. neutrons

page 25

1. filled; eight; two
2. covalent
3. polar covalent; electrical charge

page 31

1. loses; electrons; charges
2. electronegative; oxygen; nitrogen
3. bind

page 35

1. solute; solvent; solution
2. hydrogen bonds; cohesion; specific heat
3. hydrophobic; hydrophilic

page 39

1. yields; ions; accepts
2. 7; 0; 14
3. neutral (7)

Multiple-Choice

1. b, d 2. b, c 3. a 4. d 5. b 6. e 7. e 8. c

Brief Review

1. The forms are called isotopes. Isotopes of an element differ from one another in accordance with the number of neutrons they have. A regular carbon atom has six neutrons in its nucleus, while a carbon-14 atom has eight neutrons.

2. An atom's electrons move through volumes of space outside the atom's nucleus. An entire atom is about 100,000 times larger than its nucleus. Thus, most of an atom is the space through which electrons move.

3.

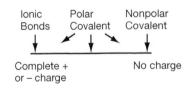

4. When its valence (outer) shell is filled, an atom is at a lower, more stable energy state.

5. Water absorbs tremendous amounts of heat from the sun and releases this heat slowly with the onset of night's colder temperature. The perspiration human beings throw off carries with it a great deal of heat, which has been absorbed by the water.

6. Living things must control their internal pH, keeping it in most instances near the neutral point of 7, because an extreme pH can begin to interfere with such critical

structures as membranes and such critical processes as the work of enzymes. Put another way, the normal structures and operations of organisms can begin to break down if pH is allowed to fluctuate very far from near-neutral levels.

CHAPTER 3

So Far . . .

page 45

1. carbon; bonds with other elements
2. atoms; carbon-based

page 48

1. monomers; polymers
2. carbon; oxygen; hydrogen; monosaccharides; polysaccharides (or complex carbohydrates)
3. starch; glycogen; cellulose; chitin

page 55

1. readily dissolve; water
2. fatty acids; glycerol; carbon atoms; hydrocarbon
3. carbon rings; estrogen; testosterone; phospholipids; phosphate

page 61

1. amino acids; amino acids; folded up
2. lipoproteins; lipids; proteins
3. nucleotides; sugar; phosphate group; nitrogen-containing bases

Multiple-Choice

1. c 2. e 3. a 4. e 5. b 6. b 7. d 8. a

Brief Review

1. Carbon is a mere trace element in Earth's atmosphere and crust and yet makes up nearly 50 percent of the dry weight of living things. It has this status because of its chemical bonding abilities: It has four outer or "valence" electrons, meaning it achieves maximum chemical stability by linking with four more electrons. This bonding capacity means it is able to form strong bonds with many other elements, which is important in creating the kind of complex molecules that are conducive to life.
2. LDL is associated with deposition of cholesterol in the arteries, so you should be concerned about high levels. HDL is associated with carrying cholesterol to the liver, away from the coronary arteries where it does damage, so if your HDL count is high, that's positive.
3. Steroids are a class of lipid molecules that have four carbon rings as a central element in their structure. Under this definition, both cholesterol and estrogen are steroids. In everyday speech, "steroids" refers to a subset of the steroid molecules—those that serve to enhance the ability of muscle to grow stronger. Testosterone is a steroid in this sense, while cholesterol and estrogen are not.

4. Proteins can take on the roles of enzymes, hormones, transport proteins, structural proteins, contractile proteins, storage proteins, and communication proteins. Proteins can do many different kinds of jobs because they take on so many different shapes. Each shape allows the protein to do a different job.
5. DNA contains or "encodes" the information for producing proteins. For a protein to be produced, the instructions for the order of its amino acids must be obtained from a length of DNA.

CHAPTER 4

So Far . . .

page 70

1. cell; cells; cell
2. eukaryotic; nucleus; prokaryotic
3. plasma membrane; nucleus; cytosol; organelles

page 76

1. DNA; proteins
2. ribosomes; rough endoplasmic reticulum (RER); Golgi complex
3. transport vesicles; endomembrane

page 83

1. smooth endoplasmic reticulum (smooth ER); lysosomes
2. energy; ATP
3. cytoskeleton

page 87

1. chloroplasts; central vacuole; cell wall
2. lysosome
3. plasmodesmata; gap junctions

Multiple-Choice

1. e 2. d 3. a 4. b 5. e 6. d 7. b 8. e

Brief Review

1. The cell would have difficulty obtaining enough materials from its external environment because its surface-to-volume ratio would be too low.
2. Eukaryotic cells have a nucleus, bound within a double membrane, that contains almost all their DNA. The DNA in prokaryotic cells is localized, but it is not bound within a membrane. Eukaryotes are usually much larger than prokaryotes. Eukaryotes are also often multicelled organisms, while prokaryotes are always single-celled. Eukaryotic cells have many types of organelles, whereas prokaryotic cells have only one type of organelle, the ribosome.
3. The information for the makeup of insulin is encoded in DNA that is copied onto an mRNA sequence, which leaves the nucleus through the pores in the nuclear envelope. The length of mRNA then arrives at a ribosome, which reads part of it before migrating to, and embedding in, the rough endoplasmic reticulum (rough ER or RER). The ribosome then continues to read the

RNA chain, and the resulting polypeptide chain drops into the cisternal space of the rough ER. There, the polypeptide chain folds up into the insulin protein, which then undergoes editing. Once this editing has been completed in the rough ER, the insulin is encased in a transport vesicle, which buds off from the rough ER and moves to the Golgi complex for further editing and for routing to its proper location. The finished insulin protein then moves through the cytoplasm in a transport vesicle that fuses with the cell's outer or "plasma" membrane, thereby exporting it from the cell.

4. Cilia and flagella are cell extensions formed by microtubules that are either a means of propulsion or, in the case of some cilia, a means of moving material around a cell. Cilia exist as a profusion of hair-like growths extending from cells; they move back and forth very rapidly, while only a few flagella sprout from a given cell—indeed, there is often just a single, tail-like flagellum. In the human body, cilia are found in the nasal passages and in the lungs. The only animal cell that has a flagellum is a sperm cell.
5. Plant cells would be isolated from each other by their thick cell walls. Because communication among cells is critical for the functioning of a plant, the result would be that the plant could not live.
6. A gap junction consists of clusters of protein assemblages that shoot through the plasma membrane of an animal cell from one side to the other, forming a tube. When these protein assemblages line up in two adjacent cells, the result is a communication channel between them. Gap junctions allow for the passage of small molecules and electrical signals between animal cells.

CHAPTER 5

So Far . . .

page 97

1. phospholipid bilayer; cholesterol; proteins; glycocalyx
2. hydrophilic; water; hydrophobic; water
3. receptors; transport proteins

page 100

1. higher concentration; lower concentration; energy
2. semipermeable; solute concentration; solute concentration
3. out of; into

page 104

1. active transport; passive transport; protein channel; protein channel
2. concentration gradient
3. transport vesicle; plasma membrane; phagocytosis; pinocytosis

Multiple-Choice

1. c 2. d 3. a 4. c 5. e 6. b 7. b 8. a

Brief Review

1. Receptor proteins usually are specific to a single communication molecule. This is so because each receptor has a shape that severely restricts the type of communication molecule it can bind with. The receptor in question has a shape that allows it to bind with glucose, but not to insulin; thus, the insulin molecules it comes into contact with simply pass it by.

2. Because steroids are lipids, they pass easily across the phospholipid bilayer by dissolving in it. Thus, they can affect most cells in the body.

3. Because the phospholipid's phosphate "heads" are charged, hydrophilic groups, they are attracted to the polar water molecules that lie on either side of the plasma membrane, and they orient themselves accordingly. Meanwhile, the phospholipid's "tails" are hydrophobic fatty acid chains that do not bond with water and thus end up oriented away from it, toward each other in the interior of the plasma membrane.

4. In clathrin-mediated endocytosis, a group of receptors extending from the surface of the plasma membrane bind with a given target substance (for example, cholesterol) and then migrate laterally to a depression on the membrane surface—a pit whose underside is coated with the protein clathrin. This pit deepens, or invaginates, eventually becoming a transport vesicle that buds off from the plasma membrane, carrying the target substance into the cell.

5. You would not expect that recognition and transport would be as important inside the cell as outside. Thus, the glycocalyx seen on the plasma membrane is unnecessary inside the cell, and proteins on the surface of interior membranes serve different functions than those on the surface of the plasma membrane.

CHAPTER 6

So Far . . .

page 112

1. potential; kinetic
2. created; destroyed; transformed; disorder (or entropy)
3. heat

page 114

1. products; reactants; reactants; products
2. ATP; phosphate group
3. ADP; phosphate group

page 119

1. protein; accelerates
2. substrate; product; substrate
3. initiate; lowering

Multiple-Choice

1. a 2. c 3. d 4. e 5. e 6. c 7. d 8. e

Brief Review

1. Plants abide by the second law of thermodynamics in that, in building themselves up, they are contributing to the total amount of entropy in the universe: They release heat as a by-product of the process by which they build leaves from carbon dioxide, water, and minerals. A plant leaf represents only a local increase in order.

2. The cocking of the extensions was an uphill or endergonic reaction because the extensions were in a higher energetic state when the reaction was completed than when it started. Any such endergonic reaction must be powered by an energy-releasing exergonic reaction. Thus, the two kinds of reactions are linked together—they are coupled. In this case, the binding of ATP to the extensions, and the resulting release of the ATP molecule's third phosphate group, was the exergonic reaction that powered the change in the extension's position.

3. In animals, the energy stored and released by ATP comes from food. ATP is an energy transfer molecule in that it receives energy from food and then passes that energy on when it powers chemical reactions in the body.

4. Enzymes are involved with every aspect of cellular life. They are necessary for breaking things down but they also are used to rearrange molecules or to make larger molecules out of smaller ones.

5. Allosteric regulation of an enzyme occurs when a molecule binds with an enzyme at a site other than its active site, thereby either decreasing or increasing the rate at which the enzyme will bind with its substrate. Such binding has the effect of either decreasing or increasing the amount of product turned out by the enzyme.

CHAPTER 7

So Far . . .

page 126

1. food; phosphate group; ATP
2. oxidation; reduction; redox
3. electron carriers; NAD^+; NADH

page 128

1. glycolysis; Krebs; electron transport chain (ETC); cytosol; mitochondria
2. energetic electrons; the ETC
3. ATP; NADH; pyruvic acid

page 132

1. acetyl CoA (acetyl coenzyme A)
2. energetic electrons; electron transport chain (ETC); carbon dioxide (CO_2)
3. NAD^+/NADH; FAD/$FADH_2$

page 137

1. lose (donate); membrane; hydrogen ions (H^+ ions)
2. H^+ ions; ATP synthase; phosphate groups; ATP

3. oxygen

Multiple-Choice

1. b 2. a 3. a 4. c 5. d 6. b 7. d 8. d

Brief Review

1. The food that we eat contains energetic molecules, such as glucose. In cellular respiration, foods are oxidized—they have electrons removed from them—and the energy released by the "fall" of these electrons from a higher to a lower energetic state powers phosphate groups onto ADP molecules, making them energetic ATP molecules.

2. We would expect people to have more mitochondria in their muscle cells. This is so because muscle cells use a great deal more energy than skin cells, and the organelles that supply that energy are mitochondria.

3. Hydrogen ions (H^+ ions or protons) are pumped across the mitochondrial inner membrane—against their concentration and charge gradients—and their energetic fall back through the ATP synthase in the membrane releases enough energy to move phosphate groups onto ADP.

4. The electron carriers NADH and $FADH_2$ are oxidized at the ETC; the energetic fall of the electrons that are removed from them powers the movement of the H^+ ions across the membrane.

5. No. In short bursts of activity, the energy we are using comes primarily from stored ATP and from glycolysis.

CHAPTER 8

So Far . . .

page 146

1. electrons; carbon dioxide; carbohydrate (a sugar)
2. chloroplasts; leaves; chlorophyll *a*
3. light reactions; primary electron acceptor; energy state

page 149

1. electrons; NADPH; ATP; oxygen
2. Calvin or C_3
3. sugar; atmosphere; electrons: ATP

page 153

1. low-energy sugar; carbon; oxygen; photorespiration
2. warm-weather; C_4
3. CAM; at night; during the day

Multiple-Choice

1. c 2. e 3. a 4. d 5. e 6. c 7. b 8. c

Brief Review

1. Yes, plants are as dependent on cellular respiration as we are. Plants make food—carbohydrates—in photosynthesis. But just as we have to break down the food we eat to get the energy transferred to ATP, so plants have to break down the food they make to move the energy into ATP.

2. The sunlight that makes it to the Earth's surface is composed of a spectrum of energetic rays (measured by their "wavelengths") that range from very short ultraviolet rays, through visible light rays, to the longer and less-energetic infrared rays. Photosynthesis is driven by part of the visible light spectrum—mainly by blue and red light of certain wavelengths.

3. A photosystem includes, first, several hundred antennae pigments consisting of both chlorophyll *a* and accessory pigments. These molecules collect solar energy and pass it along to another part of the photosystem, the reaction center. The reaction center consists of a pair of special chlorophyll *a* molecules and an initial electron acceptor molecule. These reaction center compounds receive both the solar energy from the antennae pigments and electrons derived from the splitting of water.

4. The C_4 plant would be likely to grow more rapidly in a warm-weather climate. Warm weather causes all plants to close their stomata for longer periods of time as a means of preserving water. When their stomata are closed, however, plants lose access to atmospheric carbon dioxide. In C_3 plants, this series of events leads to an increase in photorespiration, since C_3 plants utilize an enzyme, rubisco, that can bind to internally produced oxygen as well as to atmospheric CO_2. Hence, photorespiration—which undercuts plant growth—is increased in C_3 plants in warm weather. Meanwhile, C_4 never experience photorespiration since they utilize an initial CO_2-fixing enzyme that will not bind to oxygen.

5. The ATP is used to power the steps of the Calvin cycle. ATP is used in two separate steps during the cycle: once when 3-PGA (3-phosphoglyceric acid) is being energized by electrons produced by the light reactions and again when G3P is being transformed into the RuBP that begins the Calvin cycle.

CHAPTER 9

So Far . . .

page 160

1. proteins; bases; A, T, G, C
2. amino acids; bases; gene
3. messenger RNA (mRNA); ribosome; amino acids; mRNA bases; protein

page 164

1. replicate; duplicate
2. proteins; sister chromatids
3. homologous; X; X; Y

page 169

1. chromosomes; daughter cells
2. mitotic: interphase
3. sister chromatids; chromosome

page 171

1. cytokinesis; cell wall; plasma membrane
2. nucleus; plasma membrane; binary fission

Multiple-Choice

1. e 2. d 3. d 4. e 5. a 6. c 7. b 8. c

Brief Review

1. DNA contains information for the production of proteins. These proteins are "workers" and building blocks that serve a vast array of functions in organisms such as ourselves. Through the work of proteins, our bodies develop and carry out everyday functions.

2. The cell is in metaphase. There are eight chromatids present in this stage, and each daughter cell will have four chromosomes.

3. Mitosis serves to equally divide a cell's genetic material into two portions of a parent cell that will become daughter cells. Cytokinesis is the physical separation of a parent cell into two daughter cells.

4. Prophase—Duplicated chromosomes condense and become visible; the centrosome duplicates and centrosomes migrate to the poles; the nuclear membrane breaks down; and the mitotic spindle is formed. Metaphase—Chromosome pairs align along the cell midline or metaphase plate and attach to the microtubules extending from the cellular poles. Anaphase—The sister chromatids paired along the metaphase plate separate and then migrate to the two poles of the cell. Telophase—The condensed chromosomes unwind at their respective poles, and new nuclear membranes are formed around the chromosomes. At this point, division of genetic material is complete. The cell is ready for cytokinesis.

5. Plant cells have cell walls, while animal cells do not. In plant cells, membrane-lined vesicles, filled with a complex sugar, migrate to an area near the metaphase plate and begin fusing together, eventually forming a cell plate that runs from one side of the parent cell to the other. The membrane portion of the plate fuses with the original parent-cell plasma membrane, thus dividing the parent cell in half via formation of two new plasma membranes. The material inside the cell-plate membrane then forms the foundation of the new cell walls of the daughter cells.

6. The 23 pairs of human chromosomes are matched (or homologous) in the sense that the two members of each pair contain information about similar functions, such as hair color, metabolic processes, and so forth. The one exception to the matched-pair rule comes in human males, who have 22 pairs of matched chromosomes, but then one X chromosome and one Y chromosome, which are not matched. Human females have 23 matched pairs, including two X chromosomes.

7. (**a**) Four different bases—adenine, thymine, guanine, and cytosine, or A, T, G, and C, respectively; (**b**) in the nucleus; (**c**) messenger; (**d**) mRNA is used as a cellular messenger; DNA's information is copied onto it in the nucleus, after which it carries this information to the cytoplasm, where the information is used within ribosomes to put together sequences of amino acids that form proteins; (**e**) amino acids; (**f**) in ribosomes residing in the cytoplasm.

CHAPTER 10

So Far . . .

page 178

1. eggs; sperm; diploid; haploid
2. homologous chromosomes; sister chromatids
3. 46; 23

page 182

1. homologous chromosomes; homologous chromosome pairs
2. differ
3. X; X; Y

page 187

1. stem; prior to birth
2. polar bodies
3. identical

Multiple-Choice

1. b 2. c 3. a 4. b 5. b 6. d 7. d 8. a 9. d

Brief Review

1. In mitosis, a single round of chromosome duplication is followed by a single round of cell division. In this cell division, it is sister chromatids (of the duplicated chromosomes) that line up on opposite sides of the metaphase plate and then separate from each other. In meiosis, in contrast, a single round of chromosome duplication is followed by two rounds of cell division. In the first of these rounds, in meiosis I, it is duplicated homologous chromosomes, rather than sister chromatids, that line up on opposite sides of the metaphase plate and then separate from one another. In the second of these rounds, in meiosis II, sister chromatids separate, going to separate cells.

2. Chromosome reduction takes place during meiosis I.

3. The cells in males that go through meiosis, the primary spermatocytes, are themselves the product of cells called spermatogonia. These spermatogonia are stem cells in that, with each cellular division, they give rise not only to primary spermatocytes but to more spermatogonia as well. It is this dual capability in spermatogonia that allows males to keep producing sperm throughout their lifetimes.

4. Female meiotic cytokinesis differs from mitotic cytokinesis in the selective shunting of cytoplasm. In mitosis, cytokinesis divides the cytoplasmic material of a parent cell equally among daughter cells. In female meiosis, cytokinesis preferentially shunts cytoplasmic material to one daughter cell—the cell destined to become the ovum—and

away from the other cells, which become polar bodies.

5. Somatic cells are diploid cells that undergo mitosis. They include every cell in the body except the body's reproductive cells, its gametes, which are sperm in males and eggs in females. Gametes are haploid cells that are derived from diploid cells through the process of meiosis.

6. (a) metaphase I, meiosis I; (b) anaphase II, meiosis II; (c) anaphase, mitosis; (d) metaphase II, meiosis II; (e) metaphase, mitosis.

7. Meiosis ensures genetic diversity in two ways. In the process called *crossing over* or *recombination*, homologous chromosomes swap reciprocal portions of themselves with each other. Then, in the process called *independent assortment*, homologous chromosome pairs line up in a random way, relative to one another, along the metaphase plate.

8. A sperm has 23 chromosomes and an egg has 23 chromosomes; when sperm fertilizes egg, the result is a zygote with 46 chromosomes—22 homologous pairs of chromosomes and either two X chromosomes (if the zygote is female) or an X and a Y chromosome (if the zygote is male).

CHAPTER 11

So Far . . .

page 196

1. phenotype; genotype
2. dominant; dominant; recessive
3. alleles; homologous chromosomes

page 201

1. alleles; separate
2. identical; differing
3. dominant; recessive

page 204

1. heterozygous; homozygous
2. independent; heterozygous
3. expressed; a second recessive allele

page 208

1. many; polygenic; false; polygenic inheritance tends to produce continuous variation among organisms.
2. bell curve; average
3. environmental

Multiple-Choice

1. a 2. a 3. c 4. b 5. b 6. e 7. a, d 8. e

Brief Review

1. (a) Phenotype is a physiological feature, behavior, or physical feature of an organism, while genotype is the genetic composition responsible, at least in part, for the phenotype. In an example from the text, the genotypes YY or Yy resulted in the phenotype of yellow peas, while the genotype yy resulted in the phenotype of green peas. (b) The term *dominant* is used to refer to an allele that is expressed in the heterozygous genotype. In the heterozygous genotype Yy,

for example, Y is expressed (as yellow color) and thus is said to be dominant over y. The term *recessive* is used to describe an allele that is not expressed in the heterozygous genotype. Looking again at the heterozygous genotype Yy, the green y allele is not expressed, since any Yy seed will be yellow. The y allele is thus is said to be recessive to Y. (c) Codominance refers to the condition in which a heterozygote simultaneously exhibits the phenotypes associated with each of the alleles in its genotype. This is seen in blood types, where an AB individual produces both A and B cell surface molecules. Incomplete dominance is displayed when the heterozygote displays a phenotype that is intermediate between the dominant and recessive phenotypes. An example is the generation of pink flowers resulting from a parental cross of one red-flowering and one white-flowering snapdragon.

2. True.

3. Each person is likely to possess two alleles for any given gene; one allele is inherited from the individual's father, the other from the person's mother.

4. In Mendelian genetics, two different genotypes may bring about a dominant phenotype; for example, YY and Yy bring about yellow seed color.

5. About 50 percent of the progeny will be yellow peas.

6. Mendel's "element of inheritance" is now referred to as the gene.

7. Mendel's first law (law of segregation): Members of a gene pair will segregate from each other during gamete formation such that each gamete receives only one of the original two genes from the gene pair. Mendel's second law (law of independent assortment): During gamete formation, gene pairs assort independently of one another.

8. (a) Aa × aa; (b) Aa × Aa; (c) Aabb × aaBb; (d) AaBb × AaBb.

Genetics Problems

1. a 2. b 3. b 4. b 5. c 6. e 7. c 8. c

9. Since the purple allele is dominant, flowers will be purple whether the allele is present in two identical copies (homozygous state) or in one copy (heterozygous state). In contrast, expression of the recessive white allele is masked if a purple allele is present in the genotype. Therefore, it must be in homozygous form for the development of white flowers.

10. b

11. (a) 3. (b) The rule of multiplication. (c) 18.75 percent of the offspring should be purple flowered with green seeds. This answer is the product of the joint occurrence of two independent events: the probability of purple flower color (0.75) and the probability of green seed color (0.25).

12. It is possible to unambiguously determine genotype for snapdragons because incomplete dominance governs their color; every genotype manifests as a different phenotype. In the case of flower color in peas, phenotype cannot always unambiguously tell you about genotype. For white flowers, genotype can be assigned from phenotype, but for purple flowers, there are two possible genotypes, PP and Pp.

13. d
14. c

CHAPTER 12

So Far . . .

page 217

1. functional allele; faulty allele; functional allele
2. True; her second X chromosome contains functional alleles, which are enough to keep her from being color-blind.
3. heterozygous; one faulty allele

page 220

1. genetic; families
2. chromosomes; full set
3. separate; one chromosome too many; one too few

page 228

1. a, b, and c
2. mitosis; meiosis; line
3. segment; chromosome

Multiple-Choice

1. c 2. a 3. d 4. e 5. d 6. e 7. c 8. a

Brief Review

1. Male. Sex-linked diseases usually are associated with the X chromosome, which females have two copies of. A female can carry one faulty version (or allele) of an X chromosome gene and still be protected by a functional allele on her second X chromosome. Males, however, have only a single copy of the X chromosome. Should an allele on it be faulty, they have no second, protective copy of it.

2. Aneuploidy goes widely unrecognized because, in most instances, it is directly affecting embryos rather than children or adults. The most common result of aneuploidy is a miscarriage of the embryo. In many instances, prospective parents will not realize that a miscarriage has taken place, and even when a miscarriage is recognized as such, prospective parents would rarely be able to identify aneuploidy as its cause.

3. An aneuploidy that results in cancer would take place during mitosis, or the division of a regular, nonsex cell in the body. In consequence, not every cell in the body would be affected by this aneuploidy; only the line of cells stemming from the original aneuploid cells would be affected. Conversely, an ane-

uploidy that gives rise to a Down syndrome child takes place during meiosis—the formation of eggs or sperm—and hence affects every cell in the body.

4. Deletions—A portion of the chromosome is completely lost.

Inversions—A portion of the chromosome is broken off and rejoins the original chromosome, but in a reversed order.

Translocations—Occur when two chromosomes that are not homologous exchange pieces, leaving both with improper gene sequences.

Duplications—A portion of a chromosome is duplicated, in some instances by gaining a chromosome piece during abnormal crossing over.

5. (a) nondisjunction; (b) polyploidy.

6. Because people who have Klinefelter syndrome have a Y chromosome, which confers the male sex, but they also have two copies of the X chromosome, rather than the one copy that males normally possess. Females normally have two copies of the X chromosome. Thus, it makes sense that those with Klinefelter syndrome would exhibit some female characteristics.

7. A heterozygous genotype for hemoglobin would be advantageous in areas of mosquito infestation, while neither homozygous genotype would be advantageous in such areas. Those who are homozygous for hemoglobin A would not have the increased resistance to malaria; those who are homozygous for hemoglobin S would inherit sickle-cell anemia. Those who are heterozygous would have malaria resistance and yet would not inherit sickle-cell anemia.

Genetics Problems

1. None will be affected (although half, on average, will be carriers).

2. One-half of her sons can be expected to be affected. The chance that her first child is affected is 1/4 since there is a 1/2 chance the first child is a boy and a 1/2 chance that any boy is affected (another application of the rule of multiplication).

3. Recessive. Neither of the parents shows the autosomal trait, yet one of their offspring does.

4. His genotype is *aa*.

5. Her genotype must be *Aa*. (Reasoning: if she were *AA*, none of her children would be affected, whereas one is; if she were *aa*, she would manifest the trait herself, which she does not.)

6. One-half can be expected to be affected.

7. d

8. Her genotype is X^+X^P. (Reasoning: She is not affected, her mate is not affected, yet they have affected sons. This is possible only if she is a carrier.)

9. One-quarter of children and one half of their sons will show this trait (no daughters will have the trait).

10.

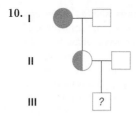

The chance that the son is color blind is 1/2. This is because the woman in question must be a carrier.

11. d

12. One-half of sons and daughters will have hyperphosphatemia. This is in sharp contrast to what would be observed if the trait were X-linked recessive. In this case, half the sons and none of the daughters would be affected.

CHAPTER 13

So Far . . .

page 238

1. structure of DNA
2. A; C
3. bases; protein

page 241

1. new, complementary strands
2. DNA polymerases
3. mutation

Multiple-Choice

1. e 2. e 3. d 4. e 5. c 6. e 7. b 8. b

Brief Review

1. "Something old, something new" is a short-hand means of conveying that, in DNA replication, each newly formed DNA double helix is a mixture of the old and new. Each one is made of an existing "template" strand of DNA and a new strand that is complementary to it.

2. First, the structure of DNA suggested an answer to the question of how genetic information can be passed on from one cell to the next, or from one generation to the next. The answer was: through base-pairing between DNA bases on an existing strand of DNA and bases that are complementary to them. Second, the varied way that bases can be arranged along the "rails" of the DNA helix suggested the means by which DNA could be a versatile enough molecule to contain information for the production of the huge number of proteins found in cells.

3. True—DNA polymerases can remove a mismatched nucleotide and replace it with a correct nucleotide.

4. A mutation is a permanent alteration in a DNA base sequence. A change in a DNA base sequence only becomes permanent when it goes uncorrected by a cell's DNA error-correcting mechanisms, meaning the change will be copied over and over during DNA replication. Not all mutations are harmful. Most have no effect at all, and a

very small proportion actually are useful to organisms as they result in the production of new, functional proteins.

5. Huntington disease results from an abnormal number of repeats of the bases CAG in the gene that codes for the huntingtin protein. The faulty protein clogs up nerve cells, eventually killing them.

CHAPTER 14

So Far . . .

page 246

1. amino acids
2. messenger RNA (mRNA); ribosome
3. ribosome; transfer RNA (tRNA)

page 252

1. complementary base pairing
2. DNA; RNA; amino acid
3. amino acid; messenger RNA codon (triplet)

page 259

1. DNA; transcription
2. micro-RNAs; messenger RNAs
3. editing; messenger RNAs; introns; exons

Multiple-Choice

1. e 2. a 3. c 4. d 5. e 6. d 7. c 8. a

Brief Review

1. The replication of DNA and the production of proteins from DNA.

2. (a) mRNA (messenger RNA), which takes DNA information to ribosomes; (b) rRNA (ribosomal RNA), which helps make up the ribosomes that act as the sites of protein synthesis; and (c) tRNA (transfer RNA), which brings amino acids to the ribosomes and binds with mRNA codons there.

3. Transcription is the process by which the information encoded in DNA sequences is put into the form of mobile mRNA sequences. Translation is the process by which the information encoded in mRNA sequences is put into the form of amino acid sequences; this results in the production of a protein.

4. The enzyme complex RNA polymerase both unwinds DNA that is to be transcribed and pairs DNA bases with their complementary RNA bases.

5. Three; one.

6. The genetic operation is self-regulating in that some of the proteins produced through it go on to regulate the production of other proteins. This is accomplished by means of the regulating proteins (called *transcription factors*) binding to non-coding sequences of DNA, thus facilitating or impeding the work of RNA polymerase, which transcribes genes.

7. Some of the evidence providing reason to doubt the importance of genes, relative to the importance of the regulation of genes is: (1) There appears to be no correlation between the number of genes an organism has

and the complexity of that organism; (2) There is a clear correlation between the proportion of non-coding DNA in an organism's genome and the complexity of that organism; and (3) Scientists who study evolution by looking at the development of animals have uncovered evidence indicating that mutations to non-coding DNA sequences have been more important than mutations to coding sequences in bringing about the evolution of differing features in animals.

CHAPTER 15

So Far . . .

page 268

1. genes; another species
2. restriction enzymes
3. human; protein

page 270

1. genetic copy
2. adult mammals
3. provided the donor cell containing DNA

page 275

1. (a)
2. all; ordinary
3. own cells

page 276

1. DNA
2. small
3. short tandem repeats (STRs)

Multiple-Choice

1. c 2. d 3. e 4. e 5. a 6. c 7. c 8. a

Brief Review

1. It is useful because some human beings cannot turn out sufficient quantities of their own supply of needed human proteins; this is so with some diabetics and the protein insulin, for example.
2. The production of sticky ends is useful because this type of end allows different restriction fragments to be joined together easily to create recombinant DNA.

   Fragment sequences:

   ATCG   GATCCTCCG
   TAGCCTAG   GAGGC

3. Dolly looked like the sheep that donated the udder cell, rather than the sheep that donated the egg, because the udder cell was the source of Dolly's DNA, while the DNA in the egg was removed. It was therefore the DNA in the donor cell that provided the instructions for Dolly's development.
4. PCR is valuable because it allows scientists to quickly make a large quantity of a given segment of DNA from a very small starting sample.
5. Because iPS cells are derived from ordinary adult cells, there is no moral controversy surrounding them, as there is with embryo-derived ESCs. In addition, through iPS cells it may be possible for patients to be sources of their own therapeutic cells. Cells from a

patient could be reprogrammed into iPS cells, which could then yield quantities of cells of the desired type. These cells would then be implanted in the patient. Should this prove unfeasible because of cost, it may be possible to develop banks of cells, derived from iPS cells, that are specialized for both cell type and immune-system type. The result would be readily available collections of cells that would not set off immune system reactions when transplanted into patients.

CHAPTER 16

So Far . . .

page 284

1. species; common ancestor
2. reproductive advantage; common
3. descended from; separate

page 291

1. False; common descent with modification was an idea that predated Darwin. Darwin was, however, the first person to perceive natural selection as an evolutionary mechanism.
2. Alfred Russel Wallace
3. Common descent with modification; natural selection

page 297

1. radiometric dating; proportions
2. Homologous; common ancestor
3. vestigial

Multiple-Choice

1. b 2. a, b, d 3. a, c, d, e 4. a. Lyell—geological forces observable today caused changes in the Earth; b. Wallace—natural selection as a mechanism underlying evolution; c. Lamarck—one form of organism can evolve into another; d. Cuvier—evidence of extinction of species 5. a, c, and d are homologous; b and e do not belong 6. c 7. a, b, d, e 8. a, c, e

Brief Review

1. The term *homology* describes structures in different species that are similar due to common ancestry. Homology provides evidence for evolution because it is consistent with the idea of common descent with modification.
2. Figure 16.13 shows that, in a gene shared by pigs, moths, and yeast, there are fewer DNA base differences between the forms of the gene found in humans and pigs than between the forms found in humans and moths. This is what you would expect if humans and pigs shared a common ancestor more recently than did humans and moths.
3. Congruent lines of evidence that are consistent with the theory of evolution: (a) Fossils of creatures believed to exist only in different evolutionary periods are not found together in the same geologic samples, and the ages of these samples, as determined by radiometric dating, are consistent with the fossils found in

them. (b) Evidence from molecular clocks is consistent with fossil and radiometric dating evidence regarding the degree of relatedness among species.
4. Darwin brought back many birds that he thought were the blackbirds, wrens, and warblers he was familiar with in Britain, but he found they were in fact all species of finches. Darwin perceived this as an example of descent with modification. Without taking the *Beagle* voyage, Darwin would not have been exposed to such extravagant examples of branching evolution, or have made various other biological observations that spurred his thinking about evolution by natural selection.
5. Fifteen years or so following the publication of *On the Origin of Species,* almost all scientists accepted the theory of evolution's principle of common descent with modification—the idea that all living things on Earth are descended from other living things, and that all living things ultimately share a single common ancestor. Not so readily accepted was the theory of evolution's principle of natural selection, which holds that evolutionary modification is driven primarily by differences in reproductive success among individuals.

CHAPTER 17

So Far . . .

page 303

1. population; single species
2. alleles; alleles; population
3. allele frequencies

page 308

1. allele frequencies
2. chance; allele frequencies; small
3. mating partners

page 313

1. False: Evolutionary fitness exists only in a relative sense; in a population, one organism is more or less fit than another depending on whether it has more or fewer offspring than another.
2. intermediate; extreme
3. directional selection; one extreme

Multiple-Choice

1. c 2. a. gene pool—the set of all alleles in a population; b. allele—a variant form of a gene; c. allele frequency—the relative representation of a given form of a gene in a population; d. genotype—the genetic makeup of an organism; e. gene flow—exchange of genes between populations 3. a 4. a, c, e 5. d 6. b, d 7. a. mutation—changes in the genetic material; b. gene flow—movement of alleles between populations by migration; c. natural selection—a process through which traits that confer a reproductive advantage to individuals are seen with greater frequency in succeeding generations of a population; d. genetic

drift—chance alterations of allele frequencies, having the greatest effect on small populations; **e.** founder effect—genetic drift brought about by migration of a subpopulation **8. c**

Brief Review

1. An individual may be selected for survival—and hence greater reproduction—because of the qualities that individual has, such as coloration or height. But this individual's characteristics do not change because it possesses these qualities. An individual does not evolve, in other words. An individual can pass on more of its alleles relative to other individuals in a population, however, and this causes the population's allele frequencies to change, meaning the population has evolved.

2. A gene pool is the sum total of alleles that exist in a population. The inheritable characteristics of living things are based on the alleles they possess. Thus, for a population to change in a way that is passed on from one generation to the next—for the population to evolve—the mixture of alleles in that population must change. Thus the evolution of a population is based at root on changes in that population's gene pool.

3. The five causes of microevolution are (**1**) Mutation—Alterations in the DNA that result in new alleles. (**2**) Gene flow—Brings alleles from other populations into the target population. (**3**) Genetic drift—The chance alteration of allele frequencies in a population. Random events can differentially increase or decrease the frequency of alleles in a population. Such events tend to have much greater effects on small populations than on large ones. Genetic drift can have large effects on small populations through two common scenarios: if a new population is founded by only a few individuals (the founder effect) or if the size of a population is decreased suddenly (the bottleneck effect). (**4**) Sexual selection—Allele frequency change based on the differential success that some members of a population have in securing mating partners. (**5**) Natural selection—Traits that confer a reproductive advantage to individuals in a population will become more common in that population over successive generations.

4. An individual in a population has to have greater reproductive success relative to other members of the population in order to contribute more to the gene pool of the succeeding generation.

5. Mutation and genetic drift alter allele frequencies in random directions and hence have nothing necessarily to do with adaptation. Gene flow doesn't necessarily bring in alleles that will be suited to the new environment, and sexual selection concerns mate choice rather than an organism's fit

with its environment. Through natural selection, however, individuals who are best suited to their environments pass on more alleles to the succeeding generation; in this way, natural selection works to adapt populations to their environment.

6. Evolutionary fitness—the relative success in contributing alleles to the next generation—depends crucially on the environment. It is the fit between environment and organism that determines which organisms will have the greatest success in survival and reproduction. Thus, the evolutionary fitness of any given individual would be expected to vary greatly from one environment to another. In the Grants' study of the Galapagos finches, a deeper bill was favored after the drought, but this situation later reversed.

CHAPTER 18

So Far . . .

page 322

1. breed
2. gene flow; populations
3. geographic separation; intrinsic isolating mechanisms

page 325

1. ecological, temporal, behavioral, mechanical, and gametic isolation and hybrid inviability or infertility
2. infertility
3. geographic separation

page 332

1. a new environment
2. relatedness
3. genus

page 335

1. unique; common ancestor
2. relatedness

Multiple-Choice

1. b 2. b, c, d 3. a, c, d
4. **a.** temporal isolation—mating occurs at different times of day or year; **b.** ecological isolation—populations utilize different habitats; **c.** behavioral isolation—populations employ different courtship or mating displays; **d.** gametic isolation—egg and sperm do not fuse; **e.** hybrid sterility—progeny of a cross are unable to reproduce
5. b, c, e 6. b–d–a–e–c 7. b, c, d 8. b, d, e

Brief Review

1. In the biological species concept, two organisms are in the same species if they actually or potentially interbreed successfully in nature.

2. In microevolution, changes in the frequency of the gene-variants called alleles determine the evolution of individual populations. To the extent that a given set of alleles increases in frequency from one generation to the next within a population, the characteristics produced by those alleles will be exhibited to a greater extent

within the population. In macroevolution, it is a drastic reduction of gene flow between populations of the same species that is the first step in bringing about speciation.

3. Without the evolution of intrinsic isolating mechanisms, two populations that have become geographically separated would simply resume interbreeding, remaining one species, if any physical barriers to interbreeding were removed. Thus, the evolution of intrinsic isolating mechanisms must take place if geographically separated populations are to become two separate species.

4. A first requirement of allopatric speciation is that two populations of the same species must become separated geographically, such that gene flow between them is restricted. This allows the forces operating in microevolution—natural selection, genetic drift, mutation, and so forth—to work separately on the two populations. Eventually, the populations may develop intrinsic isolating mechanisms such that, should they be reunited, they would no longer interbreed. In sympatric speciation, intrinsic isolating mechanisms evolve in the absence of geographical separation. The quality that both sympatric and allopatric speciation have in common is the development of intrinsic reproductive isolating mechanisms.

5. Convergent evolution is the evolution of a similar character in two unrelated organisms, caused when the organisms experience similar types of natural selection pressures in their environments. For example, many unrelated species of desert plants have succulent leaves that store water. But these similar characters are not homologous (they are analogous), so they cannot be used to determine relationships in a phylogenetic study.

CHAPTER 19

So Far . . .

page 346

1. life-forms; fossils
2. False. To judge by the fossil record, animals and plants don't appear until the last 16 percent of life's history.
3. self-replicating

page 350

1. Domains: Bacteria, Archaea, and Eukarya. Within Eukarya, the kingdoms are Protista, Plantae, Animalia, and Fungi.
2. 3.8 billion; oxygen; bacteria.
3. animal

page 359

1. green algae
2. tetrapods; fish
3. out of water

Multiple-Choice

1. b, e, f, c, a, g, d 2. d 3. b. 4. b, d, e
5. b, a, d, c, e 6. c, d 7. a, b, d 8. b, d, c, a, e

Brief Review

1. The oldest evidence we have of life dates from 3.8 billion years ago. The only forms of life that existed for 1.8 billion years following that were ocean-going microbes from Domains Bacteria and Archaea.
2. The "RNA world" forms part of the conceptual framework for the origin of life known as replicator-first. Any self-replicating RNA molecule would have had to possess the information-bearing qualities of today's DNA and the enzymatic capabilities of today's proteins.
3. All plants evolved from green algae. All land-dwelling vertebrates evolved from fish, specifically from lobed-finned fish.
4. The amniotic egg allowed terrestrial animals to lay eggs outside an aquatic environment, thus allowing such animals to live away from water. The amniotic egg evolved in reptiles.
5. Mammals have hair, which helps in heat retention, and the females among them have mammary glands that allow them to feed their offspring with milk.

CHAPTER 20

So Far . . .

page 366

1. six and seven million; chimpanzee
2. Late-evolving. The hominin line is dated to as much as 7 Mya, but modern human beings appeared only about 200,000 years ago.
3. African

page 370

1. bipedal; tooth
2. bipedal; brain
3. mosaic

page 375

1. Africa
2. No; the Neanderthals lived in Europe long before human beings migrated there, and the species *Homo erectus* reached Asia by 1.8 Mya.
3. 12,000; Indonesia

Multiple-Choice

1. a, d 2. d 3. b, c, e 4. a, c 5. d 6. b, d, e
7. a, e 8. a, c, e

Brief Review

1. No. A single common primate ancestor gave rise to both the chimpanzee evolutionary line and the hominin evolutionary line (which includes humans), but present-day chimpanzees evolved relatively recently—about the same time as modern human beings did.
2. The fossil evidence we have is not sufficient to allow us to be confident about who de-

scended from whom among the hominins. Placements on the tree vary in accordance with interpretations of the evidence we have.
3. Hominin evolution is thought to have begun 6 or 7 Mya, but the oldest hominin fossils found outside Africa date from only 1.8 Mya. Nearly all the early- and mid-period hominin fossils have been found in a swath of East Africa that runs from South Africa up through Tanzania, Kenya, and Ethiopia, although some early-period fossils may now have been identified much farther to the west.
4. *Sahelanthropus tchadensis* (Toumaï), *Australopithecus afarensis* (Lucy), *Homo erectus, Homo neanderthalensis.*
5. Neanderthals and modern human beings were very similar species and as such were highly likely to compete for the same kinds of resources, such as prey animals and shelter. If humans frequently outcompeted Neanderthals for such resources, over the course of many thousands of years, the Neanderthals may simply have lacked the resources to survive.

CHAPTER 21

So Far . . .

page 385

1. Bacteria, Archaea; protists, plants, animals, fungi
2. production of oxygen; fixation of nitrogen; breakdown of organic matter
3. living cells

page 392

1. mutualism
2. toxic
3. Both are strictly microscopic, single-celled, and prokaryotic (their cells do not have nuclei)

page 397

1. nucleus; microscopic; aquatic
2. oxygen; food chains
3. algae

Multiple-Choice

1. e 2. d 3. e 4. e 5. c 6. a, c, e 7. c, d, e
8. b, d

Brief Review

1. In nature, plants get their nitrogen from certain bacteria and archaea that are able to take in atmospheric nitrogen and turn it into a form plants can use.
2. Viruses cannot replicate, or carry out many of life's other basic functions, without using the machinery of the cells they invade. Most biologists would say that an entity that lacks such abilities should not be regarded as a living thing.
3. They must kill microorganisms while leaving human cells unharmed.
4. Like bacteria, archaea are single-celled and prokaryotic—their cells lack a nucleus.

Archaeal cells are, however, fundamentally different from bacterial cells at the level of deep chemical structure. The molecules that make up archaeal cells are chemically quite different from the molecules that make up bacterial cells (or any other kind of cell). The structural differences seen in archaeal cells are based on genetic differences between them and other life-forms.
5. Cells with nuclei, sexual reproduction, and multicellularity.
6. An amoeba is a protist that moves through use of pseudopodia or "false feet," meaning an extension of one part of the cell and a flowing of the rest of the cell into that extension. Some amoebae are parasites, and some of these are human parasites that cause the class of diseases known as amoebic dysentery.

CHAPTER 22

So Far . . .

page 406

1. hyphae; mycelium
2. (b) make their own food
3. breaking down and recycling organic matter

page 412

1. spore
2. asexual
3. yeasts

page 413

1. fungus; algae; bacteria
2. fungus; algae or bacteria
3. fungus; plant

Multiple-Choice

1. c, d, e 2. d 3. b, d, e 4. a, c, d 5. a, b, c, e
6. d 7. d 8. c

Brief Review

1. Animals take in their food prior to digesting it. Fungi cannot do this because food is made of relatively large molecules and such molecules cannot pass through fungal cell walls. Thus, fungi digest their food externally—using digestive enzymes they secrete—after which they ingest the smaller molecules that this food has been broken into.
2. Only a tiny fraction of the spores that fungi release will be able to germinate, or grow into a new mycelium. The fungi's adaptation to this fact has been to "buy many tickets"—to create a huge number of spores, which scatter to diverse environments strictly because of their numbers.
3. A spore is a reproductive cell that can give rise to a complete organism without fusing with another reproductive cell. A gamete (an egg or sperm) is a reproductive cell that must fuse with another reproductive cell for a complete organism to be produced—egg must fuse with sperm.
4. Basidiomycota—club fungi, rusts and smuts, toadstools; Ascomycota—sac fungi,

morel mushrooms, truffles; Zygomycota—bread molds, spore-releasing sporangium; Chytridiomycota—mobile, water-dwelling, early-evolving.

5. Yeast are single-celled fungi that tend to reproduce through the process of budding.

CHAPTER 23

So Far . . .

page 418

1. blastula; embryonic
2. mobile or motile; multicelled; heterotrophic; cell walls
3. small

page 421

1. tissues; symmetry
2. bilateral; opposite sides
3. body cavity

page 424

1. moving water
2. medusa; the undersides; polyp; on top
3. circulatory

page 427

1. snails or slugs; oyster, clams, or mussels; octopus, squid, or nautilus
2. exoskeleton; paired, jointed
3. exoskeleton, sessile living

page 430

1. eggs; sperm
2. asexual reproduction; unfertilized egg
3. hermaphrodite

page 434

1. broadcast; no
2. fewer; greater
3. reptiles; out of water

page 437

1. stays within; leaves the vessels
2. exoskeleton; external covering
3. molting; a periodic shedding of an old skeleton followed by the growth of a new one

Multiple-Choice

1. a, d 2. d 3. a 4. b 5. e 6. b, c, e 7. a 8. d

Brief Review

1. All animals are believed to have a single ancestor, probably an ocean-dwelling single-celled protist. All animals go through a blastula stage of development, whereas no other life-forms do. It's difficult to imagine a feature as specific as a blastula stage of development arising more than once in evolution.

2. Sponges have no organs, or even true tissues, and each of their cells functions with a great deal of independence. Thus, the cells in a sponge have a lower level of specialization and integration with one another than is the case in more complex animals.

3. A coelom provides an animal with flexibility, allows for the expansion and contraction of organs such as the heart and stomach,

and helps protect an animal's organs from being damaged by external blows.

4. Cnidaria—jellyfish, sea anemones; nematoda—roundworms; mollusca—snails, squid; annelida—earthworms, leeches; arthropoda—insects, lobsters, spiders; echinodermata—sea stars, sea urchins; chordata—fish, amphibians, reptiles.

5. Arthropods have an exoskeleton; were it not for shedding an existing exoskeleton through the process of molting, an arthropod's growth would be limited by the size of its original exoskeleton.

CHAPTER 24

So Far . . .

page 444

1. (b) no cell wall
2. spores; eggs; sperm

page 449

1. embryo; food; protective casing
2. (c) spruce tree and (d) orchid
3. sperm

page 455

1. wind; animals
2. differential
3. nights

Multiple-Choice

1. b, c, d 2. a, c, e 3. b, d 4. a. moss—bryophyte; b. cactus—angiosperm; c. pine tree—gymnosperm; d. rose—angiosperm; e. fern—seedless vascular plant 5. c, d 6. d 7. b 8. e

Brief Review

1. The gametophyte generation is the multicellular, gamete-producing generation of plant, meaning the generation that produces the reproductive cells called eggs and sperm. The sporophyte generation is the multicellular, spore-producing generation of plant, meaning the generation that produces the reproductive cells called spores. The cells of the sporophyte generation are diploid, and thus contain two sets of chromosomes each, while the cells of the gametophyte generation are haploid, and thus contain a single set of chromosomes each.

2. Seeds, which are produced only by plants, result from the fusion of two gametes—an egg and a sperm. Seeds amount to the embryo produced by sperm and egg fusion, food for this embryo, and a tough outer coating that serves to protect the embryo.

3. The pollen of most angiosperms is carried from one plant to another by animals. Such pollination allows the sperm from one plant—contained inside a pollen grain—to fertilize the egg in a second plant. The seeds of some angiosperms are dispersed by animals that ingest plant fruits.

4. Gravitropism is the bending of a plant root or shoot in response to gravity; it allows plants to control the direction of the growth of both their roots and shoots—

roots into the ground and shoots into the air. Phototropism is the curvature of shoots in response to light; it allows plants to maximize their capture of sunlight, which drives photosynthesis. Thigmotropism is the growth of plant shoots in response to touch; it allows plant shoots to grow upwards on other objects, thus maximizing access to sunlight.

5. Photoperiodism is controlled by the daily duration of darkness a plant is experiencing, relative to the daily duration of light.

CHAPTER 25

So Far . . .

page 465

1. water; minerals
2. photosynthesis
3. reproductive

page 468

1. dicots; monocots
2. periphery; fluid transport
3. water; minerals; food produced in photosynthesis

page 470

1. the tips; indefinitely (throughout the life of the plant)
2. meristematic; apical meristems

page 472

1. tracheids; vessel elements
2. solar energy
3. load; sieve element; pressure

page 474

1. spores; sporophyte; gametophyte; pollen grains; embryo sac
2. pollen; stigma; sperm; egg
3. zygote; sporophyte; food; endosperm

page 476

1. seed coat; protect
2. ovary; seed coat

Multiple-Choice

1. e 2. b, c 3. a 4. b, d 5. a 6. b, c 7. c, e 8. e 9. c, e

Brief Review

1. The stomata allow the movement of carbon dioxide into the plant and oxygen out of it. These same openings also allow water to escape from the plant as water vapor. The plant deals with the resulting problem of water loss by moving large quantities of water up through the roots and stem and out through the stomata.

2. Roots serve to anchor the plant and they are the main absorptive structures for the plant. They absorb water and minerals from their surroundings and make them available to the above-ground parts of the plant. In some species, roots also store substantial reserves of food. Taproots and fibrous roots are the two main types of roots produced by flowering plants.

3.

Flower Part	Function
pedicel	Flower stalk; lifts flower up to make it noticeable to pollinators.
sepals	Leaf-like structures that protect flower buds before they open.
petals	Generally most conspicuous part of the flower; often brightly colored; sometimes fragrant; attract pollinators.
stamens	Male reproductive structures; consist of a stalk called a filament, which holds aloft the pollen-producing sacs called anthers.
pollen	The male gametophyte; the vehicle that conducts male sperm to the female reproductive structures; composed at maturity of an outer coat, one tube cell, and two sperm cells.
carpel	Female reproductive structure; consists of the ovary, stigma, and style—the ovary produces and protects the egg-containing female gametophyte, and after fertilization turns into the fruit; the stigma is the receptive surface that captures pollen and promotes germination of pollen; and the slender style raises the stigma to make it accessible to pollinators.

4. Meristematic tissue gives rise to all other tissue types in the plant. Meristematic cells remain perpetually embryonic: They are able to keep giving rise to more of themselves as well as to cells that differentiate into all the plant's various tissue types. Meristematic tissue is concentrated in apical meristems—tissue located at the tips of roots and shoots that gives angiosperms their primary or vertical growth. There is a second location for meristematic tissue in the shoot—the area nestled between leaf and stem known as a lateral bud.

5. The water-conducting xylem cells come in two types: tracheids and vessel elements. Both are thick walled, and both die at maturity, after which their contents are cleared out. Because they are stacked on top of one another, lines of these cells become water-conducting tubes. The food-conducting phloem cells, called sieve elements, are alive at maturity but lack nuclei. Their housekeeping needs are taken care of by one or more adjacent companion cells. A collection of sieve element cells makes up a sieve tube, which transports sucrose, along with hormones and other compounds.

6. When the two sperm cells from a pollen grain enter the embryo sac of a plant, two fertilization events take place. In the first of these, a sperm cell fuses with the embryo sac's egg cell, thus setting in motion development of a new plant embryo. In the second fertilization event, the second sperm cell fuses with the two nuclei of the embryo sac's central cell. This event sets in motion the development of endosperm—food for the growing embryo.

CHAPTER 26

So Far . . .

page 483

1. anatomy; physiology
2. reduced
3. stable

page 488

1. cell, tissue, organ, organ system
2. epithelial, connective, muscle, nervous
3. muscle; nervous

page 491

1. skin; epidermis; dermis
2. just beneath the skin; organs; abdomen
3. follicle

page 498

1. bones; cartilage; ligaments
2. production of blood cells; storage of energy reserves as fat

page 500

1. fibers; length
2. sliding; sarcomere
3. myosin; actin; sarcomere

Multiple-Choice

1. d 2. a 3. b 4. e 5. d 6. c 7. a 8. d

Brief Review

1. In negative feedback, an element that brings about a response is affected negatively by that response. Put another way, the activity of the element is reduced by the response. In the example in the text, the kidneys released a hormone (EPO) that produced red blood cells whose oxygen content fed back on the kidneys, causing them to reduce their output of EPO.

2. Lymphatic organs such as lymph nodes have high concentrations of immune cells within them that monitor passing lymphatic fluid for signs of invading microorganisms.

3. Our skin is water resistant because the surface epidermal layer of the skin is formed of tightly interlocking cells made almost entirely of the protein keratin, which is water resistant.

4. Subcutaneous fat is found in a layer, varying in thickness throughout the body, that exists just beneath the skin. Visceral fat is found surrounding organs deep within the abdomen.

5. Three functions of the skeletal system are support, storage of minerals and fats, and blood cell production.

6. The sample is from the end (epiphysis) of a long bone.

CHAPTER 27

So Far . . .

page 509

1. central; brain; spinal cord; peripheral
2. from; somatic; autonomic; to
3. neurons; dendrites; axon

page 513

1. electrical charge
2. Na^+ ions; neighboring portion
3. neurotransmitters; synaptic cleft

page 518

1. sensory neurons; motor neurons; reflex
2. fight-or-flight; rest-and-digest
3. cerebral cortex; cerebrum

page 522

1. sensory receptors; electrical signals
2. smell (olfaction); thalamus; cerebral cortex
3. combinations

page 525

1. taste buds; taste cells
2. compressed
3. fluid; hair

page 528

1. retina; cornea; lens
2. rods; black-and-white; cones; color
3. optic nerves

Multiple-Choice

1. c 2. c 3. e 4. e 5. c, d, e 6. b 7. a 8. b

Brief Review

1. The sensory neuron receives input about conditions inside and outside the body and conveys this received information to the central nervous system (CNS). The motor neuron cell body exists in the CNS, but its axon extends into the peripheral nervous system (PNS); it thus can send instructions from the CNS to such structures as muscles or glands. The interneuron exists solely in the CNS and serves to interconnect neurons and integrate signals from them.

2. Neurons have special extensions of themselves, called axons and dendrites, that respectively carry nervous system signals away from and toward the neuron cell body. In addition, the outer or plasma membrane of each neuron has a charge difference, from one side to the other, that can change rapidly with the proper stimulation, going from negative on the membrane's interior to briefly positive, then back to negative. This change in membrane potential can be propagated down the length of the neuron's axon, after which stimulation of an adjacent neuron can take place through release of neurotransmitters that diffuse from the sending neuron to the receiving neuron across a synaptic cleft.

3. Neurotransmitters function in the synapses of the nervous system—the physical areas that include the tip of one neuronal axon and the cell body of a second neuron (or effector cell). The activity of neurotransmitters can be limited in time by the process of reuptake, in which a sending neuron takes a secreted neurotransmitter back into itself. Conversely, neurotransmitters can be degraded by enzymes that are secreted into the synaptic cleft by the sending cell.

4. A simple reflex arc works by means of a sensory neuron sending an afferent message about some stimulation to the spinal cord. There, the sensory neuron will synapse with a motor neuron (or perhaps an interneuron), after which the motor neuron sends a signal that brings about some action at an effector such as a muscle. The brain is not involved in such an arc.

5. In the senses of hearing, touch, taste, and vision, various types of sensory receptors respond to their respective forms of stimulation and then act as transducers, transforming the stimulation they receive into the electrical impulses of the nervous system. They did the latter by releasing neurotransmitters to receiving neurons (or by not releasing neurotransmitters, in the case of vision). In each case, the resulting nerve signal went first to the brain's thalamus and then to different areas of its cerebral cortex for processing.

CHAPTER 28

So Far . . .

page 537

1. cells; bloodstream; cells
2. endocrine; bloodstream
3. amino acid; peptide; steroid; peptide; steroid

page 539

1. negative feedback; stable
2. hypothalamus; anterior; posterior; adrenal
3. anterior; other glands

page 547

1. insulin; glucagon; pancreas
2. glycogen; glucagon
3. adrenal glands; storage; used

Multiple-Choice

1. a, c, d 2. d 3. d 4. b 5. b, d, e 6. c 7. b, c
8. b, c, e

Brief Review

1. The hormones of the endocrine system take at least several seconds to have any effect. This time-frame is fine for maintaining fluid levels, but of no use in carrying out the rapid, complex movements required to shoot a basketball—the nervous system handles those.

2. Amino-acid-based hormones are derived from a chemical modification of a single amino acid. Peptide hormones are built from chains of amino acids. The building block of all steroid hormones is the cholesterol molecule. Amino-acid-based and peptide hormones generally bind with receptors that are on the surface of target cells. Steroid hormones generally pass through the outer membrane of a target cell and bind with a receptor inside the cell.

3. The hypothalamus produces hormones oxytocin and vasopressin, which it releases

from the posterior pituitary gland; through nervous system signals, it directly controls the release of the hormones adrenaline and noradrenaline from the adrenal medulla; and it controls release of six hormones from the anterior pituitary through its secretion of releasing or inhibiting hormones.

4. Two hormones control circulating glucose levels in the body. Insulin, released from beta cells in the body's pancreas, has the effect of moving glucose into cells, where it may be stored or used. Glucagon, released from alpha cells in the pancreas, has the effect of moving glucose out of storage in both muscle and liver cells. Muscle cells retain all the glucose that has been liberated in them—using it to power their own activities—while liver cells release into the bloodstream much of the glucose liberated within them.

5. Cortisol helps liberate stores of energy in the body, particularly during times of stress. When it stays in circulation over extended periods of time, it can suppress immune system activity, reduce the insulin sensitivity of cells, and produce a narrowing of arteries. Human beings are thought to be uniquely vulnerable to these effects because human beings alone have the capacity to experience stress continuously over long periods because of their ability to envision the future.

CHAPTER 29

So Far . . .

page 553

1. elicits an immune system response
2. barriers; skin
3. foreign; specific microbial invaders

page 556

1. sensors; channel
2. phagocytes

page 561

1. antibodies; cells; B; T
2. lymphatic network
3. antigen-presenting; dendritic

page 564

1. antigen; B; exported
2. plasma; memory B
3. helper T

page 570

1. readiness; antigens
2. autoimmune disorders; allergies; organ transplantation
3. regulatory T cells (T-regs); toll-like receptors (TLRs)

Multiple-Choice

1. b 2. b, c, e 3. a. mast cells—cells that release histamine; b. cytokines—communication proteins; c. toll-like receptors—first sensors of infection; d. phagocytes—cells capable of ingesting invading cells; e. fibrin proteins—proteins that seal off infection site 4. d
5. a, d, e 6. c 7. e 8. c, e

Brief Review

1. The immune system increases blood flow near the site of injury and increases the permeability of capillaries near the site (so that more substances can be transported out); it delivers cells and proteins to the site that kill the invaders; and it releases substances that help seal off the site of injury, thus limiting the area of the infection.

2. A dendritic cell is the most important of the immune system's antigen-presenting cells (APCs). Dendritic cells ingest and are invaded by pathogens and then display antigens from the invaders on their surface. They then migrate to a lymph node and present the invader's antigens to CD4 and CD8 cells that have receptors specific to the invader. In the interaction that follows with the dendritic cell, the CD4 and CD8 cells are transformed into activated helper T and killer T cells, respectively.

3. HIV has so many effects because its ability to eliminate helper T cells allows it to weaken the immune system, which normally fights off so many kinds of invaders.

4. The immune system regards any transplanted organ as nonself and thus will initiate an attack against it.

5. Vaccines are able to provide immunity to infectious illness because of the immune system's memory B and T cells. These cells remain in the body long after an infection has passed and allow the immune system to mount a more rapid and effective attack against any second attack by a given invader. Memory B and T cells can be produced by the microbial antigens contained in vaccines; thus vaccines can elicit a state of immune-system readiness against a given invader even in the absence of an actual attack by that invader.

CHAPTER 30

So Far . . .

page 578

1. fluid
2. red blood cells; white blood cells; platelets; water
3. away from; toward; capillaries

page 580

1. heart and lungs; heart and the rest of the body
2. systemic; pulmonary
3. electrical signals

page 584

1. blockage; coronary artery
2. away from the heart
3. Capillaries

page 587

1. oxygen; carbon dioxide
2. alveoli; capillaries
3. hemoglobin; red blood cells

Multiple-Choice

1. b, d, e 2. e 3. b 4. c 5. a, e 6. a 7. d 8. e

Brief Review

1. Red blood cells transport oxygen and carbon dioxide; white blood cells are central to the body's immune system function; and platelets are active in the process of blood clotting.

2. The left and right atrial chambers of the heart pump blood only into their respective ventricles, while the ventricles pump blood to locations outside the heart—the right ventricle to the lungs, the left ventricle to all the tissues of the body.

3. Capillaries are the only blood vessels whose walls are thin enough to permit diffusion of substances in and out along their length; they are composed of but a single layer of cells, whereas arteries and veins have a three-layered structure.

4. Eating animal fats raises the levels of the low-density lipoproteins (LDLs) that lodge within the coronary artery tissue; smoking may damage LDLs in a way that triggers the immune response against them; exercise lowers LDL levels while raising the levels of high-density lipoproteins or HDLs, which help clear or neutralize LDLs.

5. Anatomical structures of the respiratory system include the lungs, the nose, the nasal cavity, the sinuses, the pharynx (upper throat), the larynx (voice box), the trachea (windpipe), the left and right bronchus (the body's two large air-conducting passageways), and the bronchioles (the smaller air passageways, branching off the left and right bronchus, that deliver air to the lungs).

6. A muscular sheet in our chest, the diaphragm, contracts, causing the ribs to rise, which expands the body's thoracic cavity, thus decreasing air pressure within the lungs. Since gases always move from areas of higher pressure to areas of lower pressure, air moves into the lungs. In exhalation, the diaphragm relaxes, and the thoracic cavity shrinks in response. This increases the air pressure inside the lungs, and air is expelled as a result.

7. Oxygen enters the bloodstream at a capillary that covers an alveolus in the lungs. Oxygen is inhaled into the sac-like alveolus and then diffuses across the alveolar tissue into an adjacent capillary.

CHAPTER 31

So Far . . .

page 595

1. digestive tract; mouth; anus
2. circulatory system
3. muscles; peristalsis

page 597

1. small intestine
2. liver; gallbladder; digestive enzymes; chemical buffers

3. esophagus, stomach, small intestine, large intestine

page 600

1. energy; structural building block; regulate
2. water, minerals, vitamins; proteins, carbohydrates, lipids
3. elements; compounds; small

page 605

1. energy; thousand grams; 1 degree Celsius
2. 9; energy; 4
3. amino acids; animal; essential amino acids; plant

page 608

1. simple sugars; starches; fibers
2. vitamins; minerals
3. blood glucose; lower

page 610

1. fatty acids
2. oils; fats
3. animal; plant

page 614

1. blood; renal arteries; blood; renal veins; bladder
2. blood vessels
3. waste; water; circulatory system

Multiple-Choice

1. b, d, e 2. b 3. c 4. a, c, d 5. b, d 6. a, b, e 7. b, c 8. c

Brief Review

1. Food has not been broken down in the stomach to an extent that it can pass out of the digestive system into adjacent capillaries (in the case of carbohydrates and proteins) or into lymphatic vessels (in the case of lipids). Partway through the small intestine, foods have been broken down to this extent, thanks in large part to the digestive enzymes and bile that move into the small intestine from the pancreas, liver, and gallbladder.

2. All carbohydrates and proteins that move out of the digestive tract are first transported to the liver through the hepatic portal vein. The liver controls which of these nutrients it will store and which it will release into general circulation. The liver also is the sole producer of bile, which facilitates the digestion of fats, and it packages waste products for removal by the kidneys.

3. Apart from waste storage and compaction, the large intestine conserves water by moving it back into circulation, and it absorbs vitamins produced by resident bacteria.

4. Vitamins are compounds—they are composed of several different elements—whereas minerals are individual elements. Vitamins function only to facilitate chemical reactions in the body, whereas minerals facilitate chemical reactions and provide structural building blocks for the body. A consequence of this difference is that our diets must contain greater quantities of minerals than vitamins.

5. The food rich in unprocessed whole grains would be preferred nutritionally because it is likely to (a) provide vitamins and minerals in addition to calories, (b) have a lower glycemic load, and (c) have a higher fiber content.

6. Animal fats, such as those found in bacon or beef, are predominately composed of saturated fatty acids. Vegetable oils, such as olive and canola oils, are predominately composed of unsaturated fatty acids.

7. Blood cells and most proteins are too large to pass out of the glomerulus capillaries and into the filtrate; they remain in the circulatory system.

8. The urination signal we are aware of is an involuntary contraction of the urinary bladder. This increases the fluid pressure inside the bladder, which can be uncomfortable.

CHAPTER 32

So Far . . .

page 623

1. zygote; embryo
2. endoderm; mesoderm; ectoderm; inner; middle; outer
3. induce; brain; spinal cord

page 626

1. morphogens
2. transcription factors; genes
3. anterior; center

page 628

1. conserved; transcription factors
2. movement; adhesion; death
3. fertilization (conception); the human life

Multiple-Choice

1. b, d, c, e, a 2. c 3. d 4. a 5. a, c, d 6. e 7. b

Brief Review

1. After fertilization, the cleavage stage of development begins. This first results in the formation of a tightly packed ball of cells, the morula, which is then transformed into a hollow, fluid-filled ball of cells with a central cavity, the blastula. Next, cells in the blastula undergo rearrangement and movement in the process called gastrulation, which results in an embryo composed of three layers of cells—the endoderm, mesoderm, and ectoderm.

2. The concentration of a given morphogen will decrease as distance increases from the cells that secrete the morphogen. Such a concentration gradient exists for all morphogens. In the fruit fly *Drosophila*, a concentration gradient of the morphogen bicoid affects the development of anterior and center-section structures of the fly. Bicoid concentrations are highest at the anterior end of the *Drosophila* embryo, and this high concentration has the effect of bringing about anterior structures of the fly, such as its head. Lower bicoid

concentrations at the center of the embryo help bring about center-section structures.

3. After gastrulation in the chick embryo, a small group of cells is induced to form the wing of the chick. This group of cells forms a structure called the wing bud, which eventually develops into the wing. A group of the cells in the wing bud are called the zone of polarizing activity (ZPA). The ZPA sends out a morphogen that directs the proper order of digit production in the chick's wing.

4. The conservation of the homeobox sequence tells us that this sequence is extremely important. If it were less important, the mutations that naturally occur to DNA over evolutionary time would have left contemporary mice and fruit flies with different DNA sequences in the homeobox portions of their developmental genes.

5. Cell adhesion molecules allow different varieties of cells to adhere selectively to one another. This allows for all kinds of cell organization, including the organization of the embryo into different layers of cells.

6. Cell death works to create spaces that define shapes in a developing organism. Without this death, the human hand would not have separate fingers but would have a webbed structure similar to that of a duck.

CHAPTER 33

So Far . . .

page 638

1. oocytes; ovaries
2. ovulation; uterine (or Fallopian) tubes
3. endometrium; fertilization of an egg

page 641

1. testes; epididymis
2. semen; sperm; glands
3. stem cells; spermatocytes

page 650

1. one; chromosomes
2. uterus; placenta
3. contractions; muscles

Multiple-Choice

1. a, c, d 2. a 3. b, c, e 4. acrosome—enzyme-containing compartment in sperm; spermatogonium—sperm stem cell; spermatocyte—maturing sperm cell; prostate gland—produces fluid found in semen; urethra—duct through which sperm are ejaculated 5. d 6. e 7. c 8. c, a, e, b, d

Brief Review

1. Gonadotropin-releasing hormone, which is released by the hypothalamus, stimulates the release of follicle-stimulating hormone (FSH) and luteinizing hormone (LH). Both of these hormones are released by the anterior pituitary gland. FSH promotes the development of the follicles, and LH stimulates the production of estrogen. As estrogen levels increase, FSH levels at first begin to decrease, but as estrogen levels begin to peak due to the development of the tertiary follicle, both FSH and LH levels spike. This results in ovulation. The corpus luteum then begins to synthesize progesterone, which acts on the hypothalamus to reduce FSH and LH to original levels, resulting in degeneration of the endometrium and menstruation.

2. Sperm development is impaired by temperatures that are either too hot or too cold. The anatomy and physiology of the testes act to maintain a correct temperature for sperm development. Sperm are protected from the high temperatures that exist elsewhere in the body by virtue of the location of the testes outside the body's torso. In addition, a muscle that surrounds the testes contracts when temperatures drop, so that the testes are pulled in closer to the warm body.

3. Two hypotheses currently are favored to explain the existence of menstruation. One is that the menstrual cycle of tissue buildup and breakdown is less costly, in terms of energy expenditure, than the alternative of keeping the endometrium in a permanent state of readiness for embryo implantation. The second hypothesis is that, when it is ready for embryo implantation, the endometrium is in a form that cannot be maintained permanently and that must arise from an earlier form. Thus, it makes sense that the inner endometrium would wash away every 28 days and then enter a new cycle of growth and development.

4. The tertiary follicle first houses a developing oocyte and then releases that oocyte from the ovary. Following this action, the tertiary follicle becomes the corpus luteum, a structure that releases hormones that first prepare the female reproductive tract for pregnancy and that then maintain the tract during the early phases of pregnancy.

5. Fusion of a sperm with an oocyte prompts the oocyte to release granules whose secretions harden a membrane surrounding the oocyte while inactivating sperm receptors on the surface of the membrane.

6. Prior to implantation, the fertilized egg divides to form a morula. This tightly packed ball of cells continues to divide, forming a hollow ball of cells, called the blastocyst, which is composed of two primary structures. One of these is a group of cells called the inner cell mass—the portion of the blastocyst that develops into the baby. The other is a group of cells called the trophoblast—cells in the blastocyst that first attach to, then extend into the maternal endometrium. In time, these cells grow into the fetal portion of the placenta.

7. Any baby born before 37 weeks of gestation is regarded as premature.

8. Birth control pills work using a combination of synthetic estrogen and progestin. Normally, low estrogen levels trigger the beginning of follicle development. The pill creates high estrogen levels that suppress the release of FSH from the hypothalamus. The progestin in the pill suppresses the release of LH to prevent ovulation of any follicle that might develop in the presence of high estrogen levels.

CHAPTER 34

So Far . . .

page 661

1. population; community; ecosystem
2. limit the growth of a population
3. density; support

page 667

1. few; abundant; many; little or no
2. greater
3. average number of children born to each woman; 2.1 births per woman

Multiple-Choice

1. d 2. c 3. c 4. e 5. b, c, e 6. a, b, d 7. b, e

Brief Review

1. population, community, ecosystem, biosphere

2. K-selected species experience their environment as relatively stable, spend most of their lives in populations that are close to carrying capacity (K), and provide a relatively large amount of care to a relatively small number of offspring. In contrast, r-selected species experience their environment as relatively unstable, have populations whose numbers are limited largely by reproductive rate, and provide little or no parental care to a relatively large number of offspring. Humans and oak trees are K-selected species; flies and ragweed are r-selected species.

3. Environmental resistance is the term used to describe all the environmental forces that act to limit population growth. Organisms will run out of food or have their sunlight blocked; temperatures will plunge, or rain will cease; greater numbers of predators will discover the population; the wastes produced by the organisms will begin to be toxic to the population.

4. Populations of K-selected species tend to have their growth limited by the carrying capacity (K) of the environments in which they live. A given environment can provide only so much food and habitat; as the density of a K-selected population increases within an environment, a lack of such resources will tend to limit the population's growth. The limitations on a K-selected population are thus said to be density dependent.

5. The Earth's human population is experiencing a drop in its total fertility rate—the average number of children born to each woman. Whereas this rate stood at 5 during the 1950s, it now stands at about 2.56. For

now, the Earth's human population is still growing; in fact, it is projected to grow from about 7 billion people in 2012 to about 9.1 billion in 2050. However, it is growing at a slower rate than it did through much of the twentieth century. By 2050, it will be growing by an estimated 31 million people per year, and may stabilize or even drop to some extent thereafter.

CHAPTER 35

So Far . . .

page 674

1. absence from
2. species diversity; geographic diversity of species populations; genetic diversity within species' populations
3. physical surroundings; normally be found; occupation

page 675

1. limited, vital resource; local extinction
2. resource partitioning

page 681

1. predation; parasitism
2. Batesian; Müllerian
3. beneficial to both; helped; unaffected

page 686

1. replacements; stable state
2. increase; longer-lived; increase
3. survive a major ecological disturbance

Multiple-Choice

1. d 2. c, e 3. a 4. b 5. a 6. b, d 7. d

Brief Review

1. In ecology, a keystone species is one whose absence from a community would bring about significant change in that community. Just as no other stone within an arch can assume the role of a keystone, so no other species within a community can assume the role of a keystone species. When the sea star *Pisaster* was removed from its community in coastal Washington, the community underwent significant change, in terms of its species makeup, because no other predator in the community could assume *Pisaster's* role in maintaining the populations of other species.
2. Competition; predation (and a special variety of it, parasitism); mutualism; and commensalism.

3. This interaction is one of parasitism of the caterpillar by the ichneumon wasp; in this interaction, the caterpillar is the host.
4. If the fungi were not providing any benefits to the algae, the mode of interaction between them would be parasitism—the fungi would be parasites on the algae. Since both the algae and the fungi are benefiting from their relationship, the mode of interaction between them is mutualism.
5. This is an example of Batesian mimicry, in which one species (the red salamander) has evolved to acquire the appearance of a species with superior protective capabilities (the red-spotted newt). The red-spotted newt is the model, the red salamander is the mimic, and the dupe is any predator species that would avoid the red salamander, believing it to be a red newt.
6. Because this succession begins from a state of little or no life and no soil, it is an example of primary succession.

CHAPTER 36

So Far . . .

page 698

1. community; physical environment
2. photosynthesis; decomposition; bacteria; fungi
3. bacteria; bacteria

page 703

1. photosynthesis; producers; herbivore
2. decomposers; biodegradable
3. energy; trophic level

page 709

1. oxygen; stratosphere; ultraviolet radiation
2. heat; carbon dioxide; methane
3. rise; decrease

page 716

1. cools; lose; absorbs
2. climate
3. tundra, taiga, temperate deciduous forest, tropical rainforest

page 722

1. decreases; decreases
2. phytoplankton; perform photosynthesis
3. flows into an ocean

Multiple-Choice

1. a, b, d 2. c, d 3. a. herbivore—organism that eats plants; b. net primary production—

material accumulated through photosynthesis; c. gross primary production—material produced through photosynthesis; d. trophic level—position in an ecosystem's food chain; e. producer—photosynthesizing organism 4. a 5. a 6. d 7. b 8. b 9. c 10. a

Brief Review

1. Within any ecosystem, the amount of available energy drops significantly at each trophic level. This is so because much of the energy locked up in organisms at each trophic level is used for the organisms' metabolic processes (building up tissue, staying warm), while additional energy is lost as heat. The drop in available energy at each trophic level means there can be fewer predator than prey animals.
2. Warm air (a) rises and (b) carries more moisture than cold air. Near the equator, Earth gets warm due to the direct rays coming from the sun. As this warm air rises, it cools and drops moisture. This cooler air moves toward the poles in both directions and descends at about 30°N and 30°S, warming as it goes, thus absorbing moisture from the land, which is dry as a result.
3. Climate essentially defines the large-scale vegetation patterns that are seen on Earth. Variations within large-scale climate regions tend to be mountains, whose climates can vary greatly from base to peak.
4. It may be that excessive eutrophication has occurred in the pond. In such occurrences, large algal blooms result from excess nutrients that come into the body of water. As the algae die and their dead organic matter falls to the lower depths, decomposing bacteria consume the organic matter but consume so much oxygen that they deplete the water of oxygen, thus killing fish.
5. Permafrost makes the tundra wet during summer months, even with low rainfall, and it is too cold for trees to grow. Taiga has a less-severe climate, a longer growing season and no permafrost; coniferous trees grow there and support a larger animal community.

Glossary

2n In a living cell, the condition of being diploid: of having two sets of chromosomes. (Contrast with **n:** In a living cell, the condition of being haploid; of having a single set of chromosomes.)

A

abiotic Pertaining to nonliving things.

acid Any substance that yields hydrogen ions in solution. An acid has a number lower than 7 on the pH scale.

acid rain Rain whose pH level has been skewed toward the acidic side of the pH scale, with air pollution the cause of this shift.

acrosome A structure located on the front end of a vertebrate sperm cell; contains enzymes that help the sperm penetrate the accessory cells surrounding the oocyte.

action potential A temporary reversal of neuronal cell membrane potential at one location that results in a conducted nerve impulse down an axon.

activation energy The energy required to initiate a chemical reaction. Enzymes lower the activation energy of a reaction, thereby greatly speeding up the rate of the reaction.

active site The portion of an enzyme that binds with a substrate, thus helping transform it.

active transport Transport of materials across the plasma membrane in which energy is expended. Through active transport, solutes can be moved against their concentration and electrical gradients. The sodium-potassium pump is an example of active transport.

adaptation A modification in the form, physical functioning, or behavior of organisms in a population over generations in response to environmental change.

adaptive immune response The human immune response that provides protection against specific microbial invaders; compare to innate immune response.

adaptive radiation The rapid evolution of many species from a single species that has been introduced to a new environment.

adenosine triphosphate (ATP) A nucleotide that serves as the most important energy-transfer molecule in living things. ATP powers a broad range of chemical reactions by donating one of its three phosphate groups to these reactions. In the process, it becomes adenosine diphosphate (ADP), which reverts to being ATP when a third phosphate is added to it.

afferent division The division of the peripheral nervous system that carries sensory information toward the central nervous system, having gathered information about the body or environment.

algae Protists that perform photosynthesis.

algal bloom An overabundance of algae in a body of water, resulting from an excess of nutrients. The many dead algae that fall to the bottom allow decomposing bacteria to flourish, using up so much oxygen that fish can suffocate.

alkaline Basic, as in solutions. Alkaline (basic) solutions have numbers above 7 on the pH scale.

allele One of the alternative forms of a single gene. In pea plants, a single gene codes for seed color, and it comes in two alleles—one codes for yellow seeds, the other for green seeds.

allergen A foreign substance that triggers an allergic reaction. These substances are usually derived from living things, including pollen, dust mites, foods, and fur.

allergy An immune system overreaction to an antigen that results in the release of histamine.

allopatric speciation Speciation that involves the geographic separation of populations. Most speciation involves geographic separation, followed by the development of intrinsic isolating mechanisms in the separated populations.

allosteric regulation The regulation of an enzyme's activity by means of a molecule binding to a site on the enzyme other than its active site.

alternation of generations A life cycle practiced by plants in which successive plant generations alternate between the diploid sporophyte condition and the haploid gametophyte condition.

alternative splicing A process in genetics in which a single primary transcript can be edited in different ways to yield multiple messenger RNAs, which in turn yield multiple proteins.

alveoli Tiny, hollow, air-exchange sacs that exist in clusters at the end of each of the air-conducting passageways in the lungs, the bronchioles.

amino-acid–based hormones Hormones that are derived from a single amino acid. One of three principal classes of hormones, the other two being peptide and steroid hormones.

amniotic egg An egg with a hard outer casing and an inner series of membranes and fluids that provide protection, nutrients, and waste disposal for a growing embryo. The evolution of the amniotic egg, in reptiles, freed them from the constraint of having to reproduce near water.

amniotic fluid A protective and nutritive fluid that surrounds the fetus of mammals, including filling the lungs.

analogy A structure found in different organisms that is similar in function and appearance but is not the result of shared ancestry. Analogies must be distinguished from homologies to get a true picture of evolutionary relationships.

ancestral character A character that existed in the common ancestor of a group of organisms. Cladistics distinguishes ancestral from derived characters and uses these characters to determine evolutionary relationships.

aneuploidy A condition in which an individual organism has either more or fewer chromosomes than is normally found in its species' full set. Down syndrome is the result of aneuploidy—generally three copies of chromosome 21, rather than the standard two.

angiosperm A flowering seed plant whose seeds are enclosed within the tissue called fruit. Angiosperms are the most dominant and diverse of the four principal types of plants. Examples include roses, cacti, corn, and deciduous trees.

animal pole The end of a zygote with relatively less yolk and lying closer to the cell's nucleus. The location of the egg's poles defines the orientation in which the embryo develops.

anther The part of a flower within which pollen grains are produced. The anther is on top of a filament, and together they make up the flower's stamen.

antibiotics Chemical compounds produced by one microorganism that are toxic to another microorganism.

antibody A protein of the immune system found on the surface of B cells, or exported by them, that is able to bind to a specific antigen, thus playing a role in eliminating it from the body.

antibody-mediated immunity An immune system capability that works through the production of proteins called antibodies.

anticodon The end of the transfer RNA molecule that can bind with a particular codon on the mRNA transcript.

antidiuretic hormone (ADH) Also known as vasopressin, a substance produced by the hypothalamus and released by the posterior pituitary gland that functions as a hormone within the kidneys and as a neurotransmitter within the brain. In the kidneys, ADH acts to conserve water by increasing the amount of it sent back into blood circulation. In the brain, vasopressin acts to facilitate social affiliation in both humans and at least one other species of mammal.

antigen Any foreign substance that elicits a response by the immune system. Certain proteins or carbohydrates on the surface of an invading bacterial cell, for instance, act as antigens that trigger an immune response.

antigen-presenting cell (APC) Any immune system cell that presents, on its surface, fragments of an antigen that it has ingested. Dendritic cells are the immune system's most important type of antigen-presenting cell.

aorta The enormous artery extending from the heart that receives all the blood pumped by the heart's left ventricle. Branches stemming from the aorta supply oxygenated blood to all the tissues in the body.

apical meristem Groups of plant cells, located at the tips of the roots and shoots, that give rise to all tissues in the plant.

appendicular skeleton The division of the skeletal system consisting of the bones of the paired appendages, including the pelvic and pectoral girdles to which they are attached.

aquifer Porous underground rock in which groundwater is stored.

Archaea With Bacteria and Eukarya, one of three domains of the living world, composed solely of microscopic, single-celled organisms superficially similar to bacteria but genetically quite different. Many of the Archaea live in extreme environments, such as boiling-hot vents on the ocean floor.

arithmetical increase An increase in numbers by an addition of a fixed number in each time period.

artery A blood vessel that carries blood away from the heart.

asexual reproduction Reproduction that occurs without the union of two reproductive cells (sexual reproduction). Offspring produced through asexual reproduction are genetically identical to their parent organism.

atmosphere The layer of gases that surrounds the Earth.

atomic number The number of protons in the nucleus of an atom. Gold has 79 protons in its nucleus and thus has the atomic number 79. All elements are ordered on the periodic table according to atomic number.

ATP synthase An enzyme functioning in cellular respiration that brings together ADP and inorganic phosphate molecules to produce ATP.

autoimmune disorder An attack by the immune system on the body's own tissues.

autonomic nervous system That portion of the peripheral nervous system's efferent division that provides involuntary regulation of smooth muscle, cardiac muscle, and glands.

autosomal dominant disorder A genetic disorder caused by a single faulty allele located on an autosomal (non-sex chromosome). Huntington disease is one example.

autosomal recessive disorder A recessive dysfunction caused by a faulty allele on an autosome (non-sex chromosome). Sickle-cell anemia is one example.

axial skeleton The division of the skeletal system that forms the central column, including the skull, vertebral column, and rib cage.

axon A single, large extension of the cell body of a neuron that carries signals away from the cell body toward other cells.

B

Bacteria With Archaea and Eukarya, one of three domains of the living world, composed solely of single-celled, microscopic organisms that superficially resemble Archaea but that are genetically quite different.

ball-and-stick model A diagram showing the three-dimensional structure of a molecule, with the atoms drawn as balls and the bonds between them drawn as sticks. This type of representation clearly shows the spatial relationship of the atoms to each other.

base Any substance that accepts hydrogen ions in solution. A base has a number higher than 7 on the pH scale.

Batesian mimicry A type of mimicry in which one species evolves to resemble a species that has superior protection against predators.

bell curve A distribution of values, found commonly in nature, that is symmetrically largest around the average.

bilateral symmetry A bodily symmetry in which opposite sides of a sagittal plane are mirror images of one another. Animals generally are bilaterally symmetrical.

bile Substance produced by the liver that facilitates the digestion of fats. Bile can be released either directly by the liver or by the gallbladder, which stores and concentrates this substance.

binary fission The form of reproduction carried out by prokaryotic cells in which the chromosome replicates and the cell pinches between the attachment points of the two resulting chromosomes to form two new cells.

binomial nomenclature The system of naming species that uses two names (genus and species) for each species. This system helps identify groupings among living things.

biodegradable Capable of being broken down by living organisms.

biodiversity Variety among living things. There are three principal types of biodiversity: species diversity, geographic distribution of species populations, and genetic diversity within species populations.

biogeochemical cycling The movement of water and nutrients back and forth between biotic (living) and abiotic (nonliving) realms.

biological legacies A living thing, or product of a living thing, that survives a major ecological disturbance.

biological species concept A definition of species that relies on the breeding behavior of populations in nature. It defines species as groups of actually or potentially interbreeding natural populations that are reproductively isolated from other such groups.

biology The study of life.

biomass Material produced by living things, generally measured by dry weight.

biome Large, terrestrial regions of the Earth that have similar climates and hence similar vegetative formations. Six biome types are recognized at a minimum: tundra, taiga, temperate deciduous forest, temperate grassland, desert, and tropical rainforest.

biosphere The interactive collection of all the world's ecosystems. Also thought of as that portion of the Earth that supports life.

biotechnology The use of technology to control biological processes as a means of meeting societal needs.

biotic Pertaining to living things.

bipedalism Among primates, the trait of walking upright, on two legs. Along with tooth structure, the most important trait in defining species that are classified as hominins, meaning members of the taxon of human-like primates.

bivalves A class of molluscs that includes mussels, clams, and oysters, among other organisms.

blade In plants, the major, broad part of a leaf.

blastocyst Hollow, fluid-filled ball of cells that is formed in the early stages of the embryonic development of humans and other mammals. In non-mammalian animals, the blastocyst is known as the blastula.

blastula An early-stage animal embryo composed of one or more layers of cells surrounding a liquid-filled cavity known as a blastocoel. A key feature in defining animals as all animals go through a blastula stage in development, but no other organisms do.

B-lymphocyte cell (B cell) The central cells of antibody-mediated immune system function. B cells produce antibodies, which can function as antigen receptors on the surface of B cells. Conversely, antibodies may be exported from B cells as freestanding entities to fight antigens.

body segmentation A repetition of body parts in an animal. An example can be found in the vertebrae that make up the human vertebral column or backbone.

bone A connective tissue that provides support and structure to the body and that often is the site of fat storage and blood cell production.

bottleneck effect A change in allele frequencies in a population due to chance following a sharp reduction in the population's size. One of the factors that potentiates genetic drift.

bronchiole Tiny air-conducting passageway in the lungs that has at its end several alveoli, the hollow air-exchange sacs of the lungs.

bryophytes A plant that lacks a vascular (fluid transport) structure. Bryophytes are the most primitive of the four principal varieties of living plants. Mosses are the most familiar example.

bud An undeveloped plant shoot, composed mostly of meristematic tissue.

buffering system A physiological system that functions to keep pH within normal limits in an organism. Buffering systems generally utilize weak acids or bases to neutralize any sudden infusion of acid or base.

C

C₄ photosynthesis A form of photosynthesis in which carbon dioxide is first fixed into a four-carbon molecule and then transferred to special bundle sheath cells in which the Calvin cycle is undertaken. C_4 photosynthesis is used primarily by plants in warm-weather environments as a means of reducing the photorespiration that undercuts carbohydrate production in C_3 plants.

calorie (in nutrition) The amount of energy necessary to raise the temperature of 1,000 grams of water by 1°C. Sometimes written as Calorie to distinguish it from a standard calorie, which is defined as the amount of energy needed to raise the temperature of 1 gram of water by 1°C.

Calvin cycle The set of steps in photosynthesis in which an energy-rich sugar is produced by means of two essential processes—the fixing of atmospheric carbon dioxide into a sugar and the energizing of this sugar with the addition of electrons supplied by the light-dependent reactions of photosynthesis. Also known as the Calvin-Benson and C_3 cycle.

CAM photosynthesis (crassulacean acid metabolism photosynthesis) A form of photosynthesis, undertaken by some plants in hot, dry climates, in which carbon fixation takes place at night and the Calvin cycle during the day. Practiced by succulent plants in particular, CAM metabolism allows plants to preserve water by opening their stomata only at night.

Cambrian Explosion The sudden appearance of the ancestors of most modern animals beginning in the Cambrian Period, 542 million years ago.

capillary The smallest type of blood vessel, connecting the arteries and veins in the body's tissues. Gases, nutrients, and wastes are exchanged between the blood and the body's tissues through the thin walls of capillaries.

capsid A protein coat that surrounds the genetic material in almost all viruses.

carbohydrate An organic molecule that always contains carbon, oxygen, and hydrogen and that, in many instances, contains nothing but carbon, oxygen, and hydrogen. Carbohydrates usually contain exactly twice as many hydrogen atoms as oxygen atoms. The building blocks or monomers of carbohydrates are monosaccharides, which combine to create the polymers of carbohydrates, the polysaccharides, such as starch and cellulose.

cardiac muscle The type of striated muscle tissue that forms the muscles of the heart.

cardiovascular system A fluid transport system of the body, consisting of the heart, all the blood vessels in the body, the blood that flows through these vessels, and the bone marrow tissue in which red blood cells are formed.

carnivore An animal that eats meat.

carpel The female reproductive structure of a flower, consisting of an ovary, a style, and a stigma.

carrier A person who does not suffer from a recessive genetic debilitation, but who carries an allele for the condition that can be passed along to offspring.

carrying capacity (K) The maximum population density of a species that can be sustained in a given geographical area over time. In ecology, this is often denoted as K.

cartilage A connective tissue that serves as padding in most joints, forms the human larynx (voicebox)

and trachea (windpipe), and links ribs to the breastbone.

catalyst A substance that retains its original chemical composition while bringing about a change in a substrate. Enzymes are catalysts in chemical reactions; one enzyme can carry out hundreds or thousands of chemical transformations without itself being transformed.

cell cycle The repeating pattern of growth, genetic duplication, and division seen in most cells.

cell wall A relatively thick layer of material that forms the periphery of all plant and fungal cells and many types of bacterial, archael, and protist cells.

cell-mediated immunity An immune system capability that works through the production of cells that destroy infected cells in the body.

cellular respiration The three-stage, oxygen-dependent harvesting of energy that goes on in most cells. The three stages are glycolysis, the Krebs cycle, and the electron transport chain.

cellulose A structural, complex carbohydrate produced by plants and other organisms.

central nervous system (CNS) The portion of the nervous system consisting of the brain and spinal cord.

central vacuole A large, watery plant organelle whose functions include the maintenance of cell pressure, the storage of nutrients, and the retention and degradation of waste products.

centrosome A cellular structure that acts as an organizing center for the assembly of microtubules. A cell's centrosome duplicates prior to mitosis and plays an important part in the development of the cell's mitotic spindle.

cephalopods A class of molluscs that includes squid, octopus, nautilus, and cuttlefish.

cerebellum A region of the brain that refines movements and the sense of balance based on sensory inputs it receives from various parts of the body.

cerebral cortex Thin outer covering of the region of the brain known as the cerebrum. Responsible for the highest human thinking and processing.

cerebrospinal fluid A fluid that circulates in both the brain and spinal cord, supplying nutrients, hormones, and immune system cells and providing the nervous tissue with protection against jarring injury.

cerebrum The largest region of the human brain, responsible for much of the human capacity for higher mental functioning.

cervix The lower part of the uterus, a narrow neck that opens into the vagina.

CFCs A class of human-made chlorine compounds that destroys the atmospheric ozone that protects life on land from damaging ultraviolet radiation.

chemical bonding General term for a bond created when electrons of two atoms interact and rearrange into a new form that allows the atoms to become attached to each other. Ionic, covalent, and hydrogen bonds are all chemical bonds.

chitin A complex carbohydrate that gives shape and strength to the external skeleton of arthropods, including insects, spiders, and crustaceans.

chlorophyll *a* The primary pigment of chloroplasts, found embedded in its membranes. Together with the accessory pigments, chlorophyll *a* absorbs some wavelengths of sunlight in the first step of photosynthesis.

chloroplast The organelle within plant and algae cells that is the site of photosynthesis.

cholesterol A steroid molecule that forms part of the outer membrane of all animal cells and that acts as a precursor for many other steroids, among them the hormones testosterone and estrogen.

chromatid One of the two identical strands of chromatin (DNA plus associated proteins) that make up a chromosome in its duplicated state.

chromatin A molecular complex of DNA and its associated proteins that makes up the chromosomes of eukaryotic organisms.

chromosome Structural unit containing part or all of an organism's genome, consisting of DNA and its associated proteins (chromatin). The human genome is made up of 23 pairs of chromosomes, or 46 chromosomes in all.

chyme The soupy mixture of food and gastric juices that passes from the stomach to the small intestine.

cilia Hair-like extensions of a cell, composed of microtubules. Many cilia protrude from the surface of some cells, moving rapidly back and forth, serving to propel the cells or to move material around it.

citric acid cycle Another name for the Krebs cycle, one of the three main sets of steps in cellular respiration; named for the first product of the cycle, citric acid.

cladistics The branch of systematics that uses shared derived characters to determine the order of branching events in speciation and therefore which species are most closely related. Cladistics is concerned only with evolutionary relationships, not classification.

cladogram An evolutionary tree constructed using the cladistic system.

cleavage The developmental process in which a zygote is repeatedly divided into smaller individual cells through cell division.

climate The average weather conditions, including temperature, precipitation, and wind, in a particular region.

climax community The relatively stable community that develops at the end of any process of ecological succession.

clone An exact genetic copy. Also, used as a verb—to make one of these copies. A single gene or a whole, complex organism can be cloned.

cloning vector A self-replicating agent that, in the cloning process, serves to transfer genetic material. Examples include bacterial plasmids and the viruses known as bacteriophages.

closed circulation system A type of circulatory system, found in all vertebrates and in some invertebrates, in which blood stays within vessels.

coastal zone The region lying between the high-tide point on shore and the point offshore where the continental shelf drops off.

cochlea The coiled, fluid-filled, membranous portion of the inner ear in which fluid vibrations are transformed into the nervous system signals perceived as sound.

codominance A condition in which two alleles of a given gene have different phenotypic effects, with both effects manifesting in organisms that are heterozygous for the gene.

codon An mRNA triplet that codes for a single amino acid or a start or a stop command in the translation stage of protein synthesis.

coelom A central body cavity, found in most animal phyla.

coenzyme A type of accessory molecule that binds to the active site of an enzyme, thus allowing the enzyme to bind to its substrate. Many vitamins are coenzymes.

coevolution The interdependent evolution of two or more species. Coevolution can benefit both species, as in flowering plants and their animal pollinators, or it can be an arms race between species, as in a plant and its predators.

coexistence The condition in which two species live in the same habitat, dividing up resources in a way that allows both to survive.

colonial multicellularity A form of life in which individual cells form stable associations with one another but do not take on specialized roles.

commensalism An interaction between two species in which one benefits while the other is neither harmed nor helped.

common descent with modification The process by which species of living things undergo modification in successive generations, with such modification sometimes resulting in the formation of new, separate species.

community All the populations of all species of living things that inhabit a given area. The term also is used to mean a collection of populations in a given area that potentially interact with each other.

compact bone Dense bone that forms the outer portion of bones, structured as a set of parallel osteons and their associated nerves and blood vessels.

competitive exclusion principle When two species compete for the same limited, vital resource, one will always outcompete the other and thus bring about the latter's local extinction.

competitive inhibition A reduction in the activity of an enzyme by means of a compound other than the enzyme's usual substrate binding with it in its active site.

concentration gradient A gradient within a given medium defined by the difference between the highest and lowest concentrations of a solute. The solute will have a natural tendency to move from the areas of higher concentration to lower, thus diffusing.

cones In human vision, photoreceptors that respond best to bright light and that provide color vision.

connective tissue A tissue, active in the support and protection of other tissues, whose cells are surrounded by a material that they have secreted. In humans, one of the four principal types of tissue.

consumer Any organism that eats other organisms rather than producing its own food.

continental drift The movement of continental plates over the globe, allowing continents to divide and rejoin in different patterns.

convergent evolution Evolution that occurs when similar environmental influences shape two separate evolutionary lines in similar ways.

coral reef Ocean structure, found in shallow, warm waters, that consists primarily of the piled-up remains of many generations of the animals called coral polyps. Such reefs provide habitat for a rich diversity of marine organisms.

coronary artery An artery that delivers oxygenated blood to the muscles of the heart. A heart attack is a complete blockage of a coronary artery.

corpus luteum The structure that develops in the mammalian ovary from the ruptured tertiary follicle following ovulation. The corpus luteum secretes hormones that help prepare the reproductive tract for pregnancy.

cotyledon An embryonic leaf. A major division in plants is between the monocots, which have one embryonic leaf, and the dicots, which have two embryonic leaves.

coupled reaction A chemical reaction in which an endergonic reaction is powered by an exergonic reaction. All "uphill," or endergonic, reactions require an input of energy; this energy is supplied by "downhill," or exergonic, reactions.

covalent bond A type of chemical bond in which two atoms are linked through a sharing of electrons.

Cretaceous Extinction A mass extinction event that occurred at the boundary between the Cretaceous and Tertiary periods. This event, which included an asteroid impact, resulted in the extinction of the dinosaurs along with many other organisms.

crossing over (genetic recombination) A process, occurring during meiosis, in which homologous chromosomes exchange reciprocal portions of themselves.

cross-pollinate To pollinate one plant with pollen of another plant. Mendel used this technique in conducting his experiments to uncover rules of heredity.

cytokinesis The physical separation of one cell into two daughter cells.

cytoplasm The region of a cell inside the plasma membrane and outside the nucleus. Usually, this region is filled with the jelly-like cytosol containing the cell's extranuclear organelles.

cytoskeleton A network of protein filaments that functions in cell structure, cell movement, and the transport of materials within the cell. Microfilaments, intermediate filaments, and microtubules are all parts of the cytoskeleton.

cytosol The protein-rich, jelly-like fluid in which a cell's organelles that are outside the nucleus are immersed.

cytotoxic T cell (killer T cell) Type of T-lymphocyte cell that binds to and kills the body's own cells when they have become infected.

D

deciduous Refers to plants that show a coordinated, seasonal loss of leaves. This strategy allows plants to conserve water during a time they could perform little photosynthesis anyway.

decomposer A type of detritivore that, in feeding on dead or cast-off organic material, breaks it down into its inorganic components. Most decomposers are fungi or bacteria.

deletion A chromosomal condition in which a piece of a chromosome has been lost. Occurs when a chromosomal fragment that breaks off does not rejoin any chromosome.

dendrites Extensions of a neuron that carry signals toward the neuronal cell body.

density dependent In ecology, effects on a population that increase or decrease in accordance with the size of that population. Density-dependent effects tend to involve biological factors.

density independent In ecology, effects on a population that are not related to the size of that population. Density-independent effects tend to involve physical forces, such as temperature and rain.

deoxyribonucleic acid (DNA) The primary information-bearing molecule of life, composed of two chains of nucleotides linked together in the form of a double helix. Proteins are put together in accordance with the information encoded in DNA.

derived character A character unique to groupings of organisms (taxa) descended from a common ancestor.

dermis In certain animals, the thick layer of the skin—composed mostly of connective tissue—that underlies, nourishes, and supports the epidermis.

desert A biome in which rainfall is less than 25 centimeters, or 10 inches, per year and water evaporation rates are high relative to rainfall.

detritivore An organism that feeds on the remains of dead organisms or the cast-off material from living organisms.

dicotyledon (dicot) A type of plant that has two embryonic leaves within its seed. More than three-quarters of all flowering plants are broad-leafed dicotyledons.

diffusion The movement of molecules or ions from areas of their higher concentration to areas of their lower concentration. Over time, the random movement of molecules will result in the even distribution of the material.

digestive system The organ system that transports food into the body, secretes digestive enzymes that help break down food to allow it to be absorbed by the body, and excretes waste products. This system consists of the esophagus, stomach, and small and large intestines plus accessory glands such as the pancreas and gallbladder.

digestive tract A muscular passageway for food and food waste that runs through the human body from the mouth to the anus.

dihybrid cross An experimental cross in which the plants used differ in two of their characters.

dikaryotic Having two haploid nuclei in one cell. A phase of the life cycle of many fungi.

diploid Possessing two sets of chromosomes. All human cells are diploid with the exception of human gametes (eggs and sperm), which are haploid. Such haploid cells possess only a single set of chromosomes.

directional selection In evolution, the type of natural selection that moves a character toward one of its extremes. Compare to stabilizing and disruptive selection.

disruptive selection In evolution, the type of natural selection that moves a character toward both of its extremes, operating against individuals that are average for that character. This type of selection seems to be less common in nature than either stabilizing or directional selection.

DNA polymerase An enzyme that is active in DNA replication, separating strands of DNA, bringing bases to the parental strands, and correcting errors by removing and replacing incorrect base pairs.

dominant Term used to designate an allele that is expressed in the heterozygous condition.

dominant disorder Genetic conditions in which a single faulty allele can cause damage, even when a second, functional allele exists.

dormancy A state in which growth is suspended and there is a prolonged low level of metabolic activity. Dormancy allows organisms to conserve energy during times of unfavorable environmental conditions.

dorsal nerve cord A rod-shaped dorsal structure consisting of nerve cells, running from a chordate animal's head to its tail.

double fertilization A fusion of gametes and of nutritive cells that occurs at the same time in angiosperm plants.

Down syndrome A disorder in humans in which affected individuals usually have three copies of chromosome 21 rather than the standard two. Individuals with this syndrome have short stature, shortened life span, and low IQ.

E

ecological dominants A species that is abundant and obvious in a given community. In any community, a few species, usually plants, will dominate in numbers.

ecology The study of the interactions that living things have with each other and with their environment.

ecosystem A community of living things and the physical environment with which they interact.

ectopic pregnancy An abnormal pregnancy in which the blastocyst has attached to a location other than the uterine wall.

efferent division The division of the peripheral nervous system that carries motor commands from the central nervous system (CNS) toward effectors (muscles and glands).

electron With protons and neutrons, one of three basic constituents of an atom. Electrons carry a negative electrical charge and are distributed in an atom at a distance from the nucleus.

electron carrier A molecule that serves to transfer electrons from one molecule to another in ATP

formation. The most important electron carrier in ATP formation is NAD+ (NADH in its reduced form). The other major carrier is FAD ($FADH_2$).

electron transport chain (ETC) The third stage of cellular respiration, occurring within the inner membrane of the mitochondria, in which most of the ATP is formed.

electronegativity The measure of the strength of attraction an atom has for electrons that are being shared in a covalent bond. An atom with higher electronegativity will tend to pull electrons toward itself, away from atoms with lower electronegativity.

element A substance that cannot be reduced to any simpler set of components through chemical processes. An element is defined by the number of protons in its nucleus.

embryo A developing organism. In humans, the developing organism from the time a zygote undergoes its first division through the end of the eighth week of development.

embryo sac The mature female gametophyte plant. Cells of the embryo sac include the egg that will be fertilized by one sperm cell from the pollen grain, and the central cell, whose two nuclei will fuse with a second sperm cell from the pollen grain, thus producing food for the embryo.

embryonic stem cell A cell from the blastocyst stage of a human embryo that is capable of giving rise to all the types of cells in the adult body.

endergonic reaction A chemical reaction in which the ending set of molecules (the products) contains more energy than the starting set of molecules (the reactants).

endocrine gland A gland that releases its materials directly into surrounding tissues or into the bloodstream, without using ducts.

endocrine system The organ system that sends signals throughout the body through use of the chemical messengers called hormones.

endocytosis The process by which cells bring relatively large materials into themselves through use of transport vesicles.

endomembrane system An interactive group of membrane-lined organelles and transport vesicles that functions within eukaryotic cells.

endometrium The tissue lining the interior of the uterus in mammals, which thickens in response to hormonal secretion during ovulation and is shed during menstruation. If pregnancy occurs, this tissue initially houses the embryo.

endosperm The nutrient tissue that surrounds an angiosperm embryo in the seed. The rice and wheat grains that we eat consist mostly of endosperm.

energy The capacity to bring about movement against an opposing force.

energy-flow model A conceptualization of ecosystems as units in which energy is first captured by given organisms and then transferred to other organisms.

environmental resistance All the forces in the environment that act to limit the size of a population.

enzyme A chemically active protein that speeds up, or in practical terms enables, chemical reactions in living things.

epidermis The outermost layer of skin in animals or the outermost cell layer in plants.

epididymis A collection of tubules near the testis in which sperm complete their development and are stored.

epithelial tissue A tissue that covers surfaces exposed to an external environment. In humans, skin is an epithelial tissue, as is the lining of the digestive tract.

essential amino acid In nutrition, one of nine amino acids that the body cannot make and that hence must be supplied by food.

estrogen A class of hormones, produced primarily by cells of the ovary, that supports egg development, growth of uterine lining, and development of female sex characteristics.

estuary An area where a river or stream flows into the ocean, bringing freshwater and saltwater habitat together. Estuaries are among the most productive ecosystems on Earth.

Eukarya With Bacteria and Archaea, one of three domains of the living world, composed of four subordinate kingdoms: Plantae, Animalia, Fungi, and Protista. All members of domain Eukarya are composed of single cells or groups of cells that have a nucleus.

eukaryote An organism that is a member of domain Eukarya.

eukaryotic cell A cell whose primary complement of DNA is contained within a membrane-lined nucleus. Eukaryotic cells have several other organelles in addition to the nucleus. All organisms except bacteria and archaea either are single eukaryotic cells or are composed of eukaryotic cells.

evolution Any genetically based phenotypic change in a population of organisms over successive generations. Evolution can also be thought of as the process by which species of living things can undergo modification over successive generations, with such modification sometimes resulting in the formation of new species.

exergonic reaction A chemical reaction in which the starting set of molecules (the reactants) contain more energy than the final set of molecules (the products).

exocrine gland A gland that secretes its materials through ducts (tubes). For example, sweat glands conduct perspiration through ducts to the skin.

exocytosis The means by which relatively large volumes of material are moved from the inside of a cell to the outside. In exocytosis, a transport vesicle fuses with a cell's plasma membrane, after which the contents of the vesicle are ejected outside the cell.

exoskeleton An external material covering the animal body, providing support and protection.

exponential growth A form of population growth in which the rate of growth is proportional to the starting size of the population. Exponential growth results in a J-shaped growth curve because, when plotted on a graph, the population's increase resembles the letter J.

exponential increase An increase in numbers that is proportional to the number already in existence.

This type of increase occurs in populations of living things, and it carries the potential for enormous growth of populations.

extremophile An organism that grows optimally in one or more conditions that would kill most other organisms.

extrinsic isolating mechanism A barrier to interbreeding of populations that is not an inherent characteristic of the organisms in the populations. Geographic barriers such as rivers are extrinsic isolating mechanisms.

F

facilitated diffusion A passage of materials through the cell's plasma membrane that is aided by a transport protein.

facilitation In succession, the actions or qualities of earlier-arriving species that in some way assist the establishment of later-arriving species within a community.

fat A dietary lipid that is solid at room temperature (e.g., butter, the fat in a piece of bacon).

fatty acid A molecule, found in many lipids, composed of a hydrocarbon chain bonded to a carboxyl group.

fertilization The fusion of two gametes to form a zygote. In humans (and many other organisms), the gametes known as sperm and egg fuse, resulting in a zygote.

fetus In humans, the developing organism from the start of the ninth week of development to the moment of birth.

fibers In skeletal muscle, a single elongated muscle cell, containing hundreds of long, thin myofibrils that run the length of the cell. In nutrition, one of the three principal classes of dietary carbohydrate, defined as a complex carbohydrate that is indigestible. The other classes of dietary carbohydrate are simple sugars and starches.

fibrous root system A plant root system that consists of many roots, all about the same size.

filament The part of a stamen (male reproductive part of a flower) that is shaped like and functions as a stalk and has an anther at the top.

first filial generation (F_1) The offspring of the parental generation in an experimental genetic cross.

first law of thermodynamics Energy cannot be created or destroyed, but can only be transformed from one form to another.

fitness In evolution, the success of an organism, relative to other members of its population, in passing on its genes to the next generation of offspring.

fixation The process of the incorporation of a gas into an organic molecule. In photosynthesis, atmospheric carbon dioxide (CO_2) is fixed into the sugars of photosynthesizing organisms, such as plants. In ecology, atmospheric nitrogen (N_2) is fixed into ammonia (NH_3) by certain bacteria.

flagella The relatively long, tail-like extensions of some cells, composed of microtubules, that function in cell movement. Often, cells will have but a single flagellum, as with mammalian sperm cells.

fluid-mosaic model A conceptualization of the cell's plasma membrane as a fluid, phospholipid bilayer that has within it a mosaic of both stationary and mobile proteins.

follicle In the vertebrate ovary, the complex of the oocyte (developing egg) and the cells and fluids that surround and nourish it.

follicle-stimulating hormone (FSH) A hormone, secreted by the anterior pituitary, that promotes egg development and stimulates secretion of estrogens in women and supports sperm production and testosterone secretion in men.

formed elements Cells and cell fragments that form the nonfluid portion of blood. Formed elements include red blood cells, white blood cells, and platelets. Contrast with plasma, the fluid portion of blood, consisting mostly of water.

founder effect The phenomenon by which an initial gene pool for a population is established by means of that population migrating to a new area. One of the conditions that potentiates genetic drift.

fraternal twins Twins who are produced first through multiple ovulations in the mother, followed by multiple fertilizations from separate sperm of the father, and then multiple implantations of the resulting embryos in the uterus.

free radical A molecule with an unpaired electron, usually existing for only a very brief time. Although free radicals are natural products of biological processes, these molecules can be destructive in living tissues.

fruit The mature ovary of any flowering plant. Many fruits protect the underlying seeds, and many attract animals that will eat the fruit and disperse the seeds.

functional group A group of atoms that confers a special property on a carbon-based molecule. Functional groups usually are transferred as a unit among carbon-based molecules and often confer an electrical charge or polarity on the molecules they are part of.

G

gallbladder Organ of the body that stores and concentrates the digestive material bile, which is produced by the liver. Bile facilitates the breakdown of fats by digestive enzymes.

gamete A haploid reproductive cell, either egg or sperm.

gametophyte generation The haploid generation in plants that produces gametes (eggs and sperm). In the flowering plants (angiosperms), this generation is microscopic but gives rise to the visible sporophyte generation.

ganglion Any collection of nerve-cell bodies in the peripheral nervous system.

gap junction A protein assemblage that forms a communication channel between adjacent animal cells. Gap junctions open only as necessary, thus allowing small molecules and electrical signals to move between cells.

gastropods A class of molluscs that includes snails and slugs, among other organisms.

gastrulation The process in early animal development in which an embryo's cells migrate to form three layers of tissue: the endoderm, the mesoderm, and the ectoderm. Each of these layers then goes on to give rise to differing tissues and organs in the organism.

gene flow The movement of genes from one population to another.

gene pool The entire collection of alleles, or variant forms of genes, in a population.

genetic code The inventory of linkages between nucleotide triplets and the amino acids they code for. With few exceptions, the genetic code is universal in living things.

genetic drift The chance alteration of allele frequencies in a population, with such alterations having greatest impact on small populations.

genetics The study of physical inheritance among living things.

genome The complete collection of an organism's genetic information. More narrowly, the complete haploid set of an organism's chromosomes.

genotype The genetic makeup of an organism, including all the genes that lie along its chromosomes.

germ-line cell The succession of parent and daughter cells that ultimately produce either eggs or sperm.

gland An organ or group of cells that secretes one or more substances.

glomerulus Knotted network of capillaries in each of the kidneys' nephrons that receives blood and lets some smaller blood-borne materials pass out of it (and into the surrounding Bowman's capsule) while retaining larger materials.

glucagon A hormone, secreted by cells in the pancreas, that brings about an increase in blood levels of glucose.

glycemic load A measure of how blood glucose levels are affected by defined portions of given carbohydrates. Lower glycemic loads are associated with improved human health.

glycocalyx An outer layer of the plasma membrane, composed of short carbohydrate chains that attach to membrane proteins and phospholipid molecules. Such chains serve as the actual binding sites on many membrane proteins, act to lubricate the cell, and can form an adhesion layer that allows one cell to stick to another.

glycogen A complex carbohydrate molecule that serves as the primary form in which carbohydrates are stored in animals.

glycolysis The first stage of cellular respiration, occurring in the cytosol. For some organisms, glycolysis is the sole means of extracting energy from food. In most organisms, it is a means of extracting some energy and a necessary precursor to the other two stages of cellular respiration, the Krebs cycle and the electron transport chain.

glycoprotein A molecule that combines protein and carbohydrate. Glycoproteins play important roles as cell receptors and some types of hormones, among other functions.

Golgi complex A network of membranes, found in the cytoplasm of eukaryotic cells, that processes and distributes proteins that come to it from the rough endoplasmic reticulum.

gonadotropin-releasing hormone A hormone released in tiny amounts from the brain's hypothalamus that stimulates the anterior pituitary to release two other hormones (follicle-stimulating hormone and luteinizing hormone) important in reproduction.

gravitropism The bending of a plant's roots or shoots in response to gravity. This capability helps a plant orient its roots and shoots properly—roots toward the center of the Earth, shoots away from it.

gross primary production The amount of material that a photosynthesizing organism produces through photosynthesis.

groundwater Water contained within underground rock formations.

gymnosperm A seed plant whose seeds do not develop within fruit tissue. One of the four principal varieties of plants, gymnosperms reproduce through wind-aided pollination. Coniferous trees, such as pine and fir, are the most familiar examples

H

habitat The type of surroundings in which individuals of a species are normally found.

haploid Possessing a single set of chromosomes. Human gametes (eggs and sperm) are haploid cells because they have only a single set of chromosomes. All other cells in the human body are diploid, meaning they possess two sets of chromosomes. Some organisms are strictly haploid. Bacteria, for example, have only a single chromosome, making them haploid.

heart attack A complete blockage of one of the heart's coronary arteries, resulting in the death of groups of heart cells from lack of a blood supply.

helper T cell Type of T-lymphocyte cell that stimulates both T-cell and B-cell immunity. Referred to in AIDS therapy as a CD-4 cell.

hemoglobin The iron-containing protein in red blood cells that binds to both oxygen and carbon dioxide, thus assisting in their transportation.

herbivore An animal that eats only plants.

hermaphroditic A state in which one animal possesses both male and female sex organs.

heterozygous Possessing two different alleles of a gene for a given character.

high-density lipoprotein (HDL) A type of protein that transports fat or lipid molecules (usually cholesterol) from various tissues in the body to the liver. Sometimes known as the "good cholesterol," HDLs help remove, and possibly neutralize, the LDLs, or low-density lipoproteins, that can harmfully reside in coronary arteries.

histamine A compound that, in immune system activity, brings about blood vessel dilation and increased blood vessel permeability.

HIV Human immunodeficiency virus, the cause of the disease AIDS.

homeostasis The maintenance of a relatively stable internal environment in living things.

Hominini The taxonomic grouping of human-like primates. Modern human beings, or *Homo sapiens*, are one of the species within Hominini. All other hominin species are now extinct.

Homo sapiens (**H. sapiens**) The species of modern human beings. The last surviving species within the taxonomic category of Hominini or human-like primates.

homologous In anatomy, having the same structure owing to inheritance from a common ancestor. Forelimb structures in whales, bats, cats, and gorillas are homologous.

homologous chromosomes Chromosomes that are the same in function and hence size. Species that are diploid (have two sets of chromosomes) have matching pairs of homologous chromosomes; one member of each homologous pair is inherited from the male, the second member of each homologous pair is inherited from the female.

homology A structure that is shared in different organisms owing to inheritance from a common ancestor. Homologies are used to help decipher evolutionary relationships.

homozygous Having two identical alleles of a gene for a given character.

hormone A substance that, when released in one part of an organism, goes on to prompt physiological activity in another part of the organism. Both plants and animals have hormones.

host The prey in a parasitic relationship.

human genome The 3.2 billion base pairs of DNA that make up the full complement of DNA found in the nucleus of each human cell.

hydrocarbon A compound made of hydrogen and carbon. Hydrocarbons are nonpolar covalent molecules and therefore are not easily dissolved in water.

hydrogen bond A chemical bond that links an already covalently bonded hydrogen atom with a second, relatively electronegative atom.

hydrophilic The property, possessed by some compounds, of being able to form chemical bonds with water molecules. Table salt (NaCl) is hydrophilic and thus will readily dissolve in water.

hydrophobic The property, possessed by some compounds, of being unable to form chemical bonds with water molecules. Oil is hydrophobic and thus will not readily dissolve in water.

hydroxide ion Strongly basic OH⁻ ion, often used to shift solutions toward neutral or basic on the pH scale.

hypertonic solution A solution that has a high concentration of solutes relative to an adjacent solution.

hyphae (singular, hypha) The slender filaments that make up the bulk of most fungi.

hypothalamus Portion of the brain important in drives and in the maintenance of homeostasis, the latter capacity coming about because of the hypothalamus' control over a good deal of the body's hormonal release.

hypothesis A tentative, testable explanation of an observed phenomenon.

hypotonic solution A solution that has a low concentration of solutes relative to an adjacent solution.

I

identical twins Twins who develop from a single zygote; strictly speaking, identical twins are a single organism at one point in their development and as such have exactly the same genetic makeup.

immune system The collection of cells and proteins that, in vertebrates, function together to kill or neutralize invading microorganisms.

incompletely dominant A genetic condition in which the heterozygote phenotype is intermediate between either of the homozygous phenotypes.

independent assortment The random distribution of homologous chromosome pairs on differing sides of the metaphase plate during meiosis.

induced pluripotent stem cell (iPS cell) A cell that has been induced to a state of pluripotency through the introduction of genes from outside its genome. In humans, a pluripotent cell is a cell that can give rise to all the types of cells found in the body.

induction In animals, the capacity of some embryonic cells to direct the development of other embryonic cells. For example, cells of the notochord induce the tissue above them to form the neural tube.

inflammation A localized immune system response to tissue injury. Inflammation can also be systemic, or body-wide, and chronic, or ongoing. Chronic, systemic inflammation has been linked to illnesses such as type 2 diabetes.

innate immune response The human immune response that does not target specific microbial invaders; compare to adaptive immune response.

inner cell mass In mammalian development, the group of cells in the embryo that will develop into the baby rather than into the placenta.

insulin A hormone, secreted by cells in the pancreas, that brings about a decrease in blood levels of glucose.

integral protein A protein of the plasma membrane that is attached to the membrane's hydrophobic interior.

integumentary system The organ system that protects the body from the external environment and assists in regulation of body temperature. This system consists of the skin and associated structures, such as glands, hair, and nails.

intermediate filament Filaments of the cytoskeleton, intermediate in diameter between microfilaments and microtubules, that help stabilize the positions of the nucleus and other organelles within the cell.

interneuron A type of neuron, located only within the brain or spinal cord, that connects other neurons. These neurons are responsible for the analysis of sensory inputs and the coordination of motor commands.

interphase That portion of the cell cycle in which the cell simultaneously carries out its work and—in preparation for division—duplicates its chromosomes. The other primary phase of the cell cycle is mitotic phase (or M phase), which includes both mitosis (in somatic cells) and cytokinesis.

interspecific competition Competitive interaction between individuals of two different species.

intertidal zone The region within the coastal zone of the ocean that extends from the ocean's low-tide mark to its high-tide mark.

intrinsic isolating mechanism A difference in anatomy, physiology, or behavior that prevents interbreeding between individuals of the same species or of closely related species. One or more intrinsic isolating mechanisms must develop for two populations of the same species to evolve into separate species.

intrinsic rate of increase (r) The rate at which a population would grow if there were no external limits on its growth. In ecology, often denoted as *r*.

inversion A chromosomal abnormality that comes about when a chromosomal fragment that rejoins a chromosome does so with an inverted orientation.

invertebrate An animal without a vertebral column.

ion An atom whose number of electrons differs from its number of protons, thus giving it an electrical charge.

ionic bonding A linkage in which two or more ions are bonded to each other by virtue of their opposite charge.

ionic compound A collection of the atoms of two or more elements that have become linked through ionic bonding.

isotonic solution A solution that has the same concentration of solutes as an adjacent solution.

isotope A form of an element as defined by the number of neutrons contained in its nucleus. Different isotopes of an element have the same number of protons but differing numbers of neutrons.

K

karyotype A pictorial arrangement of a full set of an organism's chromosomes.

keratin A flexible, water-resistant protein, abundant in the outer layers of skin, that also makes up hair and fingernails.

keystone species A species whose absence from a community would bring about significant change in that community.

kidneys The filtering organs of the urinary system that produce urine while conserving useful blood-borne materials.

kilocalorie The amount of energy it takes to raise 1,000 grams (1 kilogram) of water 1°C. Food consumption is measured in kilocalories, often written as Calories.

kinetic energy Energy in motion. A rolling rock has kinetic energy.

Krebs cycle The second stage of cellular respiration, occurring in the inner compartment of mitochondria. The Krebs cycle is the major source of electrons that power the third stage of respiration, the electron transport chain. Also known as the citric acid cycle.

K-selected species A species that tends to be relatively long-lived, that tends to have relatively few offspring for whom it provides a good deal of care, and whose population size tends to be relatively stable, remaining at or near its environment's carrying capacity (*K*). Also known as an equilibrium species.

L

labor The regular contractions of the uterine muscles that sweep over the fetus, creating pressure that opens the cervix and expels the baby and the placenta.

large intestine That portion of the digestive tract that begins at the small intestine and ends at the anus. The large intestine serves largely to compact and store material left over from the digestion of food, turning this material into the solid waste known as feces.

law of conservation of mass In a chemical reaction, matter can neither be created nor destroyed.

law of independent assortment During gamete formation, gene pairs assort independently of one another. Also known as Mendel's Second Law, this is one of the principles of inheritance formulated by Gregor Mendel.

law of segregation Differing characters in organisms result from two genetic elements (alleles) that separate in gamete formation, such that each gamete gets only one of the two alleles. Also known as Mendel's First Law, this is one of the principles of inheritance formulated by Gregor Mendel.

lichen A composite organism composed of a fungus and either algae or photosynthesizing bacteria.

life cycle The repeating series of steps that occur in the reproduction of an organism.

life sciences A set of disciplines that focus on various aspects of the living world. The life sciences include biology and related disciplines such as medicine and forestry.

life table A table showing how likely it is for an average species member to survive a given unit of time.

ligaments In anatomy, a connective tissue that links one bone to another.

lipid A member of a class of biological molecules whose defining characteristic is their relative insolubility in water. Examples include triglycerides, cholesterol, steroids, and phospholipids.

lipoprotein A molecule composed of both lipid and protein. Lipoproteins transport fat molecules through the bloodstream to all parts of the body.

liver An organ that is central to the body's metabolism of nutrients.

logistic growth A form of population growth in which exponential growth slows and then stops in response to environmental resistance. Also known as S-shaped growth because, when plotted on a graph, changes in the population's size resemble the letter S.

low-density lipoprotein (LDL) A type of protein that transports fat or lipid molecules (usually cholesterol) from the liver and small intestine to various tissues throughout the body. Sometimes known as the "bad cholesterol," LDLs can initiate heart disease by coming to reside within coronary arteries.

luteinizing hormone (LH) A hormone secreted by the anterior pituitary; in women, LH induces ovulation and stimulates the ovary to secrete estrogens and progestins to prepare the body for possible pregnancy. In men, LH stimulates the testes to produce androgens such as testosterone.

lymphatic network In humans, the transport network that collects interstitial fluid, transports it as lymph through lymphatic vessels, checks the fluid for infection, and delivers the fluid to blood vessels.

lysosome An organelle found in animal cells that digests worn-out cellular materials and foreign materials that enter the cell.

M

macroevolution Evolution that results in the formation of new species or other large groupings of living things.

mammary glands A set of glands that, in female mammals, provide milk for the young.

marsupial A type of mammal in which the young develop within the mother to a limited extent, inside an egg having a membranous shell. Early in development, the egg's membrane disappears, after which the mother delivers a developmentally immature but active marsupial. Kangaroos are one example of a marsupial.

mass A measure of the quantity of matter in an object. On Earth, equivalent to the weight of an object.

medulla oblongata A region of the brain concerned with the regulation of unconscious functions such as breathing, blood pressure, and digestion.

meiosis A process in which a single diploid cell divides to produce four haploid reproductive cells.

membrane potential The electrical charge difference that exists from one side of a neuron's plasma membrane to the other.

memory B cell One of two types of cells that the B lymphocyte or B cell develops into (the other type being a plasma cell). Memory B cells remain in the system long after a first infection by a microorganism has ended and serve to produce more plasma B cells quickly should the microorganism ever invade again.

menopause The cessation of the monthly ovarian cycle that occurs when women reach about 50 years of age.

menstruation The cyclical release of blood and the specialized uterine lining, the endometrium; occurs about once every 28 days in human females, except when the oocyte is fertilized.

messenger RNA (mRNA) A type of RNA that encodes, and carries to ribosomes, information for the synthesis of proteins.

metabolic pathway A sequential set of enzymatically controlled chemical reactions in which the product of one reaction serves as the substrate for the next.

metabolism The sum of all chemical reactions carried out by a cell or larger organism.

metaphase plate A plane located midway between the poles of a dividing cell.

microevolution A change of allele frequencies in a population over a short period of time. The basis for all large-scale evolution (macroevolution).

microfilaments The most slender of the eukaryotic cell's cytoskeletal fibers, made of the protein actin and functioning in both cell movement and support.

micrograph A picture taken with the aid of a microscope.

micrometer A millionth of a meter, abbreviated as μm.

microtubule The largest of the cytoskeletal filaments, microtubules take the form of hollow tubes composed of the protein tubulin. They help give structure to the cell, serve as the "rails" on which transport vesicles move, and form the cellular extensions known as cilia and flagella.

midbrain A region of the brain that helps maintain muscle tone and posture through control of involuntary motor responses.

mimicry A phenomenon in which one species evolves to resemble another species.

mineral An element essential to the functioning of a living organism.

mitochondria Organelles that are the primary sites of energy conversion within eukaryotic cells.

mitosis The separation of a somatic cell's duplicated chromosomes prior to cytokinesis.

mitotic phase (M phase) That portion of the cell cycle that includes both mitosis and cytokinesis. Mitosis is the separation of a somatic cell's duplicated chromosomes; cytokinesis is the physical separation of one cell into two daughter cells.

mitotic spindle The microtubules active in cell division, including those that align and move the chromosomes.

modern synthesis The unified evolutionary theory that resulted from the convergence of several lines of biological research between 1937 and 1950.

molecular biology The investigation of life at the level of its individual molecules.

molecular formula A notation specifying the elements in a molecule, with the number of atoms of each element in the molecule shown as a subscript. This notation reveals the constituent elements of a molecule, but not the spatial arrangement of those elements.

molecule An entity consisting of a defined number of atoms covalently bonded together in a defined spatial relationship.

molting A periodic shedding of an old exoskeleton followed by the growth of a new one; practiced by animals in the phyla Nematoda and Arthropoda.

monocotyledon (monocot) A type of plant that has one embryonic leaf within the seed. Although comprising only one-quarter of all flowering plants, most important food plants are the narrow-leafed monocotyledons.

monohybrid cross An experimental cross in which organisms are tested for differences in one character.

monomer A small molecule that can be combined with other similar or identical molecules to make a larger polymer.

monosaccharide A building block, or monomer, of carbohydrates. Monosaccharides combine to form complex carbohydrates, or polysaccharides. Glucose is an example of a monosaccharide.

monotremes Egg-laying mammals, represented by the duck-billed platypus and spiny anteaters found in Australia.

monounsaturated fatty acid A fatty acid with one double bond between the carbon atoms of its hydrocarbon chain.

morphogen A diffusible substance whose concentration in a region of an animal embryo affects development in that region.

morphology The physical form of an organism.

morula A tightly packed ball of early embryonic cells.

motor neuron A neuron that sends signals from the central nervous system (CNS) to such structures as muscles or glands. Given the direction of this transmission, motor neurons are efferent neurons.

Müllerian mimicry A type of mimicry in which several species that have protection against predators evolve to look alike.

multiple alleles Three or more alleles—alternative forms of a gene—occurring in a population.

muscle fiber A single skeletal muscle cell; called a fiber because of its extreme length relative to most cells.

muscle tissue Tissue that has the ability to contract. In humans, one of the four principal types of tissue.

muscular system The organ system composed of all the skeletal muscles of the body, which is to say all muscles that are under voluntary control.

mutation A permanent alteration of a DNA base sequence.

mutualism A form of relationship between two organisms in which both organisms benefit.

mycelium A web of fungal hyphae that makes up the major part of a fungus.

mycorrhizae Associations of plant roots and fungal hyphae. The fungal hyphae absorb minerals, growth hormones, and water that are then available to the plant, and the fungus gets carbohydrates from the photosynthesizing plant.

myelin Membranous covering of some neuronal axons, provided by glial cells, that allows faster nerve signal transmission through these axons.

N

n In a living cell, the condition of being haploid: of having a single set of chromosomes.

nanometer A billionth of a meter; abbreviated nm.

natural selection The process through which traits that confer a reproductive advantage to individual organisms grow more common in populations of organisms over successive generations.

Neanderthal A now-extinct species of hominin that lived in Europe and Asia from approximately 350,000 years ago to 28,000 years ago.

negative feedback A system of control in which the product of a process reduces the activity that led to the product.

nephron Functional unit of the kidneys, composed of a nephron tubule, its associated blood vessels, and the interstitial fluid in which both are immersed.

nerve A bundle of axons in the peripheral nervous system that transmits information to or from the central nervous system.

nervous system The organ system that monitors an animal's internal and external environment, integrates the sensory information received, and coordinates the animal's responses. This system consists of all the body's neurons, plus the supporting neuroglia cells, plus the sensory organs.

nervous tissue A tissue specialized for the rapid conduction of electrical impulses. In humans, one of the four principal tissue types.

net primary production The amount of material a plant (or other photosynthesizing organism) accumulates through photosynthesis. Net primary production is gross primary production minus energy lost to heat and the plant's expenditures of energy on its own maintenance.

neural crest cells Cells that break away from the top of the vertebrate neural tube as it folds together and then migrate to varying parts of the embryo, giving rise to various tissues and organs.

neural tube A dorsal, ectodermic structure that gives rise in vertebrates to both the brain and spinal cord.

neurotransmitter A chemical, secreted into a synaptic cleft by a neuron, that affects nervous system signaling by binding with receptors on an adjacent neuron or effector cell.

neutron One of three primary constituents of an atom, possessing no electrical charge and found in the atom's nucleus. Isotopes are defined by the number of neutrons in an atom.

niche A characterization of an organism's way of making a living that includes its habitat, food, and behavior.

nicotinamide adenine dinucleotide (NAD) The most important intermediate electron carrier in cellular respiration.

nitrogen fixation The conversion of atmospheric nitrogen into a form that can be taken up by living things. Bacteria fix nitrogen, which is essential to life.

nondisjunction A failure of homologous chromosomes or sister chromatids to separate during cell division.

nonessential amino acid In nutrition, one of the 11 amino acids that can be produced by the body and that hence does not need to supplied by food.

nonpolar covalent bond A type of covalent bond in which electrons are shared equally between atoms.

notochord A dorsal, rod-shaped support organ that exists in embryonic development in all vertebrates and in the adults of some vertebrates.

nuclear envelope The double membrane that lines the nucleus in eukaryotic cells.

nucleolus The area within the nucleus of a cell devoted to the production of ribosomal RNA.

nucleotide The building block of nucleic acids, including DNA and RNA, consisting of a phosphate group, a sugar, and a nitrogen-containing base.

nucleus A membrane-lined compartment that encloses the primary complement of DNA in eukaryotic cells.

nutrient (in human nutrition) A substance found in food that does at least one of three things: provides energy, provides a structural building block, or regulates a physical process. There are six classes of nutrients: water, minerals and vitamins; and carbohydrates, lipids, and proteins.

nutrient A chemical element that is used by living things to sustain life.

nutrition The study of the relationship between food and health.

O

oil A dietary lipid that is liquid at room temperature (e.g., olive oil, canola oil).

olfaction The sense of smell.

omnivore An animal that eats both plants and animals.

oocyte The precursor cell of eggs in the vertebrate ovary. Diploid primary oocytes develop from oogonia and in turn give rise to haploid secondary oocytes in the process of meiosis.

oogonia (singular, oogonium) The diploid cells that are the starting female cells in gamete (egg) production. Diploid oogonia develop into diploid primary oocytes, which give rise to haploid secondary oocytes.

open circulation A type of circulation, found in many invertebrates, in which arteries carry blood into open spaces called sinuses. The blood then bathes surrounding tissues and is channeled into veins, through which it flows back to the heart.

organ A highly organized unit within an organism, performing one or more functions, that is formed of several kinds of tissue. Kidneys, heart, lungs, and liver are all familiar examples of organs in humans.

organ system A group of interrelated organs and tissues that serve a particular set of functions in the body. For example, the digestive system includes the mouth, stomach, pancreas, and intestines and functions in digestion of food and the elimination of waste.

organelle A highly organized structure within a cell that carries out specific cellular functions. Almost all organelles (meaning "tiny organs") are bound by membranes. The lone exception is the ribosome, which has no membrane and is the single organelle possessed by prokaryote cells (bacteria and archaea). Organelles in eukaryotic cells include the cell nucleus, mitochondria, lysosomes, chloroplasts, and ribosomes.

organic chemistry A branch of chemistry devoted to the study of molecules that have carbon as their central element.

osmosis The net movement of water across a semipermeable membrane from an area of lower solute concentration to an area of higher solute concentration.

osteoblast An immature bone cell that secretes organic material that becomes bone matrix, thus producing new bone.

osteoclast A type of bone cell that dissolves bone matrix, thus liberating the minerals stored in it.

osteocyte Mature bone cell that maintains the structure and density of bone by continually recycling calcium compounds around itself.

ovarian follicle In human reproduction in females, the complex of an oocyte (developing, unfertilized egg) and its accessory cells and fluids.

ovary In flowering plants, the area, located at the base of the carpel, where fertilization of the egg and early development of the embryo occur. In animals, the female reproductive organ in which eggs develop.

oviparous A condition, seen in all birds and many reptiles, in which fertilized eggs are laid outside the mother's body and then develop there.

ovulation The release of an oocyte from the ovary in animals.

oxidation Loss of one or more electrons by an atom or a molecule. Important in energy transfer in living things as part of redox reactions, in which one substance undergoes reduction (a gain in electrons) by oxidizing another.

ozone A gas in the Earth's atmosphere consisting of three oxygen atoms bonded together that serves to protect living things from the sun's ultraviolet radiation.

P

paired, jointed appendages Appendages, such as legs, that come in pairs and have joints. Such appendages are characteristic of all arthropods.

paleoanthropologist A scientist who studies human evolution by means of analyzing fossils.

pancreas In digestion, a gland that secretes, into the small intestine through ducts, digestive enzymes along with buffers that raise the pH of chyme. In nutrient metabolism, a gland that secretes, directly into the bloodstream, the hormones insulin and glucagon, which regulate blood levels of glucose.

parasites Organisms that feed off their prey but do not kill them, at least not immediately and perhaps not ever.

parasitism A type of predation in which the predator gets nutrients from the prey but does not kill the prey immediately and may never kill it.

parasympathetic division The division of the autonomic nervous system that generally has relaxing effects on the body.

parental generation (P) The generation that begins an experimental cross between organisms. Such a cross is used to study genetics and heredity of traits.

passive transport Transport of materials across the cell's plasma membrane that involves no expenditure of energy. Simple and facilitated diffusion are examples of passive transport.

pathogenic Disease-causing. Viruses, bacteria, protists, and fungi are spoken of as being pathogenic or nonpathogenic.

pedigree A familial history of genetically transmissible conditions; generally takes the form of a diagram.

peptide hormones Hormones composed of chains of amino acids. By far the largest class of the three principal classes of hormones, the other two being amino-acid–based and steroid hormones.

peripheral nervous system (PNS) The part of the nervous system that includes all of the neural tissue outside the central nervous system (brain and spinal cord). The PNS brings information to and from the central nervous system; it also provides voluntary control of the skeletal muscles and involuntary control of the smooth muscles, cardiac muscles, and glands.

peripheral protein A protein of the plasma membrane that lies on the inside or outside of the membrane but is not attached to the membrane's hydrophobic interior.

peristalsis Waves of contraction carried out by two sets of muscles in the digestive tract that help digest material and push it through the tract.

permafrost The permanently frozen ground that begins about a meter below the surface in the tundra biome of the far north. Neither roots nor water can penetrate this layer.

Permian Extinction The greatest mass extinction event in Earth's history. This event, in which up to 96 percent of all species on Earth were wiped out, occurred about 251 million years ago.

petal The colorful, leaf-like structure of a flower; petals attract pollinators.

petiole The stalk of a leaf, attaching it to a branch or trunk.

pH scale A scale utilized in measuring the relative acidity or alkalinity of a solution. The scale, ranging from 0 to 14, quantifies the concentration of hydrogen ions in a solution. The lower the pH number, the more acidic the solution; the higher the number, the more basic the solution.

phagocyte An immune system cell capable of ingesting another cell, parts of cells, or other materials. Phagocytes ingest both invading microorganisms and tissue fragments or the body's own cells when they have become damaged.

phagocytosis The movement of large materials into a cell by means of wrapping extensions of the plasma membrane around the materials and fusing the extensions together. One of two primary forms of endocytosis, the other being pinocytosis.

pharyngeal slits In animals, openings to the pharyngeal cavity. All chordates possess pharyngeal slits at some point in their development.

pharynx In humans, the passageway at the back of the mouth that links the mouth with both the food-transporting esophagus and the air-transporting trachea. In some animals, the pharynx can be everted, or turned inside-out, and used to obtain nutrients.

phenotype A physiological feature, bodily characteristic, or behavior of an organism.

phloem In vascular plants, the fluid-transporting tissue that conducts the food produced in photosynthesis along with some hormones and other compounds.

phosphate group A phosphorus atom surrounded by four oxygen atoms.

phospholipid A charged lipid molecule composed of two fatty acids, glycerol, and a phosphate group. The phospholipid's phosphate group is hydrophilic, while its fatty acid chains are hydrophobic. Phospholipids are a major constituent of cell membranes.

phospholipid bilayer One of the chief components of the plasma membrane, composed of two layers of phospholipids, arranged with their fatty acid chains pointing toward each other.

photoperiodism The ability of a plant to respond to changes it experiences in the daily duration of darkness relative to light.

photoreceptor Sensory receptor cell for vision, located in the eye's retina, that transforms light into nervous system signals. Photoreceptors come in two varieties: rods, which function in low-light situations but provide only black-and-white vision; and cones, which respond best to bright light and provide color vision.

photorespiration A process in which the enzyme rubisco undercuts carbon fixation in photosynthesis by binding with oxygen instead of with carbon dioxide. This wasteful reaction takes place most frequently in C_3 plants. The warm-weather C_4 plants have evolved a means of reducing photorespiration.

photosynthesis The process by which certain groups of organisms capture energy from sunlight and convert this solar energy into chemical energy that is initially stored in a carbohydrate.

photosystem An organized complex of molecules within a thylakoid membrane that, in photosynthesis, collects solar energy and transforms it into chemical energy.

phototropism The bending of a plant's shoots in response to light. Generally, this capability helps a plant grow toward the sun to get the most available sunlight.

phylogeny A hypothesis about the evolutionary relationships of a group of organisms.

phylum A category of living things, directly subordinate to the category of kingdom, whose members share traits as a result of shared ancestry. In animals, a group of animals that have a similar structural makeup.

physiology The study of the physical functioning of animals and plants.

phytoplankton Small photosynthesizing organisms that drift in the upper layers of oceans or bodies of freshwater, often forming the base of aquatic food webs.

pinocytosis The movement of relatively large materials into a cell by means of the creation of transport vesicles that are produced through an invagination of the plasma membrane. One of two primary forms of endocytosis, the other being phagocytosis.

placenta A complex network of maternal and embryonic blood vessels and membranes that develops in mammals in pregnancy. The placenta allows nutrients and oxygen to flow to the embryo from the mother, while allowing carbon dioxide and waste to flow from the embryo to the mother.

placental mammal A type of mammal that is nurtured before birth by the placenta, a network of maternal and embryonic blood vessels and membranes. Embryonic placental mammals derive their nutrition not from food stored in an egg, but directly from the mother's circulation.

plasma The fluid portion of blood, consisting mostly of water but also containing proteins and other molecules. Contrast with formed elements—the cells and cell fragments that form the nonfluid portion of blood.

plasma cell One of two types of cells the B lymphocyte develops into (the other type being a memory B cell). Plasma cells are specialized to produce the free-standing antibodies that fight invaders.

plasma membrane A membrane forming the outer boundary of many cells, composed of a phospholipid bilayer interspersed with proteins and cholesterol molecules and coated, on its exterior face, with short carbohydrate chains associated with proteins and lipids.

plasmid A ring of DNA that lies outside the chromosome in bacteria. Plasmids can move into bacterial cells in the process called transformation, thus making them a valuable tool in biotechnology.

plasmodesmata Channels in the plant cell wall that make possible communication between plant cells. The structure of these channels is such that the cytoplasm of one plant cell is continuous with that of another.

platelet One of the three varieties of formed elements within blood, platelets are small fragments of cells that facilitate blood clotting by releasing clotting enzymes and clumping together at the site of an injury.

point mutation A mutation of a single base pair in a genome.

polar body Nonfunctional cell produced during meiosis in females.

polar covalent bond A type of covalent bond in which electrons are shared unequally between atoms, so that one end of the molecule has a slight negative charge and the other end a slight positive charge.

polarity A difference in electrical charge at one end of a molecule compared to the other.

pollen grain A sperm-bearing gametophyte plant, consisting at maturity of three cells and an outer coat. One sperm cell within the pollen grain will fertilize the egg cell in the female gametophyte, thus producing a new generation of sporophyte plant.

pollination The transfer of pollen—by wind, animal, or other means—to a plant's female reproductive structure.

polygenic Having multiple genes affecting a given character, such as height in humans.

polygenic inheritance Inheritance of a genetic character that is determined by the interaction of multiple genes, with each gene having a small additive effect on the character.

polymer A large molecule made up of many similar or identical subunits, called monomers.

polymerase chain reaction (PCR) A technique for generating many copies of a DNA sequence from a small starting sample.

polypeptide A series of amino acids linked in linear fashion. Polypeptide chains fold up to become proteins.

polyploidy A form of sympatric speciation in which one or more sets of chromosomes are added to the genome of an organism. Human beings cannot survive in a polyploid state, but many plants flourish in it. Polyploidy is a means by which speciation can occur (most often in plants) in a single generation.

polysaccharide A polymer of carbohydrates, composed of many monosaccharides. Examples include starch, glycogen, cellulose, and chitin.

polyunsaturated fatty acid A fatty acid with two or more double bonds between the carbon atoms of its hydrocarbon chain.

pons A region of the brain whose primary function is to relay messages between the cerebrum and the cerebellum.

population All the members of a species that live in a defined geographic region at a given time.

postanal tail A tail, existing at some point in the development of all chordates, that is located posterior to the anus.

potential energy Stored energy. A rock perched at the top of a hill has potential energy.

predation One organism feeding on parts or all of a second organism.

primary consumer Any organism that eats producers (organisms that make their own food).

primary oocyte A diploid cell produced in females that may mature into an egg, initially by giving rise to haploid secondary oocytes. After the female reaches puberty, an average of one oocyte per month is selected to continue the process of maturation in the ovary.

primary spermatocyte A diploid cell in a male that will undergo meiosis to produce haploid secondary spermatocytes, which ultimately give rise to mature sperm cells.

primary structure The sequence of amino acids in a protein. This sequence dictates the final shape of the protein because electrochemical bonding and repulsion forces act on the structure to create the folded-up protein.

primary succession In ecology, succession in which the starting state is one of little or no life and a soil that lacks nutrients.

producer Any organism that manufactures its own food. Plants, algae, and certain bacteria are producers. Producers capture solar energy and convert it into biomass that is then passed along in food webs.

product A substance formed in a chemical reaction. The products are written on the right side of a chemical equation.

prokaryote A single-celled organism whose complement of DNA is not contained within a nucleus.

prokaryotic cell A cell whose DNA is not located in the membrane-bound organelle known as a nucleus. Prokaryotes are microscopic forms of life, and all are either bacteria or archaea.

prostate gland In human males, a gland surrounding the urethra near the urinary bladder that contributes fluids to the semen.

protective immunity A state of long-lasting protection that the immune system develops against specific microorganisms.

protein A large polymer of amino acids, composed of one or more polypeptide chains. Proteins come in many forms, including enzymes, structural proteins, and hormones.

protist A eukaryotic organism that does not have all the defining characteristics of a plant, animal, or fungus. The catchall term *protist* is used to refer to several distinct evolutionary lines of eukaryotic organisms, most of them single-celled and aquatic.

proton A basic constituent of an atom, found in the nucleus of the atom and having positive electrical charge. Elements are defined by the number of protons in their nucleus.

pulmonary circulation The system that circulates blood between the heart and the lungs, with the result that blood is oxygenated.

Q

quaternary structure The way in which two or more polypeptide chains come together to form a protein.

R

radial symmetry A type of animal symmetry in which body parts are distributed evenly about a central axis. Jellyfish are radially symmetrical.

radiometric dating A technique for determining the age of objects by measuring the decay of the radioactive elements within them. The age of fossils can be determined with this technique.

reactant A substance (atoms, molecules, or ions) that goes into a chemical reaction. Reactants interact to form the product(s) of a chemical reaction.

reaction center A molecular complex in a chloroplast that, in photosynthesis, transforms solar energy into chemical energy.

receptor protein A protein that generally protrudes from the plasma membrane of a cell that is active in the transmission of signals between cells. Receptor proteins, often called receptors, function by binding with signaling molecules such as hormones.

recessive Term used to designate an allele that is not expressed in the heterozygous condition.

recessive disorder A medical condition that will not occur when an organism possesses a single functional allele for a given trait. Red-green color blindness is an example of a recessive disorder in that only one set of functional alleles need be present for normal color vision.

recombinant DNA Two or more segments of DNA that have been combined by humans into a sequence that does not exist in nature.

red blood cell (RBC) The blood cells, also known as erythrocytes, that transport oxygen to and carry carbon dioxide from every part of the body.

red marrow A tissue, found in cavities of bones in the human body, within which all of the adult body's blood cells are produced.

redox reaction A combination of a reduction and an oxidation reaction in which the electrons lost from one substance in oxidation are gained by another in reduction.

reduction The gain of one or more electrons by an atom or a molecule. Important in energy transfer in living things as part of redox reactions, in which one substance is reduced by oxidizing (or removing electrons from) another substance.

reflex Automatic nervous system response that helps an organism avoid danger or preserve a stable physical state. The knee-jerk response is a well-known reflex.

regulatory T cell A type of immune system cell that acts to limit the body's immune system response, thus protecting the body's own tissues from attack.

reproductive cloning Cloning intended to produce adult mammals of a defined genotype.

reproductive isolating mechanisms Any factor that, in nature, prevents interbreeding between individuals of the same or closely related species.

reproductive system In humans, the organ system that develops gametes and delivers them to a location where they can fuse with other gametes to produce a new individual.

resource partitioning The dividing of scarce resources among species that have similar requirements. Such partitioning allows species to coexist in the same habitat.

respiratory system The organ system that brings oxygen into the body and expels carbon dioxide from the body. In humans, this system includes the lungs and passageways that carry air to the lungs.

restriction enzyme A type of enzyme, occurring naturally in bacteria, that recognizes a specific sequence of DNA bases and cuts DNA strands at a specific location within the sequence. Restriction enzymes are used in biotechnology to cut DNA in specific places.

retina A layer of tissue at the back of the human eye whose cells convert light signals into neural signals.

ribonucleic acid (RNA) A nucleic acid that is active in the synthesis of proteins and that forms part of the structure of ribosomes. Varieties include messenger RNA (mRNA), transfer RNA (tRNA), ribosomal RNA (rRNA), and micro-RNA.

ribosomal RNA (rRNA) A type of RNA that, along with proteins, forms ribosomes.

ribosome An organelle, located in the cell's cytoplasm, that is the site of protein synthesis. The translation phase of protein synthesis takes place within ribosomes.

ribozyme A molecule composed of RNA that can both encode genetic information and act as an enzyme. Molecules similar to these may have been necessary early in the origin of life.

RNA polymerase In the transcription phase of protein synthesis, the enzyme that unwinds the DNA double helix and puts together a chain of RNA nucleotides complementary to the exposed DNA nucleotides.

rods Photoreceptors that function in low-light situations but that do not provide color vision.

root hair In plants, a threadlike extension of a root cell. Root hairs greatly increase the surface area of roots, thus allowing greater absorption of water and nutrients.

rough endoplasmic reticulum A network of membranes, found in the cytoplasm of eukaryotic cells, that aids in the processing of proteins.

r-selected species A species that tends to be relatively short-lived, that tends to produce relatively many offspring for which it provides little or no care, and whose population size tends to fluctuate widely in reaction to an environment that it experiences as highly variable. Also known as an opportunist species.

rubisco An enzyme that allows plants to incorporate atmospheric carbon dioxide into their own sugars during the process of photosynthesis.

rule of addition In probability theory, the principle that, when an outcome can occur in two or more different ways, the probability of that outcome is the sum of the respective probabilities.

rule of multiplication In probability theory, the principle that the probability of any two events happening is the product of their respective probabilities.

S

sarcomere The functional unit of a striated muscle that contracts when thin filaments slide past thick filaments. The sarcomeres shorten, thus contracting the whole muscle.

saprophyte An organism that obtains its nutrition from dead organic material.

saturated fatty acid A fatty acid with no double bonds between the carbon atoms of its hydrocarbon chain.

science A means of coming to understand the natural world through observation and the testing of hypotheses. Also, a collection of insights about nature, the evidence for which is an array of facts.

scientific method The process by which scientists investigate the natural world. The scientific method involves the testing of hypotheses through observation and experiment.

sebaceous glands A type of gland in the skin that produces a waxy, oily secretion (sebum) that lubricates the hair shaft and inhibits bacterial growth in the surrounding area.

second law of thermodynamics Energy transfer always results in a greater amount of disorder (entropy) in the universe.

secondary consumer Any organism that eats a primary consumer.

secondary structure The structure proteins assume after having folded up.

secondary succession In ecology, succession in which the final state of a habitat has been disturbed by some force, but life remains and the soil has nutrients. A farmer's field that has been abandoned is a site of secondary succession.

seed A reproductive structure in plants that includes a plant embryo, its food supply, and a tough protective casing.

seed coat The tough outer layer of a seed, derived from the integuments of the ovule, which protect the embryo from mechanical damage and water loss.

seedless vascular plant A plant that has a vascular (fluid transport) structure but that does not reproduce through use of seeds. One of the four principal varieties of plants. Ferns are the most familiar example.

semen The mixture of sperm and glandular secretions that is ejaculated from the human male through the urethra.

seminiferous tubule A convoluted tubule inside the testes where sperm development begins. Immature sperm are eventually released into the interior cavity of a tubule and travel to the epididymis, where sperm maturation is completed.

sensory neuron A neuron that senses conditions inside or outside the body and that converts this sensory information into electrical signals that travel through the nervous system.

sepal The leaf-like structure that, with other sepals, protects the flower before it opens.

sessile Fixed in location; organisms such as mushrooms and mature sponges are sessile.

sex chromosome The chromosomes that determine the sex of an organism. The X or Y chromosomes in humans.

sexual reproduction A means of reproduction in which the nuclei of the reproductive cells from two separate organisms fuse to produce offspring.

sexual selection A form of natural selection that produces differential reproductive success based on differential success in obtaining mating partners.

sieve element In plants, a type of cell that conducts phloem sap.

simple diffusion Diffusion through the plasma membrane that requires only concentration gradients, as opposed to concentration gradients and special protein channels. Water, oxygen, carbon dioxide, and steroid hormones can all cross the plasma membrane through simple diffusion.

simple sugars The smallest and simplest form of carbohydrates, which serve as energy-yielding molecules and as the building blocks, or monomers, of complex carbohydrates. In nutrition, one of the three principal classes of carbohydrates. Simple sugars can either be monosaccharides (e.g., glucose or fructose) or disaccharides (e.g., sucrose). The other classes of dietary carbohydrate are starches and fibers.

sinoatrial node A collection of specialized heart muscle cells that function as the heart's pacemaker.

skeletal muscle In humans, muscle that is attached to bone, that is under conscious control, and that microscopically has a striped or "striated" appearance owing to the parallel orientation of the long, fibrous units that make it up.

skeletal system The human organ system that forms an internal supporting framework for the body and protects delicate tissues and organs. This system consists of all the bones and cartilages in the body and the connective tissues and ligaments that connect the bones at the joints.

skin In humans, an organ consisting of two tissue layers, an outer epidermis and inner dermis, and covering the outside of the body. The skin protects the body and receives signals from the environment.

small intestine That portion of the digestive tract that runs between the stomach and large intestine.

smooth endoplasmic reticulum A network of membranes within the eukaryotic cell that is the site of the synthesis of various lipids and site at which potentially harmful substances are detoxified.

smooth muscle In humans, muscle that is not under voluntary control and that lacks a striated appearance. Smooth muscle is responsible for contractions of the uterus, digestive tract, blood vessels, and passageways of the lungs.

solute The substance being dissolved by a solvent to form a solution.

solution A homogeneous mixture of two or more substances. In biology, solutions often consist of a solute dissolved in water, which produces an aqueous solution.

solvent The substance in which a solute is dissolved to form a solution. In an aqueous solution, the solvent is water.

somatic cell Any cell that is not and will not become an egg or sperm cell.

somatic cell nuclear transfer (SCNT) A means of cloning animals through fusion of one somatic (non-sex) cell with an egg cell whose nucleus has been removed (an "enucleated" cell).

somatic nervous system That portion of the peripheral nervous system's efferent division that provides voluntary control over skeletal muscle.

somite One of the blocks of mesodermal tissue in the vertebrate embryo that lies on both sides of the notochord and gives rise to muscles and the vertebrae that enclose the spinal cord.

space-filling model A representation of a molecule showing its three-dimensional structure, particularly showing how big its atoms are in relation to each other and the overall shape of the molecule.

speciation The development of new species through evolution.

species A group of actually or potentially interbreeding natural populations that are reproductively isolated from other such populations.

specific heat The amount of energy needed to raise the temperature of 1 gram of a substance by 1°C.

sperm cell In flowering plants, either of two cells in a pollen grain, one of which fertilizes an egg, the other of which fertilizes the central cell in an embryo sac. In animals, the male gamete, which fertilizes the female gamete (the egg).

spermatocyte An immature sperm cell. Spermatocytes develop from spermatogonia and develop into spermatids, which eventually develop into mature sperm.

spermatogonia Diploid cells that are the starting cells in sperm production in males. Spermatogonia are reproductive stem cells in that, when dividing, each of them produces one primary spermatocyte (which will develop into four mature sperm cells) and one spermatogonium.

spongy bone Type of bone that is porous and less dense than compact bone. Spongy bone fills the expanded ends of long bones.

spore A reproductive cell that can develop into a new organism without fusing with another reproductive cell. (The term *spore* also refers to a dormant, stress-resistant form of a bacterial or fungal cell.)

sporophyte generation The diploid, spore-producing plant generation. This generation is the dominant, visible generation in flowering plants. Contrast with gametophyte generation.

stabilizing selection In evolution, the type of natural selection in which intermediate forms of a given character are favored over either extreme. This process tends to maintain average traits for a character. Compare to directional and disruptive selection.

stamen The male reproductive structure in a flower, consisting of a stalk-like filament topped by a pollen-producing anther.

starch A complex carbohydrate that serves as the major form of carbohydrate storage in plants.

Starches—found in such forms as potatoes, rice, carrots, and corn—are important sources of food for animals. In human nutrition, one of the three principal classes of dietary carbohydrates, defined as a complex carbohydrate that is digestible. The other classes of dietary carbohydrates are simple sugars and fibers.

steroid A member of the class of lipid molecules that have four carbon rings as a central element in their structure. One steroid differs from another in accordance with the varying side chains that can be attached to these rings. Cholesterol, testosterone, and estrogen are steroid molecules.

steroid hormones Hormones such as testosterone and estrogen that are constructed around the chemical framework of the cholesterol molecule. One of three principal classes of hormones, the other two being peptide and amino-acid–based hormones.

stigma In flowering plants, the tip end of a flower's carpel, where pollen grains are deposited prior to fertilization.

stomach An organ that performs digestion and that serves as a temporary, expandable storage site for food.

stomata Microscopic pores, found in greatest abundance on the undersides of leaves, that allow plants to exchange gases with the atmosphere. Carbon dioxide moves into plants through the stomata, while oxygen and water vapor move out.

stratosphere The layer of the Earth's atmosphere situated above the troposphere, at about 20 to 35 kilometers (13 to 21 miles) above sea level. The ozone layer lies in this level.

stroma In plants and algae, the liquid material of chloroplasts that is the site of the Calvin cycle.

structural formula A two-dimensional representation of a molecule that shows how its atoms are arranged and the types of bonds between them.

style In flowering plants, the stalk-like extension of a carpel that connects its stigma and ovary.

substrate A substance whose chemical alteration is facilitated by an enzyme.

succession In ecology, a series of replacements of community members at a given location until a stable final state is reached.

sweat gland In humans, a type of duct-containing (exocrine) gland that produces perspiration.

symmetry An equivalence of size, shape, and relative position of parts across a dividing line or around a central point.

sympathetic division The division of the autonomic nervous system that generally has stimulatory effects on the body.

sympatric speciation A type of speciation that occurs in the absence of the geographic separation of populations. Polyploidy is a special form of sympatric speciation.

synapse An area in the nervous system consisting of a sending neuron, a receiving neuron or effector cell (i.e., a muscle cell), and the gap between them, called the synaptic cleft.

synaptic cleft The tiny gap that exists between a neuron sending a nervous system signal and a neuron (or effector cell) that is receiving this signal.

systematics The field of biology dealing with the diversity and relatedness of organisms. Systematists study the evolutionary history of groups of organisms.

systemic circulation One of the body's two general networks of blood vessels that serves to transport blood between the heart and the rest of the body following oxygenation of this blood in the body's pulmonary circulation.

T

taiga The biome consisting of boreal (northern) forest, characterized by cold, dry conditions, a relatively short growing season, and large expanses of coniferous trees.

taproot system The type of plant root system that consists of a large central root and many smaller lateral roots.

target cells The set of cells in the body that will be affected by a given hormone. The target cells for each hormone bear receptors capable of binding with that hormone.

taxon Any of the taxonomic categories used in the classification of Earth's organisms, both living and extinct. In order of increasing inclusiveness, these categories are species, genus, family, order, class, phylum, kingdom, and domain.

tendons The connective tissue that attaches a skeletal muscle to a bone.

tertiary consumer Any organism that eats secondary consumers.

tertiary structure The large-scale twists and turns in a protein conformation.

testis The organ in the male reproductive system in which sperm begin development and testosterone is produced.

tetrad The grouping formed by the linkage of two homologous chromosomes in prophase I of meiosis. The four sister chromatids involved in this linkage give it the name tetrad.

tetrapods Any four-limbed vertebrate. All amphibians, reptiles, and mammals are tetrapods.

thalamus The portion of the brain through which most sensory perceptions are channeled before being relayed to the cerebral cortex.

theory A general set of principles, supported by evidence, that explains some aspect of nature.

thigmotropism The growth of a plant in response to touch. This capability allows tendrils to wrap around other objects, thus helping a plant climb upward toward light.

thylakoid A flattened, membrane-bound sac in the interior of a chloroplast that serves as the site for the light reactions in photosynthesis.

tissue An organized assemblage of similar cells that serves a common function. Nervous, epithelial, and muscle tissue are some familiar examples.

T-lymphocyte cell (T cell) A class of lymphocytes that plays a central role in cell-mediated immunity. T cells come in several varieties that play specific roles in recognizing and killing infected cells in the body.

toll-like receptors Receptors, generally existing on the surface of immune system cells, that are the primary sensors of microbial infection in the human body.

top predator A species in a community that preys on other species but is not itself preyed on.

total fertility rate The average number of children born to each woman in a human population. The most important statistic used in predicting human population changes.

tracheid In plants, a slender, tapered cell of the xylem that has perforations (bordered pits) that match up with adjacent cells to allow water to move between them.

transcription In protein synthesis, the process in which DNA's information is copied onto messenger RNA (mRNA).

transcription factor A protein that binds to a regulatory DNA sequence, thus influencing the production of one or more other proteins.

transfer RNA (tRNA) In protein synthesis, a form of RNA that binds with amino acids, transfers them to ribosomes, and then binds with a messenger RNA sequence.

transformation A cell's incorporation of genetic material from outside its boundary. Some bacteria readily undergo this process, and others can be induced to for uses in biotechnology.

transgenic organism An organism whose genome has stably incorporated one or more genes from another species.

translation The process in which a polypeptide chain is produced within a ribosome based on the information encoded in messenger RNA. This process, the second major stage in protein synthesis (after transcription), occurs in the cell's cytoplasm.

translocation The swapping of fragments by nonhomologous chromosomes, resulting in gene sequences that are out of order on both chromosomes.

transpiration The process by which plants lose water when water vapor leaves the plant through open stomata. More than 90 percent of the water that enters a plant evaporates into the atmosphere via transpiration.

transport protein A protein that forms a hydrophilic channel through the hydrophobic interior of the cell's plasma membrane, allowing hydrophilic materials to pass through the membrane.

transport vesicle A membrane-lined sphere that moves within the cell's endomembrane system, carrying within it proteins or other molecules.

triglyceride A lipid molecule formed from three fatty acids bonded to glycerol.

trimester A period lasting about 3 months during a human pregnancy. There are three trimesters during the 9-month pregnancy.

trophic level A position in an ecosystem's food chain or web, with each level defined by a transfer of energy from one kind of organism to another. Plants and other photosynthesizers are producers of food and thus occupy the first trophic level. Organisms that consume producers are primary consumers and occupy the second trophic level, and so on.

trophoblast The cells at the periphery of the developing mammalian embryo that establish physical links with the mother's uterine wall and eventually develop into the fetal portion of the placenta.

tropical rainforest A biome found in Earth's equatorial regions characterized by warm year-round temperatures, abundant rainfall (averaging 200–450 cm per year), and great species diversity.

tropical savanna A grassland biome characterized by seasonal drought, small seasonal changes in the generally warm temperatures, and stands of trees that punctuate the grassland.

troposphere The lowest layer of the Earth's atmosphere, extending from sea level to about 12 kilometers (7.4 miles) above sea level. This layer contains most of the gases in the atmosphere.

true multicellularity A form of life in which individual cells exist in stable groups, with different cells in a group specializing in different functions.

tundra A biome of Earth's far-northern latitudes characterized by very cold temperatures, very little rainfall (averaging 25 cm per year), and a short growing season.

U

umbilical cord In human pregnancy, the tissue linking the fetus with the placenta.

ureters Two tubes in which urine is transported from the kidneys to the urinary bladder.

urethra Tube in which urine flows from the bladder to the outside of the body in both males and females. In males, the urethra also transmits semen.

urinary bladder A hollow, muscular organ that serves as a temporary, expandable storage site for the waste product urine.

urinary system The organ system that eliminates waste products from the blood through formation of urine. In humans, this system consists of the kidneys, where the urine is formed; and the ureters, urinary bladder, and urethra, which transport urine from the kidneys to the outside of the body.

uterine tube In human females, the tube that transports an ovulated developing egg (an oocyte) from the ovary to the uterus, during which time fertilization may occur. Also called the fallopian tube.

V

variable An element of an experiment that is changed compared to an initial condition.

vas deferens In human males, the tube that carries the sperm from the epididymis to the urethra for ejaculation.

vasopressin See antidiuretic hormone (ADH).

vegetal pole The end of the zygote with relatively more yolk and lying farther from the cell's nucleus. The location of the egg's poles defines the orientation in which the embryo develops.

vegetative reproduction A form of asexual reproduction practiced by plants in which a portion of an initial plant can grow into a second plant. Severed "runners" of aspen trees can grow into separate trees through vegetative reproduction.

vein A blood vessel that carries blood toward the heart.

ventilation The physical movement of air into and out of the lungs, brought about by contractions and relaxations of muscles in the chest.

vertebral column A flexible column of bones extending from the anterior to posterior end of an animal. Also known as a backbone, the vertebral column distinguishes vertebrates from other chordates.

vessel element One of two types of cells that make up xylem tissue, which transports water and dissolved minerals through plants. At maturity, vessel elements are dead and empty of cellular contents, thus facilitating the rapid conduction of water.

vestigial character A structure in an organism whose original function has been lost during the course of evolution.

virus A noncellular replicating entity that must invade a living cell to replicate itself.

vitamin A chemical compound found in foods that is needed in small amounts to facilitate a chemical reaction in the human body.

viviparous A condition in animals in which fertilized eggs develop inside a mother's body.

W

wax A lipid composed of a single fatty acid linked to a long-chain alcohol.

wetlands Lands that are wet for at least part of the year. Wetlands are sites of great biological productivity, and they provide vital habitat for migrating birds.

white blood cell (WBC) The central cells of the immune system. Types of white blood cells include T cells, B cells, neutrophils, eosinophils, and macrophages, each playing a specific role in immune responses.

X

xylem The tissue through which water and dissolved minerals flow in vascular plants.

xylem sap The water and dissolved minerals that are conducted through xylem in plants.

Y

yellow marrow In human beings, a tissue largely made up of energy-storing fat cells found in the marrow cavity of long bones.

Z

zero population growth State of a population in which births exactly equal deaths in a given period.

zooplankton Microscopic aquatic animals that occupy a trophic level above that of phytoplankton, or photosynthesizing aquatic microorganisms.

zygote A fertilized egg. In humans, the developing organism from the time of fertilization through the time of the first cell division (about 30 hours after fertilization).

Credits

CHAPTER 1 CO-01 verso Frans Lanting/CORBIS CO-01 recto R. Michael Stuckey/Jupiter Images 1-1a James King-Holmes/SPL/Photo Researchers, Inc. 1-1b Ethan Miller/Getty Images 1-2 Pearson Science/Kristin Piljay 1-6a Krzysztof Wiktor/ Shutterstock 1-ESS-01 John Valls 1-6b Mark Kostich/iStockphoto 1-6c George Holton/Photo Researchers, Inc. 1-7a,b Jose B. Ruiz/naturepl.com

CHAPTER 2 CO-02 verso Michael Durham/ National Geographic Stock CO-02 recto Shutterstock 2-3 HooRoo Graphics/iStockphoto 2-4 Mike Nelson/CORBIS 2-ESS-01 Vienna Report Agency/ Sygma/CORBIS 2-13 Stephen C. Harrison; From A.K. Aggarwal, D.W. Rogers, M. Drottar, M. Ptashne, S.C. Harrison, 1988, "Science," 242:899; Courtesy, S.C. Harrison. 2-15 Doug Allen/Photolibrary 2-16a Herman Eisenbeiss/Photo Researchers, Inc. 2-16b Pasieka/SPL/Photo Researchers, Inc. 2-17 David Woodfall/Getty Images

CHAPTER 3 CO-03 verso David Noton/ naturepl.com CO-03 recto Arkady/Shutterstock 3-1 Getty Images 3-3 Dorling Kindersley Media Library 3-5 Richard Megna/Fundamental Photographs 3-Table03a Dr. Jeremy Burgess/SPL/ Photo Researchers, Inc. 3-Table03b edImage/Photo Researchers, Inc. 3-Table03c Biophoto Associates/ Photo Researchers, Inc. 3-Table03d Eye of Science/ Photo Researchers, Inc. 3-13 Eye of Science/Photo Researchers, Inc. 3-14 Quest/SPL/Photo Researchers, Inc. 3-17a,b Peter M. Colman

CHAPTER 4 CO-04 verso David Scharf/Science Faction CO-04 recto LSHTM/Photo Researchers, Inc. 4-01UNa Prof. P. Motta/SPL/Photo Researchers, Inc. 4-01UNb Photo Researchers, Inc. 4-01UNc Andrew Syred/Photo Researchers, Inc. 4-1 NCI/ Photo Researchers, Inc. 4-ESS1-01a-c Tony Brain/ David Parker/SPL/Photo Researchers, Inc. 4-6 Biophoto Associates/Photo Researchers, Inc. 4-7 Don W. Fawcett/Photo Researchers, Inc. 4-9 P. Motta & T. Naguro/SPL/Photo Researchers, Inc. 4-11 P. Motta & T. Naguro/SPL/Photo Researchers, Inc. 4-12a Tomasz Szul/Visuals Unlimited/COR-BIS 4-12b Nancy Kedersha/SPL/Photo Researchers, Inc. 4-12c Dr. Peter Dawson/SPL/Photo Researchers, Inc. 4-13 Photo Lennart Nilsson/Albert Bonniers Forlag 4-ESS2-01 Scott Camazine/Photo Researchers, Inc. 4-14b Steve Gschmeissner/SPL/Photo Researchers, Inc. 4-14c Leroy Francis/SPL/Photo Researchers, Inc. 4-18a Ed Kanze/Dembinsky Associates 4-18b Lee W. Wilcox, Univ. of Wisconsin at Madison 4-19 Eldon H. Newcomb & William P. Wergin 4-ESS3-01a Brian J. Ford 4-ESS3-01b National Library of Medicine

CHAPTER 5 CO-05 verso Sinclair Stammers/ Photo Researchers, Inc. CO-05 recto John Burbidge/ Photo Researchers, Inc. 5-4a-c Pearson Science/Eric Shrader 5-10 Jurgen Bohmer and Linda Hufnagel 5-11a M.M. Perry 5-11b Biology Media/Science Source/Photo Researchers, Inc.

CHAPTER 6 CO-06 verso Michael Durham/ National Geographic Stock CO-06 recto Markus Gann/Shutterstock 6-1 Alamy imagebroker/Alamy 6-10 Thomas A. Steitz

CHAPTER 7 CO-07 verso Michael & Patricia Fogden/National Geographic Stock CO-07 recto Mike Kemp/Photolibrary 7-01UN Neal Beidleman/ Woodfin Camp & Associates, Inc. 7-2 Victor De Schwanberg/SPL/Photo Researchers, Inc. 7-ESS-01 Olaf Doering/Alamy

CHAPTER 8 CO-08 verso Roderick Chen/Jupiter Images CO-08 recto Kati Molin/Shutterstock 8-1a Andriy Solovyov/Shutterstock 8-1b Georgette Douwma/naturepl.com 8-1c M. I. Walker/Photo Researchers, Inc. 8-2 Catalin Petolea/Alamy 8-7 Eldon H. Newcomb & William P. Wergin 8-11 Jay Directo/AFP/Getty Images

CHAPTER 9 CO-09 verso SPL/Photo Researchers, Inc. CO-09 recto Dr. Kari Lounatmaa/Photo Researchers, Inc. 9-1 Ariel Skelley/Getty Images 9-7 Biophoto Associates/Photo Researchers, Inc. 9-8a,b Biophoto Associates/Photo Researchers, Inc. 9-10 Ed Reschke/photolibrary.com 9-11 Don W. Fawcett/ Photo Researchers, Inc. 9-14 CNRI/Photo Researchers, Inc.

CHAPTER 10 CO-10 verso Hans Dieter Brandl/ Foto Natura/National Geographic Stock CO-10 recto Xtremer/iStockphoto 10-5 David Young-Wolff/ Getty Images 10-6 Andrew Syred/ Photo Researchers, Inc. 10-9 David Phillips/The Population Council/ Photo Researchers, Inc. 10-10 Suzanne L. Collins/ Photo Researchers, Inc. 10-11 Fred McConnaughey/ Photo Researchers, Inc.

CHAPTER 11 CO-11 verso Christi Carter/ photolibrary.com CO-11 recto Miroslava Vasileva Arnaudova/Shutterstock 11-1 Getty Images Inc./ Hulton Archive Photos 11-4 Dr. Maban K. Bhattarrya 11-11 Gary Roberts 11-12a Peter Morenus 11-13 Steffen Hauser/botanikfoto/Alamy

CHAPTER 12 CO-12 verso Andrew Syred/Photo Researchers, Inc. CO-12 recto Sebastian Kaulitzki/ Shutterstock 12-3 Oliver Meckes & Nicole Ottawa/ Photo Researchers, Inc. 12-8 PHANIE/Photo Researchers, Inc. 12-ESS1-01a Pascal Goetgheluck/ Photo Researchers, Inc. 12-ESS1-01b Dept. of Clinical Cytogenetics, Addenbrookes Hospital/ SPL/ Photo Researchers, Inc. 12-9 Sandra Hanks and Nazneen Rahman, Institute of Cancer Research, Sutton, Surrey, UK 12-10a,b Irene Uchida 12-ESS2-01a Photo Researchers, Inc.

CHAPTER 13 CO-13 verso Zygote Media/ 3Dscience.com CO-13 recto John Harwood/Getty Images 13-1 Omikron/Photo Researchers, Inc. 13-2 Science Source/Photo Researchers, Inc. 13-3 Science Source/Photo Researchers, Inc. 13-4 George Silk/Time Life Pictures/Getty Images

CHAPTER 14 CO-14 verso Dr. Torsten Wittman/ Photo Researchers, Inc. CO-14 recto George Underwood/Getty Images 14-11b Dr. Elena Kiseleva/ Photo Researchers, Inc. 14-14a Photo Researchers, Inc. 14-14b Oliver Meckes/Photo Researchers, Inc. 14-14c James King-Holmes/SPL/ Photo Researchers, Inc. 14-14d Niall Benvie/naturepl.com 14-17a Tony Brain/David Parker/ SPL/Photo Researchers, Inc. 14-17b Photo Researchers, Inc. 14-17c Niall Benvie/ naturepl.com 14-17d James King-Holmes/SPL/ Photo Researchers, Inc. 14-17e Max Westby 14-17f Redmond Durrell/ Alamy 14-17g Shishov Mikhail/ Shutterstock

CHAPTER 15 CO-15 verso Matthias Schrader/dpa/Landov Media CO-15 recto Zirafek/ iStockphoto 15-1 RIKEN Center for Developmental Biology 15-2 GTC Biotherapeutics 15-4 Dr. Gopal Murti/Science Photo Library/Photo Researchers, Inc. 15-6 Jon Christensen/Pearson Education/PH College 15-7 Photograph courtesy of The Roslin Institute 15-12 Pearson Education/PH College

CHAPTER 16 CO-16 verso Tony Campbell/ Shutterstock CO-16 recto Lifeonwhite.com/Getty Images 16-1 Paul Souders/CORBIS 16-2 Painting by John Collier, 1883. London, National Portrait Gallery. ©Archiv/Photo Researchers 16-3 Christopher Ralling 16-5 WaterFrame/Alamy 16-6 Juniors BIildarchiv/age footstock 16-7 Photolibrary 16-8a Bruce Coleman/Photoshot Holdings Ltd. 16-8b Frans Lanting/DanitaDelimont.com 16-8c Tui Dee Roy/National Geographic Stock 16-9 Mark Kauffman/Time Life Syndication 16-11 Sinclair Stammers/Science Photo Library/Photo Researchers, Inc. 16-ESS-01 Darrell Gulin/Getty Images

CHAPTER 17 CO-17 verso Winfried Wisniewski/ Foto Natura/National Geographic Stock CO-17 recto Dan Wilton/iStockphoto 17-4a Bob Abraham/ Pacific Stock 17-4b Bruce G. Baldwin 17-7 Ray Scott Smith/CORBIS 17-ESS-01 RFcompany/ age footstock 17-8 Tui De Roy/Photoshot 17-13 Hans Reinhard/Photoshot

CHAPTER 18 CO-18 verso David Cottridge/ Nature Picture Library CO-18 recto Stefan Klein/ iStockPhoto 18-1a Tim Davis/CORBIS 18-1b Jeff Lepore/Photo Researchers, Inc. 18-2 David Welling Photography 18-4a,b Tom & Pat Leeson/Photo Researchers, Inc 18-5 Lenz/age footstock 18-6 Guy L. Bush 18-7a,b Kevin T. Kaneshiro 18-9a,b Axel Meyer, Dept. of Biology University of Konstanz 18-ESS-01 JD Dallet/Photolibrary

CHAPTER 19 CO-19 verso Chip Clark CO-19 recto Andy Crawford/Dorling Kindersley 19-1 Anup Shah/naturepl.com 19-2 Jack Dermid/ Photoshot 19-4 Gerhard Zwerger-Schon/age footstock 19-5 Jim Sugar/CORBIS 19-7 B. Murton/ Southampton Oceanography Centre/Photo Researchers, Inc. 19-8 Stanley Awramik 19-10 The Natural History Museum, London 19-11 Radius Images/Photolibrary 19-13 Prof. David L. Dilcher 19-15 Raul Martin 19-ESS1-01 Andrew Gillis 19-ESS1-02 Ted Daeschler 19-ESS1-03 University of Chicago 19-17 M. Loup/Jacana/Photo Researchers, Inc. 19-18a Kevin Schafer/Photolibrary 19-18b Kevin Schafer/age footstock 19-18c J&C Sohns/Photolibrary

CHAPTER 20 CO-20 verso John Reader/Photo Researchers, Inc. CO-20 recto Kunsthalle Tubingen 20-3a AFP Photo/Getty Images 20-3b Michel Brunet 20-4 Michel Brunet 20-5a-c Viktor Deak 20-7 Kenneth Garrett/Kenneth Garrett Photography 20-ESS-01 Jeffrey H. Schwartz 20-10a University of Wollongong

CHAPTER 21 CO-21 verso A. Smith/Photo Researchers, Inc. CO-21 recto Eric V. Grave/Photo Researchers, Inc. 21-1a Tim Davis /CORBIS 21-1b Ralph A. Clevenger/CORBIS 21-1c Andrew Darrington/Alamy 21-1d Roland Birke/Photolibrary 21-4b Biozentrum, University of Basel/SPL/Photo Researchers, Inc. 21-5 Jim Mahoney/The Dallas MorningNews/CORBIS 21-7a David Scharf/ Photolibrary 21-7b Dr. Gary Gaugler/Photo Researchers, Inc. 21-7c CNRI/SPL/Photo Researchers, Inc. 21-12a Micrographia 21-12b Manfred Kage/Photolibrary 21-12c Dave King/ Dorling Kindersley Media Library 21-13a Visuals Unlimited/CORBIS 21-13b P.M. Motta and F.M. Magliocca/SPL/Photo Researchers, Inc. 21-14a Wim van Egmond/Getty Images 21-14b Raymond McNeil 21-15a,b Phototake/Alamy 21-ESS2-01a CORBIS- NY 21-ESS2-01b Image Works/Mary Evans Picture Library Ltd 21-ESS2-01c Claude Huston/Time Life Pictures/Getty Images

CHAPTER 22 CO-22 verso Igor Shpilenok/ Nature Picture Library CO-22 recto Shutterstock 22-1 George Barron 22-2a Chris Mattison/age footstock 22-2b Science Photo Library/Photo Researchers, Inc. 22-2c Michael & Patricia Fogden/ CORBIS 22-5a,b Jack H. Barger, US Forest Service 22-7 Breck P. Kent 22-8a Nigel Bean/naturepl.com 22-8b Inga Spence/Photo Researchers, Inc. 22-9a Ed Reschke/Photolibrary 22-9b Niall Benvie/ Nature Photo Library 22-10a Jeremy Burgess/SPL/ Photo Researchers, Inc. 22-10b Gary Gaugler/

Peter Arnold/Photolibrary 22-11a Martha J. Powell 22-11b Lee Berger 22-12 David Scharf/Photo Researchers, Inc. 22-ESS-01 Photo Researchers, Inc. 22-13 John Eastcott & Yva Momatiuk/The Image Works 22-15 Visuals Unlimited/CORBIS

CHAPTER 23 CO-23 verso Tim Fitzharris/ National Geographic Stock CO-23 recto Eric Isselée/ iStockphoto 23-1a Paul Edmondson/CORBIS 23-1b Image Quest Marine 23-1c Marevision/age footstock 23-1d Solvin Zankl/naturepl.com 23-1e Herman Eisenbeiss/Photo Researchers, Inc. 23-1f Frans Lanting/DanitaDelimont.com 23-7 JUNIORS BILDARCHIV/age footstock 23-9 GEORGETTE DOUWMA/naturepl.com 23-11 Photo Researchers, Inc. 23-13 Kjell Sandved/SANDV/Photoshot 23-14 Image Quest Marine 23-16a K. Sulik 23-16b K. Sulik 23-18 Dr. Clive Kocher/Photo Researchers, Inc. 23-19 Suzanne L. Collins/Photo Researchers, Inc. 23-22 Michael & Patricia Fogden/National Geographic Stock 23-25 Dr. Liu Jinyuan/Dalian Museum of Natural History 23-26a Gunter Ziesler/Peter Arnold/Photolibrary 23-26b John Cancalosi/Peter Arnold/Photolibrary 23-26c Arctic-Images/Getty Images 23-29 Ron Borland/ Photoshot

CHAPTER 24 CO-24 verso Tim Fitzharris/ National Geographic Stock CO-24 recto Dimitar Bosakov/Shutterstock 24-1 Photo Researchers, Inc. 24-2a Stuart Gregory/Photolibrary 24-2b Al Harvey/ Masterfile Corporation 24-2c Stepan Jezek/ Shutterstock 24-6a Lubomir Jendrol/iStockphoto 24-6b Vladimir Maravic/iStockphoto 24-6c Anders Aagesen/iStockphoto 24-6d Jirsak/Shutterstock 24-7a Maurizio Bachis/Photolibrary 24-7b Ed Reschke/Photolibrary 24-7c Daniel Vega/age footstock 24-8a Ted Mead/Photolibrary 24-8b Pablo Galan Cela/agefootstock 24-8c Michael P. Gadomski/Photo Researchers, Inc. 24-9a Robert McGouey/Photolibrary 24-9b blickwinkel/Alamy 24-12a Carr Clifton/National Geographic Stock 24-12b Sundlof—TRAV/Alamy 24-12c Charlie Waite/Getty Images 24-ESS-01 Diane Schiumo/ Fundamental Photographs, NYC 24-13a Kristian Sekulic/iStockphoto 24-13b Steve Byland/Shutterstock 24-13c Merlin D. Tuttle/Bat Conservation International/Photo Researchers, Inc. 24-14a Leonard Lessin/Photo Researchers, Inc. 24-14b Leonard Lessin/Photo Researchers, Inc. 24-16a Erwin and Peggy Bauer/Photoshot 24-16b Scott Camazine/Photo Researchers, Inc. 24-19 Morley Read/Alamy 24-20a Don Johnston/age fotostock

CHAPTER 25 CO-25 verso Brian Johnston/ Microscopy-UK CO-25 recto Vitaly Raduntsev/ Shutterstock 25-1 Win Initiative/Getty Images 25-2 Missouri Botanical Garden Library 25-3a Dorling Kindersley Media Library 25-3b Fotosearch/ Photolibrary 25-3c Photo Researchers, Inc. 25-5a Ed Reschke/Photolibrary 25-5b Nigel Cattlin/ Alamy 25-6 Ed Reschke/Photolibrary 25-9 Steve Gschmeissner/Photo Researchers, Inc. 25-12a blickwinkel/Alamy 25-12b Peter Holmes/ Photolibrary 25-14a Dr. Jeremy Burgess/Photo

Researchers, Inc. 25-14b Andrew Syred/SPL/Photo Researchers, Inc. 25-15 Carolina Biological Supply Company/Alamy 25-17a Ed Reschke/Peter Arnold/ Photolibrary 25-17b Biophoto Associates/Photo Researchers, Inc. 25-17c Steve Gschmeissner/Photo Researchers, Inc. 25-19a POWER AND SYRED/ Photo Researchers, Inc. 25-19b Kenneth Eward/ Photo Researchers, Inc. 25-21 Lee W. Wilcox 25-ESS-01 Steve Kaufman/Peter Arnold, Inc./ Photolibrary

CHAPTER 26 CO-26 verso Thomas Hoepker/ Magnum Photos, Inc. 26-7a Steve Gschmeissner/ Photo Researchers, Inc. 26-ESS1-01 Photo Researchers, Inc. 26-ESS2-01 Stockbyte/Getty Images 26-10 Pietro M. Motta/Photo Researchers, Inc.

CHAPTER 27 CO-27 verso Veer Inc. CO-27 recto DNY59/iStockphoto 27-01UN Picture Desk, Inc./ Kobal Collection 27-3a Patrick J. Lynch/Photo Researchers, Inc. 27-ESS-01 P. Motta/SPL/Photo Researchers, Inc. 27-17b Omikron/Photo Researchers, Inc

CHAPTER 28 CO-28 verso Sanofi Pasteur Limited (Connaught Campus) Archives, Toronto, Canada CO-28 recto Shishov Mikhail/Shutterstock 28-ESS-01 Samuel Ashfield/Photo Researchers, Inc.

CHAPTER 29 CO-29 verso Jim West/Alamy CO-29 recto Knorre/Shutterstock 29-01UN Manfred Kage/Peter Arnold/Photolibrary 29-2 Photo Researchers, Inc. 29-6 David Scharf/Photo Researchers, Inc. 29-11 Dr. P. Marazzi/Photo Researchers, Inc. 29-ESS1-01 Thomas Deerinck, NCMIR/Photo Researchers, Inc. 29-ESS2-01 AFP/ Getty Images

CHAPTER 30 CO-30 verso Koji Aoki/Veer CO-30 recto Spectral-Design/Shutterstock 30-3 Science Photo Library/Photolibrary 30-8c SPL/ Photo Researchers 30-10c Prof Cinti & V. Gremet/ Photo Researchers, Inc. 30-12 Javier Soriano/ AFP/Getty Images

CHAPTER 31 CO-31 verso LWA/Getty Images CO-31 recto Alessio Cola/Shutterstock 31-8 Dirk R. Frans/Peter Arnold/Photolibrary 31-10a Christian Schmidt/zefa/CORBIS 31-10b CORBIS

CHAPTER 32 CO-32 verso Lennart Nilsson/ Scanpix Sweden AB CO-32 recto Dr. Yorgos Nikas/ Photo Researchers, Inc. 32-1b Dr. Lloyd M. Beidler/ Photo Researchers, Inc. 32-5 Ed Reschke/ Photolibrary 32-6 National Museum of Health and Medicine 32-9 Eye of Science/Photo Researchers, Inc. 32-10 Alexander Tsiaras/Photo Researchers, Inc.

CHAPTER 33 CO-33 recto Ichou/Veer CO-33 verso Gleb Semenjuk/Shutterstock 33-1 David M. Phillips/Photo Researchers, Inc. 33-5 Jean-Christophe Lousse, M.D., and Jacques Donnez, M.D., Ph.D. 33-6b Lennart Nilsson/ Scanpix Sweden AB 33-10 Lennart Nilsson/Scanpix Sweden AB 33-12a Neil Harding/Getty Images 33-12b John Watney/Photo Researchers, Inc. 33-12c James Stevenson/SPL/Photo Researchers, Inc. 33-13 Publiphoto/Photo Researchers, Inc.

Index